Modern Organic Chemistry

JOHN D. ROBERTS

Professor of Organic Chemistry
California Institute of Technology

MARJORIE C. CASERIO

Associate Professor of Chemistry
University of California, Irvine

W. A. BENJAMIN, INC.   1967
NEW YORK · AMSTERDAM

Modern Organic Chemistry

Library of Congress Catalog Card Number 66-29618
Manufactured in the United States of America

*The manuscript was put into production on April 25, 1966;
this volume was published on March 17, 1967*

W. A. Benjamin, Inc.
NEW YORK, NEW YORK 10016

PREFACE

PROGRESS IN organic chemistry is like that of a forest fire—fastest when
fanned by the winds of new ideas; brightest when passing through heavily
wooded virgin areas. Although organic chemistry is more than 150 years old,
its fire rages faster and brighter than ever, as the result of a veritable hurricane
of new theoretical concepts and experimental techniques from other areas of
science. The new ideas are leading to a new kind of organic chemist, one who is
versed in all the disciplines of chemistry from chemical physics to chemical biol-
ogy and who may be called an organic chemist solely because he happens to
work on the chemistry of carbon compounds.

The gradual recognition that physical chemical principles are vital to the understanding and improvement of synthetic reactions has helped more than anything else to broaden the outlook of organic chemists. One of the pioneers in
this respect was Professor Howard J. Lucas of the California Institute of Technology—whose text, *Organic Chemistry,* published in 1935, made the first real
attempt to suffuse thermodynamics and quantum mechanics into the teaching of
elementary organic chemistry. This textbook was very much ahead of its time—
so much so that no other book published in the intervening years has gone quite
so far, particularly in the application of thermodynamics to organic chemistry.

The present text owes much to Professor Lucas, because it was originally con-
ceived as a revision of the second edition of his *Organic Chemistry* and follows a
somewhat similar order of presentation, as well as placing a similar emphasis on
thermochemistry as an aid to the understanding of organic reactions. This
emphasis should be of general value in undergraduate education because the
gradual shift of teaching in elementary physical chemistry toward quantum
mechanics and statistical mechanics has tended to displace the study of many
applications of thermodynamics from the undergraduate chemistry curriculum.

Much has been said and written about possible orders of presentation of topics
in elementary organic chemistry texts. Whether or not to mix aliphatic and aromatic chemistry, whether or not to go heavily into organic structural theory before discussing reactions—these and similar questions have been subjected to
serious debate without any clear decision (if one is indeed possible). The approach in this book has been an intermediate one which takes cognizance of the
fact that it is difficult, if not impossible, to teach everything at once and that a certain degree of repetition is helpful to the learning process. Thus, we cover elec-

tronic theory of organic chemistry lightly in Chapter 1 (Lewis structures), extensively in Chapter 5 (atomic orbital models), extensively again in Chapter 9 (the resonance method and rudiments of molecular orbital theory), and finally lightly in Chapter 31 (bonding between carbon and elements such as silicon, boron, and phosphorus).

At each juncture, the intention has been to introduce only as many new ideas as important for the subject at hand. As a result, Chapters 6 and 7 cover the basic physical and chemical properties of alkenes, yet do not cover the methods by which alkenes are prepared simply because the reactions involved could not be properly understood at this juncture.

We cannot claim that there is much that is revolutionary or original about the format or arrangement of our book and yet we believe there is an element of newness about the way we have approached the subject, with unceasing effort to test both traditional and current concepts to see if they really ring true when hit hard. Sometimes, a sort of schizophrenia has resulted, because we have not been able to decide which of two different theoretical treatments is more useful. Usually, we have not made clearcut decisions to accept or reject, but have presented the alternatives. This may be unsettling for elementary students expecting, for example, a consistent treatment of bond angles, in terms of either hybridization or electron repulsion (Chapter 5); or of unsaturated compounds, in terms of either the resonance method or molecular orbital theory (Chapter 9). We regret this, but the fact is we couldn't make up our own minds on how best to handle these subjects.

The present book is a shortened version of our "Basic Principles of Organic Chemistry." In the shortening process, not many important ideas were omitted. Instead we removed many details and tables which, although providing valuable background and breadth of coverage, could be safely deleted without changing the fundamental nature of our approach to organic chemistry. Whenever the reader desires fuller explanations than possible in this book, we hope he will look for them in the longer version. Despite the shortening, the number of topics covered is large and an instructor with limited time for presentation of an elementary organic course may well find himself in the position of having a small appetite at a sumptuous buffet supper. This is not a problem unique to our book. At least, we have made an attempt to solve it by following the suggestion of Dr. Christian E. Kaslow, that each important topic be assigned a section number, so that an instructor pressed for time, or wishing to ignore some of our alternative treatments, can quickly and easily plan and assign an appropriate table d'hôte menu for his students.

Two features of the book seem to call for special comment. First, the exercises, of which there are many—not only at the ends of the chapters but also integrated into the text. None of these exercises is of the "Write twelve reactions of aldehydes" type. Such questions may well provide useful review but our concept of the purpose of exercises was different. We hoped to make the students think, make them scour the text for clues, and, in many cases, lead them into areas rather beyond those explicitly covered in the text. Some of the exercises may be exasperating to instructor and student alike because they do not have well-defined, precise answers. However, such exercises often have the advantage of helping to stimulate classroom discussions. There are many more exercises than a student could be expected to work in a year course, but here, again, the idea has been to provide the instructor with a wide range of possible choices.

The other feature of the book which seems to merit separate discussion is the emphasis on applications of the various forms of spectroscopy to problems in organic chemistry. Chapter 2 is particularly controversial in this respect — some reviewers liked it, some thought it belonged in an appendix, and some believed it had no place at all in an elementary text. The importance of spectroscopic methods to structural analysis of organic compounds cannot be questioned. Despite the qualms of the older generation in this respect, it really is the proper thing to take spectra before determining the melting point of a new compound — vastly more information can be obtained thereby. However, this does not mean that instruction in spectroscopic methods is necessary or even desirable in elementary organic courses. There is always a limit to how much material can be covered and an argument can be made for possible pedagogical disadvantages to teaching subjects which may be of no very immediate value to the student.

The material on spectroscopy is available in Chapter 2 and in parts of later chapters — to be used or not at the discretion of the instructor. We see no important difficulties with omitting all of it, if the instructor so desires. If spectroscopy is covered, the student should be given to understand that it is not necessary for him to grasp all the material in Chapter 2 at once. Rather, he should expect to enhance his ability to comprehend and use spectroscopic methods by returning to this chapter for study and reference material as new applications are encountered with the different classes of compounds. The extensive use we have made of nuclear magnetic resonance spectroscopy may seem to reflect too much of our own research interests. Nonetheless, we feel this requires no apology because, for qualitative analysis, nmr spectroscopy is usually quite superior to infrared spectroscopy and has the further advantage of being much easier to understand.

Besides the many friends and colleagues who made valuable suggestions for the improvement of our earlier version, we are much indebted to Professor Johannes Dale of the University of Oslo for a recent very detailed critique much of which we were able to take advantage of in this book.

We shall be grateful for further suggestions for improvements on matters of fact, interpretation, or presentation.

JOHN D. ROBERTS
MARJORIE C. CASERIO

Pasadena, California
November 1966

CONTENTS

MODERN
ORGANIC CHEMISTRY

Structure, Identification, and Nomenclature

The purpose of this chapter is severalfold. First, we review briefly some of the reasons for the differences in properties between typically covalent organic compounds and inorganic salts. This is followed by a discussion of ways of representing organic substances both by structural formulas and by molecular models.

Methods for establishing the purity and identity of organic compounds by chromatography and analysis are considered—then some of the steps used in structural determinations are illustrated for the alkaloid, nicotine. Finally, we take up some of the problems posed by the nomenclature of organic compounds, a subject which has its "dry as dust" aspects and is often the bane of the beginning student, despite the fact that it has its root in the warmly human objective of facilitating communication of information and ideas about organic substances and their reactions.

Structure, Identification, and Nomenclature

Organic chemistry was originally defined as the chemistry of those substances which are formed by living matter. After the discovery by Wöhler in 1828 that a supposedly typical organic compound, urea, could be prepared by heating an inorganic salt, ammonium cyanate, this definition lost its significance and now organic chemistry seems best taken as the chemistry of carbon-containing compounds. However, the designation "organic" is still very pertinent because the chemistry of carbon compounds is more important to everyday life than that of any other element. The following list is representative, but not exhaustive, of the many categories of organic compounds with biological and commercial importance.

Petroleum products
Rubber and other elastomers
Perfumes and flavors
Antibiotics and vitamins
Alkaloids and hormones
Agricultural chemicals
    (insecticides and fertilizers)

Explosives and propellants
Plastics and synthetic fibers
Refrigerants
Dyes and pigments
Sugars
Proteins
Surface coatings (paints)

1-1 BONDING IN CARBON COMPOUNDS

We might well wonder why a whole branch of chemistry is centered on a single element. One reason is that carbon-to-carbon bonds are strong, so that long chains of carbon atoms bonded to one another are possible. However, this is not a sufficient reason for an element to have a unique and varied chemistry because the atoms of many other elements such as boron, silicon, phosphorus, etc., form strong chains of bonds to one another in the elementary state. The uniqueness of carbon stems more from the fact that it customarily forms strong carbon-carbon bonds which are also strong when the carbons are in combination with other elements. Thus, while the carbon-hydrogen and carbon-fluorine compounds shown below are highly stable and relatively unreactive chemically, the corresponding compounds of boron, silicon, phosphorus, etc., either cannot be prepared or are rather highly reactive substances.

$$
\begin{array}{ccc}
\overset{\displaystyle H}{\underset{\displaystyle |}{|}} \quad \overset{\displaystyle H}{\underset{\displaystyle |}{|}} & & \overset{\displaystyle F}{\underset{\displaystyle |}{|}} \quad \overset{\displaystyle F}{\underset{\displaystyle |}{|}} \\
H-C-C-H & \text{and} & F-C-C-F \\
\overset{\displaystyle |}{\underset{\displaystyle H}{}} \quad \overset{\displaystyle |}{\underset{\displaystyle H}{}} & & \overset{\displaystyle |}{\underset{\displaystyle F}{}} \quad \overset{\displaystyle |}{\underset{\displaystyle F}{}}
\end{array}
$$

The special properties of carbon can be attributed to its being a relatively small atom having two electrons in a filled inner K shell and four valence electrons in the outer L shell. To form simple, *electrovalent*, binary salts such as sodium chloride, carbon would have either to lose the four valence electrons of the L shell to an element such as fluorine and be converted to a quadripositive ion, $C^{4\oplus}$, or else to fill up the L shell by gaining four electrons from an element such as lithium and form a quadrinegative ion, $C^{4\ominus}$. Loss of four electrons would be energetically very unfavorable because each electron would have to be pulled away from the positive carbon nucleus. Gain of four electrons would also be very unfavorable because of mutual repulsion between the electrons. These interelectronic repulsions will be much less important in adding one electron to a fluorine atom to give $F^{\ominus}$ than in adding four electrons to a carbon atom to give $C^{4\ominus}$ because, even though the total number of outer shell electrons is the same for each ion, fluorine has a much greater nuclear charge. Customarily, carbon completes its valence-shell octet by sharing electrons with other atoms. In compounds with shared electron bonds (or covalent bonds) such as methane (CH_4), ethane (C_2H_6), or carbon tetrafluoride (CF_4), carbon has its valence shell filled, as shown in the following Lewis structures:

$$
\begin{array}{ccc}
H & H \quad H & :\!\overset{\cdot\cdot}{F}\!: \\
H:\overset{\cdot\cdot}{\underset{\cdot\cdot}{C}}:H & H:\overset{\cdot\cdot}{\underset{\cdot\cdot}{C}}:\overset{\cdot\cdot}{\underset{\cdot\cdot}{C}}:H & :\!\overset{\cdot\cdot}{F}\!:\overset{\cdot\cdot}{\underset{\cdot\cdot}{C}}:\overset{\cdot\cdot}{F}\!: \\
H & H \quad H & :\!\overset{\cdot\cdot}{F}\!:
\end{array}
$$

$$
\text{methane} \qquad\qquad \text{ethane} \qquad\qquad \text{carbon tetrafluoride}
$$

The above-mentioned interelectronic repulsions associated with the completion of the L shell are, in these compounds, compensated by the electron-attracting powers of the positively charged nuclei of the atoms to which the carbon is bonded.

The properties of some of the hydrides of the elements in the first horizontal row of the periodic table illustrate the influence of transitions in bond type which occur with increasing atomic number for a given valence shell. Lithium hydride (m.p. 680°) can be regarded as a salt-like *ionic* compound. Either structure, $Li^{\oplus}:H^{\ominus}$ or $H^{\oplus}:Li^{\ominus}$, might be written, depending upon whether lithium or hydrogen is more electron-attracting. Although lithium would be expected to be the more electron-attracting because of its higher nuclear charge (+3), this is more than offset by the greater atomic radius and the "screening" effect of the two inner-shell electrons of lithium. Hence, hydrogen actually has the greater electron affinity and the $Li^{\oplus}:H^{\ominus}$ structure is correct. Strong interionic electrostatic attractions cause lithium hydride to have high melting and boiling points like those of sodium chloride, lithium fluoride, etc.

Methane, CH_4, boils at −161°, which is at least 1000° lower than the boiling point of lithium hydride. One reason for this difference in boiling point is the almost spherical shape of methane which, by exposing only one kind of atom, reduces the attractive forces between neighboring molecules and allows them to "escape" more easily as gaseous molecules. However, it also turns out that carbon and hydrogen are well matched with respect to electron-attracting power. As a result, the electrons in the C—H bonds are nearly equally shared and the bonds have but little ionic character. In contrast to lithium hydride, methane may be characterized as a *nonpolar* substance.

Hydrogen fluoride has a boiling point some 200° higher than that of methane. Fluorine, with its high nuclear charge, is substantially more electron-attracting than carbon and forms a partially ionic bond in combination with hydrogen. The bonding electron pair of HF is drawn somewhat toward fluorine so that the

$$\delta\oplus \quad \delta\ominus$$

bond may be formulated as H---F. In liquid hydrogen fluoride, the molecules tend to aggregate in chains and rings so that the positive hydrogen on one molecule attracts a negative fluorine on the next:

$$\begin{array}{cccccccc} \delta\ominus & \delta\oplus & \delta\ominus & \delta\oplus & \delta\ominus & \delta\oplus & \delta\ominus & \delta\oplus \\ F\text{---}H & \cdots & F\text{---}II & \cdots & F\text{---}H & \cdots & F\text{---}H \end{array}$$

When liquid hydrogen fluoride is vaporized, the temperature must be raised sufficiently to overcome these intermolecular electrostatic attractions and, hence, the boiling point is high compared to liquid methane. Hydrogen fluoride is best characterized as a *polar,* but not ionic, substance. Although the O—H and N—H bonds of water and ammonia have rather less ionic character than the H—F bonds of hydrogen fluoride, these substances are also relatively polar in nature.

The chemical properties of lithium hydride, methane, and hydrogen fluoride are in accord with the above formulations. With substances such as water, which can either donate or accept protons, the hydride ion of lithium hydride accepts a proton to give a hydrogen molecule:

$$\overset{\oplus}{Li}:\overset{\ominus}{H} \;+\; H:\overset{\cdot\cdot}{\underset{\cdot\cdot}{O}}:H \;\longrightarrow\; Li^{\oplus}\;:\overset{\cdot\cdot}{\underset{\cdot\cdot}{O}}:\overset{\ominus}{H} \;+\; H:H$$

On the other hand, hydrogen fluoride donates a proton and is converted to a fluoride salt:

$$\overset{\text{H}}{\underset{\cdot\cdot}{\text{H}:\overset{\cdot\cdot}{\underset{\cdot\cdot}{\text{O}}}:}} + \overset{\delta\oplus}{\text{H}} \overset{\delta\ominus}{\underset{\cdot\cdot}{:\overset{\cdot\cdot}{\underset{\cdot\cdot}{\text{F}}}:}} \longrightarrow \text{H}:\overset{\cdot\cdot}{\underset{\cdot\cdot}{\text{O}}}:\text{H} + \overset{\ominus}{\underset{\cdot\cdot}{:\overset{\cdot\cdot}{\underset{\cdot\cdot}{\text{F}}}:}}$$

($\delta\oplus$ $\delta\ominus$ denotes partial ionic bond)

Methane, with its covalent bonds, is inert to almost all proton-donating or proton-accepting substances under anything but very extreme conditions. As would be expected, methyl cations, $CH_3^{\oplus}$, and methide ions, $CH_3:^{\ominus}$, are very difficult to generate and are extremely reactive.

$$\overset{\text{H}}{\underset{\text{H}}{\text{H}:\overset{\cdot\cdot}{\underset{\cdot\cdot}{\text{C}}}:\text{H}}} + \text{H}:\overset{\cdot\cdot}{\underset{\cdot\cdot}{\text{O}}}:\text{H} \longrightarrow \text{no chemical reaction}$$

Carbon forms electron-pair bonds not only with hydrogen but with many other elements. Even its compounds with elements at the extreme ends of the rows in the periodic table, such as lithium methide ($LiCH_3$) and methyl fluoride (CH_3F), are relatively nonpolar compared to substances such as lithium fluoride — although, of course, substantially more polar than methane (CH_4).

Carbon atoms are unique in their ability to link with themselves and form stable chains or rings. The combination of hydrogen with carbons linked together affords an extraordinarily wide variety of carbon hydrides, or **hydrocarbons,** as they are usually called. In contrast, none of the other first-row elements except boron gives a very extensive system of hydrides and most of the boron hydrides are very sensitive to hydrolytic and oxidative reagents.

1-2 STRUCTURAL ORGANIC CHEMISTRY

The building block of structural organic chemistry is the tetravalent carbon atom. With few exceptions, carbon compounds can be formulated with four covalent bonds to each carbon, regardless of whether combination is with carbon or some other element. The two-electron bond which is illustrated by the carbon-to-hydrogen bonds in methane or ethane and the carbon-to-carbon bond in ethane is called a **single bond.** In these and many related substances, each carbon is attached to four other atoms. There exist, however, compounds like ethylene, C_2H_4, in which two electrons from each of the carbon atoms are mutually shared, producing a four-electron bond, called a **double bond.**

$$\overset{\text{H}}{\underset{\text{H}}{\cdot}}\overset{\cdot}{\text{C}}::\overset{\cdot}{\text{C}}\overset{\text{H}}{\underset{\text{H}}{\cdot}} \qquad \text{ethylene}$$

Similarly, in acetylene, C_2H_2, three electrons from each carbon atom are mutually shared, producing a six-electron bond, called a **triple bond.**

$$\text{H}:\text{C}:::\text{C}:\text{H} \qquad \text{acetylene}$$

In all cases, of course, each carbon has a full octet of electrons. Carbon also forms double and triple bonds with several other elements which can exhibit a covalency of two or three.   The carbon-oxygen (or carbonyl) double bond appears in carbon dioxide and many important organic compounds such as formaldehyde and acetic acid.   Similarly, a carbon-nitrogen triple bond appears in hydrogen cyanide and acetonitrile.

$$\ddot{\ddot{O}}::C::\ddot{\ddot{O}}: \qquad\qquad \begin{matrix} H \\ \vdots\ddot{C}::\ddot{\ddot{O}}: \\ H \end{matrix} \qquad\qquad \begin{matrix} & \ddot{\ddot{O}}: \\ H & \vdots \\ H:\ddot{C}:C:\ddot{\ddot{O}}:H \\ H \end{matrix}$$

         carbon dioxide   formaldehyde   acetic acid

$$H:C:::N: \qquad\qquad \begin{matrix} H \\ \ddot{} \\ H:\ddot{C}:C:::N: \\ H \end{matrix}$$

            hydrogen cyanide   acetonitrile

By convention, a single straight line connecting the atomic symbols is used to represent a single (two-electron) bond, two such lines to represent a double (four-electron) bond, and three a triple (six-electron) bond.   Representations of compounds by these symbols are called **structural formulas.**

         ethane   ethylene   acetylene   hydrogen cyanide

  carbon dioxide   formaldehyde   acetic acid   acetonitrile

To save space and time in the representation of organic structures, it is common practice to use "condensed formulas" in which the bonds are not always shown explicitly.   In using condensed formulas, normal atomic valences are understood throughout.

   CH_3CH_3 CH_2CH_2 CHCH CH_2O

   ethane   ethylene   acetylene   formaldehyde

   CH_3CO_2H HCN CH_3CN

   acetic acid   hydrogen cyanide   acetonitrile

Representations which are intermediate between condensed and structural formulas are for the most part reasonably clear and yet economical of space. These will be the ones which we shall use most often.

Proceeding as above, one can formulate a wide variety of substances with single, double, and triple bonds having tetravalent carbon, monovalent hydrogen and halogens, divalent oxygen, and trivalent nitrogen. Figure 1-1 illustrates a number of types of simple compounds.

Figure 1-1 Some simple types of organic compounds.

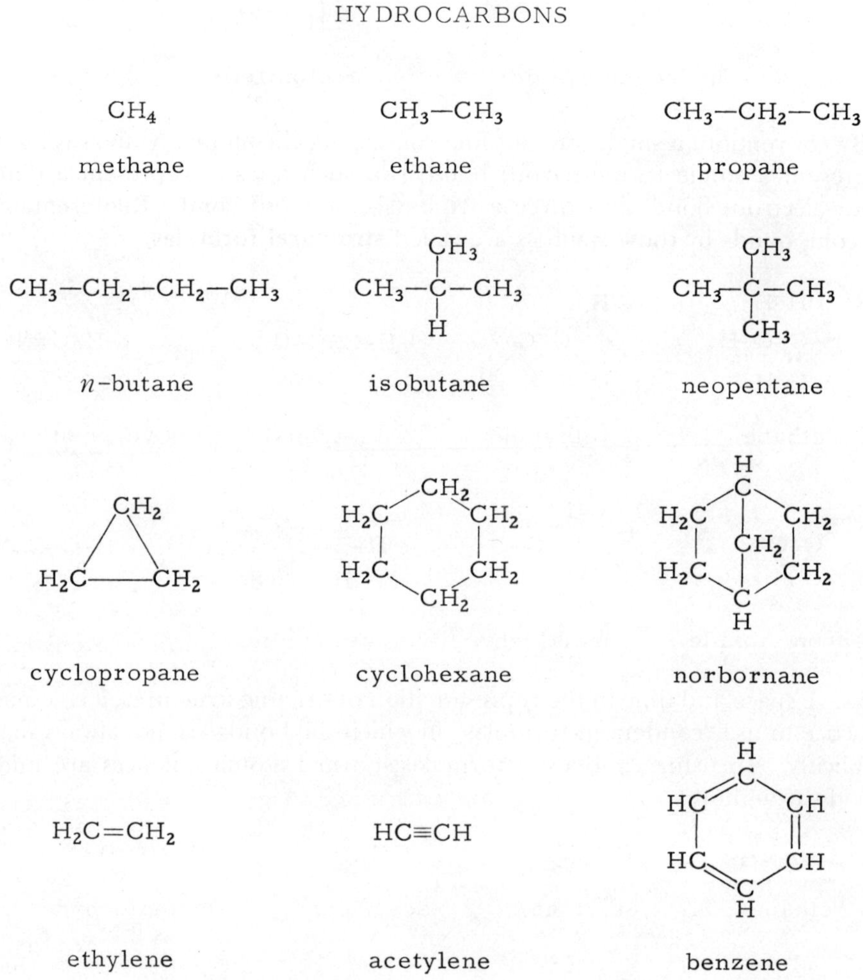

HYDROCARBONS

CH_4

methane

CH_3-CH_3

ethane

$CH_3-CH_2-CH_3$

propane

$CH_3-CH_2-CH_2-CH_3$

n-butane

isobutane

neopentane

cyclopropane

cyclohexane

norbornane

$H_2C=CH_2$

ethylene

$HC\equiv CH$

acetylene

benzene

Figure 1-1 (Continued)

HALIDES

CH_3Br

methyl
bromide

CCl_4

carbon
tetrachloride

CF_2Cl_2

difluoro-
dichloromethane

ALCOHOLS

$CH_3—OH$

methanol

$CH_3—CH_2—O—H$

ethanol

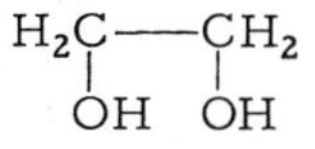

$$H_2C———CH_2$$
$$\quad OH \quad OH$$

ethylene glycol

ETHERS

$CH_3—O—CH_3$

dimethyl ether

$CH_3—CH_2—O—CH_2—CH_3$

diethyl ether

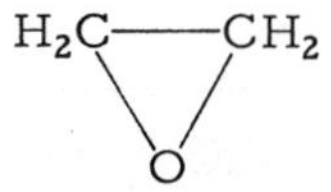

$H_2C———CH_2$
$\diagdown O \diagup$

ethylene oxide

CARBONYL ($>C=O$) COMPOUNDS

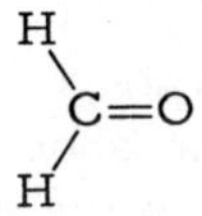

$$\begin{matrix} H \\ \diagdown \\ \quad C=O \\ \diagup \\ H \end{matrix}$$

formaldehyde

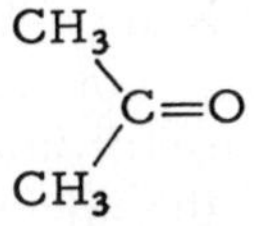

$$\begin{matrix} CH_3 \\ \diagdown \\ \quad C=O \\ \diagup \\ CH_3 \end{matrix}$$

acetone

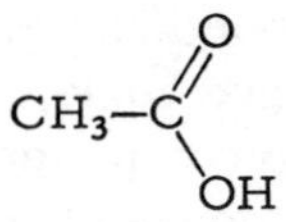

$$CH_3-C\begin{matrix}\overset{O}{\diagup\diagup}\\ \diagdown OH\end{matrix}$$

acetic acid

$$CH_3-C\begin{matrix}\overset{O}{\diagup\diagup}\\ \diagdown O—CH_2—CH_3\end{matrix}$$

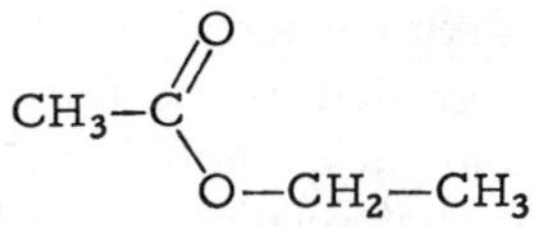

ethyl acetate

NITROGEN COMPOUNDS

$CH_3—NH_2$

methylamine

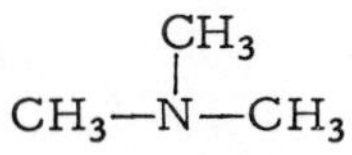

$$\begin{matrix} CH_3 \\ | \\ CH_3—N—CH_3 \end{matrix}$$

trimethylamine

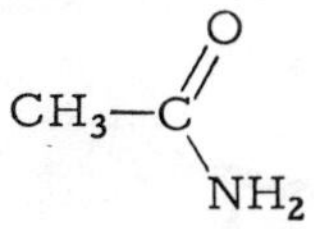

$$CH_3-C\begin{matrix}\overset{O}{\diagup\diagup}\\ \diagdown NH_2\end{matrix}$$

acetamide

$$CH_3\overset{\oplus}{N}\begin{matrix}\overset{O}{\diagup\diagup}\\ \diagdown O^{\ominus}\end{matrix}$$

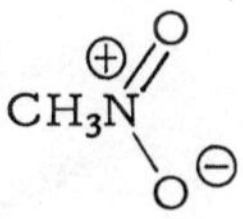

nitromethane

EXERCISE 1-1   Draw Lewis structures for the following substances whose structural formulas
are shown in Figure 1-1. Use distinct, correctly placed dots for the electrons.
Mark all atoms which are not neutral with charges of the proper sign.

a.	propane	f.	ethylene oxide
b.	cyclopropane	g.	sodium acetate ($CH_3CO_2^{\ominus}Na^{\oplus}$)
c.	benzene	h.	methylamine
d.	methyl bromide	i.	acetamide
e.	methanol	j.	nitromethane

EXERCISE 1-2   Write all the structural formulas you can for the different covalent isomers of
the following molecular formulas which have normal valences for each of the
atoms involved:

a.	C_3H_6 (two)	d.	C_2H_4ClF (two)
b.	C_3H_4 (three)	e.	C_3H_9N (three)
c.	C_2H_4O (three)	f.	$C_2H_4O_2$ (ten)

EXERCISE 1-3   Write an expanded structural formula with a line for each bond (like the
formulas on p. 7) for each of the substances represented below by a condensed
formula:

a.	$CH_3CH(CH_3)_2$	e.	$CH_3CONHCH_3$
b.	CH_3CCCH_3		
c.	CH_2ClOCH_2CHO	f.	$\overline{CH_2CH_2OCH_2CH_2O}$
d.	$(CH_2)_4$		

1-3 BOND ANGLES AND BALL-AND-STICK MODELS

It is well established that the normal carbon atom forms its four bonds in
compounds of the type CX_4 so that the four attached atoms lie at the corners of
a regular tetrahedron. The bond angles X—C—X are 109.5° and this value is
regarded as the normal valence angle of carbon. For many purposes, "ball-
and-stick" models of organic compounds give useful information about the
spatial relationships of the atoms and, for CX_4, the angles between the sticks
are set at 109.5° (Figure 1-2). Organic molecules strongly resist deformation

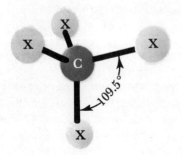

Figure 1-2

Ball-and-stick model of CX_4.

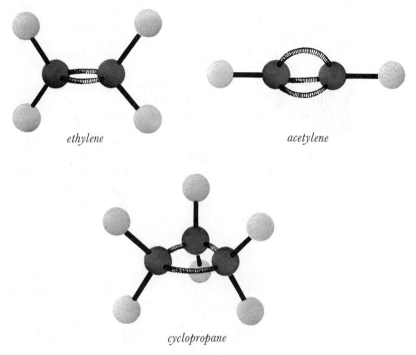

ethylene   *acetylene*

cyclopropane

Figure 1-3   Ball-and-stick models of hydrocarbons with bent bonds.

forces which alter their valence angles from normal values. Therefore, ball-and-stick models give a better correspondence to the behavior of actual molecules if the sticks are made to be rather stiff.

Ball-and-stick models of many organic substances with normal carbon valence angles of 109.5° are easily constructed. However, for other compounds, such as ethylene, acetylene, cyclopropane, formaldehyde, or ethylene oxide, the valence angles must be substantially less than the normal value if straight sticks are used to represent bonds. As a matter of convenience, models of such substances (Figure 1-3) are usually constructed with balls having holes drilled at the customary tetrahedral angles, but using reasonably flexible couplings, such as steel springs, to form "bent bonds."

Substances that require models with bent bonds are normally found to be much less stable (and more reactive) than analogous substances for which models can be constructed with straight sticks and tetrahedral angles.

1-4   ROTATIONAL CONFORMATIONS

In connection with the use of ball-and-stick models, if one allows the sticks to rotate freely in the holes, it will be found that for ethane, CH_3—CH_3, an infinite number of different atomic arrangements are possible, depending on the angular relationship between the hydrogens on each carbon. Two extreme arrange-

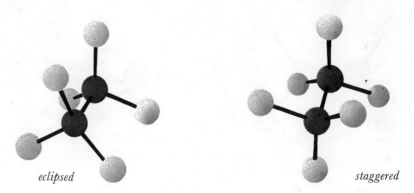

eclipsed　　　　　　　　　　　　　　　　　　　　　　　　*staggered*

Figure 1-4　Two rotational conformations of ethane.

ments or **conformations** are shown in Figure 1-4. In end-on views of the models, the *eclipsed* conformation is seen to have the hydrogens on the forward carbon directly in front of those on the back carbon. The *staggered* conformation has each of the hydrogens on the forward carbon set between each of the hydrogens on the back carbon. It has not been possible to obtain separate samples of ethane which correspond to these or intermediate arrangements because actual ethane molecules appear to have essentially "free rotation" about the single bond joining the carbons. Free, or at least rapid, rotation is possible around all single bonds, except under special circumstances, as when the groups attached are so large that they cannot pass by one another, or when the attached groups are connected together by chemical bonds (e.g., in ethylene or ring compounds such as cyclopropane or cyclohexane). For ethane and its derivatives, the staggered conformation is always somewhat more stable than the eclipsed conformation because, in the staggered conformation, the atoms are as far away from one another as possible and offer the least interaction.

Many problems in organic chemistry require consideration of structures in three dimensions, and it is very helpful to be able to use ball-and-stick models for visualization of the relative positions of the atoms in space. Unfortunately, we are very often forced to communicate three-dimensional concepts by means of drawings in two dimensions, and not all of us are equally gifted in making or visualizing such drawings. Obviously, communication by means of drawings such as the ones shown in Figure 1-4 would be impractically difficult and time-consuming—some form of abbreviation is necessary. Three styles of abbreviating the eclipsed and staggered conformations of ethane are shown in Figure 1-5. Of these, we strongly favor the "sawhorse" convention because, although it is perhaps the hardest to visualize and the hardest to master, it is the only three-dimensional convention which is simple and easy enough to draw to be useful for complex natural products. With the sawhorse drawings, we always consider that we are viewing the molecule slightly from above and from the right, just as we have shown in Figure 1-4.

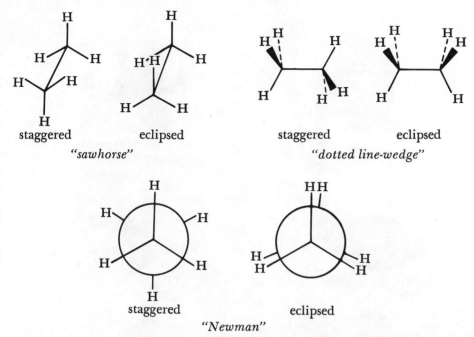

Figure 1-5   Conventions for showing the staggered and eclipsed conformations of ethane. In "saw-horse" drawings the lower left-hand carbon is always taken to be towards the front. In the dotted line-wedge convention, the wedges represent bonds coming out of the paper, the ordinary lines are bonds within the paper, and the dotted lines are bonds going in back of the paper.

EXERCISE 1-4   Show how the three conventions of Figure 1-5 can be used to represent the *different* possible staggered conformations of the following substances:
a. ethyl chloride (CH₃CH₂Cl)
b. 1,2-dichloro-1-fluoroethane (CHClFCH₂Cl)
c. 1,2-dichloroethane (CH₂ClCH₂Cl)
d. *n*-butane (CH₃CH₂CH₂CH₃); consider how you could extend each convention to a four-carbon system

---

1-5 SPACE-FILLING MODELS

Ball-and-stick models of molecules are very useful for visualization of the relative positions of the atoms in space but are unsatisfactory whenever we also want to show how large the atoms are. Actually, atomic radii are so large relative to the lengths of chemical bonds that when a model of a molecule like methyl chloride is constructed with atomic radii and bond lengths, both to scale, the bonds connecting the atoms are not clearly evident. Nonetheless, this type of "space-filling" model, made with truncated balls (Stuart, Fisher-Hirschfelder, etc.) held together with snap fasteners, is widely used to determine the possible closeness of approach of groups to each other and the degree of crowding of atoms in various arrangements (see Figure 1-6).

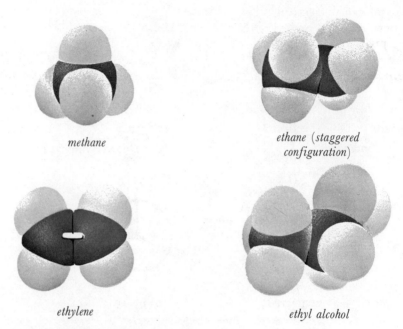

methane

ethane (staggered configuration)

ethylene

ethyl alcohol

Figure 1-6   Stuart models of organic compounds.

1-6 IDENTIFICATION AND STRUCTURE DETERMINATION

It is well known that more than one stable substance can correspond to a given molecular formula. Examples are *n*-butane and isobutane, each of which has the molecular formula C_4H_{10}, and dimethyl ether and ethanol of formula C_2H_6O.

$$CH_3-CH_2-CH_2-CH_3 \qquad CH_3-\overset{\overset{\textstyle CH_3}{|}}{\underset{\underset{\textstyle H}{|}}{C}}-CH_3 \qquad CH_3-O-CH_3 \qquad CH_3-CH_2-O-H$$

  n-butane   isobutane   dimethyl ether   ethanol

              C_4H_{10} C_2H_6O

Compounds having the same number and kind of atoms are called **isomers.** Only one stable substance is known corresponding to CH_4, but thirty-five isomers have been prepared of the formula C_9H_{20}. From this one may sense the richness of the flora of organic chemistry which leads to many problems — in telling one compound from another, in determining structures, and also in finding suitable nomenclature to permit communication with other workers. In the sections to follow, we will describe the experimental approach that is used to establish the purity, identity, and structures of organic compounds.

A. Physical Properties and Chromatography

The structure of an organic compound is most easily determined if it can be shown by its physical properties (melting point, boiling point, refractive index, density, solubility, electromagnetic absorption spectrum, mass spectrum, X-ray diffraction, etc.), or by its chemical properties to be identical with some previously prepared substance of known structure. It follows that purity is of paramount importance in identifying compounds through comparison of their properties with those of known substances. The purity of a given sample may often be gauged by its melting or boiling point and solubility behavior—the melting behavior usually being the most sensitive to impurities and easiest to determine. In general, however, small amounts of impurities are often difficult to detect by such procedures, and it is now common to evaluate purity by application of various "super-separation" methods to see if any contaminants can be separated and whether the properties of the sample are changed thereby.

The most popular separation methods are based on **chromatography,** or separation of the components of a mixture by differences in the way they become distributed (partitioned) between two phases. As we have defined it, chromatography includes simple separation techniques, such as extraction in a separatory funnel (a liquid-liquid, two-phase system) and fractional distillation (a gas-liquid, two-phase system). However, these techniques require fairly large amounts of material and they may also give unsatisfactory separations, which may be attributed to the small degree of separation possible in any given one-stage, or even a several-stage, partitioning process. The super-separation methods involve multistage partitioning of very small amounts of sample, a few milligrams or less, wherein extraordinary separations can often be achieved. To this end, the most frequently employed combination of phases are gas-liquid and liquid-solid.

Liquid-solid chromatography was originally developed for the separation of colored substances, hence the name chromatography which stems from the Greek word *chroma* meaning color. In a typical examination, a colored substance suspected of containing colored impurities is dissolved in a suitable solvent and the solution allowed to pass through a column packed with some solid adsorbent (e.g., alumina), as shown in Figure 1-7. The "chromatogram" is then "developed" by passing through a suitable solvent which washes the **adsorbate** down through the column. Hopefully, and this is the crux of the entire separation, the components are adsorbed unequally by the solid phase, and distinct bands or zones of color appear. The bands at the top of the column contain the most strongly adsorbed components; and the bands at the bottom, the least strongly held components. The zones may be separated mechanically, or else sufficient solvent can be added to wash, or **elute,** the zones separately from the column for further analysis. If all attempts to resolve a given substance chromatographically are unsuccessful, evidence (albeit negative) is thus provided for the presence of a single pure chemical entity. Although the method is not restricted to colored substances, visual techniques of detecting and isolating the various zones cannot be used when some or all of the components of a mixture are colorless. Nonetheless, the principles behind the separation remain unchanged.

In recent years, gas-liquid chromatography (more familiarly known as vapor-phase chromatography, v.p.c.) has added a new dimension for the analysis of volatile substances. The importance of gas-liquid chromatography can be

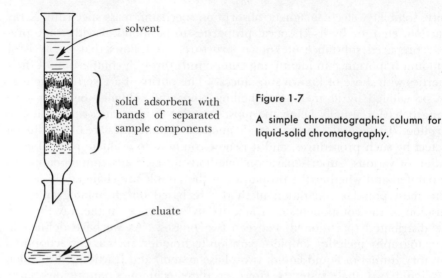

Figure 1-7

A simple chromatographic column for liquid-solid chromatography.

judged from the fact that it could be applied to the analysis of mixtures of any of the compounds whose structures are shown in Figure 1-1, most of which are low-boiling liquids. In the usual form of v.p.c., a few microliters of a liquid to be analyzed are injected into a vaporizer and carried with a stream of gas (most frequently helium) into a long heated column, packed with some porous solid (such as crushed firebrick) impregnated with a nonvolatile liquid or oil. Gas-liquid partitioning occurs, and small differences between partitioning of the components can be magnified by the large number of repetitive partitions possible in a long column. Detection is usually achieved by measuring changes in

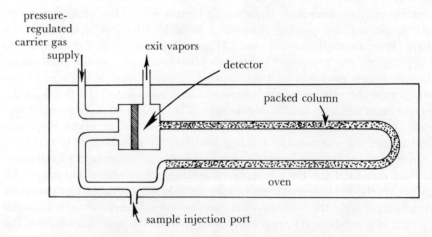

Figure 1-8   Schematic diagram of a vapor-phase chromatography apparatus. The detector is arranged to measure the difference in some property of the carrier gas alone versus the carrier gas plus effluent sample at the exit. Differences in thermal conductivity are particularly easy to measure and give high detection sensitivities.

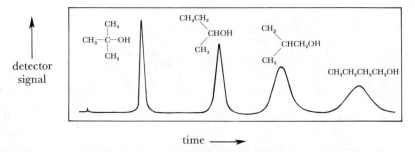

detector
signal

time ⟶

Figure 1-9   A vapor-phase chromatogram of a mixture of isomeric butyl alcohols, C_4H_9OH.

thermal conductivity of the effluent gases.   A schematic diagram of the apparatus and a typical separation are shown in Figures 1-8 and 1-9.   While observation of a single peak in the v.p.c. analysis of a material is, of course, only negative evidence for purity, the method is extraordinarily useful for detection of minute amounts of impurities when these are separated from the main peak. V.p.c. can also be used effectively to purify materials as well as to detect impurities.   To do this, the sample size and the size of the apparatus are generally increased, and the vapor of the pure component is condensed as it emerges from the column.

B. Identification

Once assured of the purity of a certain compound, the next problem is one of identification.   We may have reason to suspect the compound to be an already characterized substance.   If so, the best way to determine whether two substances are in fact identical is to compare their infrared, nuclear magnetic resonance, and mass spectra.   These spectra are essentially "fingerprints" of molecules and practically always are individualistic enough for nonidentical compounds to provide positive differentiation.   Spectroscopic methods of analysis are currently of such importance in organic chemistry as to warrant discussion in a separate chapter (see Chapter 2).

C. Determination of the Structural Formula

It is important to recognize that the determination of the structural formula of a previously unreported compound is really a different type of problem from identifying it with some already known substance.   Such an undertaking usually has two parts: first, determination of the molecular formula, that is, the number and kind of atoms in a given molecule, and second, the determination of the manner in which the several atoms are linked together in the molecule.   The determination of the molecular formula of an organic compound is an analytical problem.   The percentages of all elements present and the molecular weight must be determined.   These data suffice to give the molecular formula.

The vast majority of organic substances are compounds of carbon with hydrogen, oxygen, nitrogen, or the halogens.   All of these elements can be determined directly by routine procedures.   Carbon and hydrogen in combustible

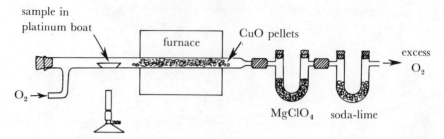

Figure 1-10   Schematic representation of a combustion train for determination of carbon and hydrogen in combustible substances.

compounds can be measured by combustion of a weighed sample in a stream of oxygen (Figure 1-10) and gravimetric determination of the resulting water and carbon dioxide through absorption in anhydrous magnesium perchlorate and soda lime, respectively.   Routine carbon-hydrogen analyses by combustion procedures utilize 3-to-5 mg samples and attain an accuracy of ±0.1 to 0.2 per cent. Complete elemental analyses permit computation of empirical formulas which are equal to, or are submultiples of, the molecular formulas.   A knowledge of the molecular weight is needed to determine which of the multiples of the empirical formula corresponds to the molecular formula.   For example, the empirical formula of the important sugar, glucose, is CH_2O, but the molecular weight defines the molecular formula as $(CH_2O)_6$ or $C_6H_{12}O_6$.

Molecular weights of gaseous organic compounds may be determined directly by vapor-density experiments.   Liquid substances of moderate volatility may be vaporized, and their vapor densities determined.   However, molecular weights of volatile compounds are not often determined in present-day organic research, because the molecular weight of a given substance may usually be estimated from the boiling point, to perhaps 25 per cent accuracy, by knowledge of the boiling points of related compounds.   Molecular weights of high-boiling liquids and slightly volatile solids are generally determined by measurements of freezing-point depressions or boiling-point elevations of solutions in suitable solvents. Solutions in a substance like camphor, which gives a very large freezing-point depression (37.7° per mole of solute dissolved in 1000 g of camphor), are particularly suitable for small-scale operations and can, with ordinary equipment, permit reasonably accurate molecular-weight measurements by determination of melting points.

There are many other more or less specialized techniques available, the choice of which depends on the problem at hand and accessibility of equipment.   Thus, molecular weights of even slightly volatile substances may often be obtained by mass spectrometry, but since mass spectrometers have not been standard laboratory equipment as have infrared spectrometers, their use for this purpose is only now becoming common.   In many circumstances, however, mass spectrometry is the method of choice, particularly since resolution is routinely achieved for masses as high as 600.   The molecular weights of very high molecular weight compounds such as proteins and polymeric materials are frequently determined by end-group analysis, measurement of osmotic pressure, viscosity, light scattering, and sedimentation. Some of these methods will be discussed in more detail in later chapters.

EXERCISE 1-5   A 0.005372-g sample of a liquid carbon-hydrogen-oxygen compound on combustion gave 0.01222 g of CO_2 and 0.00499 g of H_2O.

Show how these results lead to the empirical formula of C_3H_6O. Write at least five isomers that correspond to this formula with univalent H, divalent O, and tetravalent C.

Determination of the structural formula of an unknown compound, once the molecular formula is established, can be easy or difficult. The usual procedure is to obtain as much spectroscopic and chemical information as possible about the kinds of groups that are present. If this does not suffice to define the structure, then chemical means are used to convert the substance into known compounds. Usually this involves degradation, that is, cutting the molecule up into smaller pieces. The natures of the known compounds and the reactions involved are then used to deduce the structure of the unknown. If extensive degradation is necessary to produce known compounds, then deduction of the structure is something like deducing the structure of a building by examination of a pile of its component bricks. In the ideal case, only one structural formula will be compatible with the physical and chemical properties of a given compound. This ideal is often difficult to attain, and actual location of the atoms in space by X-ray or electron diffraction techniques may be required to settle difficult structural questions. The final proof of structure is usually sought by synthesizing a compound with the indicated structure by some unambiguous route. If the synthetic compound and the actual compound are identical, the proposed structure is considered correct.

An example will illustrate the general approach to a problem in structure determination:

Nicotine is a compound which belongs to an important class of naturally occurring substances called **alkaloids.** These are basic nitrogen-containing compounds of vegetable origin, nicotine itself being a liquid which occurs in tobacco leaves and has b.p. 265°. The analysis and molecular weight of nicotine are consistent with the molecular formula $C_{10}H_{14}N_2$. On oxidation with chromic acid, nicotine is degraded to smaller fragments. One of these fragments is an acidic material of composition $C_6H_5O_2N$ which has been shown to be identical with pyridine-3-carboxylic acid [1]. This information indicates that nicotine contains a pyridine ring substituted at the 3-position by the grouping $C_5H_{10}N$.

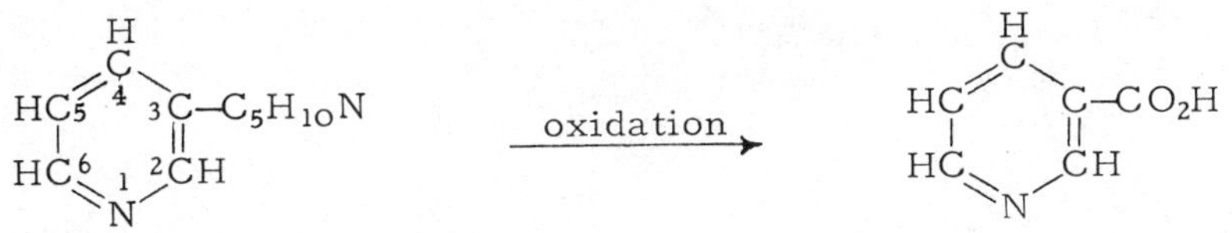

nicotine   oxidation   pyridine–3–carboxylic acid

[1]

In order to determine the structure of the $C_5H_{10}N$ grouping, a series of reactions can be carried out which modify the pyridine ring, so that oxidation now attacks this ring, leaving the $C_5H_{10}N$ grouping untouched. One fragment isolated after this oxidation is an acid ($C_6H_{11}O_2N$) which is identical with N-methylproline [2], a compound of known structure.

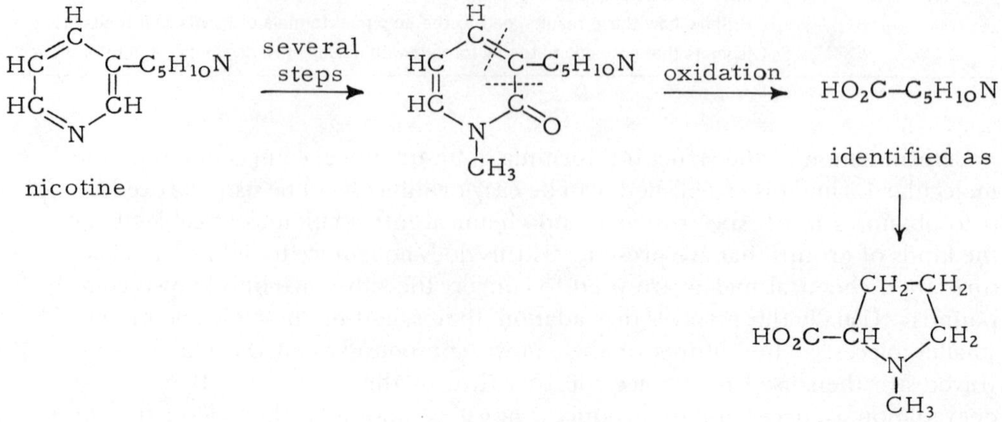

nicotine

several steps

oxidation

$HO_2C-C_5H_{10}N$

identified as

N-methylproline

[2]

Piecing the fragments [1] and [2] together strongly suggests that nicotine has the following structure:

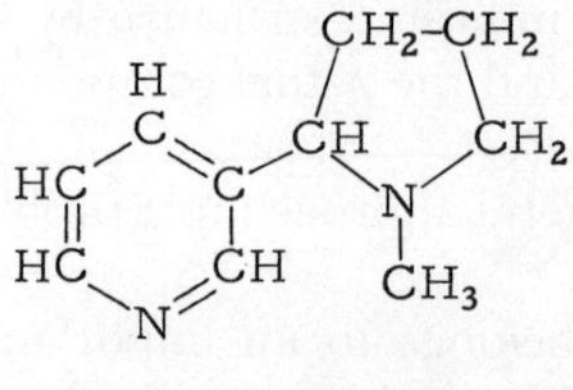

nicotine

A compound of this structure has been synthesized unambiguously in at least two different ways, and since it proved to be identical with naturally occurring nicotine, the proposed structure for nicotine is now accepted as correct.

EXERCISE 1-6   A compound shown by analysis to have the formula C_9H_{10} gives benzoic acid on vigorous oxidation.

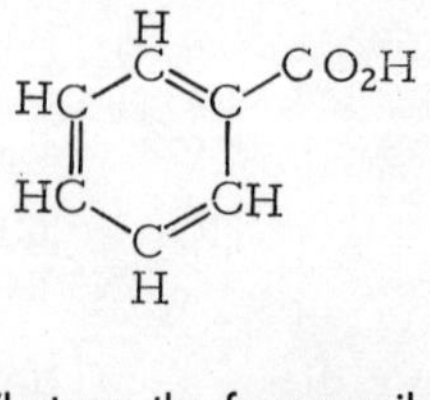

benzoic acid

What are the four possible structures for this compound?

1-7 NOMENCLATURE OF ORGANIC COMPOUNDS

Progress in science depends on communication of facts and ideas. The abundance and complexity of varieties of organic compounds make the problem of organic nomenclature one of singular importance. Ideally, every organic substance would have a completely descriptive and systematic name to permit only one structural formula to be written for it. This ideal has been approached closely enough in some of the current nomenclature systems so that reasonably useful indexes can be made for the extensive catalogs of factual information about organic compounds. Unfortunately, the truly systematic nomenclatures are virtually hopeless for conversational or routine scriptorial purposes and, except for rigid cataloging or indexing, a hodgepodge of trivial and semisystematic designations is in common usage. Eradication of undesirable or antiquated nomenclature systems is extraordinarily difficult, and in order to read or talk organic chemistry without a glossary, one has to be familiar with a variety of nomenclatural schemes. Insofar as possible, completely undescriptive names should be avoided, although clearly this is not always practical since the best descriptive names may be impossibly unwieldy. Clearly, 9-(2,6,6-trimethyl-1-cyclohexenyl)-3,7-dimethyl-2,4,6,8-nonatetraen-1-ol has phonetic disadvantages as a handy name for vitamin A.

Semidescriptive and trivial names for organic compounds are being coined continually and their use is widespread. In comparison with workers in other branches of science, organic chemists have been reasonably objective in choosing names for compounds, and, with a few exceptions, have ignored personal or nationalistic affiliations. Discrete substances of unknown constitution are generally named first after their place of origin. These names, which include penicillin, streptomycin, strychnine, etc., usually persist long after more systematic names are possible. Occasionally, compounds of new types may be designated in accord with their colors (if distinctive) or resemblance of the shapes of their molecular formulas to common objects—examples are azulene (blue), coronene (crown), etc.

We shall strive as far as possible to use systematic nomenclature in this text, but unavoidably there will be some crossing between systems. For example, the relatively simple compound [3] has three acceptable names: *t*-butyl alcohol,[1] trimethylcarbinol, and 2-methyl-2-propanol. The first name is the one most commonly used and, accordingly, we choose to refer to [3] as *t*-butyl alcohol.

$$\underset{[3]}{\underset{\displaystyle CH_3}{\overset{\displaystyle CH_3}{CH_3-\overset{|}{\underset{|}{C}}-OH}}} \qquad\qquad \underset{[4]}{\underset{\displaystyle CH_3}{\overset{\displaystyle CH=CH_2}{CH_3-\overset{|}{\underset{|}{C}}-OH}}}$$

Compound [4] is only slightly more complicated, and is called both α,α-dimethylallyl alcohol and 2-methyl-3-buten-2-ol. Both names are correct and both are used. In a situation like this, we shall frequently use the most systematic name,

---

[1] The abbreviation *t*- stands for *tertiary*, which will be defined in a later chapter.

2-methyl-3-buten-2-ol, and indicate the semisystematic name, α,α-dimethyl-allyl alcohol, parenthetically. For example,

$$CH_2{=}CH{-}CH_2{-}CH_2Br$$

4-bromo-1-butene

(allylcarbinyl bromide)

To explain the system behind these names would be of no benefit at this point. Various aspects of nomenclature will be referred to at intervals in subsequent chapters of this book as a logical adjunct to the main subject under discussion.

SUPPLEMENTARY EXERCISES

1-7 (This problem is in the nature of review of elementary inorganic chemistry and may require reference to a book on general chemistry.) Write Lewis structures for each of the following compounds. Use distinct, correctly placed dots for the electrons. Mark all atoms which are not neutral with charges of the proper sign.

a. ammonia
b. ammonium nitrate
c. hydrogen cyanide
d. ozone ($\angle$ O—O—O = 120°)
e. carbon monoxide
f. perchloric acid

g. hydrogen peroxide
h. hydroxylamine, $HONH_2$
i. sulfur trioxide
j. sulfuric acid
k. boron trifluoride

1-8 Use ball-and-stick models or suitable three-dimensional drawings to determine which members of the following sets of formulas represent identical compounds, provided "free rotation" is considered to be possible around all single bonds (except when these bonds are present in a cyclic structure):

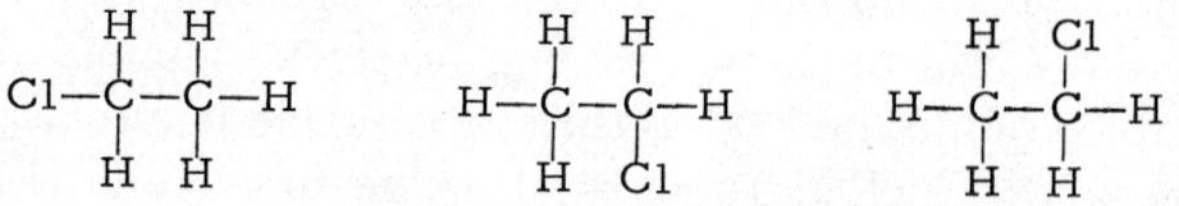

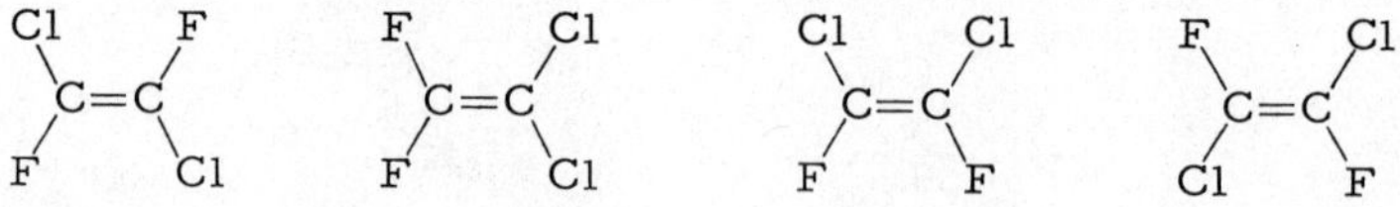

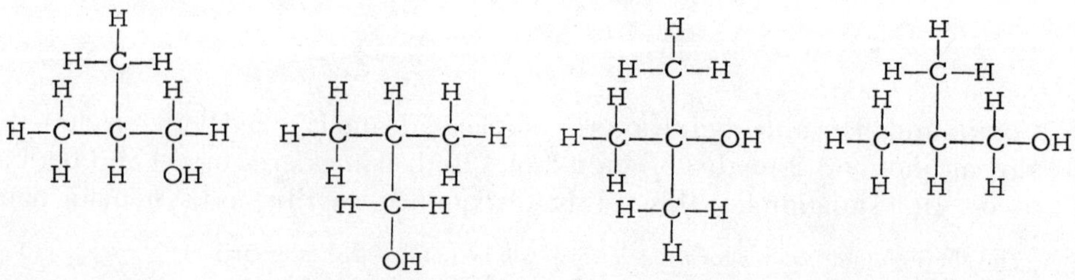

d.

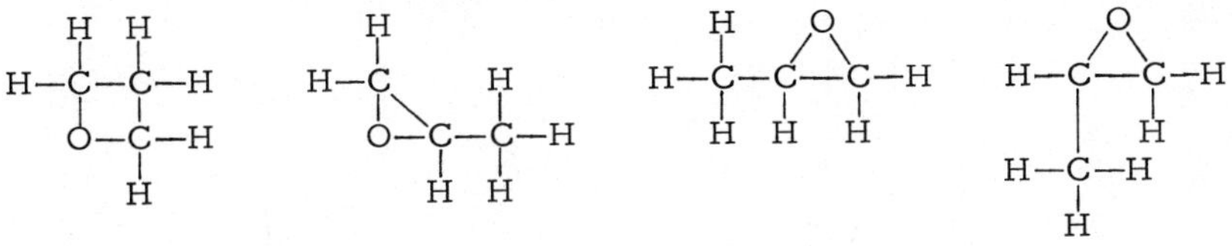

1-9 Write structural formulas for each of the following, using tetravalent carbon, divalent oxygen, and univalent hydrogen:

  a. three isomeric substances of formula C_3H_8O

  b. two isomeric substances of formula C_5H_6O, each of which has a carbon-oxygen double bond and two methyl (CH_3-) groups

  c. a compound of formula C_5H_{12} which would have all of its hydrogens located in chemically *identical* positions

  d. two isomeric substances of formula C_5H_{10}, each of which would have two, and only two, methyl (CH_3-) groups located in chemically identical positions. (Best to check with models.)

1-10 Translate the following condensed formulas into representations in which each bond is drawn individually, as in the formulas shown in Exercise 1-8. All atoms are to have their normal valences in the final formulas.

  a. $CH_3CHBrC(CH_3)_2OCH_3$

  b. $[(CH_3)_2CH]_2CHOH$

  c. $C(CH_2OH)_2(CHCl_2)_2$

  d. $C(CH_3)_2C(CH_3)_2$

  e. $(CH_2)_2CHCl$

  f. $(CH_2)_5C(CHO)_2$

  g. $(CH_3)_2C(CN)CH_2Cl$

  h. $CH_3CO_2CH_3$

Spectroscopy of
Organic Molecules

The modern organic chemist makes intensive use of spectroscopy for structural and quantitative analysis. When a new compound is prepared, the first order of business, after (or even before) determination of its melting point or boiling point, is investigation of its spectral properties. No set of chemical tests can give so much information so quickly. In recognition of this fact, the important spectral properties of each of the major classes of organic molecules will be discussed in this book along with their chemical properties. This chapter presents the principles of the most widely used spectroscopic methods in more detail than necessary for study of the early parts of the book. It is recommended that the material be reviewed as new spectral data are introduced in later chapters.

We have placed considerable emphasis on nuclear magnetic resonance (n.m.r.) spectroscopy, even though it has only come into general use in the last few years. The reasons for this emphasis are that n.m.r. spectra turn out to be more easily predicted and interpreted and, in general, are better suited for routine characterization, detection of impurities, and analysis of simple mixtures of organic compounds than the other varieties of spectra.

It is possible to defer study of all or part of Chapter 2 until after Chapter 5, which is concerned with the formulation of organic molecules in terms of atomic orbital models—a subject of importance to understanding electronic spectra. Alternatively, the material in Chapter 5 could be taken up ahead of Chapters 2 through 4.

Spectroscopy of Organic Molecules

CHAPTER $\mathcal{2}$

Virtually all parts of the spectrum of electromagnetic radiation, from X rays to radio waves, have found some practical application for the study of organic molecules. The use of **X-ray diffraction** for determination of the structures of molecules in crystals is of particular value to organic chemistry, but unfortunately the method is not at present adaptable to routine use. Even with the aid of high-speed digital computers, the determination of a complex structure often requires one or two years of research. **Electron** and **neutron diffraction** have special applications where X-ray diffraction is either difficult (substances which are normally gases or liquids) or of insufficient accuracy (location of atoms like hydrogen with very low scattering power). Although, as mentioned, the diffraction methods have the power of determining the complete structure of organic molecules, their failure to be routinely applicable precludes their general utilization in practical organic chemistry.

Attention will be focused in this chapter mainly on those forms of spectroscopy which are adaptable for routine use, either now or in the immediate future. As will be seen, these methods are used by organic chemists in more or less empirical ways. Each spectral method involves certain reversible changes in atoms and molecules through excitation when subjected to radiation. The common kinds of spectroscopy are as follows:

For atoms:

Absorption spectroscopy of atoms—also called *atomic spectra,* or *line spectra;* involves electronic excitation

For molecules:

Microwave spectroscopy — rotational excitation

Infrared and Raman spectroscopy — vibrational and rotational excitation

Ultraviolet and visible spectroscopy — electronic excitation accompanied by
vibrational and rotational changes

Nuclear magnetic resonance spectroscopy — excitation of magnetic atomic
nuclei in a magnetic field
induced by radiofrequency
radiation

Mass spectrometry — bombardment of molecules by medium-energy
electrons and determination of the distribution and
masses of the resulting charged fragments. These
changes are not reversible

2-1 ABSORPTION OF ELECTROMAGNETIC RADIATION

Absorption of electromagnetic radiation by *monatomic* gases such as sodium
vapor results in highly specific changes in electronic configurations. If one
determines and plots absorption as a function of wavelength, it is found that a
series of very sharp absorption bands or lines are observed.

Each absorption line corresponds to a change in electronic energy as befits the
excitation of an electron from one quantum-mechanical orbit to another. For a
particular line, which is the result of a change from the normal or ground state
(E_1) to a higher energy state (E_2), we have a change in energy ΔE_{12}.

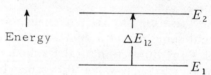

The difference in energy ΔE_{12} is related to the frequency (ν sec^{-1}) or wavelength
(λ cm) of the absorbed radiation by the equations

$$\Delta E_{12} = h\nu = \frac{hc}{\lambda}$$

where h is Planck's constant and c is the velocity of light. Since in general we
will be interested in the energy change in kilocalories (1 kcal = 10^3 cal) which
would result if 1 gram-atom (or mole) of atoms (or molecules) absorbs light, we
can rewrite the above equation in the form

$$\Delta E_{12} = \frac{286,000}{\lambda(A)} \text{ kcal}$$

where λ is now in angstrom (A) units (1 A = 10^{-8} cm). As defined here, ΔE_{12}
corresponds to 1 *einstein* of radiation.

EXERCISE 2-1   Calculate the energy in kcal which corresponds to the absorption of 1 einstein
of light of 5893 A (sodium D line) by sodium vapor. Explain how this absorption
of light by sodium vapor might have chemical utility.

The spectra of molecules, even simple diatomic molecules, are far more complex than are the spectra of atoms. In addition to the energy associated with attractive and repulsive electrical forces in a molecule, there is kinetic energy due to the rotational motions of the molecule or its parts, and vibrational motions of the atoms in each chemical bond with respect to one another. The total energy E of a molecule (apart from the nuclear energy) can be expressed as the sum of three energy terms:

$$E = E_{electronic} + E_{vibrational} + E_{rotational}$$

Absorption of electromagnetic radiation by molecules can occur not only by electronic excitation of the type described for atoms, but also by changes in the vibrational and rotational energies.

Both rotations and vibrations of molecules are quantized. This means that only particular values of rotational angular momentum or vibrational energy are possible. We speak of the permitted values of the energies as the vibrational and rotational energy levels.

Rotational energy levels are normally very closely spaced so that rather low-energy radiation, such as is provided by radio transmitters operating in the microwave region, suffices to change molecular rotational energies. Since electronic and vibrational energy levels are spaced much more widely and changes between them are induced only by higher energy radiation, microwave absorptions can be characterized as essentially pure "rotational spectra." It is possible to obtain rotational moments of inertia from microwave spectra and from these the bond angles and bond distances for simple molecules. However, microwave spectroscopy requires rather specialized apparatus, and the spectra are far from simple to interpret; as a result, microwave absorption is not as yet used as a routine analytical method in organic chemistry.

2-2 INFRARED SPECTROSCOPY

By all odds, the single most widely used tool for investigating organic structures is the infrared spectrometer. Spectra for infrared radiation over the region of wavelength from 2 to 15 microns (1 micron $= \mu = 10^{-4}$ cm) are of most interest. Recording infrared spectrophotometers with excellent resolution and reproducibility are commercially available and are widely used in organic research. The operating parts of a spectrometer are shown in Figure 2-1. The sample containers (cells) and optical parts of infrared spectrophotometers are made of rock salt (NaCl) or similar materials, since glass is opaque to infrared radiation. Gaseous, liquid, or solid samples can be used. Solids are often run as finely ground suspensions (mulls) in various kinds of oils or are ground up with potassium bromide and compressed by a hydraulic press into wafers. Considerable differences are often observed between the spectra of a solid and its solutions.

Typical infrared spectra are shown in Figure 2-2 for acetone, $CH_3\overset{\displaystyle O}{\overset{\displaystyle \|}{-C-}}CH_3$,

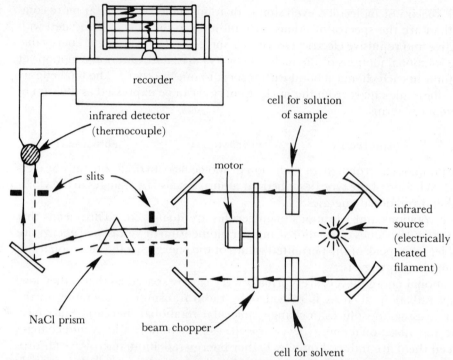

Figure 2-1   Schematic representation of a "double-beam" recording infrared spectrophotometer. The beam chopper permits radiation passing alternately through sample cell and solvent cell to reach the thermocouple.   This procedure permits the difference in absorption by solute and solvent to be measured as an *alternating* electric current from the thermocouple.   The alternating-current output is particularly desirable for electronic amplification.   The usual commercial instruments operate on a "null" principle with the recorder pen linked mechanically to a "comb" (not shown here), which is placed across the solvent-cell beam and moved by a servomechanism to reduce or increase the solvent-cell-beam intensity.   The servomechanism is actuated by the amplified thermocouple output to make the solvent-beam intensity equal to the solution-beam intensity, that is, to reduce the thermocouple output to zero or the null point.   The spectrum can be scanned through the various wavelengths by rotation of the prism in synchronization with the motion of the recorder drum.   The use of a diffraction grating in place of the prism is becoming increasingly common.

and methyl ethyl ketone, CH_3—$\overset{\displaystyle O}{\overset{\displaystyle \|}{C}}$—$CH_2$—$CH_3$. In accord with current practice, the infrared spectra given here are linear in wave numbers (ν cm^{-1}) that are related to radiation frequencies ($\boldsymbol{\nu}$ sec^{-1}) so that $\nu = \boldsymbol{\nu}/c$. A supplementary non-linear wavelength scale in microns is shown, and to convert wave numbers ν to λ in microns we use the relation $\lambda = 10^4/\nu$.

Considerable confusion exists as to the units used to express wavelength or frequency for various kinds of spectra.   For electronic spectra, λ is most commonly expressed in angstrom units (10^{-8} cm) or millimicrons (10^{-7} cm).   For infrared spectra,

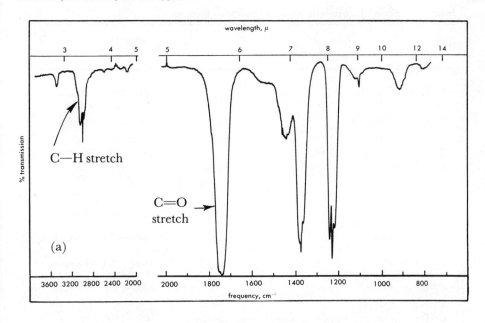

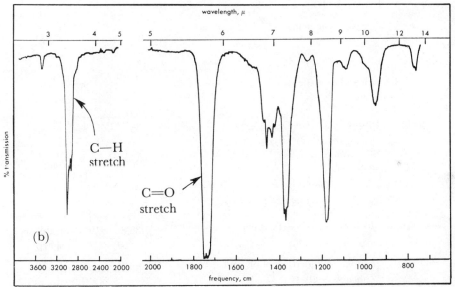

Figure 2-2   Infrared absorption spectra of acetone (a) and methyl ethyl ketone (b) in the vapor phase.

absorbed radiation may be defined by its wavelength λ in microns (10^{-4} cm) or by its frequency ν in units of wave numbers ($10^4/\lambda$ cm^{-1}).

Absorption from about 5000 to 1250 cm^{-1} is generally associated with changes in the vibrational states of the various bonds and is relatively characteristic of the types of bonds present (see Table 2-1).   Thus the bands observed for acetone (Figure 2-2a) at 3050 and 1740 cm^{-1} are due to absorption of infrared radiation, the absorbed energy causing transitions between the energy levels for the

Table 2-1   Some Characteristic Infrared Absorption Frequencies

Bond	Type of compound	Frequency, cm^{-1}	Intensity
$-\overset{\shortmid}{\underset{\shortmid}{C}}-H$	alkanes	2850–2960	strong
$-\overset{\shortmid}{\underset{\shortmid}{C}}-D$	alkanes	~2200	strong
$=\overset{\shortmid}{C}-H$	alkenes and arenes	3010–3100	medium
$\equiv C-H$	alkynes	3300	strong, sharp
$-\overset{\shortmid}{\underset{\shortmid}{C}}-\overset{\shortmid}{\underset{\shortmid}{C}}-$	alkanes	600–1500^a	weak
$C=C$	alkenes	1620–1680	variable
$-C\equiv C-$	alkynes	2100–2260	variable
$-C\equiv N$	nitriles	2200–2300	variable
$-\overset{\shortmid}{\underset{\shortmid}{C}}-O-$	alcohols $-\overset{\shortmid}{\underset{\shortmid}{C}}-OH$, ethers $-\overset{\shortmid}{\underset{\shortmid}{C}}-O-\overset{\shortmid}{\underset{\shortmid}{C}}-$, carboxylic acids $-C\overset{O}{\underset{O-H}{}}$, esters $-C\overset{O}{\underset{O-\overset{\shortmid}{\underset{\shortmid}{C}}-}{}}$	1000–1300	strong
$C=O$	aldehydes $-\overset{O}{\overset{\|}{C}}-H$	1720–1740	strong
$C=O$	ketones $-\overset{\shortmid}{\underset{\shortmid}{C}}-\overset{O}{\overset{\|}{C}}-\overset{\shortmid}{\underset{\shortmid}{C}}-$	1705–1725	strong
$C=O$	acids $-C\overset{O}{\underset{O-H}{}}$, esters $-C\overset{O}{\underset{O-\overset{\shortmid}{\underset{\shortmid}{C}}-}{}}$	1700–1750	strong
$-O-H$	alcohols $-\overset{\shortmid}{\underset{\shortmid}{C}}-O-H$, phenols $=\overset{\shortmid}{C}-O-H$	3590–3650	variable, sharp
$-O-H$	hydrogen-bonded, alcohols and phenols $-O-H\cdot\cdot O$	3200–3400	strong, broad
$-O-H$	hydrogen-bonded, acids $-O-H\cdot\cdot O$	2500–3000	variable, broad
$-NH_2$	amines $-\overset{\shortmid}{\underset{\shortmid}{C}}-NH_2$	3300–3500 (double peak)	medium
$-\overset{\shortmid}{N}-H$	amines $-\overset{\shortmid}{\underset{\shortmid}{C}}-\overset{H}{\underset{\shortmid}{N}}-\overset{\shortmid}{\underset{\shortmid}{C}}-$	3300–3500 (single peak)	medium

^{a} In general, C—C single-bond stretching frequencies are not useful for identification.

stretching vibrations of the C—H and C=O bonds, respectively. Absorption bands between 1250 and 675 cm^{-1} are generally associated with complex vibrational and rotational energy changes of the molecule as a whole and are quite characteristic of particular molecules. This part of the spectrum is often called the "finger-print" region and is of extreme usefulness for determining whether samples are chemically identical. The spectra of acetone and methyl ethyl ketone are seen to be very similar in the region 4000 to 1250 cm^{-1} but quite different from 1250 to 675 cm^{-1}.

EXERCISE 2-2   Show the approximate positions and intensities of the characteristic infrared bands corresponding to stretching vibrations in the following molecules:

a. trideuteroacetone,

$$\begin{array}{ccccc} H & & O & & D \\ | & & \| & & | \\ H-C & - & C & - & C-D \\ | & & & & | \\ H & & & & D \end{array}$$

b. methylacetylene,

$$\begin{array}{c} H \\ | \\ H-C-C\equiv C-H \\ | \\ H \end{array}$$

c. ethyl acetate,

$$\begin{array}{ccccccc} H & & O & & H & & H \\ | & & \| & & | & & | \\ H-C & - & C & -O- & C & - & C-H \\ | & & & & | & & | \\ H & & & & H & & H \end{array}$$

d. acrylonitrile,

$$\begin{array}{cc} H & \quad\quad H \\ \diagdown & \diagup \\ C&=C \\ \diagup & \diagdown \\ H & \quad\quad C\equiv N \end{array}$$

e. pyruvic acid,

$$\begin{array}{ccccc} H & & O & & O \\ | & & \| & & \| \\ H-C & - & C & - & C-O-H \\ | & & & & \\ H & & & & \end{array}$$

f. ethyl alcohol,

$$\begin{array}{ccccc} H & & H \\ | & & | \\ H-C & - & C-O-H \\ | & & | \\ H & & H \end{array}$$

(pure liquid and in dilute solution)

EXERCISE 2-3   The infrared spectra shown in Figure 2-3a and b are for compounds of formula C_3H_6O and $C_4H_6O_2$, respectively. Use the data in Table 2-1 in conjunction with the molecular formulas to deduce a structure for each of these substances from its infrared spectrum. Indicate clearly which lines in the spectra you identify with the groups in your structures.

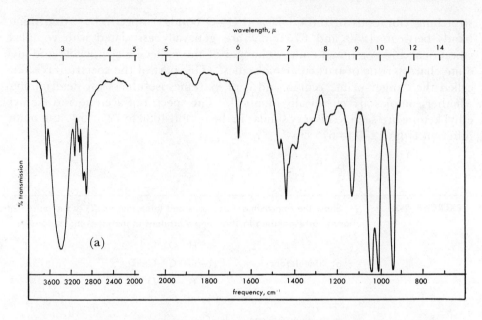

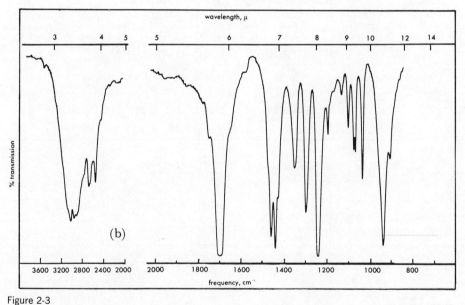

Figure 2-3

Infrared spectra for Exercise 2-3.

2-3 ELECTRONIC SPECTRA OF ORGANIC MOLECULES

Absorption of visible and ultraviolet light produces changes in the electronic energy of molecules associated with excitation of an electron from a stable to an unstable orbital. For most such changes, it is not possible to draw a very explicit structure for the excited state with conventional bond diagrams because the

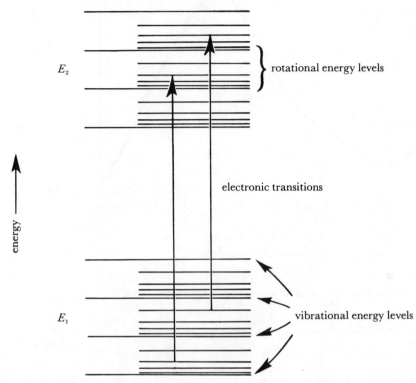

Figure 2-4   Schematic representation of electronic, vibrational, and rotational energy levels.

excited electron is not in a normal bonding orbital.   The transition of an electron from the ground state E_1 to an excited electronic state E_2 is accompanied
by vibrational and rotational changes in the molecule, as shown in Figure 2-4.
It is not usually possible to resolve the resulting absorption *bands* well enough to
see the fine structure due to vibration-rotation transitions.   Consequently, absorptions due to electronic excitation are relatively broad.

The ultraviolet spectrum of acetone is shown in Figure 2-5.[1]   The weak absorption which peaks (i.e., has λ_{max}) at 2800 A is the result of excitation of one
of the unshared electrons on oxygen to a higher energy level.   The same kind
of transition occurs at about the same wavelength and intensity for many simple
compounds of the type $R_2C{=}O$ and $RCH{=}O$ where R represents a hydrocarbon
chain containing no double bonds.

Table 2-2 lists the wavelengths of maximum absorption for some typical electronic absorption bands of simple molecules (more complex substances will be
considered in later chapters).

[1] The experimental arrangement for determining such spectra is usually quite similar to that of
infrared spectrometers shown in Figure 2-1.   The principal differences lie in the use of a tungsten
lamp (3200 to 8000 A) or hydrogen arc (1800 to 4000 A) as the light source; quartz prism and sample
cells; and a photoelectric cell, rather than a thermocouple, as the radiation detector.   In these
spectrometers, the prism is placed ahead of the sample.

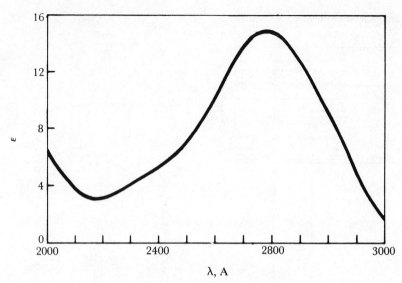

Figure 2-5   The ultraviolet spectrum of acetone in cyclohexane.

Table 2-2   Some Electronic Transitions of Simple Organic Molecules

Compound	λ_{max}, A	ε_{max}[a]	Solvent[b]
$(CH_3)_2C{=}O$	2800	15	cyclohexane
	1900	1,100	
	1560	strong	
$CH_2{=}CH_2$	1620	10,000	vapor
$CH_2{=}CH{-}CH{=}CH_2$	2170	20,900	hexane
$CH_3{-}CH{=}CH{-}CH{=}CH{-}CH_3$	2270	22,500	hexane
$CH_2{=}CH{-}CH_2{-}CH_2{-}CH{=}CH_2$	1850	20,000	alcohol
$CH_3{-}C{\equiv}CH$	1865	450	cyclohexane
$CH_2{=}CH{-}C{=}O$	3240	24	alcohol
$\qquad\qquad\quad \mid$	2190	3,600	
$\qquad\qquad\quad CH_3$			
CH_4	1219	strong	vapor
$CH_3{-}CH_3$	1350	strong	vapor
$CH_3{-}Cl$	1725	weak	vapor
$CH_3{-}Br$	2040	200	vapor
$CH_3{-}I$	2575	365	pentane
$CH_3{-}O{-}H$	1835	150	vapor
$CH_3{-}O{-}CH_3$	1838	2,520	vapor
$(CH_3)_3N$	2273	900	vapor

[a] The molar extinction coefficient ε is a measure of the absorption efficiency at the wavelength λ_{max}. Since the amount of absorption will be proportional to the concentration (c moles/liter) and thickness of the sample (l cm), ε is obtained from the equation

$$\varepsilon = \frac{1}{cl}\log_{10}\frac{I_0}{I}$$

where I_0/I is the ratio of intensity of incident light I_0 to transmitted light I. The per cent transmission of a solution is $(I/I_0) \times 100$. Substances for which ε is independent of concentration are said to obey Beer's law (or the Beer-Lambert law).

[b] It is necessary to specify the solvent since λ_{max} and ε_{max} vary somewhat with solvent.

EXERCISE 2-4   Calculate the percentage of the incident light which would be absorbed by an 0.010-M solution of acetone in cyclohexane contained in a quartz cell 0.1 cm long at 2800 A and 1900 A.

2-4 NUCLEAR MAGNETIC RESONANCE SPECTROSCOPY

Nuclear magnetic resonance (n.m.r.) spectroscopy is very useful for identification and analysis of organic compounds. The principles of this form of spectroscopy are quite simple. The nuclei of some kinds of atoms act like tiny magnets and become lined up when placed in a magnetic field. In n.m.r. spectroscopy, we measure the energy required to change the alignment of magnetic nuclei in a magnetic field.

A schematic diagram of a very simple form of an n.m.r. instrument is shown in Figure 2-6. When a substance such as ethyl alcohol, CH_3—CH_2—OH, the hydrogens of which have nuclei that are magnetic, is placed in the center of the coil between the magnet pole faces and the magnetic field is increased gradually, at certain field strengths, energy is absorbed by the sample and the current flow in the coil is increased. The result is a spectrum such as the one shown in Figure 2-7. This spectrum is detailed enough to serve as a most useful "fingerprint" for ethyl alcohol but is also simple enough for the origin of each line to be accounted for, as we shall see.

For what kinds of substances can we expect nuclear magnetic resonance absorption to occur? Magnetic properties are always found with nuclei of odd-numbered masses, ^1H, ^{13}C, ^{15}N, ^{17}O, ^{19}F, ^{31}P, etc., and nuclei of even mass but odd atomic number, ^2H, ^{10}B, ^{14}N, etc. Nuclei like ^{12}C, ^{16}O, ^{32}S, etc., with even mass and atomic numbers have no magnetic properties and do not give nuclear magnetic resonance signals. For various reasons, routine use of n.m.r. spectra in organic chemistry is confined to ^1H, ^{19}F, and ^{31}P. We shall be concerned here principally with n.m.r. spectra of hydrogen (^1H).

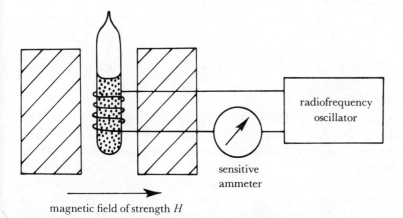

radiofrequency
oscillator

sensitive
ammeter

magnetic field of strength H

Figure 2-6   Essential features of a simple n.m.r. spectrometer.

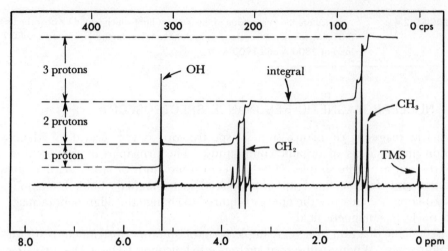

Figure 2-7   N.m.r. spectrum of ethyl alcohol (containing a trace of hydrochloric acid). Chemical shifts are relative to tetramethylsilane, $(CH_3)_4Si$ or TMS $= 0.00$ ppm. The stepped line is an integral of the areas under each of the resonance lines.

Nuclear magnetic resonance spectra may be so simple as to have only a single absorption peak but can also be much more complex than the spectrum of Figure 2-7. On the one hand, complexity is helpful because it makes the spectra more individualistic and better suited as fingerprints for characterization of organic molecules. However, complexity can hinder the use of n.m.r. spectra for qualitative analysis and structure proofs. Fortunately, with the aid of isotopic substitution and an electronic technique known as "double resonance," it is now possible to analyze completely spectra that show literally hundreds of lines. The ways of doing this are beyond the scope of this book—however, it is important to recognize that no matter how complex an n.m.r. spectrum appears to be, it can be analyzed in terms of just *three* elements: chemical shifts, spin-spin splittings, and kinetic (reaction-rate) processes.

The kind of n.m.r. spectroscopy we shall discuss here is limited in its applications, because it can only be carried on with liquids or solutions. Fortunately, the allowable range of solvents is large, from hydrocarbons to concentrated sulfuric acid, and for most compounds it is possible to find a suitable solvent.

A. The Chemical Shift

Ethyl alcohol, CH_3—CH_2—OH, has three kinds of hydrogens: methyl (CH_3), methylene (CH_2), and hydroxyl (OH). In a magnetic field, the nuclei (protons) of each of these kinds of hydrogens have slightly different magnetic environments as the result of the motions of their valence electrons and those of neighboring atoms in response to the magnetic field. The magnetic field strength at a particular nucleus is usually less than the strength of the applied external magnetic field, because the motions of the electrons result in a shielding effect (the so-called *diamagnetic shielding effect*). The important point is that the effects arising from the motions of the electrons will be different for each kind of hydrogen, and, therefore, the resonance signal produced for each kind of hydrogen will come at different field strengths. A plot of signal against field strength (Figure 2-7) thus shows three principal groups of lines for ethyl alcohol with areas under each corresponding to the three varieties of hydrogen.

Differences in the field strengths at which signals are obtained for nuclei of the same kind, such as protons or ^{19}F, but located in different molecular environments, are called **chemical shifts.**

Chemical shifts are always measured with reference to a standard. For protons in organic molecules, the customary standard is tetramethylsilane, $(CH_3)_4Si$, which has the advantage of giving a strong, sharp n.m.r. signal in a region where only a very few other kinds of protons absorb. Chemical shifts are usually expressed in cycles per second (cps) relative to tetramethylsilane (TMS). These may seem like odd units for magnetic field strength but since resonance occurs at a radio frequency, either frequency units (cps, radians/sec) or magnetic field units (gauss) are appropriate.

Most n.m.r. spectrometers for routine use operate with rf oscillators set at 40, 60, or 100 megacycles per second (Mcps). Since chemical shifts turn out to be strictly proportional to the spectrometer frequency, we expect lines 100 cps apart at 60 Mcps to be 167 cps apart at 100 Mcps. To facilitate comparisons between chemical shifts measured at different frequencies, shifts in cps are often divided by the oscillator frequency and reported as ppm (parts per million). Thus, if a proton signal comes 100 cps at 60 Mcps downfield (toward higher frequencies) relative to tetramethylsilane, it can be designated as being $(+100 \text{ cps}/60 \times 10^6 \text{ cps}) \times 10^6 = +1.67$ ppm relative to tetramethylsilane. At 100 Mcps, the line will then be $1.67 \times 100 \times 10^{-6} \times 10^6 = 167$ cps downfield from tetramethylsilane. A table of typical proton chemical shifts relative to TMS is given in Table 2-3.[1] The values quoted for each type of proton may, in practice, show variations of 5 to 20 cps. This is not unreasonable, because the chemical shift of a given proton is expected to depend somewhat on the nature of the particular molecule involved and also on the solvent, temperature, and concentration.

EXERCISE 2-5   Figure 2-8 shows the proton n.m.r. spectrum of $(CH_3)_2C(OH)CH_2COCH_3$ with tetramethylsilane as standard. The stepped line is an electronic integration of the areas under the signal peaks. (*a*) List the chemical shift of each proton signal in ppm, and deduce, from the data of Table 2-3 and the trace of the integrated areas, the identity of the protons that give rise to each line. (*b*) List the line positions in cps relative to tetramethylsilane expected at 100 Mcps. (*c*) Sketch out the spectrum and integral expected for $CH_3COC(CH_3)_2CHO$ at 60 Mcps.

---

[1] An excellent summary of chemical shifts and many illustrative n.m.r. spectra run under standard conditions are available in the NMR Spectra Catalog, Varian Associates, Palo Alto, California.

Table 2-3   Typical Proton Chemical Shift Values (dilute chloroform solutions)

Type of proton[a]	Chemical shift[b]		Type of proton[a]	Chemical shift[b]	
	ppm	cps[c]		ppm	cps[c]
R—CH₃	0.9	54	O=C—CH₃ with R below C	2.3	126
R—CH₂—R	1.3	78			
R₃CH	2.0	120	R—CH₂—Cl	3.7	220
R₂C=CH₂	~5.0	300	R—CH₂—Br	3.5	210
R₂C=CH with R below	~5.3	320	R—CH₂—I	3.2	190
			RCH(—Cl)₂[d]	5.8	350
benzene ring with CH heavy	7.3	440	R—O—CH₃	3.8	220
			(R—O—)₂CH₂[d]	5.3	320
R—C≡C—H	2.5	150	R—C—H (=O)	9.7	580
R₂C=C—CH₃ with R below	~1.8	108	R—O—H	~5[e]	300[e]
toluene-type ring C—CH₃	2.3	140	phenol-type ring C—OH	~7[e]	420[e]
			R—C—OH (=O)	~11[e]	660[e]

[a] The proton undergoing resonance absorption is shown in heavy type. The group R denotes a saturated hydrocarbon chain.

[b] Relative to tetramethylsilane as 0.00 ppm.

[c] Spectrometer frequency, 60 Mcps (14,100 gauss magnetic field).

[d] Note how the shift produced by two chlorines or two RO— groups is greater than, but by no means double, that produced by one chlorine or RO— group.

[e] Sensitive to solvent, concentration, and temperature.

B. Spin-Spin Splitting

We have noted that organic molecules with protons on contiguous carbon atoms, such as ethyl derivatives $CH_3CH_2X(X \neq H)$, show principal resonance signals for protons of different chemical shifts (see Figure 2-7). Each of these signals is actually a group of lines that results from **"spin-spin splitting."** Taking as a typical example the protons of ethyl iodide (Figure 2-9), the chemical-shift difference between the methyl and methylene protons gives the two main groups of lines. These are split ("first-order" effect) into *equally spaced* sets of three and four lines by mutual magnetic interactions that are called "spin-

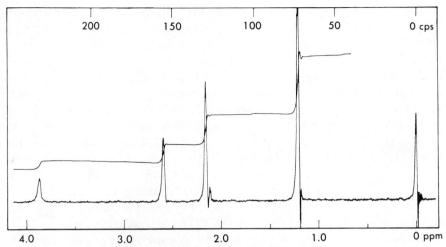

Figure 2-8   N.m.r. spectrum of diacetone alcohol, $(CH_3)_2C(OH)CH_2COCH_3$, at 60 Mcps relative to TMS 0.00 ppm.   The stepped line is the integrated spectrum.

spin interactions."   Several of these lines are further discernibly split as the result of "second-order" spin-spin splitting.

How do we know what we are dealing with when there are so many lines present?   First, the chemical shift is easily recognizable as such by the fact that the spacing between the main groups is directly proportional to the oscillator frequency ν.   If we double ν, the spacing doubles.   In contrast, the line spacings for the first-order splitting are *independent* of ν, and for this reason the first-order splitting is easily recognized, also.   Finally, the second-order splitting turns out to depend on ν for rather complicated reasons; it tends to disappear as ν is increased.

It can be shown by isotopic substitution with heavy hydrogen (deuterium, D) that the three-four pattern of lines observed for spin-spin splitting with compounds having ethyl groups (XCH_2CH_3, see Figure 2-9) arises from magnetic

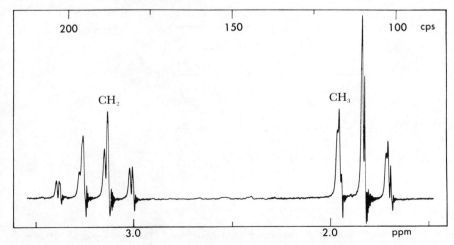

Figure 2-9   N.m.r. spectrum of ethyl iodide, CH_3CH_2I, at 60 Mcps relative to TMS, 0.00 ppm.

interaction of each group of protons with the other. Deuterons have much smaller magnetic moments than protons, and substitution of one deuteron on the methyl of an ethyl group (XCH_2CH_2D) produces a triplet resonance for the methylene group (actually somewhat broadened because of the small magnetic effect of the deuteron); substitution of two deuterons (XCH_2CHD_2) produces a doublet resonance with the splitting caused by the remaining proton. Three deuterons (XCH_2CD_3) give a one-line XCH_2 spectrum (see Figure 2-10). Thus, for this particular simple case, the multiplicity of lines can be seen to be $(n + 1)$ where n is the number of protons on contiguous carbons. That the methylene resonance of an ethyl group is not complicated beyond the observed quartet by interaction of the methylene protons with each other is, for our purposes here, best condensed into a simple catechism—protons with the *same* chemical shift do not normally split one another's absorption lines. Thus, only single resonance lines are observed for H_2, CH_4, C_2H_6, $(CH_3)_4Si$, etc.

In general, the magnitude of the spin-spin splitting effect of one proton on another proton (or group of equivalent protons) depends on the number and kind of intervening chemical bonds, and on the spatial relations between the groups. For simple systems without double bonds and with normal bond angles, we find for nonequivalent protons (i.e., having different chemical shifts):

$$H-\overset{|}{\underset{|}{C}}-H \qquad\qquad H-\overset{|}{\underset{|}{C}}-\overset{|}{\underset{|}{C}}-H \qquad\qquad H-\overset{|}{\underset{|}{C}}-\overset{|}{\underset{|}{C}}-\overset{|}{\underset{|}{C}}-H$$

$$\begin{array}{ccc} 10\text{--}15 & 5\text{--}8 & \sim 0 \\ \text{cps} & \text{cps} & \text{cps} \end{array}$$

Where restricted rotation or double- and triple-bonded groups are involved, widely divergent splittings are observed. Thus, while the "four-bond" coupling is essentially zero in compounds having no double or triple bonds, a small *nine-*

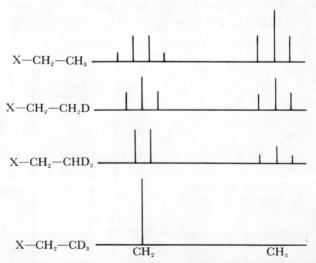

Figure 2-10   Schematic spectra of deuterated ethyl derivatives. The right-hand set of lines is always a triplet when observable because of the two protons of the $X-CH_2-$ group.

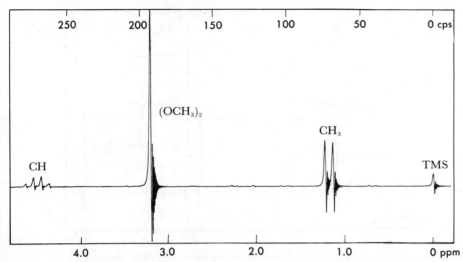

Figure 2-11   N.m.r. spectrum of dimethyl acetal, $(CH_3O)_2CHCH_3$, at 60 Mcps relative to TMS, 0.00 ppm.

bond coupling has been observed for CH_3—$C\equiv C$—$C\equiv C$—$C\equiv C$—CH_2X. Furthermore, even though "long-range" couplings are often large for compounds with double bonds, the two-bond coupling between two nonequivalent

hydrogens located at one end of a double bond (i.e., $\begin{matrix} H \\ \diagdown \\ \diagup \\ H \end{matrix} C=$) is characteris-

tically small, 0 to 3 cps.

The ratios of the line intensities in spin-spin splitting patterns usually follow simple rules when the chemical shifts are large with respect to the splittings. A symmetrical doublet is produced by a single proton, a $1:2:1$ triplet by two protons in a group, a $1:3:3:1$ quartet by three protons in a group, $1:4:6:4:1$ quintet by four protons, etc. The intensities follow the binomial coefficients.

The spectrum of $(CH_3O)_2CHCH_3$ (Figure 2-11) provides an excellent example of how n.m.r. shows the presence of contiguous protons. The symmetrical doublet and $1:3:3:1$ quartet are typical of interaction between a single proton and an adjacent group of three. The methyl protons of the (CH_3O) groups are too far from the others to give demonstrable spin-spin splitting.

EXERCISE 2-6   Sketch out the n.m.r. spectrum and integral expected at 60 Mcps, with TMS as standard, for the following substances. Show the line positions in cps; neglect spin-spin couplings smaller than 1 to 2 cps and all second-order effects. Note that chlorine, bromine, and iodine (but not fluorine) act as nonmagnetic nuclei.

a. CH_3Cl
b. CH_3CH_2Cl
c. $(CH_3)_2CHCl$
d. $CH_3CD_2CH_2Cl$
e. $(CH_3)_3CCl$

f. $CHCl_2CHBr_2$
g. $CH_3CHClCOCH_3$
h. $CH_3CH_2CO_2CH_2CH_3$
i. $ClCH_2CH_2CH_2I$
j. $(ClCH_2)_3CH$

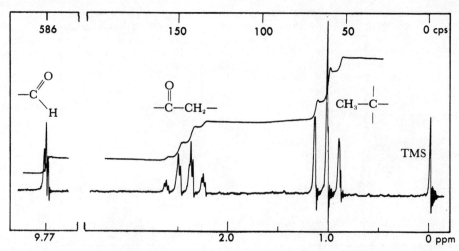

Figure 2-12   N.m.r. spectrum and integral for compound of formula C_3H_6O at 60 Mcps relative to TMS.

C. Use of Nuclear Magnetic Resonance Spectroscopy in Qualitative Analysis

The solution of a typical qualitative analysis problem by n.m.r. can be illustrated with the aid of the spectrum shown in Figure 2-12. Here, we see three principal groups of lines at 9.8, 2.4, and 1.0 ppm for a compound of formula C_3H_6O. The relative heights of the principal steps of the integrated spectrum show these groups to arise from one, two, and three hydrogens, respectively. The single hydrogen at 9.8 ppm is seen from Table 2-3 to have a chemical shift compatible with either RCHO or RCO_2H. The latter possibility is of course excluded because the compound has only one oxygen. The only structure that can be written for C_3H_6O possessing an RCHO group is CH_3CH_2CHO (propionaldehyde), and this structure is completely compatible with the other features of the spectrum. Thus, the CH_3— resonance comes at 1.0 ppm (0.9 ppm predicted for CH_3R) and the —CH_2— resonance at 2.4 ppm (2.3 ppm predicted for CH_3COR).

The spin-spin splitting pattern agrees with the assigned structure, there being the same 7 cps spacings in the characteristic three-four pattern of the CH_3—CH_2— group shown by ethyl iodide (Figure 2-9). The doubling up (somewhat obscured by second-order splitting) of each of the —CH_2— resonance lines is due to a small (~2 cps) coupling between the —CHO and —CH_2— protons. This interaction also causes the —CHO resonance to be split into a $1:2:1$ triplet, as expected from the $n + 1$ rule. Three-bond couplings between —CHO and adjacent —CH_2— protons appear to be generally much smaller than —CH_2—CH_3 couplings.

EXERCISE 2-7   Figure 2-13 shows n.m.r. spectra and integrals at 60 Mcps for three simple organic compounds. Write a structure for each substance that is in accord with both its molecular formula and n.m.r. spectrum. Explain how you assign each of the lines in the n.m.r. spectrum.

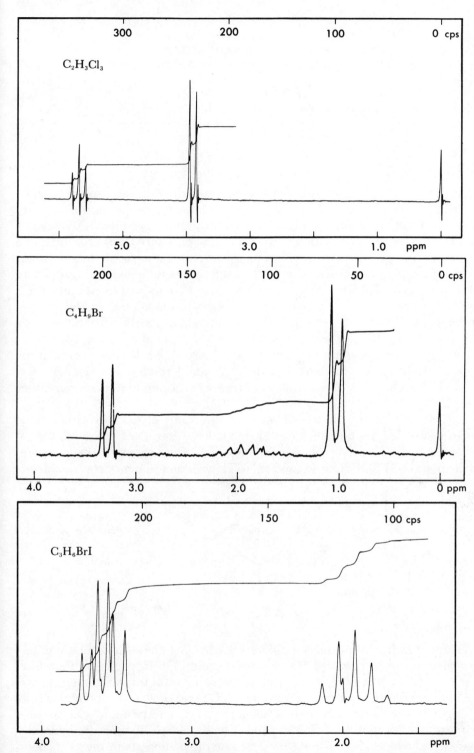

Figure 2-13   N.m.r. spectra and integrated spectra of some simple organic compounds at 60 Mcps relative to TMS, 0.00 ppm.   See Exercise 2-7.

EXERCISE 2-8   Figure 2-14 shows the n.m.r. spectrum of a compound, $C_5H_8O_2$. Which of the following structures fits the spectrum best? Explain.

$CH_3CH\!=\!CHCO_2CH_3$ $CH_2\!=\!CHCH_2CO_2CH_3$

$CH_2\!=\!CHCO_2CH_2CH_3$ $HCO_2CH_2CH_2CH\!=\!CH_2$

$CH_2\!=\!C(CH_3)CO_2CH_3$

$CH_2\!=\!C(OCH_3)COCH_3$ $\overline{OCH_2CH_2CH_2CH_2C}\!=\!O$

$(CH_2)_2CHCO_2CH_3$

D. Nuclear Magnetic Resonance and Rate Processes

An n.m.r. spectrometer is unusual among instruments used to study molecules through absorption of electromagnetic radiation in that it acts like a camera
with a relatively slow shutter speed.   In fact, its shutter speed is quite commonly
about the same as a conventional camera having exposure times of a 100th of a
second or so.   When we take an n.m.r. spectrum of a molecule that is undergoing any rapid motion or reaction, the result is something like taking a picture
of a turning spoked wheel with a box camera.   If the wheel turns only once a
minute, a photograph at a 100th of a second will show the individual spokes
without much blurring.   On the other hand, if the wheel turns 100 or more
times a second, then a photograph does not show the individual spokes at all,
but only the average outline of the rim and hub as a border to the gray of the
spokes.   Pictures showing blurred individual spokes result only when the wheel
is turning neither very rapidly nor very slowly in relation to the camera shutter
speed.

A vivid example of the use of n.m.r. in the study of motions within molecules is afforded by the fluorine (^{19}F) resonance spectrum of 1,2-difluorotetra-
chloroethane.   This molecule is most stable in three staggered rotational conformations [1-3]   Of these, [2] and [3] will have identical n.m.r. spectra.   How-

[1]   [2]   [3]

ever, the fluorines of [1] have a different environment and should have different chemical shifts from the fluorines of [2] and [3].   In principle, therefore,
one would expect to observe separate n.m.r. resonances for the isomers, but, at
room temperature, rotation around the C—C bond occurs so rapidly that only
a single fluorine resonance line is obtained.   The line position is an average
position, the location of which depends on the length of time the molecules
exist separately as [1], [2], and [3].   The rate of rotation about the C—C bond
becomes slower with decreasing temperature and is so slow at $-120°$ that one

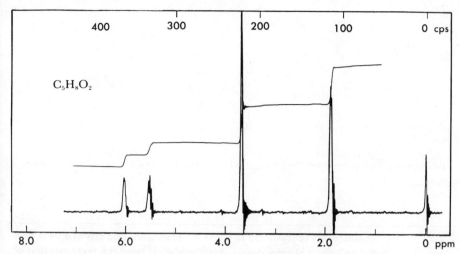

Figure 2-14 Spectrum of a compound C₅H₈O₂ at 60 Mcps relative to TMS as standard, see Exercise 2-8.

can observe the separate resonances of [1] and the isomers [2] and [3] as shown in Figure 2-15. Studies of the blurring of the n.m.r. spectrum of 1,2-difluoro-tetrachloroethane with temperature provide a means of evaluating the amount of energy the molecules must have to allow rotation to take place.

The loss of identity of particular protons by rapid rate processes makes the n.m.r. spectra of ethyl derivatives much simpler than they would otherwise be. Inspection of a ball-and-stick model of an ethyl derivative in the staggered configuration (see Figure 1-4) shows that one of the CH_3 hydrogens (marked here with *) should not have exactly the same chemical shift as the other two. However, rotation about the single bond is sufficiently fast (10^{-6} sec) to average out

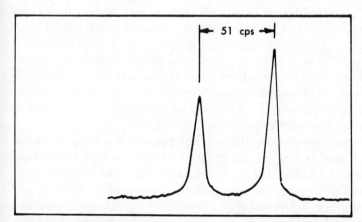

Figure 2-15   N.m.r. spectrum of 1,2-difluorotetrachloroethane, FCl_2C—CCl_2F, at − 120° and 56.4 Mcps.

$$\text{H}\overset{*}{\underset{\overset{\displaystyle \text{H}}{\overset{\displaystyle |}{\text{C}}}}{\text{—C—H}}}$$

the differences between the protons, and an average resonance line position is observed.

EXERCISE 2-9   In reasonably concentrated solutions in water, acetic acid acts as a weak acid (less than 1 per cent dissociated). Acetic acid gives two n.m.r. resonance lines at 2 and 11 ppm, relative to TMS, while water gives a line at 5 ppm. Nonetheless, mixtures of acetic acid and water are found to give just two lines. The *position* of one of these lines depends on the acetic acid concentration, while the other one does not. Explain and show how you would expect the position of the concentration-dependent line to change over the range of acetic acid concentrations from 0 to 100 per cent.

2-5 MASS SPECTROMETRY

The application of mass spectrometry to organic molecules involves bombardment with a beam of medium-energy electrons in high vacuum and analysis of the charged particles and fragments so produced. Commercial mass spectrometers are set up to analyze positively charged fragments, although negative-ion mass spectrometry is also under active investigation. The elements of a mass spectrometer are shown in Figure 2-16. The positive ions produced by electron bombardment are accelerated by the negatively charged accelerating plates and are swept down to the curve of the analyzer tube where they are sorted as to their mass to charge (m/e) ratio by the analyzing magnet. With good resolution, only the ions of a single mass number will pass through the slit and impinge on the collector, even when the mass numbers are in the neighborhood of several hundred or a thousand. The populations of the whole range of mass numbers of interest can be determined by plotting the rate of ion collection as a function of the magnetic field of the analyzing magnet.

Mass spectra of acetone, methyl ethyl ketone, and propionaldehyde are shown in Figure 2-17. Each peak is due to fragmentation of the molecule, by electron impact, into ions such as $CH_3^{\oplus}$, $CH_3CH_2^{\oplus}$, $CH_3CO^{\oplus}$, etc. The "cracking patterns" are, of course, functions of the energy of the bombarding electrons and serve as an extraordinarily individual fingerprint of the particular molecules. For instance, acetone and propionaldehyde are isomers, yet their cracking patterns are strikingly different.

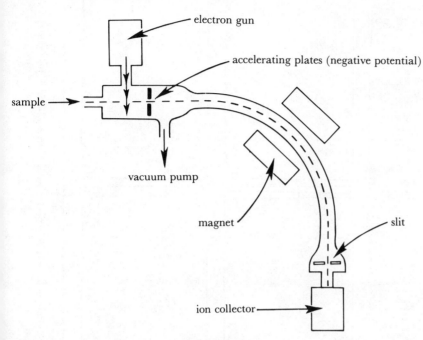

Figure 2-16 Schematic diagram of a mass spectrometer.

The intense peak that is highest in mass number is of considerable importance; in the absence of any combination reactions of cracked fragments, this corresponds to the parent molecule minus just one electron and provides a highly accurate method for measuring molecular weights.

In recent years, considerable success has been achieved in the correlation of the relative abundances of various-sized fragments with molecular structure. Thus, structural information for molecules like nicotine (p. 19) can be gained by measuring the sizes of the abundant fragments which would correspond to breaking the molecule at particularly weak junction points. This type of use of mass spectrometry will be discussed in more detail in Chapter 30.

EXERCISE 2-10   Show how the molecular weights of acetone, propionaldehyde, and methyl ethyl ketone can be estimated from the spectra in Figure 2-17. Suggest a possible origin for the strong peaks of mass 57 in the spectra of methyl ethyl ketone and propionaldehyde, which is in accord with the fact that this peak is essentially absent in acetone, although acetone shows a strong peak at 43.

EXERCISE 2-11   Explain how a mass spectrometer, capable of distinguishing between ions with m/e values differing by 1 part in 50,000, could be used to tell whether an ion of mass 29 is $C_2H_5^{\oplus}$ or $CHO^{\oplus}$.

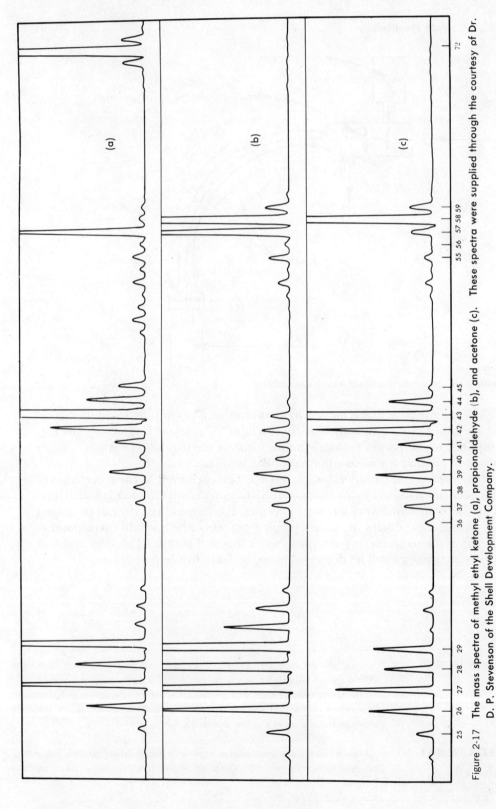

Figure 2-17 The mass spectra of methyl ethyl ketone (a), propionaldehyde (b), and acetone (c). These spectra were supplied through the courtesy of Dr. D. P. Stevenson of the Shell Development Company.

48

BIBLIOGRAPHY

The following are particularly useful for reference either to the principles or the practice of spectroscopy as applied to organic chemistry:

Electronic Spectroscopy
Electronic Absorption Spectroscopy, A. E. Gillam and E. S. Stern, Arnold, London, 1954.

Infrared Spectroscopy
Infrared Spectroscopy—Practical, K. Nakanishi, Holden-Day, San Francisco, 1962.
The Infrared Spectra of Complex Molecules, L. J. Bellamy, Wiley, New York, 1958.
Infrared Spectroscopy: a Chemist's Tool, G. C. Pimentel, *J. Chem. Educ.,* **37**, 651 (1960).

Nuclear Magnetic Resonance
Nuclear Magnetic Resonance, J. D. Roberts, McGraw-Hill, New York, 1959.
Applications of Nuclear Magnetic Resonance Spectroscopy in Organic Chemistry, L. M. Jackman, Pergamon, London, 1959.
Nuclear Magnetic Resonance Spectroscopy, J. D. Roberts, *J. Chem. Educ.,* **37**, 581 (1961).
An Introduction to Spin-Spin Splitting in High-Resolution Nuclear Magnetic Resonance Spectra, J. D. Roberts, Benjamin, New York, 1961.
NMR Spectroscopy as an Analytical Tool in Organic Chemistry, J. C. Martin, *J. Chem. Educ.,* **38**, 286 (1961).

Mass Spectrometry
Mass Spectrometry. Organic Chemical Applications, K. Biemann, McGraw-Hill, New York, 1962.
The Use of Mass Spectrometry in Organic Analysis, E. L. Eliel, T. J. Prosser, and G. W. Young, *J. Chem., Educ.,* **34**, 72 (1957).

Alkanes

*A*lthough this chapter is concerned with the chemistry of just one class of compound, the saturated hydrocarbons or alkanes, several very fundamental principles are developed which we shall use extensively in later chapters. The study of some of these principles has been traditionally associated more with physical chemistry than with organic chemistry. We include them here, at the very beginning of our discussion of organic reactions, because they provide a sound basis for understanding the key questions concerning the practical use of a reaction.—Is the equilibrium point far enough along to be useful? Can conditions be found where the reaction will take place at a practical rate? How can unwanted side reactions be suppressed?

Our initial topic is the naming of alkanes. This is quite important because a great many organic compounds are substitution products of alkanes and are usually named as such. The physical properties of the alkanes are considered next, with emphasis on how regular changes in properties are found as we add more and more carbon atoms to a hydrocarbon chain.

Chemical reactions of alkanes are discussed with special emphasis on combustion and substitution with chlorine. These reactions are employed to illustrate how we can predict and use energy changes—particularly ΔH, the heat evolved or absorbed by a reacting system, which can often be estimated very simply from tables of bond energies.

The problems involved in predicting reaction rates are considered in connection with the chlorination of methane. The example is a complex one, but has virtue in that we are able to break it down into quite simple steps. The principles involved are then applied to the formation of mixtures of isomers in substitution reactions.

Methods of synthesis of alkanes will be discussed in later chapters.

Alkanes

Compounds composed of the elements carbon and hydrogen are called **hydrocarbons;** there are several different types, depending upon how the carbon atoms are compounded. Open-chain or **acyclic** hydrocarbons having no double or triple bonds are the so-called alkanes or saturated paraffin hydrocarbons and conform to the general formula C_nH_{2n+2}. Methane, CH_4, is the simplest alkane of the series. Other types of hydrocarbons include alkenes, alkynes, cycloalkanes, cycloalkenes, and arenes, all of which will be discussed in subsequent chapters; the present chapter is devoted primarily to the alkanes.

3-1 NOMENCLATURE

Before one can begin to discuss the chemistry of organic compounds, one must know how to name them; without convenient and systematic rules for nomenclature that are universally adopted, catastrophic confusion would result. The most definitive set of rules currently in use were evolved through several international conferences and are known as the International Union of Pure and Applied Chemistry Rules (IUPAC rules). Unfortunately, practically no one adheres strictly to the IUPAC rules, and it is necessary to be conversant with a number of other naming systems; these are often simple and conveniently applied to simple compounds but become cumbersome or ambiguous with more complex compounds. We shall begin in this chapter with the naming of alkanes and continue in subsequent chapters with the naming of unsaturated open-chain hydrocarbons (alkenes and alkynes), cycloalkanes, and aromatic and polycyclic hydrocarbons.

The alkanes are classified as "continuous chain" (i.e., unbranched) if all the carbon atoms in the chain are linked to no more than two other carbons; or "branched chain" with one or more carbon atoms linked to more than two other carbons.

$$CH_3-CH_2-CH_2-CH_2-CH_2-CH_3$$

$$
CH_3-\underset{\underset{H}{|}}{\overset{\overset{CH_3}{|}}{C}}-\underset{\underset{H}{|}}{\overset{\overset{CH_3}{|}}{C}}-CH_3 \qquad CH_3-\underset{\underset{CH_3}{|}}{\overset{\overset{CH_3}{|}}{C}}-CH_2-CH_3
$$

continuous-chain hydrocarbon   branched-chain hydrocarbons

The first four continuous-chain hydrocarbons have nonsystematic names.

$$CH_4 \qquad CH_3-CH_3 \qquad CH_3-CH_2-CH_3 \qquad CH_3-CH_2-CH_2-CH_3$$

methane   ethane   propane   butane

The higher members, beginning with pentane, are named systematically with a numerical prefix (pent-, hex-, hept-, etc., to denote the number of carbon atoms) and with the ending *-ane* to classify the compound as a paraffin hydrocarbon. Examples are listed in Table 3-1. These names are generic of both branched and unbranched hydrocarbons, and, to specify a continuous-chain hydrocarbon, the prefix *n-* (for normal) is usually attached. However, in the absence of any qualifying prefix the hydrocarbon is considered to be "normal" or unbranched.

$$CH_3-CH_2-CH_2-CH_2-CH_3$$

pentane or *n*-pentane

The possibility of branched-chain hydrocarbons isomeric with the continuous-chain hydrocarbons begins with butane ($n = 4$). The total number of theo-

Table 3-1   Alkanes (C_nH_{2n+2})

No. of carbons, n	Name	No. of isomers
1	methane	1
2	ethane	1
3	propane	1
4	butane	2
5	pentane	3
6	hexane	5
7	heptane	9
8	octane	18
9	nonane	35
10	decane	75
20	eicosane	366, 319
30	triacontane	4.11×10^9

retically possible isomers for each alkane up to $n = 10$ is given in Table 3-1 and is seen to increase very rapidly with n. It was reported in 1946 that all 75 possible paraffin hydrocarbons from $n = 1$ to $n = 9$ inclusive have been synthesized.

The prefix *iso-* is reserved for substances with two methyl groups at the end of an otherwise straight chain. The prefix *neo-* is used to denote three methyl groups at the end of a chain. Thus, the isomeric butanes and pentanes are named as follows:

$$CH_3-CH_2-CH_2-CH_3 \qquad CH_3-\overset{\overset{\displaystyle CH_3}{|}}{CH}-CH_3$$

n-butane   isobutane

$$CH_3CH_2CH_2CH_2CH_3 \qquad CH_3-\overset{\overset{\displaystyle CH_3}{|}}{CH}-CH_2-CH_3 \qquad CH_3-\overset{\overset{\displaystyle CH_3}{|}}{\underset{\underset{\displaystyle CH_3}{|}}{C}}-CH_3$$

n-pentane   isopentane   neopentane

The system outlined so far permits the naming of only three of the five isomers of hexane.

$$CH_3-CH_2-CH_2-CH_2-CH_2-CH_3 \qquad CH_3-\overset{\overset{\displaystyle CH_3}{|}}{CH}-CH_2-CH_2-CH_3 \qquad CH_3-\overset{\overset{\displaystyle CH_3}{|}}{\underset{\underset{\displaystyle CH_3}{|}}{C}}-CH_2-CH_3$$

n-hexane   isohexane   neohexane

The remaining two hexane isomers (and all the higher alkanes except *n*-alkanes) are named by regarding them as substitution products of simpler hydrocarbons. The substituent groups (sometimes called "radicals") are named by replacing the ending *-ane* of the alkane by *-yl*. We have then the alk*yl* groups, the simplest examples being methyl (CH_3-) and ethyl (CH_3CH_2-) groups. Additional examples are listed in Table 3-2, and these have further classified according to whether they are primary, secondary, or tertiary. To explain, an alkyl group is described as **primary** if the carbon at the point of attachment is bonded to only *one* other carbon, as **secondary** if bonded to *two* other carbons, and **tertiary** if bonded to *three* other carbons.

Some hydrocarbons are conveniently named as derivatives of methane or ethane.

triisopropylmethane   hexamethylethane

Table 3-2   Typical Alkyl Radicals (C_nH_{2n+1})

Primary (RCH_2—)

CH_3— CH_3CH_2— $CH_3CH_2CH_2$—

methyl   ethyl   *n*-propyl

$CH_3CH_2CH_2CH_2$—
$$\begin{array}{c} CH_3 \\ \diagdown \\ CH-CH_2- \\ \diagup \\ CH_3 \end{array}$$

n-butyl   isobutyl

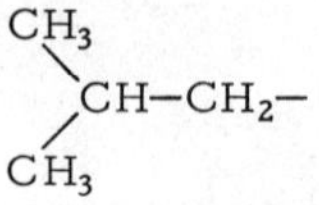

$CH_3CH_2CH_2CH_2CH_2$—
$$\begin{array}{c} CH_3 \\ \diagdown \\ CH-CH_2-CH_2- \\ \diagup \\ CH_3 \end{array}$$
$$\begin{array}{c} CH_3 \\ | \\ CH_3-C-CH_2- \\ | \\ CH_3 \end{array}$$

pentyl   isopentyl   neopentyl
(*n*-amyl)   (isoamyl)

$CH_3CH_2CH_2CH_2CH_2CH_2$—
$$\begin{array}{c} CH_3 \\ \diagdown \\ CH-CH_2-CH_2-CH_2- \\ \diagup \\ CH_3 \end{array}$$
$$\begin{array}{c} CH_3 \\ | \\ CH_3-C-CH_2CH_2- \\ | \\ CH_3 \end{array}$$

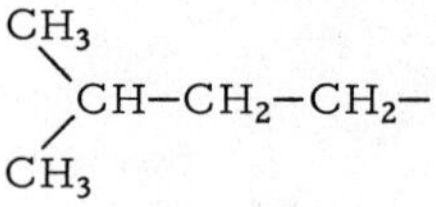

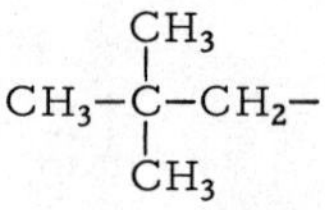

n-hexyl   isohexyl 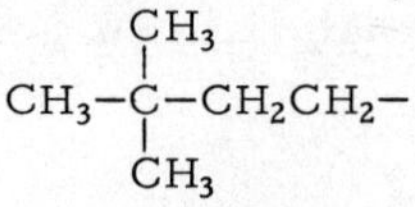   neohexyl

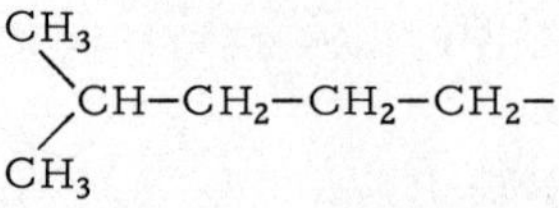

Secondary (R_2CH—)

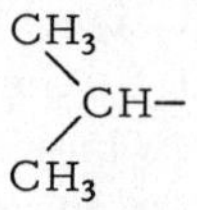

$$\begin{array}{c} CH_3 \\ \diagdown \\ CH- \\ \diagup \\ CH_3 \end{array}$$
$$\begin{array}{c} CH_3CH_2 \\ \diagdown \\ CH- \\ \diagup \\ CH_3 \end{array}$$

isopropyl 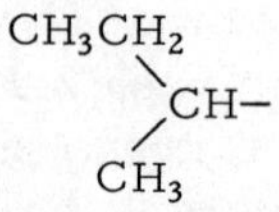   *s*-butyl

Tertiary (R_3C—)

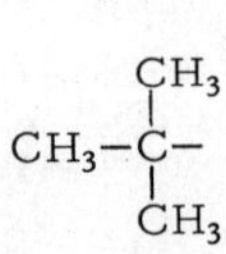

$$\begin{array}{c} CH_3 \\ | \\ CH_3-C- \\ | \\ CH_3 \end{array}$$
$$\begin{array}{c} CH_3 \\ | \\ CH_3CH_2-C- \\ | \\ CH_3 \end{array}$$

t-butyl 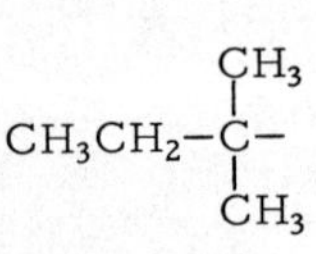   *t*-pentyl
                            (*t*-amyl)

The IUPAC rules for the systematic naming of alkanes follow.

a. The *longest* continuous chain of carbon atoms is taken as the framework on which the various alkyl groups are considered to be substituted. Thus the hydrocarbon [1] is a pentane rather than a butane derivative, since the longest chain is one with five carbons.

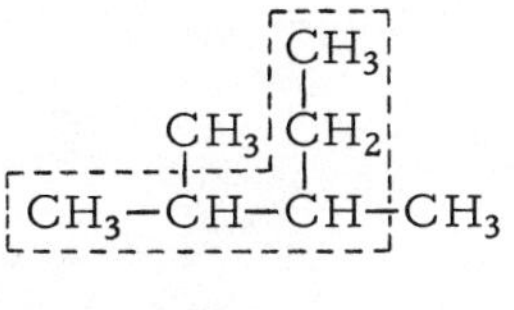

$$
\begin{array}{c}
\boxed{CH_3} \\
| \\
CH_3\ \boxed{CH_2} \\
| \\
\boxed{CH_3-CH-CH}\ CH_3
\end{array}
$$

(dotted lines enclose
longest chain of suc-
cessive carbon atoms)

[1]

b. The parent hydrocarbon is then numbered starting from the end of the chain, and the substituent groups are assigned numbers corresponding to their positions on the chain. The direction of numbering is chosen to give the lowest sum for the numbers of the side-chain substituents. Thus, hydrocarbon [1] is 2,3-dimethylpentane rather than 3,4-dimethylpentane.

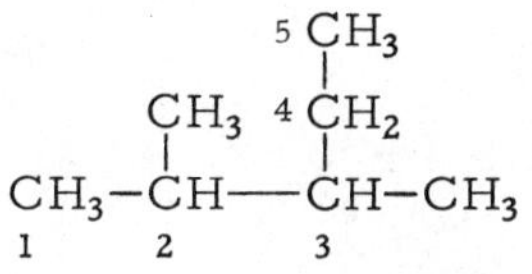

$$
\begin{array}{c}
5\ CH_3 \\
| \\
CH_3\ \ 4\ CH_2 \\
|\qquad\quad | \\
CH_3-CH\!-\!\!-\!CH-CH_3 \\
1\quad\ 2\qquad\ 3
\end{array}
\qquad \underline{not} \qquad
\begin{array}{c}
1\ CH_3 \\
| \\
CH_3\ \ 2\ CH_2 \\
|\qquad\quad | \\
CH_3-CH\!-\!\!-\!CH-CH_3 \\
5\quad\ 4\qquad\ 3
\end{array}
$$

2, 3-dimethylpentane   3, 4-dimethylpentane

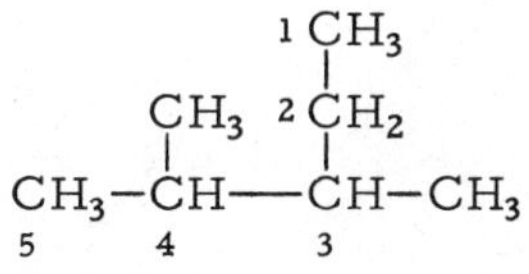

c. Where there are two identical substituents at one position, as in [2], numbers are supplied for each.

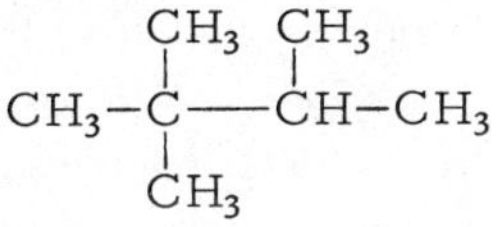

$$
\begin{array}{c}
CH_3\ \ CH_3 \\
|\qquad | \\
CH_3-C\!-\!\!-\!CH-CH_3 \\
| \\
CH_3
\end{array}
$$

2, 2, 3-trimethylbutane

[2]

d. Branched-chain substituent groups are given appropriate names by a simple extension of the system used for branched-chain hydrocarbons. The longest chain of the substituent is numbered starting with the carbon attached directly to the parent hydrocarbon chain. Parentheses are used to separate the numbering of the substituent and the main hydrocarbon chain.

$$
\begin{array}{c}
\overset{2}{C}H_3 \quad \overset{3}{C}H_2{-}CH_3 \\
\diagdown \overset{1}{\diagup} \\
\overset{1}{C}H \\
| \\
CH_3{-}CH_2{-}CH_2{-}CH_2{-}CH{-}CH_2{-}CH_2{-}CH_2{-}CH_2{-}CH_3 \\
\,1 \quad\; 2 \quad\;\; 3 \quad\;\; 4 \quad\;\; 5 \quad\;\; 6 \quad\;\; 7 \quad\;\; 8 \quad\;\; 9 \quad\; 10
\end{array}
$$

5-(1-methylpropyl)-decane

(5-*s*-butyldecane)

The IUPAC rules permit use of the substituent group names in Table 3-2, so that *s*-butyl can be used in place of (1-methylpropyl) for this example.

e. When there are two or more different substituents present, the question arises as to what order they should be cited in naming the compound. Two systems are commonly used which cite the alkyl substituents (1) in order of increasing complexity or (2) in alphabetical order. We shall adhere to the latter system mainly because it is the practice of *Chemical Abstracts*.[1] Examples are given below.

$$
\begin{array}{c}
CH_3{-}CH_2 \quad CH_3 \\
| \qquad\;\; | \\
CH_3{-}CH_2{-}CH_2{-}CH{-}CH{-}CH_2{-}CH_3 \\
\;7 \qquad 6 \qquad\; 5 \qquad 4 \quad\;\; 3 \quad\;\; 2 \qquad 1
\end{array}
$$

4-ethyl-3-methylheptane

(i. e. , ethyl is cited before methyl)

$$
\begin{array}{c}
CH_3 \\
| \\
CH_3{-}C{-}CH_3 \\
| \\
CH_3{-}CH_2{-}CH_2{-}C{-}CH_2{-}CH_2{-}CH_2{-}CH_2{-}CH_2{-}CH_3 \\
\,1 \quad\;\; 2 \quad\;\; 3 \quad\; 4| \;\; 5 \quad\;\; 6 \quad\;\; 7 \quad\;\; 8 \quad\;\; 9 \quad\;\; 10 \\
CH_3{-}CH \\
| \\
CH_3
\end{array}
$$

4-*t*-butyl-4-isopropyldecane

Derivatives of paraffin hydrocarbons, such as haloalkanes R—Cl and nitro-alkanes R—NO$_2$, where R denotes an alkyl group, are named similarly by the IUPAC system. Definite orders of precedence are assigned substituents of different types when two or more are attached to a hydrocarbon chain. Thus, alkanes with halogen and alkyl substituents are generally named as haloalkyl-alkanes (not as alkylhaloalkanes); alkanes with halogen and nitro substituents are named as halonitroalkanes (not as nitrohaloalkanes).

---

[1] A biweekly publication of the American Chemical Society; an index to, and a digest of, recent chemical publications.

$CH_3-CH_2-CH_2-CH_2-Cl$

$$CH_3-CH_2-\underset{\underset{NO_2}{|}}{CH}-\overset{\overset{CH_3}{|}}{CH}-CH_3$$

1-chlorobutane

(*n*-butyl chloride)

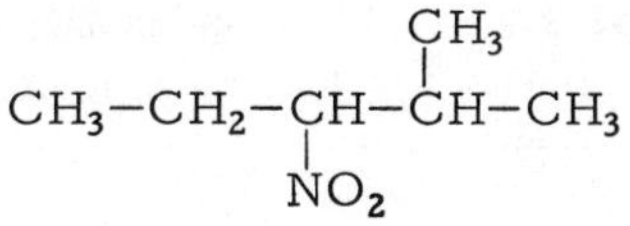

3-nitro-2-methylpentane

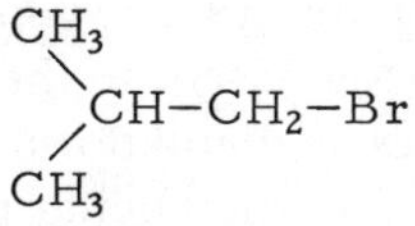

$$\underset{CH_3}{\overset{CH_3}{\diagdown}}CH-CH_2-Br$$

$$\overset{\overset{CH_3}{|}}{Cl-CH}-CH_2-CH_2-NO_2$$

1-bromo-2-methylpropane

(isobutyl bromide)

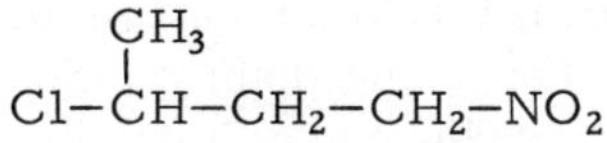

3-chloro-1-nitrobutane

EXERCISE 3-1   Name each of the following hydrocarbons by the IUPAC system and as an alkyl-substituted methane.

a. 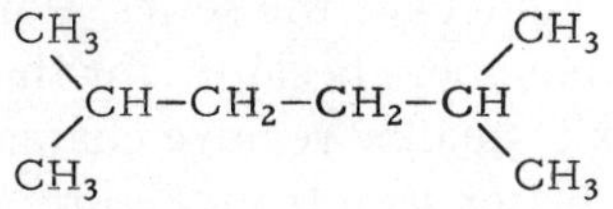 $\underset{CH_3}{\overset{CH_3}{\diagdown}}CH-CH_2-CH_2-\overset{CH_3}{\underset{CH_3}{\diagup}}CH$

b. 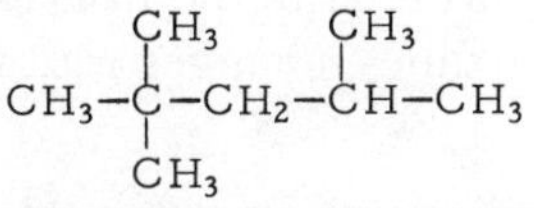 $CH_3-\underset{\underset{CH_3}{|}}{\overset{\overset{CH_3}{|}}{C}}-CH_2-\overset{\overset{CH_3}{|}}{CH}-CH_3$

c. $\underset{CH_3}{\overset{CH_3-CH_2}{\diagdown}}CH-CH_2-\overset{CH_3}{\underset{CH_3}{\diagup}}CH$

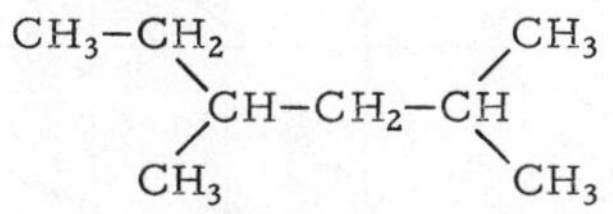

d. 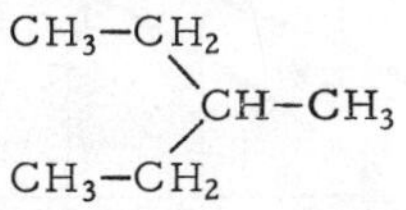 $\underset{CH_3-CH_2}{\overset{CH_3-CH_2}{\diagdown}}CH-CH_3$

e. $(CH_3-CH_2-CH_2\underset{4}{\overbrace{}})C$

f. 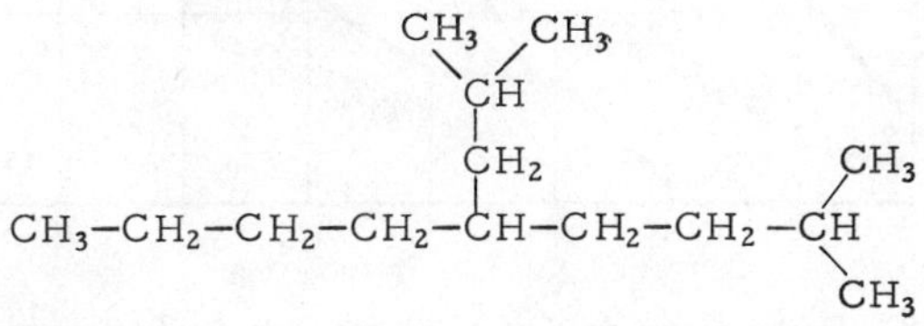 $CH_3-CH_2-CH_2-CH_2-\overset{\overset{\overset{\overset{CH_3\diagup}{\diagdown}CH_3}{CH}}{|}}{CH}-CH_2-CH_2-\overset{CH_3\diagup}{\underset{CH_3\diagdown}{}}CH$

EXERCISE 3-2   Write structures for all seventeen possible monochlorohexanes and name
them by the IUPAC system.

3-2 PHYSICAL PROPERTIES OF ALKANES—
CONCEPT OF HOMOLOGY

The series of straight-chain alkanes $CH_3(CH_2)_{n-2}CH_3$ shows a remarkably
smooth gradation of physical properties (see Table 3-3 and Figure 3-1). As the
series is ascended, each additional CH_2 group contributes a fairly constant in-
crement to the boiling point and density, and to a lesser extent to the melting
point. This makes it possible to estimate the properties of an unknown member
of the series from those of its neighbors. For example, the boiling points of
hexane and heptane are 69° and 98°, respectively; a difference in structure of
one CH_2 group therefore makes a difference in boiling point of 29°; this places
the boiling point of the next higher member, octane, at 98° + 29°, or 127°,
which is close to the actual boiling point of 126°.

Members of a group of compounds with similar chemical structures and
graded physical properties and which differ from one another by the number of
atoms in the structural backbone, such as the *n*-alkanes, are said to constitute a
homologous series. The concept of **homology,** when used to forecast the
properties of unknown members of the series, works most satisfactorily for the
higher molecular weight members because, for these, the introduction of additional CH_2 groups makes a smaller relative change in the over-all composition
of the molecule. This is better seen from Figure 3-2, which shows how ΔT, the
differences in boiling point and melting point between consecutive members of
the homologous series of *n*-alkanes, changes with the number of carbons, *n*.

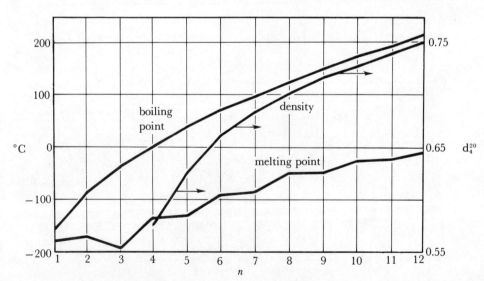

Figure 3-1   Dependence on *n* of melting points, boiling points, and densities (d_4^{20}) of straight-chain
alkanes, $CH_3(CH_2)_{n-2}CH_3$.

Table 3-3   Physical Properties of n-Alkanes, $CH_3(CH_2)_{n-2}CH_3$

n	Name	B.p., °C (760 mm)	M.p., °C	d_4^{20}	$n^{20}D$
1	methane	−161.5	−183	0.424[a]	
2	ethane	−88.6	−172	0.546[a]	
3	propane	−42.1	−188	0.501[b]	
4	butane	−0.5	−135	0.579[b]	1.3326[b]
5	pentane	36.1	−130	0.626	1.3575
6	hexane	68.7	−95	0.659	1.3749
7	heptane	98.4	−91	0.684	1.3876
8	octane	125.7	−57	0.703	1.3974
9	nonane	150.8	−54	0.718	1.4054
10	decane	174.1	−30	0.730	1.4119
11	undecane	195.9	−26	0.740	1.4176
12	dodecane	216.3	−10	0.749	1.4216
15	pentadecane	270.6	10	0.769	1.4319
20	eicosane	342.7	37	0.786[c]	1.4409[c]
30	tricontane	446.4	66	0.810[c]	1.4536[c]

[a] At the boiling point.
[b] Under pressure.
[c] For the supercooled liquid.

Branched-chain alkanes do not exhibit the same smooth gradation of physical properties as the n-alkanes. Usually, there is too great a variation in molecular structure for regularities to be apparent. Nevertheless, in any one set of isomeric hydrocarbons, volatility increases with increased branching. This can be seen from the data in Table 3-4, in which are listed the physical properties of

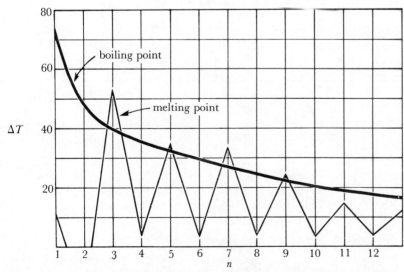

Figure 3-2   Dependence of ΔT (difference in boiling and melting points between consecutive members of the series of normal alkanes) on n (number of carbon atoms).

Table 3-4   Physical Properties of Hexane Isomers

Isomer	Structure	B.p., °C	M.p., °C	Density at 20°, d_4^{20}
n-hexane	$CH_3(CH_2)_4CH_3$	68.7	−94	0.659
3-methylpentane	$\underset{\textstyle\quad}{CH_3} \\ \mid \\ CH_3CH_2CHCH_2CH_3$	63.3	−118	0.664
2-methylpentane (isohexane)	$CH_3 \\ \mid \\ CH_3CHCH_2CH_2CH_3$	60.3	−154	0.653
2,3-dimethylbutane	$CH_3 \ \ CH_3 \\ \mid \ \ \ \ \mid \\ CH_3CH{-}CHCH_3$	58.0	−129	0.661
2,2-dimethylbutane (neohexane)	$CH_3 \\ \mid \\ CH_3CCH_2CH_3 \\ \mid \\ CH_3$	49.7	−98	0.649

the five hexane isomers; the most striking feature is the 20° difference between the boiling points of hexane and neohexane.

EXERCISE 3-3   Use the data of Tables 3-3 and 3-4 to estimate the boiling points of tetra-decane, heptadecane, 2-methylhexane, and 2,2-dimethylpentane.

3-3 SPECTROSCOPIC PROPERTIES OF ALKANES

The infrared spectra of the alkanes show clearly the C—H stretching frequencies at 2850 to 3000 cm^{-1}. The C—C stretching frequencies are variable and usually weak. Methyl (CH$_3$—) and methylene (—CH$_2$—) groups normally have characteristic C—H bending vibrations at 1400 to 1470 cm^{-1}, whereas methyl groups show a weaker band near 1380 cm^{-1}. Two sample infrared spectra that illustrate these features are given in Figure 3-3.

Pure alkanes show no ultraviolet absorption above 2000 A (see Table 2-2) and hence are often excellent solvents for the determination of the ultraviolet spectra of other substances.

The n.m.r. spectra of the alkanes are reasonably characteristic but difficult to interpret, because the chemical shifts between the various kinds of protons are rather small. Whether an alkane is branched or not can be readily ascertained by inspection of the ratio of the integral of the CH$_3$ resonances centered on 0.9 ppm versus the integral of the CH$_2$ resonances centered on 1.25 ppm (see Figure 3-4).

Mass spectrometry is excellent for the analysis of alkane mixtures and is widely used for this purpose.

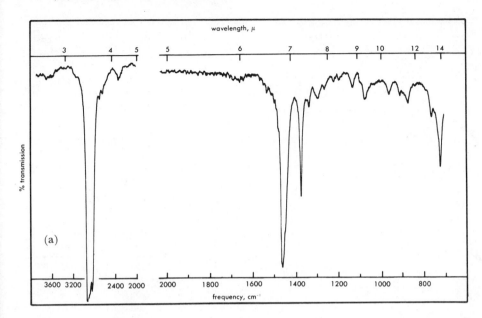

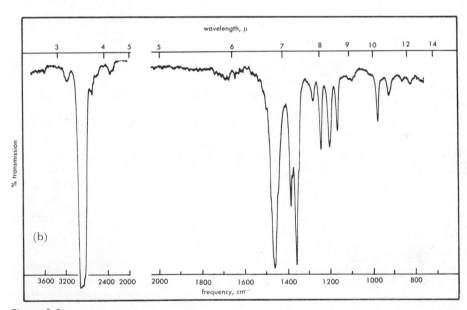

Figure 3-3

Infrared spectra of *n*-octane (a) and
2,2,4-trimethylpentane (b) as pure
liquids.

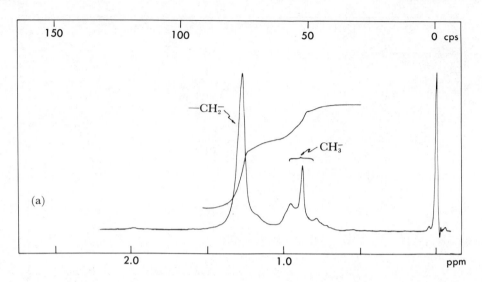

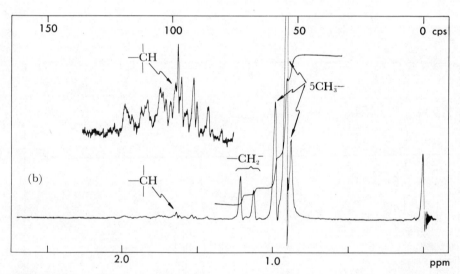

Figure 3-4

Nuclear magnetic resonance spectra of
n-octane (a) and 2,2,4-trimethylpentane
(b) at 60 Mcps relative to TMS as standard.   The upper left curve of (b) represents the spectrum from 1.25 to 2.25
ppm at increased sensitivity to show the

details of the $-\overset{|}{\underset{|}{C}}-$H absorption.

CHEMICAL REACTIONS OF ALKANES

3-4 COMBUSTION OF ALKANES

As a class, alkanes are singularly unreactive. Hence the name saturated hydrocarbon or "paraffin," which literally means "not enough affinity" [L. *par(um)*, not enough, + *affins*, affinity], arises because their chemical "affinity" for most common reagents may be regarded as "saturated" or satisfied. Thus none of the C—H or C—C bonds in a typical saturated hydrocarbon, such as ethane, are attacked at ordinary temperatures by a strong acid such as sulfuric acid or by an oxidizing agent such as bromine (in the dark), oxygen, or potassium permanganate. Ethane is similarly stable under ordinary conditions to reducing agents such as hydrogen in the presence of such catalysts as platinum, palladium, or nickel.

However, all saturated hydrocarbons are attacked by oxygen at elevated temperatures and, if oxygen is in excess, complete combustion occurs to carbon dioxide and water. Vast quantities of hydrocarbons from petroleum are utilized as fuels for the production of heat and power by combustion. Although petroleums differ in composition with their source, a representative petroleum [1] on distillation yields the following fractions: (a) *Gas* fraction, boiling point up to 40° C, contains normal and branched alkanes from C_1 to C_5. Natural gas is mainly methane and ethane while "bottled" gas (liquefied petroleum gas) is mainly propane and butane. (b) *Gasoline,* boiling point from 40 to 180° C, contains hydrocarbons from C_6 to C_{10}. Over 100 compounds have been identified in gasoline, and these include normal and branched alkanes, cycloalkanes, and alkylbenzenes (arenes). The branched alkanes make better gasoline than their straight-chain isomers because they have much higher antiknock ratings. (c) *Kerosine,* boiling point 180 to 230° C, contains hydrocarbons from C_{11} to C_{12}. Much of this is utilized as jet engine fuels and much is "cracked" to simpler alkanes (and alkenes). (d) *Light gas oil,* boiling point 230 to 305° C, C_{13} to C_{17}, is utilized as diesel and furnace fuels. (e) *Heavy gas oil and light lubricating distillate,* boiling point 305 to 405° C, C_{18} to C_{25}. (f) *Lubricants and waxes,* boiling point 405 to 515° C, C_{26} to C_{38}, lubricating oils, paraffin wax and petroleum jelly (Vaseline). The distillation residues are better known as asphalts.

3-5 ESTIMATION OF HEATS OF COMBUSTION. BOND ENERGIES

The combustion of alkanes obtained from petroleum is a major source of heat and power. Consequently, it is of practical interest to be able to estimate the amount of heat liberated in the combustion of different kinds of hydrocarbons. This can be done quite simply with the aid of tables of bond energies—and the method is very important because it can be used to estimate the heats of a wide variety of other organic reactions as well.

In discussing heats of reaction we shall confine our attention to the total amount of heat evolved or absorbed when the products and reactants are at the same temperature, usually 25° C. For combustion of a hydrocarbon, this can

[1] See "Hydrocarbons in Petroleum" by F. D. Rossini, *J. Chem. Ed.,* **37,** 554 (1960).

be measured by igniting a mixture of the hydrocarbon with excess oxygen in a closed vessel contained in a bath initially at 25° and then determining the amount of heat which has to be removed from the bath to bring the temperature back to 25°. The temperature inside the vessel may be 1000° or more during the burning but this is immaterial, because the total heat evolved will be the same, as long as the initial and final states of the system are the same. Thus very slow oxidation at 25° will result in evolution of exactly the same amount of heat as a rapid burning, provided combustion is complete in both cases.

It turns out that the heat liberated or absorbed in a *constant-volume* process, such as just described for combustion of a hydrocarbon in a closed vessel, is not quite the same as in a *constant-pressure* process. Since most organic reactions are carried out at constant pressure, it is customary to take the **heat of reaction** ΔH as the heat liberated or absorbed at *constant pressure*. By convention, ΔH is given a *negative* sign when heat is evolved (**exothermic reaction**) and a *positive* sign when heat is absorbed (**endothermic reaction**).

For the combustion of 1 mole of methane at 25° C, we find by experiment (corrected from constant volume to constant pressure, if necessary) that the reaction is exothermic by 212.8 kcal. This statement can be expressed in abbreviated form by the following equation:

$$CH_4(g) + 2O_2(g) \rightarrow CO_2(g) + 2H_2O(l) \qquad \Delta H = -212.8 \text{ kcal}$$

Here (g) and (l) denote that, for this value of ΔH, the reactants and products are in the gaseous state except for the water which is liquid. If we wish to have ΔH with gaseous water $H_2O(g)$ as the product we have to make a correction for the heat of vaporization of water (10.4 kcal/mole at 25°).

$$CH_4(g) + 2O_2(g) \rightarrow CO_2(g) + 2H_2O(l) \qquad \Delta H = -212.8 \text{ kcal}$$

$$2H_2O(l) \rightarrow 2H_2O(g) \qquad \Delta H = +2 \times 10.4 \text{ kcal}$$

$$CH_4(g) + 2O_2(g) \rightarrow CO_2(g) + 2H_2O(g) \qquad \Delta H = -192.0 \text{ kcal}$$

To estimate heats of combustion from bond energies, we take the difference between the heats calculated to break the bonds in the reactants and to make the bonds of the products remembering that bond-breaking requires heat and bond-making evolves heat. The necessary bond energies are given in Table 3-5. These bond energies apply only to *complete dissociation of gaseous substances to gaseous atoms at 25° C*. Also they do not apply, without suitable corrections, to many compounds like benzene which have more than one double bond. This limitation will be discussed in Chapter 9.

EXERCISE 3-4   The heat of combustion of 1 mole of liquid n-decane to give carbon dioxide and liquid water is 1620.1 kcal. The heat of vaporization of n-decane at 25° is 11.7 kcal. Calculate the heat of combustion which would be observed for all the participants in the vapor phase.

EXERCISE 3-5   Kilogram for kilogram, would the combustion of gaseous methane or of liquid n-decane (to liquid water) give more heat?

Table 3-5   Bond Energies (kcal/mole at 25°C)[a]

			Diatomic Molecules			
H—H	104.2	F—F	36.6	H—F	134.6
O=O	119.1	Cl—Cl	58.0	H—Cl	103.2
N≡N	225.8	Br—Br	46.1	H—Br	87.5
C=O[b]	255.8	I—I	36.1	H—I	71.4

			Polyatomic Molecules			
C—H	98.7	C—C	82.6	C—F	116
N—H	93.4	C=C	145.8	C—Cl	81
O—H	110.6	C≡C	199.6	C—Br	68
S—H	83	C—N	72.8	C—I	51
P—H	76	C=N	147	C—S	65
N—N	39	C≡N	212.6	C=S[c]	128
N=N	100	C—O	85.5	N—F	65
O—O	35	C=O[d]	192.0	N—Cl	46
S—S	54	C=O[e]	166	O—F	45
N—O	53	C=O[f]	176	O—Cl	52
N=O	145	C=O[g]	179	O—Br	48

[a] The bond energies in this table are derived from those of T. L. Cottrell, "The Strengths of Chemical Bonds," Butterworths, London, 2nd ed., 1958, and L. Pauling, "The Nature of the Chemical Bond," Cornell University Press, Ithaca, N.Y., 3rd ed., 1960.
[b] Carbon monoxide.
[c] For carbon disulfide.
[d] For carbon dioxide.
[e] For formaldehyde.
[f] Other aldehydes.
[g] Ketones.

To calculate ΔH for the combustion of methane, first we break bonds as follows, using 98.7 kcal for the energy of the C—H bonds,

$$\text{H}:\overset{\text{H}}{\underset{\text{H}}{\text{C}}}:\text{H}(g) \rightarrow \cdot \dot{\text{C}} \cdot (g) + 4\,\text{H} \cdot (g) \qquad \Delta H = +4 \times 98.7 \text{ kcal}$$
$$= +394.8 \text{ kcal}$$

and then 119.1 kcal for the energy of the double bond in oxygen.

$$2:\ddot{\text{O}}::\ddot{\text{O}}:(g) \rightarrow 4:\ddot{\text{O}}(g) \qquad \Delta H = +2 \times 119.1 \text{ kcal}$$
$$= +238.2 \text{ kcal}$$

Then we make bonds, using 192 kcal for each O=C bond in carbon dioxide,

$$\cdot \dot{\text{C}} \cdot (g) + 2:\ddot{\text{O}}(g) \rightarrow :\ddot{\text{O}}::\text{C}::\ddot{\text{O}}:(g) \qquad \Delta H = -2 \times 192.0 \text{ kcal}$$
$$= -384.0 \text{ kcal}$$

and 110.6 kcal for each of the H—O bonds of water:

$$2 : \overset{..}{\underset{..}{O}} \ (g) + 4H \cdot (g) \ \rightarrow \ 2 \ H : \overset{..}{\underset{..}{O}} : H(g) \qquad \Delta H = -4 \times 110.6 \text{ kcal}$$

$$= -442.4 \text{ kcal}$$

The net of these ΔH changes is $394.8 + 238.2 - 384.0 - 442.4 = -193.4$ kcal, which is reasonably close to the value of 191.8 kcal for the heat of combustion of methane determined experimentally.

The same type of procedure can be used to estimate ΔH values for many other kinds of reactions of organic compounds in the vapor phase at 25°. Moreover, if appropriate heats of vaporization or solution are available, it is straightforward to compute ΔH for liquid, solid, or dissolved substances.

EXERCISE 3-6   Use the bond-energy table to calculate ΔH for the following reactions in the vapor phase at 25°:

    a. $CH_3CH_2CH_3 + 5O_2 \ \rightarrow \ 3CO_2 + 4H_2O$

    b. n-decane $+ \frac{31}{2} O_2 \ \rightarrow \ 10CO_2 + 11H_2O$

    c. $CH_4 + \frac{3}{2}O_2 \ \rightarrow \ CO + 2H_2O$

    d. $CO + 3H_2 \ \rightarrow \ CH_4 + H_2O$

    e. $CH_4 + Cl_2 \ \rightarrow \ CH_3Cl + HCl$

    f. $CH_4 + I_2 \ \rightarrow \ CH_3I + HI$

EXERCISE 3-7   Calculate ΔH for $C(s) \rightarrow C(g)$ from the heat of combustion of 1 gram-atom of carbon as 94.05 kcal, and the bond energies in Table 3-5.

EXERCISE 3-8   Dissociation of the first O—H bond in gaseous water at 25°C has ΔH equal to $+119.9$ kcal. What is ΔH for dissociation of the second O—H bond?

3-6 HALOGENATION OF ALKANES AND GENERAL PROBLEMS REGARDING ORGANIC SYNTHESIS

The simplest possible reaction of chlorine with methane involves formation of chloromethane (methyl chloride) and hydrogen chloride.

$$CH_4 + Cl_2 \ \longrightarrow \ CH_3Cl + HCl$$

Although the equation for this reaction is simple, considerably more information must be available in order to predict in advance whether the reaction as written would have practical utility for the preparation of methyl chloride. Two general theoretical problems are involved. First, it must be known whether or not the reaction can proceed. This is a problem in equilibrium constants and, in general, qualitative predictions of equilibrium constants for simple organic reactions are usually not difficult to make, as will be discussed in a subsequent section. The second (and more vexing) problem is, if the reaction has a favorable equilibrium constant and therefore can proceed, whether or not it will proceed at a suitable velocity under the given set of conditions. No general solution to the reaction-rate problem has as yet been achieved, although a number of useful correlations have been made.

Given the knowledge that a particular reaction will proceed at a suitable rate, a host of practical considerations are necessary for satisfactory operation, including surveys of possible side reactions which give products other than those desired, the ease of separation of the desired products from the reaction mixture, and costs of materials, apparatus, and labor.

We shall try to consider something about the above problems in connection with important synthetic reactions.

A. Equilibrium Constants

Presumably, methane could react with chlorine to give methyl chloride and hydrogen chloride, or methyl chloride could react with hydrogen chloride to give methane and chlorine. If conditions were found where both reactions proceeded at a finite rate, equilibrium would ultimately be established and then the rates of the reactions in each direction would be the same.

$$CH_4 + Cl_2 \rightleftharpoons CH_3Cl + HCl$$

At equilibrium, the familiar equilibrium equation would apply:

$$K = \frac{[CH_3Cl]\,[HCl]}{[CH_4]\,[Cl_2]}$$

The quantities within the brackets denote either concentrations for liquid reactants or partial pressures for gaseous reactants. If the equilibrium constant K were greater than 1, then on mixing together equal volumes of each of the reactants (all are gases above $-24°$), the reaction would proceed to the right as written above. On the other hand, if the equilibrium constant were *less than 1*, the reaction would proceed to the left. For methane chlorination, it is known from experiment that K is much greater than unity, but it would be most helpful in planning other organic preparations to be able to predict the magnitude of K in advance.

If the tendencies for reactions to proceed, as measured by their equilibrium constants, are compared with the amounts of heat they evolve, some striking parallels are found. For example, the reaction of hydrogen with oxygen, once initiated, is highly *exothermic* and has an equilibrium constant of 10^{40} at 25°. The reverse reaction only occurs materially at greatly elevated temperatures.

$$H_2 + 1/2\,O_2 \longrightarrow H_2O \qquad \Delta H = -57.8 \text{ kcal}$$

$$K = \frac{[H_2O]}{[H_2]\,[O_2]^{1/2}} = 10^{40} \quad (25°)$$

We might conclude from examples such as this that the more heat evolved, the greater the tendency of reaction to occur and the larger the value of K. However, this correlation between equilibrium constants and heats of reactions is neither rigorous nor universal. Reactions are known, for example, which are endothermic and yet have equilibrium constants greater than unity. Obviously, an equilibrium constant must depend on something more than the heat evolved in the reaction, so that, in the long run, any attempt to make a precise correlation between K's and heats of reaction is bound to fail. The additional variable is the entropy of reaction ΔS.

The exact thermodynamic relationship between the equilibrium constant K of a reaction, the heat of reaction ΔH, and the entropy of reaction ΔS is given by the equation

$$-2.303RT \log_{10} K = \Delta H - T\Delta S \tag{3-1}$$

where R is the well-known gas constant (1.986 cal/°mole) and T is the absolute temperature in degrees Kelvin.

Clearly, if we could calculate ΔH and ΔS for a reaction, we could then calculate the equilibrium constant for that reaction at any given temperature. Unfortunately, estimation of ΔS is not as easy as estimation of ΔH.

The value of ΔH calculated for the formation of methyl chloride and hydrogen chloride from methane and chlorine is −27 kcal, using the bond energies in Table 3-5. Although we are assured that the process is exothermic, we cannot be certain that the reaction will in fact occur as written (i.e., $K > 1$). Even so, we know from experience that K *usually is greater than unity for most reactions with ΔH more negative than −15 kcal and is usually less than unity for ΔH more positive than +15 kcal.* We shall henceforth use this as a "rule of thumb" to predict whether K is greater or less than unity for vapor-phase reactions involving simple molecules.

B. Reaction Rates

The calculated value of ΔH for the chlorination of 1 mole of methane is −27 kcal, and the equilibrium constant K is known to be approximately 10^{18}. Nevertheless, methane and chlorine do not react at a measurable rate in the dark at room temperature, although an explosive reaction may occur if such a mixture is irradiated with strong violet or ultraviolet light. Evidently, light makes possible a very effective reaction path by which chlorine may react with methane.

Any kind of a theoretical prediction or rationalization of the rate of this or

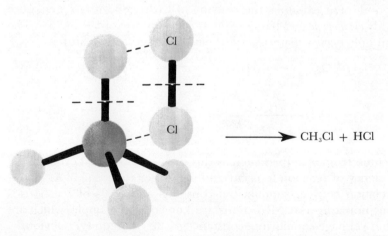

Figure 3-5   Four-center collision of chlorine with methane as visualized with ball-and-stick models.

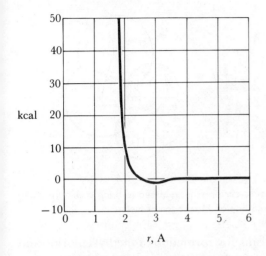

Figure 3-6

Graph of the potential energy of pairs of neon atoms as a function of the inter-nuclear distance. The energy values are per mole of neon atoms.

other reactions must inevitably take into account the details of how the reactants are converted to the products, in other words, the *reaction mechanism*. One possible path for methane to react with chlorine would have a chlorine molecule collide with a methane molecule in such a way that hydrogen chloride and methyl chloride are formed directly (see Figure 3-5). The failure of methane to react with chlorine in the dark at moderate temperatures is strong evidence against this path. There are two reasons for expecting that the simple collision mechanism might not be important. First, it involves a very precisely oriented "four-center" collision between chlorine and methane which would have a low probability of occurrence. Second, it requires pushing a chlorine molecule sufficiently deeply into a methane molecule so that one of the chlorine atoms comes close enough to the carbon atom to form a bond and yield methyl chloride.

Generally speaking, to bring nonbonded atoms to near-bonding distances (1.2 to 1.8 A) requires a very large expenditure of energy, as can be seen from Figure 3-6. Interatomic repulsive forces increase very rapidly at short distances, and pushing a chlorine molecule into a methane molecule to attain distances comparable to the 1.77-A carbon-chlorine bond distance in methyl chloride requires a considerable amount of energy (see Figure 3-7). Valuable information about interatomic repulsions can be obtained with Stuart models which have radii scaled to correspond to actual atomic interference radii, the distance where the curve of Figure 3-6 starts to rise steeply. With such models, the degree of atomic compression required to bring the nonbonded atoms to within near-bonding distance is more evident than with ball-and-stick models. It may be noted that four-center reactions of the type postulated above are only rarely encountered. One of the few well-authenticated examples is the slow thermal reaction of hydrogen with iodine to give hydrogen iodide.

$$
\begin{array}{c}
\text{H-----I} \\
| \quad\quad | \\
\text{H-----I}
\end{array}
\longrightarrow \quad 2\,\text{HI}
$$

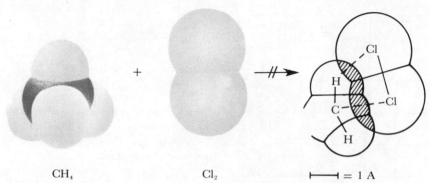

CH$_4$ Cl$_2$ $\longmapsto\!\!\longmapsto$ = 1 A

Figure 3-7   Models showing the degree of atomic compression required to bring a chlorine molecule to within bonding distance of carbon and hydrogen of methane.

If concerted "four-center" mechanisms for formation of methyl chloride and
hydrogen chloride from chlorine and methane are discarded, the remaining
possibilities are all stepwise mechanisms.   A slow stepwise reaction is dynamically
analogous to the flow of sand through a succession of funnels with different stem
diameters.   The funnel with the smallest stem will be the most important bottle-
neck and, if its stem diameter is much smaller than the others, it alone will determine the flow rate.   Generally, a multistep chemical reaction will have a slow
rate-determining step (analogous to the funnel with the small stem) and other
relatively *fast steps* which may occur either before or after the slow step.   The
prediction of the rate of a reaction proceeding by a stepwise mechanism then involves, as the central problem, a decision as to which step is rate-determining
and an analysis of the factors which determine the rate of that step.

A possible set of steps for the chlorination of methane follows:

$$(1) \quad Cl_2 \xrightarrow{\text{slow}} 2 : \overset{..}{\underset{..}{Cl}} \cdot$$

$$(2) \quad CH_4 \xrightarrow{\text{slow}} CH_3 \cdot \; + \; H \cdot$$

$$(3) \quad : \overset{..}{\underset{..}{Cl}} \cdot \; + \; CH_3 \cdot \xrightarrow{\text{fast}} CH_3Cl$$

$$(4) \quad : \overset{..}{\underset{..}{Cl}} \cdot \; + \; H \cdot \xrightarrow{\text{fast}} HCl$$

Reactions (1) and (2) involve dissociation of chlorine into chlorine atoms and the
breaking of a C—H bond of methane to give a methyl free radical and a hydrogen atom.   The methyl free radical, like chlorine and hydrogen atoms, has one
odd electron not involved in bond formation.   Atoms and free radicals are usually very highly reactive, so that formation of methyl chloride and hydrogen
chloride should proceed readily by (3) and (4).   The crux then will be whether
or not steps (1) and (2) are reasonable under the reaction conditions.

Our plan in evaluating the reasonableness of these steps is to determine how
much energy is required to break the bonds.   This will be helpful because, in the
absence of some *external* stimulus, only collisions due to the usual thermal motions of the molecules can provide the energy needed to break the bonds.   At
temperatures below 100° C, it is very rare indeed that thermal agitation alone

can supply sufficient energy to break any significant number of bonds stronger than 30 to 35 kcal/mole. Therefore, we can discard as unreasonable any step, such as the dissociation reactions (1) and (2), if the ΔH's for breaking the bonds are greater than 30 to 35 kcal. For reaction (1) we can reach a decision on the basis of the Cl—Cl bond energy from Table 3-5, which is 58.0 kcal and clearly too large to lead to bond breaking as the result of thermal agitation at or below 100°. The C—H bonds of methane are also too strong to break at 100° or less. It should now be clear why a mixture of methane and chlorine does not react in the dark at moderate temperatures.

EXERCISE 3-9   A possible mechanism for the reaction of chlorine with methane would be to have collisions where a chlorine molecule removes a hydrogen according to the following scheme:

$$CH_3 : H + \overset{..}{:}\overset{..}{Cl} : \overset{..}{Cl} : \quad \xrightarrow{\text{slow}} \quad CH_3 \cdot + H : \overset{..}{Cl} : + \overset{..}{:}\overset{..}{Cl} \cdot$$

$$CH_3 \cdot + \overset{..}{:}\overset{..}{Cl} \cdot \quad \xrightarrow{\text{fast}} \quad CH_3 : \overset{..}{Cl} :$$

Use appropriate bond energies to assess the likelihood of this reaction mechanism. What about the possibility of a similar mechanism with elemental fluorine and methane?

Conceivably, induction of the chlorination of methane by near-ultraviolet light could occur through activation of either methane or chlorine or both. However, methane is colorless and chlorine is yellow-green, which indicates that chlorine, but not methane, interacts with visible light. A quantum of near-ultraviolet light, such as is absorbed by chlorine gas, provides more than enough energy (about 70 kcal/mole of chlorine absorbing a mole of photons) to split the molecule into two chlorine atoms (see p. 26).

$$\overset{..}{:}\overset{..}{Cl} : \overset{..}{Cl} : \quad \xrightarrow{\text{violet light}} \quad 2\overset{..}{:}\overset{..}{Cl} \cdot$$

The analogous cleavage of a chlorine molecule into a chlorine cation and a chloride ion in the vapor state could not possibly be achieved by visible light, since it would require about 270 kcal/mole.

$$\overset{..}{:}\overset{..}{Cl} : \overset{..}{Cl} : \quad \longrightarrow \quad \overset{..}{:}\overset{..}{Cl} : \overset{\ominus}{} + \overset{..}{:}\overset{..}{Cl}^{\oplus} \qquad \Delta H = +270 \text{ kcal}$$

Once produced, a chlorine atom can remove a hydrogen atom from a methane molecule and form a methyl radical and a hydrogen chloride molecule. The bond energies of CH_4(102 kcal) and HCl(103.2 kcal) suggest that this reaction is exothermic by about 1 kcal/mole.

$$CH_4 + \overset{..}{:}\overset{..}{Cl} \cdot \quad \longrightarrow \quad CH_3 \cdot + HCl \qquad \Delta H = -1 \text{ kcal}$$

The attack of a chlorine atom on a methane hydrogen probably would not require a very precisely oriented collision, and the interatomic repulsions should be considerably smaller than in the four-center mechanism discussed earlier for

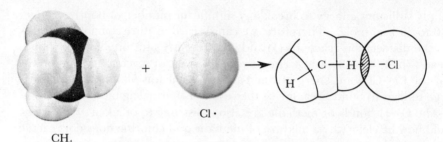

Figure 3-8   Models showing the degree of atomic compression required to bring a chlorine atom
to within bonding distance of a methane hydrogen.   Compare with Figure 3-7.

the reaction of molecular chlorine with methane because only two centers have
to come close together (Figure 3-8).

The methyl free radical resulting from the attack of atomic chlorine on a hydrogen of methane can then remove a chlorine atom from molecular chlorine
and form methyl chloride and a new chlorine atom.

$$CH_3 \cdot \ + \ Cl_2 \ \longrightarrow \ CH_3Cl \ + \ : \overset{\cdot\cdot}{\underset{\cdot\cdot}{Cl}} \cdot \qquad \Delta H \ = \ -23 \ kcal$$

This reaction is calculated to be exothermic by 23 kcal, a value large enough to
suggest that K be much greater than unity.   The attack of a methyl radical on
molecular chlorine should require a somewhat more precisely oriented collision
but no greater interatomic repulsion than the reaction of a chlorine atom with
methane.

An important feature of the mechanistic sequence postulated for the chlorination of methane is that the chlorine atom consumed in the first step is replaced
by another chlorine atom in the second step.

$$CH_4 \ + \ : \overset{\cdot\cdot}{Cl} \cdot \ \longrightarrow \ CH_3 \cdot \ + \ HCl$$

$$CH_3 \cdot \ + \ Cl_2 \ \longrightarrow \ CH_3Cl \ + \ : \overset{\cdot\cdot}{\underset{\cdot\cdot}{Cl}} \cdot$$

$$CH_4 \ + \ Cl_2 \ \longrightarrow \ CH_3Cl \ + \ HCl$$

This type of process is called a **chain reaction** since, in principle, one chlorine
atom can induce the chlorination of an infinite number of methane molecules
through operation of a "chain" or cycle of reactions.   In practice, chain reactions
are limited by so-called **termination processes,** where chlorine atoms or methyl
radicals are destroyed by reacting with one another, as shown in the following
equations:

$$CH_3 \cdot \ + \ : \overset{\cdot\cdot}{Cl} \cdot \ \longrightarrow \ CH_3Cl$$

$$2 \ CH_3 \cdot \ \longrightarrow \ CH_3CH_3$$

$$2 \ : \overset{\cdot\cdot}{\underset{\cdot\cdot}{Cl}} \cdot \ \longrightarrow \ Cl_2$$

Chain reactions may be considered to involve three phases. First, **chain-initiation** must occur, which for methane chlorination is activation and conversion of chlorine molecules to chlorine atoms by light. In the second phase, the **chain-propagation** steps convert reactants to products with no net consumption of atoms or radicals. The propagation reactions occur in competition with **chain-terminating** steps, which result in destruction of atoms or radicals.

$$Cl_2 \xrightarrow{\text{light}} 2 \; :\!\ddot{C}l \cdot \qquad\qquad \text{chain initiation}$$

$$\left.\begin{array}{l} CH_4 + :\!\ddot{C}l \cdot \longrightarrow CH_3 \cdot + HCl \\[2mm] CH_3 \cdot + Cl_2 \longrightarrow CH_3Cl + :\!\ddot{C}l \cdot \end{array}\right\} \quad \text{chain propagation}$$

$$\left.\begin{array}{l} CH_3 \cdot + :\!\ddot{C}l \cdot \longrightarrow CH_3Cl \\[2mm] :\!\ddot{C}l \cdot + :\!\ddot{C}l \cdot \longrightarrow Cl_2 \\[2mm] CH_3 \cdot + CH_3 \cdot \longrightarrow CH_3CH_3 \end{array}\right\} \quad \text{chain termination}$$

It should be noted that the chain-termination reactions for methane chlorination are expected to be exceedingly fast, since they involve combination of unstable atoms or radicals to give stable molecules. If much chain propagation is to occur before the termination steps destroy the active intermediates, the propagation steps must themselves be very fast. However, propagation is favored over termination when the concentrations of radicals (or atoms) are low because then the chance of two radicals meeting (*termination*) is much less likely than encounters of radicals with molecules which are present at relatively *high* concentrations (*propagation*).

The over-all rates of chain reactions are usually very much slowed by substances which can combine with atoms or radicals and convert them into species incapable of participating in the chain-propagation steps. Such substances are often called **radical traps**, or **inhibitors**. Oxygen acts as an inhibitor in the chlorination of methane by rapidly combining with a methyl radical to form the comparatively stable (less reactive) peroxymethyl radical, $CH_3OO\cdot$. This effectively terminates the chain. Under favorable conditions, the methane-chlorination chain may go through 100 to 10,000 cycles before termination occurs by free-radical or atom combination. The efficiency (or **quantum yield**) of the reaction is thus very high in terms of the amount of chlorination that occurs relative to the amount of light absorbed.

EXERCISE 3-10 Calculate ΔH for each of the propagation steps of methane chlorination by a mechanism of the type

$$Cl_2 \xrightarrow{h\nu} 2\,Cl\cdot \qquad\qquad \text{initiation}$$
$$\left.\begin{array}{l} Cl\cdot + CH_4 \rightarrow CH_3Cl + H\cdot \\[2mm] H\cdot + Cl_2 \rightarrow HCl + Cl\cdot \end{array}\right\} \quad \text{propagation}$$

Discuss the relative energetic feasibilities of these chain-propagation steps and compare with other possible mechanisms.

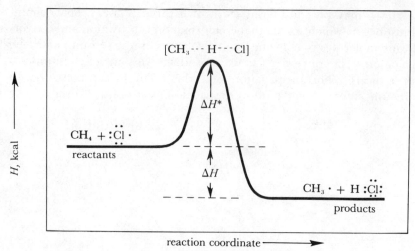

Figure 3-9   Energy diagram for the reaction, CH_4 + $:\overset{..}{\underset{..}{Cl}}\cdot$ → $CH_3\cdot$ + HCl, at constant pressure.

C. Heat of Activation

There is another facet of this or any other reaction which is very important. Consider, for example, the step in which a chlorine atom abstracts a hydrogen atom from methane. We have said that this step is exothermic by 1 kcal and that the orienting factor is unlikely to be very demanding. Nevertheless, simple collisions between the reactants, even when correctly oriented, are not generally enough to cause the reaction to take place. For a collision to be effective in this respect, the reactants must have more than average energies in order to overcome the strong repulsive forces felt on close approach of nonbonded atoms (see Figures 3-6 and 3-8). This extra energy is called the **heat of activation**, ΔH^*, and may be regarded as a sort of energy barrier between the reactants and products, as shown schematically in Figure 3-9. At the top of the barrier, we can regard the hydrogen to be bonded partly to the chlorine and partly to carbon. This bonding is what makes the energy curve of a reacting system different from a purely repulsive collision of the kind considered in Figure 3-6.

Temperature is a critical factor in determining reaction rates, as it determines how many of the molecules have the necessary minimum energy for reaction to occur. The heat of activation is actually determined by studying the effect of temperature on reaction rate.

In general, we should not expect to find a very close relation between ΔH^* and ΔH except when comparing reactions which involve closely similar reactants and mechanisms. A rather good correlation might be expected for $CH_4 + :\overset{..}{X}\cdot \rightarrow CH_3\cdot + HX$ when a comparison is made of ΔH^* and ΔH with $:\overset{..}{X}\cdot$ as fluorine, chlorine, bromine, or iodine atoms. A much poorer correlation would be anticipated for a comparison of the *over-all* ΔH^* values of methane chlorination and methane combustion with the corresponding ΔH's, because different and highly complex mechanisms are involved in these reactions. In all reactions, ΔH^* will have to be equal to, or more positive than, ΔH.

The reaction coordinate can be any desired measure of the progress of the reaction. It is often convenient to choose as the coordinate the sum of the C—H and H—Cl distances, where H is the reacting hydrogen—a large H—Cl distance is taken to be negative and a large C—H distance is taken to be positive.

EXERCISE 3-11   Calculate ΔH for the reactions, $CH_4 + :\overset{\cdot\cdot}{\underset{\cdot\cdot}{Br}}\cdot \rightarrow CH_3\cdot + HBr$ and $CH_4 + :\overset{\cdot\cdot}{\underset{\cdot\cdot}{I}}\cdot \rightarrow$ $CH_3\cdot + HI$. Draw energy diagrams analogous to Figure 3-9. What can you infer about the magnitudes of ΔH^* relative to ΔH compared to the corresponding reaction with a chlorine atom?

It should be evident from the foregoing that many complications may enter into the prediction of reaction rates. For the chlorination of methane, the rate depends not only on the wavelength and light intensity, the temperature, the concentrations of the reagents, and the rates of the individual chain-propagating and chain-terminating steps, but also on the concentrations of foreign substances which may react as radical traps or inhibitors. The example is complex but it is not uncommonly so.

3-7 PRACTICE OF HALOGENATION

The chlorination of saturated hydrocarbons can also be carried out at temperatures of about 300° in the dark. Under such circumstances the mechanism is similar to that of light-induced chlorination except that the chlorine atoms are formed by thermal dissociation of chlorine molecules. Solid carbon surfaces catalyze thermal chlorination possibly by aiding in the cleavage of the chlorine molecules.

Direct halogenation of saturated hydrocarbons works satisfactorily only with chlorine and bromine. For the general reaction

$$-\overset{|}{\underset{|}{C}}-H + X_2 \longrightarrow -\overset{|}{\underset{|}{C}}-X + H-X$$

$$X = F, Cl, Br, I$$

the calculated ΔH value is negative and very large for fluorine, negative and moderate for chlorine and bromine, and positive for iodine (see Table 3-6). With fluorine, the reaction evolves so much heat that it is difficult to control, and products from cleavage of carbon-carbon as well as of carbon-hydrogen bonds are obtained. Indirect methods for preparation of fluorine-substituted hydrocarbons will be discussed later. Bromine is generally much less reactive toward hydrocarbons than chlorine, both at high temperatures and with activation by light. Nonetheless, it is usually possible to brominate saturated hydrocarbons successfully. Iodine is unreactive.

Table 3-6 Calculated Heats of Reaction for Halogenation of Hydrocarbons

$$-\overset{|}{\underset{|}{C}}-H + X_2 \rightarrow -\overset{|}{\underset{|}{C}}-X + HX$$

X	ΔH, kcal/mole
F	-115
Cl	-27
Br	-10
I	12

The chlorination of methane does not have to stop with the formation of methyl chloride, and it is possible to obtain the higher chlorination products: dichloromethane (methylene chloride), trichloromethane (chloroform), and tetrachloromethane (carbon tetrachloride). In practice, all the substitution

$$CH_4 \longrightarrow CH_3Cl \longrightarrow CH_2Cl_2 \longrightarrow CHCl_3 \longrightarrow CCl_4$$

chloro-   dichloro-   trichloro-   tetrachloromethane   methane   methane   methane

products are formed to some extent depending on the chlorine-methane ratio employed. If monochlorination is desired, a large excess of hydrocarbon is advantageous.

For propane and higher hydrocarbons where more than one monosubstitution product is generally possible, difficult separation problems may arise when a particular product is desired. For example, the chlorination of isopentane at 300° gives all four possible monosubstitution products, [3], [4], [5], and [6].

$$CH_3\text{-}\overset{\overset{\displaystyle CH_3}{|}}{\underset{\underset{\displaystyle H}{|}}{C}}\text{-}CH_2\text{-}CH_3 \xrightarrow[300°]{Cl_2} ClCH_2\text{-}\overset{\overset{\displaystyle CH_3}{|}}{\underset{\underset{\displaystyle H}{|}}{C}}\text{-}CH_2\text{-}CH_3 \quad + \quad CH_3\text{-}\overset{\overset{\displaystyle CH_3}{|}}{\underset{\underset{\displaystyle H}{|}}{C}}\text{-}CH_2\text{-}CH_2Cl$$

isopentane   1-chloro-2-methylbutane   1-chloro-3-methylbutane

                                                         (isoamyl chloride)

                                    [3]   [4]

$$+ \quad CH_3\text{-}\overset{\overset{\displaystyle CH_3}{|}}{\underset{\underset{\displaystyle H}{|}}{C}}\text{-}CHCl\text{-}CH_3 \quad + \quad CH_3\text{-}\overset{\overset{\displaystyle CH_3}{|}}{\underset{\underset{\displaystyle Cl}{|}}{C}}\text{-}CH_2\text{-}CH_3$$

3-chloro-2-methylbutane   2-chloro-2-methylbutane

                                 (t-amyl chloride)

            [5]   [6]

On a purely statistical basis, we might expect the ratio of products to correlate with the number of available hydrogens at the various positions of substitution. That is, [3], [4], [5], and [6] would be formed in the ratio 6:3:2:1. However, in practice the product composition is substantially different, because the different kinds of hydrogens are not attacked at equal rates. Actually, the approximate ratios of the rates of attack of chlorine atoms on hydrogens located at primary, secondary, and tertiary positions are 1.0:3.3:4.4 at 300°. These results indicate that dissociation energies of C—H bonds are not exactly the same but *decrease* in the order: *primary > secondary > tertiary.*

Bromine atoms are far more selective than chlorine atoms, and bromine attacks only *tertiary* hydrogens and these not very efficiently. Thus, photochemical (light-induced) monobromination of isopentane proceeds slowly and gives quite pure *t*-amyl bromide. Bromine atoms might be expected to be more selective than chlorine atoms, since bond energies indicate that the process

$$-\overset{|}{\underset{|}{C}}-H + :\ddot{\overset{..}{B}}r \cdot \longrightarrow -\overset{|}{\underset{|}{C}} \cdot + HBr$$ is distinctly endothermic while the corres-

ponding reaction with a chlorine atom is exothermic. In such circumstances it is not surprising to find that bromine only removes those hydrogens which are relatively weakly bonded to a carbon chain.

It is interesting that the selectivity of chlorination reactions carried on in solution is markedly increased in the presence of benzene (Figure 1-1) or alkyl-substituted benzenes. The reason for this is that benzene and other arenes form loose complexes with chlorine atoms which substantially cut down chlorine-atom reactivity—thus making the chlorine atoms behave more like bromine atoms.

High-temperature chlorination of a number of paraffin hydrocarbons is carried out in large-scale industrial operations. The chlorination products have important uses as solvents and as intermediates in chemical syntheses.

It is possible to achieve chlorination of alkanes using sulfuryl chloride (SO_2Cl_2, b.p. 69°) in place of chlorine.

$$-\overset{|}{\underset{|}{C}}-H + SO_2Cl_2 \longrightarrow -\overset{|}{\underset{|}{C}}-Cl + SO_2 + HCl$$

The reaction has a free-radical chain mechanism and the chains can be initiated by light or peroxides (p. 147). The propagation steps are probably as follows:

$$-\overset{|}{\underset{|}{C}}-H + \cdot \overset{..}{\underset{..}{C}}l : \longrightarrow -\overset{|}{\underset{|}{C}} \cdot + HCl$$

$$-\overset{|}{\underset{|}{C}} \cdot + SO_2Cl_2 \longrightarrow -\overset{|}{\underset{|}{C}}-Cl + SO_2 + :\overset{..}{\underset{..}{C}}l \cdot$$

As would be expected, chlorination of alkanes with more than one kind of hydrogen using sulfuryl chloride gives a mixture of alkyl chlorides resembling that obtained with chlorine itself.

3-8 NITRATION OF ALKANES

Another reaction of commercial importance is the nitration of alkanes to give nitroparaffins. Reaction is usually carried out in the vapor phase at elevated temperatures using nitric acid or nitrogen tetroxide as the nitrating agent.

$$RH + HNO_3 \xrightarrow{\sim 425°} RNO_2 + H_2O$$

All available evidence points to a free-radical mechanism for nitration but many aspects of the reaction are not fully understood. Mixtures are obtained—nitration of propane gives not only 1- and 2-nitropropanes but nitroethane and nitromethane.

$$CH_3CH_2CH_3 \; + \; HNO_3 \; \longrightarrow \; \begin{cases} CH_3CH_2CH_2NO_2 & CH_3\underset{\underset{NO_2}{|}}{C}HCH_3 \\ \\ \text{1-nitropropane (25\%)} & \text{2-nitropropane (40\%)} \\ \\ CH_3CH_2NO_2 & CH_3NO_2 \\ \\ \text{nitroethane (10\%)} & \text{nitromethane (25\%)} \end{cases}$$

In commercial practice the yield and product distribution in nitration of alkanes is controlled as far as possible by the judicious addition of catalysts (e.g., oxygen and halogens) which are claimed to raise the concentration of alkyl radicals. The product mixtures are separated by fractional distillation.

SUPPLEMENTARY EXERCISES

3-12 There are nine heptane isomers. Write structural formulas for each. Name each as a derivative of methane and by the IUPAC system. Is "neoheptane" an unambiguous name? Explain.

3-13 Write structural formulas for each of the following and name each by the IUPAC system:
   a. *t*-butyl-isobutyl-*s*-butyl-*n*-butylmethane
   b. isononane
   c. the monochloropentane isomers; also name each as best you can as an alkyl chloride.

3-14 Calculate ΔH for the following reactions in the vapor state at 25°:
   a. $2\ CH_4 + 7\ Cl_2 \rightarrow CCl_3{-}CCl_3 + 8\ HCl$
   b. $CH_3CH_3 + \frac{7}{2}\ O_2 \rightarrow 2\ CO_2 + 3\ H_2O$
   c. $CH_3CH_3 + H_2 \rightarrow 2\ CH_4$
   d. $CH_3CH_3 + Br_2 \rightarrow 2\ CH_3Br$
   e. $CH_4 + 2Cl_2 \rightarrow C(g) + 4\ HCl$

3-15 (*a*) Would ΔH for Exercise 3-14e be greater or less if C (solid) were the reaction product? Explain. (*b*) What are the implications of the heats of reaction determined in Exercise 3-14c and d to the "saturated" character of ethane?

3-16 The C—F bond energy in Table 3-5 was computed from recent thermochemical studies of the vapor-phase reaction,

   $CH_4 + 4\ F_2 \rightarrow CF_4 + 4\ HF \qquad \Delta H = -460$ kcal

   Show how the ΔH value for this reaction may be used to calculate the energy of the C—F bond if all the other required bond energies are known.

3-17 Investigate the energetics (ΔH) of possible chain mechanisms for the light-induced monobromination of methane and compare with those for chlorination. What are the prospects for iodination of methane?

3-18 The heat of combustion of cyclopropane $(CH_2)_3$ to give carbon dioxide and liquid water is 499.8 kcal. Show how this value can be used to calculate the average C—C bond energies of cyclopropane.

3-19 Write a mechanism in harmony with that usually written for hydrocarbon chlorination which would lead to production of hexachloroethane as in Exercise 3-14a. (This reaction is used for commercial production of hexachloroethane.)

Cycloalkanes

M*any important and interesting hydrocarbons contain rings of carbon atoms linked together by single bonds and are known as cycloalkanes. The simple unsubstituted cycloalkanes of the formula* $(CH_2)_n$ *make up a particularly important homologous series in which the chemical properties change in a much more striking way than do the properties of the open-chain hydrocarbons* $CH_3(CH_2)_{n-2}CH_3$. *The reasons for this will be developed with the aid of two new concepts, steric hindrance and angle strain, each of which is simple and easy to understand, being essentially mechanical in nature.*

The conformations of the cycloalkanes, particularly cyclohexane, will be discussed in some detail, because of their importance to the chemistry of many kinds of naturally occurring organic compounds. Cycloalkanes with small rings are of special interest in exhibiting properties intermediate between those of the alkanes, which are typically saturated, and the alkenes, which are typically unsaturated.

Stereoisomerism, which is concerned with compounds having the same bond structures but different arrangements of the atoms in space, is introduced in connection with cis-trans *isomerism.*

Cycloalkanes

4-1 NOMENCLATURE

Cyclohexane is a typical cycloalkane and has six methylene (CH_2) groups joined together so as to form a six-membered ring. The cycloalkanes (or cyclo-

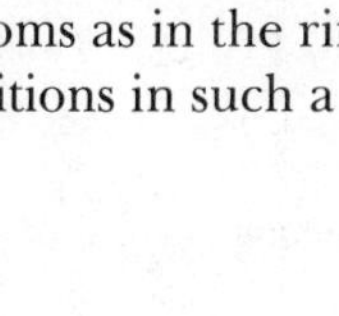

$$\begin{array}{c} \quad\quad CH_2 \\ CH_2 \quad CH_2 \\ | \quad\quad\quad | \\ CH_2 \quad CH_2 \\ \quad CH_2 \end{array}$$

cyclohexane

paraffins) with one ring have the general formula C_nH_{2n} and are named by adding the prefix *cyclo-* to the name of the corresponding *n*-alkane having the same number of carbon atoms as in the ring. Substituents are assigned numbers consistent with their positions in such a way as to keep the sum of the numbers to a minimum.

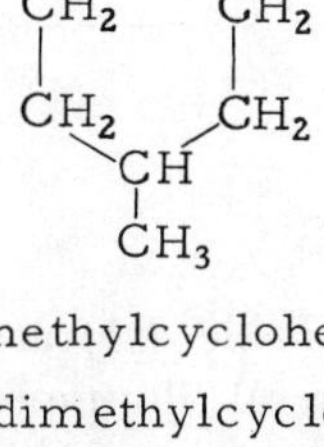

$$\begin{array}{c} CH_3 \\ CH \\ CH_2 \quad CH_2 \\ CH_2 \quad CH_2 \\ CH \\ CH_3 \end{array}$$

1,4-dimethylcyclohexane

(not 3,6-dimethylcyclohexane)

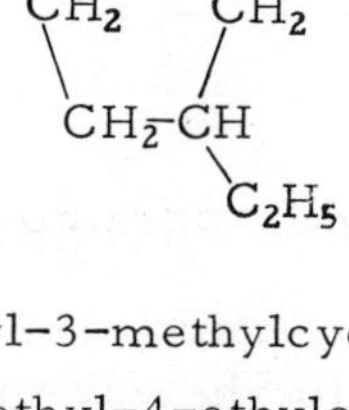

$$\begin{array}{c} CH_3 \\ CH \\ CH_2 \quad CH_2 \\ CH_2\text{-}CH \\ C_2H_5 \end{array}$$

1-ethyl-3-methylcyclopentane

(not 1-methyl-4-ethylcyclopentane)

The substituent groups derived from cycloalkanes by removing one hydrogen are named by replacing the ending -*ane* of the hydrocarbon with -*yl* to give cyclo-alkyl. Thus cyclohexane becomes cyclohexyl, cyclopentane-cyclopentyl, etc.

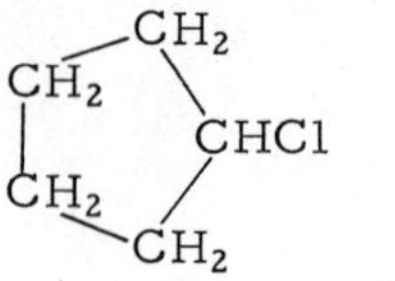

cyclopentyl chloride

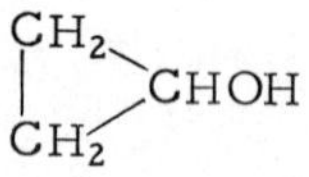

cyclopropyl alcohol
(cyclopropanol)

Frequently it is convenient to write the structure of a cyclic compound in an abbreviated form as in the following examples. Each line junction represents a carbon atom and the normal number of hydrogens is understood.

cyclobutane

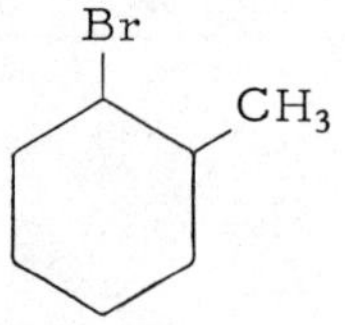

2-methylcyclohexyl bromide
(1-bromo-2-
methylcyclohexane)

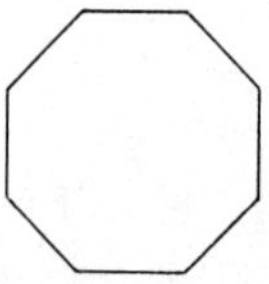

cycloöctane

EXERCISE 4-1   Write expanded structures showing the C—C bonds for each of the following condensed formulas. Name each substance by an accepted system.

a. $(CH_2)_{10}$

b. $(CH_2)_5CHCH_3$

c. $(CH_3)_2C(CH_2)_6CHC_2H_5$

d. The isomers of trimethylcyclobutane

e. $(CH_2)_6CHCH_2C(CH_3)_2CH_2Cl$

f. $[(CH_2)_2CH]_2C(CH_3)C_2H_5$

4-2 PHYSICAL PROPERTIES OF CYCLOALKANES

The melting and boiling points of cycloalkanes (Table 4-1) are somewhat higher than for the corresponding alkanes. The general "floppiness" of open-

Table 4-1   Physical Properties of Alkanes and Cycloalkanes

Compounds	B.p., °C	M.p., °C	d_4^{20}
propane	-42	-187	0.580[a]
cyclopropane	-33	-127	0.689[a]
n-butane	$-$ 0.5	-135	0.579[b]
cyclobutane	13	$-$ 90	0.689[b]
n-pentane	36	-130	0.626
cyclopentane	49	$-$ 94	0.746
n-hexane	69	$-$ 95	0.659
cyclohexane	81	7	0.778
n-heptane	98	$-$ 91	0.684
cycloheptane	119	$-$ 8	0.810
n-octane	126	$-$ 57	0.703
cycloöctane	151	15	0.830
n-nonane	151	$-$ 54	0.718
cyclononane	178	11	0.845

[a] At $-40°$.
[b] Under pressure.

chain hydrocarbons makes them harder to fit into a crystal lattice (hence lower melting points) and less hospitable to neighboring molecules of the same type than the more rigid cyclic compounds (hence lower boiling points).

4-3   SPECTROSCOPIC PROPERTIES OF CYCLOALKANES

The infrared spectra of the cycloalkanes are similar to those of the alkanes, except that, when there are no alkyl substituents, the characteristic bending frequencies of methyl groups at 1380 cm^{-1} are absent.   A moderately strong CH$_2$ "scissoring" frequency is observed between 1440 and 1470 cm^{-1}, the position depending somewhat on the size of the ring.   The general features of the infrared spectra of cycloalkanes are illustrated in Figure 4-1 using cycloöctane and methylcyclohexane as examples.

Like alkanes, the pure cycloalkanes show no ultraviolet absorption above 2000 A and are often good solvents for the determination of the ultraviolet spectra of other substances.

The n.m.r. spectra of the simple cycloalkanes show one sharp line at room temperature.   When substituents are present, differences in chemical shifts between the ring hydrogens are observed which, in the case of alkyl groups, are small and with spin-spin splitting produce more closely spaced lines than can usually be resolved (see Figure 4-2).

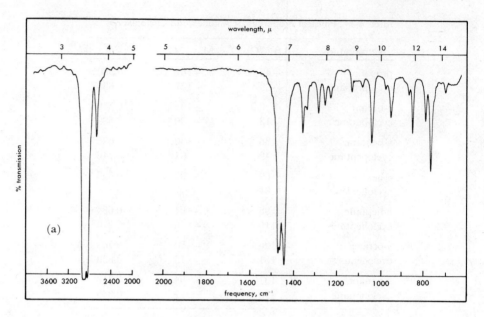

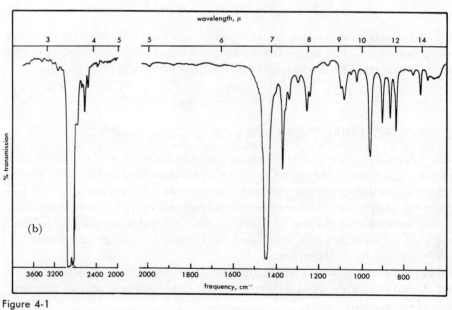

Figure 4-1

Infrared spectra of cycloöctane (a) and
methylcyclohexane (b).   These spectra
can be profitably compared with those
in Figure 3-3.

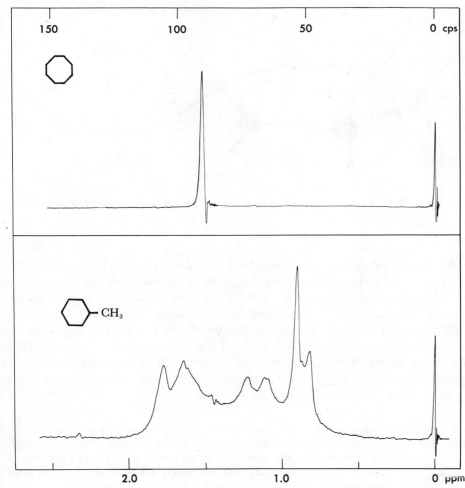

Figure 4-2   N.m.r. spectra of cyclooctane and methylcyclohexane at 60 Mcps with TMS as standard (0 ppm).

4-4 CONFORMATIONS OF CYCLOALKANES

A. Cyclohexane

We shall begin with cyclohexane, since it illustrates many important points about conformations. If cyclohexane existed as a regular *planar* hexagon with carbon atoms at the corners, the C—C—C bond angles would have to be 120°. Normal valence angles of carbon are closer to 109.5°. Thus, a cyclohexane molecule with a planar structure could be said to have an **angle strain** of 10.5° at each of the carbon atoms. We would be correct in inferring that this would lead to at least some lack of stability compared to a cyclohexane molecule with normal bond angles. The exact amount of strain associated with the planar structure is not simple to evaluate because, besides having the C—C—C bond angles

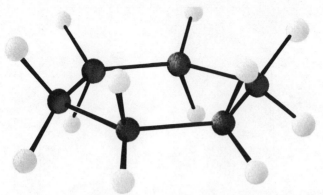

Figure 4-3   Cyclohexane in the strained planar configuration showing how the hydrogens become
eclipsed.

different from their normal values, the planar structure would also have the hydrogens in the unfavorable *eclipsed* arrangement as shown in Figure 4-3 (see also
p. 12).   The energy required to distort a C—C—C bond angle from its normal
value is approximately 17.5 cal per degree^2 per mole.   Therefore, we calculate
that the planar configuration of cyclohexane shown in Figure 4-3 is likely to be
unstable by at least $17.5 \times 10.5^2 \times 10^{-3} = 1.9$ kcal per angle or $1.9 \times 6 = 11.4$ kcal
for all six angles.   Neglecting entropy differences, this is seen by Equation (3-1)
to correspond to a K of 10^{-20} for equilibrium between unstrained, puckered
cyclohexane and strained, planar cyclohexane.

EXERCISE 4-2   Construct a graph of angle strain versus C—C—C bond angle over the range
of $\pm 20°$ from the normal value.   Use this graph to estimate the angle strain in
kcal for (a) planar cyclopentane, (b) planar cyclobutane, and (c) planar cyclo-
heptane.

Inspection of molecular models reveals that two quite different conformations
of the cyclohexane molecule may be constructed if the carbon valence angles are
held at 109.5°.   These are known as the "chair" and "boat" conformations (Figure 4-4).   It has not proved possible to separate cyclohexane into these two isomeric forms, and, actually, the two forms appear to be rapidly interconverted at
ordinary temperatures.   However, the chair conformation is considerably more
stable and comprises more than 99 per cent of the equilibrium mixture at room
temperature.
     The instability of the boat form relative to the chair form may be ascribed to
relatively unfavorable interactions between the hydrogen atoms around the ring.
If we make all the bond angles normal and orient the carbons in the ring to give
the extreme boat conformation shown in Figure 4-5, we see that a pair of 1,4-
hydrogens (the so-called "flagpole" hydrogens) have to be so close together
(1.83 A) that they fall on the rising part of the repulsion curve, as in Figure 3-6,

Figure 4-4   Two conformations of cyclohexane with 109.5° bond angles (hydrogens omitted).

for hydrogen.   Atoms interfering with one another in this way are said to cause
steric hindrance.   Obviously, steric hindrance will make molecules less stable.
and an H—H distance of 1.83 A corresponds to a repulsion energy of about 3
kcal.   There is still another factor which makes the extreme boat form unfavorable; namely, that the eight hydrogens along the "sides" of the boat are eclipsed,

interfering "flagpole" hydrogens

eclipsed
hydrogens

eclipsed
hydrogens

side view

end view

Figure 4-5   Boat form of cyclohexane showing interfering and eclipsed hydrogens.   Top, scale
models; center, ball-and-stick models; bottom, sawhorse representations.

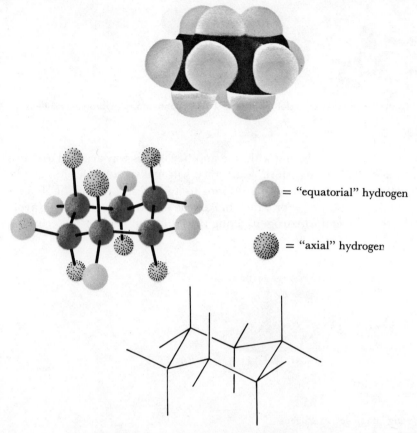

Figure 4-6   Chair form of cyclohexane showing equatorial and axial hydrogens.   Top, scale model;
center, ball-and-stick model; bottom, sawhorse representations.   Note that all the axial
positions are equivalent and all the equatorial positions are equivalent.

which brings them substantially closer together than they would be in a staggered arrangement (about 2.27 A compared with 2.50 A).   This is in striking
contrast with the chair form (Figure 4-6), for which adjacent hydrogens are seen
to be in staggered positions with respect to one another all the way around the
ring.   The chair form is therefore expected to be more stable than the boat form
since it has less repulsion between the hydrogens.

EXERCISE 4-3   The energy barrier for rotation about the C—C bond in ethane is about 3 kcal,
which suggests that the energy required to bring one pair of hydrogens into an
eclipsed arrangement is 1 kcal.   Calculate how many kilocalories the planar
form and extreme boat form of cyclohexane are likely to be unstable relative to
the chair form on account of H—H eclipsing and flagpole interactions.

Actually, the boat form of cyclohexane is not quite as strained as indicated by the
foregoing discussion.   Inspection of models reveals that the boat form is quite flexible, and even if the bond angles are held exactly at 109.5°, simultaneous rotation

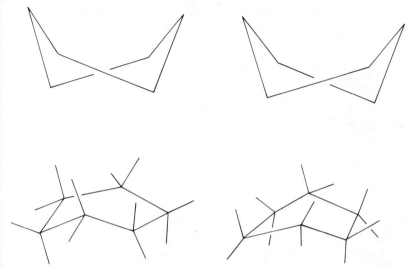

Figure 4-7   Drawings of the twist-boat conformations of cyclohexane.

around all the carbon-carbon bonds at once permits the ring to twist one way or the other to two equal energy conformations, in which the flagpole hydrogens move farther apart and the eight hydrogens along the sides become largely but not completely staggered. These arrangements are called the **twist-boat** (sometimes **skew-boat**) conformations (see Figure 4-7) and are believed to be about 5 kcal less stable than the chair form.

It will be seen that there are two distinct kinds of hydrogen in the chair form of cyclohexane — six which are almost contained by the "average" plane of the ring (called **equatorial** hydrogens) and three above and three below this average plane (called **axial** hydrogens). This raises an interesting question in connection with substituted cyclohexanes: For example, is the methyl group in methylcyclohexane equatorial or axial? Since only *one* methylcyclohexane is known, the methyl group must be either exclusively equatorial (*e*), or exclusively axial (*a*), or the two forms must be interconverted so rapidly that they cannot be separated into isomeric forms. It appears that the latter circumstance prevails; the ring going rapidly from one chair form to another by flipping one end of the

$$\begin{array}{ccc} \text{(axial)} & \xrightarrow{\text{fast}} & \text{(equatorial)} \end{array}$$

chair up and the other end down, and in so doing causing a substituent in an axial position to go to an equatorial position and *vice versa*. This process is called **ring inversion** and its rate is often called the **inversion frequency.** With cyclohexane itself, inversion is so fast that molecules flip about 10^6 times per second, going over an energy barrier of about 11 kcal.

equatorial

Figure 4-8

Scale models of equatorial and axial forms of the chair form of cyclohexyl bromide.

axial

There is considerable evidence which shows that the equatorial form of methylcyclohexane predominates over the axial form in the equilibrium mixture ($K \sim 15$). The same is true of all monosubstituted cyclohexane derivatives to a greater or lesser degree. The reason can be seen from scale models which show that a substituent group has more room in an equatorial conformation than in an axial conformation (see Figure 4-8); it is closer to the two axial hydrogens on the same side of the ring when it is in the axial position than it is to adjacent axial and equatorial hydrogens when it is in the equatorial position (see Figure 4-9). Clearly, the more stable conformation will be the one in which the nonbonded interactions are minimized.

EXERCISE 4-4   Use the sawhorse convention and draw all the possible conformations of cyclohexyl chloride with the ring in the chair and in the boat forms. Arrange these in order of expected stability. Show your reasoning.

Figure 4-9

axial   *equatorial*

Equatorial and axial monosubstituted cyclohexanes. Significant nonbonded interactions are indicated by dotted lines; these are more severe in the axial than the equatorial conformation.

Figure 4-10

Nonplanar conformation of cyclopentane.

B. Cyclopentane

The five —CH₂— groups of cyclopentane can form a regular pentagon (internal angles of 108°) with only a little bending of the normal carbon bond angles.
Actually, cyclopentane molecules are not as flat as would be expected on the
basis of having minimum distortion of the normal carbon bond angles. The
planar structure also has completely eclipsed hydrogens which would make the
planar arrangement unstable by about 10 kcal (see Exercise 4-3). The result is
that each molecule assumes a puckered conformation which is the best compromise between distortion of bond angles and eclipsing of hydrogens. The
best compromise conformations have the ring twisted with one or two of the
—CH₂— groups bent substantially out of a plane passed through the other carbons (Figure 4-10). The flexibility of the ring is such that these deformations
move rapidly around the ring.

C. Cyclobutane

Formation of a four-membered ring of carbon atoms can only be achieved
with substantial distortion of the normal valence angles of carbon regardless of
whether the ring is planar or nonplanar. If the valence bonds are assumed to

$$CH_2 \overbrace{\qquad}^{} CH_2$$
$$\underset{90°}{\big|} \qquad \big|$$
$$CH_2 \underline{\qquad} CH_2$$

cyclobutane

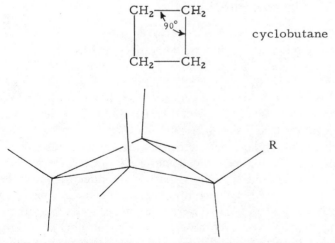

R

Figure 4-11   Nonplanar cyclobutane conformation with a substituent R in the less hindered, quasi-
equatorial position. The dihedral angle between the two halves of the bent ring is
usually 25 to 30 degrees, i.e., a 25 to 30° deviation from planarity.

lie along straight lines drawn between the carbon nuclei, each C—C—C bond angle will be 19.5° smaller than the normal 109.5° value in a planar ring. The angle distortion, of course, will be still greater if the ring is nonplanar. Nonetheless, the energy of eclipsing the hydrogens in cyclobutane is sufficient to cause the ring to be nonplanar. Substituents are probably most favorably located in what might be called the "quasi-equatorial" positions (Figure 4-11).

D. Cyclopropane

The three carbon atoms of the cyclopropane ring lie in a plane, and the angle strain is expected to be considerable, since each carbon valence angle must be deformed 49.5° from its normal value. It is likely that some relief from the strain associated with the eclipsing of the hydrogens of cyclopropane is achieved by distortion of the H—C—H and H—C—C bond angles.

$$
\begin{array}{c}
CH_2 \\
\diagup \overset{60°}{\diagdown} \\
CH_2 \!\!-\!\!-\!\! CH_2
\end{array}
\qquad\qquad \text{cyclopropane}
$$

E. Ethylene

If one is willing to consider a carbon-carbon double bond as a two-membered ring, then ethylene C_2H_4 is the simplest possible cycloalkane ("cycloethane") and as such has carbon valence angles of 0° and therefore an angle strain of 109.5° at each CH_2 group.

$$
CH_2 \overset{0°}{=\!\!=\!\!=} CH_2
$$

As we shall see in Chapter 6, ethylene is a planar molecule.

4-5   STRAIN IN CYCLOALKANE RINGS

A. The Baeyer Theory

The idea that cyclopropane and cyclobutane derivatives should have strained rings because their C—C—C bond angles cannot have the normal tetrahedral value of 109.5° was advanced by Baeyer in 1885. At the same time, it was suggested that the difficulties in synthesizing cycloalkane rings from C_7 upward was the direct result of the angle strain which would be expected if the large rings were regular planar polygons (see Table 4-2).

The Baeyer strain theory as applied to large rings is incorrect because we now know that cyclohexane and the higher cycloalkanes have puckered rings with normal or nearly normal bond angles. A good part of the difficulty in synthesizing the larger rings from open-chain compounds is due to the low probability of having reactive groups on the two fairly remote ends of a long hydrocarbon chain come together to effect cyclization. Usually, coupling of reactive groups on the ends of *different* molecules occurs in preference to cyclization, unless the reactions are carried out in very dilute solutions.

It was Sachse (1890) who pointed out that large-ring compounds need not be

Table 4-2   Strain and Heats of Combustion of Cycloalkanes

Cycloalkane, $(CH_2)_n$	n	Angle strain at each CH_2, deg	Heat of combustion,[a] ΔH, kcal/mole	Heat of combustion per CH_2, $\Delta H/n$, kcal	Total strain,[b] kcal/mole
ethylene	2	109.5	337.23	168.6	22.4
cyclopropane	3	49.5	499.83	166.6	27.6
cyclobutane	4	19.5	655.86	164.0	26.4
cyclopentane	5	1.5	793.52	158.7	6.5
cyclohexane	6	$(10.5)^c$	944.48	157.4 .	0.0
cycloheptane	7	$(19.0)^c$	1108.2	158.3	6.3
cycloöctane	8	$(25.5)^c$	1269.2	158.6	9.6
cyclononane	9	$(30.5)^c$	1429.5	158.8	11.2
cyclodecane	10	$(34.5)^c$	1586.0	158.6	12.0
cyclopentadecane	15	$(46.5)^c$	2362.5	157.5	1.5
open-chain, n-alkane	∞			157.4	

[a] For gaseous hydrocarbons to give liquid water at 25°C, data from S. Kaarsemaker and J. Coops, *Rec. Trav. Chim.*, **71**, 261 (1952), and J. Coops, H. Van Kamp, W. A. Lambgrets, B. J. Visser, and H. Dekker, *Rec. Trav. Chim.*, **79**, 1226 (1960).
[b] Calculated by subtracting ($n \times 157.4$) from the observed heat of combustion.
[c] Angle strain calculated for planar ring as per the Baeyer theory.

flat, since strain could be relieved by puckering — this was elaborated by Mohr (1918) and became the Sachse-Mohr theory of strainless large rings.

EXERCISE 4-5   Formation of a cycloalkane $(CH_2)_n$ by reactions such as Br $+CH_2)_n$ZnBr $\rightarrow$ $(CH_2)_n$ + $ZnBr_2$ occurs in competition with other reactions such as 2 Br $+CH_2)_n$ZnBr $\rightarrow$ Br $+CH_2)_n(CH_2)_n$ZnBr + $ZnBr_2$.

a. Explain why cyclization reactions of this kind carried out in *dilute* solutions are likely to give better yields of $(CH_2)_n$ than in *concentrated* solutions.

b. Make a graph which shows, as a function of n over the range 3 to 15, how the yield of cycloalkane might be expected to depend on (1) the total strain in the ring formed (see Table 4-2), and (2) the probability that at any given instant the reactive ends will be properly oriented with respect to one another so as to permit cyclization to occur.

c. Explain how the factors considered in (b) must be balanced relative to one another to account for the reported yields of cyclization products for the following ring sizes: $(CH_2)_3$, >80%; $(CH_2)_4$, 7%; $(CH_2)_6$, 45%; larger rings <10%.

B. Heats of Combustion of Cycloalkanes

The strain in ring compounds can be evaluated quantitatively by comparison of the heats of combustion per CH_2 group as in Table 4-2. The data indicate that cyclohexane is virtually strain-free, since the heat of combustion per CH_2 is the same as for n-alkanes (157.4 kcal). The increase for the smaller rings

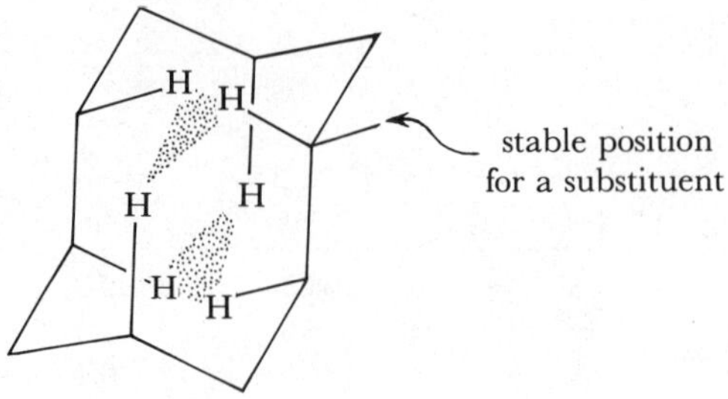

stable position
for a substituent

Figure 4-12

Conformation of cyclodecane. Shaded area indicates maximal nonbonded interactions.

clearly reflects increasing angle strain and, to some extent, unfavorable interactions between nonbonded atoms. For rings from C_7—C_{12} there appears to be a residual strain of 1 to 1.5 kcal per CH_2. These rings can be puckered into flexible conformations with normal C—C—C angles, but from C_7—C_{12} such arrangements all have pairs of partially eclipsed or interfering hydrogens. Rather surprisingly, the stable conformation of cyclodecane is a compromise structure with slightly distorted bond angles and several very short H—H distances (see Figure 4-12). A stable conformation for a substituent on the cyclodecane ring is the one indicated in Figure 4-12 and the least stable is that which replaces any of the six hydrogens shown, since nonbonded interactions are particularly strong at these positions.

The very large ring compounds like cyclopentadecane $(CH_2)_{15}$ are essentially strain-free.

4-6 CHEMICAL PROPERTIES

We have already observed how strain in the small-ring cycloalkanes affects their heats of combustion. We reasonably expect other chemical properties will also be affected by ring strain and, indeed, cyclopropane and cyclobutane are considerably more reactive than saturated, open-chain hydrocarbons. In fact, they undergo some of the reactions which are typical of compounds with carbon-carbon double bonds, their reactivity depending on the degree of angle strain and the sensitivity of the reagent to C—C bond strengths. The result of these reactions is always opening of the ring by cleavage of a C—C bond to give an open-chain compound having normal bond angles. Relief of angle strain may therefore be considered to be an important part of the driving force of these reactions. A summary of a number of ring-opening reactions is given in Table 4-3. Ethylene is highly reactive, while cyclopropane and cyclobutane are less so (in that order). The C—C bonds of the larger, relatively strain-free cycloalkanes are inert, so that these substances resemble the n-alkanes in their chemical behavior. Substitution reactions, such as chlorination of cyclopentane and higher cycloalkanes, are generally less complex than those of the corresponding alkanes because there are fewer possible isomeric substitution products. Thus, cyclohexane gives only one monochlorination product while n-hexane gives three isomeric monochloro compounds.

Table 4-3   Reactions of Cycloalkanes, $(CH_2)_n$

Reaction	"Cycloethane" $(CH_2{=}CH_2)$	Cyclo-propane	Cyclo-butane	Cyclo-pentane	Cyclo-hexane
$(CH_2)_{n-2}\big|{-}{-}{-}^{CH_2}_{CH_2} + Br_2 \rightarrow (CH_2)_{n-2}\big<^{CH_2Br}_{CH_2Br}$	very readily	slowly	inert	inert	inert
$+ H_2SO_4 \rightarrow (CH_2)_{n-2}\big<^{CH_3}_{CH_2OSO_3H}$	readily	readily	?	inert	inert
$+ KMnO_4 \rightarrow (CH_2)_{n-2}\big<^{CH_2OH}_{CH_2OH}$	readily	inert	inert	inert	inert
$+ H_2 \xrightarrow{Ni} (CH_2)_{n-2}\big<^{CH_3}_{CH_3}$	readily at room temp.	120°	200°	inert	inert

EXERCISE 4-6   Use the data of Table 4-2 and other needed bond energies to calculate ΔH for the following reaction in the vapor state at 25° with $n = 3, 4$, and 5.

$$(CH_2)_n \rightarrow CH_3(CH_2)_{n-3}CH{=}CH_2$$

What can you conclude about the stability of the cycloalkanes with $n = 3, 4$, and 5 with respect to corresponding open-chain compounds with double bonds?

EXERCISE 4-7   Use the heats of combustion (to liquid water) given in Table 4-2 and appropriate bond energies to calculate ΔH (vapor) for ring-opening of the cycloalkanes with bromine over the range $n = 2$ to $n = 6$:

$$(CH_2)_n + Br_2 \rightarrow (CH_2)_{n-2}(CH_2Br)_2$$

EXERCISE 4-8   Investigate the thermodynamic feasibility of the following propagation steps for opening the rings of cycloalkanes with $n = 2\text{-}6$ by a free-radical mechanism.

$$(CH_2)_n + Br\cdot \;\rightarrow\; BrCH_2{+}CH_2\}_{n-2}CH_2\cdot$$
$$BrCH_2{+}CH_2\}_{n-2}CH_2\cdot + Br_2 \;\rightarrow\; (CH_2)_{n-2}(CH_2Br)_2 + Br\cdot$$

Use 83 kcal for the bond-dissociation energy of a *normal* C—C bond and 68 kcal for the bond-dissociation energy of a C—Br bond. (An easy way to solve a problem of this type is to first calculate ΔH of each step for cyclohexane where there is no strain, and then make suitable corrections for the strain which is present for small values of n.)

EXERCISE 4-9   Show how the reactions described in Table 4-3 could be used to tell whether a hydro-
                      carbon of formula C_4H_8 is methylcyclopropane, cyclobutane, or 1-butene ($CH_3CH_2CH=$
                      CH_2). Write equations for the reactions used.

4-7 *CIS-TRANS* ISOMERISM OF SUBSTITUTED CYCLOALKANES

Stereoisomerism may be defined broadly as isomerism of compounds with the
same structural formulas but having different spatial arrangements of the
various groups. We have already encountered two examples of stereoisomerism: the boat and chair forms of cyclohexane and monosubstituted cyclohexanes
with the substituent either in an axial or an equatorial position, and the different
possible rotational conformations of ethane derivatives (pp. 43-46). In these
cases the stereoisomers are much too easily interconverted to be isolated separately. However, there is another type of stereoisomerism due to different
spatial arrangements of substituent groups attached to double bonds (see Chapter 6) or rings in which the stereoisomers are not readily interconverted. This
is often called **geometrical isomerism** or *cis-trans* **isomerism.** Thus, when a
cycloalkane is disubstituted at different ring positions as in 1,2-dimethylcyclo-

$$
\begin{array}{c}
\overset{\displaystyle CH_2}{\triangle} \\
CH-CH \\
CH_3 \qquad\qquad CH_3
\end{array}
$$

1, 2-dimethylcyclopropane

propane, two isomeric structures are possible according to whether the substituents are situated both above (or both below) the plane of the ring (*cis* isomer), or one above and one below (*trans* isomer), as shown in Figure 4-13.

Ring formation confers rigidity on the molecular structure such that rotation
about any of the C—C ring bonds is prevented. As a result, *cis* and *trans* isomers
cannot be interconverted without breaking one or more bonds. One way of

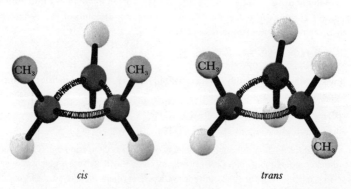

Figure 4-13 Ball-and-stick models of *cis* and *trans* isomers of 1,2-dimethylcyclopropane.

doing this is to break open the ring and then close it again with a substituent on the opposite side from where it started. Alternatively, the bond to the substituent (or the hydrogen) on the same carbon can be broken and reformed on the opposite side of the ring. Examples of both kinds of processes will be discussed in later chapters.

EXERCISE 4-10   Write structural formulas for all of the possible *cis-trans* isomers of the following compounds:
a. 1,2,3-trimethylcyclopropane
b. 1,3-dichlorocyclopentane
c. 1,1,3-trimethylcyclohexane
d. (3-methylcyclobutyl)-3-methylcyclobutane

EXERCISE 4-11   Would you expect *cis*- or *trans*-1,2-dimethylcyclopropane to be the more stable? Explain.

Cis and *trans* isomers of cyclohexane derivatives have the additional possibility of conformational isomerism. For example, 4-*t*-butylcyclohexyl chloride can theoretically exist in four stereoisomeric chair forms, [1], [2], [3], and [4].

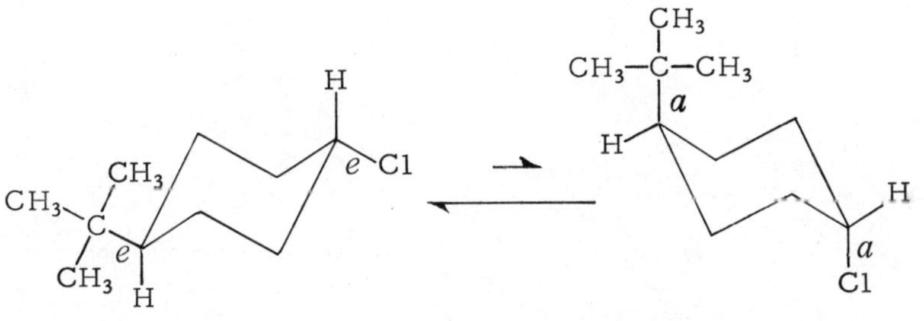

[1]   [2]

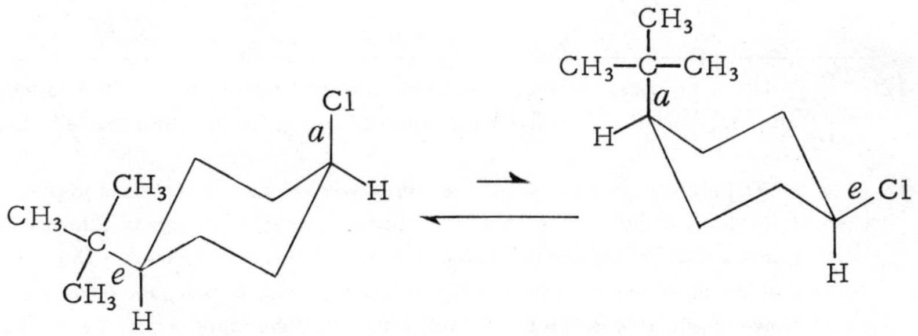

[3]   [4]

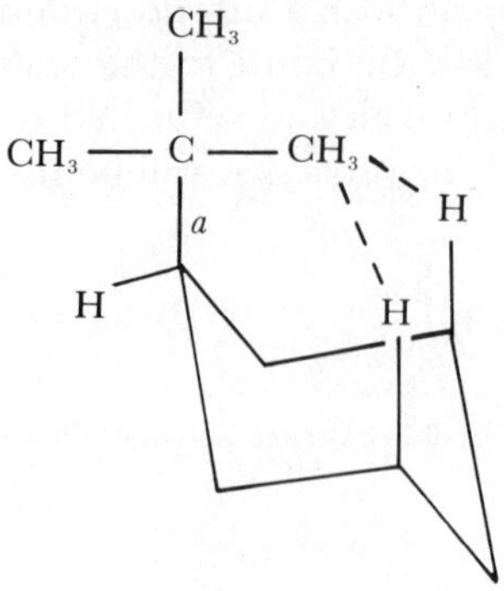

Figure 4-14

1,3-Interactions in a cyclohexane ring with an axial *t*-butyl group.

Structures [1] and [2] have the substituents *trans* to one another but in [1] they are both equatorial while in [2] they are both axial. Structures [3] and [4] have the *cis* relationship between the groups, but the *t*-butyl and chlorine are equatorial-axial in [3] and axial-equatorial in [4]. *t*-Butyl groups are very large and bulky and considerable steric hindrance results when a *t*-butyl is in an axial position (Figure 4-14). For this reason, structures [1] and [3] with the *t*-butyl group equatorial are much more favorable than [2] and [4].

When there are two substituents in the *cis*-1,4-arrangement on a cyclohexane ring, neither of which will go easily into an axial position, then it appears that the twist-boat conformation (p. 89) is most favorable (Figure 4-15).

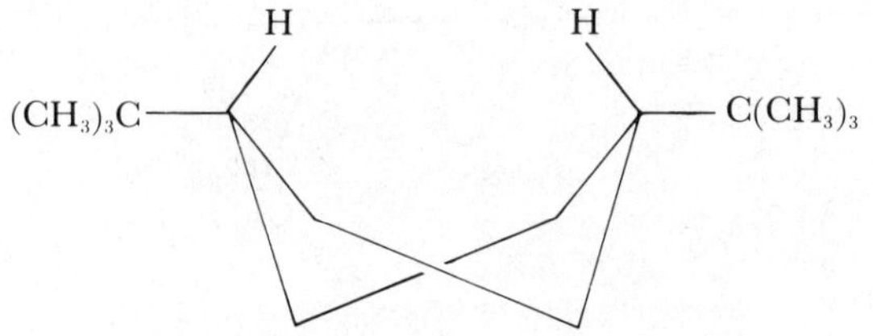

Figure 4-15

Twist-boat conformation of *cis*-1,4-di-*t*-butylcyclohexane.

EXERCISE 4-12   Draw the possible chair conformations of *trans*- and *cis*-1,3-dimethylcyclohexane. Are the *cis* or the *trans* isomers likely to be the more stable? Explain.

EXERCISE 4-13   An empirical rule known as the von Auwers-Skita rule was used to assign configurations of pairs of *cis* and *trans* isomers in cyclic systems at a time when *cis* isomers were thought to be always less stable than *trans* isomers. The rule states that the *cis* isomer will have the higher boiling point, density, and refractive index. However, the rule fails for 1,3-disubstituted cyclohexanes, where the *trans* isomer has the higher boiling point, density, and refractive index. Explain how the von Auwers-Skita rule might be restated to include such 1,3-systems.

EXERCISE 4-14   Would you expect cyclohexene oxide to be more stable in the *cis* or *trans* configuration? Give your reasons.

cyclohexene oxide

4-8 CONFORMATIONS OF DECALIN

The six-membered rings of decalin like those of cyclohexane are expected to be most stable when in the chair form.   However, there are two possible ways in which two chairs can be joined together (see Figure 4-16)—the ring-junction hydrogens may be either both on the same side of the molecule (*cis*-decalin) or on opposite sides (*trans-*

trans-decalin   *cis-decalin*

Figure 4-16 Chair conformations of the decalins.

decalin).   When the two rings are joined through two equatorial-type bonds, *trans*-decalin results, while an axial-equatorial union gives *cis*-decalin.   Both isomers are known, and the *trans* isomer is about 2 kcal more stable than the *cis* isomer, largely because of relatively unfavorable nonbonded interactions within the concave area of *cis*-decalin (see Figure 4-17).

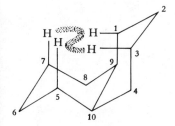

Figure 4-17

Representation of *cis*-decalin showing nonbonded interactions (shaded areas). The numbering of the decalin ring is the currently accepted convention.

EXERCISE 4-15   Use ball-and-stick models to assess the degree of stability to be expected for a decalin with chair-form rings and an axial-axial ring fusion.

SUPPLEMENTARY EXERCISES

4-16 Write structural formulas for substances (one for each part) which fit the following descriptions. Make sawhorse drawings of the substances where conformational problems are involved.

  a. a compound of formula C_9H_{18} which shows infrared absorption at 1380 cm^{-1} and has only a single sharp resonance peak in its n.m.r. spectrum

  b. a compound of formula C_5H_{10}, which shows infrared absorptions at 1380 cm^{-1} and 1440 cm^{-1} and has just two unsplit n.m.r. absorption peaks

  c. a compound of formula C_4H_8 which reacts slowly with bromine and sulfuric acid but not with potassium permanganate solution

  d. the most highly strained isomer of C_5H_{10}

  e. the possible products from treatment of 1-ethyl-2-methylcyclopropane with bromine

  f. the least stable chair and the least stable boat conformations of *trans*-1,4-dichlorocyclohexane

  g. the most stable geometrical isomer of 1,3-di-*t*-butylcyclobutane

  h. a compound with a six-membered ring which is most stable with the ring in a boat form

  i. the most stable possible conformation of *trans*-1,3-di-*t*-butylcyclohexane

  j. the most stable conformation of *cis*-2-*t*-butyl-*cis*-decalin

  k. a boat-boat conformation of *cis*-decalin

Bonding in Organic Molecules.
Atomic Orbital Models

*I*n *earlier chapters we have used structural formulas with covalent chemical bonds shown by lines or pairs of dots representing shared pairs of electrons. It is possible to study and understand much of the chemistry of organic compounds in terms of such formulas, but a greater understanding can be achieved by going more deeply into the way chemical bonding is related to the electronic structures of the atoms and the electrical forces acting between the electrons and the nuclei. A satisfying reward for this approach is the ability to interpret and make qualitative predictions of bond angles in organic compounds. Our reason for delaying discussion of bonds and bond angles to this chapter is that these subjects are usually better appreciated after some consideration of the three-dimensional character of organic molecules and the concepts of angle strain and steric hindrance.*

There are several qualitative approaches to bonding in polyatomic molecules, but we shall discuss here the most widely used and currently popular approach; it involves setting up appropriate atomic orbitals for the atoms and considering that each bond arises from the attractive electrical forces between two nuclei and a pair of electrons traveling in two overlapping atomic orbitals—each centered on a different atom. The geometry of the bonds is assumed to be determined by the geometry of the orbitals. This approach is reasonably successful but, since the bond angles very often differ from those predicted, various kinds of corrections are needed to reconcile theory with experiment.

We shall also present an alternative and more simple approach to predictions of molecular geometry which emphasizes the influence of the repulsive forces between the valence electrons. In the course of showing how each of these approaches can be applied, we shall discuss ways of formulating bonding and geometries for a number of important kinds of organic compounds.

Bonding in Organic Molecules. Atomic Orbital Models

CHAPTER 5

Hitherto, we have represented the electronic structures of organic molecules in terms of Lewis structures, for which the working principle is the accession (or loss) of electrons by each atom in the molecule to achieve an inert gas configuration. Such representations fail to indicate much about the geometry of a molecule. Why, for instance, are the bond angles 109.5° in compounds like methane and carbon tetrachloride but 104.5° in water and 92° in hydrogen sulfide? Also, Lewis structures do not adequately account for differences in strengths and reactivities of various types of bonds, particularly carbon-carbon single, double, and triple bonds. A more detailed approach to the electronic structures of organic molecules is necessary. In the following discussion, we shall show how atomic orbital models are set up for organic molecules and we shall illustrate some of their advantages and limitations.

5-1 HYDROGEN-LIKE ATOMIC ORBITALS

The modern concept of a hydrogen atom does not visualize the orbital electron traversing a simple planetary orbit. Rather, we speak of an **atomic orbital,** in which there is a probability of finding the electron in a particular volume element at a given distance and direction from the nucleus. The boundaries of such an orbital are not very distinct, because there always remains a finite, even if small, probability of finding the electron relatively distant from the nucleus.

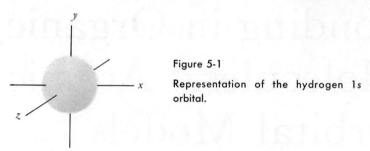

Figure 5-1

Representation of the hydrogen 1s orbital.

There are a number of discrete atomic orbitals available to the electron of a hydrogen atom. These differ in energy, size, and shape, and *exact* mathematical descriptions for each are available. That which follows will be a qualitative description of the nature of some of the hydrogen orbitals.

The most stable or "normal" state of a hydrogen atom is designated 1s. The 1s state is the state of the hydrogen atom in which the electron is on the average closest to the nucleus (i.e., it is the state with the smallest atomic orbital). The orbital of the 1s state is spherically symmetrical. This means that the probability of finding the electron at a given distance r from the nucleus is independent of the direction from the nucleus. We shall henceforth represent the 1s orbital as a sphere centered on the nucleus with a radius such that the probability of finding the electron within the boundary surface is high (0.8 to 0.95); see Figure 5-1.

The 2s orbital is spherically symmetrical like the 1s orbital; it is larger and therefore more diffuse, and it has a higher energy. There are also three orbitals of equal energies called 2p orbitals, which are quite different in geometrical form from the s orbitals. These are shown in Figure 5-2, from which we see that the respective axes passing through the tangent spheres of the three p orbitals lie at right angles to one another, and each orbital is *not* spherically symmetrical with respect to the nucleus.

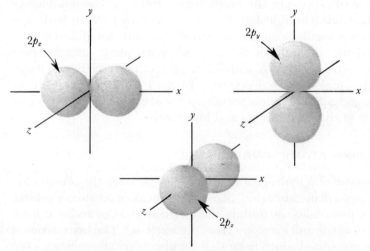

Figure 5-2   The shapes and orientations of the three 2p orbitals of a hydrogen atom.

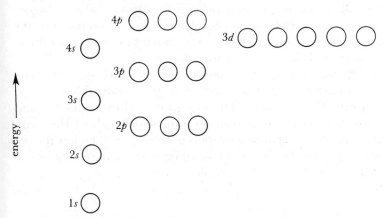

Figure 5-3   Schematic diagram of the energies of the hydrogen-like atomic orbitals.

The 3s and 3p states are similar to the 2s and 2p states but are of higher energy. The 3d, 4d, 4f, etc., orbitals have still higher energies and quite different geometries.   The 3d and 4f orbitals are not important for bonding in most organic substances, at least those which are compounds of hydrogen and elements in the first main row of the periodic table.   The relative energies of the 1s–4p orbitals are shown in Figure 5-3.

The famous **Pauli "exclusion principle"** states that no more than two electrons can occupy a given orbital and then only if they differ with respect to electron spin (which can have only two possible orientations, as may be symbolized by ↑ and ↓).   Two electrons with "paired" spins are often represented as ↑↓. Such a pair of electrons can occupy a single orbital.   The symbols ↑↑ (or ↓↓) represent two electrons that may *not* go together into a single orbital.

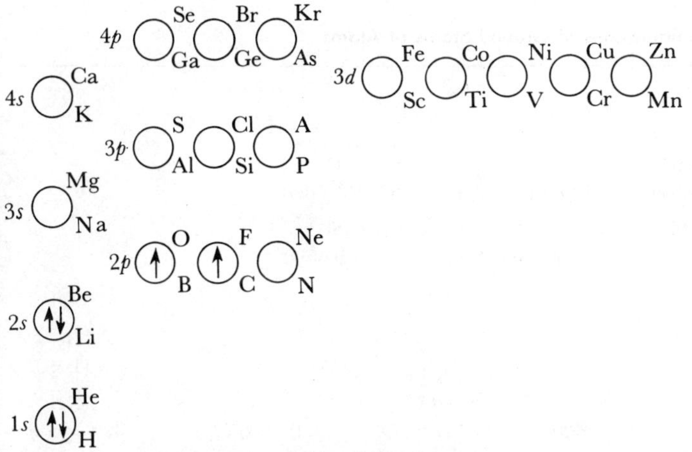

Figure 5-4   Diagram showing the most stable electron configuration of a carbon atom.   Addition of further electrons in accord with Hund's rule gives the electron configuration of the other atoms as indicated by the atomic symbols.

If we assume that all atomic nuclei have orbitals like those of the hydrogen atom, we can see how more complex atoms can be built up by adding electrons to the orbitals in order of decreasing stability. For each atom, the proper number of electrons is added to balance the nuclear charge.

Figure 5-4 shows the building up of the lowest state of a carbon atom. The two highest energy electrons are put into different $2p$ orbitals with unpaired spins in accordance with **Hund's rule.** The rationale of Hund's rule is quite simple. If there are two electrons that can go into two orbitals of the same energy (degenerate orbitals), their mutual repulsion energy will be less if they have unpaired spins ($\uparrow\uparrow$) and thus are not able to be in the same orbital at the same time. For this reason, the electronic configuration

is expected to be more stable than the configuration

is expected to be more stable than the configuration

if the orbitals have the *same* energy.

States like the one shown in Figure 5-4 for carbon are built up through the following steps. Helium has two paired electrons in the $1s$ orbital; its configuration can be written as $(1s)^2$, the superscript outside the parentheses denoting two paired electrons in the $1s$ orbital. If the electrons are not paired, then the most stable state is $(1s)(2s)$. Thus,

$$\text{He}^{2\oplus} + 2e(\uparrow\downarrow) \longrightarrow \text{He} \quad (1s)^2 \quad [\text{more stable state than } (1s)(2s), \text{ or } (2p)^2, \text{ etc.}]$$

$$\text{He}^{2\oplus} + 2e(\uparrow\uparrow) \underset{\longrightarrow}{\overset{\longrightarrow}{\diagdown}} \begin{array}{ll} \text{He} & (1s)^2 \\ \text{He} & (1s)(2s) \end{array} \quad [\text{most stable state possible for helium with unpaired electrons}]$$

Table 5-1   Electronic Configurations of Ground States of Atoms

H $(1s)$				
Li $(1s)^2(2s)$	Be $(1s)^2(2s)^2$	B $(1s)^2(2s)^2(2p)$	C $(1s)^2(2s)^2(2p)^2$	
Na $(1s)^2(2s)^2(2p)^6(3s)$	Mg $\ldots(3s)^2$	Al $\ldots(3s)^2(3p)$	Si $\ldots(3s)^2(3p)^2$	

				He $(1s)^2$
	N $(1s)^2(2s)^2(2p)^3$	O $(1s)^2(2s)^2(2p)^4$	F $(1s)^2(2s)^2(2p)^5$	Ne $(1s)^2(2s)^2(2p)^6$
	P $\ldots(3s)^2(3p)^3$	S $\ldots(3s)^2(3p)^4$	Cl $\ldots(3s)^2(3p)^5$	A $\ldots(3s)^2(3p)^6$

For $Li^{3\oplus} + 3e$, we expect Li $(1s)^2(2s)$ to be the stable state where the $(1s)^2$ electrons are paired. Continuing in this way we can derive the electronic configurations for the elements in the first two rows of the periodic table, as shown in Table 5-1. These configurations can be expected to follow Hund's rule for the most stable state.

5-2 BOND FORMATION USING ATOMIC ORBITALS

In writing the conventional Lewis structures for molecules, we assume that a covalent chemical bond between two atoms involves sharing of a pair of electrons, one from each atom. Figure 5-5 shows how atomic orbitals can be considered to be used in bond formation. Here, we postulate that a *single* bond is formed by the pulling together of two atomic nuclei by attractive forces exerted by two electrons in overlapping atomic orbitals having paired spins ($\uparrow\downarrow$). Since *two* atomic orbitals can hold a maximum of *four* electrons, it is reasonable to ask why it is that two rather than one, three, or four electrons are normally involved. The answer is that two overlapping atomic orbitals can be considered to combine to give one low-energy **bonding orbital** and one high-energy **antibonding orbital** (see the top part of Figure 5-6). Orbitals which overlap as shown in Figure 5-5 are said to overlap in the σ manner, and the bonding orbital is called a **σ orbital** while the antibonding orbital is called a **σ * orbital.** Two **paired** electrons suffice to fill the σ orbital. Any additional electrons have to go into the high-energy σ^* orbital and contribute not to bonding but to repulsion between the atoms. The hydrogen molecule-ion $H_2^{\oplus}$ can be regarded as having one electron in a σ orbital. It has been studied in the vapor state by spectroscopic means and found to have a dissociation energy to $H^{\oplus}$ and $H\cdot$ of 61 kcal compared to the 104.2 kcal bond energy for H_2. Several possible combinations of two hydrogen orbitals and from one to four electrons are shown in the lower part of Figure 5-6.

EXERCISE 5-1   Formulate the electronic configuration of He_2 and $He_2^{\oplus}$ in a manner similar to Figure 5-6. The ion $He_2^{\oplus}$ has been detected spectroscopically; suggest a reason why this ion is more stable than $H_2^{\ominus}$.

EXERCISE 5-2   Write electronic configurations for three different *excited* states of H_2. Arrange them in order of stability. Show your reasoning.

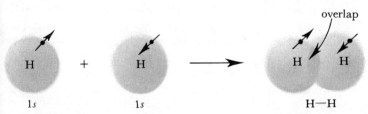

1s   1s   H—H

Figure 5-5   Representation of the formation of an H—H bond by sharing of electrons in overlapping orbitals.

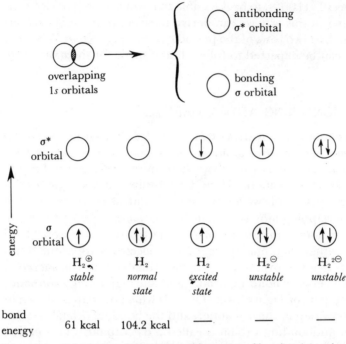

Figure 5-6 Schematic representation of formation of bonding (σ) and antibonding (σ^*) orbitals by overlap of two atomic 1s orbitals and some of the various electronic configurations that are possible with these orbitals.

5-3 DIRECTED COVALENT BONDS

To predict bond angles we can use the idea that the direction of a bond should be such as to have the orbitals of the bonding electrons overlap as much as possible for a given internuclear distance.

This idea does not apply to bonds involving only s orbitals because s orbitals are spherically symmetrical. However, it should be important in the formation of bonds with p orbitals. For bonding of a hydrogen by its 1s orbital to a given p orbital, the hydrogen nucleus is expected to lie along the axis of the p orbital as in Figure 5-7, because this arrangement will give the maximum overlap for a given degree of internuclear repulsion.

For an atom X which forms two σ bonds with p orbitals to hydrogen, the H—X—H angle is predicted to be 90° (Figure 5-8). The orbital treatment here offers improvement over Lewis structures through the idea of directed bonds and the possibility of predicting bond angles. Without further thought, it would be possible to go too far and predict that, because only s and p orbitals are commonly involved for the atoms of organic compounds of elements in the first main row of the periodic system, all bond angles for such substances would be either indeterminate (s orbitals with spherical symmetry) or 90° (p orbitals). This dilemma has been resolved by orbital hybridization, as will be described later.

A further useful postulate is that the strongest bonds are formed when the overlapping of the orbitals is at a maximum. On this basis we expect differences

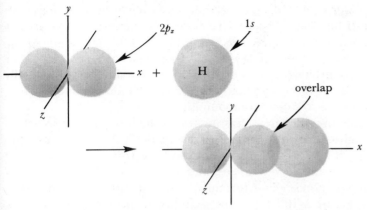

Figure 5-7   Overlap of a hydrogen 1s orbital with a 2p orbital centered on another atom.

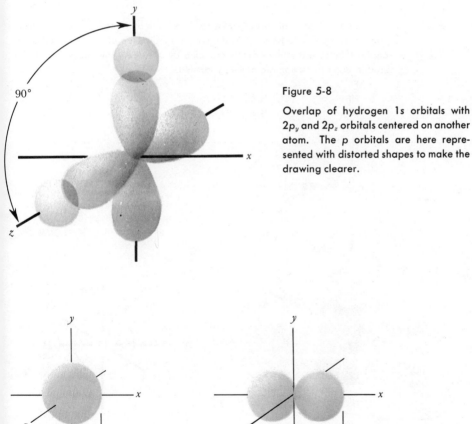

Figure 5-8

Overlap of hydrogen 1s orbitals with $2p_y$ and $2p_z$ orbitals centered on another atom. The p orbitals are here represented with distorted shapes to make the drawing clearer.

Figure 5-9   Relative extension of 2s and 2p orbitals.

in bond-forming power for s, p, d, and f orbitals since each of these orbitals have different radial distributions. The relative scales of extension for $2s$ and $2p$ orbitals are 1 and $\sqrt{3}$, respectively, as shown in Figure 5-9. The shape of the p orbitals leads to the expectation that p orbitals should be able to overlap other orbitals better than s orbitals and hence that p bonds should be generally stronger than s bonds. If there is a choice between formation of s and p bonds, p bonds should lead to more stable compounds.

The water molecule provides an interesting test of the foregoing approach to bonds and bond angles. The oxygen atom is seen from Table 5-1 to have the configuration $(1s)^2(2s)^2(2p)^4$. If we assign two paired electrons arbitrarily to the $2p_y$ orbital, then we have the $2p_x$ and $2p_z$ orbitals with one electron each to form bonds to two hydrogen atoms. This formulation in full and in an abbreviated version is shown in Figure 5-10. (It will be seen that the octet rule follows very naturally here through having all available stable orbitals filled with electrons.)

EXERCISE 5-3   Make drawings of atomic orbital models for each of the following substances. Each drawing should be large and clear with indication of the expected bond angles. Be sure that the orbitals occupied by unshared pairs as well as those used in bond formation are correctly labeled.

  a. F_2 e. $H_3O^{\oplus}$
  b. HF   f. H_2O_2
  c. NH_3 g. $H_2N\!-\!NH_2$
  d. F_2O

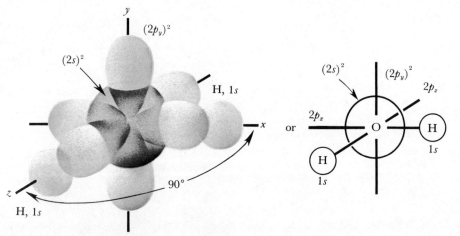

Figure 5-10   Formulation of the water molecule as involving σ overlap of $2p_x$ and $2p_z$ orbitals of oxygen with the $1s$ orbitals of hydrogen.

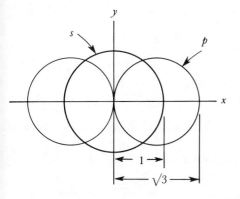

Figure 5-11

Diagram of an atom with s and p orbitals before hybridization.

5-4 HYBRID BOND ORBITALS

From what has been said so far, one might expect carbon with the $(1s)^2(2s)^2(2p)^2$ configuration to form only compounds such as :CR$_2$ with $\angle$ R—C—R $= 90°$, or else $(1s)^2(2s)(2p)^3$ compounds (CR$_4$) with three p bonds at $90°$ to one another and an s bond in an unspecified direction. Since CH$_4$, CCl$_4$, etc., have been shown beyond any possible doubt to have tetrahedral configurations, the simple orbital picture breaks down when applied to carbon.

Pauling and Slater have resolved this discrepancy between theory and experiment by introducing the concept of *orbital hybridization*. The hybridization involves determining which (if any) combinations of s and p orbitals might make more effective bonds than the individual s and p orbitals.

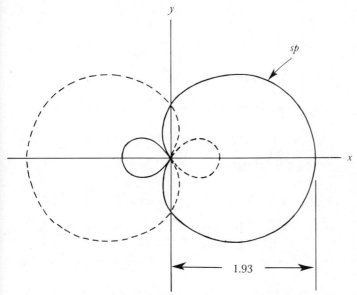

Figure 5-12   Diagram of two sp hybrid orbitals composed of an s orbital and a p_x orbital. One of the orbitals (solid line) has its greatest extension in the plus x direction, while the other orbital (dotted line) has its greatest extension in the minus x direction.

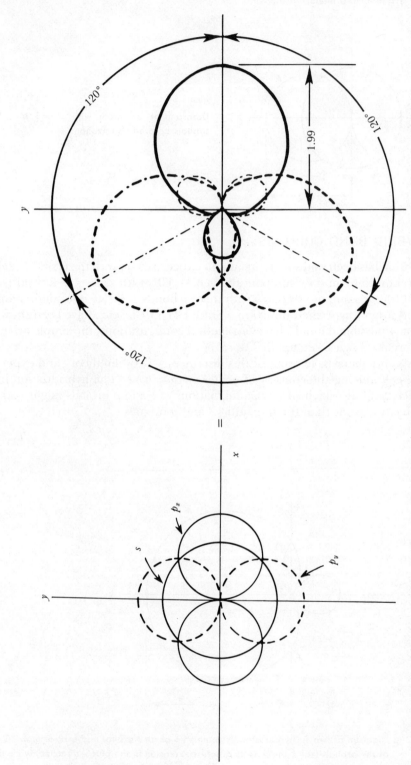

Figure 5-13   Diagram of three sp^2 hybrid orbitals made up from an s orbital, a p_x orbital, and a p_y orbital.   Each orbital is shown with a different kind of line.

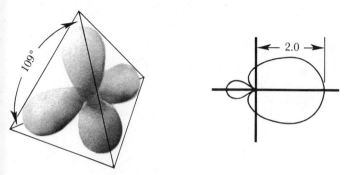

Figure 5-14   Diagram of the sp^3 hybrid orbitals.

By way of illustration, let us suppose that we have an s and a p orbital available to form two bonds, as shown in Figure 5-11. Note that neither the s nor p orbitals can utilize all their overlapping potential for an s orbital of another nucleus along the x axis. Obviously, however, if we can combine these orbitals in such a way as to utilize more of the overlapping power of the orbitals, we would have stronger bonds and more stable molecules. The results of the mathematical treatment of orbital hybridization predicts that an s and a p orbital of one atom can form two stronger covalent bonds if they combine to form two new orbitals called "sp-hybrid orbitals" (Figure 5-12). Each sp-hybrid orbital has an overlapping power of 1.93 compared to the pure s orbital taken as unity and a pure p orbital as $\sqrt{3}$. Bond angles of 180° are expected for bonds with sp-hybrid orbitals.

For atoms forming three covalent bonds we might expect sp^2 hybridization, as shown in Figure 5-13. The orbitals have their axes in a common plane because the p orbitals are thereby utilized most effectively. The predicted overlapping power of these orbitals is 1.99 and bond angles of 120° are expected.

Hybridization of one s and three p orbitals gives four sp^3-hybrid orbitals which we do not expect to lie in one plane; actually, the axes of sp^3-hybrid orbitals are predicted to be directed at angles of 109.5° to each other. The predicted relative overlapping power of sp^3-hybrid orbitals is 2.00 (see Figure 5-14).

5-5   ATOMIC ORBITAL MODELS OF ORGANIC COMPOUNDS

A. Saturated Compounds

The alkanes and their derivatives which have normal tetrahedral angles for the bonds to carbon can be readily formulated in terms of atomic orbitals with sp^3 σ bonds to carbon. An example in the abbreviated style of Figure 5-10 is shown in Figure 5-15.

B. Compounds with Double Bonds

It will be recalled from the earlier chapters that bond angles in compounds with carbon-carbon double bonds such as ethylene are far from the normal

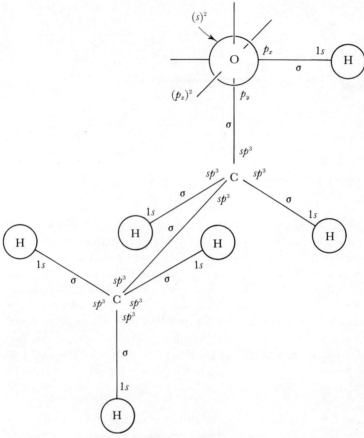

Figure 5-15   Abbreviated atomic orbital model of ethyl alcohol, CH_3CH_2OH, showing only the outer-shell electrons.

tetrahedral value of 109.5°. There are several ways in which a carbon-carbon double bond can be formulated in terms of atomic orbital models. One very popular approach is to consider that ethylene has two sp^2-hybridized carbons which form one carbon-carbon σ bond and four carbon-hydrogen σ bonds by overlap of the six sp^2 orbitals as shown in Figure 5-16. The remaining carbon-carbon bond is formulated as arising from *sidewise* overlap of the two p orbitals, one on each carbon, which are not utilized in making the sp^2 hybrids. Sidewise overlap of p orbitals is called **π overlap** to distinguish it from the endwise **σ overlap** of the type we have discussed earlier (Figure 5-17).

Formulation of ethylene in this way suggests that it should be a planar molecule with H—C—H angles of 120°. Ethylene is indeed planar, but its H—C—H angles are found to be 116.7° rather than the 120° predicted for sp^2 bonds. Whether this discrepancy is sufficient to render the model untenable seems to be a matter of opinion at this time.

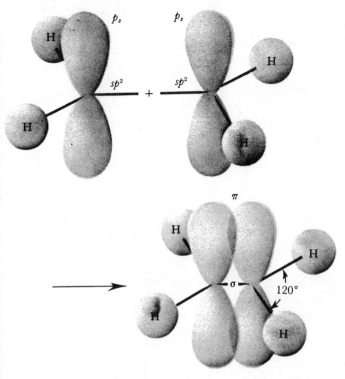

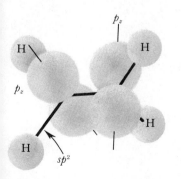

Figure 5-16   The σ,π formulation of ethylene.

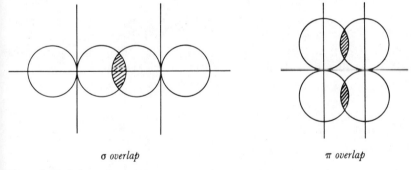

σ overlap   π overlap

Figure 5-17   Schematic representation of σ and π overlap of p orbitals.

Figure 5-18

Twisted nonplanar configuration of ethylene with reduced π overlap.

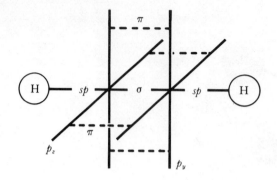

Figure 5-19

Acetylene by the σ-π formulation.

On the basis of the σ-π model of double bonds, we conclude that the twisted configuration shown in Figure 5-18 should not be very stable. Here the p_z orbitals are not in position to overlap effectively in the π manner. The favored configuration is expected to have the axes of the p-π orbitals parallel. Since considerable energy would have to be expended to break the p-π double bond and to permit rotation about the remaining sp^2-σ bond, restricted rotation and stable *cis-trans* isomers are expected.

C. Compounds with Triple Bonds

Acetylene, C_2H_2, is an organic compound which is often formulated with sp hybrid bonds. The carbon-hydrogen framework can be taken to be built up through σ overlap of two sp-hybrid orbitals, one from each carbon atom, to form a C—C bond, and σ overlap of the remaining sp orbitals with the s orbital of two hydrogens to form C—H bonds. The remaining *two* carbon-carbon bonds result through sidewise π overlap of the pure p orbitals as in Figure 5-19. This model fits well with the properties of acetylenic bonds in being linear (bond angles of 180° as predicted) with high chemical reactivity (π electrons exposed).

5-6   BOND ORBITALS FOR ATOMS CARRYING UNSHARED ELECTRON PAIRS

The electronic configuration of the nitrogen atom in its most stable state is $(1s)^2(2s)^2(2p)^3$. When nitrogen is converted to ammonia, the question may be asked whether the bonding is between the three p orbitals of nitrogen, or if hybridization occurs to give essentially three sp^3 bonds and an sp^3 unshared electron pair. For the latter event, an electron has to be promoted from s^2 to a p orbital of higher energy.

$$
\begin{array}{cccccc}
(p) & & & & & (sp^3)^2 \\[4pt]
(p) & \cdot\text{N}\colon & (s)^2 & \longrightarrow & (sp^3) \quad \cdot\ddot{\text{N}}\cdot \quad (sp^3) \\[4pt]
(p) & & & & & (sp^3)
\end{array}
$$

The promotion energy for the change from $(1s)^2(2s)^2(2p)^3$ to $(1s)^2(2s)(2p)^4$ is on the order of 200 kcal for nitrogen. Although changing from pure p to sp^3 bonds might increase the bond strengths by as much as 25 to 30 kcal, this may not be enough to compensate for promotion of the s electron. One point of view is that no important hybridization of the s and p orbitals is to be expected for ammonia and related compounds with unshared electron pairs (e.g., water). However, this is not in accord with theoretical predictions of ^{14}N—H spin splittings in n.m.r. spectra. The magnitudes of such couplings are more like what would be expected with sp^3 N—H bonds.

For atoms such as carbon, any s- to p-promotion energy is compensated by the possibility of forming more bonds, not just better bonds. Thus $C(2s)^2(2p_x)(2p_y)$ might form two p bonds (of ~80 kcal each) to hydrogen atoms and liberate 160 kcal, while $C(2s)(2p_x)(2p_y)(2p_z)$ could form four sp^3 bonds (of 103 kcal each) to hydrogen atoms and liberate 412 kcal. The energy of the latter process is clearly sufficient to accommodate the electron promotion energy (96 kcal) for $C(1s)^2(2s)^2(2p)^2 \rightarrow C(1s)^2(2s)(2p)^3$, and promotion and hybridization with the formation of four strong bonds is to be expected.

EXERCISE 5-4 Make drawings of atomic orbital models for each of the following compounds. Each drawing should be large and clear with indication of the expected bond angles. Be sure that orbitals occupied by unshared pairs as well as those used by each atom in bond formation are correctly labeled. Be sure to place charges beside any atoms that do not have their normal complements of electrons.

a. methyl fluoride, CH_3F
b. dimethyl ether, CH_3OCH_3
c. formaldehyde, $CH_2{=}O$
d. N_2
e. acetonitrile, $CH_3C{\equiv}N$
f. benzene
g. graphite

h. formic acid, HCO_2H
i. CO_2
j. BF_3
k. $(CH_3)_2Mg$
l. CH_3NO_2
m. ketene, $CH_2{=}C{=}O$

5-7 INTERELECTRONIC REPULSION AND BOND ANGLES

A simple alternative to orbital hybridization for predicting angles for covalent bonds is to use the reasonable assumption that the bonding electron pairs will strive to be as far apart as possible because of electrostatic repulsion. Thus four electron pairs about one atom, as for the carbon of methane, will be furthest apart in a tetrahedral arrangement wherein electron repulsion should be at a minimum. This approach can be easily applied to prediction of the geometry of a methyl cation formed by removing one hydrogen with its bonding electron pair from a molecule of methane. The remaining three electron pairs on carbon are expected to seek a planar arrangement with 120° angles to minimize electron repulsion.

$$\begin{array}{c} \text{H} \\ \cdot\cdot \\ \text{H} : \overset{\cdot\cdot}{\underset{\cdot\cdot}{\text{C}}} : \text{H} \\ \cdot\cdot \\ \text{H} \end{array} \qquad \xrightarrow{\; -\,:\text{H}^{\ominus}\;} \qquad \begin{array}{c} \text{H} \\ \cdot\cdot \\ \cdot\,\overset{\cdot\cdot}{\text{C}}\,\cdot \\ \text{H}\qquad\text{H} \end{array}^{\oplus}$$

tetrahedral   planar methyl cation

In a methyl anion, $CH_3:^{\ominus}$, the nonplanar configuration should be (and is) most favorable with the unshared electron pair located more or less at the corner of a tetrahedron, the other corners of which are occupied by three pairs of the C—H bonds.

$$\begin{array}{c} \text{H} \\ \cdot\cdot \\ \text{H} : \overset{\cdot\cdot}{\underset{\cdot\cdot}{\text{C}}} \cdot \text{H} \\ \cdot\cdot \\ \text{H} \end{array} \qquad \xrightarrow{\; -\;\text{H}^{\oplus}\;} \qquad \begin{array}{c} \text{H} \\ \cdot\cdot \\ \text{H} : \overset{\cdot\cdot}{\underset{\cdot\cdot}{\text{C}}} : \\ \cdot\cdot \\ \text{H} \end{array}^{\ominus}$$

non-planar methyl anion

The methyl radical, $CH_3\cdot$, is clearly expected to provide some kind of an intermediate case. The experimental evidence on this point is not conclusive. However, the radical does seem to be very close to planar in its most stable state.

It is possible to explain many of the deviations from the normal tetrahedral bond angles in organic compounds by simple consideration of interelectronic repulsions. Thus for compounds of the type CH_3X, where X is a more electron-attracting group than hydrogen, the C—X bond is polarized as $H_3\overset{\delta\oplus}{C}—\overset{\delta\ominus}{X}$ and the carbon should have some of the character of $CH_3^{\oplus}$. The H—C—H angles are thus expected to be greater than 109.5°, as, in fact, they are; in methyl chloride, for example, the H—C—H angle is about 111°.

The 116.7° H—C—H bond angles in ethylene can be seen to be reasonable on the following basis. If we take a tetrahedral carbon and pull any two electron pairs together, as would happen in formation of a double bond, then the repulsion of these pairs with the others around the carbon is reduced. Consequently, the C—H electron pairs can move farther apart. This, of course, spreads the C—H bond angles. The same effect is expected and observed for cyclopropane, the angles between the bonds to the ring of which lie between 112 and 118°.

EXERCISE 5-5   The H—C—H bond angle in formaldehyde, $H_2C{=}O$, is about 125°. Is this in accord with interelectronic repulsions? Explain.

Alkenes I

Structure, Spectra, and Stereoisomerism

In the early days of organic chemistry, the alkanes were characterized as "saturated" and the alkenes as "unsaturated" because the alkenes, but not the alkanes, were found to undergo addition reactions with substances such as halogens, hydrogen halides, sulfuric acid, and oxidizing agents. The "chemical affinity" of the alkenes was therefore "unsaturated." Later, it was recognized that these addition reactions actually involve cleavage of half of a carbon-carbon double bond. That such reactions occur with alkenes much more easily than with alkanes is because the carbon-carbon bonds of a double bond are individually weaker (more strained) than a normal carbon-carbon single bond.

The great variety and specificity of the addition reactions that compounds with double bonds undergo make them extremely important as intermediates in organic syntheses. We shall begin to discuss these reactions in Chapter 7, and shall take up in this chapter the nomenclature, spectra, and cis-trans isomerism of alkenes. The latter subject will be especially important later when we consider the mechanisms of addition reactions.

Alkenes I
Structure, Spectra,
and Stereoisomerism

CHAPTER 6

A wide variety of substances contain one or more of the unsaturated carbon-carbon double bonds characteristic of ethylene. The open-chain hydrocarbons with one double bond have the general formula C_nH_{2n} and are called alkenes. The carbon-carbon double bond is often called an "olefinic linkage" and the alkenes designated as **olefins** (oil-formers). These terms arose because the gaseous lower-molecular-weight alkenes yield "oily" products on treatment with chlorine or bromine.

6-1 NOMENCLATURE

According to the IUPAC system for naming alkenes, the longest continuous chain containing the double bond is given the name of the corresponding alkane with the ending *-ane* changed to *-ene*. This chain is then numbered so that the

$$\overset{4}{C}H_3\overset{3}{C}H_2\overset{2}{C}H=\overset{1}{C}H_2$$

1-butene

(not 3-butene)

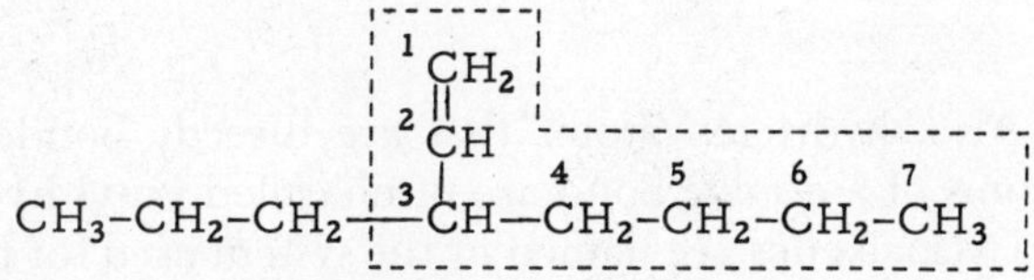

$$CH_3-CH_2-CH_2-\overset{3}{C}H-\overset{4}{C}H_2-\overset{5}{C}H_2-\overset{6}{C}H_2-\overset{7}{C}H_3$$

with the group:

$$\overset{1}{C}H_2 \overset{||}{\underset{2}{C}H}$$

3-propyl-1-heptene

(the dotted lines indicate longest continuous chain containing the double bond)

121

position of the *first* carbon of the double bond is indicated by the lowest possible number.

Other, less systematic names are often used for the simpler alkenes. By one system, alkenes are named as substituted ethylenes — in which case a prefix may be required to denote whether the substitution is symmetrical (*sym*) or unsymmetrical (*unsym*).

$$CH_2{=}CH_2 \qquad\qquad CH_3{-}CH{=}CH{-}CH_3 \qquad\qquad \overset{\displaystyle CH_3}{\overset{|}{CH_3{-}C}}{=}CH_2$$

ethylene   *sym*-dimethylethylene   *unsym*-dimethylethylene

A few, very common alkenes are named as "alkylenes" by appending the suffix *-ene* to the name of the hydrocarbon radical with the same carbon skeleton.

$$CH_2{=}CH_2 \qquad\qquad CH_3{-}CH{=}CH_2 \qquad\qquad \overset{\displaystyle CH_3}{\overset{|}{CH_3{-}C}}{=}CH_2$$

ethylene   propylene   isobutylene

The hydrocarbon radicals derived from alkenes carry the suffix *-enyl*, as in alkenyl, and numbering of the radical starts with the carbon atom with the free valence.

$$\overset{4}{C}H_3{-}\overset{3}{C}H{=}\overset{2}{C}H{-}\overset{1}{C}H_2{-} \qquad\qquad \overset{4}{C}H_2{=}\overset{3}{C}H{-}\overset{2}{C}H_2{-}\overset{1}{C}H_2{-}$$

2-butenyl   3-butenyl

However, there are a few alkenyl radicals for which trivial names are commonly used in place of systematic names. These are vinyl, allyl, and isopropenyl radicals.

$$CH_2{=}CH{-} \qquad\qquad CH_2{=}CH{-}CH_2{-} \qquad\qquad \overset{\displaystyle CH_3}{\overset{|}{CH_2{=}C}}{-}$$

vinyl   allyl   isopropenyl

(ethenyl)   (2-propenyl)   (1-methylethenyl)

Also, hydrogen atoms that are directly bonded to the unsaturated carbon atoms of a double bond are often called **vinyl hydrogens.**

Cycloalkenes are named by the system used for the open-chain alkenes, except that the numbering is always started at one of the carbons of the double bond and continued on around the ring *through* the double bond so as to keep the sum of the index numbers as small as possible.

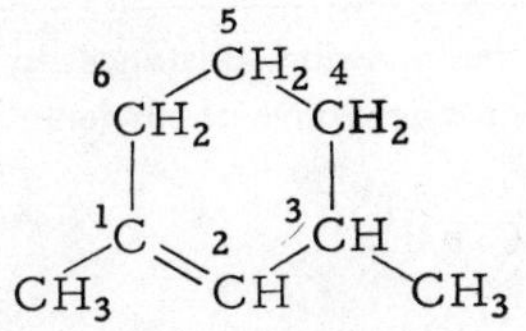

$$\begin{array}{c}
6\quad {}^5CH_2\quad 4\\
CH_2\qquad CH_2\\
|\qquad\qquad |\\
{}^1C\underset{2}{=\!=}\quad {}^3CH\\
CH_3\quad CH\quad CH_3
\end{array}$$

1, 3-dimethylcyclohexene

(not 1, 5-dimethylcyclohexene)

Many compounds contain two or more double bonds and are known as alkadienes, alkatrienes, and alkatetraenes, etc., the suffix denoting the number of double bonds. The location of each double bond is specified by appropriate numbers, as illustrated below.

$CH_2=C=CH-CH_3$ $\qquad$ $CH_2=CH-CH=CH_2$ $\qquad$ $CH_2=C=C=CH_2$

1, 2-butadiene $\qquad\qquad$ 1, 3-butadiene $\qquad\qquad$ 1, 2, 3-butatriene

A further classification is used according to the relationships of the double bonds, one to the other. Thus, 1,2-alkadienes and similar substances are said to have **cumulated** double bonds.

$CH_2=C=CH_2$ $\qquad\qquad\qquad$ $\underset{/}{\overset{\backslash}{C}}=C=\underset{\backslash}{\overset{/}{C}}$

allene $\qquad\qquad\qquad$ cumulated double bonds

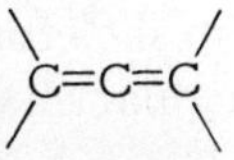

(propadiene)

1,3-Alkadienes and other compounds with alternating double and single bonds are said to have **conjugated** double bonds.

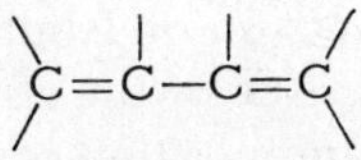

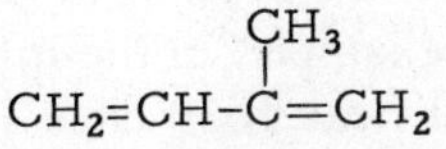

$CH_3-CH=CH-CH=CH_2$ $\qquad$ $\underset{/}{\overset{\backslash}{C}}=\overset{|}{C}-\overset{|}{C}=\underset{\backslash}{\overset{/}{C}}$ $\qquad$ $\overset{\displaystyle CH_3}{\underset{\displaystyle |}{}}$ $CH_2=CH-\overset{|}{C}=CH_2$

1, 3-pentadiene $\qquad\qquad$ conjugated $\qquad\qquad$ isoprene

$\qquad\qquad\qquad\qquad$ double bonds $\qquad$ (2-methyl-1, 3-butadiene)

Compounds with double bonds that are neither cumulated nor conjugated are classified as having isolated double-bond systems.

$CH_2=CH-CH_2-CH=CH_2$ $\qquad$ $\underset{/}{\overset{\backslash}{C}}=\overset{|}{C}\underset{\displaystyle |n}{\left(\overset{|}{C}\right)}\overset{|}{C}=\underset{\backslash}{\overset{/}{C}}$

1, 4-pentadiene $\qquad\qquad$ isolated double bond system $(n \geqq 1)$

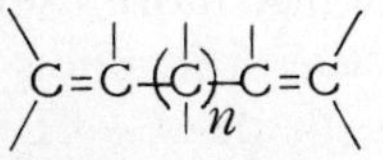

EXERCISE 6-1   Name each of the following substances by the IUPAC system and, if straightforward to do so, as a derivative of ethylene:

a. $(CH_3)_2C=CHCH_3$

b. $Cl_2C=C(CH_3)_2$

c. $(CH_3)_3CCH_2C(CH_3)=CH_2$

d. $(CH_3)_2C=C=CHBr$

e. $[(CH_3)_2CH]_2C=C[CH(CH_3)_2]_2$

f. $(CH_3)_2C \overset{\displaystyle CH}{\underset{\displaystyle CH}{\Big\|}}$

g.

EXERCISE 6-2   Write structural formulas for each of the following substances:

a. trifluorochloroethylene

b. *unsym*-dineopentylethylene

c. 1,4-hexadiene

d. 1,1-di-(1-cyclohexenyl)-ethene

e. trivinylallene

6-2 PHYSICAL PROPERTIES OF ALKENES

In general, the physical properties of the alkenes are similar to those of
alkanes. The data in Table 6-1 permits comparison of the boiling points, melting points, and densities of several alkenes with the corresponding alkanes
having the same carbon skeleton. Like *n*-alkanes, the 1-alkenes form a homologous series showing regular changes in physical properties with increasing chain
length.

6-3 SPECTROSCOPIC PROPERTIES OF ALKENES

A. Infrared Spectra

The infrared spectra of alkenes are sufficiently different from those of alkanes
to make it possible in most instances to recognize when a double bond is present.
For example, in the infrared spectrum of 1-butene (Figure 6-1) the absorption
band near 1650 cm^{-1} is characteristic of the stretching vibration of the double
bond. In general, the intensity and position of this band depends on the structure of the alkene; it varies with the degree of branching at the double bond and
with the presence of a second unsaturated group in conjugation with the first

(i.e., $C=C-C=C$ or $C=C-C=O$). In many cases, however, the ab-

sorption bands caused by the various modes of vibration of the vinyl C—H
bonds are frequently more useful for detecting a double bond and identifying
its type than is the absorption band caused by C=C stretch. With 1-butene,
absorptions due to the C—H vibrations of the $CH=CH_2$ group occur near
3100, 1420, 1000 and 915 cm^{-1}. In general, absorption bands at these frequen-

Table 6-1   Comparison of Physical Properties of *n*-Alkanes and Alkenes

Hydrocarbon	Formula	B.p., °C	M.p., °C	d_4^{20}
ethane	$CH_3—CH_3$	−88.6	−183[a]	
ethylene	$CH_2{=}CH_2$	−105	−169	
propane	$CH_3—CH_2—CH_3$	−42.1	−187[a]	0.501[b]
propene	$CH_3—CH{=}CH_2$	−47.8	−185[a]	0.514[b]
n-butane	$CH_3—CH_2—CH_2—CH_3$	−0.5	−138	0.579[b]
1-butene	$CH_3—CH_2—CH{=}CH_2$	−6.3	−185[a]	0.595[b]
cis-2-butene	$CH_3—CH{=}CH—CH_3$	3.7	−139	0.621[b]
trans-2-butene	$CH_3—CH{=}CH—CH_3$	0.9	−106	0.604[b]
pentane	$CH_3—CH_2—CH_2—CH_2—CH_3$	36.1	−129	0.626
1-pentene	$CH_3—CH_2—CH_2—CH{=}CH_2$	30.0	−165	0.641
cis-2-pentene	$CH_3—CH_2—CH{=}CH—CH_3$	37.9	−151	0.656
trans-2-pentene	$CH_3—CH_2—CH{=}CH—CH_3$	36.4	−140	0.648
hexane	$CH_3—CH_2—CH_2—CH_2—CH_2—CH_3$	68.7	−95	0.659
1-hexene	$CH_3—CH_2—CH_2—CH_2—CH{=}CH_2$	63.5	−140	0.674
cis-2-hexene	$CH_3—CH_2—CH_2—CH{=}CH—CH_3$	68.8	−141	0.687
trans-2-hexene	$CH_3—CH_2—CH_2—CH{=}CH—CH_3$	67.9	−133	0.678
cis-3-hexene	$CH_3—CH_2—CH{=}CH—CH_2—CH_3$	66.4	−138	0.680
trans-3-hexene	$CH_3—CH_2—CH{=}CH—CH_2—CH_3$	67.1	−113	0.677

[a] At the triple point.
[b] At the saturation pressure.

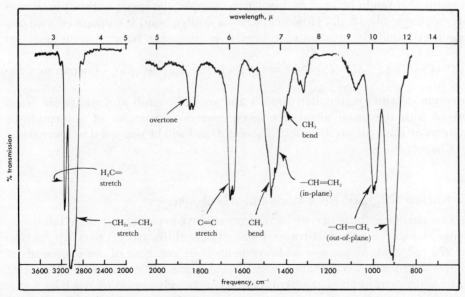

Figure 6-1   The infrared spectrum of 1-butene.

cies are diagnostic of the grouping —CH=CH$_2$. The bands near 1420 cm^{-1} are due to in-plane bending, while those at 915 to 1000 cm^{-1} arise from out-of-plane bending. The other intense absorptions, near 1460 and 3000 cm^{-1} are due to C—H vibrations of the CH$_3$CH$_2$— group. These illustrate a further point—namely, the positions of the infrared absorptions of alkyl C—H bonds are often significantly different from those of vinyl C—H bonds.

The infrared absorption of 1-butene that occurs at 1830 cm^{-1} (Figure 6-1) falls in the region where stretching vibrations are usually observed. However, this band actually arises from an overtone (harmonic) of the =CH$_2$ out-of-plane bending at 915 cm^{-1}. Such overtone absorptions come at just twice the frequency of the fundamental frequency and, whenever an absorption like this is observed, which does not seem to fit with the normal fundamental vibrations, the possibility of its being an overtone should be checked.

EXERCISE 6-3   Deduce the structures of the substances whose infrared spectra are shown in Figure 6-2. Assign as many of the bands as you can to specific stretching and bending vibrations.

B. Ultraviolet Absorption Spectra of Alkenes

The electrons of a carbon-carbon double bond of an alkene (specifically the ones designated as π electrons, pp. 114-116) are excited to higher energy states by light of wavelength 2000 to 1000 A. But, since many other substances absorb in this region of the spectrum, including air, the quartz sample cell, and most solvents that might be used to dissolve the sample, the spectra of simple alkenes are not easily obtained. However, when a double bond is conjugated with one or more similarly unsaturated bonds so that we have systems such as

$$\begin{matrix} \diagdown &&& \diagup \\ C\!=\!C\!-\!C\!=\!C \\ \diagup &&& \diagdown \end{matrix} \quad \text{or} \quad \begin{matrix} \diagdown &&& \\ C\!=\!C\!-\!C\!=\!O \\ \diagup &&& \end{matrix}$$, then the wavelengths of maximum absorption shift to greater than 2000 A and are more easily and accurately determined with the usual ultraviolet spectrometers. Examples of absorption by systems of this type are shown in Table 2-2, and will be discussed in more detail in Chapter 9.

C. Nuclear Magnetic Resonance Spectra of Alkenes

The chemical shifts of vinyl hydrogens (vinyl protons) normally fall in the range 4.6 to 5.3 ppm relative to TMS. These shifts are 2.5 to 4.5 ppm (150 to 270 cps at 60 Mcps) toward lower fields than are those of the hydrogens of simple alkanes or cycloalkanes, which means that the presence or absence of vinyl hydrogens in an organic compound is relatively easy to establish by n.m.r. spectroscopy.

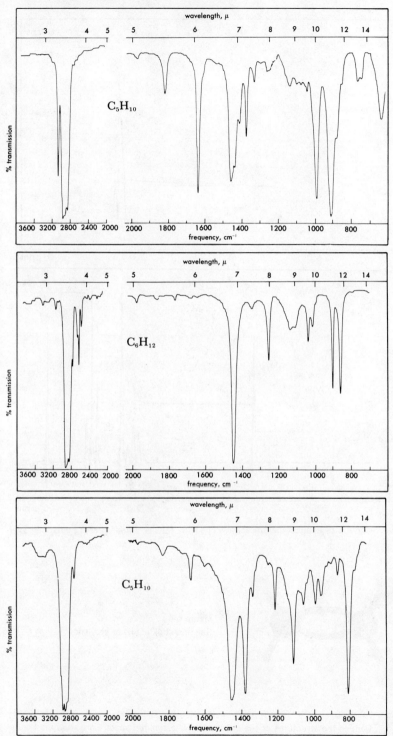

Figure 6-2

Infrared spectra, see Exercise 6-3.

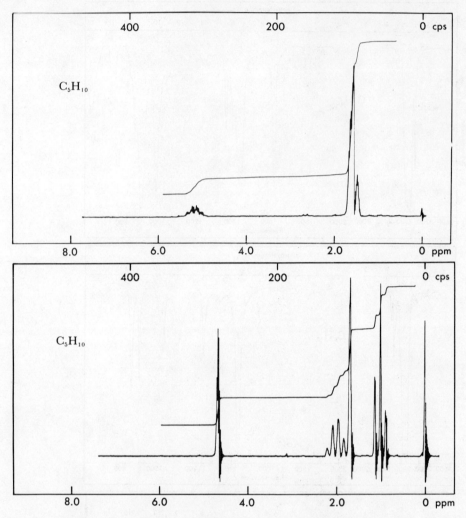

Figure 6-3   Nuclear magnetic resonance spectra at 60 Mcps with TMS as standard at 0 ppm.   See Exercise 6-4.

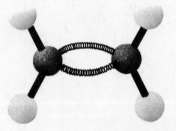

Figure 6-4
Ball-and-stick model of ethylene.

EXERCISE 6-4   Deduce the structures of the substances whose n.m.r. spectra are shown in Figure 6-3.   Analyze the spectra in as much detail as you can in terms of chemical shifts and spin-spin splitting.

6-4   THE STRUCTURE OF ETHYLENE

Both ball-and-stick and σ-π atomic orbital models of ethylene (see pp. 114-116 and Figure 6-4) suggest that all six atoms (two carbons and four hydrogens) should lie in a single plane.

This prediction is in accord with the best available physical measurements of the geometry of ethylene. However, the H—C—H bond angles for ethylene [1], as determined by electron diffraction, are 116.7° rather than the 109.5° suggested by the ball-and-stick model, or the 120° suggested by the atomic orbital model.

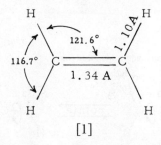

[1]

It will be recalled from Chapter 1 (p. 12) that rotation around the carbon-carbon single bond in ethane occurs relatively easily. In contrast, a ball-and-stick model of ethylene suggests that rotation around the double bond might only be achieved by first breaking one-half of the bond and rotating the two parts of the molecule about the residual single bond. The atomic-orbital description of the double bond leads to the same conclusion (see p. 116).

$$CH_2\!\!=\!\!CH_2 \;\rightleftharpoons\; \dot{C}H_2\text{-}\!\!\!\overset{}{\underset{}{(}}\!\!\!\!\overset{}{\underset{}{\div}}\!\!\!\!\overset{}{\underset{}{)}}\text{-}\dot{C}H_2$$

For rotation to occur, the necessary energy input would be roughly equal to the difference in energy between a double and a single carbon-carbon bond (i.e., 63 kcal/mole; see Table 3-5). Such an amount of energy is not available from molecular collisions at ordinary temperatures, and so it is not surprising that rotation about the double bond of ethylene, or any alkene, does not occur under these conditions.

6-5   *CIS-TRANS* ISOMERISM

As a consequence of the special geometry of the carbon-carbon double bond and restricted rotation about this bond, the possibility arises of geometric isomerism in appropriately substituted alkenes similar to that described for cycloalkanes (see pp. 96-97). For example, 2-butene can exist in a *cis* form in which the methyl groups are on the *same* side of the double bond, and a *trans* form with the methyl groups on *opposite* sides of the double bond (Figure 6-5).

The two forms are normally quite stable since interconversion by the path shown on p. 130 occurs only at relatively high temperatures or by irradiation with light of suitable wavelength.

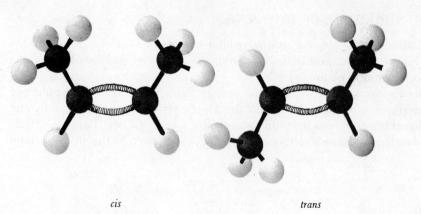

cis   *trans*

Figure 6-5 Ball-and-stick models of *cis*- and *trans*-2-butene.

cis   *trans*

For the sake of clarity, we shall redefine some of the stereochemical terms introduced so far. Isomeric substances by definition have the same molecular formula, but they may be of two types, structural isomers or stereoisomers. Structural isomers have different structural frameworks in which the bonding arrangements for the component atoms are different. 1-Butene, 2-butene, cyclobutane, and methylcyclopropane are all structural isomers.

$$CH_3CH_2CH=CH_2 \qquad CH_3CH=CHCH_3 \qquad \begin{matrix} CH_2-CH_2 \\ | \qquad | \\ CH_2-CH_2 \end{matrix} \qquad \begin{matrix} CH_2 \\ | \quad {\scriptstyle\diagdown} CHCH_3 \\ CH_2 \end{matrix}$$

1-butene   2-butene   cyclobutane   methylcyclopropane

Stereoisomers have the same structural framework but differ in the spatial arrangement of the various substituent groups. The *cis* and *trans* isomers of 2-butene are stereoisomers. They are also referred to as geometric isomers, and the specific arrangement in space is referred to as the **configuration.** Thus, the geometric isomer of 2-butene, in which the methyl substituents are on opposite sides of the double bond, has the *trans* configuration.

In discussing the stereochemistry of ethane (see pp. 11-13), we used the term *conformation* rather than *configuration.* *Conformation* is best restricted to a spatial arrangement that is in mobile equilibrium with other arrangements or conformations. No one conformation constitutes a discrete isolable substance under ordinary conditions. Thus, the distinction between conformational isomers and configurational isomers is that the latter are presumed stable and isolable, while the former are not. At room temperature, the staggered and eclipsed conformations of ethane are rapidly interconverted by rotation about the carbon-carbon bond; in contrast, *cis* and *trans* isomers of 2-butene are stable under these conditions. Obviously, we must expect borderline situations where distinction between conformations and configurations will be difficult, if not actually meaningless.

Cis-trans isomerism is very frequently encountered. By convention, the configuration of complex alkenes is taken to correspond to the configuration of the longest continuous chain as it passes through the double bond. Thus the following compound [2] is 4-ethyl-3-methyl-*trans*-3-heptene, despite the fact that two identical groups are *cis* with respect to each other, because the longest continuous chain is *trans* as it passes through the double bond.

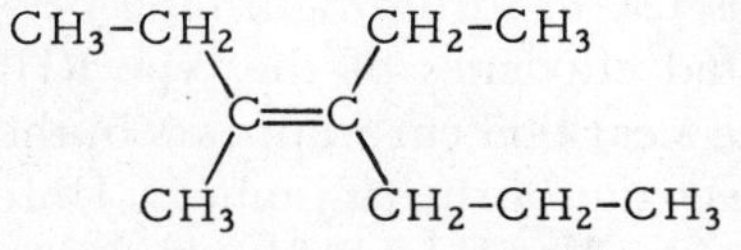

$$CH_3-CH_2 \qquad CH_2-CH_3$$
$$\diagdown \qquad \diagup$$
$$C=C$$
$$\diagup \qquad \diagdown$$
$$CH_3 \qquad CH_2-CH_2-CH_3$$

4–ethyl–3–methyl–*trans*–3–heptene

[2]

The *trans* isomers of the simple alkenes are usually more stable than the corresponding *cis* isomers. The methyl groups in *trans*-2-butene are far apart, whereas, in *cis*-2-butene, they are much closer to one another. Scale models, which reflect the sizes of the methyl groups, indicate some interference between the methyl groups of the *cis* isomer. The *cis* alkenes with large groups have very considerable repulsive interactions (steric hindrance) between the substituents and are much less stable than the corresponding *trans* isomers (see Figure 6-6).

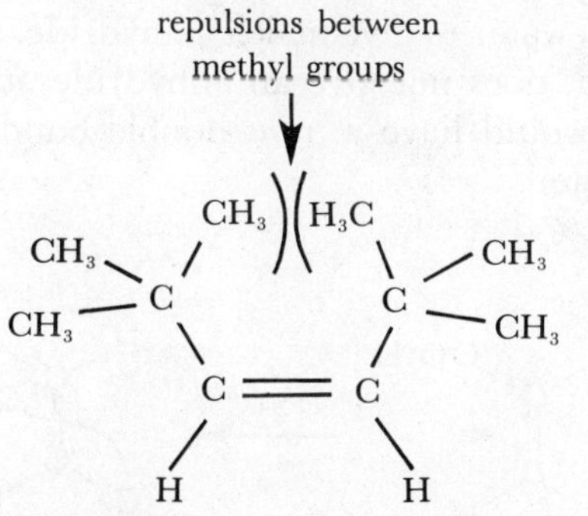

repulsions between
methyl groups

$$CH_3 \qquad CH_3 \quad \Big)\Big(\quad H_3C \qquad CH_3$$
$$\diagdown \qquad \diagup \qquad \qquad \diagdown \qquad \diagup$$
$$C \qquad \qquad \qquad C$$
$$\diagup \qquad \diagdown \qquad \qquad \diagup \qquad \diagdown$$
$$CH_3 \qquad \qquad CH_3 \qquad \qquad CH_3$$
$$C === C$$
$$\diagup \qquad \qquad \diagdown$$
$$H \qquad \qquad H$$

Figure 6-6

Repulsive interactions between the methyl groups of *cis-sym-di-t-butylethy-lene* (2,2,5,5-tetramethyl-*cis*-3-hexene).

EXERCISE 6-5   *Cis* and *trans* alkenes can be interconverted by heating them with iodine in the liquid or vapor phases. Use the bond-energy table (p. 65) to aid in evaluating a theoretically possible mechanism for this type of reaction, involving a reversible attachment of an iodine atom to one carbon of a double bond.

EXERCISE 6-6   The *trans* alkenes are generally more stable than the *cis* alkenes. Give one or more examples of unsaturated systems where you would expect the *cis* form to be more stable and explain the reason for your choice.

6-6 DETERMINATION OF CONFIGURATION OF *CIS-TRANS* ISOMERS

The physical properties of *cis* and *trans* isomers are usually quite similar (see Table 6-1), and separation of both from a mixture by techniques such as fractional distillation or crystallization is not always possible. Chromatographic methods (pp. 14-17) are generally required to separate mixtures of compounds that have as closely similar physical properties as most pairs of *cis-trans* isomers.

The data in Table 6-1 show that, except for 3-hexenes, *cis* isomers have lower melting points and higher boiling points than *trans* isomers. Although usually the differences are not large, they are of some help in assigning configurations to *cis* and *trans* isomers.

Infrared spectroscopy is useful in distinguishing between *cis* and *trans* configurations for disubstituted ethylenes of the type RHC=CHR'. With such compounds, a strong band near 965 cm^{-1} appears in the spectrum of the *trans* isomer, but not in the spectrum of the *cis* isomer. Unfortunately, similar correlations for more highly substituted double bonds are not available.

So far, we have mentioned only physical methods for the determination of configuration. There are also a number of chemical methods, which are more or less useful depending on the system under investigation. In some cases, the method of preparation of a stereoisomer is diagnostic of its configuration. This will be more likely to be so if only one isomer is obtained and the mechanism of the reaction, especially the stereochemical details, are known.

The most reliable method of determining configurations by chemical means is through reactions that lead to closure of five- or six-membered rings. In general, *cis* isomers can undergo ring closure much more readily than the corresponding *trans* isomers because it is not possible to prepare a five- or six-membered ring compound with a *trans* double bond in the ring. The kind of difference which is observed is well illustrated by maleic acid, which has a *cis* double bond and on heating to 150° loses water to give maleic anhydride. The corresponding *trans* isomer, fumaric acid, does not give an anhydride at 150° and, in fact, fumaric anhydride, which would have a *trans* double bond in a five-membered ring, has never been isolated.

maleic   maleic   fumaric   fumaric
acid   anhydride   acid   anhydride
                                                 (unknown)

Clearly, of this pair, maleic acid has the *cis* configuration and fumaric acid the *trans* configuration.

SUPPLEMENTARY EXERCISES

6-7 Write structural formulas for each of the following:

    a. The thirteen hexene isomers; name each as a derivative of ethylene and by the IUPAC system. Show by suitable formulas which isomers can exist in *cis* and *trans* forms and correctly designate each.

    b. All *trans*-1,18-di-(2,6,6-trimethyl-1-cyclohexenyl)-3,7,11,15-tetramethyl-1,3,5,7,9,11,13,-15,17-octadecanonaene ($C_{40}H_{56}$).

6-8 Calculate, from the data in Table 4-2 and any necessary bond energies, the minimum thermal energy that would be required to break one of the ring carbon-carbon bonds and interconvert *cis-* and *trans*-1,2-dimethylcyclobutanes (see pp. 92-97).

Alkenes II

Reactions of Carbon-Carbon Double Bonds

*C*arbon-carbon double bonds undergo a very wide variety of addition reactions in which half of the double bond is broken and two new bonds to carbon are formed. The importance of such reactions to synthetic organic chemistry can hardly be overemphasized.

Some double-bond additions involve free-radical intermediates, while others proceed by way of ionic intermediates. With some reagents, addition occurs exclusively by formation of both new bonds on the same side of the double bond (cis addition) and, with other reagents, a new bond is formed on one side of the double bond and another new bond on the other side of the double bond (trans addition).

It is our intention in this chapter to show the nature of the factors that control additions to double bonds. The principles involved will be found useful in understanding a variety of other kinds of reactions as well. It is most important to try to develop a working knowledge of the conditions by which double-bond additions occur. This will be particularly helpful in synthetic work for the selection of conditions in which addition will take place or not, as desired.

The chapter also includes a section devoted to discussion of some of the problems commonly encountered in devising efficient syntheses of organic compounds.

Alkenes II
Reactions of
Carbon-Carbon
Double Bonds

7-1 ADDITIONS TO ALKENES. ELECTROPHILIC AND NUCLEOPHILIC REAGENTS

The most characteristic reactions of alkenes are additions in which one-half of the double bond is broken and two new groups are attached to give a saturated compound.

$$
\begin{array}{c}
\underset{H}{\overset{H}{\diagdown}}C=C\underset{H}{\overset{H}{\diagup}} \;+\; X\!\!+\!\!X \;\longrightarrow\; H-\underset{X}{\overset{H}{\underset{|}{\overset{|}{C}}}}-\underset{X}{\overset{H}{\underset{|}{\overset{|}{C}}}}-H
\end{array}
$$

Similar reactions involving cleavage of carbon-carbon bonds do not occur with equal facility in saturated alkanes, but this is not surprising when the differences in bond energies are considered. According to bond energies (see Table 3-5), cleavage of one-half of a carbon-carbon double bond requires 63 kcal, while cleavage of a carbon-carbon single bond requires 83 kcal. As a result, addition reactions to double bonds are about 20 kcal more exothermic than the corresponding cleavage reactions of carbon-carbon single bonds.

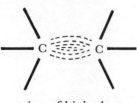

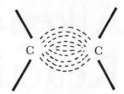

region of high electron
density

single bond

relatively diffuse region of high
electron density

double bond

Figure 7-1   Schematic representations of average positions of electrons in carbon-carbon single
and double bonds.

$$CH_2=CH_2 \ + \ Br_2 \ \longrightarrow \ \underset{\underset{Br}{|}}{CH_2}-\underset{\underset{Br}{|}}{CH_2} \qquad \Delta H \ = \ -27 \ kcal$$

$$CH_3-CH_3 \ + \ Br_2 \ \longrightarrow \ 2 \ CH_3Br \qquad \Delta H \ = \ -7 \ kcal$$

The reactivities of alkenes are enhanced relative to those of the alkanes because the electrons in a carbon-carbon double bond can be regarded as being more exposed than the electrons in a carbon-carbon single bond. This is clearly illustrated by the atomic orbital models of ethylene described in Chapter 5 (pp. 114-115). The electrons in the bonds between the two unsaturated carbons are pushed outward by their mutual repulsions. Thus, their average positions are considerably farther from the bond axis than the electron positions of a single bond (Figure 7-1). In such circumstances, reagents that act to acquire electrons in chemical reactions (**electrophilic**—"electron-loving") are expected to be particularly suitable for initiating double-bond reactions. This is actually the case and, furthermore, reagents that are primarily electron-donating (**nucleophilic**—"nucleus-loving") are notoriously poor for initiating reactions at carbon-carbon double bonds, unless there are substituents with a high degree of electron-attracting power. Consequently, in carrying out a reaction with a compound having a double bond so that addition to the double bond does *not* occur, strongly electrophilic reagents should be avoided.

EXERCISE 7-1   Considering that $\overset{\ominus}{O}H$ is a substance that tends to react with electrophilic reagents, while $H^{\oplus}$ tends to react with nucleophilic agents, classify the following as (strongly or weakly) electrophilic or nucleophilic or neither. Show your reasoning.

a. H_2SO_4 e. Br_2 i. $NaNH_2$
b. NH_3 f. CH_4 j. $AlCl_3$
c. $NaCl$ g. HBF_4 k. $(CH_2)_3$
d. H_2O h. SO_3 m. $AgBF_4$

7-2 HYDROGENATION OF ALKENES: HETEROGENEOUS CATALYSIS

The reaction of hydrogen with ethylene is substantially exothermic.

$$CH_2{=}CH_2 \ + \ H_2 \ \longrightarrow \ CH_3{-}CH_3 \qquad \Delta H = -30 \ \text{kcal} \quad \text{(calculated)}$$
$$\Delta H = -32.8 \ \text{kcal} \quad \text{(experimental)}$$

However, a mixture of hydrogen and ethylene is indefinitely stable at 200° or less in a glass vessel. Conceivably, thermal or photochemical hydrogenation of ethylene could proceed at a useful rate by free-radical mechanisms similar to those involved in the chlorination of saturated alkanes (pp. 68-73). Such free-radical chain mechanisms, however, are likely to be energetically unfavorable (see Exercise 7-2). But despite this, ethylene reacts rapidly and completely with hydrogen at low temperatures and pressures in the presence of certain metals like nickel, platinum, and palladium.

EXERCISE 7-2   Consider the feasibility of a free-radical chain mechanism for hydrogenation of ethylene in the vapor state at 25° by the following propagation steps:
$$CH_3{-}CH_2{\cdot} + H_2 \rightarrow CH_3{-}CH_3 + H{\cdot}$$
$$CH_2{=}CH_2 + H{\cdot} \rightarrow CH_3CH_2{\cdot}$$

For maximum catalytic effect, the metal is usually prepared in a finely divided state. This is achieved for platinum and palladium by reducing the metal oxides with hydrogen prior to hydrogenation of the alkene. A specially active form of nickel ("Raney nickel") is prepared from a nickel-aluminum alloy; sodium hydroxide is added to dissolve the aluminum, and the nickel remains as a black, pyrophoric powder.

$$2\,Ni{-}Al \ + \ 2OH^{\ominus} \ + \ 2H_2O \ \longrightarrow \ 2\,Ni \ + \ 2AlO_2^{\ominus} \ + \ 3H_2$$

Highly active platinum, palladium, and nickel catalysts can also be synthesized by reduction of metal salts with sodium borohydride.

Besides having synthetic applications, catalytic hydrogenation is useful for analytical and thermochemical purposes. The analysis of a compound for the number of double bonds is carried out by measuring the uptake of hydrogen for a given amount of sample.

7-3 ELECTROPHILIC ADDITION TO ALKENES

Reagents such as the halogens (Cl_2, Br_2, and I_2), the hydrogen halides (HCl and HBr), the hypohalous acids (HOCl and HOBr), water, and sulfuric acid commonly add to the double bonds of alkenes to give saturated compounds.

$$\text{C}=\text{C}$$

$$\xrightarrow{\text{Br}_2} \quad -\underset{\underset{\text{Br}}{|}}{\text{C}}-\underset{\underset{\text{Br}}{|}}{\text{C}}-$$

$$\xrightarrow{\text{HOCl}} \quad -\underset{\underset{\text{Cl}}{|}}{\text{C}}-\underset{\underset{\text{OH}}{|}}{\text{C}}-$$

$$\xrightarrow{\text{H}_2\text{SO}_4} \quad -\underset{\underset{\text{H}}{|}}{\text{C}}-\underset{\underset{\text{OSO}_3\text{H}}{|}}{\text{C}}-$$

$$\xrightarrow{\text{HCl}} \quad -\underset{\underset{\text{H}}{|}}{\text{C}}-\underset{\underset{\text{Cl}}{|}}{\text{C}}-$$

$$\xrightarrow{\text{H}_2\text{O, H}^{\oplus}} \quad -\underset{\underset{\text{H}}{|}}{\text{C}}-\underset{\underset{\text{OH}}{|}}{\text{C}}-$$

These reactions have much in common in their mechanisms and have been much studied from this point of view. They are also of considerable synthetic and analytical utility. The addition of water to alkenes (hydration) is particularly important for the preparation of a number of commercially important alcohols. Thus ethyl alcohol and t-butyl alcohol are made on a very large scale by the hydration of the corresponding alkenes (ethylene and isobutylene), using sulfuric or phosphoric acids as catalysts.

$$\text{CH}_2=\text{CH}_2 \quad \xrightarrow[240°]{\text{H}_2\text{O, } 10\% \text{ H}_2\text{SO}_4} \quad \text{CH}_3\text{CH}_2\text{OH}$$

ethyl alcohol

$$\underset{\text{CH}_3}{\overset{\text{CH}_3}{}}\text{C}=\text{CH}_2 \quad \xrightarrow[25°]{\text{H}_2\text{O, } 10\% \text{ H}_2\text{SO}_4} \quad \underset{\text{CH}_3}{\overset{\text{CH}_3}{}}\text{C}\underset{\text{OH}}{\overset{\text{CH}_3}{}}$$

t-butyl alcohol

A. The Stepwise Polar Mechanism

We shall give particular attention here to the addition of bromine to alkenes. This reaction is very conveniently carried out in the laboratory and illustrates a number of important points about addition reactions. The characteristics of bromine addition are best understood through consideration of the reaction mechanism. A particularly significant observation concerning the mechanism is that bromine addition (and the other additions listed above) proceeds in the dark and in the presence of free-radical traps. This is evidence against a free-radical chain mechanism analogous to the chain mechanism involved in the halogenation of alkanes. It does not, however, preclude operation of free-radical addition reactions under other conditions. In fact, there are light-induced, radical-trap inhibited reactions of bromine and hydrogen bromide with alkenes, which we shall describe later.

The alternative to a free-radical chain reaction is an *ionic,* or *polar,* reaction in which electron-pair bonds are regarded as being broken in a **heterolytic** manner as contrasted to the free-radical, or **homolytic,** processes discussed previously.

$$X \overset{|}{:} Y \longrightarrow X^{\oplus} + :Y^{\ominus} \qquad \text{heterolytic bond-breaking}$$

$$X \overset{|}{:} Y \longrightarrow X\cdot + \cdot Y \qquad \text{homolytic bond-breaking}$$

Most polar addition reactions do not seem to be simple four-center, one-step processes for two important reasons. First, it should be noted that such mechanisms require the formation of the new bonds to be on the same side of the double bond and hence produce *cis* **addition** (Figure 7-2). However, there is ample evidence to show that bromine and many other reagents give *trans* addition (Figure 7-3). For example, cyclohexene adds bromine and hypochlorous acid to give *trans*-1,2-dibromocyclohexane and *trans*-2-chlorocyclohexanol. Similarly, hydrogen bromide adds to 1,2-dimethylcyclohexene to give *trans*-1-bromo-1,2-dimethylcyclohexane.[1] Such *trans* additions can hardly involve simple four-center reactions between one molecule of alkene and one molecule of an addend X—Y because the X—Y bond would have to be stretched impossibly far to permit the formation of C—X and C—Y bonds at the same time.

[1] Recent evidence indicates that *cis* addition of hydrogen bromide and hydrogen chloride occurs to some other kinds of alkenes. It remains to be demonstrated how general this behavior is.

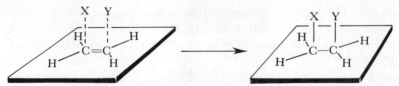

Figure 7-2   Schematic representation of *cis* addition of a reagent X—Y to ethylene by a four-center mechanism.

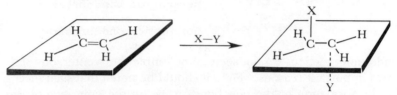

Figure 7-3   Product of *trans* addition of a reagent X—Y to ethylene.

The second piece of evidence against the four-center mechanisms is that addition reactions carried out in the presence of reagents able to react by donation of a pair of electrons (*nucleophilic* reagents, see p. 136) often give mixtures of products. Thus, the addition of bromine to an alkene in methyl alcohol solution containing lithium chloride leads not only to the expected dibromo-alkane but to products resulting from attack by chloride ions and the solvent. This intervention of extraneous nucleophilic agents in the reaction mixture is evidence against a one-step mechanism.

A somewhat oversimplified two-step mechanism that accounts for most of the facts is illustrated for the addition of bromine to ethylene. [In the formulation shown below, the curved arrows are not considered to have real mechanistic significance but are used primarily to show which atoms can be regarded as nucleophilic (donate electrons) and which electrophilic (accept electrons). The arrowheads point to the atoms that accept electrons.]

$$H_2C::CH_2 \ + \ :\ddot{Br}:\ddot{Br}: \ \longrightarrow \ \underset{\oplus}{\overset{\begin{smallmatrix}H\\|\end{smallmatrix}}{H-C}}\overset{\begin{smallmatrix}Br\\|\end{smallmatrix}}{-\underset{\begin{smallmatrix}|\\H\end{smallmatrix}}{C}-H} \ + \ :\ddot{Br}:^{\ominus}$$

electrophilic attack   (7-1)

$$:\overset{\ominus}{\ddot{Br}}: \ + \ \underset{\oplus}{\overset{\begin{smallmatrix}H\\|\end{smallmatrix}}{H-C}}\overset{\begin{smallmatrix}Br\\|\end{smallmatrix}}{-\underset{\begin{smallmatrix}|\\H\end{smallmatrix}}{C}-H} \ \longrightarrow \ \overset{\begin{smallmatrix}H\\|\end{smallmatrix}}{H-C}\overset{\begin{smallmatrix}Br\\|\end{smallmatrix}}{-\underset{\begin{smallmatrix}|\\Br\end{smallmatrix}}{C}\overset{}{}}\underset{H}{} H$$

nucleophilic attack   (7-2)

1,2-dibromoethane
(ethylene dibromide)

The first step (which involves electrophilic attack on the double bond and *heterolytic* breaking of both a carbon-carbon and a bromine-bromine bond) produces a bromide ion and a cation with the positive charge centered on a carbon atom, as shown in Eq. (7-1). A carbon cation is commonly called a **carbonium ion**. Like the free-radical intermediates postulated for the halogenation of saturated hydrocarbons, a carbonium-ion intermediate is not usually expected to be stable. It is deficient in electrons and should be highly reactive toward reagents that can provide a pair of electrons to form a covalent bond. Therefore, in the second step of the postulated mechanism, shown in Eq. (7-2), the carbonium ion combines rapidly with an available nucleophile (e.g., $:\overset{\ominus}{\ddot{Br}}:$) to give the reaction product.

Clearly, if other nucleophiles (e.g., $:\overset{\ominus}{\ddot{Cl}}:$, CH_3OH) are present in solution, they may compete with the bromide ion for the carbonium ion, as in Eqs. (7-3) and (7-4), and mixtures of products will result.

$$:\overset{\ominus}{\ddot{Cl}}: \ + \ \underset{\oplus}{\overset{\begin{smallmatrix}H\\|\end{smallmatrix}}{H-C}}\overset{\begin{smallmatrix}Br\\|\end{smallmatrix}}{-\underset{\begin{smallmatrix}|\\H\end{smallmatrix}}{C}-H} \ \longrightarrow \ \overset{\begin{smallmatrix}H\\|\end{smallmatrix}}{H-C}\overset{\begin{smallmatrix}Br\\|\end{smallmatrix}}{-\underset{\begin{smallmatrix}|\\H\end{smallmatrix}}{C}-H} \qquad\qquad (7\text{-}3)$$

(with Cl below first carbon)

$$CH_3:\ddot{O}: \ + \ \underset{\oplus}{\overset{\begin{smallmatrix}H\\|\end{smallmatrix}}{H-C}}\overset{\begin{smallmatrix}Br\\|\end{smallmatrix}}{-\underset{\begin{smallmatrix}|\\H\end{smallmatrix}}{C}-H} \ \longrightarrow \ \overset{\begin{smallmatrix}H\\|\end{smallmatrix}}{H-C}\overset{\begin{smallmatrix}Br\\|\end{smallmatrix}}{-\overset{}{C}-H} \ \xrightarrow{-H^{\oplus}} \ \overset{\begin{smallmatrix}H\\|\end{smallmatrix}}{H-C}\overset{\begin{smallmatrix}Br\\|\end{smallmatrix}}{-C-H} \quad (7\text{-}4)$$

(with $CH_3:\overset{\oplus}{\ddot{O}}:H$ and $CH_3-\ddot{O}$ H groups below)

To account for the observation that the reagents mentioned add across the double bond in the *trans* manner, we must conclude that the first and second steps take place from *opposite sides of the double bond.*

B. Why *trans* Addition?

The simple carbonium-ion intermediate of Eq. (7-1) does not account for formation of the *trans*-addition product. For one thing, there is no obvious reason why free rotation should not occur about the C—C bond of the cation—$\overset{\displaystyle |}{\underset{\displaystyle |}{C}}$—$\overset{\displaystyle |}{\underset{\displaystyle |}{C}}$⊕ derived from an open-chain alkene, and if such occurs, all stereospecificity is lost. Furthermore, the atomic-orbital representation of a carbonium ion (see pp. 111-113) predicts the positively charged carbon atom should form sp^2-hybrid σ bonds that would all lie in a plane. In this configuration, repulsion between electron pairs is minimized. We should expect that, in the addition of bromine to cycloalkenes, a bromide ion might be able to attack either side of the planar positive carbon to give a mixture of *cis* and *trans* products. *Trans* addition occurs exclusively, however.

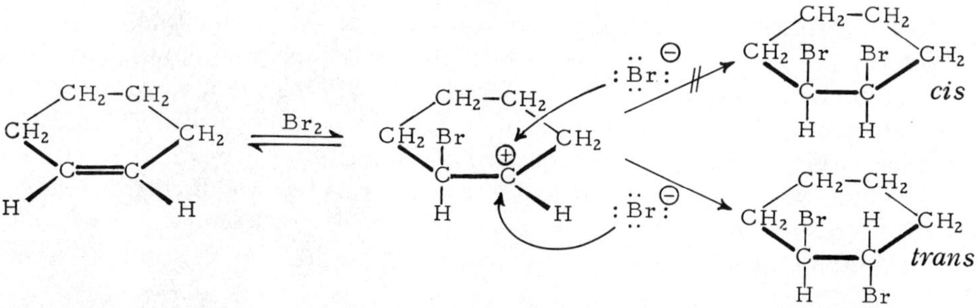

To account for the stereospecificity of bromine addition to alkenes, it has been suggested that a cyclic intermediate is formed in which bromine is bonded to both carbons of the double bond. This "bridged" ion is called a **bromonium ion** because the bromine formally carries the positive charge.

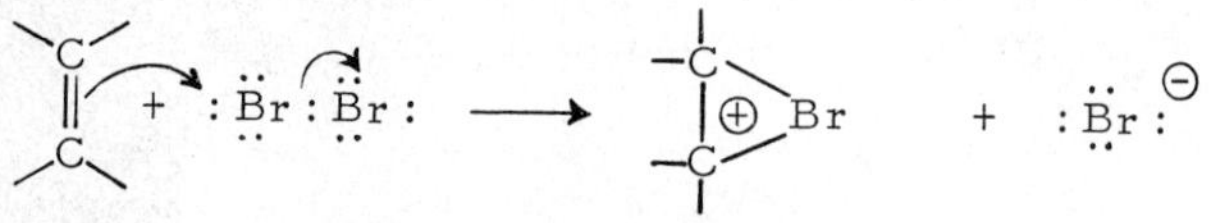

bromonium ion

Attack of bromide ion, or other nucleophile, at carbon on the side opposite the bridging group results in formation of the *trans*-addition product.

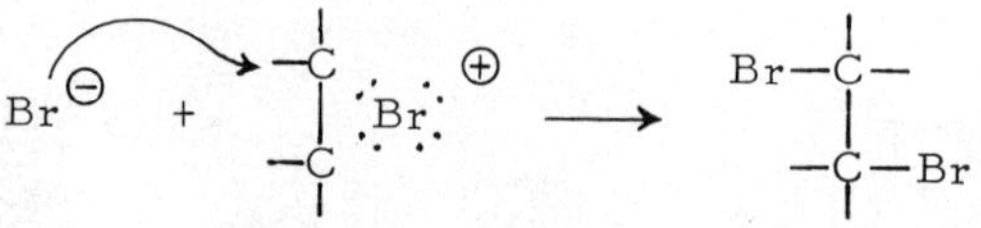

By analogy, a hydrogen-bridged intermediate can be used to account for *trans* addition of acids such as HBr, $H_3O^⊕$, H_2SO_4, etc., to alkenes. These intermediates are sometimes called **protonium** ions and might appear to violate the usual generalization

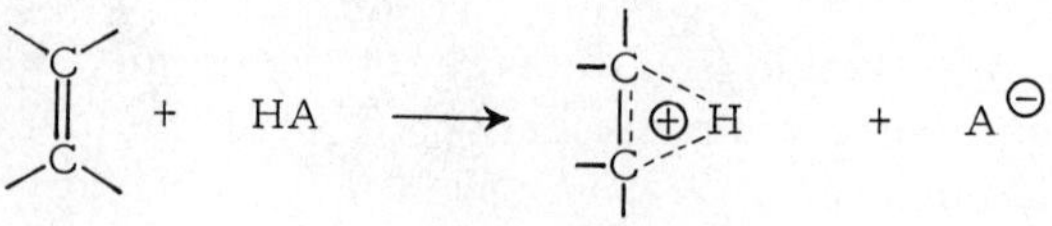

protonium ion

that hydrogen can form only one stable bond. It should be emphasized, however, that the bonding between the bridging hydrogen and the two carbon atoms is not considered to be normal electron-pair covalent bonding; it is different in that one electron pair effects the bonding of three atomic centers rather than the usual two. Protonium ions of this structure may be regarded as examples of "electron-deficient bonding," there being insufficient electrons with which to form all normal electron-pair bonds. During the past few years, a number of relatively stable substances having electron-deficient bonds to hydrogen have been carefully investigated. The simplest example is the $H_2^{\oplus}$ ion which may be regarded as a combination of a proton and a hydrogen atom (p. 107). This ion is reasonably stable in the gaseous state and has been detected and studied spectroscopically. Another and very striking example is afforded by stable diborane (B_2H_6), which has been shown to have a hydrogen-bridged structure. The bonds to each of the bridge hydrogens in diborane, like those postulated to the bridge hydrogen of an alkene-protonium ion, are examples of **three-center electron-pair** bonds.

diborane

Whether the intermediates in alkene-addition reactions are correctly formulated with bridged bromonium, chloronium, or protonium structures is still a controversial matter. Certainly, many other reactions that involve carbonium ions are far from stereospecific, and therefore bridged ions cannot be the exclusive formulation. It should also be remembered that all ions in solution, even those with only transitory existence, are strongly solvated, and this in itself may have important stereochemical consequences. In subsequent discussion, we shall most frequently write carbonium ions with the charge fully localized on one carbon atom, but it should be understood that this may not always be either the most accurate or the most desirable representation.

EXERCISE 7-3   Calculate ΔH (vapor) for addition of fluorine, chlorine, bromine, and iodine to an alkene. What can you conclude from these figures about the kind of problems that might attend practical use of each of the halogens as a reagent to synthesize a 1,2-dihalide?

EXERCISE 7-4   Use bond energies to evaluate the feasibility of addition of halogens to ethylene in the vapor state by the following free-radical chain mechanism at 25°:

$$X\cdot + CH_2{=}CH_2 \rightarrow X{-}CH_2{-}CH_2\cdot$$
$$X{-}CH_2{-}CH_2\cdot + X_2 \rightarrow X{-}CH_2{-}CH_2{-}X + X\cdot$$

What about the prospects of chain initiation by reaction of halogen with the double bond?

$$X_2 + CH_2{=}CH_2 \rightarrow X{-}CH_2{-}CH_2\cdot + X\cdot$$

Show your reasoning.

EXERCISE 7-5   *a.* Write as detailed a mechanism as you can for the *trans* addition of hypo-chlorous acid (HOCl) to cyclopentene.

   b. Use the bond-energy table to calculate ΔH values for addition of HOCl to ethylene to give CH_3CH_2OCl and CH_2OHCH_2Cl. How does the fact that HOCl is a weak acid (K_A in water $= 7 \times 10^{-10}$) make formation of CH_3CH_2OCl unlikely?

EXERCISE 7-6   Calculate ΔH for the addition of water to ethylene in the vapor state at $25°$. Why are alkenes not hydrated in aqueous sodium hydroxide solutions?

EXERCISE 7-7   Both the *cis* and *trans* isomers of cyclodecene are known. Would you expect that *trans* addition of bromine to each of these isomers would give the same or different products? Explain. (Ball-and-stick models will be particularly helpful here.)

7-4 ORIENTATION IN ADDITION TO ALKENES

A. Markownikoff's Rule

Addition of an unsymmetrical substance like HX to an unsymmetrical alkene can theoretically give two products,

$$(CH_3)_2C{=}CH_2 \ + \ HX \ \longrightarrow \ \underset{X \ \ H}{(CH_3)_2C{-}CH_2} \ \text{and/or} \ \underset{H \ \ X}{(CH_3)_2C{-}CH_2}$$

One of the most important early generalizations in organic chemistry was **Markownikoff's rule** (1870), which may be stated as follows: *In addition of HX to an unsymmetrical carbon-carbon double bond, the hydrogen of HX goes to that carbon of the double bond that carries the greater number of hydrogens.* Thus, Markownikoff's rule predicts that hydrogen chloride will add to propylene to give iso-propyl chloride and to isobutylene to give *t*-butyl chloride.

$$CH_3{-}CH{=}CH_2 \ + \ HCl \ \longrightarrow \ \underset{Cl}{CH_3{-}CH{-}CH_3}$$

$$(CH_3)_2C{=}CH_2 \ + \ HCl \ \longrightarrow \ \underset{Cl}{(CH_3)_2C{-}CH_3}$$

Additions in accord with Markownikoff's Rule

The rule by no means has universal application but, nonetheless, it is of considerable utility when limited to polar additions to hydrocarbons with only one double bond.

B. A Theoretical Basis for Markownikoff's Rule

To understand the reason for Markownikoff's rule, it will be desirable to discuss further some of the principles that are important to intelligent prediction of the course of an organic reaction. Consider the addition of hydrogen bromide to isobutylene. Two different carbonium-ion intermediates could be formed by attachment of a proton to one or the other of the double-bond carbons.

t-butyl cation *t*-butyl bromide

isobutyl cation isobutyl bromide

Subsequent reaction of the cations so formed with bromide ion gives *t*-butyl bromide and isobutyl bromide. In the usual way of running these additions, the product is quite pure *t*-butyl bromide.

How could we have predicted which product would be favored? The first step is to decide whether the prediction is to be based on (1) which of the two products is the *more stable,* or (2) which of the two products is formed *more rapidly.* If we make a decision on the basis of product stabilities, we take into account ΔH values, entropy effects, etc., to estimate an equilibrium constant K between the reactants and each product. When the ratio of the products is determined by the ratio of their equilibrium constants, we say the over-all reaction is subject to **equilibrium** (or **thermodynamic**) **control.** This will be the case when the reaction is carried out under conditions that make it *readily reversible.*

When a reaction is carried out under conditions in which it is *not reversible,* the ratio of the products is determined by the relative *rates* of formation of the various products. Such reactions are said to be under **kinetic control.** To predict relative reaction rates, we take into account steric hindrance, stabilities of possible intermediates, etc., with the purpose (whether explicitly stated or not) of estimating relative energies of activation $\Delta H *$ (pp. 74-75).

Addition of hydrogen bromide to isobutylene is predicted by Markownikoff's rule to give *t*-butyl bromide. Now, it turns out that the equilibrium constant connecting *t*-butyl bromide and isobutyl bromide is 4.5 at 25°.

$$K = \frac{[t\text{--butyl bromide}]}{[i\text{--butyl bromide}]} = 4.5$$

This means that if addition of hydrogen bromide to isobutylene actually gives 99 + per cent of *t*-butyl bromide in accord with Markownikoff's rule, then Markownikoff's rule is likely to be a *kinetic-control* rule and may very well be invalid under conditions where addition is reversible.

If Markownikoff's rule depends on kinetic control of the product ratio in the polar addition of hydrogen bromide to isobutylene, then it is proper to try to explain the direction of addition in terms of the ease of formation of the two possible carbonium-ion intermediates.

$$CH_3 \atop CH_3 \Big\rangle C=CH_2 \ + \ H^{\oplus}$$

fast $\longrightarrow$ $\left[CH_3 \atop CH_3 \right. \overset{CH_3}{\underset{}{\overset{\oplus}{C}}}\!\!-CH_3 \left. \right]$

t-butyl cation

slow $\longrightarrow$ $\left[CH_3 \atop CH_3 \right. \overset{H}{\underset{CH_2^{\oplus}}{\overset{}{C}}} \left. \right]$

isobutyl cation

The evidence is strong that alkyl groups are more electron donating than hydrogen. This means that the more alkyl groups there are on the positive carbon of a carbonium ion, the more stable and the more easily formed the carbonium ion will be. The reason is that electron-donating groups can partially compensate for the electron deficiency of the positive carbon. As a result, we can predict that the *t*-butyl cation with three alkyl groups attached to the positive center (i.e., a *tertiary* carbonium ion) will be formed more readily than the isobutyl cation with one alkyl group attached to the positive center (i.e., a *primary* carbonium ion).

This procedure reduces the theoretical problem presented by Markownikoff's rule to predicting which of the two possible carbonium-ion intermediates will be most readily formed. With the simple alkenes, we shall expect the preference to be in the order *tertiary* > *secondary* > *primary*.

EXERCISE 7-8   When *t*-butyl bromide is allowed to stand at room temperature for long periods, the n.m.r. spectrum shows that the material becomes contaminated with isobutyl bromide. Write a reasonable mechanism for the formation of isobutyl bromide and calculate the percentage of isobutyl bromide that you would expect to be present at equilibrium at 25°.

EXERCISE 7-9   Arrange ethylene, propylene, and isobutylene in order of expected ease of hydration with aqueous acid. Show your reasoning.

EXERCISE 7-10   Given that 1 mole of hydrogen bromide gas evolves 20 kcal when dissolved in water, estimate whether the addition of hydrogen bromide to ethylene is energetically more favorable in the gas phase or in aqueous solution. (Assume that the heats of solution of ethylene and ethyl bromide in water are small compared to 20 kcal.)

7-5 ADDITIONS OF UNSYMMETRICAL REAGENTS OPPOSITE TO MARKOWNIKOFF'S RULE

The early literature concerning the addition of hydrogen bromide to unsymmetrical alkenes is at best confused, and sometimes the same alkene was reported to give addition both according to, and in opposition to, Markownikoff's rule under very similar conditions. Much of the uncertainty on the addition of hydrogen bromide was removed by the classical researches of Kharasch and Mayo (1933), who showed that there must be two reaction mechanisms, each giving a different product. Under polar conditions, Kharasch and Mayo found that hydrogen bromide adds to propylene in a rather *slow* reaction to give pure isopropyl bromide.

$$CH_3CH=CH_2 \ + \ HBr \ \xrightarrow[\substack{\text{polar} \\ \text{conditions}}]{\text{slow}} \ CH_3\underset{\underset{Br}{|}}{C}HCH_3$$

With light, peroxides, free-radical initiators, and in the absence of free-radical traps, a *rapid* free-radical chain addition of hydrogen bromide occurs to yield 80 per cent or more of *n*-propyl bromide.

$$CH_3CH=CH_2 \ + \ HBr \ \xrightarrow[\text{peroxides}]{\text{fast}} \ CH_3CH_2CH_2Br$$

Similar effects have been occasionally noted with hydrogen chloride, but never with hydrogen iodide or hydrogen fluoride. A few substances apparently add to alkenes only by free-radical mechanisms and always give addition opposite to Markownikoff's rule.

The polar addition of hydrogen bromide was discussed in Section 7-4 and will not be further considered at this point. Two questions with regard to the so-called abnormal addition will be given special attention: namely, why the free-radical mechanism should give a product of different structure than the polar addition, and why the free-radical addition occurs readily with hydrogen bromide but rarely with the other hydrogen halides (see Exercise 7-12).

The abnormal addition of hydrogen bromide is strongly catalyzed by peroxides, which have the structure R—O—O—R and decompose thermally to give free radicals.

$$R-\overset{..}{\underset{..}{O}}:\overset{..}{\underset{..}{O}}-R \ \longrightarrow \ 2 \ R-\overset{..}{\underset{..}{O}}\cdot \qquad \Delta H = + 35 \text{ kcal}$$

The RO radicals can react with hydrogen bromide in two ways, as shown in the following equations:

$$RO\cdot \ + \ HBr \begin{cases} \nearrow ROH \ + \ Br\cdot & \Delta H = -23 \text{ kcal} \\ \searrow ROBr \ + \ H\cdot & \Delta H = +39 \text{ kcal} \end{cases}$$

Clearly, the formation of ROH and a bromine atom is energetically more favorable. The over-all process of decomposition of peroxide and attack on hydrogen bromide, which results in the formation of a bromine atom, can initiate a free-radical chain addition of hydrogen bromide to an alkene.

Chain propagation:
$$\begin{cases} CH_3CH=CH_2 \ + \ Br\cdot \ \longrightarrow CH_3\overset{\cdot}{C}H-CH_2Br & \Delta H = -5 \text{ kcal} \\ CH_3\overset{\cdot}{C}H-CH_2Br \ + \ HBr \rightarrow CH_3CH_2CH_2Br \ + \ Br\cdot & \Delta H = -11 \text{ kcal} \end{cases}$$

Chain termination:
$$R'\cdot \ + \ R'\cdot \ \longrightarrow R'-R' \qquad R'\cdot = \text{atom or radical}$$

The chain-propagating steps, taken together, are exothermic by 16 kcal and have a fairly reasonable energy balance between the separate steps. The reaction chains actually appear to be rather long, since the addition is strongly inhibited by radical traps and only traces of peroxide catalyst are needed.

EXERCISE 7-11   Write two different free-radical chain mechanisms for addition of hydrogen chloride to alkenes and consider the energetic feasibility for each.

EXERCISE 7-12   Calculate the ΔH values for initiation and chain propagation steps of free-radical addition of hydrogen fluoride, hydrogen chloride, and hydrogen iodide to an alkene. Would you expect these reagents to add easily to double bonds by such a mechanism?

The direction of addition of hydrogen bromide to propylene clearly depends on which end of the double bond the bromine atom attacks. The choice will

$$CH_3-\overset{\cdot}{C}H-CH_2-Br \qquad\qquad CH_3-\underset{Br}{CH}-CH_2\cdot$$

$$[1] \qquad\qquad\qquad\qquad [2]$$

depend on which of the two possible carbon free radicals that may be formed is the more stable, the 1-bromo-2-propyl radical [1] or the 2-bromo-1-propyl radical [2]. The ease of formation and stabilities of the carbon free radicals is seen to follow the sequence *tertiary > secondary > primary* (see also p. 146). By analogy, the *secondary* 1-bromo-2-propyl radical [1] is expected to be more stable and more easily formed than the *primary* 2-bromo-1-propyl radical [2]. The product of radical addition should be, and indeed is, *n*-propyl bromide.

EXERCISE 7-13   Bromotrichloromethane, $CBrCl_3$, adds to 1-octene by a free-radical chain mechanism on heating in the presence of a peroxide catalyst. Use the bond-energy tables to devise a feasible mechanism for this reaction and work out the most likely structure for the product. Show your reasoning.

7-6 ADDITION OF BORON HYDRIDES TO ALKENES

Diborane (B_2H_6) adds readily as BH_3 to most alkenes to give trialkylboron compounds (organoboranes). With ethylene, triethylborane results.

$$6\ CH_2{=}CH_2\ +\ B_2H_6\ \xrightarrow{\ 0°\ }\ 2\ (CH_3CH_2)_3B$$

This reaction is called **hydroboration**; it proceeds in three stages, but the intermediate mono- and dialkylboranes are not generally isolated, as they react rapidly by adding further to the alkene.

$$2\ CH_2{=}CH_2\ +\ B_2H_6\ \longrightarrow\ 2\ CH_3CH_2BH_2$$

$$CH_2{=}CH_2\ +\ CH_3CH_2BH_2\ \longrightarrow\ (CH_3CH_2)_2BH$$

$$CH_2{=}CH_2\ +\ (CH_3CH_2)_2BH\ \longrightarrow\ (CH_3CH_2)_3B$$

With an unsymmetrical alkene such as propylene, hydroboration occurs so that boron becomes attached to the less substituted end of the double bond — with propylene, tri-*n*-propylborane is formed.

$$6\,CH_3CH=CH_2 \;+\; B_2H_6 \;\longrightarrow\; 2\,(CH_3CH_2CH_2)_3B$$

EXERCISE 7-14   Determine from the general characteristics of additions to double bonds whether the direction of addition of B_2H_6 to propylene is consistent with a polar mechanism.

Hydroborations have to be carried out with some care, since diborane and alkylboranes are highly reactive substances, in fact, spontaneously inflammable in air. For most synthetic purposes, it is not necessary to isolate the addition products, and diborane can be generated either *in situ* or externally through the reaction of boron trifluoride with sodium borohydride.

$$3NaBH_4 \;+\; 4BF_3 \overset{\oplus\;\ominus}{\longrightarrow} 2B_2H_6 \;+\; 3NaBF_4$$

Boron trifluoride is conveniently used in the form of its stable complex with diethyl ether, $(C_2H_5)_2O{:}BF_3$; also, the reactions are usually carried out in ether solvents such as diethyl ether, $(C_2H_5)_2O$; diglyme, $(CH_3OCH_2CH_2)_2O$; or tetrahydrofuran, $(CH_2)_4O$.

The most common synthetic reactions of the resulting alkylboranes are oxidation with alkaline hydrogen peroxide to the corresponding primary alcohol, and cleavage with aqueous acid (or, better, anhydrous propionic acid, $CH_3CH_2CO_2H$) to give alkanes. Thus, for tri-*n*-propylborane:

$$(CH_3CH_2CH_2)_3B \;+\; 3\,H_2O_2 \xrightarrow[25-30°]{\overset{\ominus}{OH}} 3\,CH_3CH_2CH_2OH \;+\; B(OH)_3$$

$$(CH_3CH_2CH_2)_3B \;+\; 3\,H_2O \xrightarrow[reflux]{\overset{\oplus}{H}} 3\,CH_3CH_2CH_3 \;+\; B(OH)_3$$

The first of these processes achieves "anti-Markownikoff" addition of water to a carbon-carbon double bond as the over-all result of the two steps. The second reaction provides a method of reducing carbon-carbon double bonds without using hydrogen and a metal catalyst.

7-7 OXIDATION OF ALKENES

A. Ozonization

Most alkenes react readily with ozone, even at low temperatures, to cleave the double bond and yield cyclic peroxidic derivatives known as **ozonides.**

$$CH_3CH=CHCH_3 \xrightarrow[-80°]{O_3} \; CH_3CH \overset{\displaystyle O}{\underset{O-O}{\Big\langle}} CHCH_3$$

2–butene ozonide

Considerable evidence exists to indicate the over-all reaction occurs in three main steps, the first of which involves a *cis*-**cycloaddition** reaction that produces an unstable addition product called a **molozonide.**

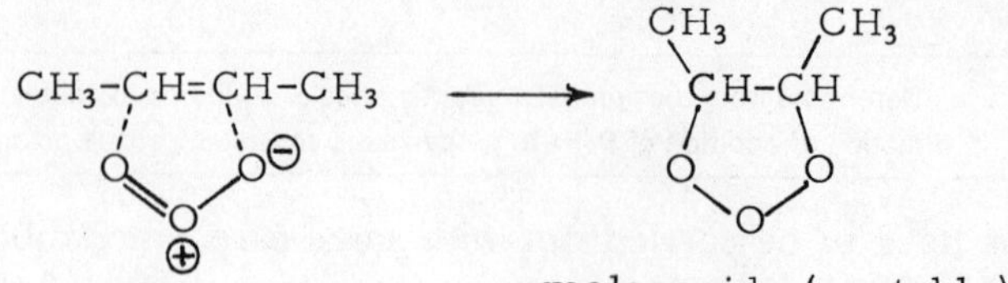

molozonide (unstable)

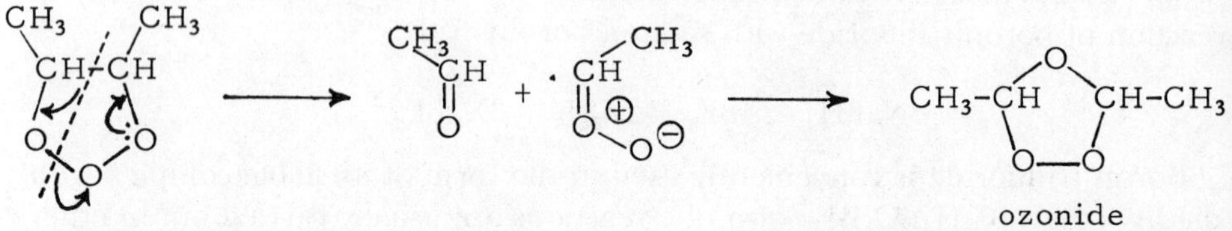

ozonide

Ozonides, like most substances with peroxide (O—O) bonds, may explode violently and unpredictably. Ozonizations must therefore be carried out with due caution. The ozonides are not usually isolated but are destroyed, by hydrolysis with water and reduction with zinc, to yield carbonyl compounds that are generally quite easy to isolate and identify.

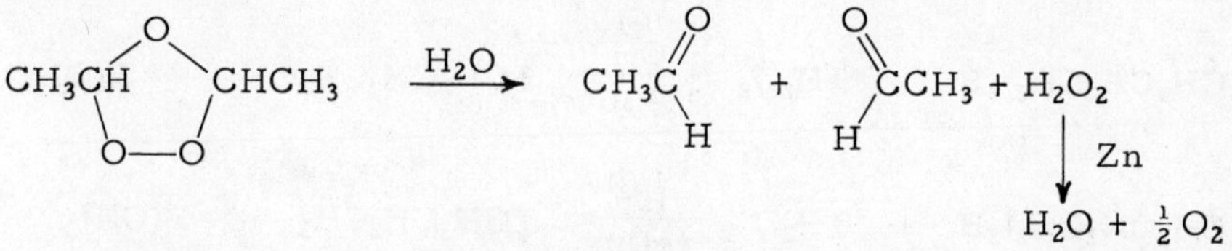

The over-all reaction sequence provides an excellent means for locating the positions of double bonds in alkenes. The potentialities of the method may be illustrated by the difference in reaction products between the 1- and 2-butenes.

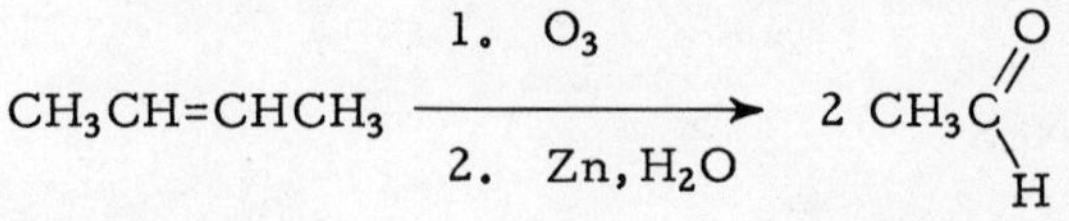

acetaldehyde

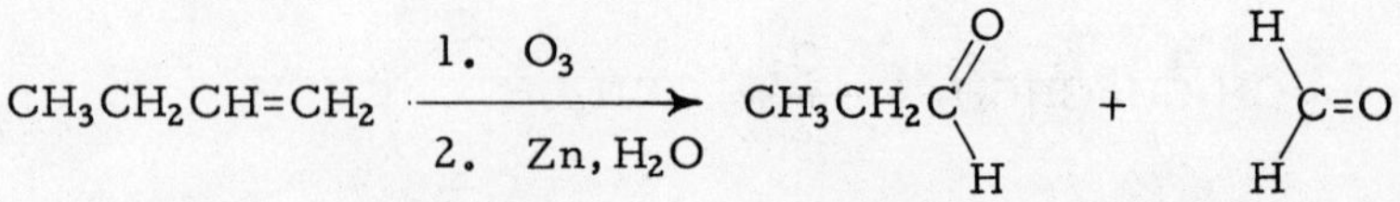

propionaldehyde   formaldehyde

EXERCISE 7-15   The following physical properties and analytical data pertain to two isomeric hydrocarbons, A and B, isolated from a gasoline:

	b.p.	m.p.	%C	%H
A	68.6°	−141°	85.63	14.34
B	67.9°	−133°	85.63	14.34

Both A and B readily decolorize bromine and permanganate solutions and give the same products on ozonization. Suggest possible structures for A and B. What experiments would you consider necessary to further establish the structure and configuration of A and B?

B. Hydroxylation

Several oxidizing reagents react with alkenes, under mild conditions, to give, as the over-all result, addition of hydrogen peroxide as HO—OH. Of particular importance are permanganate and osmium tetroxide, both of which react in an initial step by a *cis*-cycloaddition mechanism like that postulated for ozone.

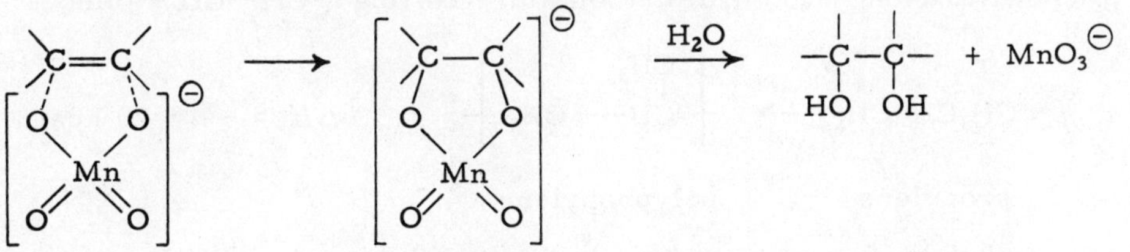

unstable

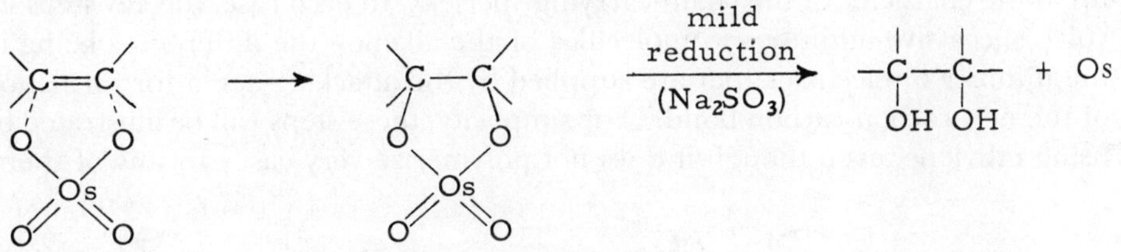

stable osmate
ester

Each of these reagents produces *cis*-dihydroxy compounds (diols) with cyclo-alkenes.

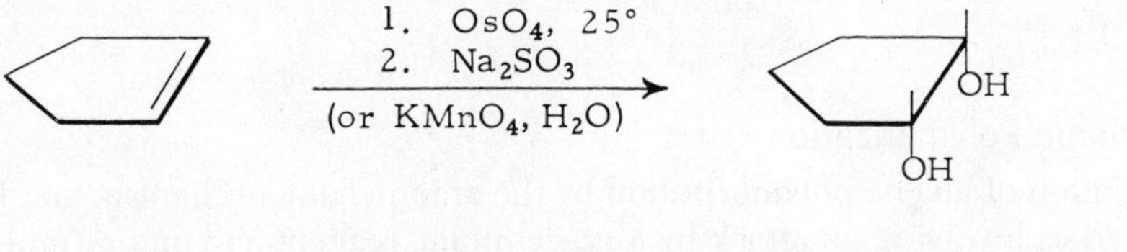

cis-1, 2-cyclopentanediol

An alternate scheme for oxidation of alkenes with hydrogen peroxide in formic acid follows a different course in that *trans* addition occurs.

$$\text{(structure)} \xrightarrow[\text{HCO}_2\text{H, }25°]{35\% \text{ H}_2\text{O}_2} \text{(structure with OH groups)}$$

trans-1, 2-cyclopentanediol

7-8 POLYMERIZATION OF ALKENES

One of the most important technical reactions of alkenes is their conversion to higher molecular-weight compounds (**polymers**). A polymer is here defined as a long-chain molecule with recurring structural units. Polymerization of pro-pylene gives a long-chain hydrocarbon with recurring $-\overset{\overset{\text{CH}_3}{|}}{\text{CH}}-\text{CH}_2-$ units.

$$n \cdot \text{CH}_3\text{CH}=\text{CH}_2 \longrightarrow \left[\overset{\overset{\text{CH}_3}{|}}{\text{CH}}\text{———}\text{CH}_2 \right]_n \qquad \Delta H = -n \cdot 20 \text{ kcal}$$

propylene   polypropylene

Most technically important polymerizations of alkenes occur by chain mecha-nisms and may be classed as anion, cation, or free-radical reactions, depending upon the character of the chain-carrying species. In each case, the key steps in-volve successive additions to molecules of the alkene—the differences being in the number of electrons that are supplied by the attacking agent for formation of the new carbon-carbon bond. For simplicity, these steps will be illustrated by using ethylene, even though it does not polymerize very easily by any of them.

$$\text{R}-\text{CH}_2-\text{CH}_2:^{\ominus} + \text{CH}_2{=}\text{CH}_2 \longrightarrow \text{R}-\text{CH}_2-\text{CH}_2-\text{CH}_2-\text{CH}_2:^{\ominus}, \text{ etc.}$$

$$\text{R}-\text{CH}_2-\overset{\oplus}{\text{CH}}_2 + \text{CH}_2{=}\text{CH}_2 \longrightarrow \text{R}-\text{CH}_2-\text{CH}_2-\text{CH}_2-\overset{\oplus}{\text{CH}}_2, \text{ etc.}$$

$$\text{R}-\text{CH}_2-\text{CH}_2 \cdot + \text{CH}_2{\overset{..}{-}}\text{CH}_2 \longrightarrow \text{R}-\text{CH}_2-\text{CH}_2-\text{CH}_2-\text{CH}_2 \cdot, \text{ etc.}$$

A. Anionic Polymerization

Initiation of alkene polymerization by the anion-chain mechanism may be for-mulated as involving an attack by a nucleophilic reagent $\text{Y}:^{\ominus}$ on one end of the double bond and formation of a carbanion.

$$Y:^{\ominus} + CH_2{=}CH_2 \longrightarrow Y:CH_2{-}CH_2:^{\ominus}$$

carbanion

Attack by the carbanion on another alkene molecule would give a four-carbon carbanion, and subsequent additions to further alkene molecules would lead to a high-molecular-weight anion.

$$Y:CH{-}CH_2:^{\ominus} + CH_2{=}CH_2 \longrightarrow Y:CH_2{-}CH_2{-}CH_2{-}CH_2:^{\ominus}$$

$$\xrightarrow{n(CH_2{=}CH_2)} Y:CH_2{-}CH_2{+}CH_2{-}CH_2{\rightarrow}_n CH_2{-}CH_2:^{\ominus}$$

The growing chain can be terminated by any reaction (such as the addition of a proton) that would destroy the carbanion on the end of the chain.

$$Y:CH_2{-}CH_2{+}CH_2{-}CH_2{\rightarrow}_n CH_2CH_2:^{\ominus} \xrightarrow{H^{\oplus}} Y:CH_2{-}CH_2{+}CH_2{-}CH_2{\rightarrow}_n CH_2{-}CH_3$$

Anionic polymerization of alkenes is quite difficult to achieve, since few anions (or nucleophiles) are able to add readily to alkene double bonds (see p. 136). Anionic polymerization occurs readily only with ethylenes substituted with sufficiently powerful electron-attracting groups to expedite nucleophilic attack.

B. Cationic Polymerization

Polymerization of an alkene by acidic reagents can be formulated by a mechanism similar to the addition of hydrogen halides to alkene linkages. First, a proton from a suitable acid adds to an alkene to yield a carbonium ion. Then, in the absence of any other reasonably strong nucleophilic reagent, another alkene molecule donates an electron pair and forms a longer chain cation. Continuation of this process can lead to a high-molecular-weight cation. Termination can occur by loss of a proton.

$$CH_2{=}CH_2 \overset{H^{\oplus}}{\rightleftharpoons} CH_3{-}CH_2^{\oplus} + CH_2{=}CH_2 \longrightarrow$$

$$CH_3{-}CH_2{-}CH_2{-}CH_2^{\oplus} \xrightarrow{n(CH_2{=}CH_2)} CH_3{-}CH_2{+}CH_2{-}CH_2{\rightarrow}_n CH_2{-}CH_2^{\oplus}$$

$$\xrightarrow{-H^{\oplus}} CH_3{-}CH_2{+}CH_2{-}CH_2{\rightarrow}_n CH{=}CH_2$$

Ethylene does not polymerize by the cationic mechanism, because it does not have sufficiently electron-donating groups to permit ready formation of the intermediate growing-chain cation. Isobutylene has electron-donating alkyl groups and polymerizes much more easily than ethylene by this type of mechanism. The usual catalysts for cationic polymerization of isobutylene are sulfuric acid, hydrogen fluoride, or a complex of boron trifluoride and water. Under nearly anhydrous conditions, a very long-chain polymer is formed called polyiso-butylene.

$$n \cdot CH_2=C\begin{smallmatrix}CH_3\\CH_3\end{smallmatrix} \xrightarrow{BF_3 \cdot H_2O} CH_3-\underset{CH_3}{\overset{CH_3}{C}}\left[-CH_2-\underset{CH_3}{\overset{CH_3}{C}}-\right]_{n-2} CH_2-\underset{CH_2}{\overset{CH_3}{C}}$$

polyisobutylene

Polyisobutylene fractions of particular molecular weights are very tacky and are used as adhesives for pressure-sealing tapes.

In the presence of 60 per cent sulfuric acid, isobutylene is not converted to a long-chain polymer, but to a mixture of eight-carbon alkenes. The mechanism is like the polymerization reaction described above, except that chain termination occurs after only one isobutylene molecule has been added. The short chain length is due to the high water concentration: the intermediate carbonium ion loses a proton to water before it can react with another alkene molecule.

$$CH_2=C\begin{smallmatrix}CH_3\\CH_3\end{smallmatrix} \xrightarrow[70^\circ]{60\% \ H_2SO_4} CH_3-\underset{CH_3}{\overset{CH_3}{C}}-CH_2-C\begin{smallmatrix}CH_2\\CH_3\end{smallmatrix} \ + \ CH_3-\underset{CH_3}{\overset{CH_3}{C}}-CH=C\begin{smallmatrix}CH_3\\CH_3\end{smallmatrix}$$

80%   20%

"diisobutylene"

Since the proton can be lost in two different ways, a mixture of alkene isomers is obtained. The alkene mixture is known as "diisobutylene" and has a number of commercial uses. Hydrogenation affords 2,2,4-trimethylpentane (often erroneously called "isoöctane") which is used as the standard "100 anti-knock rating" fuel for internal-combustion gasoline engines.

$$CH_2=C\begin{smallmatrix}CH_3\\CH_3\end{smallmatrix} \ + \ H_2SO_4 \rightleftharpoons CH_3-\overset{CH_3}{\underset{CH_3}{C}}\oplus \xrightarrow{CH_2=C\begin{smallmatrix}CH_3\\CH_3\end{smallmatrix}} CH_3-\underset{CH_3}{\overset{CH_3}{C}}-CH_2-\overset{CH_3}{\underset{CH_3}{C}}\oplus$$

$$\xrightarrow{-H^\oplus} CH_3-\underset{CH_3}{\overset{CH_3}{C}}-CH_2-C\begin{smallmatrix}CH_2\\CH_3\end{smallmatrix} \ + \ CH_3-\underset{CH_3}{\overset{CH_3}{C}}-CH=C\begin{smallmatrix}CH_3\\CH_3\end{smallmatrix}$$

diisobutylene isomers $\xrightarrow[50^\circ]{H_2 \ (Ni)}$ $CH_3-\underset{CH_3}{\overset{CH_3}{C}}-CH_2-\overset{CH_3}{CH}-CH_3$

2, 2, 4-trimethylpentane

EXERCISE 7-16   *a.* Write a mechanism for the sulfuric acid-induced dimerization of trimethyl-ethylene, indicating the products you expect to be formed.

   b. Ozonization of the actual olefin mixture that is formed gives (along with a mixture of aldehydes and ketones) substantial amounts of 2-butanone

$$CH_3-\overset{\overset{\textstyle O}{\|}}{C}-CH_2-CH_3$$

(CH_3—$\overset{\overset{\textstyle O}{\|}}{C}$—$CH_2$—$CH_3$). Write a structure and reaction mechanism for formation of a C_{10}-olefin that might *reasonably* be formed in the dimerization reaction and that, on ozonization, would yield 2-butanone and C_6-carbonyl compound. (Consider how sulfuric acid might cause the double bond in trimethylethylene to shift its position.)

C. Free-Radical Polymerization

   Ethylene may be polymerized with peroxide catalysts under high pressure (1000 atmospheres or more, literally in a cannon-barrel) at temperatures in excess of 100°. The initiation step involves formation of free radicals, and chain propagation entails stepwise addition of radicals to ethylene molecules.

Initiation: $R:\overset{..}{\underset{..}{O}}:\overset{..}{\underset{..}{O}}:R \longrightarrow 2\ R:\overset{..}{\underset{..}{O}}\cdot$

Propa-gation: $\begin{cases} R:\overset{..}{\underset{..}{O}}\cdot\ +\ CH_2{=}CH_2 \longrightarrow R:\overset{..}{\underset{..}{O}}:CH_2{-}CH_2\cdot \\ R:\overset{..}{\underset{..}{O}}:CH_2{-}CH_2\cdot\ +\ n(CH_2{=}CH_2) \longrightarrow RO{\Large(}CH_2{-}CH_2{\Large)}_n CH_2{-}CH_2\cdot \end{cases}$

Termi-nation: $2\ RO{\Large(}CH_2{-}CH_2{\Large)}_n CH_2{-}CH_2\cdot \longrightarrow \left[RO{-}(CH_2{-}CH_2{\Large)}_n CH_2{-}CH_2 \right]_2$

                                                              combination

$$RO{\Large(}CH_2{-}CH_2{\Large)}_n CH{=}CH_2\ +\ RO{\Large(}CH_2CH_2{\Large)}_n{-}CH_2{-}CH_3$$

                    disproportionation

Chain termination may occur by any reaction resulting in combination or disproportionation of free radicals. The polyethylene produced in this way has from 100 to 1000 ethylene units in the hydrocarbon chain. The polymer possesses a number of desirable properties as a plastic and is widely used for electrical insulation, packaging films, piping, and a variety of molded articles. The very low cost of ethylene (about $0.05 per pound) makes the polyethylene a particularly competitive material despite the practical difficulties involved in the polymerization process. Propylene and isobutylene do not polymerize satisfactorily by free-radical mechanisms.

EXERCISE 7-17   Write a reasonable mechanism for termination of ethylene polymerization by disproportionation. Calculate ΔH values for termination of the chain reaction by combination and disproportionation.

D. Coordination Polymerization

A relatively low-pressure low-temperature ethylene polymerization has been achieved with an aluminum-molybdenum oxide catalyst, which requires occasional activation with hydrogen (Phillips Petroleum). Ethylene also polymerizes quite rapidly at atmospheric pressure and room temperature in an alkane solvent containing a suspension of the insoluble reaction product from triethylaluminum and titanium tetrachloride (Ziegler). Both the Phillips and Ziegler processes produce very high molecular weight polyethylene with exceptional physical properties. The unusual characteristics of these reactions indicate that no simple anion, cation, or free-radical mechanism can be involved. It is believed that the catalysts act by coordinating with the alkene molecules in somewhat the way hydrogenation catalysts combine with alkenes.

Polymerization of propylene by catalysts of the Ziegler type gives a most useful plastic material. It can be made into durable fibers or molded into a variety of shapes. **Copolymers** (polymers with more than one kind of monomer unit in the polymer chains) of ethylene and propylene made with Ziegler catalysts have highly desirable rubberlike properties and are potentially the cheapest useful elastomers (elastic polymers). A Nobel Prize was shared in 1963 by K. Ziegler and G. Natta for their work on alkene polymerization.

7-9 SYNTHESIS OF ORGANIC COMPOUNDS

Exercise 7-18 is the first of many exercises in this book directed toward developing the facility of devising practical syntheses of particular compounds. The importance of this can hardly be overemphasized, for synthetic work is perhaps the primary activity in the practice of organic chemistry. The purposes of syntheses are widely divergent—thus, one might desire to confirm by synthesis the structure of a naturally occurring substance (cf. pp. 19-20) and, at the same time, develop routes whereby analogs of it could be prepared for comparisons of chemical and physiological properties. Another aim might be to make available previously unreported substances that would be expected on theoretical grounds to have unusual characteristics because of abnormal steric or electronic effects; simple examples of such substances that have not as yet been prepared are tetra-t-butylmethane, cyclopropyne, and tetracyanomethane, $C(CN)_4$. Much research is also done to develop or improve processes for synthesizing commercially important compounds; in such work, economic considerations are obviously paramount.

Regardless of why a compound is synthesized, the goal is to make it from available starting materials as efficiently and economically as possible. Naturally, what is efficient and economical in a laboratory-scale synthesis may be wholly impractical in industrial production; and, while we shall emphasize laboratory methods, we shall also indicate industrial practices in connection with the preparation of many commercially important substances.

An essential point of difference between industrial and laboratory methods is that the most efficient industrial process is almost always a completely continuous process, in which starting materials flow continuously into a reactor and products flow continuously out. In contrast, research in a laboratory is usually unconcerned with sustained production of any single substance, and laboratory preparations are therefore normally carried out in batches. Another point of difference of approach is with regard to by-products. In laboratory syntheses, a by-product such as the sulfuric acid used to hydrate an alkene is easily disposed of but, on an industrial scale, the problem of disposal or recovery of millions of pounds per year of spent impure acid might well preclude use of an otherwise satisfactory synthesis.

In our exercises, we have attempted to choose examples of practical preparations involving practical starting materials and have generally avoided synthetic interconversions of compounds that, although of possible pedagogical value, are not important in the laboratory. The aim of this approach is to aid in developing a feeling for the kinds of compounds that are readily available.

We believe that it is important, in writing out projected syntheses, to specify reagents and approximate reaction conditions as closely as possible, particularly because many combinations of reagents may have more than one possible reaction path, depending upon the solvent, temperature, etc. The addition of hydrogen bromide to alkenes (pp. 146-148) provides a cogent example of how a change in conditions can change the course of a reaction.

Most syntheses involve more than one step — indeed, in the preparation of complex natural products, it is not uncommon to have thirty or more separate steps. The planning of such syntheses can be a real exercise in logistics. The reason is that the over-all yield is the product of the yields in the separate steps; thus, if each of any three steps in a thirty-step synthesis gives only 20 per cent of the desired product, the over-all yield is limited to $(0.20)^3 \times 100 = 0.8$ per cent, even if all the other yields are 100 per cent. If 90 per cent yields could be achieved in each step, the over-all yield would still be only $(0.90)^{30} \times 100 = 4$ per cent. Obviously, in a situation of this kind, one should plan to encounter the reactions that have the least likelihood of succeeding in the earliest possible stages of the syntheses.

It is to be expected that there will be an essentially infinite number of routes by which a given starting material can be converted to a given product. The problem is to select an efficient route — efficient in the number of steps required and the over-all yield obtainable, as well as efficient through using reagents that do not themselves require multistep syntheses to prepare.

The most useful way to plan a multistep synthesis is to work backward from the product to starting material. If none of the available starting materials have the same carbon skeleton as the product, the first task is to formulate possible routes for putting together the carbon skeleton. Each route is then examined for its potential to get the desired functional groups at their proper locations. In almost all cases, it is important to use reactions that will lead to pure compounds without the necessity for isomer separations. We shall illustrate some of the above considerations by working through a specific example, which, like all our exercises, will be based primarily on the reactions in the immediate chapter but still may utilize steps discussed considerably earlier.

The example involves development of a practical synthesis of 2-chloro-2,4,4-trimethylpentane from the starting materials specified for Exercise 7-18: ethylene, propylene, isobutylene, isobutane, and inorganic reagents.

$$\begin{array}{ccc} & \underset{|}{CH_3} & \underset{|}{CH_3} \\ CH_3-\underset{|}{C}-CH_2-\underset{|}{C}-CH_3 \\ & Cl & CH_3 \end{array}$$ 2-chloro-2, 4, 4-trimethylpentane

The carbon skeleton of the desired product is different from that of any of the given starting materials. However, it can be seen to be divisible into two iso-butane units.

$$\begin{array}{ccccc} & C & | & C & \\ & | & | & | & \\ C-C-C & + & C-C \\ & | & | \\ & | & C \\ & | \end{array}$$

Using reactions that have been discussed so far, this skeleton can be put to-gether from isobutylene which with sulfuric acid dimerizes to an 80:20 mixture of 2,4,4-trimethyl-1-pentene and 2,4,4-trimethyl-2-pentene (pp. 153-154).

$$2\ CH_2{=}C(CH_3)_2 \xrightarrow[70°]{60\%\ H_2SO_4} \underset{CH_3}{\underset{|}{CH_2}}{=}\underset{|}{C}-CH_2-\underset{\underset{CH_3}{|}}{C}-CH_3 + CH_3-\underset{|}{C}{=}CH-\underset{\underset{CH_3}{|}}{C}-CH_3$$

$$80\% 20\%$$

These reactions are probably comparably convenient to carry out in the labora-tory.

   The introduction of chlorine at the proper position in the octane skeleton can be carried out by addition of hydrogen chloride to the trimethylpentene isomers, each of which, by Markownikoff's rule, is fortunately expected to give the same product (pp. 144-146). The alternative is free-radical chlorination of 2,2,4-trimethylpentane, either photochemically or thermally with chlorine (pp. 75-77), or else with sulfuryl chloride (p. 77).

$$\underset{CH_3}{\underset{|}{CH_2}}{=}\underset{|}{C}-CH_2-\underset{\underset{CH_3}{|}}{\overset{CH_3}{C}}-CH_3 + CH_3-\underset{|}{\overset{CH_3}{C}}{=}CH-\underset{\underset{CH_3}{|}}{\overset{CH_3}{C}}-CH_3$$

conc. HCl, 25°

$$CH_3-\underset{Cl}{\overset{CH_3}{\underset{|}{C}}}-CH_2-\underset{CH_3}{\overset{CH_3}{\underset{|}{C}}}-CH_3$$

$Cl_2, h\nu$

SO_2Cl_2

$$CH_3-\underset{|}{CH}-CH_2-\underset{\underset{CH_3}{|}}{\overset{CH_3}{C}}-CH_3$$

The second preparation is flawed by the fact that the chlorination is not specific for the tertiary hydrogen. This, then, would be a grossly impractical synthesis, since there is every reason to anticipate that separation of the desired isomer would be very difficult. Synthesis of the corresponding 2-bromo-2,4,4-trimethylpentane by bromination of the hydrocarbon would be much more practical, because attack at the tertiary carbon by bromine atoms is highly favored (cf. p. 76-77). The preferred synthesis of 2-chloro-2,4,4-trimethylpentane is by dimerization of isobutylene followed by addition of hydrogen chloride.

$$2\ CH_2{=}C(CH_3)_2 \xrightarrow[70°]{60\%\ H_2SO_4} CH_2{=}\underset{\underset{CH_3}{|}}{\overset{\overset{CH_3}{|}}{C}}{-}CH_2{-}\underset{\underset{CH_3}{|}}{\overset{\overset{CH_3}{|}}{C}}{-}CH_3 + CH_3{-}\underset{}{\overset{\overset{CH_3}{|}}{C}}{=}CH{-}\underset{\underset{CH_3}{|}}{\overset{\overset{CH_3}{|}}{C}}{-}CH_3$$

$$\xrightarrow[25°]{conc.\ HCl} CH_3{-}\underset{\underset{Cl}{|}}{\overset{\overset{CH_3}{|}}{C}}{-}CH_2{-}\underset{\underset{CH_3}{|}}{\overset{\overset{CH_3}{|}}{C}}{-}CH_3$$

The above example is neither complicated nor profound, but it should serve to illustrate the principle of working backward to develop various routes to the proper carbon skeleton from available starting materials and then deciding how to introduce the desired functional groups. The final choice of route will depend on the over-all efficiency in yield, number of steps required, general convenience, etc.

EXERCISE 7-18   Indicate how you would synthesize each of the following compounds from any one of the given organic starting materials and inorganic reagents. Specify reagents and the reaction conditions, and justify the practicality of any isomer separations. If separations are not readily possible, estimate the proportion of the desired compound in the final product. Starting materials: ethylene, propylene, isobutylene, isobutane.

a. $CH_3{-}\underset{\underset{OH}{|}}{\overset{\overset{CH_3}{|}}{C}}{-}CH_3$

e. $CH_3{-}\underset{\underset{CH_3}{|}}{\overset{\overset{CH_3}{|}}{C}}{-}CH_2{-}\overset{\overset{O}{||}}{C}{-}CH_3$

b. $CH_3{-}\underset{\underset{F}{|}}{\overset{\overset{CH_3}{|}}{C}}{-}CH_3$

f. $CH_3{-}\underset{\underset{H}{|}}{\overset{\overset{CH_3}{|}}{C}}{-}CH_2Br$

c. $CH_3CH{-}CH_2$ with OH and Br below

g. $ClCH_2{-}\underset{\underset{CH_3}{|}}{\overset{\overset{CH_3}{|}}{C}}{-}CH_2{-}\overset{\overset{CH_3}{|}}{CH}{-}CH_3$

d. $CH_3{-}\underset{\underset{CH_3}{|}}{\overset{\overset{CH_3}{|}}{C}}{-}CH_2{-}\underset{\underset{I}{|}}{\overset{\overset{CH_3}{|}}{C}}{-}CH_3$

h. $CH_3{-}CH_2{-}CH_2OH$

$$\text{CH}_3 \qquad \text{CH}_3 \qquad\qquad\qquad \text{CH}_3 \quad\; \text{CH}_3$$

i. HO CH$_2$—CH—CH$_2$—C—CH$_3$ *j.* CH$_3$—C—CH$_2$—C—CH$_2$

$$\qquad\qquad\qquad\qquad \text{CH}_3 \qquad\qquad\qquad \text{CH}_3 \quad \text{OH OH}$$

SUPPLEMENTARY EXERCISES

7-19 Calculate the heats ($-\Delta H$) of the following reactions in the gas phase at 25°:

$$\text{H}_2\text{O}_2 + (\text{CH}_2)_2 \rightarrow \text{HO—CH}_2\text{—CH}_2\text{—OH}$$
$$\text{H}_2\text{O}_2 + (\text{CH}_2)_6 \rightarrow \text{HO—(CH}_2)_6\text{—OH}$$

  a. What conclusion as to the rates of the above reactions can be made on the basis of the ΔH values? Explain.

  b. What change in the heats of the reactions would be expected if they were carried out in the liquid phase? Why?

  c. What agents might be effective in inducing the reactions in liquid phase? Explain.

7-20 Evaluate (show your reasoning) the possibility that the following reaction will give the indicated product:

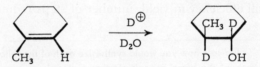

If you do not think the indicated product would be important, write the structure(s) of the product(s) you think most likely to be found.

7-21 Investigate the energetic feasibility of adding ammonia (NH$_3$) to an alkene by a free-radical chain mechanism with the aid of a peroxide (ROOR) catalyst. Would such a mechanism give addition in accord with Markownikoff's rule? Why? What practical difficulties might be encountered in attempts to add ammonia to isobutylene with a sulfuric acid catalyst?

7-22 Calculate ΔH values for the following reactions in the vapor phase per mole of the principal reactant using the bond energy tables:

  a. $n(\text{CH}_2\text{=CH}_2) \longrightarrow \text{+CH}_2\text{-CH}_2\text{+}_n$

  b. CH$_2$=CH$_2$ + O$_3$ $\longrightarrow$

$$\overset{\displaystyle\text{O}}{\underset{\displaystyle\text{O—O}}{\text{CH}_2 \qquad \text{CH}_2}}$$

Use $\Delta H = -34.5$ kcal for the reaction, $\text{O}_3 \rightarrow \tfrac{3}{2}\text{O}_2$

7-23 It has been found possible to synthesize two isomeric cycloalkenes of formula C_8H_{14}. Both of these compounds react with hydrogen in the presence of platinum to give cycloöctane, and each, on ozonization followed by reduction, gives

$$H—\overset{\overset{\textstyle O}{\|}}{C}—CH_2—CH_2—CH_2—CH_2—CH_2—CH_2—\overset{\overset{\textstyle O}{\|}}{C}—H$$

a. What are the structures of the two compounds?

b. Would the two substances give the same compound on hydroxylation with potassium permanganate?

Alkynes

*T*he alkynes are hydrocarbons with carbon-carbon triple bonds. Acetylene, C_2H_2, the simplest member of the class, is one of the most important of all starting materials for organic syntheses, especially in commercial operations.

The usefulness of alkynes in synthesis is partly due to the variety of addition reactions that the triple bond undergoes and partly due to the fact that a hydrogen attached to an acetylenic group, $-C\equiv C-H$, is weakly acidic and can be removed by strong bases to form acetylide salts. The acidity of acetylenic hydrogens is very low compared with the common mineral acids but is at least 10^{18} times greater than the acidity of the hydrogens of alkanes.

The main purpose of this chapter is to show the similarities and differences between the addition reactions of acetylenes and alkenes, as well as to explain how we can account for the acidity of acetylenic hydrogens by the concepts we have developed earlier.

Alkynes

A number of hydrocarbons, called alkynes or acetylenes, have triple bonds between carbon atoms. Acetylene, C_2H_2, the simplest member of this class of hydrocarbon, has been established by various physical measurements to be a linear molecule with a carbon-carbon triple-bond distance of 1.20 A and two carbon-hydrogen bonds of 1.06 A.

$$H\text{———}C\equiv\!\equiv\!C\text{———}H$$

1.20 A

1.06 A

According to the atomic-orbital description given in Chapter 5 (pp. 111-116), the C—H bonds of acetylene are σ bonds formed by overlap of a hydrogen s orbital with a carbon sp orbital; there is one C—C σ bond (from overlap of two carbon sp orbitals) and there are two C—C π bonds (from overlap of two perpendicular pairs of p orbitals). The bond angles expected for this model are 180°.

The linear configuration predicted for alkynes by both atomic-orbital and ball-and-stick models allows no possibility for *cis-trans* isomerism at the triple bond, and such isomerism is not observed (Figure 8-1).

Figure 8-1   Ball-and-stick model of a substance with a carbon-carbon triple bond, showing the linear arrangement expected for the carbons and attached groups.

8-1 NOMENCLATURE

The IUPAC system for naming alkynes employs the ending *-yne* in place of the *-ane* used for the name of the corresponding, completely saturated hydrocarbon.

H–C≡C–H CH_3–C≡C–CH_3

ethyne   2-butyne

(acetylene)   (dimethylacetylene)

The numbering system for location of the triple bond and substituent groups is analogous to that used for the corresponding alkenes.

$$CH_3-\overset{\overset{\displaystyle CH_3}{|}}{\underset{\underset{\displaystyle CH_3}{|}}{C}}-C\equiv C-\overset{\overset{\displaystyle CH_3}{|}}{\underset{\underset{\displaystyle H}{|}}{C}}-CH_3$$

2, 2, 5-trimethyl-3-hexyne

(isopropyl-*t*-butylacetylene)

Many alkynes are commonly named as substitution products of acetylene, as shown in parentheses in the above examples.

Open-chain hydrocarbons with more than one triple bond are called **alkadiynes, alkatriynes,** etc., according to the number of triple bonds. Hydrocarbons with both double and triple bonds are called **alkenynes, alkadienynes, alkendiynes,** etc., according to the number of double and triple bonds. A double bond takes precedence over a triple bond when both are present.

HC≡C–C≡CH H_2C=CH–C≡CH

butadiyne   butenyne

HC≡C–CH=CH–CH=CH_2 HC≡C–C≡C–CH=CH_2

1, 3-hexadiene-5-yne   1-hexen-3, 5-diyne

The hydrocarbon substituents derived from alkynes are called **alkynyl** groups:

HC≡C–   HC≡C–CH_2–

ethynyl   2-propynyl

(propargyl)

EXERCISE 8-1   Name each of the following substances by the IUPAC system and as a substituted acetylene (review the names of the substituent groups on pp. 51-57, 81-82, 121-123).

a. $CH_3C{\equiv}CCl$

b. $(CH_3)_3CC{\equiv}CCH_2C(CH_3)_3$

c. $CH_2{=}CHCH_2C{\equiv}CCH{=}CH_2$

d. $HC{\equiv}CCH_2C{\equiv}C{-}C(CH_3){=}CH_2$

e.

f. $(CH_2)_8C_2$

8-2   PHYSICAL PROPERTIES OF ALKYNES

The boiling points, melting points, and densities of the simple alkynes are generally somewhat higher than those of corresponding alkanes or alkenes. The 1-alkynes, like the *n*-alkanes (pp. 58-59), and the 1-alkenes (pp. 124-125) form a homologous series with rather regular changes in physical properties as the chain length is increased. The physical properties of some selected alkynes, and their heats of combustion, are given in Table 8-1.

8-3   SPECTROSCOPIC PROPERTIES OF ALKYNES

The infrared spectrum of a monosubstituted alkyne such as phenylacetylene, $C_6H_5C{\equiv}CH$ (see Figure 8-2), has a strong band near 3300 cm^{-1}, which is characteristic of the carbon-hydrogen stretching vibration in the grouping ${\equiv}C{-}H$. At a lower frequency (longer wavelength) around 2100 cm^{-1}, there is a band caused by the stretching vibration of the triple bond. Therefore, the presence of the grouping $-C{\equiv}CH$ in a molecule may be detected readily by infrared spectroscopy. However, the triple bond of a disubstituted alkyne, $R{-}C{\equiv}C{-}R$, is less easily detected because there is no ${\equiv}C{-}H$ absorption near 3300 cm^{-1}, and furthermore, the $C{\equiv}C$ absorption is sometimes of such low intensity that it may be indiscernible.

Alkynes, like alkenes, only absorb ultraviolet radiation very strongly at wavelengths in the relatively inaccessible region below 2000 A. When, however, the triple bond is conjugated with one or more unsaturated groups, radiation of longer wavelength is absorbed. To illustrate, acetylene absorbs at 1500 and 1730 A, while 3-buten-1-yne ($CH_2{=}CH{-}C{\equiv}CH$) absorbs at 2190 and 2275 A. The effects of such conjugation on spectra are discussed in more detail in Chapter 9 (pp. 196-198).

Table 8-1   Physical Constants and Heats of Combustion of Alkynes

IUPAC name	Common name	Formula	B.p., °C	M.p., °C	d_4^{20}	ΔH of combustion[a]
ethyne	acetylene	HC≡CH	−84	−81		310.6
propyne	methylacetylene	CH₃C≡CH	−23.2	−103		463.1
1-butyne	ethylacetylene	CH₃CH₂C≡CH	8.1	−126	0.65[b]	620.6
1-pentyne	n-propylacetylene	CH₃(CH₂)₂C≡CH	40.2	−106	0.690	778.0
1-hexyne	n-butylacetylene	CH₃(CH₂)₃C≡CH	71.5	−132	0.716	935.5
1-heptyne	n-pentylacetylene[c]	CH₃(CH₂)₄C≡CH	99.7	−81	0.733	1092.9
1-octyne	n-hexylacetylene	CH₃(CH₂)₅C≡CH	126.2	−79	0.746	1250.3
1-nonyne	n-heptylacetylene	CH₃(CH₂)₆C≡CH	150.8	−50	0.757	1407.8
1-decyne	n-octylacetylene	CH₃(CH₂)₇C≡CH	174.0	−44	0.766	1565.2
2-butyne	dimethylacetylene	CH₃C≡CCH₃	27.0	−32	0.691	620.6
2-pentyne	ethylmethylacetylene[d]	CH₃CH₂C≡CCH₃	56.1	−109	0.711	774.3
2-hexyne	methyl-n-propylacetylene[d]	CH₃(CH₂)₂C≡CCH₃	84.0	−88	0.732	
3-hexyne	diethylacetylene	CH₃CH₂C≡CCH₂CH₃	81.8	−105	0.724	

[a] Of the gaseous hydrocarbon at 25° C to give liquid water, kcal/mole.
[b] Under pressure.
[c] Or n-amylacetylene.
[d] Alphabetical, order of substituent groups (see p. 56).

166

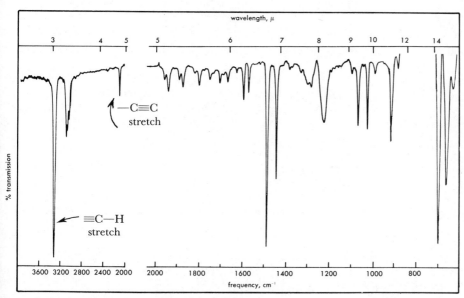

Figure 8-2   The infrared spectrum of phenylacetylene in carbon tetrachloride solution.

The nuclear magnetic resonance spectrum of phenylacetylene is shown in Figure 8-3. The peaks near 435 cps and at 185 cps correspond to resonance of the phenyl and ≡C—H protons, respectively. The difference in chemical shift between the two types of protons is considerably larger than between vinyl and aromatic protons (compare Figure 8-3 with Figure 6-3) and, in general, acetylenic

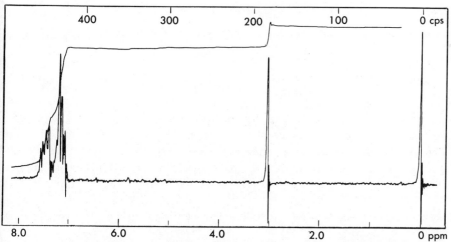

Figure 8-3   The n.m.r. spectrum and integral of phenylacetylene at 60 Mcps relative to TMS as 0.00. This spectrum illustrates nicely the use of n.m.r. for detection of impurities—the small peaks between 300 and 400 cps being due to the presence of impurities with alkene hydrogens. The integral indicates that the ratio of alkene to acetylenic hydrogens is on the order of 1:15. The impurity is most likely styrene (phenylethylene, $C_6H_5CH=CH_2$) and, if so, it is present to about 2 per cent.

protons are brought into resonance at higher magnetic fields (i.e., they are subject to more diamagnetic shielding, p. 37) than vinyl or aromatic protons. In fact, acetylenic protons have chemical shifts approaching those of alkyl protons.

EXERCISE 8-2   Sketch out the principal features you would expect for the infrared and n.m.r. spectra of the following substances. (It will be helpful to review pp. 60-62 and 124-128, as well as Sections 2-4A and 2-4B.)

a. $CH_3C\equiv CCH_3$

b. $CH_3C\equiv CH$ (expect a long-range n.m.r. coupling of 3 cps)

c. $CH_3CH_2C\equiv CCH_2CH_3$

d. $HC\equiv C-CH=CH-C\equiv CH$ (*cis* and *trans*)

e. $(CH_2)_8C_2$

8-4 ACETYLENE

Acetylene (ethyne) is customarily obtained on a commercial scale by hydrolysis of calcium carbide (CaC_2) or, in low yield, by high-temperature cracking, or partial combustion, of petroleum gases, particularly methane. Calcium carbide is obtained from the reaction of calcium oxide with carbon at about 2000° and is

$$CaO + 3C \xrightarrow{2000°} CaC_2 + CO$$

cleaved by water (acting as an acid) to give acetylene and calcium hydroxide.

$$CaC_2 + 2H_2O \longrightarrow HC\equiv CH + Ca(OH)_2$$

Acetylene is much less stable with respect to the elements than ethylene or ethane.

$$HC\equiv CH \ (g) \longrightarrow 2C\ (s) + H_2\ (g) \qquad \Delta H = -54.2 \text{ kcal}$$

$$H_2C=CH_2 \ (g) \longrightarrow 2C\ (s) + 2H_2\ (g) \qquad \Delta H = -12.5 \text{ kcal}$$

$$H_3C-CH_3 \ (g) \longrightarrow 2C\ (s) + 3H_2\ (g) \qquad \Delta H = +20.2 \text{ kcal}$$

An explosive decomposition of acetylene to carbon and hydrogen may occur if the gas is compressed to several hundred psi. Even liquid acetylene (b.p. −83°) must be handled with care. Acetylene is not used commercially under substantial pressures unless it is mixed with an inert gas and handled in rugged equipment with the minimum amount of free volume. Large-diameter pipes for transmission of compressed acetylene are often packed with metal rods to cut down on the free volume. Acetylene for welding is dissolved under 200 psi

in acetone ($CH_3-\overset{\overset{\displaystyle O}{\|}}{C}-CH_3$, b.p. 56.5°) and contained in cylinders packed with diatomaceous earth.

Flame temperatures of about 2800° can be obtained by combustion of acetylene with pure oxygen. It is interesting that acetylene gives higher flame temperatures than ethylene or ethane even though acetylene has a substantially lower heat of combustion than these hydrocarbons. The higher temperature of acetylene flames, compared with those of ethylene or ethane, is possible de-

$$C_2H_2\ (g)\ +\ \tfrac{5}{2}\ O_2\ (g)\ \longrightarrow\ 2CO_2\ (g)\ +\ H_2O\ (l) \qquad \Delta H = -311\ \text{kcal}$$

$$C_2H_4\ (g)\ +\ 3\ O_2\ (g)\ \longrightarrow\ 2CO_2\ (g)\ +\ 2H_2O\ (l) \qquad \Delta H = -337\ \text{kcal}$$

$$C_2H_6\ (g)\ +\ \tfrac{7}{2}\ O_2\ (g)\ \longrightarrow\ 2CO_2\ (g)\ +\ 3H_2O\ (l) \qquad \Delta H = -373\ \text{kcal}$$

spite the smaller heat of combustion, because the heat capacity of the products is relatively small; less water is formed and less of the heat of the reaction is used to bring the combustion products up to the flame temperatures.

8-5 ADDITION REACTIONS OF ALKYNES

The alkynes behave in some ways as typical unsaturated compounds with two double linkages. For example, bromine adds to acetylene in two steps: first to give *trans*-1,2-dibromoethylene (acetylene dibromide), and finally, to give 1,1,2,2-tetrabromoethane (acetylene tetrabromide).

$$HC{\equiv}CH \xrightarrow{\ Br_2\ } \underset{Br}{\overset{H}{}} C{=}C \underset{H}{\overset{Br}{}} \xrightarrow{\ Br_2\ } CHBr_2\text{--}CHBr_2$$

trans-1, 2-dibromo-　　　1, 1, 2, 2-tetrabromo-
ethylene　　　　　　　　　　ethane

(acetylene dibromide)　(acetylene tetrabromide)

Alkynes react readily with potassium permanganate with formation of manganese dioxide and discharge of the permanganate color. Anhydrous hydrogen fluoride adds to the triple bond of acetylene to give vinyl fluoride and finally 1,1-difluoroethane.

$$HC{\equiv}CH \xrightarrow{\ HF\ } H_2C{=}CHF \xrightarrow{\ HF\ } CH_3\text{--}CHF_2$$

vinyl fluoride

Water adds to acetylene in the presence of sulfuric acid and mercuric sulfate.

$$CH{\equiv}CH\ +\ H_2O \xrightarrow[HgSO_4]{H_2SO_4} \left[CH_2{=}C\underset{OH}{\overset{H}{\big\backslash}} \right] \longrightarrow CH_3\text{--}C\underset{H}{\overset{O}{}}$$

vinyl alcohol　　　　　　　acetaldehyde

(unstable)

The product of addition of one molecule of water to acetylene is unstable and rearranges to a carbonyl compound, acetaldehyde. With alkyl-substituted acetylenes, addition of water always occurs in accord with Markownikoff's rule.

$$CH_3-C \equiv CH \ + \ H_2O \quad \xrightarrow[HgSO_4]{H_2SO_4} \quad \left[\begin{array}{c} OH \\ | \\ CH_3-C=CH_2 \end{array} \right] \quad \longrightarrow \quad \begin{array}{c} O \\ || \\ CH_3-C-CH_3 \end{array}$$

propyne   acetone

Acetylene dimerizes under the influence of aqueous cuprous ammonium chloride. This reaction is formally analogous to the dimerization of isobutylene

$$2\,HC \equiv CH \quad \xrightarrow{Cu(NH_3)_2^{\oplus}\ Cl^{\ominus}} \quad \begin{array}{c} H \quad H \\ \diagdown \quad | \\ C=C-C \equiv CH \\ \diagup \\ H \end{array}$$

butenyne

(vinylacetylene)

under the influence of sulfuric acid (see p. 154), but the details of the reaction mechanism are not known.

Cuprous, mercuric, and nickelic ions are often specific catalysts for reaction of alkynes—perhaps because of their ability to form complexes with triple bonds. Formation of such complexes causes the water solubilities of alkynes to increase in the presence of metal ions.

$$R-C \equiv C-R \ + \ Hg^{2\oplus} \quad \rightleftharpoons \quad \begin{array}{c} Hg^{2\oplus} \\ \uparrow \\ R-C \equiv C-R \end{array}$$

Alkynes, like alkenes, react with boron hydrides by addition of B—H across the carbon-carbon triple bond (cf., pp. 148-149) and give vinylboranes.

$$CH_3CH_2-C \equiv C-H \ + \ \begin{array}{c} R \\ \diagdown \\ B-H \\ \diagup \\ R \end{array} \quad \longrightarrow \quad \begin{array}{c} CH_3CH_2 \qquad H \\ \diagdown \quad\quad \diagup \\ C=C \\ \diagup \quad\quad \diagdown \\ H \qquad B-R \\ \qquad | \\ \qquad R \end{array}$$

(a vinylborane)

Vinylboranes react readily with acetic acid under mild conditions to give alkenes. The over-all process is quite stereospecific, for a disubstituted acetylene gives only a *cis* alkene. Evidently the boron hydride adds in a *cis* manner to the triple bond, and the vinylborane produced then reacts with acid to give the corresponding *cis* alkene.

$$CH_3CH_2 \quad \underset{C}{\overset{R}{\underset{|||}{\overset{|}{C}}}} \quad \overset{R}{\underset{|}{B}} \quad \longrightarrow \quad CH_3CH_2 \quad \underset{C}{\overset{B}{\underset{|}{\overset{R}{C}}}} \quad \xrightarrow[0°]{CH_3CO_2H} \quad CH_3CH_2 \quad H$$

3-hexyne   [1]   90% cis-3-hexene

EXERCISE 8-3   Show how each of the following compounds could be synthesized from the indicated starting material and appropriate inorganic reagents. Specify the reaction conditions, mention important side reactions, and justify the practicality of any isomer separations.

a. $CH_2=CH-\overset{Cl}{\underset{|}{C}}=CH_2$ from acetylene

b. CH_3CFHCH_2Br from methylacetylene

c. $CH_3CH_2COCH_3$ from 1-butyne

d. $\underset{H}{\overset{CH_3}{\diagdown}}C=C\underset{H}{\overset{CH_3}{\diagup}}$ from 2-butyne

e. $\underset{H}{\overset{CH_3CH_2}{\diagdown}}C=C\underset{D}{\overset{H}{\diagup}}$ from 1-butyne and deuteroacetic acid (CH_3CO_2D)

8-6   1-ALKYNES AS ACIDS

A characteristic and synthetically important reaction of acetylene and 1-alkynes is salt (or "acetylide") formation with very strong bases. In such reac-

$$R-C\equiv C:H \; + \; \overset{\oplus}{K}:\overset{\ominus}{NH_2} \quad \xrightarrow[\;\rightleftharpoons\;]{\overset{liquid}{NH_3}} \quad R-C\equiv C:\overset{\ominus}{} \; \overset{\oplus}{K} \; + \; :NH_3$$

R = H or alkyl   a potassium acetylide

tions, the alkynes behave as acids in the sense that they give up protons to suitably strong bases. Water is much too weakly basic to accept protons from alkynes, and consequently no measurable hydrogen ion is expected from the ionization of alkynes in dilute aqueous solutions. Nearly anhydrous potassium hydroxide will convert an appreciable fraction of acetylene itself to potassium acetylide, but the conversion is much more favorable with potassium amide in liquid ammonia.

Table 8-2 shows approximate ionization constants of a number of substances acting as acids. Of course, the salts of the weaker of these acids, with ionization constants much smaller than that of water (10^{-16}), will be essentially completely hydrolyzed in water solution.

Table 8-2   Approximate Ionization Constants, K_A, for Various Acids

Compound	$K_A{}^a$
$HClO_4$	$>10^{10}$
$CH_3-\overset{\overset{O}{\parallel}}{C}\overset{}{\underset{OH}{}}$ (OH proton)	2×10^{-5}
H_2O	10^{-16b}
CH_3CH_2OH (OH proton)	10^{-18}
$H–C\equiv C–H$	10^{-22}
NH_3	10^{-35}
$\overset{H}{\underset{H}{}}C=C\overset{H}{\underset{H}{}}$	$\sim 10^{-40}$
$CH_3–CH_3$	$<10^{-40}$

a The ionization constants are referred to water solution, whether actually measurable in water or not, and are equilibrium constants for the reaction

$$HA \xrightleftharpoons{H_2O} H^{\oplus} + A^{\ominus} \qquad K_A = [H^{\oplus}][A^{\ominus}]/[HA]$$

b The ionization constant employed here for water is the customary value of 10^{-14} divided by the concentration of water in pure water (55 M).

$$K^{\oplus} A^{\ominus} + H_2O \; \xrightleftharpoons{} \; HA + K^{\oplus} OH^{\ominus}$$

Consequently, ionization equilibria of very weak acids must be measured in solvents which are less acidic than water, such as ammonia, ethers, or, in some cases, even hydrocarbons. Usually, no solvent can be found in which a very weak acid ($K_A < 10^{-20}$) will dissociate significantly; so the strengths of such acids (e.g., HA_1 and HA_2) are determined relative to one another by determining the position of equilibria of the following type:

$$HA_1 + K^{\oplus} A_2^{\ominus} \rightleftharpoons K^{\oplus} A_1^{\ominus} + HA_2$$

Such measurements of relative acidities, carried out in appropriate solvents, permit, with a graded series of acids, the assignment of approximate ionization constants to even extremely weak acids, just as though they were directly determinable in water solution.

EXERCISE 8-4   Acetylene has an acid ionization constant (K_A) of $\sim 10^{-22}$.

a. Calculate the concentration of acetylide ion expected to be present in a 14 M solution of potassium hydroxide that is 0.01 M in acetylene (assuming ideal solutions).

b. Outline a practical method (or methods) that you think might be suitable to determine an approximate experimental value of K_A for acetylene, remembering that water has K_A of about 10^{-16}.

c. Would you expect H—C≡N to be a stronger acid than H—C≡C—H? Why?

Acetylene is less acidic than water, but 10^{13} times more acidic than ammonia, and at least 10^{18} times more acidic than ethylene or ethane. The large acidity of acetylene and 1-alkynes relative to other hydrocarbons can be simply explained by the repulsions between the electron pair of the C—H bond and the other carbon electrons (see also pp. 117-118). We shall compare the C—H bonds of an acetylene and an alkane. First, we note that the six electrons of the acetylenic triple bond are constrained between the two carbon nuclei. As a result, the average positions of these electrons are farther from the electron pair of the C—H bond than the corresponding six electrons of a saturated tetrahedral carbon.

Consequently, less repulsion is expected between the C—H electron pair and the other six carbon electrons for an acetylenic C—H than for a saturated C—H. The C—H electron pair of an acetylene will then be able to move closer to the carbon nucleus than is normal for a saturated carbon and, hence, the hydrogen will tend to be more positive and more easily removed by a proton acceptor than will a hydrogen of an alkane.

$$R\text{------}C\text{\,}\underset{\delta\ominus}{\equiv}\text{\,}\underset{\delta\oplus}{C}\text{----}H$$

In terms of degree, the very much larger acidity of acetylene as compared with an alkane is easily understood if one remembers that electrostatic forces depend upon the inverse square of the distance. A small average movement of electrons will cause a very large electrostatic effect at the short distances which correspond to atomic diameters.

A simple and useful test for a triple bond substituted with hydrogen is provided by reaction with silver ammonia solution. Acetylenes with a terminal triple bond give solid silver salts, while disubstituted acetylenes do not react. The silver acetylides appear to have substantially covalent carbon-metal bonds and are not true salts like calcium, sodium, and potassium acetylides. Silver

$$R-C{\equiv}C-H \; + \; \overset{\oplus}{Ag}(NH_3)_2 \; \longrightarrow \; \underline{R-C{\equiv}C-Ag} \; + \; NH_3 \; + \; \overset{\oplus}{NH_4}$$

(R = H or alkyl)   silver acetylide

ammonia solution may be used to precipitate terminal acetylenes from mixtures with disubstituted acetylenes. The monosubstituted acetylenes are easily regenerated from the silver precipitates by treatment with mineral acids or sodium cyanide. It should be noted that dry silver acetylides may be quite shock-sensitive and can decompose explosively.

SUPPLEMENTARY EXERCISES

8-5 Write structural formulas for each of the following, showing possible geometrical isomers:
   a. cyclopropene dibromide
   b. 2,4-hexadiene
   c. cyclooctyne
   d. dibromoacetylene
   e. 1,5-hexadien-3-yne

8-6 Calculate ΔH values from the bond-energy tables in Chapter 3 for the following reactions in the vapor state at 25°:
   a. $HC{\equiv}CH + Br_2 \rightarrow CHBr{=}CHBr$
   b. $CHBr{=}CHBr + Br_2 \rightarrow CHBr_2{-}CHBr_2$
   c. $HC{\equiv}CH + H_2O \rightarrow CH_2{=}CHOH$

   d. $CH_2{=}CHOH \; \longrightarrow \; CH_3\overset{O}{\overset{\|}{C}}{\diagdown}_H$

   e. $2\,HC{\equiv}CH \rightarrow H_2C{=}CH{-}C{\equiv}CH$
   f. $CH_3{-}C{\equiv}C{-}H \rightarrow CH_2{=}C{=}CH_2$
   g. Calculate also a ΔH for reaction (f) from the experimental ΔH values for the following reactions:

$$CH_3C{\equiv}CH + 2\,H_2 \rightarrow CH_3CH_2CH_3 \qquad \Delta H = -69.7\,\text{kcal}$$
$$CH_2{=}C{=}CH_2 + 2\,H_2 \rightarrow CH_3CH_2CH_3 \qquad \Delta H = -71.3\,\text{kcal}$$

Explain why the value of ΔH calculated from bond energies might be unreliable for the last reaction.

8-7   Suppose you were given four unlabeled bottles, each of which is known to contain one of the following compounds: n-pentane, 1-pentene, 2-pentyne, and 1-pentyne. Explain how you could use simple chemical tests (preferably test-tube reactions) to identify the contents of each bottle. (Note that all four compounds are low-boiling liquids.)

8-8   How would you distinguish between the compounds in each of the following pairs using (1) chemical methods (preferably test-tube reactions) and (2) spectroscopic methods:

   $a.$ $CH_3CH_2C{\equiv}CH$ and $CH_3C{\equiv}CCH_3$
   $b.$ $CH_3CH_2C{\equiv}CH$ and $CH_2{=}CH{-}CH{=}CH_2$
   $c.$ $C_6H_5C{\equiv}CC_6H_5$ and $C_6H_5CH_2CH_2C_6H_5$
   $d.$ $CH_3C{\equiv}CCH(CH_3)_2$ and $CH_3CH_2C{\equiv}CCH_2CH_3$

The Resonance Method and
Some of Its Applications.
The Molecular-Orbital Approach

The structural theory of organic chemistry originated and developed from the concept of the tetrahedral carbon atom. It has received powerful impetus from the electronic theory of valence along the lines described in Chapter 5. We can now express the structures of vast numbers of organic compounds by simple bond diagrams that can be readily translated into three-dimensional models compatible with a variety of molecular properties. Nevertheless, there are many compounds for which ordinary structural theory is inadequate because conventional structures do not provide reasonable descriptions of the actual molecules. Particularly noteworthy in this category are the aromatic hydrocarbons, or arenes, of which benzene (C_6H_6) is the most notable example. While these compounds resemble polyenes in having less than $(2n + 2)/n$ hydrogens per carbon, they possess chemical stability approaching that of alkanes.

Attempts to correlate the structure of arenes with their reactivity (or lack of it) taxed classical structural theory to the extreme—almost, in fact, to an impasse. New approaches led gradually to the development of the resonance method, which has been quite successful in accommodating many of the difficulties involved and has the marked advantage of being based on simple bond diagrams. In this chapter, after considering some aspects of chemical binding for very simple molecules, we shall outline qualitatively the resonance method and show some of its applications to stability, reactions, and spectra of organic compounds.

*An alternate means for formulation and prediction of the structures and properties of organic compounds, the **molecular-orbital** approach, is also discussed briefly in this chapter.*

The Resonance
Method and Some
of Its Applications.
The Molecular-
Orbital Approach

CHAPTER 9

9-1 ELECTRON-PAIR BONDS

The energy of a typical electron-pair bond between two atoms $(Y:Y)$ is found to depend strongly on the internuclear distance, as shown in Figure 9-1. The minimum in the curve corresponds to the normal equilibrium bond length (r_e) and the bond energy (D_e) for the stable unexcited molecule, Y—Y. At much shorter distances, the energy rises very rapidly because of internuclear repulsions. At much longer distances, the energy of the system approaches that of the two entirely free atoms. The distance r_e, which corresponds to the bond length at minimum energy, *increases* with atomic number as one goes down a column of the periodic table and the atoms get larger. It *decreases* across a horizontal row of the periodic table as the electronegativity of the atoms increases and the outer-shell electrons are attracted more toward the nuclei. Other things being the same, the stronger the bond is, the shorter r_e will be. The reason is that a strong bond more nearly overcomes the repulsive forces between the nuclei and thus permits them to move closer together. For bonds between carbon atoms, r_e usually ranges between about 1.20 and 1.55 A and, if

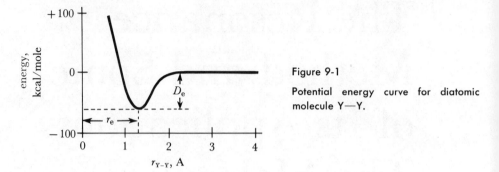

Figure 9-1

Potential energy curve for diatomic molecule Y—Y.

Figure 9-1 (or anything like it) applies to bonds between carbon atoms, we should not expect significant bonding at internuclear distances greater than 2 A.

In addition to electrostatic repulsion between the atomic nuclei of a simple molecule $Y:Y$, there are repulsions between the two bonding electrons. How, then, can we explain that a bond between separate $Y\cdot$ atoms is formed at all? The bonding energy may be considered to arise from attraction between the electrons and nuclei in the following way. The electrons in an electron-pair bond between two nuclei brought to distances near r_e (Figure 9-1) are equivalent and indistinguishable. That is, we are unable to identify one electron any more than the other with a given atom. The significance of the pairing of the electrons is that it permits each to have maximum possible freedom to move through the orbitals of the two-atom system rather than being "localized" on particular atoms (see pp. 107-108). Quantum mechanical calculations tell us that freedom of motion of the electrons is very important—as illustrated by the fact that fully five-sixths of the binding of the hydrogen molecule can be associated with the "delocalization" of the electrons between the two nuclei. Now, the basic point, which this chapter is designed to clarify, is that there are a great many compounds with structures in which electrons are delocalized over *more than two atoms*—and, in accord with the explanation advanced for the origin of bonding energy, such molecules possess an extra measure of stability over that expected for molecules with the same geometry but with electron pairs associated with just two atoms.

9-2 THE BENZENE PROBLEM

Benzene is an outstanding example of a molecule in which electron delocalization is important—and since we cannot assign all the electrons in pairs to bonds between specific nuclei, it is not possible to write a conventional bond structure for benzene that is consistent with its shape and reactivity. To fully appreciate the structural problem posed by benzene, however, we must first describe its properties.

Benzene is known, from X-ray diffraction and spectroscopic measurements, to be a flat molecule with six carbon atoms, 1.397 A apart, in a hexagonal ring. Six hydrogen atoms, one associated with each carbon, radiate out from the ring at distances of 1.09 A. All H—C—C and C—C—C angles are 120°.

In the preceding formula, all but one of the valence electrons of each carbon can be accounted for as electron-pair bonds. The fundamental question follows — should we now consider the remaining six electrons to be localized in pairs, as in the classical "cyclohexatriene" structure proposed for benzene by Kekulé in 1865? Apparently not, because this structure does not fit well with the properties of benzene. Thus, if benzene were to correspond to what we expect for

Kekule' formulation of benzene
as 1, 3, 5-cyclohexatriene

cyclohexatriene, the C—C bonds should not be of equal lengths and the reactivity of the compound should resemble that of 1,3,5-hexatriene.

$$CH_2{=}CH{-}CH{=}CH{-}CH{=}CH_2$$

Neither condition is fulfilled. In particular, hexatriene is highly reactive with a variety of reagents, and its behavior is in marked contrast to the stability of benzene with the same reagents, as illustrated by the reactions summarized in Table 9-1. The reagents that commonly *add* (in the dark) to the double bonds of alkenes (e.g., HBr, Cl_2, HOCl, H_2SO_4) attack benzene relatively slowly to *substitute* a hydrogen atom rather than to give addition products. Nevertheless, there can be no doubt that benzene is really unsaturated, since it can be hydrogenated (under forcing conditions compared with simple alkenes) to cyclohexane, and, in sunlight, adds chlorine or bromine to give 1,2,3,4,5,6-hexahalocyclohexanes. Also, benzene is attacked by ozone, and the products are those expected on the basis of Kekulé's cyclohexatriene structure.

  That benzene is more stable than can be anticipated for what we might call "classical" 1,3,5-cyclohexatriene can be gauged semiquantitatively from differences between heats of hydrogenation (or heats of combustion) observed for benzene and expected for 1,3,5-cyclohexatriene. To a first approximation, the hydrogenation of 1,3,5-cyclohexatriene should evolve three times as much heat as the hydrogenation of cyclohexene, since the former structure is considered to have three double bonds while the latter has one.

Table 9-1   Comparative Properties of Benzene and 1,3,5-Hexatriene

Benzene		1,3,5-Hexatriene	
Reagents	Products	Reagents	Products
HNO_3/H_2SO_4	nitrobenzene	HNO_3/H_2SO_4	instantaneous polymerization and oxidation
Br_2 (a metal bromide catalyst is necessary; $FeBr_3$)	bromobenzene	Br_2 (in $CHCl_3$ below 13°)	$BrCH_2-CH=CH$ $BrCH_2-CH=CH$ 1,6-dibromo-2,4-hexadiene
Br_2 (in sunlight)	hexabromocyclohexane		
H_2/PtO_2 catalyst in acetic acid for 25 hr. at 25° or $H_2/Ni/200°/200$ atm.	cyclohexane	H_2/PtO_2 catalyst in acetic acid for 1-2 hr. at 25°	$CH_3-CH_2-CH_2$ $CH_3-CH_2-CH_2$ n-hexane
Ozone (O_3)	triozonide ↓Zn/H_2O 3 glyoxal	Ozone (O_3)	triozonide ↓Zn/H_2O 2 H—C + 2 C—C
maleic anhydride	no reaction in the dark	(benzene as solvent)	Diels-Alder adduct (see Chapter 10)

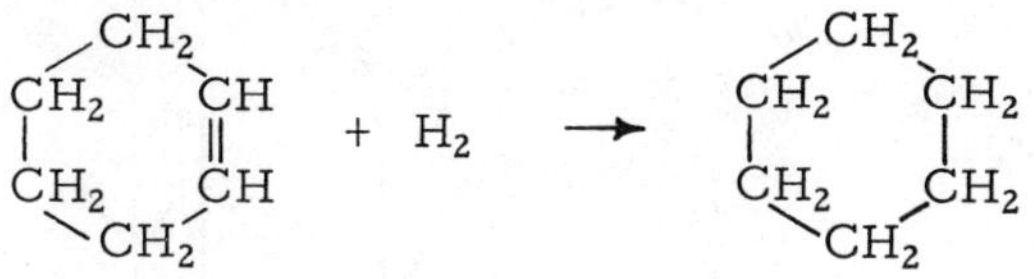

$$\text{cyclohexene} + H_2 \rightarrow \text{cyclohexane} \qquad \Delta H = -28.6 \text{ kcal/mole}$$

cyclohexene   cyclohexane

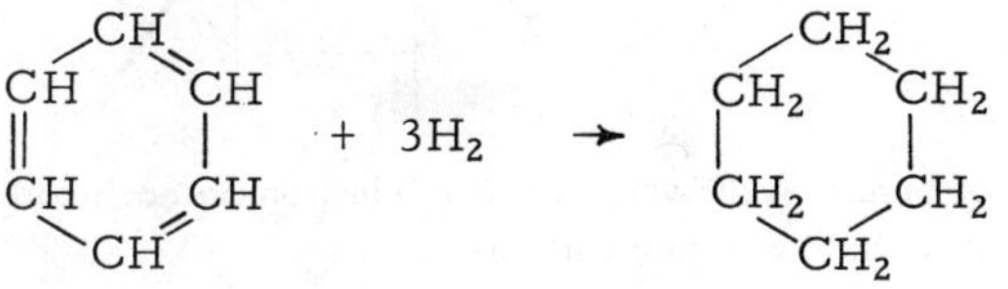

$$\text{"1,3,5-cyclohexatriene"} + 3H_2 \rightarrow \qquad \Delta H = 3 \times (-28.6)$$
$$= -85.8 \text{ kcal/mole}$$

"1, 3, 5-cyclohexatriene"

Actually, benzene evolves only 49.8 kcal/mole, or 36 kcal/mole *less* than anticipated for the cyclohexatriene.

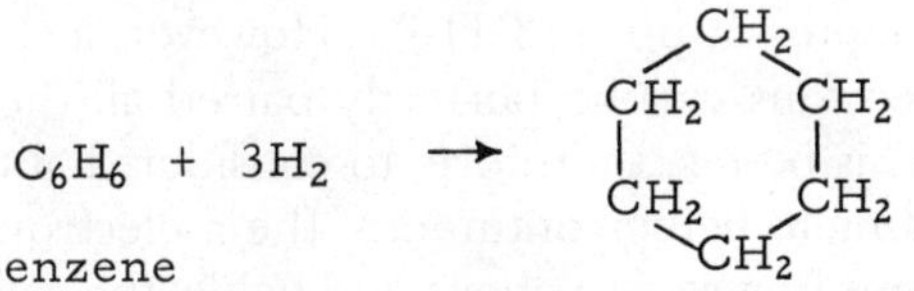

$$C_6H_6 + 3H_2 \rightarrow \qquad \Delta H = -49.8 \text{ kcal/mole}$$

benzene

Similarly, the heat of combustion of Kekulé's cyclohexatriene (to liquid water),
calculated from average bond energies, is 827 kcal/mole, while the experimental
heat of combustion of benzene is 789 kcal/mole, or 38 kcal/mole less than calculated for cyclohexatriene.   This 38 kcal we can call the **stabilization energy** of
benzene.   It is also often called the resonance energy, but we shall reserve this
term for the part of the stabilization that arises from electron delocalization (see
Section 9-6).

$$C_6H_6(g) + 15/2\ O_2(g) \rightarrow 6CO_2(g) + 3H_2O(l) \qquad \Delta H = -789 \text{ kcal/mole}$$

benzene

9-3   AN ATOMIC-ORBITAL MODEL OF BENZENE

Of the many bond structures that have been proposed for benzene, either before or since Kekulé's time, no single one may be accepted as satisfactory.
Atomic-orbital concepts, however, give a very acceptable description of benzene.
Each carbon atom in the ring can be taken as sp^2-hybridized and considered to
form three coplanar sp^2-hybrid σ bonds with bond angles of 120°.   These σ

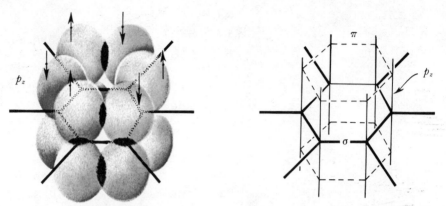

Figure 9-2   Atomic orbital model of benzene, showing how a p_z electron on each carbon can be paired with p_z electrons on both adjacent carbons.

bonds to carbon and hydrogen use three of the four valence electrons of each carbon. The total remaining six carbon electrons will be in p orbitals on adjacent carbons. We could formulate three π bonds, through overlap of adjacent p orbitals, occupied by electrons having paired spins—each of these bonds being similar to those for ethylene (see Chapter 5, pp. 113-116). However, a characteristic of benzene is that the π electrons can be perfectly paired all the way around the ring (see Figure 9-2). It is better, therefore, to consider that there are six π bonds and take the π bonding as being continuous, the π electrons being associated with all six carbon atoms in a region above and below the carbons of the ring. As mentioned previously, delocalization of the electrons indistinguishably over all six centers (as in benzene) is expected to correspond to a more stable electron distribution than any in which the electrons are considered to be localized in pairs between adjacent carbons (as in 1,3,5-cyclohexatriene).

9-4   ELECTRON-PAIRING SCHEMES—THE RESONANCE METHOD

We shall now reconsider the structure of benzene in terms of possible ways of pairing the six electrons in localized bonds. The atomic-orbital formulation immediately suggests two equivalent Kekulé structures [1] and [2]. Structures [3], [4], and [5] are also seen as acceptable ways of pairing the electrons within the planar hexagonal framework of the molecule. However, these latter structures clearly are energetically less favorable than the Kekulé forms because the atoms C_1—C_4, or C_2—C_5, or C_3—C_6 are too far apart (>2 A) for effective bond formation (see Figure 9-1). The dotted lines between distant carbon atoms in structures [3] through [5] are significant only in that they define a pairing scheme. Such lines are sometimes said to represent "formal" bonds.

[1]   [2]   [3]   [4]   [5]

According to the resonance method, the individual pairing schemes are taken to *contribute* to the actual structure of benzene to an extent that would lead to the most stable possible molecule of the *given* geometry. Benzene is considered to be a "hybrid" of the valence-bond structures [1], [2], [3], [4], and [5]. These structures are frequently called **resonance structures** and do not separately have physical reality or independent existence; indeed, the energy of the actual molecule is *less* than any one of the contributing structures. The double-headed arrow between the structures is used to indicate that they represent different electron-pairing schemes and not different substances in equilibrium.

When we use the resonance method we consider that the contribution of each of the several structures is to be weighted in some way that accords with the degree of bonding each would have if it represented an actual molecule with the specified geometry. Thus, the two Kekulé formulas are to be taken as contributing *equally* and *predominantly* to the hybrid structure of benzene, equally, because they are energetically equivalent and, predominantly, because they would contribute much more to over-all bonding than structures [3] through [5]. It follows that structures [3] through [5] can be essentially ignored in accounting for the properties of the normal state of actual benzene molecules.

In using the resonance method, we assume that all the resonance structures contributing to a given resonance hybrid have *exactly* the same spatial arrangements of the atoms but different pairing schemes for the electrons. Therefore, structures [3], [4], and [5] are not to be considered to be bicyclohexadiene [6], even though bicyclohexadiene has a similar electron pairing scheme, because bicyclohexadiene is a known (albeit unstable) nonplanar molecule with vastly different bond angles and bond lengths than benzene. Structures [3], [4], and [5] represent a grossly distorted bicyclohexadiene with each carbon at the corner of a regular hexagon and a formal bond in place of a carbon-carbon single bond.

[6]

Clearly, it is inconvenient and tedious to write down the structures of the contributing forms in order to show the structure of a resonance hybrid. A shorthand notation is therefore desirable. Frequently, dotted rather than full lines are used where the bonding electrons are delocalized over several atoms. For benzene, this would be formula [7] in place of structures [1] and [2].

or

[7]

However, it is current practice (whether desirable or not) to use a single Kekulé structure, [1] or [2], to represent benzene with the implicit understanding that the C—C bonds are all equivalent. In recent years, benzene has often been represented as a hexagon with an inscribed circle. This is a wonderfully simple notation for benzene but is quite uninformative and is even misleading with many other aromatic hydrocarbons.

EXERCISE 9-1   Discuss the meaning and merit of a statement such as "compound X resonates between forms A and B" in terms of a specific example.

9-5 RULES FOR USE OF THE RESONANCE METHOD

The discussion of the application of the resonance method to benzene in Section 9-3 may be reduced to a fairly concise prescription which is generally applicable for evaluating the properties of unsaturated systems.

1. All resonance structures are assigned (and must have) the same number of paired electrons and are evaluated for identical locations of the atoms in space. Ionic structures should also be considered if elements of widely different electron-attracting powers are present.

2. The relative energies of the various structures are estimated by considering: (a) bond energies (the formal bonds being counted as contributing no stabilization); (b) the degree of distortion from the geometrically favorable atomic positions; and (c) atomic electron-attracting powers (for ionic structures). If the geometry of the actual molecule is known, then the spatial arrangements of all the resonance structures can be taken to conform with it.

3. The electron stabilization is expected to be greatest when there are two (or more) equivalent structures of lowest energy. As a corollary, the structure of a

molecule is least likely to be satisfactorily represented by a conventional valence diagram when two (or more) energetically equivalent, lowest-energy structures may be written.

4. If there is only a single contributing structure of low energy, then, to a first approximation, the resonance hybrid may be assigned properties like those expected for that structure.

A. 1,3-Butadiene and Cyclobutene

Possible pairing schemes for 1,3-butadiene and cyclobutene are shown by formulas [8] and [9]. The positions of the atoms in these formulas correspond approximately to the configurations shown by experiment to be most stable.

[8a]   [8b]

[9a]   [9b]

These substances represent physically distinct structural isomers and *not* resonance structures, because of the difference in their geometries. Two pairing schemes may be written for both compounds, [8a], [8b] and [9a], [9b]. For butadiene, structure [8b] has a formal single bond about 4 A long—hence is not expected to make much of a contribution to the structure of butadiene, which can therefore best be represented as [8a]. For cyclobutene, structure [9b] is quite unreasonable, since it represents a grossly distorted butadiene and must therefore have an unfavorably high energy. Cyclobutene is closely approximated by the classical structure [9a], but the molecule is actually *less* stable than indicated from bond energies for the classical structure because of angle strain in the small ring.

EXERCISE 9-2   Evaluate the relative stabilities of actual molecules of butadiene in each of the three forms shown in Figure 9-3 from the standpoint of steric effects and the resonance method. Give your reasoning.

EXERCISE 9-3   Consider possible resonance forms for 1,3,5-hexatriene and write a dashed-line structure that reflects the contributions of the various forms.

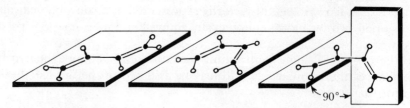

Figure 9-3   Different conformations of 1,3-butadiene.   See Exercise 9-2.

EXERCISE 9-4   Consider the importance of the following resonance for cyclobutene (give your reasoning in detail):

$$
\begin{array}{cc}
CH_2\!-\!CH & CH_2 \quad CH \\
|\qquad\ \| & \|\qquad \| \\
CH_2\!-\!CH & CH_2 \quad CH
\end{array}
\qquad \longleftrightarrow
$$

Explain what differences in geometry one would expect for a hybrid of such structures as compared with conventional cyclobutene geometry.

B. Acrolein

Acrolein ($CH_2{=}CH{-}CH{=}O$) is well approximated by structures [10a] through [10d].

$$CH_2{=}CH{-}CH{=}\overset{..}{O}: \cdot \longleftrightarrow CH_2{-}CH{=}CH{-}\overset{..}{O}: \longleftrightarrow$$

[10a]   [10b]

$$CH_2{=}CH{-}\overset{\oplus}{CH}{-}\overset{..}{\underset{..}{O}}\overset{\ominus}{:} \longleftrightarrow \overset{\oplus}{CH_2}{-}CH{=}CH{-}\overset{..}{\underset{..}{O}}\overset{\ominus}{:}$$

[10c]   [10d]

The hybrid structure may be abbreviated as in [11]

$$\overset{\delta\oplus}{CH_2}{\cdots}\overset{\delta\oplus}{CH}{\cdots}\overset{2\,\delta\ominus}{CH}{\cdots}O$$

[11]

in which the unsaturation is indicated as alternately heavy and lightly dotted extra bonds. The lightly dotted line is meant to indicate that structures [10b] and [10d] contribute little to the hybrid and thus the extent of double-bond character of the central bond is expected to be small. The greatest contribution is made by [10a]. Ionic structures, however, should be given careful consideration when elements of widely different electron-attracting powers are present; hence structures [10c] and [10d] should not be overlooked — their importance is largely felt when the molecule is excited by light energy, as will be explained later. Structures with positive oxygen and negative carbon, [12a] and [12b], need not be considered for the normal molecule because carbon is much less electron-attracting than oxygen.

$$CH_2=CH-\overset{\ominus}{\overset{\cdot\cdot}{C}}H-\overset{\oplus}{\underset{\cdot\cdot}{O}}: \longleftrightarrow \overset{\ominus}{C}H_2-CH=CH-\overset{\oplus}{\underset{\cdot\cdot}{O}}:$$

$$[12a] \qquad\qquad\qquad [12b]$$

unfavorable structures

C. The Carboxylate Anion

The anions, $RCO_2^{\ominus}$, formed by the reaction of carboxylic acids, RCO_2H, with bases, turn out to be poorly represented by the classical structure

$$R-\overset{\overset{\displaystyle O}{\|}}{\underset{\displaystyle O^{\ominus}}{C}}$$

This kind of anion has a specially favorable opportunity for resonance since there are two energetically equivalent pairing schemes ([13a] and [13b]) that may be written, and the anion is best considered as a hybrid of both structures.

$$[13a] \qquad\qquad [13b]$$

The additional structures [14a] and [14b] must be less important because they represent electrostatic rather than covalent bonding. Of the two, [14a] is sure to be the more favorable, because [14b] has like charges located on adjacent atoms and the polarity of the carbon-oxygen bond is reversed from normal.

$$[14a] \qquad\qquad [14b]$$

Write resonance structures similar to [13] and [14] for the enolate anion, $CH_2{=}CH{-}O^{\ominus}$. Assess the relative importance of the structures and draw a suitable hybrid structure. Predict the most likely positions of the atoms for the anion in its most stable configuration.

D. The Allyl Cation

An especially important type of carbonium ion is represented by the allyl cation, $CH_2{=}CH{-}CH_2^{\oplus}$. This ion can be formulated as two equivalent structures, [15a] and [15b].

$$\overset{\oplus}{CH_2{=}CH{-}CH_2} \quad \longleftrightarrow \quad \overset{\oplus}{CH_2}{-}CH{=}CH_2 \quad \sim \quad \overset{\frac{1}{2}\oplus}{CH_2}{=\!=\!=\!}CH{=\!=\!=\!}\overset{\frac{1}{2}\oplus}{CH_2}$$

$$[15a] \hspace{8em} [15b]$$

As a result we should expect the allyl cation to be appreciably more stable than other carbonium ions whose structures are well represented by a single classical formula (e.g., $CH_3CH_2^{\oplus}$). This certainly appears to be the case, because reactions that involve cationic intermediates usually proceed much more readily when an allylic-type cation can be produced than when an ethyl or n-propyl cation would be formed (p. 146).

The hybrid nature of allylic cations also serves to explain the seemingly anomalous behavior of conjugated alkadienes, such as 1,3-butadiene, in electrophilic addition reactions. For example, butadiene with 1 mole of chlorine yields the "normal" product, 1,2-dichloro-3-butene, and an "abnormal" product, 1,4-dichloro-2-butene.

$$CH_2{=}CH{-}CH{=}CH_2 + Cl_2 \rightarrow \underset{Cl \quad Cl}{CH_2{-}CH{-}CH{=}CH_2} + \underset{Cl \hspace{4em} Cl}{CH_2{-}CH{=}CH{-}CH_2}$$

The proportions of each isomer formed varies with the reaction conditions. According to the mechanism proposed for the addition of halogens to simple alkenes (pp. 138-141), the chlorine molecule may be considered to attack one of the double bonds of butadiene in a stepwise manner to first form a cationic intermediate. This intermediate is a stabilized, substituted-allyl cation, which can be represented as a hybrid of structures [16a] and [16b].

$$CH_2{=}CH{-}CH{=}CH_2 \xrightarrow{\ Cl_2\ } ClCH_2{-}\overset{\oplus}{CH}{-}CH{=}CH_2 \leftrightarrow ClCH_2{-}CH{=}CH{-}\overset{\oplus}{CH_2}$$

$$[16a] \hspace{10em} [16b]$$

$$\text{or}$$

$$ClCH_2{-}\overset{\delta\oplus}{CH}{=\!=\!=\!}CH{=\!=\!=\!}\overset{\delta\oplus}{CH_2}$$

In effect, the carbon atoms located at the 2- and 4-positions of the cation are both partially electron deficient. Therefore, a chloride ion has the choice of attacking C2 to give 1,2-dichloro-3-butene or C4 to give 1,4-dichloro-2-butene.

$$ClCH_2-CH=CH-CH_2\overset{.}{Cl}$$

1, 4-dichloro-2-butene

$$\overset{\delta\oplus}{\cancel{C}lCH_2}-CH=CH=CH_2 \quad \overset{\delta\oplus}{} \quad \overset{\ominus}{Cl}$$

$$ClCH_2-\underset{\underset{Cl}{|}}{CH}-CH=CH_2$$

1, 2-dichloro-3-butene

Bromine and hypochlorous acid react similarly with butadiene to give mixtures of 1,4- and 1,2-addition products.

$$CH_2=CH-CH=CH_2$$

$$\xrightarrow{Br_2} CH_2=CH-\underset{\underset{Br}{|}}{CH}-\underset{\underset{Br}{|}}{CH_2} + BrCH_2-CH=CH-CH_2Br$$

$$\xrightarrow{HOCl} CH_2=CH-\underset{\underset{OH}{|}}{CH}-\underset{\underset{Cl}{|}}{CH_2} + HOCH_2-CH=CH-CH_2Cl$$

E. The Cyclopentadienate Anion

The hydrogens of the —CH_2— group of the hydrocarbon 1,3-cyclopenta-diene are acidic, in fact, considerably more acidic than the acetylenic hydrogens of the 1-alkynes (pp. 171-173). This means that cyclopentadiene is some 10^{30} times more acidic than the ordinary alkanes. The reason is that loss of one of the —CH_2— protons of cyclopentadiene results in formation of an especially stabilized anion.

$$\underset{\overset{CH}{\diagdown}\underset{CH_2}{\diagup}}{\overset{CH-CH}{\|\quad\quad\|}}\overset{CH}{} \quad \underset{\overset{-H^{\oplus}}{\xrightleftharpoons{}}}{+H^{\oplus}} \quad \underset{\overset{CH}{\diagdown}\underset{\underset{\ominus}{CH}}{\diagup}}{\overset{CH-CH}{\|\quad\quad\|}}\overset{CH}{}$$

The structure of the anion may be described as a resonance hybrid of *five* energetically equivalent structures [17a] through [17e]. The unshared electron pair is therefore delocalized over five carbon atoms, and we expect the resulting delocalized anion to be much more stable than is expected for any *one* of the equivalent localized structures.

[17a]   [17b]   [17c]   [17d]   [17e]

or

After the success of the resonance method in accounting for the high acidity of cyclopentadiene, it comes as a surprise that the cyclopentadienyl cation is not comparably stabilized.   Five resonance forms, [18a] through [18e], can be written for the cation just like [17a] through [17e], and yet this cation appears to be so unstable that it has so far eluded all attempts to establish its existence even as

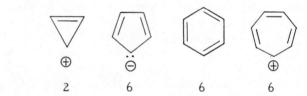

[18a]   [18b]   [18c]   [18d]   [18e]

a transient intermediate.   Apparently in *cyclic* systems of this general type, besides electron delocalization, some other factor is highly important—which is the total number of π electrons.   When a monocyclic conjugated system has 2, 6, 10, 14, etc., π electrons, it turns out to have a greater degree of stability than similar systems with 4, 8, 12, etc., electrons.   Thus, entities such as the following are relatively stable:

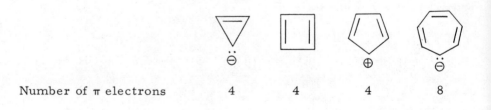

Number of π electrons   2   6   6   6

In marked contrast, it has not been possible to demonstrate the stable existence of any of the following substances except the last one, which is very much more difficult to prepare than the cyclopentadienate anion:

Number of π electrons   4   4   4   8

This body of fact provides perhaps the most troublesome deficiency in the application of the simple resonance method to organic chemistry.

EXERCISE 9-6   Evaluate the importance of resonance of the following types (it may be helpful to use ball-and-stick models):

a. [cyclopentadienyl structures] $\leftrightarrow$ [structure] $\leftrightarrow$ [structure] $\leftrightarrow$ etc.

b. [benzene ring structure] $\leftrightarrow$ [structure] $\leftrightarrow$ [structure]

c. $CH_2=CH-\overset{\oplus}{O}$ $\longleftrightarrow$ $\overset{\oplus}{C}H_2-CH=O$

d. [cyclic structure with $CH=CH$, CH, $\overset{\oplus}{C}$, CH_2, CH_2-CH_2] $\leftrightarrow$ [cyclic structure with $\overset{\oplus}{C}H-CH$, CH, C, CH_2, CH_2-CH_2]

e. [structure with CH, CH_2, $\overset{\oplus}{C}H_2$] $\longleftrightarrow$ [structure with $\overset{\oplus}{C}H$, CH_2-CH_2]

f. [cyclopropane with CH_2, CH_2, $CH-\overset{\oplus}{C}H_2$] $\longleftrightarrow$ [structure with $\overset{\oplus}{C}H_2$, CH_2, $CH=CH_2$]

g. $F-\underset{F}{\overset{F}{C}}-\overset{\ominus}{O}$ $\longleftrightarrow$ $F-\underset{F}{C}=O$ with $\overset{\ominus}{F}$

9-6 STABILIZATION AND RESONANCE ENERGY

It was shown earlier that the heat of combustion of benzene is 36 to 38 kcal/ mole *less* than calculated for the hypothetical molecule 1,3,5-cyclohexatriene.

We choose to call this energy difference the **stabilization energy** (S.E.) of benzene. An important part of this energy can be considered to be derived from the fact that the π electrons are less localized in benzene than would be the case for 1,3,5-cyclohexatriene. The stability gained by the delocalization of electrons can be called the **resonance energy** (R.E.), but stabilization and resonance energies are not necessarily equal, since the former is the net of all effects, both stabilizing and destabilizing. Thus, S.E. values derived from heats of combustion are usually calculated from a set of bond energies that neglects changes in bond strength caused by environment. For instance, *primary, secondary, tertiary,* vinyl, and acetylenic C—H bonds are assumed to have equal energies; C—C single bonds are taken as equal, regardless of whether the *other* bonds to the carbon atoms in question are single or multiple; differences in energy between double bonds that are mono-, di-, tri-, or tetra-substituted are neglected, as are often decreases in bond energies associated with steric strain. Bond energies are strictly applicable to molecules in which the bonds are of the normal lengths. In the case of benzene, which has C—C bonds with lengths intermediate between normal single and double bonds, there seems to be no clear agreement as to how to take the bond distances into account in computing the resonance energy. In spite of these shortcomings, bond energies, and hence stabilization energies, can be used to obtain a good qualitative idea of the importance of electron delocalization in organic molecules.

Tables 9-2 and 9-3 show the stabilization energies of several compounds that seem best represented as hybrid structures; and for these compounds the S.E. values are unquestionably large enough to indicate that resonance stabilization is significant. Many of the compounds in Table 9-2 have structures like that of benzene, and since their stability sets them apart from the open-chain conjugated polyenes, details of their chemistry are usually treated separately from those of the polyenes. Accordingly, much of the chemistry of these substances, which are called **aromatic compounds,** is discussed in later chapters of this book.

In Table 9-4 the stabilization energies of several conjugated polyenes are recorded. These are considerably smaller than the S.E. values of Table 9-2, and we are less confident that resonance is to be regarded as important for these molecules. The low stabilization energy of cyclooctatetraene may appear surprising, because it might seem that the π electrons should be delocalized in an eight-membered ring, much as they are in the six-membered benzene ring. However, electron and X-ray diffraction experiments show that cyclooctatetraene is not a planar molecule—it has in fact a tub, or boatlike, shape, with alternating carbon-carbon bond distances of 1.334 and 1.462 A. Since the p orbitals cannot overlap effectively in a nonplanar conformation (see Figure 9-4), extensive delocalization is precluded. Apparently, angle strain in the cyclooctatetraene ring (when planar) is large enough to outweigh any resonance energy that might be gained thereby. This may be regarded as one of many known examples of *steric inhibition of resonance* (where a hybrid structure has such an unfavorable geometry on steric grounds as to preclude consideration of resonance). In any event, the gain of stabilization through electron delocalization is likely to be small because the substance has a conjugated monocyclic system with *eight* π electrons (see p. 190).

Table 9-2   Stabilization Energies (or Approximate Resonance Energies) from
Heats of Combustion of Some Aromatic Compounds

Compound	Structure (as commonly written)	$\Delta H_{calc.}$ [a]	$\Delta H_{obs.}$	S.E.
benzene		827	789	38
toluene	—CH₃	983	944	39
biphenyl		1597	1514	83
biphenylene		1540	1481	59
naphthalene		1321	1250	71
azulene		1321	1279	42
anthracene		1816	1712	104
phenanthrene		1816	1705	111
pyridine	N	696	675	21
aniline	—NH₂	865	824	41
phenol	—OH	789	749	40

[a] Calculated from bond energies in Table 3–5, and from the heat of vaporization of water taken as 10 kcal/mole.

Table 9-3　Stabilization Energies Calculated from Heats of Combustion for Derivatives of Carboxylic Acids

Compound	Structure (as commonly written)	$\Delta H_{calc.}$[a]	$\Delta H_{obs.}$	S.E.
acetic acid	$CH_3-\overset{\overset{\displaystyle O}{\|\|}}{C}-OH$	238	220	18
methyl acetate	$CH_3-\overset{\overset{\displaystyle O}{\|\|}}{C}-OCH_3$	404	389	15
acetic anhydride	$CH_3-\overset{\overset{\displaystyle O}{\|\|}}{C}-O-\overset{\overset{\displaystyle O}{\|\|}}{C}-CH_3$	467	441	26
acetamide	$CH_3-\overset{\overset{\displaystyle O}{\|\|}}{C}-NH_2$	314	303	11
methyl carbonate	$CH_3-O-\overset{\overset{\displaystyle O}{\|\|}}{C}-O-CH_3$	375	350	25
urea	$H_2N-\overset{\overset{\displaystyle O}{\|\|}}{C}-NH_2$	195	172	23

[a] Calculated from bond energies in Table 3–5, and from the heat of vaporization of water taken as 10 kcal/mole.

Table 9-4　Stabilization Energies (S.E.) from Heats of Combustion (ΔH) of Some Conjugated Polyènes

Compound	Structure	$\Delta H_{calc.}$	$\Delta H_{obs.}$	S.E.
1,3-butadiene	$CH_2=CH-CH=CH_2$	608	608	
1,3-pentadiene	$CH_2=CH-CH=CHCH_3$	765	762	3
2-methyl-1,3-butadiene (isoprene)	$CH_2=CH-\underset{\underset{\displaystyle CH_3}{\|}}{C}=CH_2$	765	762	3
cycloöctatetraene		1103	1095	8
benzoquinone	$O=\!\!\!\!\!\bigcirc\!\!\!\!\!=O$	677	672	5

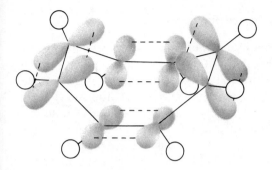

Figure 9-4

Atomic orbital model of π-electron system of nonplanar cycloöctatetraene.

EXERCISE 9-7   Calculate stabilization energies for the following compounds from their heats of hydrogenation and the heat of hydrogenation of 1-butene (30.3 kcal/mole) and cyclohexene (28.6 kcal/mole):

Compound	ΔH (hydrogenation), kcal/mole	Compound	ΔH (hydrogenation), kcal/mole
1,3-butadiene	-57.1	1,3-cyclohexadiene	-55.4
1,3-pentadiene	-54.1	phenylethylene	-77.5
1,4-pentadiene	-60.8	(styrene)	

Would you consider these stabilization energy values to be more reliable than those obtained from heats of combustion? Explain.

EXERCISE 9-8   a. The experimental $-\Delta H$ (25°C) is 707.7 kcal for combustion of gaseous 1,3-cyclopentadiene to carbon dioxide and liquid water. Compute from this value (and any required bond energies) a stabilization energy for cyclopentadiene. Show your method. Discuss briefly any uncertainties that might arise in estimating a resonance energy for cyclopentadiene which would not be similarly important for butadiene.

b. Evaluate as best you can the relative importance of resonance for 1,3-butadiene and 1,3-cyclopentadiene by consideration of the geometries of possible resonance structures.

EXERCISE 9-9   Suggest a reason why (a) the stabilization energy of biphenylene is less than twice that of benzene, and (b) why the heat of combustion of naphthalene is less than that of azulene.

EXERCISE 9-10   Calculate the heats of the following reactions in the vapor phase at 25° C with the aid of bond energies and the tables of stabilization energies on pp. 193-194.

a. $CH_3CH_2OH + O_2 \rightarrow CH_3CO_2H + H_2O$

b. $CH_3\!-\!C(OCH_3)_3 + 2CH_3CO_2H \rightarrow 3CH_3CO_2CH_3 + H_2O$

$$c. \quad 2CH_3OH + CO_2 \rightarrow CH_3\!-\!O\!-\!\overset{\displaystyle O}{\overset{\displaystyle \|}{C}}\!-\!O\!-\!CH_3 + H_2O$$

9-7   RESONANCE AND ABSORPTION SPECTRA

The electronic spectra of organic molecules were discussed briefly in Chapter 2, and it will be recalled that the absorption of ultraviolet radiation by ethylene at wavelengths near 1800 A corresponds to the excitation of one of the double-bond π electrons to an orbital of higher energy (i.e., $\pi \rightarrow \pi^*$ transition). The simple expectation is that an alkene with two or more double bonds would give an absorption spectrum similar to that of ethylene but of increased intensity, because the number of double bonds is greater. This is more or less true for compounds such as 1,4-pentadiene (H_2C=CH—CH_2—CH=CH_2) and 1,3-dimethylenecyclobutane (CH_2=⟨◇⟩=CH_2) with isolated double bonds, but it is *not* true for compounds such as 1,3-butadiene (CH_2=CH—CH=CH_2) and styrene (⟨⎔⟩—CH=CH_2), which have **conjugated** double bonds. In general, conjugated systems absorb light of longer wavelengths and with greater intensity than a comparable system of isolated double bonds.

For example, although ethylene does not absorb beyond 2000 A, 1,3-butadiene absorbs intensely at 2170 A. We may conclude that, as far as light absorption is concerned, the conjugated double bonds of butadiene are not independent of each other, and the electronic excitation produced by light of wavelength near 2170 A is associated with the double-bond system as a whole. Furthermore, since butadiene absorbs at longer wavelengths than ethylene or 1,4-pentadiene, the difference in energy between the normal and excited states of butadiene must be *less* than for ethylene or 1,4-pentadiene.[1] Clearly, if the excited electron in butadiene is delocalized over four carbon atoms rather than two, the excited state will be relatively stable. This is actually the case. The electronic excitation energy required for butadiene or any conjugated polyene is relatively small primarily because of resonance stabilization of the excited state.

One may inquire why resonance manifests itself more in the excited state of a conjugated polyene than in the normal state, and what is the hybrid structure of the excited state(s). The two questions are very closely related, but unfortunately, it is not easy to provide a simple explanation. The difficulty lies in our inability to draw very explicit structures for the excited states of molecules with conventional bond diagrams. However, of the many conventional pairing schemes that may be written for butadiene, three of which ([19] through [21])

$$CH_2=CH-CH=CH_2 \qquad \overset{\oplus}{C}H_2-CH=CH-\overset{\ominus}{\underset{..}{C}}H_2 \qquad \overset{\uparrow\text{-------------}\downarrow}{CH_2-CH=CH-CH_2}$$

$$[19] \qquad\qquad\qquad [20] \qquad\qquad\qquad\qquad [21]$$

---

[1] The difference in energy ΔE between the normal and excited states is related to the frequency (ν sec^{-1}) of the absorbed radiation such that $\Delta E = h\nu$, where h is Planck's constant; the frequency is in turn related to the wavelength (λ cm) by $\nu = c/\lambda$, where c is the velocity of light. Thus, electronic excitation at low frequencies or long wavelengths means that ΔE is small (i.e., the excited state is close to the ground or normal state).

are shown here, only *one* structure [19] has a low enough energy to be important for the normal state of butadiene. Therefore, resonance is unimportant in the normal state of butadiene. However, when the molecule is excited so that its energy becomes closer to the energies of structures [20] and [21] than to [19], resonance becomes important because [19] and [20], and other structures of comparably high energy, can now make substantial contributions to the hybrid structure of the excited state. The actual energy of the excited state is therefore lower than any one of the high-energy structures [20] and [21], etc.

The more extended the conjugated system becomes, the smaller is the energy

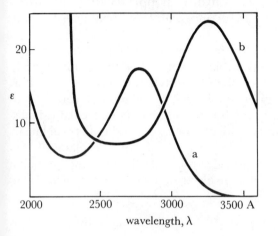

Figure 9-5

Ultraviolet spectra of methyl ethyl ketone (a) and methyl vinyl ketone (b) in cyclohexane solution.

difference between the normal and excited states. Thus, the diphenylpolyenes, C_6H_5—$(CH=CH)_n$—C_6H_5, absorb light at progressively longer wavelengths as n increases; this is apparent from the colors of these compounds, which range from colorless ($n = 1$) through yellow and orange ($n = 2$–7) to red ($n = 8$) as the wavelength increases from the ultraviolet well into the visible region of the electromagnetic spectrum.

Resonance in excited states is not restricted to compounds with conjugated carbon-carbon double bonds, for compounds with conjugated $C=N$ and $C=O$ bonds show analogous spectral effects. To illustrate, the ultraviolet spectra of methyl ethyl ketone $(CH_3\overset{\text{O}}{\overset{\|}{C}}CH_2CH_3)$ and methyl vinyl ketone $(CH_3\overset{\text{O}}{\overset{\|}{C}}CH=CH_2)$ in the region 2000 to 3500 A are shown in Figure 9-5. The band at 2770 A for methyl ethyl ketone is due to excitation of an electron from one of the unshared electron pairs on oxygen (i.e., $n \to \pi^*$ transition). In methyl vinyl ketone, this band shifts to longer wavelengths (3240 A) and is more intense. There is also an intense absorption centered on 2190 A in the spectrum of methyl vinyl ketone which is due to the excitation of one of the π electrons of the conjugated system $C=C$—$C=O$ (i.e., a $\pi \to \pi^*$ transition). A comparable band for the carbonyl group of methyl ethyl ketone is not shown in Figure 9-5 because it occurs at much shorter wavelengths, about 1850 A, which is out of the range of the spectrometer used.

9-8 MOLECULAR ORBITAL THEORY

The molecular orbital approach is a currently popular alternative to the resonance method for qualitative explanation and prediction of the properties of unsaturated systems.   In principle, molecular orbital theory is simple in that molecules are assumed to have molecular orbitals with different energies in a manner analogous to the atomic orbitals of hydrogen (pp. 103-107).   Electrons are then assigned to these orbitals in accordance with the orbital energies and Hund's rule (where applicable).

In practice, the molecular orbitals are, for want of better models, approximated by linear combinations of atomic orbitals centered on the various nuclei. This is called the **linear combination** of **atomic orbitals** (LCAO) method.   For benzene, exactly the same framework of atomic orbitals and σ bonds can be used as for the resonance method (on p. 182).   It turns out that six molecular orbitals can be constructed out of various independent and properly symmetrical linear combinations of the six $2p$-carbon orbitals perpendicular to the plane of the benzene ring.   The six extra "unsaturation electrons" are then assigned in pairs to the three lowest of these orbitals to give an electron "configuration" which can be represented schematically as follows:

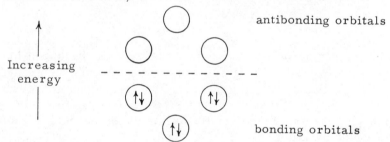

The upper (and here vacant) orbitals are of such energy that electrons in them would not contribute to binding the nuclei together; they are antibonding orbitals.

EXERCISE 9-11   The LCAO molecular orbitals of the cyclopentadienate system (C_5H_5) described on pp. 189-190 have schematic energies as follows:

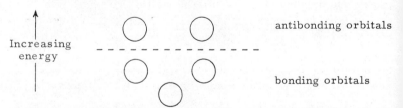

Indicate a possible point of difference between $C_5H_5^{\oplus}$ and $C_5H_5^{\ominus}$ that can be deduced from molecular orbital theory.

The LCAO method is far easier to use in actual numerical calculations[1] than the "valence-bond" method, which is the mathematical counterpart of the resonance approach. Molecular orbital theory is often employed qualitatively by assigning electrons to π-orbital systems such as the one discussed for benzene. Representation of the resulting entity with all its components is artistically taxing at the very least. It is therefore common to finesse the finer details and to depict the whole as a simple dotted-line formula similar to a resonance hybrid (p. 184). For benzene this would be

$$\begin{pmatrix} \sigma\text{-bond framework} \\ \text{of benzene with six} \\ \text{empty } p \text{ atomic} \\ \text{orbitals} \end{pmatrix}^{6\oplus} + \text{ 6 electrons } \rightarrow \begin{array}{l} \text{Benzene with three} \\ \text{bonding molecular} \\ \text{orbitals containing} \\ \text{six electrons} \end{array} \equiv$$

Such representations are singularly uninformative and may, in fact, lead to quite erroneous conclusions. In the authors' opinion, molecular orbital theory is much less suited to qualitative treatment of organic molecules than is the resonance method. We shall illustrate the difficulties by two different examples and wish to make clear that these difficulties arise only in the qualitative treatment.

Consider the π-electron systems of butadiene and trimethylenemethyl, each of which is C_4H_6 (Figure 9-6). If we postulate each system to give four molecular orbitals into which the four unsaturation electrons are placed, and then draw dotted lines between the adjacent carbons, we can see no reason for any pronounced difference between the two possible arrangements. On the other hand, inspection of possible electron-pairing schemes (as in the resonance method) leads immediately to the conclusion that butadiene is likely to be very different from trimethylenemethyl (Figure 9-7). The latter will be a diradical if there is to be an average of one electron per carbon and if each electron is to be paired with an electron on an *adjacent* carbon. A more detailed LCAO treatment of

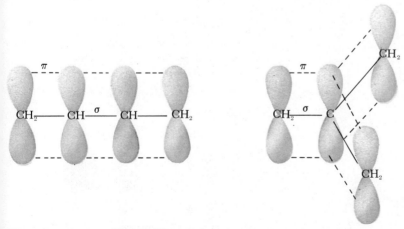

Figure 9-6   Atomic orbital models of 1,3-butadiene and trimethylenemethyl.

[1] J. D. Roberts, "Notes on Molecular Orbital Calculations," Benjamin, New York, 1961.

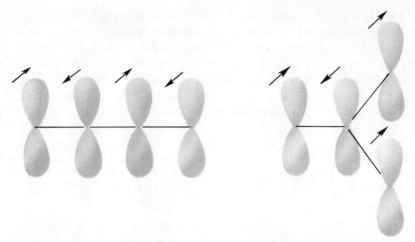

Figure 9-7   Electron-pairing schemes for 1,3-butadiene and trimethylenemethyl.

trimethylenemethyl agrees with the simple resonance method in suggesting that the substance would be a diradical, but this is difficult to deduce qualitatively.

Another (and very common) example of the failure of qualitative molecular orbital theory in simple systems is provided by the allyl cation that was discussed by the resonance approach on p. 188. Here we have three p orbitals in the π system and two electrons (Figure 9-8). The qualitative molecular orbital picture suggests that the two electrons are spread out more or less evenly over the three orbitals with, perhaps, part of the positive charge being associated with each carbon atom. This is not in accord with the experimental facts (or a detailed LCAO calculation), which suggest that the charge is primarily, if not exclusively, centered on the terminal carbons. The resonance method suggests the correct arrangement immediately, since the two important and equivalent pairing schemes have charges only on the terminal carbons (Figure 9-9).

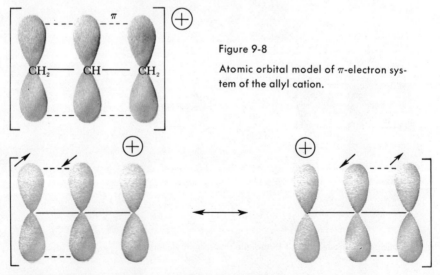

Figure 9-8

Atomic orbital model of π-electron system of the allyl cation.

Figure 9-9   Electron-pairing schemes of the allyl cation.

SUPPLEMENTARY EXERCISES

9-12 Write three structures for C_4H_2 with tetravalent carbon and univalent hydrogen. Decide on the most favorable geometrical configuration and evaluate the resonance energy for this configuration.

9-13 Propylene reacts with chlorine at 300° to yield allyl chloride.

    a. Write two chain mechanisms for this chlorination, one involving attack of a chlorine atom on the hydrogen of the —CH_3 group and the other an attack of a chlorine atom at the double bond.

    b. Consider the relative feasibilities of the two different mechanisms on the basis of bond energies. Indicate in detail any uncertainties that might make such calculations unreliable.

9-14 Use the heats of combustion of cycloöctatetraene (Table 9-4) and of cycloöctane (Table 4-2), and any required bond energies, to calculate the heat of hydrogenation of cyclo-öctatetraene to cycloöctane in the vapor phase at 25°.

9-15 Write the five Kekulé-type resonance structures of phenanthrene, and show how these can account for the fact that phenanthrene, unlike benzene, adds bromine, but only across the 9,10-positions.

phenanthrene

Bifunctional Compounds.
Alkadienes

The beginning student will find the study of organic chemistry considerably simplified through recognizing that most organic compounds can be regarded as combinations of saturated open-chain or cyclic hydrocarbons with functional groups. In the great majority of organic reactions only the functional groups are involved, the hydrocarbon part of the molecule being just "along for the ride" and affecting the outcome of the reactions mostly through indirect means such as steric hindrance, modification of solubility characteristics, and the like.

The first part of this chapter is concerned with functional groups as an aid to the classification of organic compounds. We then consider the chemistry of alkadienes, which provide our first opportunity for detailed study of a class of compound with two functional groups—in this case, with two double bonds. We shall pay special attention to the 1,3-alkadienes in which the double bonds are so located in relation to each other that their properties differ from those encountered for the simple alkenes.

Bifunctional
Compounds.
Alkadienes

10-1 FUNCTIONAL GROUPS AS AN AID TO THE CLASSIFICATION OF ORGANIC COMPOUNDS

A number of simple organic compounds were classified in Chapter 1 (see Figure 1-1) according to type, i.e., hydrocarbons, halides, alcohols, ethers, and carbonyl compounds. The properties characteristic of these and other various types of organic compounds are largely determined by the substituent, or **functional group,** common to each. Thus, different alcohols such as CH_3OH, CH_3CH_2OH, $(CH_3)_2CHOH$, and $(CH_3)_3COH$ behave more or less alike because they all possess the hydroxyl group (—OH). Similarly, alkenes are considered as a particular type or class of hydrocarbon because their most important chemical properties are those exhibited by their carbon-carbon double bonds.

A more complete list of the main classes of organic compounds and their functional groups is given in Table 10-1. Classification according to functional groups has the virtue of providing rationale for the behavior of the vast numbers of organic compounds that are known. It is logical and convenient to divide organic compounds into families with similar properties in the same way that the periodic classification of the elements divides the elements into groups or families having related properties. It is well to appreciate, however, that a real understanding of organic chemistry involves much *more* than a knowledge of the separate behaviors of classes of compounds with different functional groups.

203

Table 10-1   Classification of Organic Compounds According to Functional Groups

Class of compound	Functional group	Typical example	
		Formula	Name
alkene	$>$C=C$<$	$CH_3CH_2CH=CH_2$	1-butene
alkyne	$-$C≡C$-$	$CH_3C≡CH$	methylacetylene
alcohol	$-$OH	⬜$-$OH	cyclobutanol
ether	$-$O$-$	$CH_3OCH_2CH_3$	methyl ethyl ether
halide	F, Cl, Br or I	⬠$-$Cl	cyclopentyl chloride
aldehyde	$-$C(=O)$-$H	CH_3CH_2CHO	propionaldehyde
ketone	$>$C=O	$CH_3\overset{O}{\overset{\|}{C}}CH_2CH_3$	2-butanone
carboxylic acid	$-$C(=O)$-$OH	$CH_3CH_2CH_2CH_2CO_2H$	pentanoic acid
amine	$-$NH$_2$	CH_3NH_2	methylamine
nitro compound	$-\overset{\oplus}{N}(=O)(\overset{\ominus}{O})$ ↔ $-\overset{\oplus}{N}(\overset{\ominus}{\ddot{O}})(=O)$	CH_3CHCH_3 / NO_2	2-nitropropane
nitrile	$-$C≡N	CH_3CN	acetonitrile
organometallic	$-$C$-$Metal	$CH_3CH_2CH_2CH_2Li$	*n*-butyllithium

Indeed, it is frequently useful and instructive to consider *types of reactions* rather than *types of compounds*. For example, addition reactions are not confined to the carbon-carbon multiple bonds of alkenes and alkynes but occur generally in

compounds with unsaturated linkages such as aldehydes $\left(\begin{smallmatrix}R\\ \\H\end{smallmatrix}C=O\right)$ and

ketones $\left(\begin{smallmatrix}R\\ \\R'\end{smallmatrix}C=O\right)$, imines $\left(\begin{smallmatrix}R\\ \\R'\end{smallmatrix}C=N-R'\right)$, nitriles (R—C≡N), azo

compounds (R—N=N—R), etc. To discuss such additions in a comprehensive
manner, one needs to compare the behavior of compounds with different functional groups. In this book, organic chemistry is approached largely from the
viewpoint of functional groups, but not, we hope, to the point of de-empha-
sizing reaction types.

Returning to the list of functional groups in Table 10-1, we may ask why the
carboxyl function, $-C\begin{smallmatrix}\nearrow OH\\ \searrow O\end{smallmatrix}$, is classified neither as an alcohol nor as a ketone,

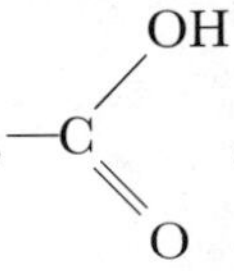

even though it possesses a hydroxyl group and a carbonyl group. The reason is
that the properties of one group are often greatly modified by the presence of
another, particularly when the groups are joined by a common bond, as in the
carboxyl group; hence the combination is best classified as a separate functional
group.

EXERCISE 10-1   Consider possible ways in which the OH and C=O groups of a carboxylic
acid, such as $CH_3CH_2CH_2CO_2H$, might interact or influence each other to confer
properties on the combination not possessed by isolated OH and C=O groups,

as in $HOCH_2CH_2CH_2\overset{\displaystyle O}{\overset{\|}{C}}H$.

Some examples of **polyfunctional** compounds (having two or more functional
groups) whose groups are in such close proximity that the properties characteristic of each are considerably modified, include the following:

$Cl-CH_2-Cl$ $CH_3-C\begin{smallmatrix}\nearrow O\\ \searrow NH_2\end{smallmatrix}$ $CH_3-C\begin{smallmatrix}\nearrow O\\ \searrow OC_2H_5\end{smallmatrix}$

dichloromethane   acetamide 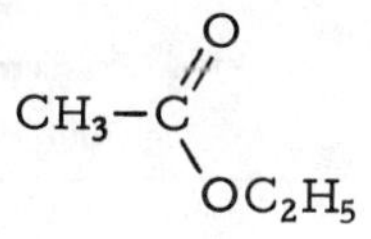   ethyl acetate

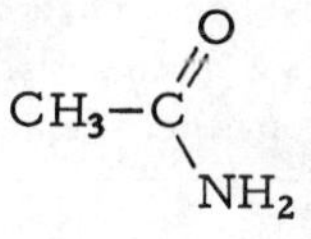

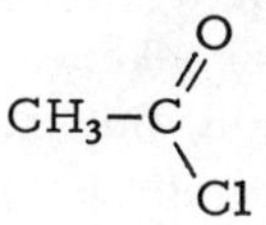

(methylene chloride)

$CH_3-C\begin{smallmatrix}\nearrow O\\ \searrow Cl\end{smallmatrix}$ $CH_2=CHCl$ $HOOC-COOH$

acetyl chloride   vinyl chloride   oxalic acid

Separation of functional groups by two or more carbons of a saturated hydrocarbon chain usually serves to insulate them from pronounced interaction, and
the properties become more nearly typical of those of the isolated functional
groups. Several examples follow:

$$\begin{matrix} & O \\ & \parallel \\ ClCH_2CH_2CH_2Cl & CH_3CCH_2CH_2NH_2 \end{matrix}$$

ClCH₂CH₂CH₂Cl

1, 3-dichloropropane

$$\overset{O}{\overset{\parallel}{CH_3C}}CH_2CH_2NH_2$$

4-amino-2-butanone

$$\overset{O}{\overset{\parallel}{CH_3C}}CH_2CH_2CH_2OC_2H_5$$

5-ethoxy-2-pentanone

$$\overset{O}{\overset{\parallel}{CH_3C}}CH_2CH_2Cl$$

4-chloro-2-butanone

CH₂=CHCH₂CH₂CH₂Cl

5-chloro-1-pentene

HOOCCH₂CH₂COOH

succinic acid

10-2 ALKADIENES

In the balance of this chapter we shall give specific consideration for the first time to the properties of an important class of *bifunctional* compounds, the alkadienes.

When there are two or more double bonds in a hydrocarbon chain, the properties of the compound will depend considerably upon the relative positions of these double bonds, that is, whether they are *cumulated, conjugated,* or *isolated* (refer to p. 123 for definitions and nomenclature). The properties of a compound with isolated double bonds (e.g., 1,4-pentadiene, CH₂=CH—CH₂—CH=CH₂) are generally similar to those of simple alkenes since the double bonds are virtually isolated by the intervening CH₂ group.

EXERCISE 10-2   In one way, 1,4-pentadiene is different from propylene in chemical properties—namely, the removal of the hydrogens at the 3-position by attack of free radicals or strong bases is much easier compared with the removal of those on the methyl group of propylene. Explain.

10-3 1,3- OR CONJUGATED DIENES

The reactions of 1,3-butadiene are reasonably typical of conjugated dienes in general. The compound undergoes the usual reactions of alkenes such as catalytic hydrogenation, and free-radical and polar addition, but it does so *more readily* than most alkenes or dienes having isolated double bonds. Further, the products are frequently those of concurrent 1,2- and 1,4-addition. This behavior was discussed briefly in Chapter 9, pp. 188-189, in the case of electrophilic addition of chlorine and can be rationalized by assuming the formation of a resonance-stabilized carbonium ion. The positive charge of the intermediate resides primarily on two carbons, and either of these positions may be attacked by chloride ion to give either the 1,4- or 1,2-addition product. The course of the analogous reaction of 1,3-butadiene with hydrogen chloride is shown below.

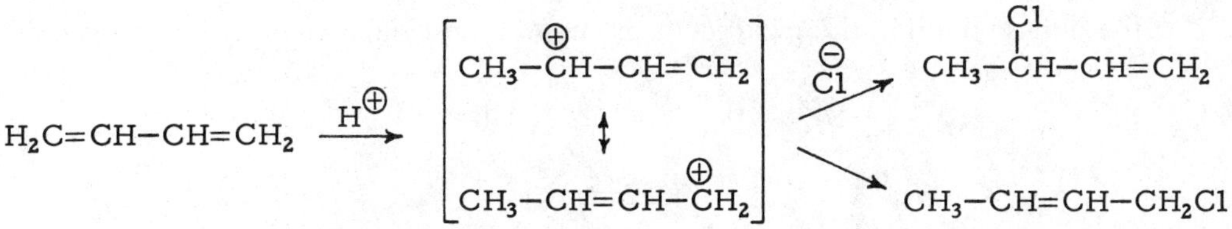

$$H_2C=CH-CH=CH_2 \xrightarrow{H^{\oplus}} \left[\begin{array}{c} CH_3-\overset{\oplus}{CH}-CH=CH_2 \\ \updownarrow \\ CH_3-CH=CH-\overset{\oplus}{CH_2} \end{array} \right] \overset{\ominus}{Cl} \begin{array}{c} \overset{Cl}{\underset{|}{CH_3-CH-CH=CH_2}} \\ \\ CH_3-CH=CH-CH_2Cl \end{array}$$

EXERCISE 10-3   Show how it is possible to account for the fact that free-radical additions to conjugated dienes frequently give both 1,2- and 1,4-addition products.

EXERCISE 10-4   Which of the following two modes of addition of bromine to styrene would you expect to be preferred?   Explain.

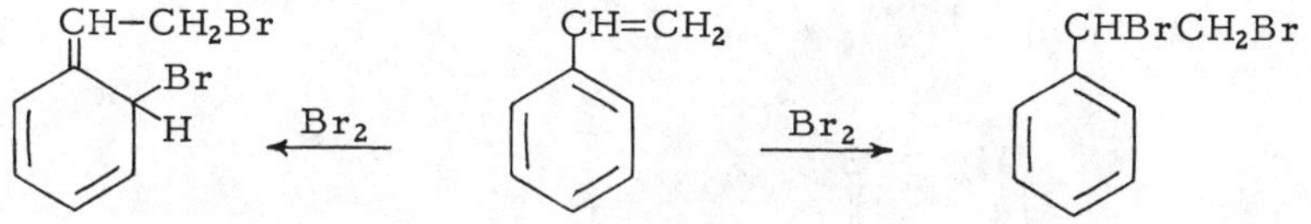

styrene

10-4   1,4-CYCLOADDITION REACTIONS OF DIENES: THE DIELS-ALDER REACTION

One of the most useful reactions in synthetic organic chemistry is the 1,4-addition of an alkene to a conjugated diene. It is known as the **Diels-Alder** re-

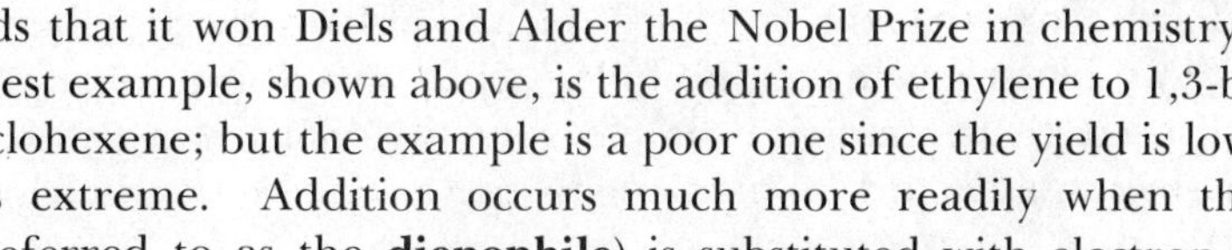

diene   dienophile   adduct

action after its discoverers and has proved of such value in the synthesis of cyclic compounds that it won Diels and Alder the Nobel Prize in chemistry in 1950. The simplest example, shown above, is the addition of ethylene to 1,3-butadiene to give cyclohexene; but the example is a poor one since the yield is low and the conditions extreme.   Addition occurs much more readily when the alkene (usually referred to as the **dienophile**) is substituted with electron-attracting groups $-CO_2H$, $-\overset{O}{\underset{||}{C}}-R$, $-C\equiv N$, and the like.   A list of the more reactive dienophiles is given in Table 10-2.

One of the reasons why the reaction has proved of value, especially in the synthesis of natural products, is that it is highly stereospecific.   First, and most obvious, the diene reacts in the *s-cis* [1] conformation of its double bonds because

[1] The designation, *s-cis*, means that the double bonds lie in a plane on the same side (*cis*) of the single bond connecting them.   The opposite and usually somewhat more stable conformation is called *s-trans*.

the double bond in the product (a six-membered ring) must necessarily have the

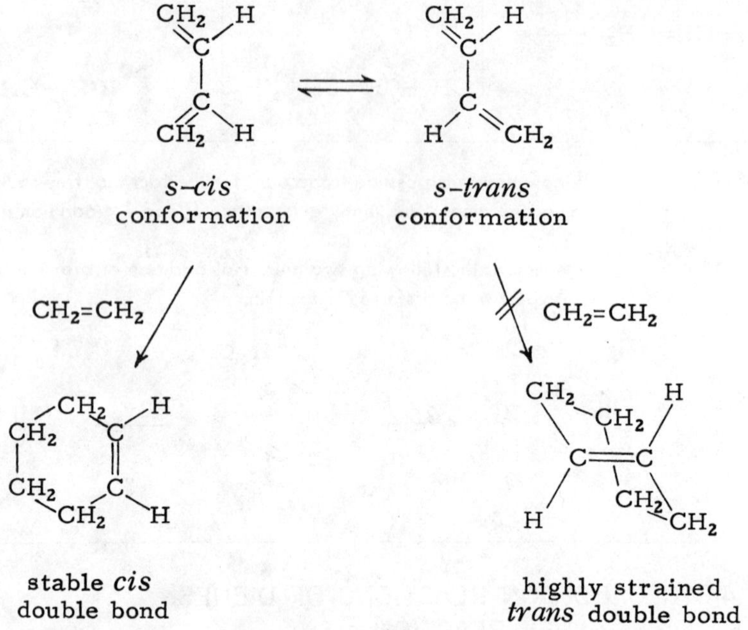

s–cis
conformation

s–trans
conformation

stable *cis*
double bond

highly strained
trans double bond

cis configuration. Cyclic dienes with five- and six-membered rings usually react
readily because they are fixed in *s-cis* configurations.

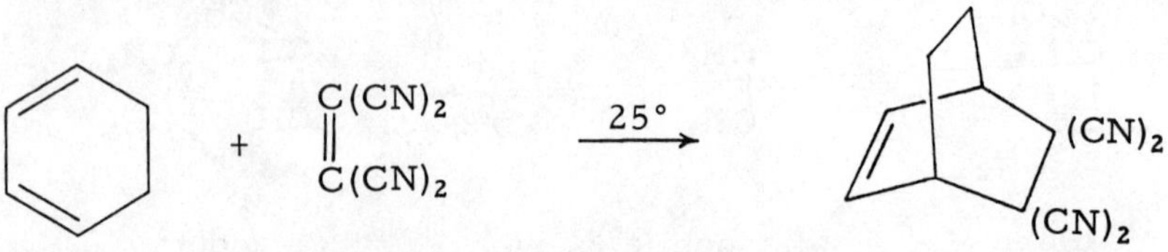

Second, the configurations of the diene and the dienophile are *retained* in the
adduct. This means that the reactants (or addends) come together to give *cis*
addition. Two illustrative examples follow which are drawn to emphasize how
cis addition occurs. In the first example, dimethyl maleate, which has *cis* ester
(CO_2CH_3) groups, adds to 1,3-butadiene to give a *cis*-substituted cyclohexene.

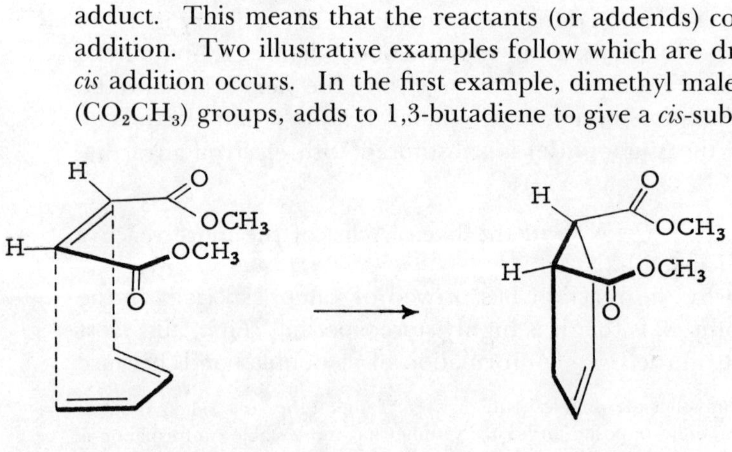

(shows retention of
configuration in the
dienophile)

cis

In the second example, *cis* addition of a dienophile to *trans,trans*-2,4-hexadiene is seen to yield a product with two methyl groups on the same side of the cyclohexene ring.

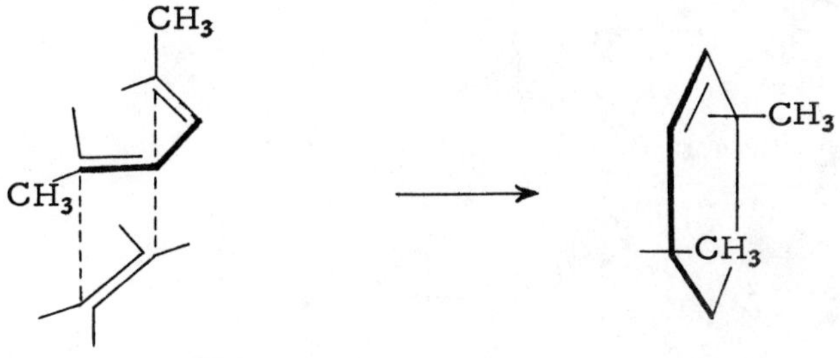

(shows retention of configuration of the diene methyl sub-stituents)

cis

EXERCISE 10-5   What products would you expect from the Diels-Alder addition of tetracyanoethylene to *cis,trans*-2,4-hexadiene and *cis,cis*-2,4-hexadiene?   Explain.

Table 10-2   Reactive Dienophiles

Name	Formula	Name	Formula
tetracyanoethylene	$(CN)_2C{=}C(CN)_2$	acrylonitrile	$CH_2{=}CH{-}CN$
crotonaldehyde	$CH_3CH{=}CH{-}CHO$	acrolein	$CH_2{=}CH{-}CHO$
cinnamic acid (*cis* and *trans*)	$C_6H_5CH{=}CH{-}CO_2H$	ethyl acrylate	$CH_2{=}CH{-}CO_2C_2H_5$
maleic anhydride	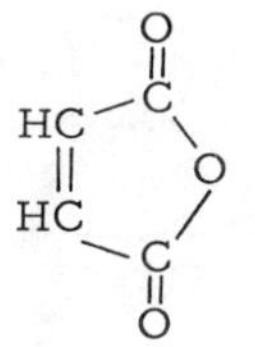	N-phenylmaleimide	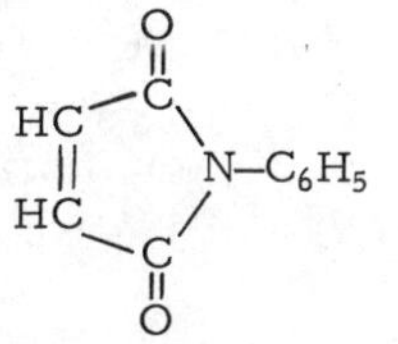
dimethyl maleate	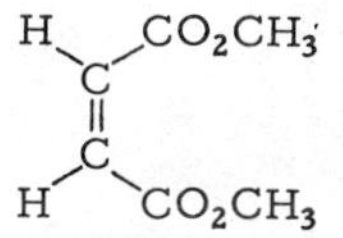	dimethyl fumarate	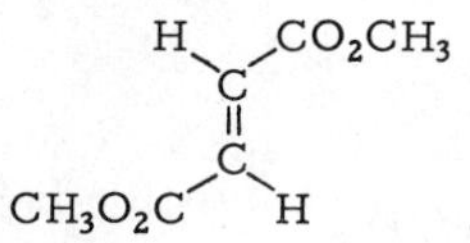
1-nitropropene	$CH_3CH{=}CH{-}NO_2$	β-nitrostyrene	$C_6H_5{-}CH{=}CHNO_2$

As for the mechanism of the Diels-Alder reaction, there is little evidence in favor of simple free-radical or polar mechanisms such as we have discussed previously.   As one possibility, the reaction can be formulated as a process in which the bonds between the diene and the dienophile are formed more or less simultaneously.

Alternately, the addends can be considered to be first oriented and *one* bond

formed. This would create two radical centers between which the second bond is subsequently formed. It seems reasonable to suppose that the odd electrons of the "diradical" remain paired (have opposite spins) at all times throughout the reaction.

10-5 1,2-CYCLOADDITION OF DIENES

Although conjugated dienes generally react with dienophiles by 1,4-addition to form six-membered ring compounds, 1,2-additions to form four-membered ring compounds are also known. The nature of the dienophile seems to be the determining factor in 1,2- vs. 1,4-addition. For example, although ethylene adds 1,4 to butadiene (see p. 207), tetrafluoroethylene adds 1,2 to butadiene.

However, tetrafluoroethylene adds to cyclopentadiene to give a mixture of 1,2- and 1,4-cycloadducts.

The contrasting behavior of tetrafluoroethylene and ethylene in cycloadditions is not as yet understood.

10-6 POLYMERIZATION OF CONJUGATED DIENES

The general character of radical and ionic types of alkene polymerization was discussed briefly in Section 7-8. The same principles apply to alkadienes with the added feature that there are additional ways of linking the monomer units.

The polymer chain may grow by either 1,2-addition or 1,4-addition to the monomer. In the latter event, there is the further possibility of *cis* or *trans* addition.

Type of addition

$$\left(\begin{array}{c} CH=CH_2 \\ | \\ CH-CH_2 \end{array} \right)_n \qquad 1, 2$$

$$n \cdot CH_2=CH-CH=CH_2 \longrightarrow \left(\begin{array}{cc} H & H \\ \diagdown & \diagup \\ C=C \\ \diagup & \diagdown \\ CH_2 & CH_2 \end{array} \right)_n \qquad cis\text{--}1, 4$$

$$\left(\begin{array}{cc} H & CH_2 \\ \diagdown & \diagup \\ C=C \\ \diagup & \diagdown \\ CH_2 & H \end{array} \right)_n \qquad trans\text{--}1, 4$$

EXERCISE 10-6   Formulate chain initiation, propagation, and termination steps for the polymerization of butadiene by a peroxide catalyst. Consider carefully possible structures for the growing-chain radical. Show the expected structure of the polymer. Calculate ΔH for the reaction.

A polymer made up of identical repeating units is called a **homopolymer.** If the units are nonidentical, as when different monomers are polymerized together, the product is called a **copolymer.** Strictly speaking, if a monomer polymerizes nonstereospecifically (giving chains formed by 1,2- and *cis* and *trans* 1,4-addition in the case of a conjugated diene), it forms a copolymer rather than a homopolymer.

Many of the polymers formed from conjugated dienes are elastic and are used to manufacture synthetic rubbers. The raw polymers are usually tacky and little direct use is found for them, except as adhesives and cements. They are transformed into materials with greater elasticity and strength by **vulcanization,** in which the polymer is heated with sulfur and various catalysts called **accelerators,** with the result that the polymer chains become "cross-linked" to one another by carbon-sulfur bonds. Some of the cross-linking appears to occur by addition to the double bonds, but the amount of sulfur added is generally insufficient to saturate the polymer. With large proportions of sulfur, hard rubber is formed such as is used in storage-battery cases.

Because of the many double bonds present, diene rubbers are usually sensitive to air oxidation unless **antioxidants** are added to inhibit oxidation.

The more important dienes for the manufacture of synthetic rubbers are 1,3-butadiene, 2-chloro-1,3-butadiene (chloroprene), and 2-methylbutadiene (isoprene).

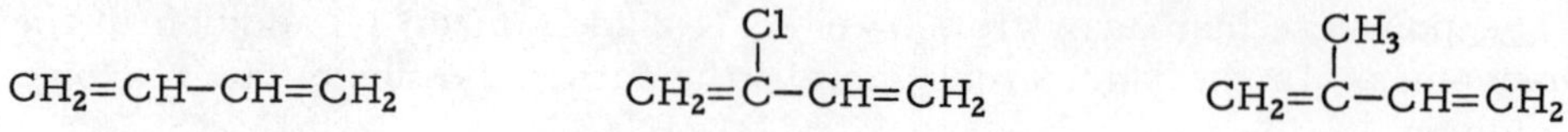

$$CH_2=CH-CH=CH_2$$

1, 3-butadiene

$$CH_2=\overset{\overset{\displaystyle Cl}{|}}{C}-CH=CH_2$$

2-chloro-
1, 3-butadiene

(chloroprene)

$$CH_2=\overset{\overset{\displaystyle CH_3}{|}}{C}-CH=CH_2$$

2-methyl-
1, 3-butadiene

(isoprene)

Various rubbers that have the desirable properties of elasticity, flexibility, abrasive resistance, and resistance to chemicals are listed in Table 10-3. The homogeneity of these polymers depends greatly on the way in which they are prepared, particularly on the polymerization catalyst employed. A synthetic rubber that is virtually identical with natural Hevea rubber is made from isoprene, using finely divided lithium metal or Ziegler-type catalysts; the product is formed almost exclusively by *cis* 1,4-addition. As mentioned earlier (p. 156), Ziegler-type catalysts may be made from a trialkylaluminum (R$_3$Al) and a metallic halide, usually titanium tetrachloride.

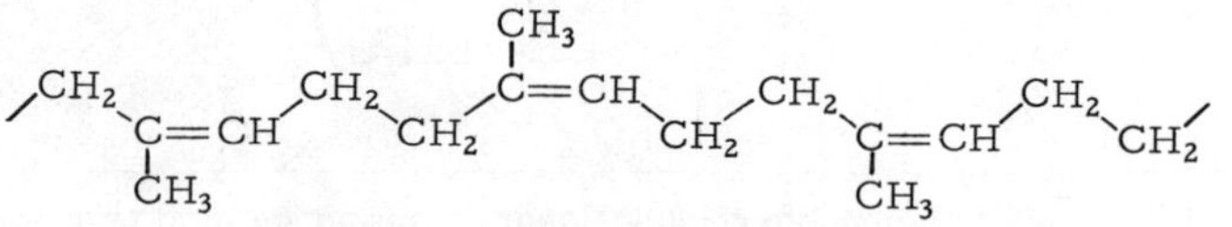

natural rubber (*cis*-1, 4-polyisoprene)

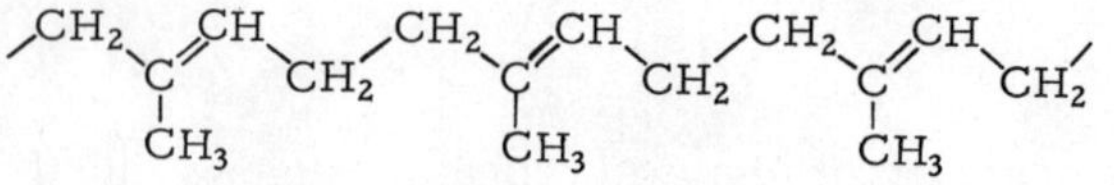

gutta-percha (*trans*-1, 4-polyisoprene)

Interestingly, gutta-percha, the *trans* 1,4-isomer of natural rubber, is hard and brittle at room temperature. The reason for the difference in properties between the *cis* and *trans* isomers can be readily seen by inspecting molecular models. The chains with *trans* double bonds are seen to be able to lie alongside of each other, ordered to form a semicrystalline array, as shown in Figure 10-1. When double bonds are *cis*,

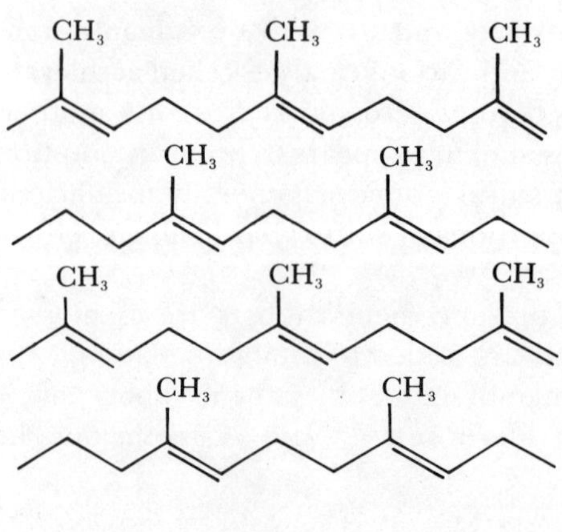

Figure 10-1

Schematic representation of the configuration of chains in gutta-percha (*trans*-1,4-polyisoprene).

Table 10-3   Synthetic Rubbers

Monomer	Formula	Catalyst	Polymer	Type of addition
1,3-butadiene	$CH_2{=}CH{-}CH{=}CH_2$	Li	polybutadiene	100% *cis* 1,4
1,3-butadiene	$CH_2{=}CH{-}CH{=}CH_2$	Na	polybutadiene	25–30% *cis* and *trans* 1,4
1,3-butadiene and styrene	$CH_2{=}CH{-}CH{=}CH_2$ $C_6H_5CH{=}CH_2$	a	*GRS*[b]	
1,3-butadiene and acrylonitrile	$CH_2{=}CH{-}CH{=}CH_2$ $CH_2{=}CH{-}CN$	a	Buna N[c]	
2-chloro-1,3-butadiene (chloroprene)	$CH_2{=}CH{-}\underset{\underset{Cl}{\vert}}{C}{=}CH_2$	a	neoprene	100% *trans* 1,4
2-methyl-1,3-butadiene (isoprene)	$CH_2{=}CH{-}\underset{\underset{CH_3}{\vert}}{C}{=}CH_2$	Li or Ziegler	identical with natural rubber	~100% *cis* 1,4
isobutylene and isoprene	$(CH_3)_2C{=}CH_2$	$AlCl_3$	butyl rubber	

[a] No simple formula can be given, but peroxide-type catalysts, particularly persulfate salts, are most commonly used.

[b] *GRS* means *G*overnment *R*ubber-*S*tyrene type and is an obsolete notation introduced during World War II.

[c] Originally developed in Germany during World War II.

however, steric hindrance prevents the chains from assuming a similar ordered structure and the bulk of the material exists in an amorphous state with randomly oriented chains. When the *cis* polymer is stretched, the chains are straightened out and tend to become oriented; but since this is an unfavorable state, the material snaps back to the amorphous state when released. Interestingly, at elevated temperatures, where gutta-percha becomes amorphous it has elastic properties. The elastic properties of polymers are discussed in more detail in Chapter 29.

Polymerization of isobutylene in the presence of small amounts of isoprene gives a copolymer with enough double bonds to permit cross-linking of the polymer chains through vulcanization. The product is a hard-wearing, chemically resistant rubber called "butyl rubber." It is highly impermeable to oxygen and is used widely as inner tubes for tires.

SUPPLEMENTARY EXERCISES

10-7   According to the proposed mechanism for the Diels-Alder reaction, explain why maleic anhydride does not add to 1,3-butadiyne.

10-8   Would you expect tetracyanoethylene, $(CN)_2C{=}C(CN)_2$, to add to the following compounds by 1,2- or 1,4-addition? Explain.

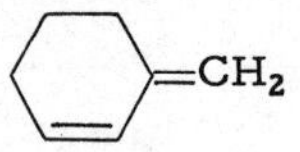

methylenecyclohexene

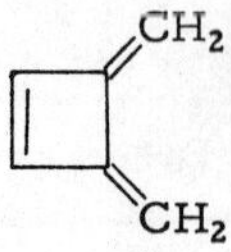

1, 2-dimethylenecyclobutene

10-9 Predict the products of the following reactions; show your reasoning.

a. $CH_2{=}CH{-}CH{=}CH_2$ + 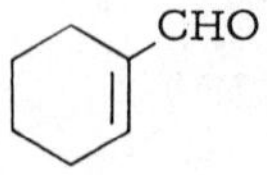

b. *cis,trans*-2,4-hexadiene and maleic anhydride

c. $C_6H_5C{\equiv}CH + F_2C{=}CF_2$

10-10 Show the last step in a synthesis of each of the following substances (give approximate reaction conditions):

a. $CH_2{=}CHCHBrCH_3$

b. 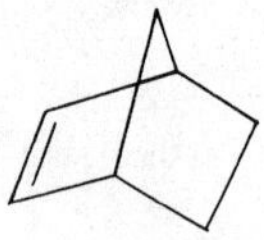

c. 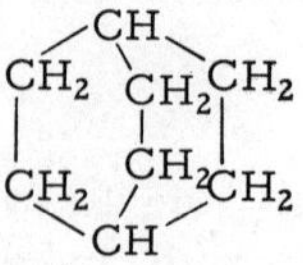

d. 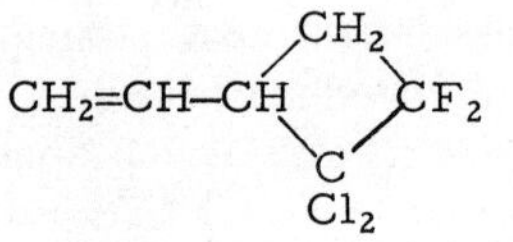

e. 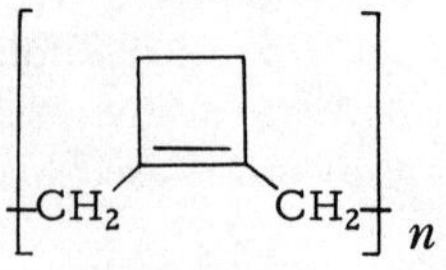

f. $\left[CH_2{-}\overset{F}{\overset{|}{C}}{=}CH{-}CH_2 \right]_n$

10-11 Explain why free-radical initiators cause styrene ($C_6H_5CH{=}CH_2$) to polymerize head-to-tail to form

$$\left[CH_2{-}\underset{}{\overset{C_6H_5}{\overset{|}{C}H}}{-}CH_2{-}\overset{C_6H_5}{\overset{|}{C}H} \right]_n$$

10-12 How many reasonably stable geometrical isomers would be expected for each of the following compounds? Indicate your reasoning and draw appropriate structural formulas.

a. isobutylene   *e.* cyclodecene

b. 1,4-pentadiene   *f.* 1,2,3-trimethylcyclopropane

c. 1,3-pentadiene   *g.* 2,4,6-octatriene

d. cyclobutene   *h.* 1,4-dichloro-1,2,3-butatriene

Nucleophilic Displacement and
Elimination Reactions.
Alkyl, Cycloalkyl, Alkenyl,
and Alkynyl Halides

There are relatively few basic types of organic reactions and of these, substitution, addition, and elimination are of the greatest importance. So far, we have discussed substitution of halogen for hydrogen, addition reactions of alkenes, and addition reactions of cycloalkanes with strained rings. In this chapter, the principal topics are the substitution or displacement by nucleophilic reagents of groups attached to carbon, and the formation of carbon-carbon double bonds by elimination reactions. These reactions are often profoundly influenced by seemingly minor variations in structure, reagents, solvent, and temperature. It is our purpose to show how these variations can be understood and, as far as possible, predicted in terms of the principles we have already discussed.

The latter part of the chapter includes correlation of the reactivity of various kinds of halides with their structures. The physical and chemical properties of fluorinated organic compounds are reviewed briefly. This class of substance provides examples of some of the most reactive as well as the most inert compounds, many being of considerable commercial importance.

Nucleophilic Displacement and Elimination Reactions. Alkyl, Cycloalkyl, Alkenyl, and Alkynyl Halides

The theory and practice of two very important reactions of organic compounds, nucleophilic displacement and elimination, are the principal concern of this chapter. Before proceeding, however, it will be helpful to consider the nomenclature of many of the organic reactants and products involved. The reader who is already acquainted with these nomenclature systems, or wishes to study them at a later time, can pass directly to page 223.

11-1 ORGANIC DERIVATIVES OF INORGANIC COMPOUNDS

Chapter 10 included a discussion of some of the merits of classifying organic compounds according to their functional groups. Another useful classification of various types of compounds considers them as organic-substitution products of water, ammonia, hydrogen sulfide, nitrous or nitric acids, etc., through

Table 11-1   Organic Compounds as Derivatives of Common Inorganic Compounds

Parent compound	Organic derivative			
	Class of compound		Example	
H—O—H	R—O—H	alcohol	CH_3OH	methanol
	R—O—R'	ether	CH_3OCH_3	dimethyl ether
	$R-\overset{\overset{O}{\|\|}}{C}-O-H$	carboxylic acid	$CH_3\overset{\overset{O}{\|\|}}{C}OH$	acetic acid
	$R-\overset{\overset{O}{\|\|}}{C}-O-R'$	carboxylic ester	$CH_3\overset{\overset{O}{\|\|}}{C}OCH_3$	methyl acetate
	$R-\overset{\overset{O}{\|\|}}{C}-O-\overset{\overset{O}{\|\|}}{C}-R$	carboxylic anhydride	$CH_3\overset{\overset{O}{\|\|}}{C}O\overset{\overset{O}{\|\|}}{C}CH_3$	acetic anhydride
H—S—H	R—S—H	thiol (mercaptan)	CH_3SH	methanethiol (methyl mercaptan)
	R—S—R'	thioether (sulfide)	CH_3SCH_3	methylthiomethane (dimethyl sulfide)
	$R-\overset{\overset{O}{\|\|}}{C}-S-H$	thio acid	$CH_3\overset{\overset{O}{\|\|}}{C}SH$	thioacetic acid
NH_3	RNH_2	*prim.* amine	CH_3NH_2	methylamine
	R_2NH	*sec.* amine	$(CH_3)_2NH$	dimethylamine
	R_3N	*tert.* amine	$(CH_3)_3N$	trimethylamine
	$R-\overset{\overset{O}{\|\|}}{C}-NH_2$	acylamine (unsubstituted amide)	$CH_3-\overset{\overset{O}{\|\|}}{C}-NH_2$	acetamide
	$R-\overset{\overset{O}{\|\|}}{C}-NHR$	(monosubstituted amide)	$CH_3-\overset{\overset{O}{\|\|}}{C}-NHCH_3$	N-methylacetamide
	$R-\overset{\overset{O}{\|\|}}{C}-NR_2$	(disubstituted amide)	$CH_3-\overset{\overset{O}{\|\|}}{C}-N(CH_3)_2$	N,N-dimethylacetamide

Table 11-1   Organic Compounds as Derivatives of Common Inorganic Compounds (*Continued*)

Parent compound	Organic derivative			
	Class of compound		Example	
H—ONO$_2$ (nitric acid)	R—ONO$_2$	alkyl nitrate	CH$_3$—ONO$_2$	methyl nitrate
H—ONO (or H—NO$_2$) (nitrous acid)	R—ONO R—NO$_2$	alkyl nitrite nitroalkane	CH$_3$—ONO CH$_3$—NO$_2$	methyl nitrite nitromethane
H—NO (hyponitrous acid, monomeric form)	R—NO	nitrosoalkane	CH$_3$—NO	nitroso-methane
H—O—S(=O)(=O)—OH	R—O—S(=O)(=O)—OH	alkyl acid sulfate	CH$_3$—O—S(=O)(=O)—OH	methyl acid sulfate
	R—O—S(=O)(=O)—O—R	dialkyl sulfate	CH$_3$—O—S(=O)(=O)—OCH$_3$	dimethyl sulfate
H—X (X=F, Cl, Br, I)	R—X	alkyl halide (haloalkane)	CH$_3$—F	methyl fluoride (fluoromethane)

replacement of one or more hydrogens with an organic group. Reference to Table 11-1 shows how alcohols, ethers, carboxylic acids, anhydrides, and esters may be regarded as derivatives of water; mercaptans and sulfides as hydrogen sulfide derivatives; amines and amides as ammonia derivatives; alkyl nitrates as derivatives of nitric acid; nitroalkanes and alkyl nitrites as derivatives of nitrous acid; and alkyl sulfates as derivatives of sulfuric acid. For the sake of completeness, we include alkyl halides, which we have already classed as substituted alkanes, but which may also be considered as derivatives of the hydrogen halides.

11-2   ALCOHOL AND ALKYL HALIDE NOMENCLATURE

In naming an alcohol by the IUPAC system, the ending *-ol* is appended to the name of the parent hydrocarbon. The latter corresponds to the longest straight chain of carbon atoms that includes the carbon carrying the hydroxyl group; it also includes the double bond when the compound is unsaturated. Note also that the *-ol* function normally takes precedence over a double bond, halogen, and alkyl in determining the suffix of the name. With respect to numbering, the carbon carrying the hydroxyl group is taken as number one if it terminates the chain, or the lowest number thereafter if it is attached to a nonterminal carbon.

$$CH_3-OH \qquad CH_3CH_2-OH \qquad C_6H_5CH_2\overset{\overset{\displaystyle OH}{|}}{C}HCH_2CH_3 \qquad ClCH_2CH=\overset{\overset{\displaystyle CH_2CH_3}{|}}{C}CH_2-OH$$

methanol   ethanol   1-phenyl-   4-chloro-2-ethyl-
                                    2-butanol   2-buten-1-ol

The most commonly used system for naming alcohols (and halides) combines the name of the appropriate hydrocarbon radical with the word *alcohol* (or *halide*). This system works well whenever the radical name is simple and easily visualized.

$$CH_3-\overset{\overset{\displaystyle CH_3}{|}}{\underset{\underset{\displaystyle CH_3}{|}}{C}}-OH \qquad\qquad CH_3-\overset{\overset{\displaystyle CH_3}{|}}{\underset{\underset{\displaystyle H}{|}}{C}}-CH_2-OH \qquad\qquad CH_2=CH-CH_2-Cl$$

t-butyl alcohol   isobutyl alcohol   allyl chloride

A prevalent but unofficial procedure names alcohols as substitution products of **carbinol,** CH_3OH, a synonym of methanol. Many alcohols that are cumbersome to name by the IUPAC system may have structures that are more easily visualized when named by the carbinol system.

$$CH_3\overset{\overset{\displaystyle CH_3}{|}}{C}H-\overset{\overset{\displaystyle H}{|}}{\underset{\underset{\displaystyle OH}{|}}{C}}-CH_2CH_2\overset{\overset{\displaystyle CH_3}{|}}{C}HCH_3 \qquad\qquad C_6H_5-\overset{\overset{\displaystyle H}{|}}{\underset{\underset{\displaystyle OH}{|}}{C}}-CH_2CH=CH_2$$

isopropylisoamylcarbinol   allylphenylcarbinol
(2,6-dimethyl-3-heptanol   (1-phenyl-3-buten-1-ol
by IUPAC system**)**   by IUPAC system)

The carbinol system has been extended to include other derivatives. Alkyl halides and alkylamines, for example, are frequently called carbinyl halides and carbinylamines.

$$\hspace{4cm}-CH_2Cl \qquad\qquad\qquad C_6H_5-\overset{}{\underset{\underset{\displaystyle NH_2}{|}}{C}}H-CH_2CH_3$$

cyclohexylcarbinyl chloride   ethylphenylcarbinylamine

11-3   ETHER NOMENCLATURE

Symmetrical ethers (both R groups in R—O—R being the same) are named simply dialkyl, dialkenyl, or diaryl ethers, as the case may be. The prefix di- to denote disubstitution is sometimes omitted as superfluous, but most current opinion regards this form of redundancy desirable to help prevent errors.

Clearly, when an ether is unsymmetrical, the names of both R groups must be included.

$$CH_3CH_2-O-CH_2CH_3 \qquad CH_3-O-CH=CH_2 \qquad C_6H_5-O-C_6H_5$$

diethyl ether   methyl vinyl ether   diphenyl ether

11-4 CARBOXYLIC ACID NOMENCLATURE

According to the IUPAC system, carboxylic acids are called alkanoic acids. The suffix -*oic* is added to the name of the longest straight-chain hydrocarbon in the molecule that includes the carbon of the carboxyl ($-CO_2H$) group. Note that the carboxyl function normally takes precedence over the hydroxyl function.

$$\overset{\overset{\textstyle Cl}{|}}{CH_3CH_2CH_2CHCO_2H} \qquad\qquad \overset{\overset{\textstyle CH_3}{|}}{CH_3CHCH}=\overset{\overset{\textstyle OH}{|}}{CHCHCO_2H}$$

2-chloropentanoic acid   2-hydroxy-5-methyl-3-hexenoic acid

The simple alkanoic acids have long been known by descriptive but unsystematic names that correspond variously to their properties, odors, or natural origin. It seems unlikely that these names will very soon be superseded by more systematic designations, particularly for the following acids:

HCO_2H	formic acid	(L. *formica*, ant)
CH_3CO_2H	acetic acid	(L. *acetum*, vinegar)
$CH_3CH_2CO_2H$	propionic acid	(*proto* + Gr. *pion*, fat)
$CH_3CH_2CH_2CO_2H$	butyric acid	(L. *butyrum*, butter)
$\overset{\textstyle CH_3}{\underset{\textstyle CH_3}{\diagdown\!\!/}}CHCO_2H$	isobutyric acid	

Esters of carboxylic acids carry the suffix -*oate* in place of -*oic* (or -*ate* in place of -*ic* for acids with descriptive names).

$$\overset{\overset{\textstyle O}{\|}}{CH_3CH_2COCH_3} \qquad \overset{\overset{\textstyle O}{\|}}{C_6H_5CH_2COCH_2CH_3} \qquad \overset{\overset{\textstyle Cl}{|}}{CH_2}=CH\overset{\overset{\textstyle O}{\|}}{CHCOCH_2CH_3}$$

methyl propionate   ethyl phenylacetate   ethyl 2-chloro-3-butenoate

11-5 THE USE OF GREEK LETTERS TO DENOTE SUBSTITUENT POSITIONS

Considerable use is made of the Greek letters α, β, γ, etc., to designate successive positions along a hydrocarbon chain. The carbon directly attached to the principal functional group is denoted as α, the second as β, etc.

$$
\begin{array}{c}
\quad\quad CH_3 \\
\quad\quad | \\
CH_2{=}CH{-}C{-}OH \\
\quad\quad | \\
\quad\quad CH_3
\end{array}
$$

$$
\begin{array}{c}
\quad\quad CH_3 \\
\quad\quad | \\
Br_2CH{-}C{-}CO_2H \\
\quad\quad | \\
\quad\quad Br
\end{array}
$$

α, α–dimethylallyl alcohol
(2–methyl–3–buten–2–ol)

α, β, β–tribromoisobutyric acid
(2, 3, 3–tribromo–2–methyl–
propanoic acid)

In general, the use of these names is to be deplored, but since it is widespread, cognizance of the system is important.

11-6   SINGLE- OR MULTIPLE-WORD NAMES

A troublesome point in naming chemical compounds concerns the circumstances that govern whether a compound is written as a single word (e.g., methylamine, trimethylcarbinol) or as two or more words (e.g., methyl alcohol, methyl ethyl ether).   When a compound is named as a derivative of substances such as methane, ammonia, acetic acid, or carbinol because of the substitution of hydrogen for some other atom or group, its name is written as a single word.

$(C_6H_5)_3CH$

triphenylmethane

$$
\begin{array}{c}
CH_3{-}N{-}C_2H_5 \\
\quad\quad | \\
\quad\quad H
\end{array}
$$

methylethylamine[1]

$$
\begin{array}{c}
CH_2{=}CH{-}CH_2{-}C(CH_3)_2 \\
\quad\quad\quad\quad\quad | \\
\quad\quad\quad\quad\quad OH
\end{array}
$$

dimethylallylcarbinol

$CH_2{=}CH{-}CH_2CO_2H$

vinylacetic acid

CH_3MgI

methylmagnesium iodide

C_6H_5Li

phenyllithium

This is correct because we do not speak of "a methane" but of the compound "methane." It follows that a derivative such as $(C_6H_5)_3CH$ is called triphenylmethane and not triphenyl methane.   We do speak, however, of an alcohol, an ether, a halide, acid, ester, sulfide, or ketone, for these words correspond to types of compounds rather than particular compounds.   Therefore additional words are required to fully identify particular alcohols, ethers, halides, etc. Several examples follow.

[1] Amine is a contraction of ammonia.

C_2H_5I

ethyl iodide

$$CH_3\overset{\overset{\displaystyle O}{\|}}{C}OH$$

acetic acid

$(CH_3)_2CHOH$

isopropyl alcohol

$$CH_3\overset{\overset{\displaystyle O}{\|}}{C}OCH_3$$

methyl acetate

$$CH_3\overset{\overset{\displaystyle O}{\|}}{C}CH_2CH_3$$

methyl ethyl ketone

CH_3SCH_3

dimethyl sulfide

$CH_3OCH_2CH_3$

methyl ethyl ether

$$(CH_3\overset{\overset{\displaystyle O}{\|}}{C})_2O$$

acetic anhydride

EXERCISE 11-1   Name each of the following by an accepted system:

a. $CH_3-\overset{\overset{\displaystyle CH_3}{|}}{\underset{\underset{\displaystyle CH_3}{|}}{C}}-CH_2-CH_2OH$

d. $BrCH_2CH_2OCH=CH_2$

b.   ⬡—$\overset{}{\underset{\underset{\displaystyle OH}{|}}{CH}}$—⬠

e. $CH_3-CH=CH-\overset{\overset{\displaystyle CH_3}{|}}{CH}-SH$

c. $CH_3-\underset{\underset{\displaystyle Br}{|}}{CH}-\underset{\underset{\displaystyle Br}{|}}{CH}-CO_2CH_3$

f.   ⬡—$\overset{\overset{\displaystyle CH_3}{|}}{\underset{\underset{\displaystyle NO}{|}}{C}}$—$CH_3$

EXERCISE 11-2   Write bond structures for each of the following:
   a. dimethylvinylamine   d. formic acetic anhydride
   b. allylcarbinyl trimethylacetate   e. α-phenylethanol
   c. N-methyl-N-ethylformamide   f. isoamyl nitrite

NUCLEOPHILIC DISPLACEMENT REACTIONS

11-7 GENERAL CONSIDERATIONS

Broadly defined, a displacement reaction involves the replacement of one functional group (X) by another (Y).

$$RX + Y \longrightarrow RY + X$$

We are here concerned with *nucleophilic* displacement reactions of alkyl derivatives; these are *ionic* or *polar* reactions involving the attack by a nucleophile (i.e., an electron-pair donating reagent) at carbon. A typical example is the reaction of hydroxide ion with methyl bromide to displace bromide ion. The electron pair of the C—O bond to be formed can be regarded as donated by the

$$H\!:\!\ddot{O}\!:^{\ominus} \quad CH_3\!\mid\!:\!\ddot{B}r\!: \quad\longrightarrow\quad CH_3\!:\!\ddot{O}\!:\!H \;+\; :\!\ddot{B}r\!:^{\ominus}$$

hydroxide ion, whereas the electron pair of the C—Br bond to be broken departs

Table 11-2   Typical S_N Displacement Reactions of Alkyl Halides, RX

1. $R\!\mid\!:X + Y\!:^{\ominus} \;\rightarrow\; R\!:\!Y + X\!:^{\ominus}$

Nucleophilic agent	Product	Product name, R = CH_3	Useful solvents
$Cl^{\ominus}$	RCl	methyl chloride	acetone, ethanol
$Br^{\ominus}$	RBr	methyl bromide	acetone, ethanol
$I^{\ominus}$	RI	methyl iodide	acetone, ethanol
$^{\ominus}OH$	ROH	methyl alcohol	water, dioxane-water
$^{\ominus}OCH_3$	$ROCH_3$	dimethyl ether	methyl alcohol
$^{\ominus}SCH_3$	$RSCH_3$	dimethyl sulfide	ethyl alcohol
$CH_3\!-\!\overset{\displaystyle O}{\underset{\displaystyle O^{\ominus}}{C}}$	$RO\!-\!\overset{\displaystyle O}{\underset{\displaystyle CH_3}{C}}$	methyl acetate	acetic acid, ethanol
$^{\ominus}\!:\!C\!\equiv\!N$	RCN	acetonitrile	acetone, dimethyl sulfoxide
$HC\!\equiv\!C\!:^{\ominus}$	$RC\!\equiv\!CH$	methylacetylene	liquid ammonia
$^{\ominus}\!:\!CH(CO_2C_2H_5)_2$	$RCH(CO_2C_2H_5)_2$	diethyl methylmalonate	ethyl alcohol
$^{\ominus}\!:\!NH_2$	RNH_2	methylamine	liquid ammonia
$:\!\overset{\ominus}{N}\!=\!\overset{\oplus}{N}\!=\!\overset{\ominus}{N}\!:$	RN_3	methyl azide	acetone
(phthalimide anion)	RN(phthalimide)	N-methylphthalimide	N,N-dimethylforma-mide
$NO_2^{\ominus}$	RNO_2	nitromethane	N,N-dimethylforma-mide

Table 11-2   Typical S_N Displacement Reactions of Alkyl Halides, RX (*Continued*)

2.
$$R\overset{|}{\underset{|}{:}}X + Y: \rightarrow R:\overset{\oplus}{Y} + \overset{\ominus}{X}:$$

Nucleophilic agent	Product	Product name, R = CH$_3$	Useful solvents
$(CH_3)_3N:$	$R\overset{\oplus}{N}(CH_3)_3 \overset{\ominus}{X}$	tetramethylammonium chloride	ether, benzene
$(C_6H_5)_3P:$	$R\overset{\oplus}{P}(C_6H_5)_3 \overset{\ominus}{X}$	triphenylmethylphos- phonium chloride	ether, benzene
$(CH_3)_2S:$	$R\overset{\oplus}{S}(CH_3)_2 \overset{\ominus}{X}$	trimethylsulfonium chloride	ether, benzene

3.
$$R\overset{|}{\underset{|}{:}}X + H:Y: \rightarrow R:\overset{\oplus}{Y}:\overset{|}{\underset{|}{H}} + X:\overset{\ominus}{} \rightarrow R:Y: + H:X$$

Nucleophilic agent	Product	Product name, R = CH$_3$	Useful solvents
H_2O	ROH	methyl alcohol	water, dioxane- water
CH_3OH	$ROCH_3$	dimethyl ether	methyl alcohol
CH_3CO_2H	$RO\overset{O}{\overset{\|}{C}}CH_3$	methyl acetate	acetic acid
NH_3	RNH_2	methylamine	ammonia, methanol

with the leaving bromide ion.   The name for this type of reaction is abbreviated S_N, S for substitution and N for nucleophilic.

A number of nucleophilic reagents commonly encountered in S_N reactions are listed in Table 11-2 along with the names of the products obtained when they react with methyl chloride.   The nucleophile may be an anion, $Y:\overset{\ominus}{}$, or a neutral molecule, Y: or HY:, and the operation of each is illustrated in the following general equations for a compound RX:

$$R\text{--}X + Y:\overset{\ominus}{} \longrightarrow R\text{--}Y + X:\overset{\ominus}{}$$

$$R\text{--}X + Y: \longrightarrow R\text{--}\overset{\oplus}{Y} + X:\overset{\ominus}{}$$

$$R\text{--}X + HY: \longrightarrow R\overset{\oplus}{Y}H + X:\overset{\ominus}{} \rightarrow RY: + HX$$

The wide range of products listed in Table 11-2 shows the synthetic utility of S_N reactions.   Displacement can result in the formation of bonds between carbon and chlorine, bromine, iodine, oxygen, sulfur, carbon, nitrogen, and phosphorus.

Nucleophilic displacements are by no means confined to alkyl halides. Other alkyl derivatives include alcohols, ethers, esters, and "onium ions."[1] Some illustrative reactions of several different alkyl compounds with various nucleophiles are assembled in Table 11-3.

As we shall see in a later section, the mechanism of an S_N reaction and the reactivity of a given alkyl compound RX toward a nucleophile Y depends upon

Table 11-3 S_N Displacement Reactions of Various Types of Compounds, RX

Type of compound, RX	Reaction
alkyl chloride	$R{-}Cl + I^\ominus \rightleftarrows RI + Cl^\ominus$
alkyl bromide	$R{-}Br + I^\ominus \rightleftarrows RI + Br^\ominus$
alkyl iodide	$R{-}I + CH_3O^\ominus \rightarrow ROCH_3 + I^\ominus$
dialkyl sulfate	$R{-}OSO_2OR + CH_3\overset{\ominus}{O} \rightarrow ROCH_3 + {}^\ominus OSO_2OR$
benzenesulfonate ester	$R{-}O\overset{\displaystyle O}{\underset{\displaystyle O}{\overset{\|}{\underset{\|}{S}}}}{-}\bigcirc + H_2O \rightarrow ROH + HO\overset{\displaystyle O}{\underset{\displaystyle O}{\overset{\|}{\underset{\|}{S}}}}{-}\bigcirc$
acetate ester	$R{-}O\overset{\displaystyle O}{\overset{\|}{C}}CH_3 + H_2O \rightarrow ROH + HO\overset{\displaystyle O}{\overset{\|}{C}}CH_3$
alcohol	$R{-}OH + HBr \rightarrow RBr + H_2O$
ether	$R{-}OR' + HBr \rightarrow RBr + R'OH$
ammonium ion	$R{-}\overset{\oplus}{N}R_3' + HO^\ominus \rightarrow ROH + NR_3'$
iodonium ion	$R{-}\overset{\oplus}{I}{-}R' + OH^\ominus \rightarrow ROH + R'I$
diazonium ion	$R{-}\overset{\oplus}{N}{\equiv}N + H_2O \rightarrow ROH + H^\oplus + N_2$

the nature of R, X, and Y, and upon the nature of the solvent. For reaction to occur at a reasonable rate, it is very important to select a solvent that will dissolve both the alkyl compound and the nucleophilic reagent; considerable assistance may be required from both the solvent and the nucleophile to break the slightly polar C—X bond. However, the highly polar nucleophilic agents most used (e.g., NaBr, NaCN, H₂O) are seldom soluble in the solvents that best dis-

---

[1] Examples of -onium cations follow:

$$R_4N^\oplus \qquad\qquad R_4P^\oplus \qquad\qquad R_3O^\oplus$$
tetraalkylammonium   *tetraalkylphosphonium*   *trialkyloxonium*

$$R_3S^\oplus \qquad\qquad R{-}\overset{\oplus}{N}{\equiv}N:$$
trialkylsulfonium   *alkyldiazonium*

solve slightly polar organic compounds. In practice, relatively polar solvents, or solvent mixtures, such as acetone, aqueous acetone, ethanol, aqueous dioxane, etc., are found to provide the best compromise for reactions between alkyl compounds and salt-like nucleophilic reagents. A number of useful solvents for typical S_N reactions are listed in Table 11-2.

11-8 MECHANISMS OF S_N DISPLACEMENTS

Two mechanisms may be written for the reaction of methyl chloride with hydroxide ion in aqueous solution that differ in the timing of bond breaking in relation to bond making. In the first mechanism, A, the reaction is written as taking place in two steps, the first of which involves a *slow* and reversible dissociation of methyl chloride to methyl cation and chloride ion. The second step involves a *fast* reaction between methyl cation and hydroxide ion (or water) to yield methanol.

Mechanism A:

$$CH_3-Cl \; \underset{\longleftarrow}{\overset{slow}{\rightleftharpoons}} \; CH_3^{\oplus} + Cl^{\ominus}$$

$$CH_3^{\oplus} + OH^{\ominus} \; \xrightarrow{fast} \; CH_3OH$$

or

$$CH_3^{\oplus} + H_2O \longrightarrow CH_3\overset{\oplus}{O}H_2 \; \xrightarrow{OH^{\ominus}} \; CH_3OH + H_2O$$

In the second mechanism, B, the reaction proceeds in a single step. Attack of hydroxide ion at carbon occurs simultaneously with the loss of chloride ion; that is, the carbon-oxygen bond is formed at the same time that the carbon-chlorine bond is broken.

Mechanism B:

$$HO\colon^{\ominus} \quad CH_3\colon Cl\colon \; \xrightarrow{slow} \; CH_3OH + \colon Cl\colon^{\ominus}$$

Of the two mechanisms, A requires that the reaction rate be determined solely by the rate of the first step (cf. earlier discussion, pp. 68-70). This means that the rate at which methanol is formed (measured in moles per unit volume per unit time) will depend on the concentration of methyl chloride, and not on the hydroxide ion concentration, because hydroxide ion is not utilized except in a *fast secondary* reaction. In contrast, mechanism B requires the rate to depend on the concentrations of both reagents since the slow step involves collisions between hydroxide ions and methyl chloride molecules. More precisely, the reaction rate (v) may be expressed in terms of Eq. (11-1) for mechanism A and Eq. (11-2) for mechanism B.

$$v = k[CH_3Cl] \qquad (11\text{-}1)$$

$$v = k[CH_3Cl][OH^{\ominus}] \qquad (11\text{-}2)$$

Customarily, v is expressed in moles of product formed per liter of solution per unit of time (most frequently in seconds). The concentration terms $[CH_3Cl]$ and $[OH^{\ominus}]$ are then in units of moles per liter, and the proportionality constant k (called the **specific-rate constant**) has the dimensions of sec^{-1} for mechanism A and $mole^{-1} \times liters \times sec^{-1}$ for mechanism B.

It is useful to speak of both the *order of a reaction with respect to a specific reactant* and the *over-all order of a reaction*. The order of a reaction with respect to a given reactant is the power to which the concentration must be raised to have direct proportionality between concentration and reaction rate. According to Eq. (11-2) the rate of the methyl chloride-hydroxide ion reaction is first order with respect to both reagents. In Eq. (11-1) the rate is first order in methyl chloride; the order with respect to hydroxide ion may be said to be zero since $[OH^{\ominus}]^0 = 1$. The **over-all order** of reaction is the sum of the orders of the respective reactants. Thus, Eqs. (11-1) and (11-2) express the rates of **first-order** and **second-order** reactions, respectively.

We have, then, a kinetic method for distinguishing between the two possible mechanisms, A and B. Experimentally, the rate of formation of methyl alcohol is found to be proportional to the concentrations of both methyl chloride and hydroxide ion. The reaction rate is second order over-all and is expressed correctly by Eq. (11-2). From this we infer that the mechanism of the reaction is the single-step process B. Reactions having this type of mechanism are generally classified as **bimolecular nucleophilic substitutions,** often designated S_N2, S for substitution, N for nucleophilic, and 2 for bimolecular. The alternate two-step mechanism A is a unimolecular S_N reaction and is accordingly designated S_N1.

EXERCISE 11-3   Ethyl chloride (0.1 M) reacts with potassium iodide (0.1 M) in acetone solution at 60° to give ethyl iodide and potassium chloride at a rate of 5.44×10^{-7} mole/liter/sec.

    a. If the reaction proceeded by an S_N2 mechanism, what would the rate of the reaction be at 0.01 M concentrations of both reactants? Show your method of calculation.

    b. Suppose the rate were proportional to the square of the potassium iodide concentration and the first power of the ethyl chloride (S_N3). What would the rate be with 0.01 M reactants?

    c. If one starts with solutions initially 0.1 M in both reactants, the rate of formation of ethyl iodide is initially 5.44×10^{-7} mole/liter/sec but falls as the reaction proceeds and the reactants are used up. Make plots of the rate of formation of ethyl iodide against the concentration of ethyl chloride as the reaction proceeds (remembering that one molecule of ethyl chloride consumes one molecule of potassium iodide) on the assumption that the rate of reaction is proportional to the first power of the ethyl chloride concentration; and to (1) the zeroth power, (2) the first power, and (3) the second power of the potassium iodide concentration.

    d. What kind of experimental data would one need to tell whether the rate of the reaction of ethyl chloride with potassium iodide is first order in each reactant or second order in ethyl chloride and zero order in potassium iodide?

Many S_N reactions are carried out using the solvent as the nucleophilic agent. They are called **solvolysis** reactions; specific solvents such as water, ethanol, acetic acid, and formic acid produce hydrolysis, ethanolysis, acetolysis, and formolysis reactions, respectively. The rates of all solvolysis reactions are necessarily first order since the solvent is in such great excess that its concentration does not change effectively during reaction, and hence its contribution to the rate does not change. But this does not mean that reaction is necessarily proceeding by an S_N1 mechanism, particularly in solvents such as water, alcohols, or amines, which are expected to be reasonably good nucleophilic agents.

One way to distinguish between S_N1 and S_N2 solvolyses in nucleophilic solvents is to add to the reaction mixture a relatively small concentration of a substance that is expected to be a more powerful nucleophile than the solvent. If the rate of nucleophilic substitution remains essentially unchanged,[1] it usually may be inferred that the reaction mechanism is S_N1; but if the rate of substitution increases significantly, the reaction mechanism is S_N2. For example, the measured rate of formation of t-butyl alcohol from t-butyl chloride is proportional only to the concentration of the halide. Addition of hydroxide ion causes no increase in the substitution rate. This then is evidence that t-butyl chloride hydrolyzes by an S_N1 mechanism.

$$(CH_3)_3C\!-\!Cl \quad \xrightarrow{\text{slow}} \quad (CH_3)_3C^{\oplus} + Cl^{\ominus}$$

$$(CH_3)_3C^{\oplus} + H_2O \quad \xrightarrow{\text{fast}} \quad (CH_3)_3C\!-\!OH + H^{\oplus}$$

$$(CH_3)_3C^{\oplus} + OH^{\ominus} \quad \xrightarrow{\text{fast}} \quad (CH_3)_3C\!-\!OH$$

If, in S_N1 reactions, more than one nucleophile is present, there will be a competition for the carbonium ion and a mixture of products will result. The ratios of the products, but not their over-all rates of formation, are determined by the relative concentrations of the nucleophiles. Thus, an S_N1 solvolysis of a halide in water in the presence of a nucleophile such as azide ion is expected to give both the organic azide and alcohol.

$$R\!-\!Br \quad \xrightarrow[H_2O]{\text{slow}} \quad R^{\oplus} \quad \xrightarrow{\text{fast}} \quad \begin{cases} \xrightarrow[-H^{\oplus}]{H_2O} ROH \\ \\ \xrightarrow{N_3^{\ominus}} RN_3 \end{cases}$$

---

[1] Some change in rate is to be expected if the added substance is a salt because salts, whether nucleophilic or not, change the physical environment of the reacting molecules. A change in rate that is specifically due to reaction of the added nucleophile is best judged by comparison with the effect produced by a *non*nucleophilic substance such as lithium perchlorate.

11-9   STEREOCHEMISTRY OF S_N2 DISPLACEMENTS

If we pause to consider the S_N2 reaction of methyl chloride with hydroxide ion in more detail, we can think of two simple ways in which the reaction could be effected; these differ in the direction of approach of the reagents, one to the other (see Figure 11-1). The hydroxide ion might attack methyl chloride directly at the site where the chlorine is attached (i.e., **front-side** approach). Alternatively, hydroxide might approach the molecule from the rear to cause expulsion of chloride ion from the front (i.e., **back-side** approach).

The stereochemical consequences of front- versus back-side displacement are different. In the case of cyclic compounds, the two types of displacement predict different products. For example, an S_N2 reaction between *cis*-3-methylcyclopentyl chloride and hydroxide ion would give the *cis* alcohol by front-side attack but the *trans* alcohol by back-side attack. The actual product is the *trans* alcohol, from which we infer that reaction occurs by back-side displacement.

back-side approach

front-side approach

Figure 11-1   Back-side (inverting) and front-side (noninverting) attack of hydroxide ion on methyl chloride, as visualized with ball-and-stick models.

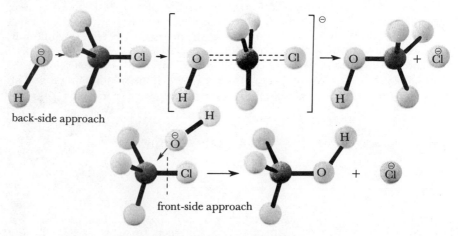

back–side displacement → *trans* alcohol

front–side displacement → *cis* alcohol (not formed)

For open-chain compounds, back-side displacement has been conclusively established with the aid of **optical isomers.** As will be discussed later (see Chapter 17), optical isomers are nonidentical mirror images related to each other as right- and left-handed gloves. For the present discussion, we shall be interested in the type of optical isomer that arises when four *different* groups are attached to a single carbon atom. An example is *s*-butyl chloride, which has four different groups, chlorine, methyl, ethyl, and hydrogen, attached to the number-two carbon and can therefore be obtained in either right-or left-handed forms (Figure 11-2).

$$CH_3CH_2-\overset{\overset{\displaystyle H}{|}}{\underset{\underset{\displaystyle Cl}{|}}{C}}-CH_3 \qquad s\text{-butyl chloride}$$

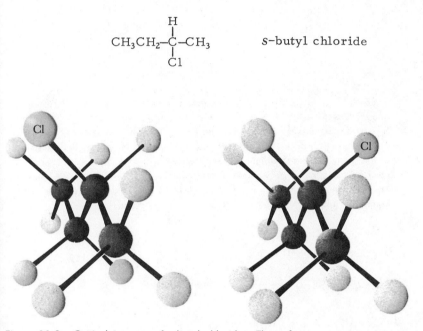

Figure 11-2   Optical isomers of *s*-butyl chloride. These forms are mirror images and are not identical.

The optical isomers of *s*-butyl chloride have identical physical properties with one notable exception. When plane-polarized light is passed through solutions of the separate isomers, one causes the plane of polarization to rotate around the axis of the beam in one direction, whereas the other causes the plane to rotate equally but in the opposite direction (see Figure 11-3).

Reference to the drawings in Figure 11-2 of the optical isomers of *s*-butyl chloride shows that *front-side* displacement of chloride by hydroxide ion will give an *s*-butyl alcohol of the *same* configuration as the original chloride, whereas *back-side* displacement will give the alcohol of *opposite* or *inverted* configuration. The results of experiments using one of the two optical isomers show that hydroxide ion attacks *s*-butyl chloride by back-side approach to give *s*-butyl alcohol of inverted configuration. Similar studies of a wide variety of displacements have established that S_N2 reactions invariably proceed with inversion of configuration via back-side attack. This stereochemical course is commonly known as **Walden inversion.**[1]

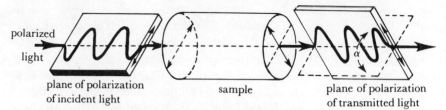

polarized light

plane of polarization of incident light

sample

plane of polarization of transmitted light

Figure 11-3　Schematic representation of the rotation of a plane of polarized light by an optically active compound, with α as the angle of rotation.

EXERCISE 11-4　　　Eqs. (11-3) through (11-5) are illustrative of the approach used by Kenyon and Phillips to establish that inversion of optical configuration accompanies S_N2-type substitutions. Explain how this conclusion can be drawn for Eq. (11-5). The symbols $(+)$ or $(-)$ designate for each compound the sign of the rotation α of the plane of polarized light that it produces. The sign of rotation *cannot* be used by itself to decide whether a compound is right-handed or left-handed. Thus, a right-handed alkyl chloride may have a $(-)$ rotation while the corresponding right-handed alcohol may have a $(+)$ rotation.

$$(+)RO \colon H + CH_3\overset{O}{\overset{\|}{C}}O\overset{O}{\overset{\|}{C}}CH_3 \rightarrow (+)RO\overset{O}{\overset{\|}{C}}CH_3 + CH_3\overset{O}{\overset{\|}{C}}OH \qquad (11\text{-}3)$$

$$(+)RO \colon H \quad \xrightarrow{\text{2 steps}} \quad (+)RO{-}SO_2R' \qquad (11\text{-}4)$$

$$(+)R \colon OSO_2R' + CH_3\overset{O}{\overset{\|}{C}}{-}O^{\ominus} \rightarrow (-)RO\overset{O}{\overset{\|}{C}}CH_3 + {}^{\ominus}OSO_2R' \qquad (11\text{-}5)$$

EXERCISE 11-5　　　Account for the fact that, in the presence of bromide ion, an optical isomer of *s*-butyl bromide **racemizes**, which means that its optical rotation diminishes to zero.

EXERCISE 11-6　　　Use appropriate drawings (Figure 11-2) (or models) to determine the stereochemical result of an S_N2 reaction of hydroxide ion with right-handed molecules of 1-chloro-2-methylbutane.

---

[1] The first documented observation that optically active compounds could react to give products having the opposite optical configuration was made by Walden in 1895. The implications were not understood, however, until the mechanisms of nucleophilic substitution were elucidated in the 1930s, largely through the work of Hughes and Ingold. It was subsequently established that S_N2-type substitutions give products of inverted configuration (see Exercise 11-4).

11-10   STEREOCHEMISTRY OF S$_N$1 REACTIONS

When one carries out an S$_N$1 reaction starting with a single pure optical isomer of a tertiary compound, the product is usually a mixture of both optical
isomers with a slight predominance of the isomer that corresponds to inversion.
Theoretically, a free carbonium ion is most stable in the planar configuration
(see p. 117) and hence might be expected to lead to exactly equal amounts of the
two optical isomers, regardless of the optical configuration of the starting material (Figure 11-4).

The extent of configuration change resulting from an S$_N$1 reaction is expected
to depend, however, upon the degree of "shielding" of the front side of the
reacting carbon by the leaving group and its associated solvent molecules.   If
the leaving group does not get away from the carbonium ion before the product-
determining step, then some preference is expected for nucleophilic attack at
the back side of the carbon, which would result in a predominance of the product of *inverted* configuration.

With an optically active saturated secondary compound, such as 2-octyl *p*-
toluenesulfonate, solvolysis may lead to 100% inversion, which result is probably better regarded as that of an S$_N$2 reaction than that of an S$_N$1 reaction.

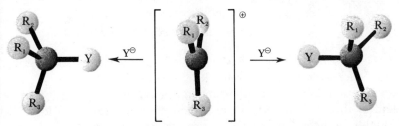

Figure 11-4   Representation of a planar carbonium ion by a ball-and-stick model, with R$_1$, R$_2$, R$_3$
as different alkyl groups, to show the probability of reaction with Y$^\ominus$ to give right-
and left-handed substitution products.

Other things being the same, the amount of inversion decreases as the stability of the carbonium-ion intermediate increases because, the more stable the ion,
the longer is its lifetime, and the more chance it has of becoming a relatively
"free" ion.   The solvent should and does have an influence on the stereochemical results of S$_N$1 reactions because the stability and lifetime of carbonium ions
depend upon the nature of the solvent (see p. 237).

EXERCISE 11-7   What can be concluded about the mechanism of the acetolysis of *n*-butyl
derivatives from the following reaction?

$$\underset{\substack{\\ \text{D}}}{\overset{\substack{\text{H}\\ |}}{CH_3CH_2CH_2-C-OSO_2}}-\!\!\!\left\langle\right\rangle\!\!\!-Br \xrightarrow{CH_3CO_2H} \underset{\substack{\\ \text{H}}}{\overset{\substack{\text{D}\\ |}}{CH_3CH_2CH_2-C}}\overset{\overset{\text{O}}{||}}{-O\overset{}{C}-CH_3}$$

(inverted)

11-11 STRUCTURAL AND SOLVENT EFFECTS IN S_N REACTIONS

We shall consider first the relation between the structures of alkyl derivatives and their reaction rates toward a given nucleophile. This will be followed by a discussion of the relative reactivities of various nucleophiles toward a given alkyl derivative. Finally, we shall comment on the role of the solvent in S_N reactions.

A. Structure of the Alkyl Group, R

The rates of S_N2-displacement reactions of simple alkyl derivatives, RX, follow the order *primary* R > *secondary* R > *tertiary* R. In practical syntheses involving S_N2 reactions, the primary compounds generally work very well, secondary isomers are fair, and the tertiary isomers are completely impractical. Steric hindrance appears to be particularly important in determining S_N2-reaction rates, and the slowness of tertiary halides is best accounted for by steric hindrance to the back-side approach of an attacking nucleophile by the alkyl groups on the α carbon. Neopentyl halides are very unreactive in S_N2 reactions, and scale models indicate this to be the result of steric hindrance by the methyl groups on the β carbon.

$$\begin{array}{c} CH_3 \\ | \\ CH_3-C-CH_2Br \\ | \\ CH_3 \end{array}$$

neopentyl bromide
(slow in S_N2-type reactions)

In complete contrast to S_N2 reactions, the rates of S_N1 reactions of alkyl derivatives follow the order *tertiary* R > *secondary* R > *primary* R.

Steric hindrance is relatively unimportant in S_N1 reactions because the rate is independent of the nucleophile. In fact, *steric acceleration* is possible in the solvolysis of highly branched alkyl halides through relief of steric compression by formation of a planar cation.

$$\begin{array}{ccc} CH_3 & CH_3 & \\ | & | & \\ CH_3-C & \text{---} & C-X \\ | & | & \\ CH_3 & CH_3 & \end{array} \xrightarrow{-X^{\ominus}} \begin{array}{ccc} CH_3 & CH_3 & \\ | & & \\ CH_3-C & & C^{\oplus} \\ | & & \\ CH_3 & CH_3 & \end{array}$$

steric crowding   relief of strain

The reactivity sequence, *tertiary* > *secondary* > *primary*, is to be expected since we know that electron-deficient centers are stabilized more by alkyl groups than by hydrogen. The reason for this is that alkyl groups are *less electron-attracting* than hydrogen.

B. The Leaving Group, X

The reactivity of a given alkyl derivative, RX, in either S_N1 or S_N2 reactions is determined in part by the nature of the leaving group, X. In general, there is a reasonable correlation between the reactivity of RX and the acid strength of H—X, the X groups that correspond to the strongest acids being the best leaving groups. Thus, since H—F is a relatively weak acid and H—I is a very strong acid, the usual order of reactivity of alkyl halides is R—I > R—Br > R—Cl > R—F. Also, the greater ease of breaking a C$\dashv$OSO$_2$C$_6$H$_5$ bond than a C—Cl bond in S_N2 reactions on carbon correlates with the greater acid strength of HOSO$_2$C$_6$H$_5$ in relation to HCl.

Alcohols are particularly *unreactive* in S_N reactions, unless a strong acid catalyst is present. The reason is that the OH$^\ominus$ group is a very poor leaving group. The acid functions by donating a proton to the oxygen of the alcohol, transforming the hydroxyl function into a better leaving group (H$_2$O in place of OH$^\ominus$). Reactions of ethers and esters are acid-catalyzed for the same reasons.

$$\text{ROH} + \text{Br}^\ominus \;\not\!\!\longrightarrow\; \text{RBr} + \overset{\ominus}{\text{OH}} \qquad\qquad\qquad S_N2$$

$$\text{R}:\overset{\cdot\cdot}{\underset{\cdot\cdot}{\text{O}}}:\text{H} + \text{H}^\oplus \;\;\rightleftharpoons\;\; \text{R}:\overset{\overset{\text{H}}{|}}{\underset{\cdot\cdot}{\text{O}}}:\text{H}^\oplus$$

$$\text{R}\!\mid\!\overset{\overset{\text{H}}{|}}{\underset{\cdot\cdot}{\text{O}}}:\text{H}^\oplus + \text{Br}^\ominus \;\longrightarrow\; \text{RBr} + \text{H}_2\text{O} \qquad\qquad S_N2$$

$$\text{R}\!\mid\!\overset{\overset{\text{H}\ \oplus}{|}}{\underset{\cdot\cdot}{\text{O}}}:\text{H} \;\longrightarrow\; \text{R}^\oplus + \text{H}_2\text{O} \;\xrightarrow{\text{Br}^\ominus}\; \text{RBr} \qquad S_N1$$

EXERCISE 11-8   The reaction of alcohols with hydrobromic acid to give alkyl bromides is an equilibrium reaction. Alkyl bromides are usually formed from alcohols and concentrated hydrobromic acid in good yields, whereas alkyl bromides hydrolyze almost completely in neutral water solution. Estimate the change in equilibrium ratio of alkyl bromide to alcohol in changing from a solution with 10 M bromide ion buffered at pH 7 to 10 M hydrobromic acid.

Heavy-metal salts, particularly those of silver, mercury, and copper, catalyze S_N1 reactions of alkyl halides in much the same way as acids catalyze the S_N reactions of alcohols. A heavy-metal ion functions by complexing with the unshared electrons of the halide, making the leaving group a metal halide rather than a halide ion. This acceleration of the rates of halide reactions is the basis for a qualitative test for alkyl halides with silver nitrate in ethanol solution. Silver halide precipitates at a rate that depends upon the structure of the alkyl group, *tertiary* > *secondary* > *primary*. Tertiary halides usually react immediately at room temperature, whereas primary halides require heating.

$$\text{R}:\overset{\cdot\cdot}{\underset{\cdot\cdot}{\text{X}}}: \;\underset{}{\overset{\text{Ag}^\oplus}{\rightleftharpoons}}\; \text{R}:\overset{\cdot\cdot}{\underset{\cdot\cdot}{\text{X}}}:\text{-----Ag}^\oplus \;\xrightarrow[(-\text{AgX})]{\text{slow}}\; \text{R}^\oplus \;\xrightarrow{\text{HY}}\; \text{RY} + \text{H}^\oplus$$

That complexes are actually formed between organic halides and silver ion is indicated by an increase in water solubility in the presence of silver ion for those halides that are slow in forming carbonium ions.

C. The Nucleophilic Reagent

The S_N2 reactivity of a particular reagent towards an alkyl derivative can be defined as its nucleophilicity, which is its ability to donate an electron pair to carbon.

Table 11-4   Reactivities of Various Nucleophiles toward Methyl Bromide in Water at 50°C

Nucleophile	Approximate reaction half-time, hr.[a]	Rate relative to water	K_B
H_2O	1,100[b]	(1)	10^{-6}
$CH_3CO_2^{\ominus}$	2.1	5.2×10^2	10^{-11}
$Cl^{\ominus}$	1	1.1×10^3	$\sim 10^{-20}$
$Br^{\ominus}$	0.17	7.8×10^3	$< 10^{-2}$
$N_3^{\ominus}$	0.11	1.0×10^4	10^{-11}
$HO^{\ominus}$	0.07	1.6×10^4	10^0
$C_6H_5NH_2$	0.04	3.1×10^4	10^{-10}
$SCN^{\ominus}$	0.02	5.9×10^4	10^{-14}
$I^{\ominus}$	0.01	1.1×10^5	$< 10^{-22}$

[a] Time in hours required for half of methyl bromide to react at constant $(1\ M)$ concentration of nucleophile.
[b] Calculated from data for pure water, assuming water to be $55\ M$.

The nucleophilicity of a reagent does not always parallel its basicity, measured by its ability to donate an electron pair to a proton.   The lack of parallelism can be seen from Table 11-4, which indicates the range of reactivities of various nucleophilic agents (toward methyl bromide in water) and their corresponding basicities.   Clearly, a strong base is a good nucleophile (e.g., $OH^{\ominus}$), but a very weak base may also be a good nucleophile (e.g., $I^{\ominus}$).

EXERCISE 11-9   The S_N1 reactions of many RX derivatives that form moderately stable carbonium ions, are substantially *retarded* by added $X^{\ominus}$ ions.   However, such retardation is diminished, at given $X^{\ominus}$ concentrations, by adding another nucleophile such as $N_3^{\ominus}$.   Explain.

EXERCISE 11-10   The relative reactivity of water and $N_3^{\ominus}$ toward methyl bromide is seen from Table 11-4 to be 1:10,000.   Would you expect the relative reactivity of these substances toward the *t*-butyl cation to be larger, smaller, or about the same? Why?

EXERCISE 11-11   The reaction of *n*-butyl chloride with sodium hydroxide to give *n*-butyl alcohol is catalyzed by sodium iodide.
   a. Write a mechanism which accounts for the iodide-ion catalysis.
   b. Work out the stereochemistry to be expected for *both* the catalyzed and the uncatalyzed reactions if right-handed 1-chlorobutane-1-D

$$(CH_3CH_2CH_2-\overset{\displaystyle H}{\underset{\displaystyle D}{\overset{|}{\underset{|}{C}}}}-Cl)$$ were used as the starting material.   Show your reasoning.

c. Does retention of optical configuration, as the over-all result of an S$_N$2 reaction, automatically preclude operation of the usual inversion mechanism? Explain.

D. The Nature of the Solvent

The rates of most S$_N$1 reactions are very sensitive to solvent changes. This is reasonable because the ionizing power of a solvent is crucial to the ease of formation of ions $\overset{\oplus}{R}\text{----}\overset{\ominus}{X}$ from RX.

Actually, two factors are relevant in regard to the ionizing ability of solvents. First, a high dielectric constant increases ionizing power by making it easier to separate ions, the force between charged particles depending inversely upon the dielectric constant of the medium. On this count, water with a dielectric constant of 80 should be much more effective than a hydrocarbon with a dielectric constant of 2. A related, and probably more important, factor is the ability of the solvent to solvate the separated ions. Cations are most effectively solvated by compounds of elements in the first row of the periodic table that have unshared electron pairs. Examples are ammonia, water, alcohols, carboxylic acids, sulfur dioxide, and dimethyl sulfoxide, $(CH_3)_2SO$. Anions are solvated most efficiently by solvents having hydrogen attached to a strongly electronegative element Y so that the H—Y bond is strongly polarized. With such solvents, hydrogen bonds between the solvent and the leaving group assist ionization in much the same way that silver ion catalyzes ionization of alkyl halides (p. 235).

| solvation of a cation by a solvent with un- shared electron pairs | solvation of an anion by a hydrogen–bonding solvent |

The most efficient ionizing solvents will be those that are most effective in solvating both anions and cations. Water appears to strike the best compromise with regard to the structural features that make up ionizing power, that is, dielectric constant and solvating ability. From the foregoing discussion, we should expect t-butyl chloride to hydrolyze more readily in water-alcohol mixtures than in ether-alcohol mixtures, since an ether can only solvate cations effectively whereas water can solvate both anions and cations.

EXERCISE 11-12   Classify the following solvents according to effectiveness expected for solvation of cations and anions:

a. acetone

b. carbon tetrachloride

c. anhydrous hydrogen fluoride

d. chloroform

e. trimethylamine, $(CH_3)_3N$

f. trimethylamine oxide, $(CH_3)_3\overset{\oplus}{N}\text{—}\overset{\ominus}{O}$

ELIMINATION REACTIONS

The reverse of addition to alkene double bonds is elimination. Generally, an alkyl derivative will, under appropriate conditions, eliminate HX, where X is commonly a halide, hydroxyl, ester, or 'onium function, and a hydrogen is located on the carbon adjacent to that bearing the X function.

$$
\begin{array}{c}
-\overset{\displaystyle |}{\underset{\displaystyle H}{C}}-\overset{\displaystyle |}{\underset{\displaystyle X}{C}}- \longrightarrow \quad \overset{\diagdown}{\diagup}C{=}C\overset{\diagup}{\diagdown} \quad + \quad HX
\end{array}
$$

$$
X \;=\; Cl,\; Br,\; I,\; -O\overset{\displaystyle O}{\overset{\|}{C}}-CH_3,\; -\overset{\oplus}{S}R_2,\; -\overset{\oplus}{N}R_3,\; -\overset{\oplus}{O}H_2
$$

Substitution and elimination usually proceed concurrently for alkyl derivatives, and, in synthetic work, it is important to be able to have as much control as possible over the proportions of the possible products. As we shall see, substitution and elimination have rather closely related mechanisms, which fact makes achievement of control much more difficult than if the mechanisms were sufficiently diverse to give very different responses to changes in experimental conditions.

11-12 THE E2 REACTION

Consider the reaction of ethyl chloride with sodium hydroxide.

$$
CH_3CH_2Cl + OH^{\ominus}
\begin{cases}
\nearrow CH_3CH_2OH + Cl^{\ominus} & S_N2 \\
\searrow CH_2{=}CH_2 + H_2O + Cl^{\ominus} & E2
\end{cases}
$$

Elimination to give ethylene competes with substitution to give ethanol. Furthermore, the rate of elimination, like the rate of substitution, is proportional to the concentrations of ethyl chloride and hydroxide ion; thus, elimination is here a second-order reaction, appropriately abbreviated as **E2.** As to its mechanism, the attacking base, $OH^{\ominus}$, removes a proton from the β carbon simultaneously with the formation of the double bond and the loss of chloride ion from the α carbon.

$$
\underset{H\overset{\ominus}{:}\overset{..}{O}:}{}\quad \overset{\beta}{CH_2}{-}\overset{\alpha}{CH_2}\overset{..}{\underset{..}{Cl}}: \longrightarrow \quad H_2O + CH_2{=}CH_2 + Cl^{\ominus}
$$

EXERCISE 11-13   An alternative mechanism for E2 elimination is the following:

$$
CH_3CH_2Cl + OH^{\ominus} \overset{fast}{\rightleftharpoons} \overset{\ominus}{\underset{..}{C}}H_2CH_2Cl + H_2O \overset{slow}{\longrightarrow} CH_2{=}CH_2 + Cl^{\ominus}
$$

> a. Would this mechanism lead to first-order kinetics with respect to the concentrations of $OH^\ominus$ and ethyl chloride? Explain.
>
> b. This mechanism has been excluded for several halides by carrying out the reaction in deuterated solvents such as D_2O and C_2H_5OD. Explain how such experiments could be relevant to the reaction mechanism.

Structural influences on E2 reactions have been studied carefully. For organic halides with a given R group, the rate of elimination varies with X in the order I > Br > Cl > F. For a given X, the ease of elimination follows the order, *tertiary* R > *secondary* R > *primary* R. E2 reactions are only slightly influenced by steric hindrance compared with S_N2 reactions and take place easily with tertiary halides.

Rather strong bases are generally required to bring about the E2 reaction. The effectiveness of a series of bases parallels base strength, and the order $NH_2^\ominus$ > $OC_2H_5^\ominus$ > $OH^\ominus$ > $O_2CCH_3^\ominus$ is observed for E2 reactions. This fact is important in planning practical syntheses, because the E2 reaction tends to predominate with strongly basic, slightly polarizable reagents such as amide ion, $NH_2^\ominus$, or ethoxide ion, $OC_2H_5^\ominus$. On the other hand, S_N2 reactions tend to be favored with weakly basic reagents such as iodide ion or acetate ion. Elimination is also favored over substitution at elevated temperatures.

EXERCISE 11-14   a. Why is potassium *t*-butoxide, $K^\oplus OC(CH_3)_3^\ominus$, an excellent base for promoting elimination reactions of alkyl halides, whereas ethylamine, $CH_3CH_2NH_2$, is relatively poor for the same purpose?

b. Potassium *t*-butoxide is many powers of ten more effective as an eliminating agent in dimethyl sulfoxide than in *t*-butyl alcohol. Explain.

With halides having unsymmetrical R groups, like *t*-amyl chloride, it is possible to have two or more different alkenes formed, depending upon which β hydrogen is removed in the rate-determining step. Most E2 eliminations tend to yield the most stable alkene, which is usually the most highly substituted alkene. However, formation of the least stable or least highly substituted alkene may be favored when the leaving group is bulky or highly electron-attracting, or the base itself is bulky.

$$CH_3-\overset{\overset{\displaystyle CH_3}{|}}{C}-\overset{\beta}{C}H_2-CH_3 \quad 86\% \quad CH_3-\overset{\overset{\displaystyle CH_3}{|}}{C}=CH-CH_3 + H_2O + \overset{\ominus}{Cl}$$

$$\overset{\beta}{CH_3}-\overset{\overset{\displaystyle \overset{\beta}{CH_3}}{|}}{\overset{\alpha}{C}}-\overset{\beta}{CH_2}-CH_3 + \overset{\ominus}{OH}$$

$$14\% \quad CH_2=\overset{\overset{\displaystyle CH_3}{|}}{C}-CH_2CH_3 + H_2O + \overset{\ominus}{Cl}$$

11-13 THE E1 REACTION

Many secondary and tertiary halides undergo **E1** type of elimination in competition with the S_N1 reaction in neutral or acidic solutions.   For example, when *t*-butyl chloride solvolyzes in 80% aqueous ethanol at 25°, it gives 83% of *t*-butyl alcohol by substitution and 17% of isobutylene by elimination.

$$CH_3-\overset{\overset{\displaystyle CH_3}{|}}{\underset{\underset{\displaystyle Cl}{|}}{C}}-CH_3 \xrightarrow{80\% \ C_2H_5OH} \begin{array}{l} \xrightarrow{E1} CH_3-\overset{\overset{\displaystyle CH_3}{|}}{C}=CH_2 \quad 17\% \\ \\ \xrightarrow{S_N1} CH_3-\overset{\overset{\displaystyle CH_3}{|}}{\underset{\underset{\displaystyle OH}{|}}{C}}-CH_3 \quad 83\% \end{array}$$

The ratio of substitution and elimination remains constant throughout the reaction, which means that each process has the same kinetic order with respect to the concentration of *t*-butyl halide.   Usually, but not always, the S_N1 and E1 reactions have a common rate-determining step, namely, slow ionization of the halide.   The solvent then has the choice of attacking the intermediate carbonium ion at carbon to effect substitution, or at a β hydrogen to effect elimination.

$$CH_3-\overset{\overset{\displaystyle CH_3}{|}}{\underset{\underset{\displaystyle Cl}{|}}{C}}-CH_3 \xrightarrow[slow]{H_2O} CH_3-\overset{\overset{\displaystyle CH_3}{|}}{\underset{\underset{\displaystyle \oplus}{}}{C}}-CH_3 \xrightarrow{fast} \begin{array}{l} \xrightarrow{H_2O} CH_3-\overset{\overset{\displaystyle CH_3}{|}}{C}=CH_2 + H_3\overset{\oplus}{O} \quad E1 \\ \\ \xrightarrow{H_2O} CH_3-\overset{\overset{\displaystyle CH_3}{|}}{\underset{\underset{\displaystyle OH}{|}}{C}}-CH_3 + H_3\overset{\oplus}{O} \quad S_N \end{array}$$

EXERCISE 11-15   In the preceding reaction, would you expect the ratio of *t*-butyl alcohol to isobutylene to vary significantly with the nature of the leaving group in the *t*-butyl derivative [i.e., Cl, Br, I or $\overset{\oplus}{S}(CH_3)_2$]?   Why?

Would you expect the same behavior if elimination were occurring by the E2 mechanism with the solvent acting as the base?   Explain.

EXERCISE 11-16   The reaction of *t*-butyl chloride with water is strongly accelerated by sodium hydroxide.   How would the ratio of elimination to substitution products be effected thereby?

EXERCISE 11-17   Write equations and mechanisms for all the products that might reasonably be expected from the reaction of s-butyl chloride with a solution of potassium hydroxide in ethanol.

EXERCISE 11-18   Why is apocamphyl chloride practically inert toward hydroxide ion?

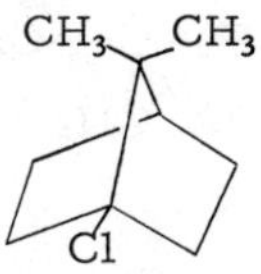

   Structural influences on the E1 reaction are similar to those for the S_N1 reactions and, for RX, the rate orders are $X = I > Br > Cl > F$ and *tertiary* R > *secondary* R > *primary* R. With halides like *t*-amyl chloride, which can give different alkenes depending upon the direction of elimination, it is found that the E1 reaction tends to favor the most stable or highly-substituted alkene.

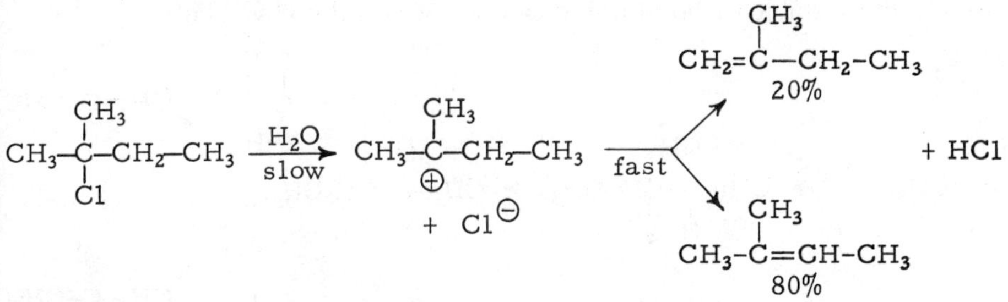

EXERCISE 11-19   Show how the following conversions may be achieved (specify reagents and conditions; note that several steps may be needed). Write a mechanism for each reaction you use. (Note that some of the steps required are described in earlier chapters.)

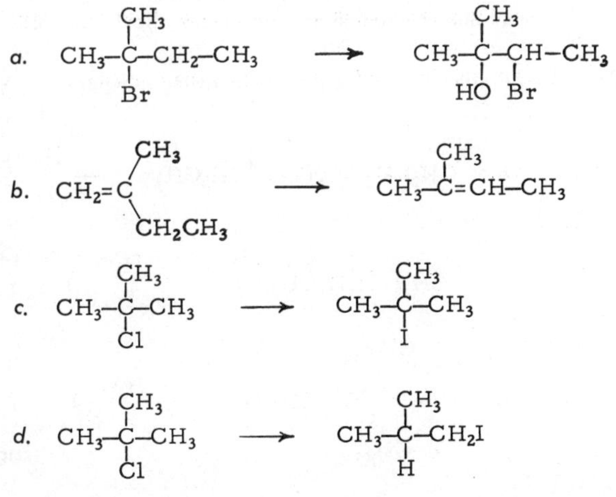

Another feature of E1 reactions (and also of S_N1 reactions) is the prevalency of the initially formed carbonium ion to rearrange, especially if, in doing so, a more stable ion results. For example, the very slow S_N1 formolysis of neopentyl iodide leads predominantly to 2-methyl-2-butene.

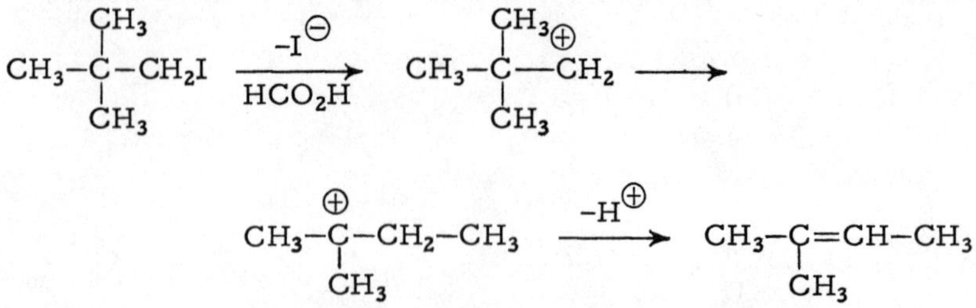

Here, ionization results in migration of a methyl group with its bonding pair of electrons from the β to the α carbon transforming an unstable primary carbonium ion to a relatively stable tertiary cation. Elimination of a proton completes the reaction.

Rearrangements involving shifts of hydrogen (as $H:^\ominus$) occur with comparable ease if a more stable carbonium ion can be formed thereby. Thus

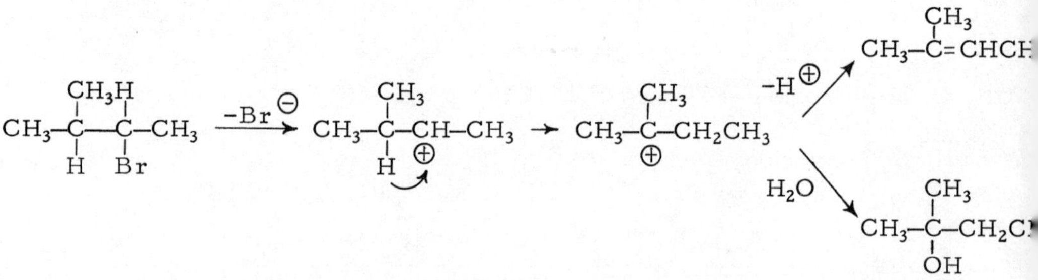

Rearrangements of this type are also discussed in Chapter 13.

EXERCISE 11-20   Explain how $(CH_3)_2CDCHBrCH_3$ might be used to determine whether trimethylethylene is formed directly from the bromide in an E1 reaction, or by rearrangement and elimination as shown in the above equations.

EXERCISE 11-21   Predict the products of the following reactions:

a. $CH_3CH_2CBr(CH_3)CH_2CH_3$ $\xrightarrow[S_N1, \ E1]{H_2O}$

b. $(CH_3)_3CCH(CH_3)Cl$ $\xrightarrow[S_N1, \ E1]{H_2O}$

c. 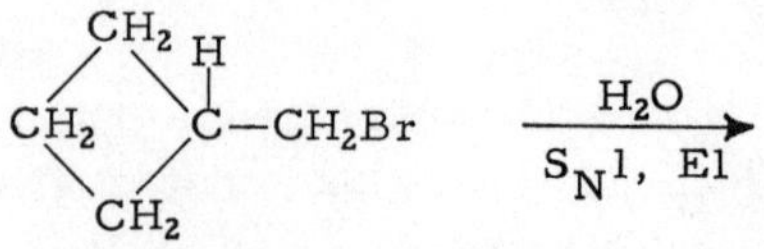 $\xrightarrow[S_N1, \ E1]{H_2O}$

ALKYL, ALKENYL, AND CYCLOALKYL HALIDES

11-14 ALKYL HALIDES

Much of importance regarding the chemistry of alkyl halides was discussed earlier in this chapter in connection with displacement and elimination reactions. The physical properties of alkyl halides are much as one might expect: Volatility decreases (a) with increasing molecular weight along a homologous series, (b) with increasing atomic number of the halogen, and (c) with the structure of the alkyl group in the order *tertiary* > *secondary* > *primary* for isomeric halides.

Methyl chloride, methyl bromide, and most of the lower fluorides are gases at room temperature. The boiling points of many halides are roughly comparable to hydrocarbons of the same molecular weight, but there are many exceptions. Examples are: methyl iodide (M.W. 142), which has b.p. 42°, whereas *n*-decane (M.W. 142) has b.p. 176°; tetrafluoromethane (M.W. 88), which has b.p. $-128°$, midway between the b.p.'s of methane (M.W. 16, b.p. $-162°$) and ethane (M.W. 30, b.p. $-89°$).

The ultraviolet and n.m.r. spectra of the simple alkyl halides were discussed in Chapter 2. The infrared spectra have relatively few bands that are specifically characteristic of alkyl halides. However, C—F bonds give rise to very intense absorption bands in the region of 1350 to 1000 cm^{-1}; C—Cl bonds absorb strongly in the region of 800 to 600 cm^{-1}; whereas C—Br and C—I bonds absorb at still lower frequencies, which are not accessible with spectrometers restricted to sodium chloride optics.

11-15 ALKENYL HALIDES

A. Vinyl Halides

The most readily available vinyl halide is vinyl chloride, which can be prepared by a number of routes.

$$CH{\equiv}CH \ + \ HCl \qquad\qquad\qquad CH_2{=}CH_2 \ + \ Cl_2$$

$$CH_2{=}CHCl$$

$$OH^{\ominus} \diagup E2 \qquad E2 \diagdown OH^{\ominus}$$

$$CH_2{=}CH_2 \ + \ Cl_2 \ \longrightarrow \ \underset{\overset{|}{Cl}\quad\overset{|}{Cl}}{CH_2{-}CH_2} \qquad\qquad CH_3{-}CHCl_2$$

The most feasible commercial preparation is probably by way of high-temperature chlorination of ethylene. Other vinyl chlorides may usually be made by similar procedures, except that direct high-temperature chlorination of alkenes other than ethylene is unlikely to be successful.

The outstanding chemical characteristic of vinyl halides is their general *inertness* in S$_N$1 and S$_N$2 reactions. Thus vinyl chloride, on long heating with solutions of silver nitrate in ethanol, gives no silver chloride, fails to react with potassium iodide by the S_N2 mechanism, and, with sodium hydroxide, only gives acetylene by a slow E2 reaction. The haloacetylenes, such as $RC{\equiv}C{-}Cl$, possess similar inertness in S_N1 and S_N2 reactions. One reason for the low reactivity of vinyl and ethynyl halides is the fact that ethylene and acetylene are stronger acids than alkanes (Table 8-2) which indicates that unsaturated carbons are more strongly electron-attracting than the saturated carbons of alkanes. We expect then, that if it is easier to remove a proton, it will be more difficult to remove a halide ion from vinyl or ethynyl halides in either S_N1 or S_N2 reactions.

The phenyl halides, C_6H_5X, are like the vinyl and ethynyl halides in being very unreactive in both S_N1 and S_N2 reactions. The chemistry of these compounds is discussed in Chapter 23.

B. Allyl Halides

Allyl chloride is made on a commercial scale by the chlorination of propylene at 400°. 1,2-Dichloropropane is a minor product under the reaction conditions.

$$CH_2{=}CH{-}CH_3 \ + \ Cl_2 \ \xrightarrow{\ 400° \ } \ CH_2{=}CH{-}CH_2Cl \ + \ HCl$$

Allyl chloride is an intermediate in the commercial synthesis of glycerol (1,2,3-trihydroxypropane) from propylene.

$$CH_2{=}CHCH_3 \ \xrightarrow{\ Cl_2 \ } \ CH_2{=}CHCH_2Cl \ \xrightarrow{\ H_2O \ } \ CH_2{=}CHCH_2OH$$

$$\xrightarrow{\ HOCl \ } \ \underset{\underset{OH \quad Cl \quad OH}{|\quad\;\;|\quad\;\;|}}{CH_2{-}CH{-}CH_2} \ \xrightarrow{\ H_2O \ } \ \underset{\underset{OH \quad OH \quad OH}{|\quad\;\;|\quad\;\;|}}{CH_2{-}CH{-}CH_2}$$

glycerol

A general method for preparing allylic halides is by addition of halogen acids to conjugated dienes, which usually gives a mixture of 1,2- and 1,4-addition products (see pp. 188-189 and 206-207).

$$CH_2{=}CH{-}CH{=}CH_2 \ + \ HCl \ \longrightarrow \ \underset{\underset{}{|}}{\overset{\overset{Cl}{|}}{CH_3{-}CH}}{-}CH{=}CH_2 \ + \ CH_3CH{=}CH{-}CH_2Cl$$

3-chloro-1-butene	1-chloro-2-butene
(α-methylallyl	(crotyl chloride)
chloride)	

EXERCISE 11-22   Deduce the structures of the two compounds whose n.m.r. and infrared spectra are shown in Figure 11-5. Assign as many of the infrared bands as you can and analyze the n.m.r. spectra in terms of chemical shifts and spin-spin splittings.

In contrast to the vinyl halides, which are characteristically inert, the allyl halides are very reactive—in fact, much more reactive than corresponding saturated compounds in both S_N1 and S_N2 reactions. Other allylic derivatives besides the halides also tend to be unusually reactive in displacement and substitution reactions—the double bond providing an activating effect on breaking the bond

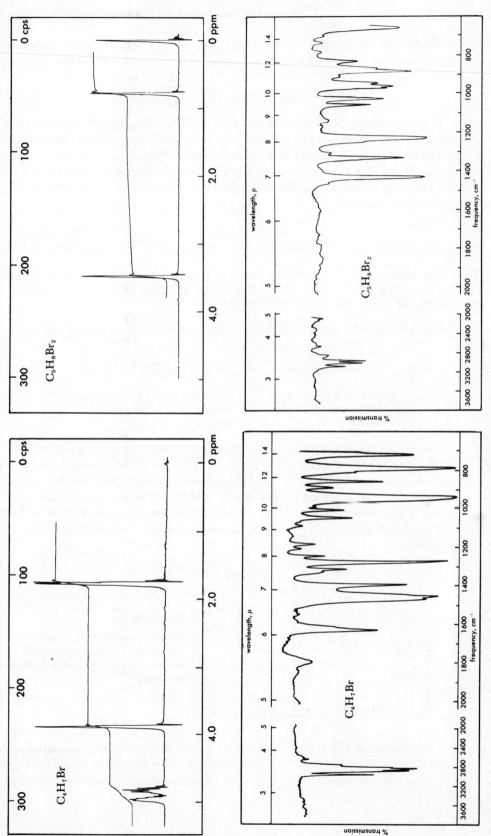

Figure 11-5 Infrared and n.m.r. spectra of substance C₄H₇Br and substance C₅H₈Br₂ (see Exercise 11-22).

to the functional group. A triple bond has a comparable effect and, for example, it is found that the chlorine of 3-chloro-1-propyne is quite labile.

$$HC\equiv C-CH_2Cl \qquad \begin{array}{l} \text{3-chloro-1-propyne} \\ \text{(propargyl chloride)} \end{array}$$

The considerable S_N1 reactivity of allyl chloride compared with n-propyl chloride can be explained by reference to the electronic energies of the intermediate carbonium ions and starting halides, as shown in Figure 11-6. As we have seen previously (p. 188), two equivalent electron-pairing schemes may be written for the allyl cation, which suggest a stabilized hybrid structure with substantially delocalized electrons.

$$CH_2=CH-CH_2Cl \rightarrow \left[CH_2=CH-\overset{\oplus}{CH_2} \leftrightarrow \overset{\oplus}{CH_2}-CH=CH_2 \sim \overset{\frac{1}{2}\oplus}{CH_2}\cdots CH\cdots \overset{\frac{1}{2}\oplus}{CH_2} \right] + Cl$$

(one low-energy electron-pairing scheme)   (two low-energy electron-pairing schemes)   (hybrid structure)

No such stabilized hybrid structure can be written for the n-propyl cation.

$$CH_3-CH_2-CH_2Cl \rightarrow CH_3-CH_2-\overset{\oplus}{CH_2} + \overset{\ominus}{Cl}$$

(one low-energy electron-pairing scheme)   (one low-energy electron-pairing scheme)

Thus, the energy of the allyl cation is *lower* than that of the n-propyl cation and, from Figure 11-6, we see that *less* energy is required to form the allyl cation from allyl chloride than to form the n-propyl cation from n-propyl chloride. A word of caution should be noted here: It is important to recognize that the ease of reaction is determined by the energy differences between the carbocations and the starting halides and not by the energies of the carbocations relative to one another.

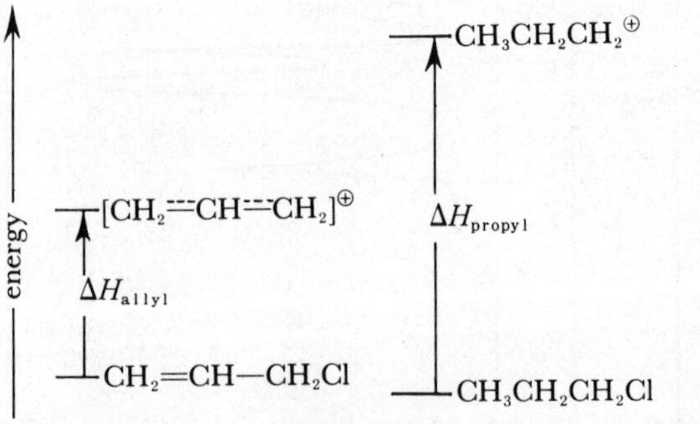

Figure 11-6

The high S_N1 reactivity of allyl chloride compared with n-propyl chloride is here related to the low energy of allyl-cation formation.

The reason for the high S_N2 reactivity of allylic compounds compared with alkyl compounds is not completely understood. One possibility is that the highest point on the energy barrier (p. 74), or transition state, between the reactants and products can be more easily reached if there is stabilization involving delocalization of the double-bond electrons.

$$CH_2=CH-CH_2Cl + \overset{\ominus}{O}H \rightarrow \left[\begin{array}{c} \overset{\delta\ominus}{}OH \\ | \\ CH_2\text{---}CH\text{---}CH_2 \\ \overset{\delta\ominus}{}Cl \end{array} \right] \rightarrow CH_2=CH-CH_2OH + Cl^\ominus$$

transition state

EXERCISE 11-23   a. Write resonance structures for the transition states of S_N2 substitution for allyl and n-propyl chlorides with hydroxide ion and show how these can account for the greater reactivity of the allyl compound.

b. Would you expect that electron-donating or electron-withdrawing groups substituted at the γ-carbon of allyl chloride would increase the S_N2 reactivity of allyl chloride?

11-16 CYCLOALKYL HALIDES

The cycloalkyl halides have physical and chemical properties which are generally similar to those of the open-chain secondary halides and can usually be prepared by the same types of reactions. All the cycloalkyl halides undergo S_N2 reactions rather slowly and, with nucleophiles that are reasonably basic ($\overset{\ominus}{O}H$, $\overset{\ominus}{O}C_2H_5$, $\overset{\ominus}{C}\equiv N$, etc.), E2 reactions can be expected to predominate. The rate of carbonium-ion formation leading to S_N1 and E1 reactions is relatively sensitive to ring size but, except for the small-ring halides, the carbonium-ion reactions are normal in most other respects.

The cyclopropyl halides are exceptional in behaving much more like vinyl halides than like secondary alkyl halides. Thus cyclopropyl chloride undergoes S_N1 and S_N2 reactions many powers of ten more slowly than isopropyl or cyclohexyl chlorides. A relationship between the reactivity of cyclopropyl chloride and vinyl chloride is of course not surprising in view of the general similarity between cyclopropane rings and double bonds (pp. 94-95). This similarity extends to cyclopropylcarbinyl derivatives as well. Cyclopropylcarbinyl chloride is reactive in both S_N1 and S_N2 reactions in much the same way as allyl chloride.

$$\begin{array}{c} CH_2 \\ | \diagdown \\ CH-CH_2Cl \\ | \diagup \\ CH_2 \end{array} \qquad \text{cyclopropylcarbinyl chloride}$$

11-17 POLYHALOGEN COMPOUNDS

Polychlorination of methane affords the di-, tri-, and tetrachloromethanes cheaply and efficiently.

$$CH_2Cl_2 \qquad\qquad CHCl_3 \qquad\qquad CCl_4$$

dichloromethane	trichloromethane	tetrachloromethane
(methylene chloride)	(chloroform)	(carbon tetrachloride)
b.p. 40°	b.p. 61°	b.p. 77°

These substances have excellent solvent properties for nonpolar and slightly polar substances. Chloroform was once widely used as an inhalation anesthetic but has a deleterious effect on the heart and is slowly oxidized by atmospheric oxygen to highly toxic phosgene ($COCl_2$). Commercial chloroform contains about 1% ethanol to destroy any phosgene formed by oxidation.

Carbon tetrachloride is very commonly employed as a cleaning solvent, although its considerable toxicity entails some hazard in indiscriminate use. Carbon tetrachloride is also used as an efficient fire-extinguishing fluid for petroleum fires, although its tendency to phosgene formation makes it undesirable for confined areas. The common laboratory practice of removing traces of water from solvents with metallic sodium should not be applied to halogenated compounds. Carbon tetrachloride-sodium mixtures can detonate and are shock sensitive.

Trichloroethylene ("Triclene," b.p. 87°) is a widely used dry-cleaning solvent. It may be prepared from either ethylene or acetylene.

$$HC\equiv CH + 2\ Cl_2 \longrightarrow CHCl_2-CHCl_2 \xrightarrow[\text{E2}]{Ca(OH)_2}$$

$$CH_2=CH_2 + 3\ Cl_2 \xrightarrow[(-3\ HCl)]{300°}$$

$$\underset{Cl}{\overset{H}{\diagdown}}C=C\underset{Cl}{\overset{Cl}{\diagup}}$$

Methylene chloride reacts with hydroxide ion by an S_N2 mechanism very much less readily than methyl chloride. The chloromethanol formed then undergoes a rapid E2 elimination to give formaldehyde, a substance that exists in water largely as dihydroxymethane (formaldehyde hydrate).

$$CH_2Cl_2 \xrightarrow[\underset{S_N2}{\text{slow}}]{\ominus OH} \left[\begin{matrix} O{-}H \\ CH_2 \\ Cl \end{matrix} \right] \xrightarrow[\underset{E2}{\text{fast}}]{OH^\ominus} H_2C=O \xrightarrow[\text{fast}]{H_2O} \left[\begin{matrix} OH \\ CH_2 \\ OH \end{matrix} \right]$$

Carbon tetrachloride is even less reactive than methylene chloride. One might expect chloroform to be intermediate in reactivity between methylene chloride and carbon tetrachloride, but chloroform is surprisingly reactive toward hydroxide ion and ultimately gives carbon monoxide, formate, and chloride ions. We may then infer that a different reaction mechanism is involved. Apparently, a strong base, such as hydroxide ion, attacks the chloroform molecule much more rapidly at hydrogen than at carbon. There is strong evidence to show that the carbanion so formed, $Cl_3C:^\ominus$, can eliminate chloride ion to give a highly reactive intermediate of bivalent carbon, $:CCl_2$, called **dichlorocarbene.** This intermediate has only *six* valence electrons around carbon (two covalent bonds), and, although it is electrically neutral, it is powerfully electrophilic, and rapidly attacks the solvent to give the final products.

$$Cl_3C\!:\!|H \;+\; \overset{\ominus}{O}H \quad \rightleftharpoons \quad Cl_3C\!:\!^{\ominus} \;+\; H_2O$$

$$Cl_3C\!:\!^{\ominus} \quad \xrightarrow{\text{slow}} \quad :CCl_2 \;+\; Cl^{\ominus}$$

$$:CCl_2 \quad \xrightarrow{H_2O,\ \text{fast}} \quad \begin{cases} CO \;+\; 2Cl^{\ominus} \\[6pt] HC\!\!\overset{O}{\underset{O^{\ominus}}{\diagup}}\ \ +\ 2Cl^{\ominus} \end{cases}$$

Note the analogy between this mechanism for the hydrolysis of chloroform and the elimination mechanism of Exercise 11-13. Both reactions involve a carbanion intermediate, but subsequent elimination from a β carbon leads to an alkene, and from an α carbon to a carbene. Carbene formation is the result of **1,1- or α-elimination.**

The electrophilic nature of dichlorocarbene, $:CCl_2$, and other carbenes, including carbene itself, $:CH_2$ (sometimes called methylene), can be profitably used in synthetic reactions. Alkene double bonds can provide electrons, and carbenes react with an alkene by *cis* addition to the double bond to give cyclopropane derivatives—by what can be characterized as a ***cis* 1,1-cycloaddition** to the double bond. We now have examples of 1,1-, 1,2- (p. 210), 1,3- (pp. 149-150), and 1,4-cycloadditions (pp. 207-210).

Activated carbenes, such as are formed from the light-induced decomposition of diazomethane (CH_2N_2), even react with the electrons of a carbon-hydrogen bond to "insert" the carbon of the carbene between carbon and hydrogen. This transforms $-C-H$ to $-C-CH_3$.

$$-\!\!\overset{|}{\underset{|}{C}}\!:\!H \;+\; :CH_2 \quad \longrightarrow \quad -\!\!\overset{|}{\underset{|}{C}}\!-CH_2\!-H$$

The $:CH_2$ formed from the light-induced decomposition of diazomethane is one of the most reactive reagents known in organic chemistry. More selective carbene reactions are possible by elimination of zinc iodide from iodomethylzinc iodide, ICH_2ZnI, which leads only to cyclopropane formation with simple alkenes.

EXERCISE 11-24   What products would you expect from the reaction of bromoform, $CHBr_3$, with potassium *t*-butoxide in *t*-butyl alcohol in the presence of (a) *trans*-2-butene, (b) *cis*-2-butene?

EXERCISE 11-25   The rate of formation of the CH_2-addition product from iodomethylzinc iodide and cyclohexene is first order in each participant. Suggest a mechanism that is in accord with this fact.

11-18 FLUORINATED ALKANES

A. Fluorochloromethanes

Replacement of either one or two of the chlorines of carbon tetrachloride by fluorine can be readily achieved with the aid of antimony trifluoride containing some antimony pentachloride. The reaction stops after two chlorines have been replaced. The antimony trifluoride may be regenerated continuously from the antimony chloride by addition of anhydrous hydrogen fluoride.

$$3\ CCl_4 + SbF_3 \xrightarrow{\ SbCl_5\ } 3\ CFCl_3 + SbCl_3$$
$$\text{b. p. } 25°$$

$$3\ CCl_4 + 2\ SbF_3 \xrightarrow{\ SbCl_5\ } 3\ CF_2Cl_2 + 2\ SbCl_3$$
$$\text{b. p. } -30°$$

Both products have considerable utility as refrigerants, particularly for household refrigerators and air-conditioning units, under the trade name "Freon." Difluorodichloromethane (Freon 12) is also employed as a propellant in aerosol bombs, shaving-cream dispensers, and other such containers. It is nontoxic, odorless, noninflammable, and will not react with hot concentrated mineral acids or metallic sodium. This lack of reactivity is quite generally characteristic of the difluoromethylene group, provided the fluorines are not located on an unsaturated carbon. Attachment of fluorine to a carbon atom carrying one or more chlorines tends greatly to reduce the reactivity of the chlorines toward almost all types of reagents.

B. Fluorocarbons

During World War II, plastics and lubricating compounds of unusual chemical and thermal stability were required for many applications and, in particular, for pumping apparatus used for separating U^{235} from U^{238}, by diffusion of very corrosive uranium hexafluoride through porous barriers. It was natural to consider the use of substances made of only carbon and fluorine (fluorocarbons) for such purposes, and considerable effort was spent on methods of preparing compounds like $+CF_2+_n$.

The obvious routes for preparation of fluorocarbons by direct fluorination of alkanes, or by antimony fluoride exchange on chlorocarbons, are not always satisfactory.

$$-(CH_2)_n + 2n \cdot F_2 \longrightarrow -(CF_2)_n + 2n \cdot HF \qquad \Delta H = -2n \cdot 115 \, \text{kcal}$$

$$-(CH_2)_n \xrightarrow{2n \cdot Cl_2} -(CCl_2)_n \xrightarrow[SbCl_5]{SbF_3} -(CF_2)_n$$

Direct fluorination is highly exothermic and exceedingly difficult to control, and neither perchlorination of an alkane, nor exchange of fluorine for chlorine of a chlorocarbon, can be carried to practical completion.

An indirect hydrocarbon-fluorination process, using cobalt trifluoride as a fluorinating intermediate, works quite well because the trifluoride is a more moderate reagent than elemental fluorine. Cobalt trifluoride is made by passing fluorine through a bed of cobalt difluoride.

$$2 \, CoF_2 + F_2 \longrightarrow 2 \, CoF_3 \qquad \Delta H = -58 \, \text{kcal}$$

The hydrocarbon is then passed through the cobalt trifluoride until only cobalt difluoride is left. The trifluoride can then be regenerated with fluorine gas. The heat of hydrocarbon fluorination with cobalt trifluoride is about one-half that of direct fluorination.

$$-(CH_2)_n + 4n \cdot CoF_3 \longrightarrow -(CF_2)_n + 2n \cdot HF + 4n \cdot CoF_2$$

$$\Delta H = -2n \cdot 57 \, \text{kcal}$$

This type of reaction yields about 90% of perfluoroheptane (C_7F_{16}, **perfluoro** means all hydrogens replaced by fluorine) with n-heptane and about 70% of a fluorocarbon oil from paraffin oil. The cost of the process is high because of the expense of preparing and handling elemental fluorine, and because half the fluorine is converted back to cheap hydrogen fluoride.

A plastic material of the type $-(CF_2)_n$ is produced in quantity by free-radical polymerization of tetrafluoroethylene.

$$n \cdot CF_2 {=} CF_2 \xrightarrow{R \cdot} -(CF_2 {-} CF_2)_n$$

The product ("Teflon") is a solid, very chemically inert substance, which is stable to around 300°. It makes excellent electrical insulation and gasket materials. It also has self-lubricating properties, which are exploited in the preparation of low-adhesion surfaces and light-duty bearing surfaces.

Tetrafluoroethylene can be made on a commercial scale by the following route:

$$3 \, CHCl_3 + 2 \, SbF_3 \xrightarrow{SbCl_5} CHClF_2$$

$$2 \, CHClF_2 \xrightarrow[90\% \text{ yield}]{700-900°} CF_2 {=} CF_2 + 2 \, HCl$$

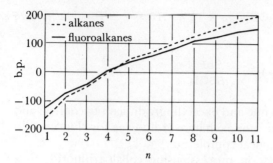

Figure 11-7

Boiling points of straight-chain fluoro-carbons (C_nF_{2n+2}) and hydrocarbons (C_nH_{2n+2}).

Free-radical polymerization of chlorotrifluoroethylene gives a useful polymer ("Kel-F") that is similar to polytetrafluoroethylene ("Teflon").

An excellent elastomer of high chemical resistance ("Viton") can be made by copolymerizing hexafluoropropylene with 1,1-difluoroethylene. The product is stable to 300° C and is not attacked by red fuming nitric acid.

C. Properties of Fluorocarbons

The fluorocarbons have extraordinarily low boiling points relative to the hydrocarbons of comparable molecular weights, and as seen in Figure 11-7, their boiling points are nearly the same or even lower than those of the alkanes with the same number of carbons. Octafluorocyclobutane boils 17° lower than cyclobutane, despite a 350% greater molecular weight. The high stability and low-boiling point of octafluorocyclobutane make it of wide potential use as a propellant in the pressure packaging of food.

$$CH_2\text{—}CH_2 \quad\quad\quad CF_2\text{—}CF_2$$
$$|\quad\quad\quad | \quad\quad\quad\quad |\quad\quad\quad |$$
$$CH_2\text{—}CH_2 \quad\quad\quad CF_2\text{—}CF_2$$

b. p. + 12°   b. p. −5°

mol. wt. = 56   mol. wt. = 200

Fluorocarbons are very insoluble in most polar solvents and are only slightly soluble in alkanes in the kerosene range. The higher-molecular-weight fluoro-carbons are not even miscible in all proportions with their lower-molecular-weight homologs.

The physiological properties of organofluorine compounds vary exceptionally widely. Dichlorodifluoromethane and the saturated fluorocarbons appear to be completely nontoxic. On the other hand, perfluoroisobutylene is exceedingly toxic, more so than the war gas, phosgene ($COCl_2$). Sodium fluoroacetate (CH_2FCO_2Na) and 2-fluoroethanol are toxic fluorine derivatives of oxygen-containing organic substances. The fluoroacetate salt is sold commercially as a rodenticide. Interestingly, sodium trifluoroacetate is nontoxic.

SUPPLEMENTARY EXERCISES

11-26 Write structural formulas for each of the following substances:

  a. isoamyl alcohol
  b. 2-methyl-3-buten-2-ol
  c. dineopentylcarbinol
  d. α,β-dibromopropionic acid
  e. methyl vinylcarbinyl ether
  f. 9-(2,6,6-trimethyl-1-cyclohexenyl)-3,7-dimethyl-2,4,6,8-nonatetraen-1-ol

11-27 Name each of the following by IUPAC system and, where applicable, by the carbinol (or substituted-acid) systems:

  a. $HC{\equiv}C-CH_2OH$

  $$d.\quad CH_3-\underset{\underset{\displaystyle CH_3}{|}}{\overset{\overset{\displaystyle CH_3}{|}}{C}}-CH_2CO_2H$$

  $$b.\quad CH_3-\underset{\underset{\displaystyle CH_3}{|}}{\overset{\overset{\displaystyle CH_3}{|}}{C}}-\underset{\underset{\displaystyle OH}{|}}{CH}-CH_3$$

  $$e.\quad CH_3-CH-\underset{\underset{\displaystyle Cl}{|}}{\overset{\overset{\displaystyle CH_3}{|}}{CH}}-\underset{\underset{\displaystyle OH}{|}}{CH}-CO_2H$$

  c.

  f.

11-28 Indicate how you would synthesize each of the following substances from the given organic starting materials and any other necessary organic or inorganic reagents. Specify reagents and conditions.

  a. dimethylacetylene from acetylene
  b. 3-chloropropyl acetate from 3-chloro-1-propene
  c. methyl ethyl ether from ethanol
  d. methyl t-butyl ether from isobutylene
  e. 1-iodo-2-chloropropane from propylene

11-29 Which one of the following pairs of compounds would you expect to react more readily with (A) potassium iodide in acetone, (B) concentrated sodium hydroxide in ethanol, and (C) silver nitrate in aqueous ethanol? Write equations for all the reactions involved and give your reasoning with respect to the predicted orders of reactivity.

  a. methyl chloride and isobutyl chloride with A, B and C.
  b. methyl chloride and t-butyl chloride with A, B and C.
  c. t-butyl chloride and 1-fluoro-2-chloro-2-methylpropane with B and C.
  d. allyl and allylcarbinyl chlorides with A, B, and C.

11-30 Explain what inferences about the stereochemistry of the E2 reaction can be gained from the knowledge that the basic dehydrohalogenation of A is exceedingly slow compared with that of B.

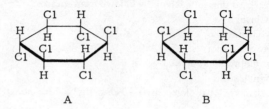

A   B

11-31 Classify each of the following reactions from the standpoint of yield, side reactions, and reaction rate as good, fair, or bad synthetic procedures for preparation of the indicated products under the given conditions. Show your reasoning and designate any important side reactions.

a. $CH_3-\overset{\underset{\displaystyle CH_3}{|}}{\underset{\underset{\displaystyle CH_3}{|}}{C}}-Cl$ + $CH_3-\overset{\underset{\displaystyle CH_3}{|}}{\underset{\underset{\displaystyle CH_3}{|}}{C}}-ONa$ $\xrightarrow{50°}$ $CH_3-\overset{\underset{\displaystyle CH_3}{|}}{\underset{\underset{\displaystyle CH_3}{|}}{C}}-O-\overset{\underset{\displaystyle CH_3}{|}}{\underset{\underset{\displaystyle CH_3}{|}}{C}}-CH_3$ + NaCl

b. CH_3-I + $CH_3-\overset{\underset{\displaystyle CH_3}{|}}{\underset{\underset{\displaystyle CH_3}{|}}{C}}-OH$ $\xrightarrow{25°}$ CH_4 + $CH_3-\overset{\underset{\displaystyle CH_3}{|}}{\underset{\underset{\displaystyle CH_3}{|}}{C}}-O-I$

c. $CH_3-\overset{\underset{\displaystyle Cl}{|}}{\underset{}{CH}}-\overset{\underset{\displaystyle CH_3}{|}}{\underset{}{CH}}-CH_3$ $\xrightarrow[100°]{H_2O}$ $CH_3-\overset{\underset{\displaystyle CH_3}{|}}{\underset{}{CH}}-CH=CH_2$ + HCl

d. $\xrightarrow[\substack{acetone,\\ reflux}]{NaI}$

e. $CH_3-\overset{\underset{\displaystyle CH_3}{|}}{\underset{\underset{\displaystyle CH_3}{|}}{C}}-CH_2Cl$ + $CH_3\overset{\displaystyle O}{\overset{\|}{C}}-\overset{\ominus\oplus}{O}Na$ $\xrightarrow{50°}$ $CH_3-\overset{\underset{\displaystyle CH_3}{|}}{\underset{\underset{\displaystyle CH_3}{|}}{C}}-CH_2-O-\overset{\displaystyle O}{\overset{\|}{C}}-CH_3$ + NaCl

f. $CH_3-\overset{\underset{\displaystyle CH_3}{|}}{\underset{\underset{\displaystyle CH_3}{|}}{C}}-Cl$ + $CH_3CH_2OCH_2CH_3$ $\xrightarrow{35°}$ $CH_3-\overset{\underset{\displaystyle CH_3}{|}}{\underset{\underset{\displaystyle CH_3}{|}}{C}}-O-CH_2CH_3$ + CH_3CH_2Cl

g. $CH_2=CHCl$ + $CH_3\overset{\displaystyle O}{\overset{\|}{C}}-\overset{\ominus\ \oplus}{O}Ag$ $\xrightarrow{25°}$ $CH_2=CH-O-\overset{\displaystyle O}{\overset{\|}{C}}-CH_3$ + AgCl

h. $CH_2=CH-CH_2Cl$ + $1/3\ SbF_3$ $\xrightarrow{50°}$ $CH_2=CH-CH_2F$ + $1/3SbCl_3$

11-32 Consider each of the following compounds to be in unlabeled bottles in pairs as indicated. Give for each pair a *chemical* test (preferably a test tube reaction) that will distinguish between the two substances.

	Bottle A	Bottle B
a.	$(CH_3)_3CCH_2Cl$	$CH_3CH_2CH_2CH_2Cl$
b.	$BrCH=CHCH_2Cl$	$ClCH=CHCH_2Br$
c.	$(CH_3)_3CCl$	$(CH_3)_2CHCH_2Cl$
d.	$CH_3CH=CHCl$	$CH_2=CHCH_2Cl$
e.	$(CH_3)_2C=CHCl$	$CH_3CH_2CH=CHCl$
f.	$CH_3CH_2CH=CHCl$	$CH_2=CHCH_2CH_2Cl$

11-33 Show how the pairs of compounds listed in Exercise 11-32 could be distinguished by spectroscopic means.

Organometallic Compounds

*R*esearch on the chemistry of organometallic compounds has progressed rapidly in recent years. A number of magnesium, aluminum, and lithium organometallics are now commercially available, and are used on a large scale despite their being extremely reactive to water, oxygen, and almost all organic solvents other than hydrocarbons or ethers. This high degree of reactivity is one reason for the interest in organometallic chemistry, because compounds with high reactivity generally enter into a wide variety of reactions and are therefore of value in synthetic work. However, just as interesting, and even more important, is the fact that organometallic compounds are often very selective in their reactions. An excellent example is provided by ethylene polymerization. The Ziegler catalysts discussed in Chapter 7, which can be made from trialkylaluminum compounds and titanium tetrachloride, convert ethylene to high-molecular-weight polymer. On the other hand, triethylaluminum achieves the polymerization of ethylene to relatively short-chain 1-alkenes (C_4, C_6, C_8, C_{10}, and C_{12}).

In this chapter we shall try to correlate the chemical and physical properties of some of the important kinds of organometallic compounds, a very significant common denominator being the degree of ionic character of the carbon-metal bonds. The synthetic usefulness and limitations of the organomagnesium compounds (Grignard reagents) will be considered in detail. Finally, we shall discuss the stereochemistry of reactions of organometallic compounds, a subject that is of particular current interest.

Organometallic Compounds

Organometallic compounds are most simply defined as substances possessing carbon-metal bonds. This definition excludes substances like sodium acetate and sodium methoxide, since these are best regarded as having oxygen-metal bonds. Among the common metallic elements that form reasonably stable organic derivatives are the alkali metals of Group I of the periodic table (lithium, sodium, and potassium), the alkaline earth metals of Group II (magnesium and calcium), aluminum of Group III, tin and lead of Group IV, and the transition metals, such as zinc, cadmium, iron, nickel, chromium, and mercury. The organic group can be alkyl, alkenyl, alkynyl, or aryl. Some typical examples follow:

Group I (alkali)	*Group II* (alkaline earth)	*Group III*	*Group IV*
$CH_2=CHLi$ vinyllithium	C_6H_5MgBr phenylmagnesium bromide	$[(CH_3)_2Be]_n$ dimethylberyllium (polymer)	CH_3SnCl_3 methyltin trichloride
CH_3CH_2Na ethylsodium	$(CH_3)_2Ca$ dimethylcalcium	$[(CH_3)_3Al]_2$ trimethylaluminum (dimer)	$(CH_3CH_2)_4Pb$ tetraethyllead

257

Transition Metals

$(C_2H_5)_2Zn$	CH_3CdCl	C_6H_5HgCl	$(CH_3CH_2)_2Hg$
diethylzinc	methylcadmium chloride	phenylmercuric chloride	diethylmercury

Less typically metallic elements (the metalloids) such as boron, silicon, germanium, selenium, arsenic, etc., also form organic derivatives, some of which are quite important, but these fall between true metallic and nonmetallic organic compounds. They are best considered separately and will not be included in the present discussion.

12-1 GENERAL PROPERTIES OF ORGANOMETALLIC COMPOUNDS

The physical and chemical properties of organometallic compounds vary over an extraordinarily wide range and can be well correlated with the degree of ionic character of the carbon-metal bonds present. This varies from substantially ionic, in the case of sodium acetylide, $CH{\equiv}C{:}^{\ominus}Na^{\oplus}$, to essentially covalent, as in tetraethyllead $(C_2H_5)_4Pb$. The more electropositive the metal, the more ionic is the carbon-metal bond, with carbon at the negative end of the dipole,

$$\overset{\delta\ominus}{-\underset{|}{\overset{|}{C}}{:}} \quad \overset{\delta\oplus}{Metal}$$

Values for the estimated per cent ionic character of various carbon-metal bonds of saturated (tetrahedral) carbon are given in Table 12-1.

The reactivity of organometallic compounds increases with the ionic character of the carbon-metal bond. It is not then surprising that organosodium and organopotassium compounds are among the most reactive organometallics. They are spontaneously inflammable in air, react violently with water and carbon dioxide, and, as might be expected from their saltlike character, they are involatile and do not readily dissolve in nonpolar solvents. In contrast, the more covalent compounds like organomercurials [e.g., $(CH_3)_2Hg$] are far less reactive; they are relatively stable in air, much more volatile, and will dissolve in nonpolar solvents.

The fact that organometallic compounds have only partly covalent carbon-metal bonds means that the metal atom does not normally have a full shell of valence electrons. Thus, an aluminum atom in trimethylaluminum has formally six electrons in its outer valence shell.

$$\underset{CH_3 \quad CH_3}{\overset{CH_3}{\overset{\cdot\cdot}{\underset{\cdot\cdot \quad \cdot\cdot}{Al}}}} \qquad \text{trimethylaluminum}$$

Table 12-1   Per Cent Ionic Character of Carbon-Metal Bonds [a]

C—K	51	C—Mg	35	C—Sn	12
C—Na	47	C—Al	22	C—Pb	12
C—Li	43	C—Zn	18	C—Hg	9
C—Ca	43	C—Cd	15		

[a] L. Pauling, *The Nature of the Chemical Bond*, Cornell University Press, 1960, Chap. 3.

Some, but by no means all, organometallic compounds of this kind have a considerable tendency to exist as dimers or even as polymers, the bonding between the metal atoms involving the alkyl groups or halogen, if present. Examples include

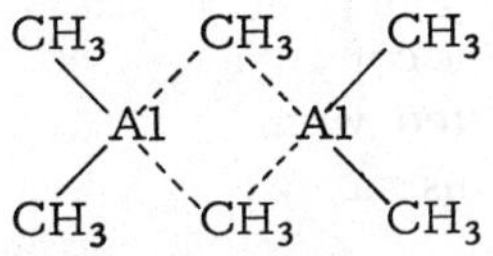

trimethylaluminum

(dimer)

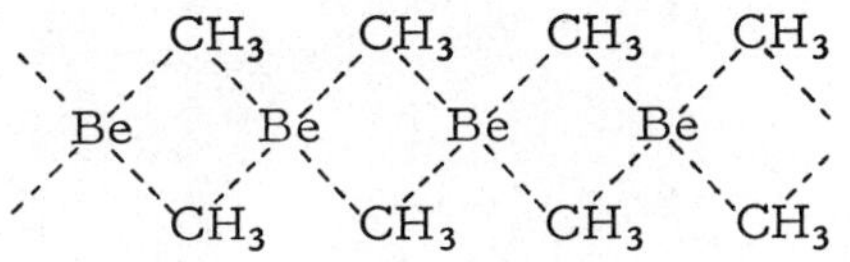

dimethylberyllium

(polymer)

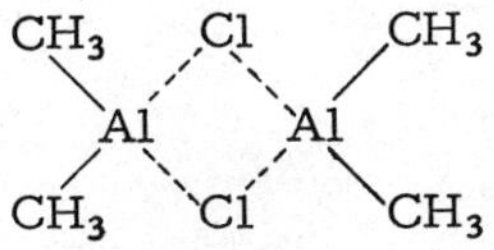

dimethylaluminum chloride

(dimer)

These substances are further examples of electron-deficient compounds such as diborane, B_2H_6, discussed on p. 143. In solvents (such as ethers) which have unshared electron pairs, the dimers may be broken down as the result of preferential coordination of the metal with the solvent.

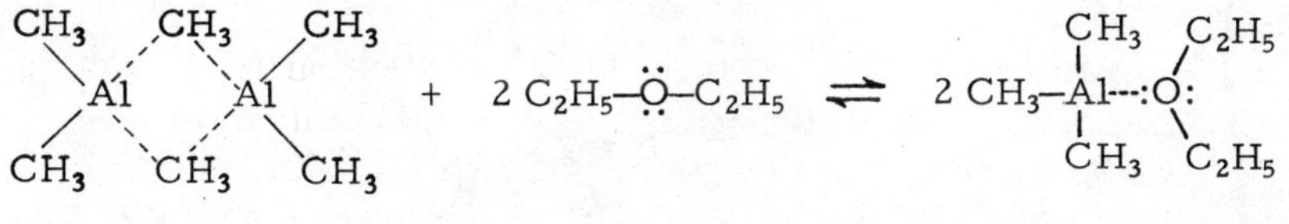

A selection of properties for a number of organometallic compounds of special synthetic importance is given in Table 12-2. To further illustrate the manner in which many organometallic compounds are used in organic syntheses, the reactions between methyllithium and each of the reagents listed in Table 12-2 are compiled in Figure 12-1. It will be seen that each reaction is characterized

Table 12-2   Physical Properties and Reactivities of Typical Organometallic Compounds

	Compound	m.p.	b.p.	Solubility in alkanes	Reactivity						
					HCl	H_2O	O_2	$(CH_3)_2C{=}O$	CO_2	$(C_2H_5)_2O$	$\diagdown C{=}C\diagup$
Decreasing electron-attracting power of metal ↑	CH_3Na	d.	–	–	+	+	+[a]	+	+	+	+[b]
	CH_3Li	d.	–	+	+	+	+[a]	+	+	+	+[b]
	$(CH_3)_2Mg$	?	+[c]	–	+	+	+[a]	+	+	–	–
	$(CH_3)_2Zn$	−40°	46°	+	+	+	+[a]	+	–	–	–
	$(CH_3)_2Hg$	<0°	96°	+	+	–	–	–	–	–	–

[a] Spontaneously inflammable in air.
[b] Reaction may occur with some members of the class and rather active carbon-carbon double bonds.
[c] Slightly volatile at elevated temperatures.

by attack of an electron-seeking (electrophilic) reagent on the negatively charged carbon of the carbon-lithium bond. Furthermore, in each reaction except the last, lithium becomes associated with a more electronegative atom than carbon. All but the last two reactions listed are extremely fast, even at −80°, and may occur violently on rapid mixing of the reagents.

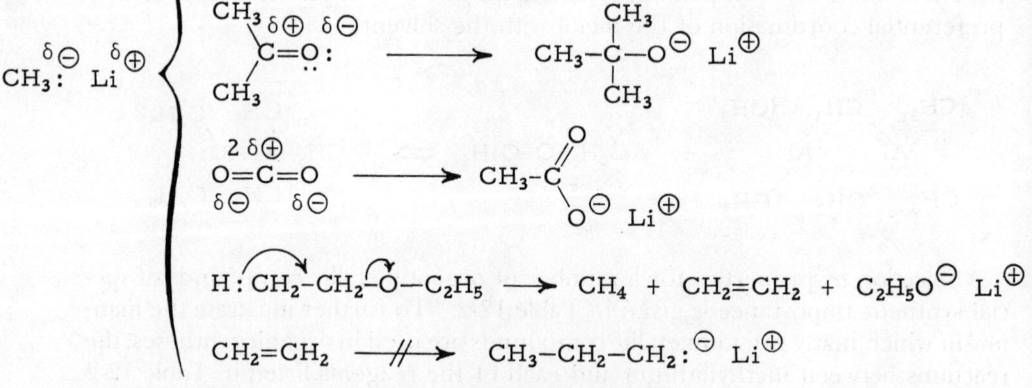

Figure 12-1   Reactions of methyllithium with a variety of reagents.

12-2 PREPARATION OF ORGANOMETALLIC COMPOUNDS

A. Metals with Organic Halides

The reaction of a metal with an organic halide is a convenient method for preparation of organometallics derived from reasonably active metals such as lithium, magnesium, and zinc. Dialkyl ethers, particularly diethyl ether, provide an inert, slightly polar medium in which organometallic compounds are usually soluble. Care is necessary to exclude moisture, oxygen, and carbon dioxide, which would otherwise react with the organometallic compound, and this is usually done by using an inert atmosphere of nitrogen or helium.

$$CH_3Br \ + \ 2\ Li \xrightarrow{\ (CH_3CH_2)_2O\ } \quad CH_3Li \quad + \quad LiBr$$

methyllithium

$$CH_3CH_2Br \ + \ Mg \xrightarrow{\ (CH_3CH_2)_2O\ } \quad CH_3CH_2MgBr$$

ethylmagnesium
bromide

The reactivity order of the various halides is $I > Br > Cl \gg F$. Alkyl fluorides do not react with lithium or magnesium. Concerning the metal, zinc reacts well with bromides and iodides, whereas mercury is satisfactory only if amalgamated with sodium.

$$2\ CH_3I \ + \ Hg(Na) \quad \longrightarrow \quad (CH_3)_2Hg \ + \ 2\ NaI$$

Sodium presents a special problem because of the high reactivity of organo-sodium compounds toward ether and organic halides. Both lithium and sodium alkyls attack diethyl ether, but, whereas the lithium compounds usually react slowly, the sodium compounds react so rapidly as to make diethyl ether impractical as a solvent for the preparation of most organosodium compounds. Hydrocarbon solvents are usually necessary. Even so, special preparative techniques are necessary in order to avoid having organosodium compounds react with the organic halide as fast as formed to give hydrocarbons by either S_N2 displacement or E2 elimination, depending on whether the sodium derivative attacks carbon or a β hydrogen of the halide.

S_N2 displacement:

$$CH_3CH_2{:}^{\ominus}\ Na^{\oplus} \ + \ CH_3CH_2{:}\ddot{B}r \ \longrightarrow \ CH_3CH_2CH_2CH_3 \ + \ Na^{\oplus}\ Br^{\ominus}$$

E2 elimination:

$$CH_3CH_2{:}^{\ominus}\ Na^{\oplus} \ + \ H{-}CH_2CH_2{:}\ddot{B}r \ \longrightarrow \ CH_3CH_3 \ + \ CH_2{=}CH_2 \ + \ Na^{\oplus}\ Br^{\ominus}$$

Displacement reactions of this kind brought about by sodium and organic halides (often called **Wurtz coupling** reactions) are only of limited synthetic importance. Some related and more useful reactions are discussed on pp. 269–270.

EXERCISE 12-1   What products would you expect to be formed in an attempt to synthesize hexamethylethane from *t*-butyl chloride and sodium? Write equations for the reactions involved.

B. Organometallic Compounds with Metallic Halides

The less-reactive organometallic compounds are best prepared from organomagnesium halides (Grignard reagents) and metallic halides.

$$CH_3MgCl + HgCl_2 \longrightarrow CH_3HgCl + MgCl_2$$

$$2\ CH_3MgCl + HgCl_2 \longrightarrow (CH_3)_2Hg + MgCl_2$$

These reactions, which could be written to proceed in either direction, actually go so as to have the most electropositive metal ending up combined with halogen. On this basis, sodium chloride can be predicted confidently not to react with dimethylmercury to yield methylsodium and mercuric chloride.

C. Organometallic Compounds and Acidic Hydrocarbons

A few organometallics are most conveniently prepared by the reaction of an alkylmetal derivative with an acidic hydrocarbon such as an acetylene or cyclopentadiene.

$$CH_3MgBr + CH_3C{\equiv}CH \rightarrow CH_4 + CH_3C{\equiv}CMgBr$$

Such reactions may be regarded as reactions of the salt of a weak acid (methane, $K_A < 10^{-40}$) with a stronger acid (methylacetylene, $K_A \sim 10^{-22}$).

The more reactive organometallic compounds are seldom isolated from the solutions in which they are prepared; these solutions are not generally stored for any length of time but are used directly in subsequent reactions. However, ether solutions of certain organomagnesium halides (phenyl-, methyl-, and ethylmagnesium halides) are obtainable commercially; also, *n*-butyllithium is available dissolved in mineral oil and in paraffin wax. Manipulation of any organometallic compounds should always be carried out with caution, owing to their extreme reactivity, and, in many cases, their considerable toxicity (particularly organic compounds of mercury, lead, and zinc).

EXERCISE 12-2   Write balanced equations for the preparation of each of the following organometallic compounds starting from suitable alkyl halides and inorganic reagents. Specify reaction conditions and solvents.

  a. $(CH_3)_2Zn$ *c.* $(CH_3CH_2)_4Pb$
  b. CH_3MgCl *d.* $(CH_3)_2CHLi$

12-3 ORGANOMAGNESIUM COMPOUNDS

The most important organometallic compounds for synthetic purposes are the organomagnesium halides, or **Grignard reagents.** They are so named after Victor Grignard, who discovered them and developed their use as synthetic reagents, for which he received a Nobel prize in 1912. As already mentioned, these substances are customarily prepared in dry ether solution from magnesium turnings and an organic halide.

$$CH_3I \ + \ Mg \quad \xrightarrow{\text{ether}} \quad CH_3MgI$$
$$95\% \text{ yield}$$

Chlorides often react sluggishly and, in addition, may give an unwelcome precipitate of magnesium chloride, which, unlike magnesium bromide and iodide, is only very slightly soluble in ether. Organomagnesium fluorides are not known.

It is clearly evident that while organomagnesium compounds possess moderately polar carbon-magnesium bonds, extensive ionization to $R:^{\ominus}$ does not occur, because the carbanion so formed would rapidly attack ether in the manner associated with the highly polar alkylsodium compounds.

$$\overset{\delta\ominus}{R}\text{----}\overset{\delta\oplus}{Mg}\text{--}X \quad \underset{\longleftarrow}{\longrightarrow} \quad R:^{\ominus} \ + \ \overset{\oplus}{Mg}X$$

Although Grignard reagents as prepared in ether solution do not attack the solvent, they are very highly associated with it. Not all the ether can be removed, even under reduced pressure at moderate temperatures, and the solid contains one or more moles of ether for every mole of organomagnesium compound. The ether molecules appear to be coördinated through the unshared electron pairs of oxygen to magnesium.

12-4 REACTIONS OF GRIGNARD REAGENTS

A. Active Hydrogen Compounds

Grignard reagents react with acids, even very weak acids such as alcohols, acetylene, and primary and secondary amines. These reactions may be regarded as involving the neutralization of a strong base ($R:^{\ominus}$ of RMgX). The products are hydrocarbon, RH, and a magnesium salt.

$$\overset{\delta\ominus}{CH_3}\text{---}\overset{\delta\oplus}{MgI} \ + \ \overset{\delta\ominus}{CH_3CH_2O}\text{---}\overset{\delta\oplus}{H} \quad \longrightarrow \quad CH_4 \ + \ CH_3CH_2OMgI$$

This type of reaction occasionally provides a useful way of replacing a halogen bound to carbon by hydrogen as in a published synthesis of cyclobutane from cyclobutyl bromide.

$$
\begin{array}{ccc}
CH_2-CH-Br & & CH_2-CH-MgBr & & CH_2-CH_2 \\
| \qquad | & \xrightarrow{\ Mg\ } & | \qquad | & \xrightarrow{\ H_2O\ } & | \qquad | \\
CH_2-CH_2 & & CH_2-CH_2 & & CH_2-CH_2
\end{array}
$$

B. Oxygen, Sulfur, and Halogens

Grignard reagents react with oxygen, sulfur, and halogens to form substances containing C—O, C—S, and C—X bonds, respectively.

$$RMgX + O_2 \longrightarrow R—O—O—MgX \xrightarrow{RMgX} 2\ ROMgX \xrightarrow{H_2O,\ H^{\oplus}} 2\ ROH$$

$$8\ RMgX + S_8 \longrightarrow 8\ RSMgX \xrightarrow{H_2O,\ H^{\oplus}} 8\ RSH$$

$$RMgX + I_2 \longrightarrow RI + MgXI$$

These reactions are not usually important for synthetic work because the products, ROH, RSH, and RX, can usually be obtained more conveniently and directly from alkyl halides by S_N1 and S_N2 displacement reactions, as described in Chapter 11. However, when both S_N1 and S_N2 reactions are slow or otherwise impractical, as for neopentyl derivatives, the Grignard reactions can be very useful.

$$\underset{\text{neopentyl chloride}}{CH_3\text{--}\overset{\overset{\displaystyle CH_3}{|}}{\underset{\underset{\displaystyle CH_3}{|}}{C}}\text{--}CH_2Cl} \xrightarrow{Mg} CH_3\text{--}\overset{\overset{\displaystyle CH_3}{|}}{\underset{\underset{\displaystyle CH_3}{|}}{C}}\text{--}CH_2MgCl \xrightarrow{I_2} \underset{\text{neopentyl iodide}}{CH_3\text{--}\overset{\overset{\displaystyle CH_3}{|}}{\underset{\underset{\displaystyle CH_3}{|}}{C}}\text{--}CH_2I}$$

Also, oxygenation of a Grignard reagent at *low* temperatures provides an excellent method for the synthesis of hydroperoxides.

$$RMgX + O_2 \xrightarrow{-70°} ROOMgX \xrightarrow{H^{\oplus}} ROOH$$

To prevent formation of excessive amounts of the alcohol, **inverse addition** is desirable (i.e., a solution of Grignard reagent is added to ether through which oxygen is bubbled rather than have the oxygen bubble through a solution of the Grignard reagent).

C. Additions to Carbonyl Groups

The most important synthetic use of Grignard reagents is for formation of new carbon-carbon bonds by addition to multiple bonds, particularly carbonyl bonds. In each case, magnesium is transferred from carbon to a more electronegative element. An example is the addition of methylmagnesium iodide to formaldehyde.

$$\overset{\delta\ominus\ \ \delta\oplus}{CH_3\text{:}MgI} + \overset{\delta\oplus\ \ \delta\ominus}{H_2C=O} \longrightarrow CH_3\text{:}CH_2\text{--}O\text{--}MgI \xrightarrow[H^{\oplus}]{H_2O} CH_3CH_2OH$$

$$\underset{\text{new carbon--carbon bond}}{}$$

The yields of addition products are generally high in these reactions, and, with suitable variations of the carbonyl compound, a wide range of compounds can be built up from substances containing fewer carbon atoms per molecule. The products formed from a number of types of carbonyl compounds with Grignard reagents are listed in Table 12-3. (The nomenclature of carbonyl compounds is considered in Section 13-1.)

The products are complex magnesium salts from which the desired organic product is freed by acid hydrolysis.

$$\text{ROMgX} + \text{HOH} \longrightarrow \text{ROH} + \text{HOMgX}$$

$$\underset{\text{HCl}}{\big\downarrow} \longrightarrow \text{H}_2\text{O} + \text{MgXCl}$$

If the product is sensitive to strong acids, the hydrolysis may be conveniently carried out with a saturated solution of ammonium chloride; basic magnesium salts precipitate while the organic product remains in ether solution.

The reaction of carbon dioxide with Grignard reagents gives initially RCO_2MgX.

$$\text{RMgX} + \text{CO}_2 \longrightarrow \underset{\text{OMgX}}{\overset{\text{O}}{\underset{\|}{R\!-\!C}}}$$

This substance is a salt of a carboxylic acid; it contains a carbon-oxygen double bond and is expected to be able to react further with the Grignard reagent.

$$\text{RCO}_2\text{MgX} + \text{RMgX} \longrightarrow \underset{R}{\overset{\text{OMgX}}{\underset{|}{R\!-\!C\!-\!\text{OMgX}}}}$$

In practice, the second reaction is found to be slow, even at room temperature, and can be essentially eliminated by pouring the Grignard solution onto finely powdered stirred solid carbon dioxide ("Dry Ice").

Acid chlorides like acetyl chloride, $\text{CH}_3\text{C}\overset{\text{O}}{\underset{\text{Cl}}{\diagup}}$, usually combine with 2 moles of Grignard reagent to give a tertiary alcohol. Presumably, the first step is addition to the carbonyl bond.

$$\underset{\text{Cl}}{\overset{\text{O}}{\text{CH}_3\text{C}}} + \text{RMgX} \longrightarrow \underset{R}{\overset{\text{OMgX}}{\underset{|}{\text{CH}_3\!-\!\text{C}\!-\!\text{Cl}}}}$$

Table 12-3   Products from the Reaction of Grignard Reagents as RMgX with Carbonyl Compounds

Reactant	Product	Hydrolysis product	Customary yield
formaldehyde $H{-}C({=}O){-}H$	RCH_2OMgX	*prim.* alcohol RCH_2OH	good
aldehyde $R'{-}C({=}O){-}H$	$R{-}\underset{H}{\overset{R'}{C}}{-}OMgX$	*sec.* alcohol $R{-}\overset{R'}{C}HOH$	good
ketone $R'{-}C({=}O){-}R''$	$R{-}\underset{R''}{\overset{R'}{C}}{-}OMgX$	*tert.* alcohol $R{-}\underset{R''}{\overset{R'}{C}}{-}OH$	good to poor
carbon dioxide CO_2	RCO_2MgX	carboxylic acid RCO_2H	good
carboxylic acid $R'{-}C({=}O){-}OH$	$R'CO_2MgX + RH$	carboxylic acid $R'CO_2H$	good
carboxylic ester $R'{-}C({=}O){-}OR''$	$R{-}\underset{R}{\overset{R'}{C}}{-}OMgX$	*tert.* alcohol $R{-}\underset{R}{\overset{R'}{C}}{-}OH$	good to poor
acid chloride $R'{-}C({=}O){-}Cl$	$R{-}\underset{R}{\overset{R'}{C}}{-}OMgX$	*tert.* alcohol $R{-}\underset{R}{\overset{R'}{C}}{-}OH$	good to poor
N,N-dimethylcarboxamide $(CH_3)_2N{-}C({=}O){-}R'$	$R{-}\underset{N(CH_3)_2}{\overset{R'}{C}}{-}OMgX$	ketone $\overset{R'}{\underset{R}{C}}{=}O$	good to poor

The initial intermediate is unstable and immediately decomposes to a ketone and magnesium halide. The ketone then reacts with more Grignard reagent to give the salt of a tertiary alcohol.

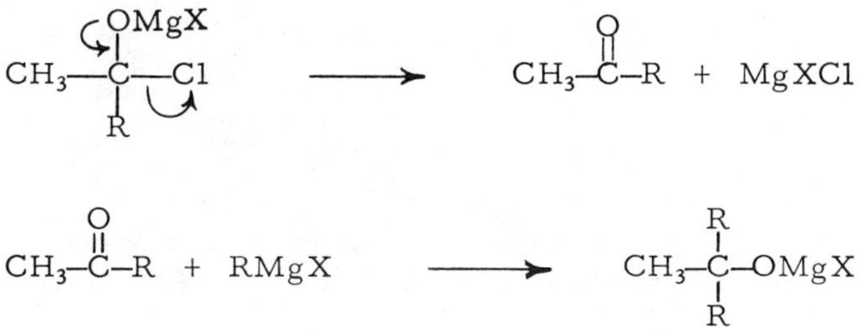

$$CH_3-\underset{\underset{R}{|}}{\overset{\overset{OMgX}{|}}{C}}-Cl \longrightarrow CH_3-\overset{\overset{O}{\|}}{C}-R \ + \ MgXCl$$

$$CH_3-\overset{\overset{O}{\|}}{C}-R \ + \ RMgX \longrightarrow CH_3-\underset{\underset{R}{|}}{\overset{\overset{R}{|}}{C}}-OMgX$$

EXERCISE 12-3   Would you expect the same products if, instead of addition to the carbonyl group, the acyl halides were to undergo a simple S_N2 displacement of halogen with the Grignard reagent acting to furnish $R:^{\ominus}$? Explain why simple displacement is unlikely to be the correct mechanism from the fact that acid fluorides react with Grignard reagents faster than acid chlorides, which in turn react faster than acid bromides.

The reaction of an acid chloride with RMgX is impractical for the synthesis of ketones because RMgX usually adds rapidly to the ketone as it is formed. However, this addition can often be moderated to the point where the ketone can be isolated by working at low temperatures.

Reaction of esters with Grignard reagents is similar to the reaction of acid chlorides and is very useful for synthesis of tertiary alcohols with two identical groups attached to the carbonyl carbon.

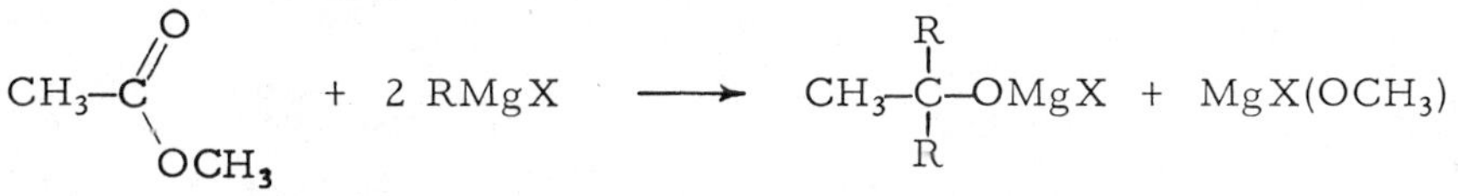

$$CH_3-\overset{\overset{O}{\|}}{\underset{\underset{OCH_3}{\diagdown}}{C}} \ + \ 2\ RMgX \longrightarrow CH_3-\underset{\underset{R}{|}}{\overset{\overset{R}{|}}{C}}-OMgX \ + \ MgX(OCH_3)$$

Many additions of Grignard reagents to carbonyl compounds proceed in nearly quantitative yields, while others give no addition product whatsoever. Trouble is most likely to be encountered in the synthesis of tertiary alcohols with bulky alkyl groups, since then the R group of the Grignard reagent will be hindered from reaching the carbonyl carbon of the ketone and side reactions may compete more effectively.

EXERCISE 12-4   Write structures for the products of the following reactions involving Grignard reagents. Show the structures of both the intermediate substances and the substances obtained after hydrolysis with dilute acid. Unless otherwise specified, assume that sufficient Grignard reagent is used to cause those reactions to go to completion which occur readily at room temperatures.

a. $C_6H_5MgBr + C_6H_5CHO$

b. $CH_3MgI + CH_3CH_2CO_2C_2H_5$

c. $(CH_3)_3CMgCl + CO_2$

d. $CH_3CH_2MgBr + ClCO_2C_2H_5$

e. $CH_3MgI + CH_3COCH_2CH_2CO_2C_2H_5$
   (1 mole)   (1 mole)

f. $C_6H_5MgBr + CH_3O{-}\overset{\overset{\displaystyle O}{\|}}{C}{-}OCH_3$

g. $(CH_3)_3CCH_2MgBr + CH_3\overset{\overset{\displaystyle O}{\|}}{C}{-}O{-}\overset{\overset{\displaystyle O}{\|}}{C}CH_3$

EXERCISE 12-5   Show how each of the following substances can be prepared by a reaction involving a Grignard reagent:

a. 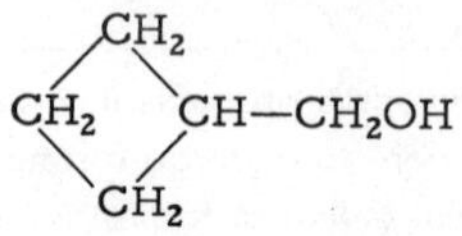 $\underset{\displaystyle CH_2}{\overset{\displaystyle CH_2}{CH_2{\diagdown}{\diagup}}}CH{-}CH_2OH$ (two ways)

b. $CH_2{=}CH{-}C(CH_3)_2OH$

c. $CH_3CH_2CH(OH)CH_3$ (two ways)

d. $(CH_3CH_2)_3COH$ (three ways)

e. 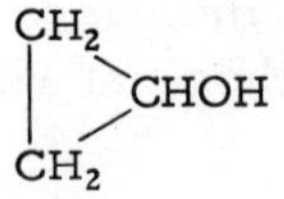 $\underset{\displaystyle CH_2}{\overset{\displaystyle CH_2}{|}}{\diagdown}CHOH$

D. Addition to Carbon-Carbon Double Bonds

We would not expect Grignard reagents to add to carbon-carbon double bonds nearly as readily as they add to carbonyl groups. Not only is a carbon-carbon double bond less susceptible to nucleophilic attack of $R{:}^{\ominus}$ of RMgX, but it is also less readily attacked by the electrophilic $^{\oplus}MgX$ group of RMgX.

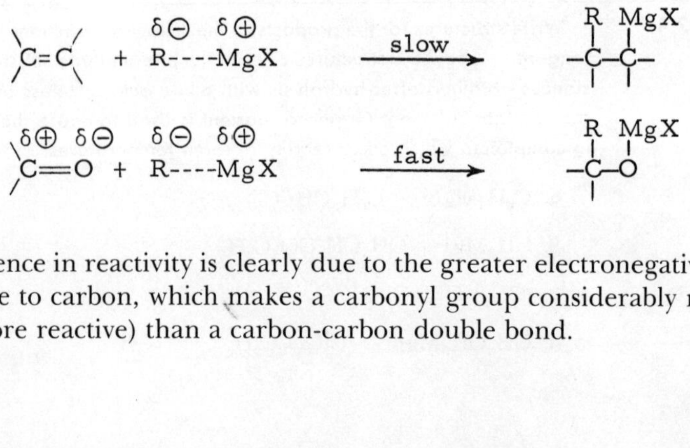

$$\underset{\diagup}{\overset{\diagdown}{C}}{=}\underset{\diagdown}{\overset{\diagup}{C}} \;+\; \overset{\delta\ominus\;\;\;\delta\oplus}{R{-}{-}{-}{-}MgX} \quad\xrightarrow{\;\;slow\;\;}\quad \overset{R\;\;\;MgX}{\underset{|\;\;\;\;\;|}{{-}\overset{|}{C}{-}\overset{|}{C}{-}}}$$

$$\overset{\delta\oplus\;\;\delta\ominus}{\underset{\diagup}{\overset{\diagdown}{C}}{=}O} \;+\; \overset{\delta\ominus\;\;\;\delta\oplus}{R{-}{-}{-}{-}MgX} \quad\xrightarrow{\;\;fast\;\;}\quad \overset{R\;\;\;MgX}{\underset{|}{{-}\overset{|}{C}{-}O}}$$

The difference in reactivity is clearly due to the greater electronegativity of oxygen relative to carbon, which makes a carbonyl group considerably more polar (hence, more reactive) than a carbon-carbon double bond.

E. Addition to Carbon-Nitrogen Triple Bonds

Nitrogen is a more electronegative element than carbon and the nitrile group is polarized in the sense $-\overset{\delta\oplus}{C}\equiv\overset{\delta\ominus}{N}$. Accordingly, Grignard reagents add to nitrile groups in much the same way as they add to carbonyl groups.

$$R'\overset{\delta\oplus}{-}\overset{\delta\ominus}{C}\equiv N \;+\; \overset{\delta\ominus}{R}\overset{\delta\oplus}{-}\text{-}\text{-}MgX \longrightarrow \underset{R}{\overset{R'}{C}}=N-MgX$$

Hydrolysis of the adducts lead to ketimines, which are unstable under the reaction conditions and rapidly hydrolyze to ketones.

$$\underset{R}{\overset{R'}{C}}=N-MgX \xrightarrow{\;H^{\oplus},\;H_2O\;} \left[\underset{R}{\overset{R'}{C}}=NH\right] \xrightarrow{\;H_2O\;} \underset{R}{\overset{R'}{C}}=O \;+\; NH_3$$

ketimine

F. Displacement Reactions

In principle, Grignard reagents can participate in S_N2 reactions by furnishing $R:^{\ominus}$ as a nucleophile. We have already referred to this general type of reaction

$$CH_2=CH-CH_2\overset{\curvearrowright}{:}\underset{\curvearrowleft}{\overset{..}{Cl}}: +\; \overset{\delta\ominus}{R}\text{-}\text{-}\text{-}\overset{\delta\oplus}{MgX} \longrightarrow CH_2=CH-CH_2-R \;+\; MgXCl$$

as Wurtz coupling (p. 262). However, such displacements with Grignard reagents do not proceed well with alkyl halides, but only with allyl halides and a few alkyl derivatives such as alkyl sulfates, sulfonates, and α-chloroethers which have particularly high S_N2 reactivity. Coupling may be a real problem in the preparation of allylmagnesium halides from allyl halides and, with such halides, it is usually necessary to use a large excess of magnesium and dilute halide solutions to minimize the coupling reaction.

EXERCISE 12-6 Complete the following equations:
  a. $C_6H_5CH_2CH_2MgBr + (CH_3)_2SO_4 \;\rightarrow$
  b. $C_2H_5MgBr + CH_3C\equiv C-CH_2Br \;\rightarrow$
  c. $CH_2=CH-CH_2Li + CH_2=CH-CH_2Cl \;\rightarrow$
  d. $CH_3CH_2CH_2MgBr + ClCH_2OCH_3 \;\rightarrow$

Grignard reagents react with most small-ring cyclic ethers by S_N2 displacement. The angle strain in three- and four-membered rings facilitates ring-opening, whereas strainless five- and six-membered cyclic ethers are not attacked by Grignard reagents.

$$RMgX \ + \ CH_2\!\!-\!\!CH_2 \quad \longrightarrow \quad RCH_2\!-\!CH_2OMgX$$

$$\underset{O}{\diagdown}$$

ethylene oxide

$$RMgX \ + \ \underset{CH_2}{\overset{CH_2}{CH_2}}\!\!\!\diagup\! O \quad \longrightarrow \quad RCH_2CH_2CH_2OMgX$$

trimethylene oxide

12-5 ORGANOSODIUM AND ORGANOLITHIUM COMPOUNDS

Alkylsodium and alkyllithium derivates behave in much the same way as organomagnesium compounds, but with increased reactivity. As mentioned previously, they are particularly sensitive to air and moisture, and react with ethers, alkyl halides, active hydrogen compounds, and multiple carbon-carbon, carbon-oxygen, and carbon-nitrogen bonds.   In additions to carbonyl groups they give fewer side reactions than Grignard reagents and permit syntheses of very highly branched tertiary alcohols.   Triisopropylcarbinol can be made from diisopropyl ketone and isopropyllithium but not with the corresponding Grignard reagent.

$$\underset{CH_3}{\overset{CH_3}{\diagdown}}CH\!-\!\overset{O}{\overset{\|}{C}}\!-\!CH\underset{CH_3}{\overset{CH_3}{\diagup}} \ + \ \underset{CH_3}{\overset{CH_3}{\diagdown}}CH\!-\!Li \ \longrightarrow \ \left(\underset{CH_3}{\overset{CH_3}{\diagdown}}CH\right)_{\!3}\!\!C\!-\!OH$$

triisopropylcarbinol

Tri-*t*-butylcarbinol can be prepared from di-*t*-butyl ketone, *t*-butyl chloride, and sodium. The product has a high degree of steric hindrance between its methyl groups and suffers considerable breakdown into smaller fragments when attemps are made to prepare the corresponding chloride with hydrochloric acid.

$$CH_3\!-\!\overset{CH_3}{\underset{CH_3}{\overset{|}{C}}}\!-\!\overset{O}{\overset{\|}{C}}\!-\!\overset{CH_3}{\underset{CH_3}{\overset{|}{C}}}\!-\!CH_3 \ + \ CH_3\!-\!\overset{CH_3}{\underset{CH_3}{\overset{|}{C}}}\!-\!Cl \ + \ Na \ \longrightarrow \ CH_3\!-\!\overset{CH_3}{\underset{CH_3}{\overset{|}{C}}}\!-\!\overset{OH}{\overset{|}{C}}\!-\!\overset{CH_3}{\underset{CH_3}{\overset{|}{C}}}\!-\!CH_3$$

$$CH_3\!-\!\overset{|}{\underset{CH_3}{\overset{|}{C}}}\!-\!CH_3$$

di-*t*-butyl ketone   tri-*t*-butylcarbinol

12-6 COMMERCIAL APPLICATIONS OF ORGANOMETALLIC COMPOUNDS

Tetraethyllead, b.p. 202°, is the most important organometallic compound in commercial use. It greatly improves the antiknock rating of gasoline in concentrations on the order of 1 to 3 cc per gallon. Ethylene dibromide is added to leaded gasoline to convert the lead oxide formed in combustion to volatile lead bromide and thus diminish deposit formation. Most tetraethyllead is made by the reaction of a lead-sodium alloy with ethyl chloride. The excess lead is reconverted to the sodium alloy. Tetramethyllead shows some advantage over tetraethyllead in high-performance engines.

$$4 \ C_2H_5Cl \ + \ 4 \ PbNa \ \longrightarrow \ (C_2H_5)_4Pb \ + \ 4 \ NaCl \ + \ 3 \ Pb$$

Some alkylmercuric halides, such as ethylmercuric chloride, have fungicidal properties and are used to preserve seeds.

Organoaluminum compounds add to alkenes more readily than do Grignard reagents. With triethylaluminum, successive additions of ethylene give a mixture of tri-n-alkylaluminum compounds with 2, 4, 6, 8, etc., carbons in each alkyl group.

$$CH_3CH_2Al(C_2H_5)_2 \ \xrightarrow{CH_2=CH_2} \ CH_3CH_2CH_2CH_2Al(C_2H_5)_2 \ \xrightarrow{CH_2=CH_2}$$

$$CH_3CH_2CH_2CH_2CH_2CH_2Al(C_2H_5)_2 \ \xrightarrow{CH_2=CH_2}$$

$$CH_3(CH_2)_5Al(CH_2CH_2CH_2CH_3)(C_2H_5) \ etc.$$

The longer-chain alkyl groups undergo a reversible elimination of dialkylaluminum hydride.

$$CH_3CH_2CH_2CH_2CH_2CH_2AlR_2 \ \rightleftharpoons \ CH_3CH_2CH_2CH_2CH=CH_2 \ + \ HAlR_2$$

In the presence of ethylene, this reaction goes to the right because the hydride adds to the ethylene to give an ethyldialkylaluminum.

$$HAlR_2 \ + \ CH_2=CH_2 \ \longrightarrow \ CH_3CH_2AlR_2$$

Further insertion of ethylene units between this ethyl group and aluminum, followed by elimination of dialkylaluminum hydride and then formation of a new ethyl group, is seen to result in polymerization of ethylene to a mixture of 1-alkenes.

$$n \cdot CH_2=CH_2 \ \xrightarrow{(C_2H_5)_3Al} \ CH_3CH_2(CH_2CH_2)_{n-2}CH=CH_2$$

This process is used commercially for large-scale syntheses of 1-alkenes.

EXERCISE 12-7   What experimental conditions of temperature, ethylene pressure, and triethylaluminum concentrations would you expect to be most favorable for conversion
of ethylene to 1-butene?   To 1-decene?   Explain.

12-7   ELECTROPHILIC DISPLACEMENT REACTIONS AT CARBON

Inasmuch as many of the reactions of organometallic compounds may be classified as electrophilic displacements, S_E, it is convenient to discuss them at this point.   They contrast with nucleophilic displacements, S_N (Chapter 11), in that substitution at carbon involves attack of an electron-seeking or electrophilic reagent rather than a nucleophilic reagent.

$$R \,\vdots\, X + Y: \longrightarrow R:Y + X: \qquad\qquad S_N$$
$$\text{nucleophile}$$

$$R \,:\vdots\, X + Y \longrightarrow R:Y + X \qquad\qquad S_E$$
$$\text{electrophile}$$

Some typical examples of electrophilic substitution at carbon follow:

$$CH_3\,\vdots\, MgBr + :\overset{..}{B}r\,\vdots\,:\overset{..}{B}r: \longrightarrow CH_3Br + MgBr_2$$

$$C_2H_5\,\vdots\, HgC_2H_5 + ClHg\,\vdots\,:\overset{..}{C}l: \longrightarrow C_2H_5HgCl + C_2H_5HgCl$$

$$CH_2{=}CH{-}CH_2\,\vdots\, Li + H\,\vdots\,{-}OH \longrightarrow CH_2{=}CHCH_3 + LiOH$$

Some ambiguity in the designations S_N and S_E arise for reactions which result in the formation of a carbon-carbon bond.   For example, Wurtz coupling by a polar mechanism involves both nucleophilic attack on carbon of the alkyl halide and electrophilic attack on carbon of the organometallic compound.   For our purposes here, we shall focus on the electrophilic aspects of the reaction.

$$\overset{\delta\oplus}{CH_3}\,\vdots\,\overset{\delta\ominus}{\;Br} + \overset{\delta\ominus}{CH_3}\,\vdots\,\overset{\delta\oplus}{Na} \longrightarrow CH_3CH_3 + NaBr$$

$$\text{electrophile} \qquad \text{nucleophile}$$

Clearly, we can envisage two possible mechanisms of electrophilic displacement by analogy with nucleophilic displacements.   The first is a two-step reaction involving ionization to a carbanion intermediate followed by reaction with an electrophile to form the products (S_E1).

$$R \,\vdots\, X \;\rightleftharpoons\; R:^{\ominus} + X^{\oplus}$$

$$R:^{\ominus} + Y^{\oplus} \longrightarrow R:Y$$

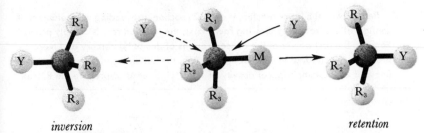

inversion   *retention*

Figure 12-2   Representation by ball-and-stick models of the course of electrophilic substitution by front-side or back-side attack on an optically active organometallic compound.

The second mechanism is a single-step reaction in which the bond to the entering group is formed at the same time as the bond to the leaving group is broken (S_E2).

$$Y^{\oplus} + R{:}X \longrightarrow R{:}Y + X^{\oplus}$$

However, the mechanisms of electrophilic displacements have not been investigated as extensively as nucleophilic displacements, partly because they are not as prevalent and partly because reactions involving organometallics, which are the obvious ones to study, are not always amenable to kinetic and stereochemical investigation.   In spite of this, sufficient work has been carried out to confirm the incidence of both S_E1 and S_E2 mechanisms, and to indicate the stereochemical course of these reactions.

Stereochemistry of S_E2 Displacements

If an optically active form of an organometallic compound were available, we could ascertain that S_E2 reactions involve front-side or back-side attack, depending on whether the configuration of the products is retained or inverted (Figure 12-2, see also pp. 230–232).

So far, relatively few optically active organometallic compounds have been prepared.   Synthesis of Grignard reagents from optically active alkyl halides almost always leads to racemization (i.e., the Grignard reagent contains equal amounts of the two optical isomers).   However, less active organometallic compounds have been resolved (see Exercise 12-8), and from these we find that electrophilic substitution at carbon normally proceeds by *front-side* attack with *retention of configuration.*

EXERCISE 12-8   Optically active s-butylmercuric bromide (the optically active s-butyl group being here symbolized by R*) reacts with optically inactive s-butylmagnesium bromide (the optically inactive s-butyl group being symbolized as R) to give R*HgR (di-s-butylmercury).

$$R^*HgBr + RMgBr \rightarrow R^*HgR + MgBr_2$$

Treatment of the R*HgR with mercuric bromide gives s-butylmercuric bromide.

$$R^*HgR + HgBr_2 \rightarrow R^*HgBr + RHgBr$$

Reason why the latter reaction is an S_E2 reaction, proceeding with retention of configuration, from the following facts: First, the reaction rate is directly proportional to the first power of the concentrations of di-s-butylmercury and mercuric bromide. Second, at the end of the reaction, the butylmercuric bromide has just one-*half* of the initial optical activity of the R*HgBr used to prepare the R*HgR.

SUPPLEMENTARY EXERCISES

12-9 Write balanced equations for reactions that you expect would occur between the following substances (1 mole) and 1 mole of *n*-amylsodium. Indicate your reasoning where you make a choice between several possible alternatives.

a. water
b. diethyl ether *
c. *t*-butyl chloride
d. *n*-amyl iodide
e. propylene
f. allyl chloride
g. acetic acid (added slowly to the *n*-amylsodium)
h. acetic acid (*n*-amylsodium added slowly to it)

12-10 Predict the products of each of the following Grignard reactions before and after hydrolysis. Give reasoning or analogies for each.

a. $CH_3MgI + HCO_2C_2H_5 \rightarrow$
b. $CH_3CH_2MgBr + CS_2 \rightarrow$
c. $CH_3CH_2MgBr + NH_3 \rightarrow$

12-11 Show how each of the following substances can be synthesized from the indicated starting materials by a route that involves organometallic substances in at least one step:

a. $(CH_3)_3C—D$ from $(CH_3)_3CCl$

b. $CH_3C{\equiv}C—CO_2H$ from $CH{\equiv}CH$

c. $CH_3{-}\overset{\overset{\displaystyle CH_3}{|}}{\underset{\underset{\displaystyle CH_3}{|}}{C}}{-}CH_2I$ from $(CH_3)_4C$

d. $CH_3{-}\overset{\overset{\displaystyle CH_3}{|}}{\underset{\underset{\displaystyle OH}{|}}{C}}{-}CH(CH_3)_2$

e.
$$\left(\boxed{}\right)_3 COH \text{ from } \boxed{}Br$$

f. $CH_3{-}\overset{\overset{\displaystyle CH_3}{|}}{\underset{\underset{\displaystyle CH_3}{|}}{C}}{-}CH_2CH_2CH_2CH_2OH$ from $(CH_3)_3CCH_2Cl$

12-12 Each of the following equations represents "possible" Grignard syntheses. Consider each equation and decide whether or not you think the reaction will go satisfactorily. Give your reasoning and, for those reactions that are unsatisfactory, give the expected product or write "No Reaction" where applicable.

a. methylmagnesium iodide + butyryl chloride $\longrightarrow\longrightarrow$ *n*-propyl methyl ketone

b. methylmagnesium iodide + $CH_3CH{=}N{-}CH_3$ $\longrightarrow\longrightarrow$ $CH_3CH_2{-}\overset{\overset{\displaystyle CH_3}{|}}{N}{-}CH_3$

c. 2-bromoethyl acetate $\xrightarrow[\text{ether}]{\text{Mg}}$ Grignard reagent $\xrightarrow{CH_2{=}O}$ $\longrightarrow$ 3-hydroxy-propyl acetate

d. allylmagnesium chloride + ethyl bromide $\longrightarrow$ 1-pentene

Alcohols and Ethers

*A*lcohols, ROH, and ethers, ROR, can be regarded as substitution products of water. With alcohols, we shall be interested, on the one hand, in reactions that proceed at the O—H bond without involving the C—O bond or the organic radical directly and, on the other hand, with processes that result in cleavage of the C—O bond or changes in the organic radical. The reactions involving the O—H bond are expected to be similar to the corresponding reactions of water.

The simple ethers do not have O—H bonds, and most of the reactions that they undergo involve the substituent groups. The cyclic ethers with small rings show enhanced reactivity because of ring strain and will be seen to be valuable intermediates in organic synthesis.

Alcohols and Ethers

CHAPTER 13

Among the representative reactions of alcohols that involve the O—H bond are salt and ester formation. In each of these, the C—O bond remains intact.

Salt formation:

$$CH_3OH + HBr \rightleftharpoons CH_3{-}\overset{\oplus}{O}H_2 \quad \overset{\ominus}{Br}$$

$$2CH_3OH + 2Na \longrightarrow 2\,CH_3{-}\overset{\ominus}{O} \quad Na^{\oplus} + H_2$$

Ester formation:

$$C_2H_5OH + CH_3{-}\overset{O}{\overset{\|}{C}}{-}OH \overset{H^{\oplus}}{\rightleftharpoons} C_2H_5{-}O{-}\overset{O}{\overset{\|}{C}}{-}CH_3 + H_2O$$

Typical reactions involving the C—O bond and the organic radical are alkyl halide formation and oxidation.

Alkyl halide formation:

$$(CH_3)_3C{-}OH + HCl \longrightarrow (CH_3)_3CCl + H_2O$$

Oxidation:

$$(CH_3)_2CH{-}OH \xrightarrow{CrO_3} (CH_3)_2C{=}O \ + \ H_2O$$

Clearly, ethers are limited in the extent that they can undergo reactions of the above types and, in general, their chemistry is considerably less variegated than that of alcohols. This fact is turned to advantage in the widespread use of ethers as solvents and reaction media for a variety of organic reactions, as we have already seen in the specific case of Grignard reagents (Chapter 12).

13-1 NOMENCLATURE OF CARBONYL COMPOUNDS

A number of carbonyl compounds will be very important to our discussion of syntheses and reactions of alcohols and, therefore, it will be well to have in hand the nomenclature of such substances. Since the procedures used in naming carbonyl compounds follow along lines discussed previously for other types of compounds, the most widely used nomenclature systems are summarized in Table 13-1 without further discussion. Nonsystematic names for carbonyl compounds such as *mesityl oxide* for $(CH_3)_2C{=}CHCOCH_3$ (4-methyl-3-penten-2-one) and *pinacolone* for $(CH_3)_3CCOCH_3$ (3,3-dimethyl-2-butanone) are not uncommon and will be given in the proper context when encountered.

Table 13-1   Nomenclature Systems for Carbonyl Compounds

Aldehydes, $R{-}\overset{\displaystyle O}{\underset{\displaystyle H}{C}}$

Formula	IUPAC name = longest straight chain[a] + suffix -al	Name as derivative of a carboxylic acid (i.e., a carboxaldehyde)
$H_2C{=}O$	methanal	formaldehyde
$ClCH_2CH_2CHO$	3-chloropropanal	β-chloropropionaldehyde
$CH_2{=}\overset{\displaystyle CH_3}{\underset{\displaystyle \,}{C}}CHO$	2-methylpropenal	methacrolein (methacrylaldehyde)[b]
▷$-CHO$	cyclopropylmethanal	cyclopropanecarboxaldehyde[c]

[a] The longest straight chain which includes the functional group is understood.

[b] Propenoic acid is commonly called *acrylic acid* and 2-methylpropenoic acid *methacrylic acid.*

[c] The acid $(CH_2)_2CHCO_2H$ is commonly called *cyclopropanecarboxylic acid.*

Table 13-1   Nomenclature Systems for Carbonyl Compounds (*Continued*)

Ketones, $\begin{matrix}R\\\diagdown\\ \ \ \ \ C{=}O\\\diagup\\R'\end{matrix}$

Formula	IUPAC name = longest straight chain[a] + suffix -*one*	Name as a substituted ketone[d]
$(CH_3)_2C{=}O$	propanone	dimethyl ketone (acetone)[e]
$CH_3\overset{O}{\overset{\|}{C}}CH_2CH{=}CH_2$	4-penten-2-one	methyl allyl ketone
phenyl–$\overset{O}{\overset{\|}{C}}$–$CH_3$	phenylethanone	methyl phenyl ketone (acetophenone)[e]
cyclohexyl=O	cyclohexanone	—

Acyl Halides, $R{-}C\overset{\diagup\!O}{\diagdown_X}$

Formula	IUPAC = longest straight chain[a] + suffix -*oyl* + name of halide	Name as a derivative of a carboxylic acid (i.e., a carbonyl halide)
$CH_3{-}\overset{O}{\overset{\|}{C}}{-}Cl$	ethanoyl chloride	acetyl chloride
$(CH_3)_2CH{-}\overset{O}{\overset{\|}{C}}{-}Br$	2-methylpropanoyl bromide	isobutyryl bromide
$CH_2{=}CH{-}CH_2{-}\overset{O}{\overset{\|}{C}}{-}Cl$	3-butenoyl chloride	vinylacetyl chloride
cyclopropyl–$\overset{O}{\overset{\|}{C}}{-}Br$	cyclopropylmethanoyl bromide	cyclopropanecarbonyl bromide

[d] Ketone is a separate word even though aldehyde is not.   Thus $(CH_3CH_2)_2CO$ is diethyl ketone but $(CH_3CH_2)_2CHCHO$ is diethylacetaldehyde (see pp. 222–223).

[e] A few ketones are named as derivatives of carboxylic acids.   Names by this system stem from the synthesis (real or imagined) of the ketone by the reaction $RCO_2H + R'CO_2H \rightarrow RCOR' + CO_2 + H_2O$.

EXERCISE 13-1   Draw structural formulas for each of the following substances.
                                    a. hexanal   *d.* 3-phenyl-2-butenal
                                    b. divinyl ketone   *e.* cyclohexyldimethylcarbinylcarbonyl
                                    c. phenylacetyl chloride   bromide

EXERCISE 13-2   Name the following substances according to the systems developed in Table
13-1.
                                  a. $CH_3CH{=}CHCHO$ *d.* CF_3COCF_3
                                    b. $N{\equiv}CCH_2COCl$ *e.* $CH_3CH{-}CHCHO$
                                                                                        OH CH_3

                                  c. $C_6H_5COCH_2COC_6H_5$ *f.* $(CH_3)_2C(CH_2)_2CHCOBr$

13-2 PHYSICAL PROPERTIES OF ALCOHOLS—HYDROGEN BONDING

Comparison of the physical properties of alcohols with those of hydrocarbons of comparable molecular weight shows several striking differences, especially for the lower members.   Alcohols are substantially less volatile, have higher melting points and greater water solubility than the corresponding hydrocarbons (see Table 13-2), although the differences become progressively smaller as molecular weight increases.

The reason for these differences in physical properties is related to the high polarity of the hydroxyl group which, when substituted on a hydrocarbon chain, confers a measure of polar character to the molecule.   As a result, there is a significant attraction of one molecule for another that is particularly pronounced in the solid and liquid states.   It leads to association of alcohol molecules through the rather positive hydrogen of one hydroxyl group with a correspondingly negative oxygen of another hydroxyl group.

This type of association is called "hydrogen bonding," and, although the strengths of such bonds are much less than those of most conventional chemical bonds, they are still significant (about 5 to 10 kcal per bond).   Clearly then, the reason that alcohols boil higher than corresponding alkyl halides, ethers, or hydrocarbons is because, for the molecules to vaporize, additional energy is required to break the hydrogen bonds.   Alternatively, association through hydrogen bonds may be regarded as effectively raising the molecular weight, hence reducing volatility.

EXERCISE 13-3   *Cis*-cyclopentane-1,2-diol is appreciably more volatile (b.p. 124° at 29 mm)
than *trans*-cyclopentane-1,2-diol (b.p. 136° at 22 mm).   Explain.

Table 13-2   Comparison of Physical Properties of Alcohols and Hydrocarbons

Alcohol	Hydrocarbon	Mol. wt.	B.p., °C	M.p., °C
CH_3OH		32	65	−98
	CH_3CH_3	30	−89	−172
CH_3CH_2OH		46	78.5	−117.3
	$CH_3CH_2CH_3$	44	−42.2	−189.9
$CH_3CH_2CH_2OH$		60	97.2	−127
	$CH_3CH_2CH_2CH_3$	58	−0.6	−135
$CH_3(CH_2)_3CH_2OH$		88	138	−79
	$CH_3(CH_2)_4CH_3$	86	69	−95
$CH_3(CH_2)_8CH_2OH$		158	228	6
	$CH_3(CH_2)_9CH_3$	156	196	−26

The water solubility of the lower-molecular-weight alcohols is pronounced and is readily understood as the result of hydrogen bonding with water molecules (water itself being extensively associated). In methanol, the hydroxyl

$$\overset{\delta \oplus}{---O}\;\overset{\delta \ominus}{—H}\;\overset{\delta \oplus}{---O}\;\overset{\delta \ominus}{—H}\;\overset{}{---O}\;\overset{}{—H---}$$
$$\;\;\;|\qquad\qquad|\qquad\qquad|$$
$$\;\;\;H\qquad\qquad R\qquad\qquad H$$

group accounts for almost half of the weight of the molecule, and it is not then surprising that the substance is miscible with water in all proportions. As the size of the hydrocarbon group of an alcohol increases, the hydroxyl group accounts for progressively less of the molecular weight, and hence water solubility decreases (Figure 13-1). Indeed, the physical properties of higher-molecu-

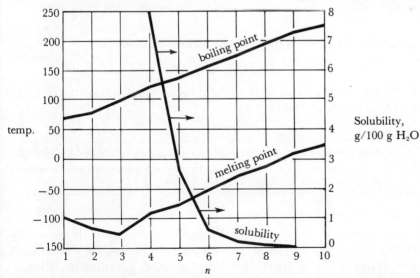

Figure 13-1   Dependence of melting points, boiling points, and water solubilities of straight-chain primary alcohols ($C_nH_{2n+2}O$) on n.

lar-weight alcohols are very similar to those of the corresponding hydrocarbons (Table 13-2).

13-3 SPECTROSCOPIC PROPERTIES OF ALCOHOLS— HYDROGEN BONDING

The hydrogen-oxygen bond of a hydroxyl group gives a characteristic absorption band in the infrared and, as we might expect, this absorption is considerably influenced by hydrogen bonding. For example, in the *vapor state* (in which there is essentially no hydrogen bonding), ethanol gives an infrared spectrum with a fairly sharp absorption band at 3700 cm^{-1}, owing to a free or unassociated hydroxyl group (Figure 13-2a); in contrast, this band is barely visible at 3640 cm^{-1} in the spectrum of a 10 per cent solution of ethanol in carbon tetrachloride (Figure 13-2b). However, there is a relatively broad band around 3350 cm^{-1} which is characteristic of hydrogen-bonded hydroxyl groups. The shift in frequency of about 300 cm^{-1} is not surprising, since hydrogen bonding weakens the O—H bond; its absorption frequency will then be lower. The association band is broad because the hydroxyl groups are associated in aggregates of various sizes and shapes, giving rise to a variety of different kinds of hydrogen bonds and therefore a spectrum of closely spaced O—H absorption frequencies.

In very dilute solutions of alcohols in nonpolar solvents, hydrogen bonding is minimized; but as the concentration is increased, more and more of the molecules become associated and the intensity of the infrared absorption band due to associated hydroxyl groups increases at the expense of the free-hydroxyl band. Furthermore, the frequency of the association band is a measure of the strength of the hydrogen bond. The lower the frequency relative to the position of the free hydroxyl group, the stronger is the hydrogen bond. As we shall

see in Chapter 16, the hydroxyl group in carboxylic acids $\left(RC\begin{smallmatrix}O\\\\OH\end{smallmatrix}\right)$ forms

stronger hydrogen bonds than alcohols and, accordingly, absorbs at lower frequencies (lower by about 400 cm^{-1}).

EXERCISE 13-4   What type of infrared absorption bands due to hydroxyl groups would you expect for *trans*-cyclobutane-1,2-diol and butane-1,2-diol (a) in very dilute solution, (b) in moderately concentrated solution, and (c) as pure liquids?

From the foregoing discussion of the influence of hydrogen bonding on the infrared spectra of alcohols, it should come as no surprise that the *nuclear magnetic resonance spectra* of the hydroxyl protons of alcohols are similarly affected. Thus the chemical shift of a hydroxyl proton is influenced by the degree of

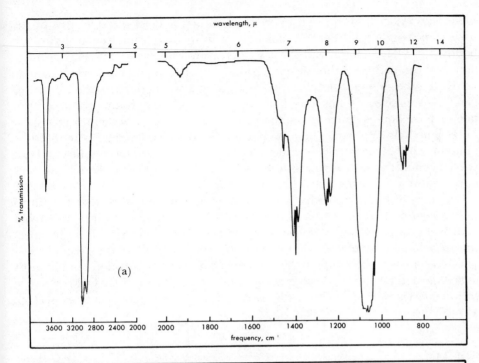

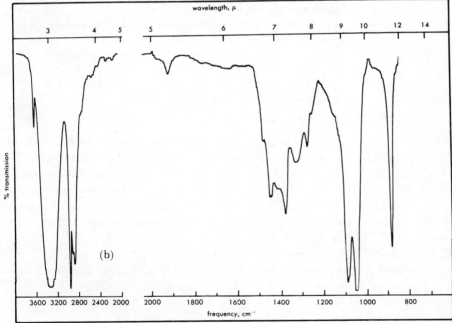

Figure   13-2

Infrared spectrum of ethanol in the
vapor phase (a) and as a 10 per cent
solution in carbon tetrachloride (b)

molecular association through hydrogen bonding and on the strengths of the hydrogen bonds. Except for alcohols that form intramolecular hydrogen bonds, the OH chemical shift varies extensively with temperature, concentration, and the nature of the solvent. Also, resonance appears at lower magnetic fields (i.e., the chemical shift is larger relative to TMS) as the strengths of hydrogen bonds increase. Thus, the chemical shifts of the OH protons of simple alcohols as pure liquids generally fall between 4 and 5 ppm downfield with respect to tetramethylsilane, but, when the degree of hydrogen bonding is reduced by dilution with carbon tetrachloride, the OH resonances move upfield. With ethyl alcohol, the shift is found to be 3 ppm between the pure liquid and very dilute solution in carbon tetrachloride.

One may well question why it is that absorptions are observed in the infrared spectrum of alcohols which correspond both to free and hydrogen-bonded hydroxyl groups, while only one OH resonance is observed in their n.m.r. spectra. The answer is that the lifetime of any one molecule in the free or unassociated state is long enough to be detected by infrared absorption but too short to be detected by n.m.r. Consequently, one sees only the average OH resonance for all species present. (For a discussion of n.m.r. and rate processes, see pp. 43–46.)

EXERCISE 13-5   Suggest a likely structure for the compound of molecular formula C_4H_6O whose n.m.r. and infrared spectra are shown in Figure 13-3a. Show your reasoning. Do the same for the compound of formula $C_3H_8O_2$, whose spectra are shown in Figure 13-3b.

13-4 PREPARATION OF ALCOHOLS

Many of the common laboratory methods for the preparation of alcohols are discussed in other chapters and, to avoid undue repetition, we shall not consider them in detail at this time. Included among these are hydration (p. 138) and hydroboration (pp. 148–149) of alkenes, addition of hypohalous acids to alkenes (pp. 138–139) and alkadienes (p. 189), S_N1 and S_N2 hydrolysis of alkyl (pp. 227–229) and alkenyl halides (pp. 244–247), addition of Grignard reagents to carbonyl compounds (pp. 264–267), and the reduction of carbonyl compounds (pp. 327–329).

A few of the reactions mentioned have been adapted for large-scale production. Ethanol, for example, is made in quantity by the hydration of ethylene, using an excess of steam under pressure at temperatures around 300° in the presence of phosphoric acid.

$$CH_2{=}CH_2 \;+\; H_2O \;\xrightleftharpoons{\; 300°,\; H_3PO_4 \;}\; CH_3CH_2OH$$

A dilute solution of ethanol is obtained which can be concentrated by distillation to a constant boiling point mixture that contains 95.6 per cent ethanol by

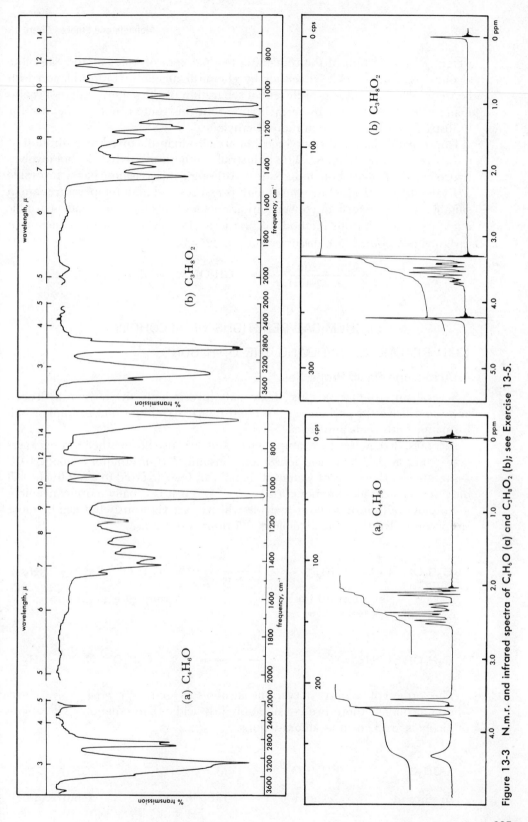

Figure 13-3 N.m.r. and infrared spectra of C_4H_6O (a) cnd $C_3H_8O_2$ (b); see Exercise 13-5.

285

weight. Dehydration of the remaining few per cent of water to give "absolute alcohol" is usually achieved either by chemical means or by distillation with benzene, which results in preferential separation of the water. Ethanol is also made in large quantities by fermentation, but this route is not competitive for industrial uses with the hydration of ethylene.

Isopropyl alcohol and *t*-butyl alcohol are also manufactured by hydration of the corresponding alkenes. The industrial synthesis of methyl alcohol involves hydrogenation of carbon monoxide. Although this reaction has a favorable ΔH value of -28.4 kcal, it requires high pressures and high temperatures and a suitable catalyst; excellent conversions are achieved using a zinc oxide–chromic oxide catalyst. Various methods of synthesis of other alcohols by reduction of carbonyl compounds are discussed on pp. 327–329.

$$CO + 2H_2 \xrightarrow[\text{ZnO–CrO}_3]{400°, \ 200 \ \text{atm.}} CH_3OH \qquad \Delta H = -28.4 \ \text{kcal}$$

CHEMICAL REACTIONS OF ALCOHOLS

13-5 · REACTIONS INVOLVING THE O—H BOND

A. Acidic and Basic Properties

Several important reactions of alcohols involve only the oxygen-hydrogen bond and leave the carbon-oxygen bond intact. An important example is salt formation with acids and bases.

Alcohols, like water, are amphoteric and are usually neither strong bases nor strong acids. The acid ionization constant (K_A) of ethanol is about 10^{-18} —slightly less than that of water. Ethanol can be converted to a salt by the salt of a weaker acid like ammonia ($K_A \sim 10^{-35}$), but it is usually more convenient to employ sodium or sodium hydride which react vigorously but can be more easily controlled than the analogous reactions with water.

$$C_2H_5OH + Na^{\oplus} NH_2^{\ominus} \ \underset{\longleftarrow}{\longrightarrow} \ C_2H_5O^{\ominus} Na^{\oplus} + NH_3$$

$$\begin{array}{cc} \text{sodium amide} & \text{sodium ethoxide} \\ \text{(sodamide)} & \end{array}$$

$$C_2H_5OH + Na^{\oplus} H^{\ominus} \ \longrightarrow \ C_2H_5O^{\ominus} Na^{\oplus} + H_2$$

The order of acidity of various alcohols is generally *prim.* > *sec.* > *tert.*; *t*-butyl alcohol is therefore considerably less acidic than ethanol. The anions of alcohols are known as **alkoxide** ions.

$$CH_3O^{\ominus} \qquad C_2H_5O^{\ominus} \qquad (CH_3)_2CHO^{\ominus} \qquad (CH_3)_3CO^{\ominus}$$

$$\begin{array}{cccc} \text{methoxide} & \text{ethoxide} & \text{isopropoxide} & \textit{t}\text{-butoxide} \end{array}$$

Alcohols are bases comparable in strength to water and are converted into more or less stable salts with strong acids. An example is the reaction of methanol with hydrogen bromide to give methyloxonium bromide.

$$CH_3:\overset{\cdot\cdot}{\underset{\cdot\cdot}{O}}:H \ + \ HBr \ \rightleftharpoons \ CH_3:\overset{\overset{H}{|}}{\underset{\cdot\cdot}{O}}:H^{\oplus} \ + \ Br^{\ominus}$$

methyloxonium bromide

The reaction of hydrogen bromide with water proceeds in an analogous manner:

$$H:\overset{\cdot\cdot}{\underset{\cdot\cdot}{O}}:H \ + \ HBr \ \rightleftharpoons \ H:\overset{\overset{H \ \oplus}{|}}{\underset{\cdot\cdot}{O}}:H \ + \ Br^{\ominus}$$

hydroxonium bromide

B. Ether Formation

Alkoxide formation is important as a means of generating a powerful nucleophile that will readily enter into S_N2 reactions. Whereas ethanol reacts very slowly with methyl iodide to give methyl ethyl ether, sodium ethoxide in ethanol solution reacts quite rapidly.

$$CH_3I \ + \ C_2H_5OH \ \overset{slow}{\rightleftharpoons} \ CH_3OC_2H_5 \ + \ HI$$

$$CH_3I \ + \ C_2H_5O^{\ominus} \ Na^{\oplus} \ \xrightarrow{fast} \ CH_3OC_2H_5 \ + \ NaI$$

In fact, the reaction of alkoxides with alkyl halides or alkyl sulfates is an important general method for the preparation of ethers, and is known as the **Williamson synthesis.** Complications can occur because the increase of nucleophilicity associated with the conversion of an alcohol to an alkoxide ion is always accompanied by an even greater increase in eliminating power by the E2-type mechanism. The reaction of an alkyl halide with alkoxide may then be one of elimination rather than substitution, depending on the temperature, the structure of the halide, and the alkoxide (pp. 238–239). For example, if we wish to prepare isopropyl methyl ether, better yields would be obtained if we were to use methyl iodide and isopropoxide ion rather than isopropyl iodide and methoxide ion because of the prevalence of E2-type elimination with the latter combination.

$$CH_3I \ + \ (CH_3)_2CHO^{\ominus} \ \xrightarrow{S_N2} \ (CH_3)_2CHOCH_3 \ + \ I^{\ominus}$$

$$(CH_3)_2CHI \ + \ CH_3O^{\ominus} \ \xrightarrow{E2} \ CH_3CH{=}CH_2 \ + \ CH_3OH \ + \ I^{\ominus}$$

Potassium *t*-butoxide is often an excellent reagent to achieve E2-type elimination, since it is strongly basic but so bulky as to not undergo S_N2 reactions readily.

EXERCISE 13-6　　　　　Predict the major products of the following reactions:

a. $(CH_3)_3CCH_2I + C_2H_5O^\ominus \rightarrow$

b. $(CH_3)_3CBr + CH_3O^\ominus \rightarrow$

c. 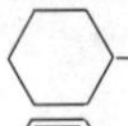 ⬡—$Cl + (CH_3)_3CO^\ominus \rightarrow$

d. 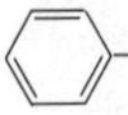 ⬡—$CH_2Br + (CH_3)_2CHCH_2O^\ominus \rightarrow$

e. $(CH_3)_2CHCH_2Br + C_6H_5CH_2O^\ominus \rightarrow$

C. Ester Formation

Other electron-pair acceptors besides protons can combine with the unshared pairs on the oxygen of an alcohol. One such substance is boron trifluoride; the boron atom has only six electrons in its outer valence shell and has therefore a strong tendency to coordinate with an unshared electron pair to complete its octet.

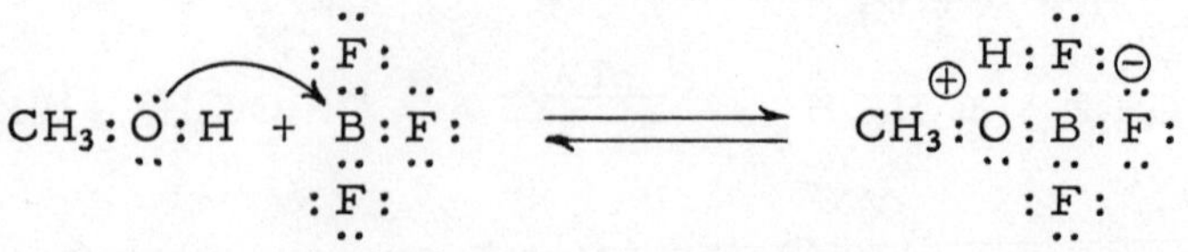

$$CH_3 : \ddot{O} : H \; + \; B : \ddot{F} : \quad\rightleftharpoons\quad CH_3 : \overset{\oplus}{O} : B : \ddot{F} :^\ominus$$

Coordination processes of this general type are important in the mechanisms of formation of esters from alcohols and acyl halides, carboxylic anhydrides, and carboxylic acids. For example, acyl halides have a rather positive carbonyl carbon because of the polarization of the carbon-oxygen and carbon-halogen bonds. Addition of an electron-pair donating agent like the oxygen of an alcohol occurs rather easily.

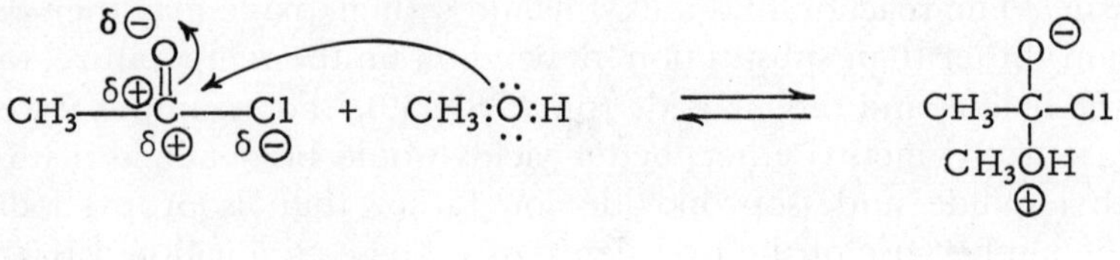

$$CH_3 \overset{\delta\oplus}{-}\overset{\delta\ominus O}{\underset{\delta\oplus}{C}} \overset{}{-} \underset{\delta\ominus}{Cl} \; + \; CH_3 : \ddot{O} : H \quad\rightleftharpoons\quad CH_3 - \underset{\underset{\oplus}{CH_3OH}}{\overset{\overset{O^\ominus}{|}}{C}} - Cl$$

$$[1]$$

The complex [1] contains both an acidic group $(CH_3 - \overset{\oplus}{O} - H)$ and a basic group

$(-\overset{\overset{O^\ominus}{|}}{\underset{|}{C}}-)$, so that a proton shifts from one oxygen to the other to give [2], which then rapidly loses hydrogen chloride by either an E1- or E2-type elimination to form the ester.

$$\underset{\substack{CH_3\overset{\oplus}{O}H}}{\overset{\overset{O^{\ominus}}{\underset{|}{CH_3-\overset{|}{C}-Cl}}}{}} \rightleftharpoons \underset{CH_3\overset{..}{O}}{\overset{\overset{H}{\underset{|}{O}}}{CH_3-\overset{|}{C}-Cl}} \longrightarrow \overset{O}{\underset{||}{CH_3-C-O-CH_3}} + HCl$$

$$[1] \qquad\qquad [2]$$

The over-all reaction resembles an S_N2 displacement, but the mechanism is quite different in being an *addition-elimination* rather than an inversion process.

A similar but more reversible reaction occurs between acetic acid and methanol.

$$\overset{O}{\underset{||}{CH_3-C-OH}} + CH_3:\overset{..}{\underset{..}{O}}:H \rightleftharpoons \underset{\substack{CH_3-\overset{|}{O}-H \\ \oplus}}{\overset{\overset{O^{\ominus}}{\underset{|}{CH_3-\overset{|}{C}-OH}}}{}} \rightleftharpoons$$

$$\underset{\substack{CH_3-O}}{\overset{\overset{OH}{\underset{|}{CH_3-\overset{|}{C}-OH}}}{}} \rightleftharpoons \overset{O}{\underset{||}{CH_3-C-OCH_3}} + H_2O$$

This reaction is slow in either direction in the absence of a strong mineral acid. Strong acids catalyze ester formation from the alcohol provided they are not present in large amount. The reason for the "too much of a good thing" behavior of the catalyst is readily apparent from a consideration of the reaction mechanism. A strong acid like sulfuric acid may donate a proton to the unshared oxygen electron pairs of either acetic acid or methanol.

$$\underset{OH}{\overset{O}{CH_3-C\lessgtr}} + H_2SO_4 \rightleftharpoons \underset{OH}{\overset{\overset{\oplus}{OH}}{CH_3-C\lessgtr}} + HSO_4^{\ominus}$$

$$[3]$$

$$CH_3-O-H + H_2SO_4 \rightleftharpoons \overset{\overset{H}{\underset{|}{CH_3-O-H}}}{}^{\oplus} + HSO_4^{\ominus}$$

Clearly, formation of methyloxonium bisulfate can only operate to *reduce* the reactivity of methanol toward the carbonyl carbon of acetic acid. However, this anticatalytic effect is more than balanced (at low concentrations of H_2SO_4)

by protonation of the carbonyl oxygen of the carboxylic acid [3], since this greatly enhances the electron-pair accepting power of the carbonyl carbon.

$$\left[\begin{array}{c} \overset{\oplus}{O}H \\ \parallel \\ CH_3-C-OH \end{array} \longleftrightarrow \begin{array}{c} OH \\ \mid \\ CH_3-\underset{\oplus}{C}-OH \end{array} \right] \; + \; CH_3-O-H \; \rightleftharpoons \; \begin{array}{c} OH \\ \mid \\ CH_3-C-OH \\ \mid \\ CH_3-\overset{}{O}\overset{\oplus}{-}H \end{array}$$

[3]   [4]

The resulting intermediate [4] is in equilibrium with its isomer [5], which can lose a water molecule to give the oxonium salt of the ester [6].

$$\begin{array}{c} OH \\ \mid \\ CH_3-C-OH \\ \mid \\ CH_3-\underset{\oplus}{O}-H \end{array} \rightleftharpoons \begin{array}{c} \overset{\oplus}{O}H_2 \\ \mid \\ CH_3-C-OH \\ \mid \\ CH_3O \end{array} \rightleftharpoons \begin{array}{c} \overset{\oplus}{O}H \\ \parallel \\ CH_3-C-OCH_3 \end{array} + H_2O \rightleftharpoons$$

[4]   [5]   [6]

$$\begin{array}{c} O \\ \parallel \\ CH_3-C-OCH_3 \end{array} + \overset{\oplus}{H_3O}$$

methyl acetate

Transfer of a proton from [6] to water gives the reaction product.

At high acid concentrations, essentially all the methanol would be converted to inert methyloxonium ion and the rate of esterification would then be very slow, even though more of the oxonium ion of acetic acid would be present.

EXERCISE 13-7   In the esterification of an acid with an alcohol, how could you distinguish between C—O and O—H cleavage of the alcohol using heavy oxygen (^{18}O) as a tracer?

$$CH_3O\text{-}H \; + \; \begin{array}{c} O \\ \parallel \\ RC\text{-}OH \end{array} \quad \xrightarrow{\;H^{\oplus}\;} \quad \begin{array}{c} O \\ \parallel \\ RCOCH_3 \end{array} + H_2O$$

or

$$CH_3\text{-}OH \; + \; \begin{array}{c} O \\ \parallel \\ RCO\text{-}H \end{array} \quad \xrightarrow{\;H^{\oplus}\;} \quad \begin{array}{c} O \\ \parallel \\ RCOCH_3 \end{array} + H_2O$$

What type of alcohols might conceivably react by C—O cleavage, and what side reactions would you anticipate for such alcohols?

As mentioned earlier, esterification is reversible and, with ethanol and acetic acid, has an equilibrium constant of about 4 at room temperature, which corresponds to 66 per cent conversion to ester.

$$CH_3\overset{\displaystyle O}{\overset{\|}{C}}{-}OH \ + \ C_2H_5OH \ \rightleftharpoons \ CH_3\overset{\displaystyle O}{\overset{\|}{C}}{-}O{-}C_2H_5 \ + \ H_2O$$

$$K \ = \ \frac{[CH_3CO_2C_2H_5]\,[H_2O]}{[CH_3CO_2H]\,[C_2H_5OH]} \ \sim 4$$

The reaction may be driven to completion by removing the ester and/or water as they are formed.

Steric hindrance is very important in determining rates of esterification, and esters with highly branched groups, in either the acid or alcohol parts, are formed at slower rates and with smaller equilibrium constants than their less highly branched analogs. In general, the ease of esterification for alcohols is *prim.* > *sec.* > *tert.*, with a given carboxylic acid.

13-6   REACTIONS INVOLVING THE C—O BOND OF ALCOHOLS

A. Halide Formation

Alkyl halide formation from an alcohol and a hydrogen halide affords an important example of a reaction wherein the C—O bond of the alcohol is broken.

$$R{-}OH \ + \ HBr \ \rightleftharpoons \ RBr \ + \ H_2O$$

The reaction is reversible and the favored direction depends on the water concentration (see Exercise 11-8, p. 235). Primary bromides are often best prepared by passing dry hydrogen bromide into the alcohol heated to just slightly below its boiling point.

Reaction proceeds at a useful rate only in the presence of strong acid, which can be furnished by excess hydrogen bromide or, usually and more economically, by sulfuric acid. The alcohol accepts a proton from the acid to give an alkyloxonium ion, which is more reactive in subsequent displacement with bromide ion than the alcohol, since it can more easily lose a neutral water molecule than the alcohol can lose hydroxide ion (see p. 235).

$$Br^{\ominus} \ + \ R\overset{\displaystyle H}{\underset{\oplus}{\overset{\|}{O}}}{-}H \ \longrightarrow \ RBr \ + \ H_2O \qquad\qquad S_N2$$

or

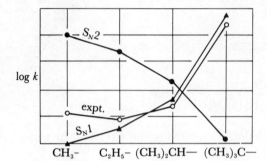

$$R{-}\underset{\oplus}{\overset{\overset{\displaystyle H}{|}}{O}}{-}H \quad \underset{\xrightarrow{\hspace{1.2cm}}}{\overset{(-H_2O)}{\rightleftharpoons}} \quad R^{\oplus} \quad \xrightarrow{Br^{\ominus}} \quad RBr \qquad\qquad S_N1$$

Figure 13-4

Schematic representation of reactivities of a series of alcohols with hydrogen bromide as compared to normal S_N1 and S_N2 reactivity orders. The points shown for S_N1 reactivity of methanol and the S_N2 reactivity of t-butyl alcohol are estimated and may only represent upper limits.

Whether the displacement reaction is an S_N1 or S_N2 process depends on the structure of the alcohol. To illustrate, the relative rates of reaction of a series of primary, secondary, and tertiary alcohols with hydrogen bromide are shown schematically in Figure 13-4 and are compared to the relative reactivities expected for both S_N1 and S_N2 mechanisms.

Neither the normal S_N1 nor S_N2 reactivity order is observed. The most reasonable interpretation of the reactivity sequence is to consider the primary alcohols to be reacting by S_N2 and the secondary and tertiary alcohols by S_N1 mechanisms.

Hydrogen chloride is less reactive than hydrogen bromide toward primary alcohols, and a catalyst (zinc chloride) may be required. A solution of zinc chloride in concentrated hydrochloric acid (Lucas reagent) is widely used as a convenient reagent to differentiate between the lower primary, secondary, and tertiary alcohols. Tertiary alcohols react very rapidly to give an insoluble layer of alkyl chloride at room temperature. Secondary alcohols react in several minutes, whereas primary alcohols form chlorides only on heating. The order of reactivity is typical of S_N1-type reactions. Zinc chloride probably assists in the breaking of the C—O bond of the alcohol much as silver ion aids ionization of RX (p. 235).

$$ROH + ZnCl_2 \rightleftharpoons R{-}\underset{\overset{|}{H}}{O}{-}{-}{-}ZnCl_2 \quad \xrightarrow{-[HOZnCl_2]^{\ominus}} R^{\oplus} \quad \xrightarrow{Cl^{\ominus}} RCl$$

Thionyl chloride, $SOCl_2$, is a useful reagent for the preparation of alkyl chlorides, especially when the use of zinc chloride and hydrochloric acid is undesirable. Addition of 1 mole of an alcohol to 1 mole of thionyl chloride gives an unstable alkyl chlorosulfite, which generally decomposes on mild heating to yield the alkyl chloride and sulfur dioxide.

$$ROH + SOCl_2 \xrightarrow{-HCl} R{-}O{-}\underset{\overset{\|}{}}{\overset{\overset{\displaystyle O}{\|}}{S}}{-}Cl \longrightarrow RCl + SO_2$$

alkyl chlorosulfite

B. Esters of Sulfuric Acid—Dehydration of Alcohols

Alkyl acid sulfate formation from alcohols and concentrated sulfuric acid may occur by a reaction rather closely related to alkyl halide formation.

$$ROH + H_2SO_4 \rightleftharpoons R\overset{\oplus}{O}H_2 + H\overset{\ominus}{S}O_4 \longrightarrow ROSO_3H + H_2O$$

alkyl acid sulfate

Conversion of the oxonium acid sulfate to the alkyl acid sulfate probably goes by an S_N2 mechanism with primary alcohols and an S_N1 mechanism with tertiary alcohols. An alternative mechanism which operates in 100 per cent or fuming sulfuric acid is addition of sulfur trioxide to the OH group.

$$ROH + SO_3 \longrightarrow \left[R\overset{\underset{\displaystyle\oplus}{H}}{—O—}SO_3{}^{\ominus} \right] \longrightarrow R—O—SO_3H$$

On heating, alkyl acid sulfates readily undergo elimination of sulfuric acid to give alkenes and, in the reaction of an alcohol with hot concentrated sulfuric acid, which gives over-all dehydration of the alcohol, the acid sulfate may well be a key intermediate. This is the reverse of acid-catalyzed hydration of alkenes discussed previously (p. 138) and goes to completion if the alkene is allowed to distill out of the reaction mixture as it is formed.

$$CH_3CH_2OH + H_2SO_4 \xrightarrow{(-H_2O)} CH_3CH_2OSO_3H \underset{\text{-----}}{\overset{150°}{\rightleftharpoons}} CH_2{=}CH_2 + H_2SO_4$$

The mechanism of elimination of sulfuric acid from ethyl acid sulfate is probably of the E2 type, with water or bisulfate ion acting as the base. An alternative mechanism is an E2-type reaction of bisulfate ion or water on the oxonium salt of the alcohol.

$$HSO_4{}^{\ominus} + \underset{\overset{|}{H}}{C}H_2{-}CH_2{-}\overset{\oplus}{O}H_2 \longrightarrow H_2SO_4 + CH_2{=}CH_2 + H_2O$$

At lower temperatures, alkyl acid sulfate may react by a displacement mechanism with excess alcohol in the reaction mixture with formation of a dialkyl ether. Diethyl ether is made commercially by this process; although each step in the reaction is reversible, ether formation can be favored by distilling away the ether as fast as it forms.

$$CH_3CH_2OSO_3H + CH_3CH_2OH \xrightarrow{130°} CH_3CH_2{-}\overset{\underset{\displaystyle\oplus}{H}}{O}{-}CH_2CH_3 + HSO_4{}^{\ominus}$$

$$\Updownarrow$$

$$CH_3CH_2OCH_2CH_3 + H_2SO_4$$

Most alcohols will also dehydrate at fairly high temperatures to give alkenes and/or ethers in the presence of solid catalysts such as silica gel or aluminum oxide. The behavior of ethanol is reasonably typical of primary alcohols and is summarized in the following equations:

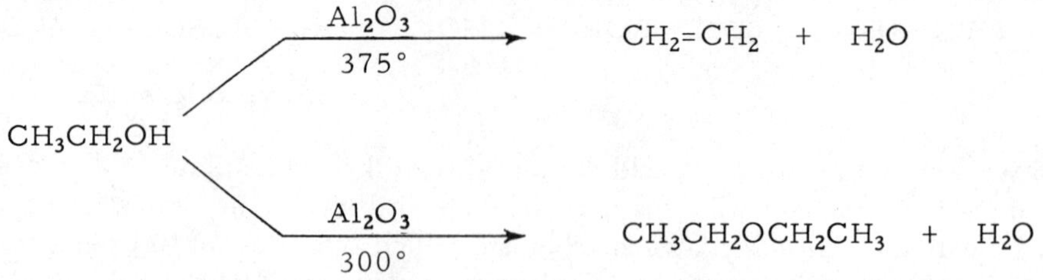

$$CH_3CH_2OH \xrightarrow[\text{375°}]{Al_2O_3} CH_2{=}CH_2 \; + \; H_2O$$

$$CH_3CH_2OH \xrightarrow[\text{300°}]{Al_2O_3} CH_3CH_2OCH_2CH_3 \; + \; H_2O$$

Tertiary alcohols react with sulfuric acid at much lower temperatures than do most primary alcohols. The following S_N1 and E1 reactions may be written for t-butyl alcohol and sulfuric acid.

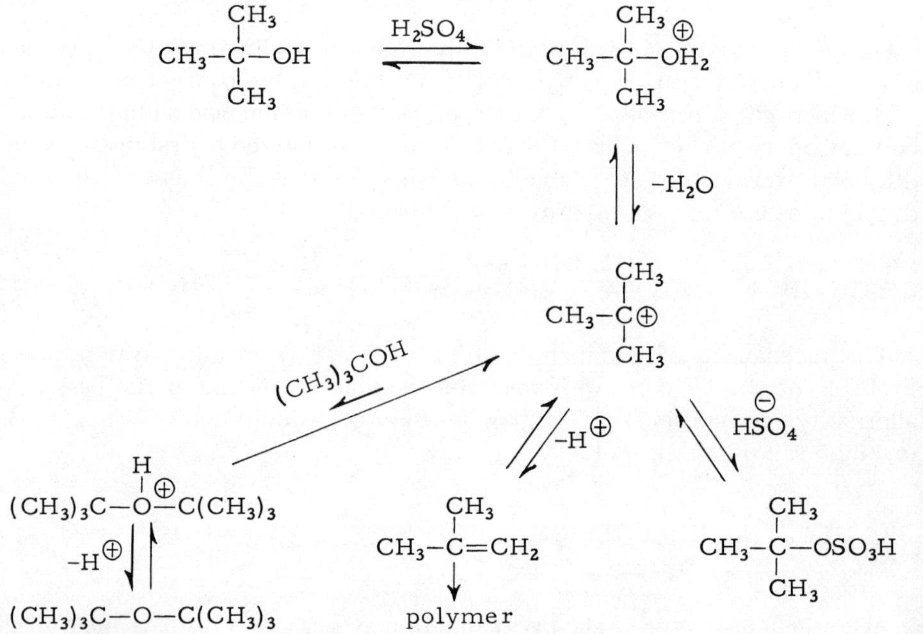

$$
\begin{array}{c}
CH_3 \\
| \\
CH_3{-}C{-}OH \\
| \\
CH_3
\end{array}
\xrightleftharpoons{H_2SO_4}
\begin{array}{c}
CH_3 \quad \oplus \\
| \\
CH_3{-}C{-}OH_2 \\
| \\
CH_3
\end{array}
$$

$$\Big\updownarrow \; -H_2O$$

$$
\begin{array}{c}
CH_3 \\
| \\
CH_3{-}C\oplus \\
| \\
CH_3
\end{array}
$$

$(CH_3)_3COH$

$$
\begin{array}{c}
H \\
| \; \oplus \\
(CH_3)_3C{-}O{-}C(CH_3)_3
\end{array}
$$

$-H^\oplus$ ⇅

$(CH_3)_3C{-}O{-}C(CH_3)_3$

$-H^\oplus$

$$
\begin{array}{c}
CH_3 \\
| \\
CH_3{-}C{=}CH_2 \\
\downarrow \\
\text{polymer}
\end{array}
$$

$HSO_4^\ominus$

$$
\begin{array}{c}
CH_3 \\
| \\
CH_3{-}C{-}OSO_3H \\
| \\
CH_3
\end{array}
$$

Di-t-butyl ether is unstable in sulfuric acid solution and it has never been detected in reaction mixtures of this type. Its low stability may be due to steric crowding between the alkyl groups.

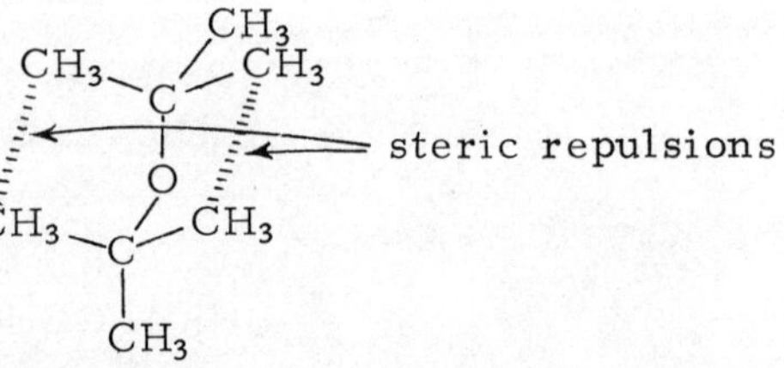

$$
\begin{array}{c}
\qquad CH_3 \\
CH_3 \diagdown \quad \diagup CH_3 \\
\qquad C \\
\qquad | \\
\qquad O \\
CH_3 \diagdown \quad \diagup CH_3 \\
\qquad C \\
\qquad | \\
\qquad CH_3
\end{array}
\longleftrightarrow \text{steric repulsions}
$$

Isobutylene can be removed from the reaction mixture by distillation and is easily made the principal product by appropriate adjustment of the reaction conditions. If the isobutylene is not removed as it is formed, polymer is the most important end product. Sulfuric acid is often an unduly strenuous reagent for dehydration of tertiary alcohols and potassium acid sulfate, copper sulfate, iodine, phosphoric acid, or phosphorous pentoxide may give better results by causing less polymerization and less oxidative degradation which, with sulfuric acid, results in formation of sulfur dioxide.

Secondary alcohols react with sulfuric acid by mechanisms on the borderline between S_N2 and S_N1 and E2 and E1. Often di-*sec*-alkyl ethers are not easily prepared by dehydration of secondary alcohols.

EXERCISE 13-8   What would be the products of the following reactions? Indicate your reasoning.

a. $(CH_3)_3COH + CH_3OH \xrightarrow[0°]{\text{conc. } H_2SO_4}$

b. 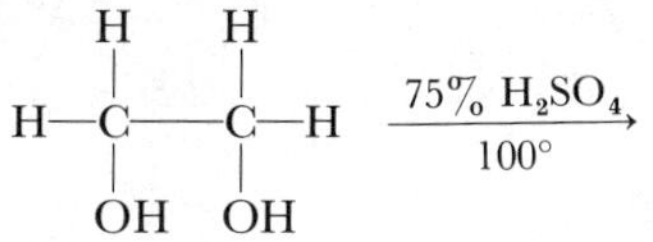 $H-\underset{\underset{OH}{|}}{\overset{\overset{H}{|}}{C}}-\underset{\underset{OH}{|}}{\overset{\overset{H}{|}}{C}}-H \xrightarrow[100°]{75\% \text{ } H_2SO_4}$

c. $CH_3-\underset{\underset{CH_3}{|}}{\overset{\overset{CH_3}{|}}{C}}-CH_2-OH$ $\begin{cases} \xrightarrow[25°]{95\% \text{ } H_2SO_4} \\ \xrightarrow[25°]{100\% \text{ } H_2SO_4} \end{cases}$

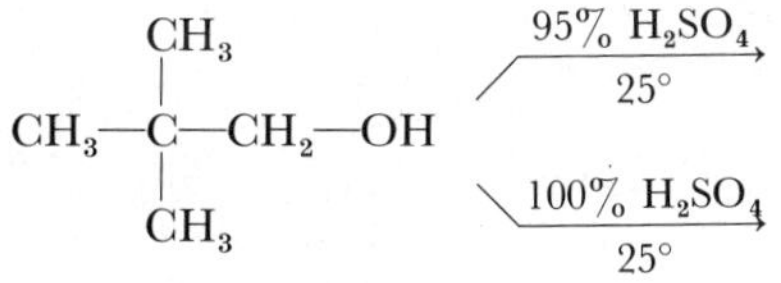

d. 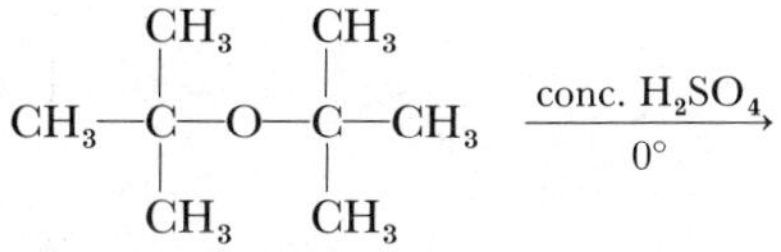 $CH_3-\underset{\underset{CH_3}{|}}{\overset{\overset{CH_3}{|}}{C}}-O-\underset{\underset{CH_3}{|}}{\overset{\overset{CH_3}{|}}{C}}-CH_3 \xrightarrow[0°]{\text{conc. } H_2SO_4}$

Rearrangement of the alkyl group of an alcohol is very common in dehydration, particularly in the presence of sulfuric acid, which is highly conducive to carbonium ion formation. Typical examples showing both methyl and hydrogen migration follow.

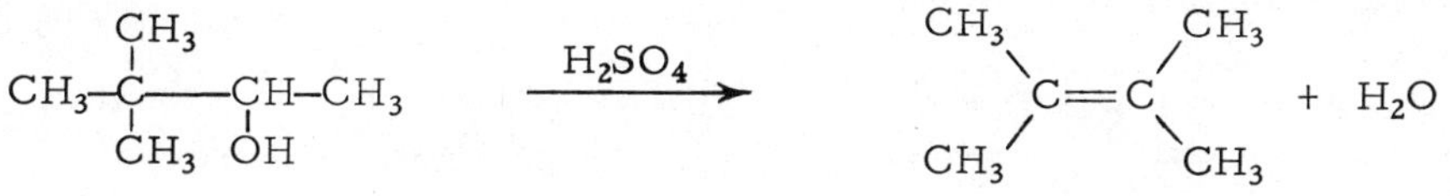

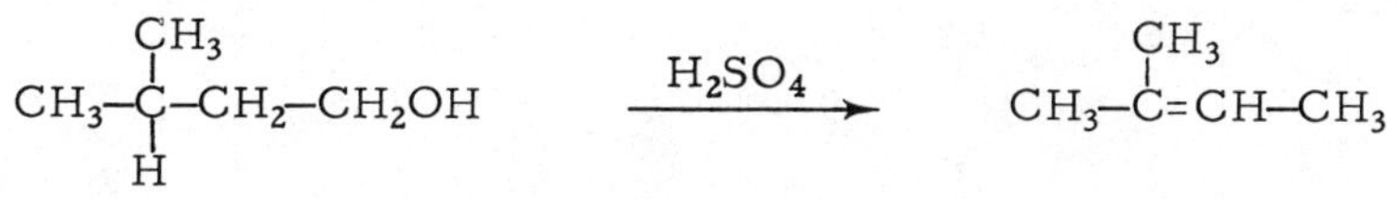

$$CH_3-\underset{\underset{CH_3}{|}}{\overset{\overset{CH_3}{|}}{C}}-\underset{\underset{OH}{|}}{\overset{}{C}}H-CH_3 \xrightarrow{H_2SO_4} \underset{CH_3}{\overset{CH_3}{}}C=C\underset{CH_3}{\overset{CH_3}{}} + H_2O$$

$$CH_3-\underset{\underset{H}{|}}{\overset{\overset{CH_3}{|}}{C}}-CH_2-CH_2OH \xrightarrow{H_2SO_4} CH_3-\overset{\overset{CH_3}{|}}{C}=CH-CH_3$$

The key step in each such rearrangement involves an isomerization of a carbonium ion along lines discussed in Chapter 11 (p. 242). Except in a few circumstances where thermodynamic control dominates and leads to different results from kinetic control, the final products always correspond to rearrangement of a less stable carbonium ion to a more stable carbonium ion.

reactants →

$$
\begin{array}{cc}
\text{R} & \oplus \\
| & | \\
-\text{C}-\text{C}- \\
| & |
\end{array}
\quad \rightarrow \quad
\begin{array}{cc}
\oplus & \text{R} \\
| & | \\
-\text{C}-\text{C}- \\
| & |
\end{array}
\quad \rightarrow \quad \text{products}
$$

less stable   more stable
carbonium ion   carbonium ion

For the particular case of the dehydration of methyl-*t*-butylcarbinol, the sequence is

$$
\begin{array}{c}
\text{CH}_3 \\
| \\
\text{CH}_3-\overset{|}{\underset{|}{\text{C}}}-\text{CH}-\text{CH}_3 \\
| \\
\text{CH}_3 \;\; \text{OH}
\end{array}
\underset{}{\overset{\text{H}_2\text{SO}_4}{\rightleftharpoons}}
\left[
\begin{array}{c}
\text{CH}_3 \\
| \\
\text{CH}_3-\overset{|}{\text{C}}-\text{CH}-\text{CH}_3 \\
| \\
\text{CH}_3 \oplus
\end{array}
\right. \longrightarrow
$$

secondary
carbonium
ion

$$
\left.
\begin{array}{c}
\text{CH}_3\;\text{CH}_3 \\
| \quad | \\
\text{CH}_3-\text{C}-\overset{|}{\text{C}}-\text{CH}_3 \\
\underset{\oplus}{} \quad \text{H}
\end{array}
\right]
\underset{}{\overset{-\text{H}^{\oplus}}{\rightleftharpoons}}
\begin{array}{c}
\text{CH}_3 \quad\quad \text{CH}_3 \\
\diagdown \quad\quad \diagup \\
\text{C}=\text{C} \\
\diagup \quad\quad \diagdown \\
\text{CH}_3 \quad\quad \text{CH}_3
\end{array}
$$

tertiary
carbonium
ion

13-7 OXIDATION OF ALCOHOLS

Apart from combustion to carbon dioxide and water, oxidation of primary and secondary alcohols to carbonyl compounds is possible through dehydrogenation. Primary alcohols first give aldehydes and thence carboxylic acids, whereas secondary alcohols give ketones.

$$
\text{RCH}_2\text{OH} \xrightarrow{\;[\text{O}]\;}
\begin{array}{c}
\overset{\text{O}}{\overset{\|}{}} \\
\text{R}-\text{C} \\
\diagdown \\
\text{H}
\end{array}
\xrightarrow{\;[\text{O}]\;}
\begin{array}{c}
\overset{\text{O}}{\overset{\|}{}} \\
\text{R}-\text{C} \\
\diagdown \\
\text{OH}
\end{array}
$$

$$
\begin{array}{c}
\text{R} \\
\diagdown \\
\quad\;\text{CHOH} \\
\diagup \\
\text{R}
\end{array}
\xrightarrow{\;[\text{O}]\;}
\begin{array}{c}
\text{R} \\
\diagdown \\
\quad\;\text{C}=\text{O} \\
\diagup \\
\text{R}
\end{array}
$$

Tertiary alcohols are oxidized with considerable difficulty and then only with degradation into smaller fragments by cleavage of carbon-carbon bonds. Similarly, oxidation of secondary alcohols beyond the ketone stage does not proceed readily and leads to degradation.

Laboratory oxidation of alcohols is most often carried out with chromic acid (H_2CrO_4), which is usually prepared as required from chromic oxide (CrO_3) or from sodium dichromate ($Na_2Cr_2O_7$) in combination with sulfuric acid. Acetic acid is the most generally useful solvent for such reactions.

$$3 \; \begin{matrix} CH_3 \\ | \\ CH-OH \\ | \\ CH_3 \end{matrix} + 2\,CrO_3 + 6\,H^{\oplus} \longrightarrow 3 \; \begin{matrix} CH_3 \\ | \\ C=O \\ | \\ CH_3 \end{matrix} + 2\,Cr^{3\oplus} + 6\,H_2O$$

The mechanism of the chromic acid oxidation of isopropyl alcohol to acetone has been investigated very thoroughly and is highly interesting in that it reveals how changes of oxidation level can occur involving a typical inorganic and a typical organic compound. The initial step is reversible formation of isopropyl acid chromate [7], which is quite unstable and is not usually isolated (although it can be isolated by working rapidly at low temperatures).

$$\begin{matrix} CH_3 \\ | \\ CH-OH \\ | \\ CH_3 \end{matrix} + CrO_3 \; \rightleftharpoons \; \begin{matrix} CH_3 \\ | \\ CH-O-CrO_3H \\ | \\ CH_3 \end{matrix}$$

$$[7]$$

The subsequent step is the slowest in the reaction and appears to involve attack of a base (water) at the *alpha* hydrogen of the chromate ester concurrent with elimination of the grouping $HCrO_3^{\ominus}$. There is an obvious analogy between this step and an E2 reaction (pp. 238–240).

$$\longrightarrow \quad \begin{matrix} CH_3 \\ | \\ C=O \\ | \\ CH_3 \end{matrix} + H_3O^{\oplus} + HCrO_3^{\ominus}$$

The transformation of chromic acid (H_2CrO_4) to H_2CrO_3 amounts to the reduction of chromium from an oxidation state of +6 to +4. Disproportionation of Cr^{IV} occurs rapidly to give compounds of Cr^{III} and Cr^{VI}.

$$3\,H_2CrO_3 + 6\,H^{\oplus} \longrightarrow CrO_3 + 2\,Cr^{3\oplus} + 6\,H_2O$$

Unsaturated alcohols can be oxidized to unsaturated ketones by chromic acid, since the reagent usually attacks double bonds relatively slowly.

In contrast, neutral potassium permanganate oxidizes unsaturated groups more rapidly than alcohols.

However, complications are to be expected when the double bond of an unsaturated alcohol is particularly reactive or when the alcohol rearranges readily under strongly acidic conditions.

13-8   POLYHYDRIC ALCOHOLS

The simplest example of an alcohol with more than one hydroxyl group is methylene glycol, $HOCH_2OH$, the term "glycol" meaning a *diol*, a substance with two alcoholic hydroxyl groups.   Methylene glycol is reasonably stable in water solution but attempts to isolate it lead only to its dehydration product, formaldehyde.

$$HO-CH_2-OH \quad \rightleftharpoons \quad H_2C=O \;+\; H_2O$$

This behavior is typical of *gem*-diols (*gem* = geminal, i.e., with both hydroxyl groups on the same carbon atom), and the very few *gem*-diols that are isolable are those which carry strongly electron-attracting substituents such as chloral hydrate and hexafluoroacetone hydrate.

chloral hydrate   hexafluoroacetone hydrate

Polyhydric alcohols in which the hydroxyl groups are situated on different carbons are relatively stable, and, as we might expect for substances with a multiplicity of polar groups, they have high boiling points, considerable water solubility but low solubility in nonpolar solvents.

ethylene glycol	tetramethylene glycol	glycerol
1, 2-ethanediol	1, 4-butanediol	1, 2, 3-propanetriol
b.p. 197°	b.p. 230°	b.p. 290°

1,2-Diols are usually prepared from alkenes by oxidation with reagents such as osmium tetroxide, potassium permanganate, or hydrogen peroxide (pp. 151–152).   However, ethylene glycol is made on a large scale commercially from ethylene oxide, which in turn is made by air oxidation of ethylene at high temperatures over a silver catalyst.

$$CH_2{=}CH_2 \ + \ \tfrac{1}{2}O_2 \ \xrightarrow[\;300^\circ\;]{Ag} \ \underset{\underset{O}{\diagdown\diagup}}{CH_2{-}CH_2} \ \xrightarrow{H_2O, \ H^\oplus} \ \underset{\underset{OH \ \ OH}{|\ \ \ \ |}}{CH_2{-}CH_2}$$

ethylene oxide

Ethylene glycol has important commercial uses. It is an excellent permanent antifreeze for automotive cooling systems, since it is miscible with water in all proportions and a 50 per cent solution freezes at -34° C (-29°F). It is also used as a solvent and as an intermediate in the production of polymers (polyesters) and other products, as shown on p. 303.

The trihydric alcohol, glycerol, is a nontoxic, water-soluble, viscous, hygroscopic liquid that is widely used as a humectant (moistening agent). It is an important component of many food, cosmetic, and pharmaceutical preparations. At one time, glycerol was obtained on a commercial scale only as a by-product of soap manufacture through hydrolysis of fats, which are glycerol esters of long-chain alkanoic acids (see pp. 361–363), but now the main source is by synthesis from propylene as described on p. 244. The trinitrate ester of glycerol (nitroglycerin) is an important but shock-sensitive explosive. Dynamite is a much safer and more controllable explosive, made by absorbing nitroglycerin in porous material like sawdust or diatomaceous earth. Smokeless powder is nitroglycerin mixed with partially nitrated cellulose.

$$\begin{array}{l} CH_2ONO_2 \\ | \\ CHONO_2 \\ | \\ CH_2ONO_2 \end{array} \qquad \begin{array}{l} \text{nitroglycerin} \\ \text{(glyceryl trinitrate)} \end{array}$$

Glycerol plays an important role in animal metabolism as a constituent of fats and lipids.

13-9   UNSATURATED ALCOHOLS

The simplest unsaturated alcohol, vinyl alcohol, is unstable with respect to acetaldehyde and has never been isolated.

$$\underset{\text{vinyl alcohol}}{\underset{H}{\overset{H}{\diagdown}}C{=}C\underset{H}{\overset{OH}{\diagup}}} \qquad \rightleftharpoons \qquad \underset{\text{acetaldehyde}}{CH_3{-}C\overset{O}{\underset{H}{\diagup\diagdown}}}$$

Other simple vinyl alcohols undergo similar transformations to carbonyl compounds. However, ether and ester derivatives of vinyl alcohols are known and can be prepared by the addition of alcohols and carboxylic acids to acetylenes. The esters are used to make many commercially important polymers.

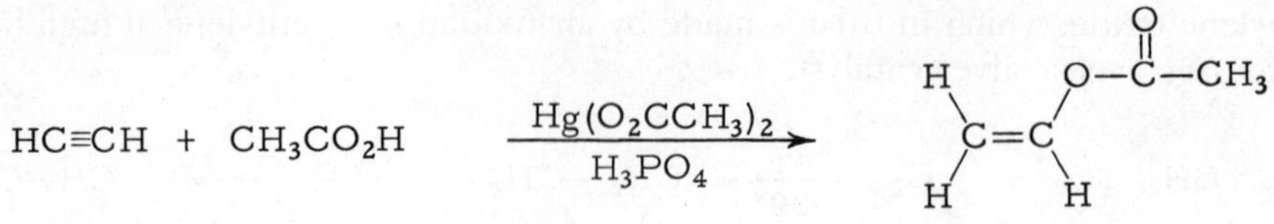

$$HC\equiv CH + CH_3CO_2H \xrightarrow[H_3PO_4]{Hg(O_2CCH_3)_2}$$

vinyl acetate

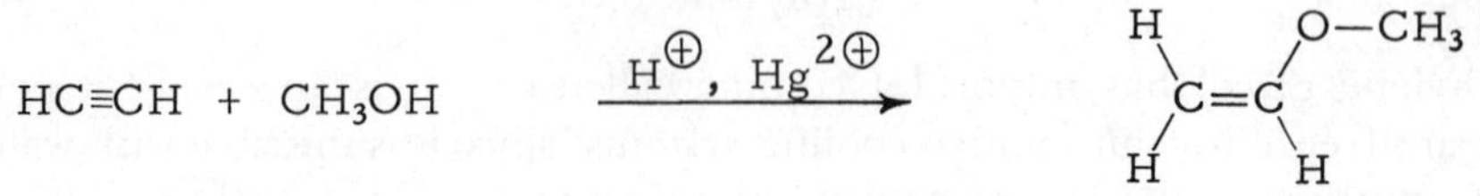

$$HC\equiv CH + CH_3OH \xrightarrow{H^{\oplus}, Hg^{2\oplus}}$$

methyl vinyl ether

EXERCISE 13-9   Use bond energies and estimated stabilization energies to predict the positions of the following equilibria (see pp. 193–194).

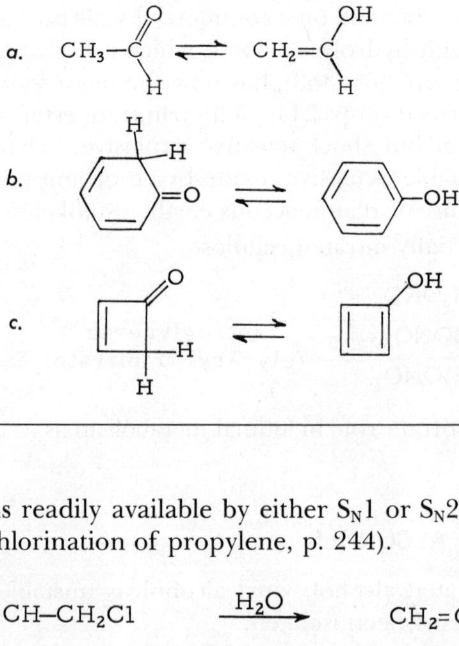

Allyl alcohol is readily available by either S_N1 or S_N2 hydrolysis of allyl chloride (made by chlorination of propylene, p. 244).

$$CH_2=CH-CH_2Cl \xrightarrow{H_2O} CH_2=CH-CH_2OH$$

allyl alcohol

It displays most of the usual double-bond reactions and, as expected from the behavior of allylic halides, it is much more reactive than saturated primary alcohols toward reagents like Lucas reagent, which cleave the C—O bond.

When the double bond and hydroxyl group are separated by two or more CH_2 groups, as in 3-buten-1-ol, they behave reasonably independently of one another.

$$CH_2=CH-CH_2-CH_2OH$$

3–buten–1–ol

ETHERS

13-10 TYPES AND REACTIONS OF SIMPLE ETHERS

Substitution of the hydroxyl hydrogens of alcohols by hydrocarbon groups give compounds known as ethers. These may be further classified as open-chain, cyclic, saturated, unsaturated, aromatic, etc.

$$CH_3CH_2OCH_2CH_3 \qquad\qquad CH_3OCH{=}CH_2$$

$$\underset{\displaystyle \diagdown\!\!\diagup O}{CH_2\text{---}CH_2}$$

diethyl ether   methyl vinyl ether   ethylene oxide

b. p. 35°   b. p. ~ 12°   b. p. 11°

methyl phenyl ether   tetrahydrofuran   1, 4-dioxane
(anisole)

b. p. 155°   b. p. 65°   b. p. 101. 5°

The most generally useful methods of preparation of ethers have already been discussed in connection with the reactions of alcohols (pp. 287 and 293).

In general, ethers are low on the scale of chemical reactivity, since the carbon-oxygen bond is not cleaved readily. For this reason, ethers are frequently employed as inert solvents in organic synthesis. Particularly important in this connection are diethyl ether, diisopropyl ether, tetrahydrofuran, and 1,4-dioxane. The mono and dialkyl ethers of ethylene glycol and diethylene glycol are useful high-boiling solvents. Unfortunately, they have acquired irrational names like "polyglymes," "cellosolves," and "carbitols"; for reference, **cellosolves** are monoalkyl ethers of diethylene glycol; **carbitols** are monoalkyl ethers of diethylene glycol; **polyglymes** are dimethyl ethers of di- or triethylene glycol, diglyme, and triglyme, respectively.

$$CH_3OCH_2CH_2OH \qquad\qquad C_4H_9OCH_2CH_2OCH_2CH_2OH$$

methyl cellosolve   butyl carbitol

b. p. 124°   b. p. 231°

$$CH_3OCH_2CH_2OCH_2CH_2OCH_3$$

diglyme

b. p. 161°

Unlike alcohols, ethers are not acidic and do not usually react with bases. However, exceptionally powerfully basic reagents, particularly certain alkali-metal alkyls, will react destructively with many ethers (see also p. 261).

$$CH_3^{\ominus} \ Na^{\oplus} \ + \ H{:}CH_2{-}CH_2{-}\ddot{O}{-}CH_2CH_3 \longrightarrow$$

$$CH_4 \ + \ CH_2{=}CH_2 \ + \ CH_3CH_2\overset{\ominus}{O} \overset{\oplus}{Na}$$

Ethers, like alcohols, are weakly basic and are converted to unstable oxonium salts by strong acids (e.g., H_2SO_4, $HClO_4$, and HBr) and to relatively stable coordination complexes with Lewis acids (e.g., BF_3 and RMgX).

$$C_2H_5\ddot{O}C_2H_5 \ + \ HBr \quad \rightleftharpoons \quad C_2H_5\overset{H \ \oplus}{\ddot{O}}C_2H_5 \ + \ Br^{\ominus}$$

diethyloxonium bromide

$$C_2H_5\ddot{O}C_2H_5 \ + \ BF_3 \quad \longrightarrow \quad C_2H_5\overset{F{\diagdown}\overset{F}{\underset{B}{|}}{\diagup}F}{\ddot{O}}C_2H_5$$

boron trifluoride etherate

Dialkyloxonium ions are more susceptible to nucleophilic displacement and elimination reactions than are neutral ether molecules; the reasons are the same as for the activation of alcohols by strong acids (p. 235). Therefore, strongly acidic conditions are required for cleavage reactions of ethers to occur readily.

$$C_2H_5{-}O{-}C_2H_5 \ + \ H^{\oplus} \ \rightleftharpoons \ C_2H_5{-}\overset{H}{\underset{\oplus}{O}}{-}C_2H_5 \ \xrightarrow[S_N2]{Br^{\ominus}} \ C_2H_5Br \ + \ C_2H_5OH$$

$$(CH_3)_3C{-}O{-}C(CH_3)_3 \ + \ H^{\oplus} \quad \rightleftharpoons \quad (CH_3)_3C{-}\overset{H}{\underset{\oplus}{O}}{-}C(CH_3)_3$$

$$\Big\downarrow \ {}^{\ominus}HSO_4 \quad E_1$$

$$(CH_3)_2C{=}CH_2 \quad \longleftarrow \quad (CH_3)_3C{-}OH \ + \ (CH_3)_2C{=}CH_2 \ + \ H_2SO_4$$

EXERCISE 13-10   Predict the products likely to be formed on cleavage of the following ethers with hydrobromic acid.

a. $CH_2{=}CH{-}CH_2{-}O{-}CH_3$

b. $CH_3CH_2{-}O{-}CH{=}CH_2$

c. $(CH_3)_3CCH_2{-}O{-}CH_3$

d. $\begin{array}{c} CH_2{-}CH_2 \\ | \qquad \quad \diagdown \\ \qquad \qquad O \\ CH_2{-}CH_2 \diagup \end{array}$

e. (aryl)—$O{-}CH_3$

Ethers are susceptible to attack by free radicals, and for this reason are not good solvents for free-radical reactions. In fact, ethers are potentially hazardous chemicals since, in the presence of atmospheric oxygen, a radical-chain process can occur, resulting in the formation of peroxides which are unstable, explosion-prone compounds. This process is called **autoxidation** and occurs not only with ethers but with many aldehydes and hydrocarbons. Commonly used ethers such as diethyl ether, tetrahydrofuran, and dioxane often become contaminated with peroxides formed by autoxidation on prolonged storage and exposure to air and light. Purification of ethers is frequently necessary before use, and caution should always be exercised in their distillation as the distillation residues may contain dangerously high concentrations of explosive peroxides.

13-11   CYCLIC ETHERS

Ethylene oxide, the simplest cyclic ether, is an outstanding exception to the generalization that most ethers are resistant to cleavage. Like cyclopropane, the three-membered ring is highly strained and readily opens under mild conditions. Indeed, the importance of ethylene oxide lies in its readiness to form other important compounds; for example, ethylene glycol, diethylene glycol, the cellosolves and carbitols, dioxane, and ethylene chlorohydrin, and polymers (Carbowax).

The lesser known four-membered cyclic ether, trimethylene oxide $(CH_2)_3O$, is also cleaved readily, but less so than ethylene oxide. Tetramethylene oxide (tetrahydrofuran) is relatively stable and is a water-miscible compound with desirable properties as an organic solvent. It is often used in place of diethyl ether in Grignard reactions and reductions with lithium aluminum hydride.

SUPPLEMENTARY EXERCISES

13-11 Write structural formulas for each of the following:
  a. bromomethyl 1,2-dimethylcyclopropyl ketone
  b. divinylmethylcarbinyl ketone
  c. 4-bromo-2-methyl-3-butynal
  d. diacetylacetylene
  e. α,β-dimethylbutyric acetic anhydride
  f. 3-acetyl-2-cyclohexenone

13-12 The reaction of methyl acetate with water to give methanol and acetic acid is catalyzed by strong mineral acids such as sulfuric acid. Furthermore, when hydrolysis is carried out in ^{18}O water, the following exchange takes place *faster* than formation of methanol.

No methanol-^{18}O ($CH_3{}^{18}OH$) is formed in hydrolysis under these conditions.
  a. Write a step-wise mechanism which is in harmony with the acid catalysis and with the results obtained in ^{18}O water. Mark the steps of the reaction that are indicated to be fast or slow.
  b. The reaction depends on methyl acetate having a proton-accepting ability comparable to that of water. Why? Consider different ways of adding a proton to methyl acetate and decide which is most favorable on the basis of structural theory. Give your reasoning.
  c. Explain how the reaction could be slowed down in the presence of high concentrations of sulfuric acid.

13-13 Indicate how you would synthesize each of the following substances from the given organic starting materials and other necessary organic or inorganic reagents. Specify reagents and conditions.

  a. $CH_3CH_2CH_2C(CH_3)_2Cl$ from $CH_3CH_2CH_2OH$

  b. $CH_3CH_2\underset{\underset{\displaystyle O}{\overset{\displaystyle |}{O-\underset{\displaystyle \parallel}{C}-CH_3}}}{C}HCH_2CH_3$ from CH_3CH_2OH

  c. $(CH_3)_2CH-CH_2Br$ from $(CH_3)_3COH$

d. $CH_3CH_2CHCH_3$ from $CH_3CH_2CH_2CH_2OH$
           OSO_3H

e. $CH_3CH_2C(CH_3)_2CHO$ from $(CH_3)_2C(OH)CH_2CH_3$

f. $CH_3OCH_2CH_2OCH_3$ from   ethylene

g. 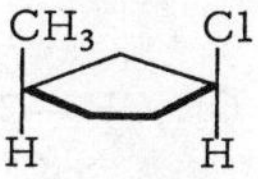   from

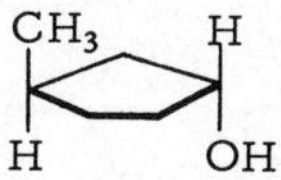

(*cis*)   (*trans*)

h.

$$CH_3\!-\!\underset{\underset{CH_3}{|}}{\overset{\overset{CH_3}{|}}{C}}\!-\!CH_2\!-\!CH_3 \quad\text{from}\quad CH_3\!-\!\underset{\underset{CH_3}{|}}{\overset{\overset{CH_3}{|}}{C}}\!-\!OH$$

i. $(CH_2{=}CHCH_2)_2O$ from $CH_2{=}CHCH_2Cl$

j. 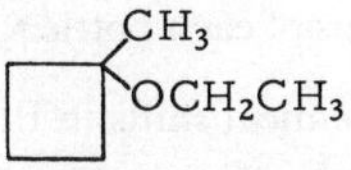   from

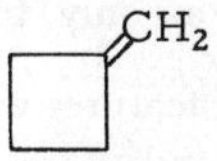

k. 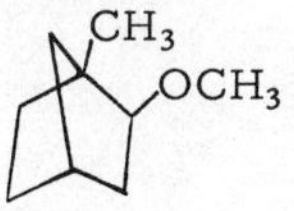   from

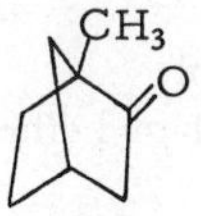

13-14 Give for each of the following pairs of compounds a chemical test, preferably a test-tube reaction, which will distinguish between the two substances. Write an equation for each reaction.

a.

$$CH_3\!-\!\underset{\underset{OH}{|}}{\overset{\overset{CH_3}{|}}{C}}\!-\!CH_3 \qquad\text{and}\qquad CH_3\!-\!\underset{\underset{H}{|}}{\overset{\overset{CH_3}{|}}{C}}\!-\!CH_2OH$$

b. $CH_2{=}CH{-}CH_2CH_2OH$ and $CH_3CH{=}CH{-}CH_2OH$

c.

$$CH_3\!-\!\underset{\underset{CH_3}{|}}{\overset{\overset{CH_3}{|}}{C}}\!-\!CH_2OH \qquad\text{and}\qquad CH_3\!-\!\underset{\overset{|}{CH_3}}{\overset{\overset{CH_3}{|}}{CH}}\!-\!CH_2CH_2OH$$

d. $CH_3CH_2{-}O{-}SO_2{-}O{-}CH_2CH_3$ and $CH_3CH_2CH_2CH_2{-}O{-}SO_3H$

e.

$$CH_3\!-\!\overset{\overset{O}{\|}}{C}\!-\!Cl \qquad\text{and}\qquad ClCH_2\overset{\overset{O}{\|}}{C}\!-\!OH$$

f.

$$CH_3\!-\!\overset{\overset{^{18}O}{\|}}{C}\!-\!OCH_3 \qquad\text{and}\qquad CH_3\!-\!\overset{\overset{O}{\|}}{C}\!-\!{}^{18}OCH_3$$

g. 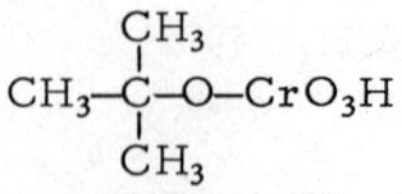
$$CH_3-\underset{\underset{CH_3}{|}}{\overset{\overset{CH_3}{|}}{C}}-O-CrO_3H$$
and
$$CH_3-\underset{\underset{H}{|}}{\overset{\overset{CH_3}{|}}{C}}-CH_2-O-CrO_3H$$

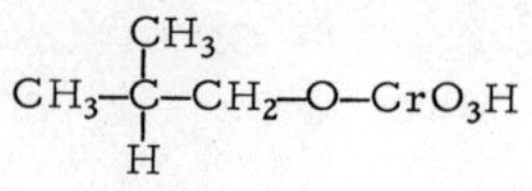

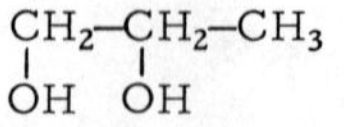

h.
$$\underset{\underset{OH}{|}}{CH_2}-\underset{\underset{OH}{|}}{CH_2}-CH_3$$
and
$$\underset{\underset{OH}{|}}{CH_2}-CH_2-\underset{\underset{OH}{|}}{CH_2}$$

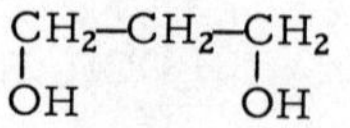

i. 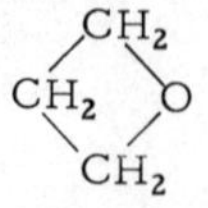
$$\underset{\diagdown CH_2 \diagup}{\overset{\diagup CH_2 \diagdown}{CH_2 \quad O}}$$
and
$$CH_3CH\!-\!\!-\!CH_2 \atop \diagdown O \diagup$$

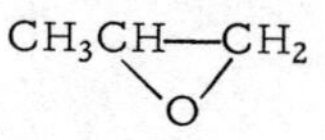

j. 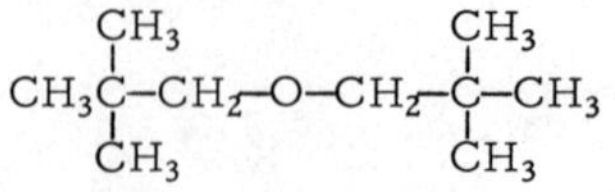
$$CH_3\underset{\underset{CH_3}{|}}{\overset{\overset{CH_3}{|}}{C}}-CH_2-O-CH_2-\underset{\underset{CH_3}{|}}{\overset{\overset{CH_3}{|}}{C}}-CH_3$$
and
$$CH_3\underset{\underset{CH_3}{|}}{\overset{\overset{CH_3}{|}}{C}}-O-CH_2-CH_2-\underset{\underset{CH_3}{|}}{\overset{\overset{CH_3}{|}}{C}}-CH_3$$

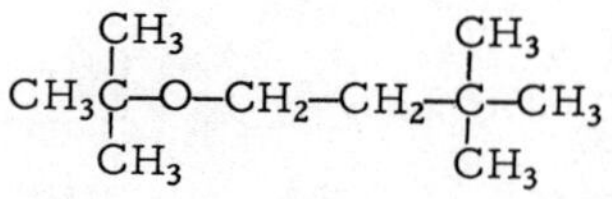

13-15 Suppose you were given unlabeled bottles, each of which is known to contain one of the following compounds: 1-pentanol, 2-pentanol, *t*-amyl alcohol, 3-penten-1-ol, 4-pentyn-1-ol, di-*n*-butyl ether, and 1-pentyl acetate. Explain how you could use simple chemical tests (test-tube reactions only) to identify the contents of each bottle.

13-16 Predict the principal features with approximate chemical shifts in the n.m.r. spectra of the following compounds:

    a. isobutyl alcohol

    b. neopentyl alcohol

    c. methyl *β*-methylvinyl ether

    d. *t*-butyl alcohol

    e. *t*-butyl alcohol in carbon tetrachloride

Aldehydes and Ketones
Reactions at the Carbonyl Group

The chemistry of carbonyl compounds is virtually the backbone of synthetic organic chemistry. We shall divide our study of these substances into three parts. In this chapter we shall consider first methods for the synthesis of simple aldehydes and ketones and then the reactions of aldehydes and ketones which involve only their carbonyl groups. In Chapter 15 consideration will be given to the way in which the carbonyl function activates groups on adjacent carbons. In Chapter 16 we shall discuss the role of the carbonyl group in reactions of carboxylic acids and their derivatives. Throughout these discussions attention will be given to the differences in behavior of various kinds of carbonyl groups—differences that may be correlated with electrical and steric effects.

Aldehydes and Ketones Reactions at the Carbonyl Group

14-1 PREPARATION OF ALDEHYDES AND KETONES

A number of useful reactions for the preparation of aldehydes and ketones, such as ozonization of alkenes and hydration of alkynes, have been considered in earlier chapters. Only a few rather general methods which have not been discussed earlier will be taken up here.

A. Oxidation of 1,2-Diols and Alkenes

Aldehydes and ketones can often be prepared by oxidation of alkenes to 1,2-diols (pp. 151–152), followed by oxidative cleavage of the 1,2-diols with lead tetraacetate or sodium periodate. For example,

$$\text{(ring)}=CH_2 \xrightarrow[\substack{\text{(or neutral} \\ \text{KMnO}_4)}]{\substack{H_2O_2, \\ HCO_2H}} \text{(ring)} \begin{array}{l} OH \\ CH_2OH \end{array} \xrightarrow[\text{(or NaIO}_4)]{Pb(O_2CCH_3)_4} \text{(ring)}{=}O + CH_2{=}O$$

Cleavage of glycols with these reagents usually proceeds in good yield, according to the following stoichiometry:

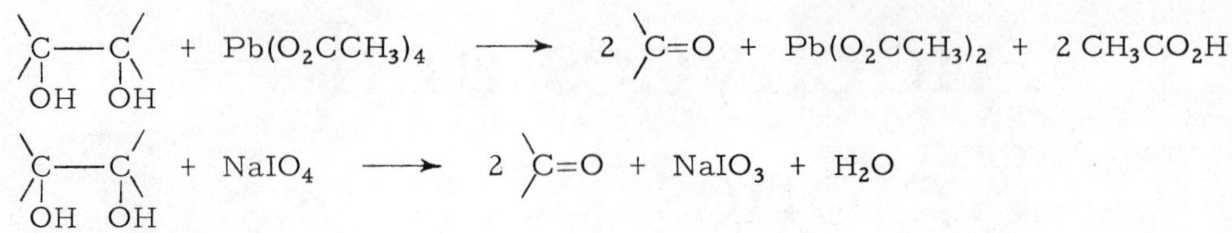

$$\underset{\underset{OH}{|}}{\overset{\diagdown}{C}}-\underset{\underset{OH}{|}}{\overset{\diagup}{C}} + Pb(O_2CCH_3)_4 \longrightarrow 2 \overset{\diagdown}{\underset{\diagup}{C}}=O + Pb(O_2CCH_3)_2 + 2 CH_3CO_2H$$

$$\underset{\underset{OH}{|}}{\overset{\diagdown}{C}}-\underset{\underset{OH}{|}}{\overset{\diagup}{C}} + NaIO_4 \longrightarrow 2 \overset{\diagdown}{\underset{\diagup}{C}}=O + NaIO_3 + H_2O$$

B. Reduction of Carboxylic Acids to Aldehydes

Conversion of a carboxylic acid to an aldehyde by direct reduction is not easy to achieve because acids are generally difficult to reduce, whereas aldehydes are easily reduced. Thus the problem is to keep the reaction from going too far.

The most useful procedures involve conversion of the acid to a derivative that either is more easily reduced than an aldehyde, or else is reduced to a substance from which the aldehyde can be generated. The so-called **Rosenmund reduction** involves the first of these schemes; in this procedure, the acid is converted to an acyl chloride, which is reduced with hydrogen over a palladium catalyst to the aldehyde in yields up to 90 per cent. The rate of reduction of the aldehyde to the corresponding alcohol is kept at a low level by poisoning the catalyst with sulfur.

$$R-CO_2H \xrightarrow{SOCl_2} RCOCl \xrightarrow[Pd(S)]{H_2} RCHO + HCl$$

EXERCISE 14-1   Compare calculated ΔH values for the reduction of CH_3CO_2H and CH_3COCl with hydrogen (to give CH_3CHO) with reduction of CH_3CHO to CH_3CH_2OH (use any necessary data from Table 9-3). Would you expect CH_3CONH_2 to be reduced to the aldehyde more or less easily than CH_3COCl? Why?

Reduction of an acid to a substance that can be converted to an aldehyde is usefully achieved by way of lithium aluminum hydride reduction of the nitrile corresponding to the acid. The following scheme outlines the sequence of reactions involved starting with the acid:

$$RCO_2H \xrightarrow{SOCl_2} RCOCl \xrightarrow{NH_3} RCONH_2$$

$$\xrightarrow{POCl_3} RC{\equiv}N \xrightarrow{LiAlH_4} [R-\overset{\overset{H}{|}}{C}=N-Li]$$

$$\xrightarrow{H_2O} R-\overset{\overset{H}{|}}{C}=NH \xrightarrow{H^{\oplus},\ H_2O} R-\overset{\overset{H}{|}}{C}=O$$

The reduction step is usually successful only if *inverse* addition is used; i.e., a solution of lithium aluminum hydride is added to a solution of the nitrile in ether preferably at low temperatures.

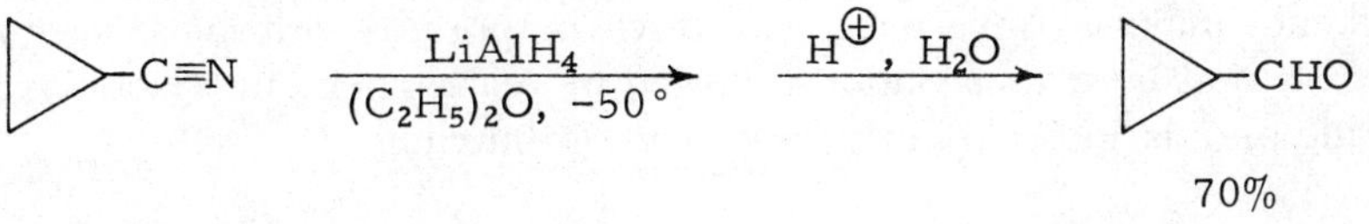

cyclopropanecarbonitrile   cyclopropanecarboxaldehyde

If the nitrile is added to the hydride, the reduction product is a primary amine, RCH_2NH_2.

C. Rearrangements of 1,2-Glycols

Many carbonyl compounds can be usefully synthesized by acid-catalyzed rearrangements of 1,2-glycols, the so-called "pinacol-pinacolone" rearrangement.

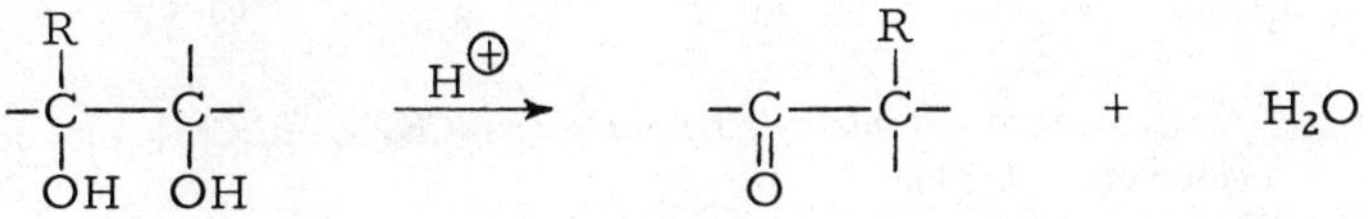

R = alkyl, aryl or hydrogen

The general characteristics of the reaction are similar to those of carbonium ion rearrangements (see pp. 242, 295–296). The acid functions to protonate one of the —OH groups and make it a better leaving group. The carbonium ion which results can then undergo rearrangement by shift of the neighboring group R with its pair of bonding electrons to give a new, more stable, species with a carbon-oxygen double bond.

An important example is provided by the rearrangement of pinacol to pinacolone as follows:

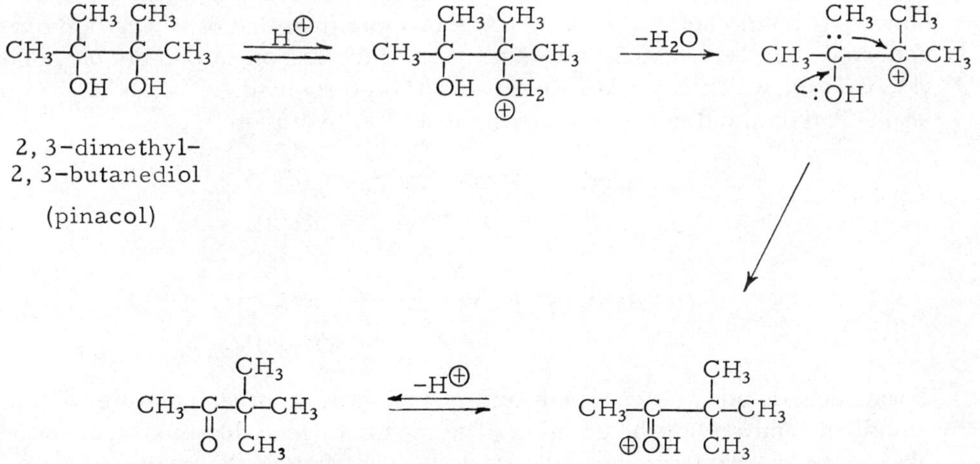

2,3-dimethyl-
2,3-butanediol

(pinacol)

3,3-dimethyl-2-butanone
(pinacolone)

Alkenes may be converted to carbonyl compounds with the same number of carbon atoms by hydroxylation followed by rearrangement. Isobutyraldehyde is made on a large scale in this way from isobutylene.

$$CH_3-\underset{\displaystyle CH_3}{C}=CH_2 \xrightarrow{Cl_2} CH_3-\underset{\displaystyle CH_3}{\overset{\displaystyle CH_3}{C}}-\underset{\displaystyle Cl}{CH_2} \xrightarrow{H_2O} CH_3-\underset{\displaystyle OH}{\overset{\displaystyle CH_3}{C}}-\underset{\displaystyle OH}{CH_2} \xrightarrow{H^{\oplus}} CH_3-\underset{\displaystyle H}{\overset{\displaystyle CH_3}{C}}-CHO$$

EXERCISE 14-2   The acid-catalyzed rearrangement of isobutylene glycol is given above as affording isobutyraldehyde. Would you expect any concomitant formation of methyl ethyl ketone? Explain.

EXERCISE 14-3   Predict the products to be expected from acid-catalyzed rearrangements of 1,2-propanediol and 2-methyl-2,3-butanediol.

EXERCISE 14-4   Treatment of tetramethylethylene oxide $(CH_3)_2C\overset{\displaystyle \diagup\diagdown}{\underset{\displaystyle O}{}}C(CH_3)_2$ with acid produces pinacolone. Explain.

EXERCISE 14-5   How might one dehydrate pinacol to 2,3-dimethyl-1,3-butadiene without forming excessive amounts of pinacolone in the process?

14-2 CARBONYL GROUPS OF ALDEHYDES AND KETONES

A. Comparison with Carbon-Carbon Double Bonds

The carbon-oxygen bond is both a strong double bond and a reactive double bond. Its bond energy (179 kcal) is rather more than that of two carbon-oxygen single bonds (2 × 85.5 kcal) in contrast to the carbon-carbon double bond (145.8 kcal), which is weaker than two carbon-carbon single bonds (2 × 82.6 kcal). A typical difference in reactivity is seen in hydration.

$$CH_2=O + H_2O \rightleftharpoons \underset{\displaystyle OH \quad H}{CH_2-O}$$

$$CH_2=CH_2 + H_2O \rightleftharpoons \underset{\displaystyle OH \quad H}{CH_2-CH_2}$$

Formaldehyde adds water rapidly and reversibly at room temperature without an added catalyst; but the addition of water to ethylene does not occur in the absence of a very strongly acidic catalyst, even though the equilibrium constant is considerably larger.

The reactivity of the carbonyl bond is primarily due to the difference in electronegativity between carbon and oxygen, which leads to a considerable contribution of the dipolar resonance form with oxygen negative and carbon positive.

$$\underset{/}{\overset{\backslash}{C}}{=}O \quad \longleftrightarrow \quad \underset{/}{\overset{\backslash}{\overset{\oplus}{C}}}{-}\overset{..}{\underset{..}{O}}{:}^{\ominus} \quad \sim \quad \underset{/}{\overset{\backslash}{\overset{\delta\oplus}{C}}}{=\!=\!=\!=}\overset{\delta\ominus}{O}$$

The polarity of the carbonyl bond is expected to facilitate addition of water and other polar reagents such as $\overset{\delta\oplus}{H}{-}\overset{\delta\ominus}{X}$ and $\overset{\delta\ominus}{R}{-}\overset{\delta\oplus}{Mg}X$ relative to addition of the same reagents to alkene double bonds. However, we must always keep in mind the possibility that, whereas additions to carbonyl groups may be rapid, their equilibrium constants may be small, because of the strength of the carbonyl bond.

The polarity of the carbonyl group is manifested in many of the other properties of aldehydes and ketones. Boiling points for the lower members of the series are 50 to 80° higher than hydrocarbons of the same molecular weight; this may be seen from the data of Table 14-1 (physical properties of aldehydes and ketones) and that of Table 3-3 (physical properties of n-alkanes). The water solubility of the lower-molecular-weight aldehydes and ketones is pronounced.

B. Spectroscopic Properties

The infrared stretching frequencies for the carbonyl groups of aldehydes and ketones generally fall in the range 1705 to 1740 cm^{-1} and the absorption intensities are much greater than for carbon-carbon double bonds. The ultraviolet spectra of simple carbonyl compounds have been discussed earlier (pp. 33–34).

The character of the carbonyl bond is such as to give very low field n.m.r. absorptions for protons of the aldehyde group (RCHO). As Table 2-3 shows, these absorptions come some 4 ppm below vinylic hydrogens. Much of this difference is probably due to the polarity of the carbonyl group. It is carried over in much smaller degree to hydrogens in the α position and we find that

protons of the type $CH_3{-}\overset{\overset{\displaystyle O}{\|}}{C}{-}R$ come at lower fields (0.3 ppm) than those of

$CH_3{-}\overset{\overset{\displaystyle R}{|}}{C}{=}CR_2$.

EXERCISE 14-6   Show how structures may be deduced for the two substances with respective infrared and n.m.r. spectra as shown in Figure 14-1.

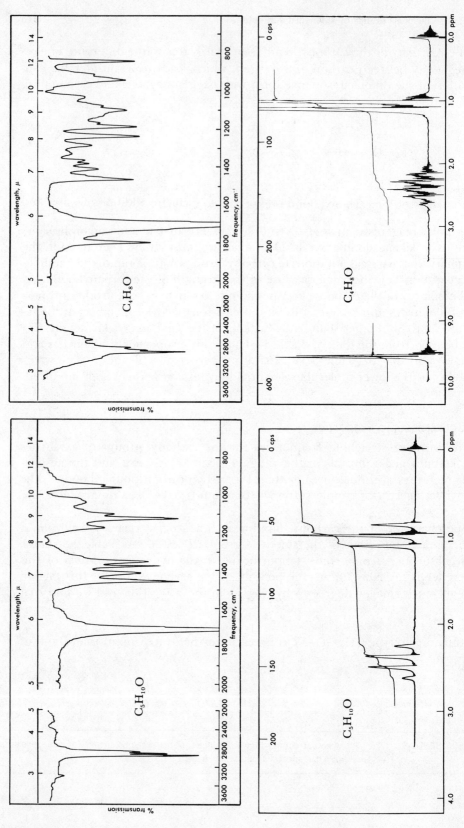

Figure 14-1   Infrared and proton n.m.r. spectra of four organic compounds.   See Exercise 14-6.

Table 14-1   Physical Properties of Aldehydes and Ketones

Compound	Formula	M.p., °C	B.p., °C	d_4^t, g/ml
formaldehyde	CH_2O	-92	-21	0.815^{-20}
acetaldehyde	CH_3CHO	-121	21	0.7951^{10}
propionaldehyde	CH_3CH_2CHO	$-81.$	49	0.7966^{25}
acrolein (2-propenal)	$CH_2{=}CHCHO$	-87	52	0.8410^{20}
crotonaldehyde	$CH_3CH{=}CHCHO$	-69	104–105	0.8575^{15}
butyraldehyde	$CH_3CH_2CH_2CHO$	-99	76	0.8170^{20}
isobutyraldehyde	$(CH_3)_2CHCHO$	-66	64	0.7938^{20}
benzaldehyde	C_6H_5CHO	-26	179	1.0504^{15}
acetone	CH_3COCH_3	-94	56	0.7899^{20}
methyl ethyl ketone	$CH_3COCH_2CH_3$	-86	80	0.8054^{20}
methyl vinyl ketone	$CH_3COCH{=}CH_2$		80	0.8636^{20}
cyclobutanone	(structure)$=O$		99	0.9548^{0}
cyclopentanone	(structure)$=O$	-58.2	130	0.9480^{20}
cyclohexanone	(structure)$=O$	-45	155	0.9478^{20}
mesityl oxide (4-methyl-3-penten-2-one)	$(CH_3)_2C{=}CHCOCH_3$	-59	130	0.8653^{20}
acetophenone	$C_6H_5COCH_3$	20.5	202	1.0236^{25}
biacetyl	$CH_3COCOCH_3$		88	0.9904^{15}
acetylacetone	$CH_3COCH_2COCH_3$	-23	139^{746}	0.9721^{25}
benzil (dibenzoyl)	$C_6H_5COCOC_6H_5$	95	346	

C. Further Considerations of Reactivity

The important reactions of carbonyl groups characteristically involve addition at one step or the other. We have already discussed additions achieved by Grignard reagents as part of Chapter 12. It will be recalled that steric hindrance plays an important role in determining the ratio between addition and other competing reactions. Similar effects are noted in a wide variety of other reactions. We shall expect the reactivity of carbonyl groups in addition processes to be influenced by the size of the substituents thereon because when addition occurs, the substituent groups are pushed back closer to one another. On this basis, we anticipate *decreasing* reactivity with increasing bulkiness of substituents, as in the following series.

$$\underset{H}{\overset{H}{}}C=O \;>\; \underset{CH_3}{\overset{H}{}}C=O \;>\; \underset{CH_3}{\overset{CH_3}{}}C=O \;\gg\; \underset{\underset{CH_3\quad CH_3}{\overset{|}{C}}}{\overset{\overset{CH_3\quad CH_3}{\overset{|}{C}}}{\underset{CH_3}{\overset{CH_3}{|}}}}C=O$$

The term "reactivity" is often used somewhat loosely in connection with discussions of this type. It probably is best confined to considerations of reaction rate but is also rather widely employed in connection with equilibrium constants, that is, how far the reaction goes, not just how fast it goes. Usually, we expect that, if steric hindrance is high, equilibrium reactions will not go either very fast or very far. In the case of carbonyl additions, this is generally true, but there are exceptions which will be noted later.

Cyclic ketones almost always react more rapidly in addition processes than open-chain analogs.

$$\underset{\underset{CH_2-CH_2}{CH_2\qquad CH_2}}{\overset{\overset{O}{\overset{\|}{C}}}{}} \qquad > \qquad \underset{\underset{CH_3\;\; CH_3}{CH_2\qquad CH_2}}{\overset{\overset{O}{\overset{\|}{C}}}{}}$$

This is because the alkyl groups of the open-chain compounds have considerably more freedom of motion and produce greater steric hindrance in transition states for addition.

Electrical effects are also important in influencing the ease of addition to carbonyl groups. Electron-attracting groups facilitate the addition of nucleophilic reagents to carbon by increasing its positive character. Thus we find that compounds such as the following add nucleophilic reagents readily.

$$\underset{\text{trichloroacetaldehyde (chloral)}}{CCl_3-\overset{\overset{O}{\|}}{C}-H} \qquad\qquad \underset{\text{oxomalonic acid}}{HO_2C-\overset{\overset{O}{\|}}{C}-CO_2H}$$

EXERCISE 14-7   Arrange the following pairs of compounds in order of expected reactivity toward addition of a common nucleophilic agent such as hydroxide ion to the carbonyl bond. Indicate your reasoning.

$$a.\quad CH_3-\overset{\overset{O}{\|}}{C}-CH_3 \qquad and \qquad CH_3-\overset{\overset{O}{\|}}{C}-CCl_3$$

$$
\begin{array}{ccc}
& \overset{\displaystyle O}{\underset{\displaystyle \|}{}} & \overset{\displaystyle O}{\underset{\displaystyle \|}{}}
\end{array}
$$

b. $(CH_3)_3C{-}\overset{\displaystyle O}{\overset{\|}{C}}{-}H$ and $CH_3{-}\overset{\displaystyle O}{\overset{\|}{C}}{-}CH_3$

c. $CH_3{-}\overset{\displaystyle O}{\overset{\|}{C}}{-}OCH_3$ and $CH_3{-}\overset{\displaystyle O}{\overset{\|}{C}}{-}CH_3$

d. $CH_3{-}\overset{\displaystyle O}{\overset{\|}{C}}{-}Cl$ and $CH_3{-}\overset{\displaystyle O}{\overset{\|}{C}}{-}CH_3$

e.   (cyclopentanone)   and   (cyclobutanone)

14-3 SOME TYPICAL CARBONYL ADDITION REACTIONS

Although Grignard reagents, organolithium compounds, and the like generally add to aldehydes and ketones (Chapter 12) rapidly and irreversibly, this is not true of many other reagents; their addition reactions may require acidic or basic catalysts and have relatively unfavorable equilibrium constants. We shall not attempt to provide a catalog of addition reactions but will try to emphasize the principles involved by discussion of a few examples in considerable detail.

A. Cyanohydrin Formation

Hydrogen cyanide adds to many aldehydes and ketones to give α-cyanoalcohols, usually called cyanohydrins.

$$
CH_3{-}\overset{\displaystyle O}{\overset{\|}{C}}{-}CH_3 \; + \; HCN \quad \underset{\longleftarrow}{\overset{base}{\longrightarrow}} \quad CH_3{-}\underset{\underset{\displaystyle C{\equiv}N}{|}}{\overset{\overset{\displaystyle OH}{|}}{C}}{-}CH_3
$$

The products are useful in synthesis — for example, in the preparation of cyano-alkenes and hydroxy acids.

$$
CH_3{-}\underset{\underset{\displaystyle C{\equiv}N}{|}}{\overset{\overset{\displaystyle OH}{|}}{C}}{-}CH_3
$$

acetone cyanohydrin

$\xrightarrow{(-H_2O)}$ $CH_2{=}\underset{}{\overset{\overset{\displaystyle CH_3}{|}}{C}}{-}C{\equiv}N$

α-methacrylonitrile

$\xrightarrow[(-NH_3)]{H_2O,\ H^{\oplus}}$ $CH_3{-}\underset{\underset{\displaystyle CO_2H}{|}}{\overset{\overset{\displaystyle OH}{|}}{C}}{-}CH_3$

2-hydroxy-2-methylpropionic acid

(dimethylglycolic acid)

An important feature of cyanohydrin formation is that it requires a basic
catalyst. In the absence of base, the reaction does not proceed, or is at best very
slow. In principle the basic catalyst might activate either the carbonyl group or
hydrogen cyanide. With hydroxide ion as the base, one reaction to be expected
is a reversible addition of hydroxide to the carbonyl group.

$$
\begin{array}{ccc}
CH_3 & & CH_3 \quad O^{\ominus} \\
_{\delta\oplus}_{\delta\ominus} & & \\
C{=}O \quad + \quad {}^{\ominus}OH & \rightleftharpoons & C \\
CH_3 & & CH_3 \quad OH \\
\end{array}
$$

[1]

However, such addition is not likely to facilitate formation of cyanohydrin,
because it represents a competitive saturation of the carbonyl double bond.
Indeed, if the equilibrium constant for this addition were large, an excess of
hydroxide ion could inhibit cyanohydrin formation by tying up acetone as the
adduct [1].

Hydrogen cyanide itself has no unshared electron pair on carbon and is unable to form a carbon-carbon bond to a carbonyl carbon (we shall see later how
hydrogen cyanide, when it does react as a nucleophilic agent toward carbon,
forms C—N rather than C—C bonds). However, an activating function of hydroxide ion is clearly possible through conversion of hydrogen cyanide to cyanide ion, which substance can function as a nucleophile toward carbon. A complete reaction sequence for cyanohydrin formation is then as follows:

$$H{-}C{\equiv}N \;+\; {}^{\ominus}OH \;\rightleftharpoons\; :C{\equiv}N^{\ominus} \;+\; H_2O$$

The last step regenerates the base catalyst. All steps of the over-all reaction are reversible but, with aldehydes and most nonhindered ketones, formation of the cyanohydrin is reasonably favorable. In practical syntheses of cyanohydrins, it is convenient to add a strong acid to a mixture of sodium cyanide
and the carbonyl compound, so that hydrogen cyanide is generated *in situ*.
The amount of acid added should be insufficient to consume all the cyanide
ion, so that sufficiently alkaline conditions are maintained for rapid addition.

EXERCISE 14-8   One possible way of carrying out the cyanohydrin reaction would be to dis-
pense with hydrogen cyanide and just use the carbonyl compound and sodium

cyanide. Reason whether the equilibrium constant for cyanohydrin formation would be more favorable or less favorable with acetone and hydrogen cyanide in water compared to acetone and sodium cyanide in water.

Table 14-2 shows the extent of reaction for some simple carbonyl compounds. The effect of introducing an isopropyl group in the 2-position of cyclohexanone is seen to be considerable and is probably steric in origin. However, in other

Table 14-2   Equilibrium in Cyanohydrin Formation in 96% Ethanol Solution at 20°

Carbonyl compound	Equilibrium constant, liter/mole	% Cyanohydrin at equilibrium[a]
CH_3COCH_3	32.8	84
$CH_3COCH_2CH_3$	37.7	85
$CH_3COCH(CH_3)_2$	81.2	90
$CH_3COC(CH_3)_3$	32.3	84
(cyclopentanone)	67	89
(cyclohexanone)	11,000	~100
(menthone)	15.3	78

[a] Starting with $1M$ concentrations of carbonyl compound and hydrogen cyanide.

cases where steric effects might be expected to be important, no evidence for such effects is reported. Thus virtually the same equilibrium constant is found for acetone and methyl *t*-butyl ketone. This is difficult to explain, and it appears that the factors governing cyanohydrin formation require further study.

EXERCISE 14-9   What should be the rate law for the formation of acetone cyanohydrin by the mechanism given on p. 318 if the first step is slow and the others fast? If the second step is slow and the others fast?

EXERCISE 14-10   *a.* Calculate ΔH for the formation of acetone cyanohydrin from hydrogen cyanide and acetone in the vapor phase at 25°. Do the same for the formation of dimethylethynylcarbinol from acetylene and acetone.
          b. What are the prospects for carrying out addition of acetylene to acetone by the same procedure used for hydrogen cyanide? Explain.

B. Addition of Ammonia to Aldehydes

Ammonia adds readily to many aldehydes. For example,

$$CH_3\!\!-\!\!C(H)\!\!=\!\!O + :NH_3 \rightleftharpoons CH_3\!\!-\!\!\overset{\overset{\displaystyle \oplus}{NH_3}}{\underset{H}{C}}\!\!-\!\!O^{\ominus} \rightleftharpoons CH_3\!\!-\!\!\overset{\overset{\displaystyle NH_2}{|}}{\underset{H}{C}}\!\!-\!\!OH$$

acetaldehyde ammonia
m. p. 97°

The aldehyde-ammonia adducts are usually not very stable, undergoing dehydration and polymerization readily. We shall encounter similar substances as intermediates in several important reactions.

C. Hemiacetal and Acetal Formation

Hemiacetals and acetals are products of addition of alcohols to aldehydes. Thus for acetaldehyde and methanol,

$$\underset{H}{\overset{CH_3}{\diagdown}}C\!\!=\!\!O \quad\underset{\longleftarrow}{\overset{CH_3OH}{\longrightarrow}}\quad \underset{H\quad OCH_3}{\overset{CH_3\quad OH}{\diagdown\;\diagup}}C \quad\underset{\longleftarrow}{\overset{CH_3OH,\ -H_2O}{\longrightarrow}}\quad \underset{H\quad OCH_3}{\overset{CH_3\quad OCH_3}{\diagdown\;\diagup}}C$$

hemiacetal   acetaldehyde dimethyl acetal

(1-methoxyethanol)   (1, 1-dimethoxyethane)

First, we shall consider hemiacetal formation, which is catalyzed by *both* acids and bases. The base catalysis is similar to that involved in cyanohydrin formation. The slow step here is the addition of alkoxide ion to the carbonyl group.

$$CH_3OH + \overset{\ominus}{O}H \rightleftharpoons CH_3\overset{\ominus}{O} + H_2O$$

$$\underset{H}{\overset{CH_3}{>}}C\!\!=\!\!\overset{\ominus}{O}\;\;\overset{\ominus}{O}\!-\!CH_3 \underset{}{\overset{slow}{\rightleftharpoons}} \underset{H}{\overset{CH_3\;\;OCH_3}{>}}C\underset{\overset{\ominus}{O}}{}$$

$$\underset{H}{\overset{CH_3\;\;OCH_3}{>}}C\underset{\overset{\ominus}{O}}{} + H_2O \overset{fast}{\rightleftharpoons} \underset{H}{\overset{CH_3\;\;OCH_3}{>}}C\underset{OH}{} + \overset{\ominus}{O}H$$

Acid catalysis of hemiacetal formation might involve activation of either the alcohol or the carbonyl compound. However, the only simple reaction one would expect between various species of alcohols and proton donors is oxonium salt formation, which hardly seems the proper way to activate an alcohol for nucleophilic attack at the carbonyl group of an aldehyde.

$$CH_3OH + H^{\oplus} \rightleftharpoons CH_3\!-\!\underset{\oplus}{\overset{\overset{H}{|}}{O}}\!-\!H$$

methyloxonium ion

On the other hand, formation of the oxonium salt (or **conjugate acid**)[1] of the carbonyl compound is expected to provide activation for hemiacetal formation by increasing the positive character of the carbonyl carbon.

$$\underset{H}{\overset{CH_3}{>}}C\!\!=\!\!O + H^{\oplus} \rightleftharpoons \left[\underset{H}{\overset{CH_3}{>}}\overset{\oplus}{C}\!\!=\!\!\overset{}{O}H \longleftrightarrow \underset{H}{\overset{CH_3}{>}}\overset{\oplus}{C}\!\!-\!\!OH\right]$$

conjugate acid of acetaldehyde

$$\underset{H}{\overset{CH_3}{>}}C\!\!=\!\!\overset{}{O}H + \underset{H}{\overset{}{O}}\!-\!CH_3 \rightleftharpoons \underset{H}{\overset{CH_3\;\;\overset{\oplus}{O}\diagup^{CH_3}}{>}}C\underset{OH}{H} \rightleftharpoons \underset{H}{\overset{CH_3\;\;O\!-\!CH_3}{>}}C\underset{OH}{} + H^{\oplus}$$

hemiacetal

---

[1] The terms **conjugate acid** and **conjugate base** are very convenient to designate substances which are difficult to name simply as bases or acids. The conjugate acid of a compound X is $XH^{\oplus}$, while the conjugate base of a compound HY is $Y^{\ominus}$. Thus $H_3O^{\oplus}$ is the conjugate acid of water, while $\overset{\ominus}{O}H$ is the conjugate base of water; water itself is both the conjugate base of $H_3O^{\oplus}$ and the conjugate acid of $OH^{\ominus}$.

In water solution most aldehydes form hydrates. This reaction is analogous to hemiacetal formation and is catalyzed both by acids and bases.

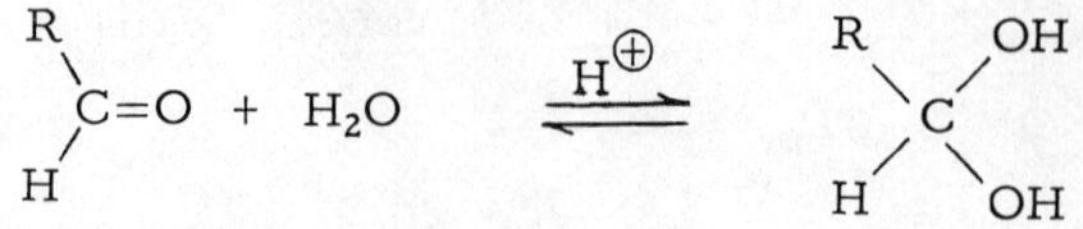

The equilibrium for hydrate formation depends both on steric and electrical factors.

EXERCISE 14-11   The equilibrium constant for hydration is especially large for formaldehyde, trichloroacetaldehyde, and cyclopropanone. Explain.

In contrast to hemiacetal formation, acetal formation is catalyzed *only* by acids. Addition of a proton to a hemiacetal can occur in two ways to give [2] or [3].

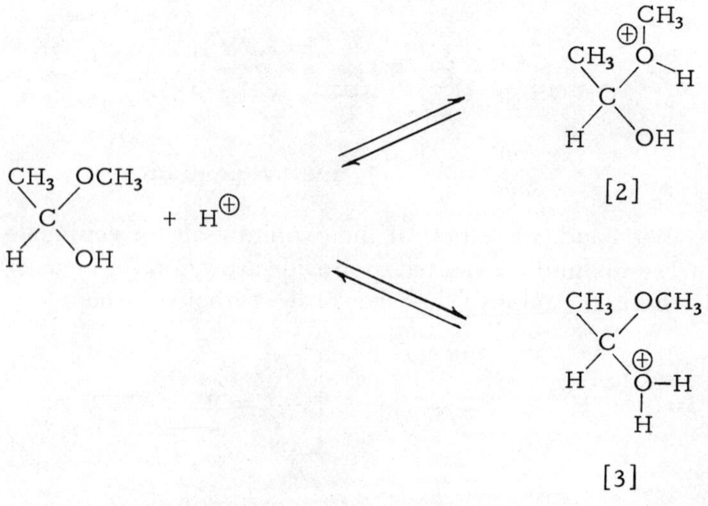

The first of these [2] can lose CH_3OH and yield the conjugate acid of acetaldehyde. This is the reverse of acid-catalyzed hemiacetal formation.

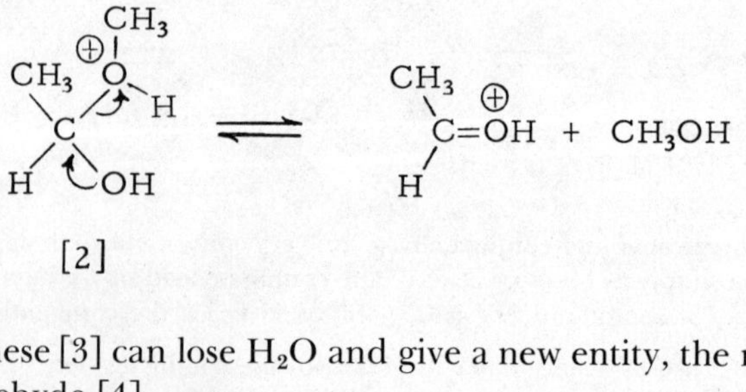

The second of these [3] can lose H_2O and give a new entity, the methyloxonium cation of the aldehyde [4].

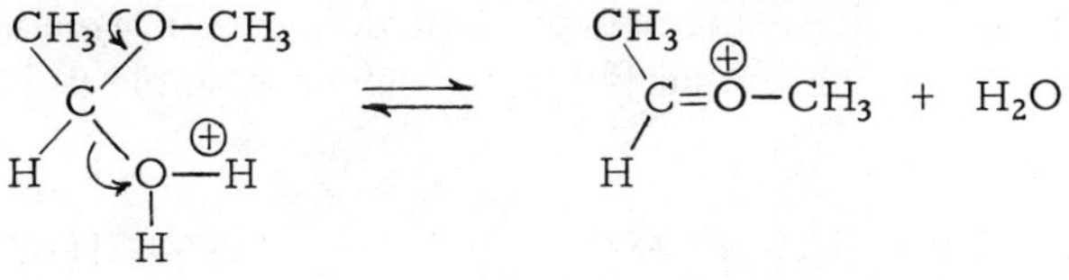

[3]   [4]

The reaction of [4] with water gives back [3], but reaction with alcohol leads to the conjugate acid of the acetal [5]. Loss of a proton from [5] gives the acetal.

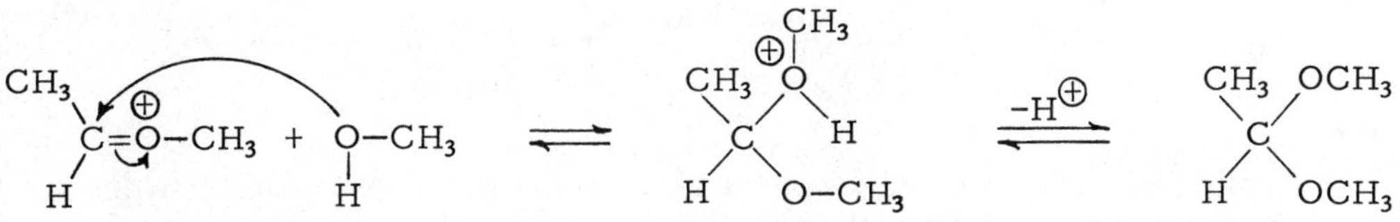

[4]   [5]

EXERCISE 14-12   The slow step in an alternative mechanism for acetal formation might be as follows:

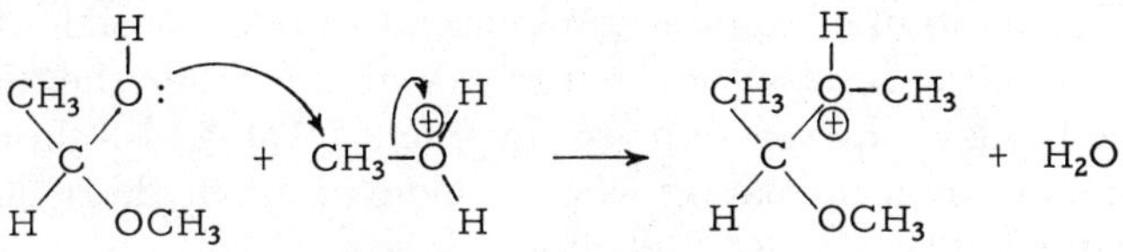

How could this mechanism be distinguished experimentally from the one given above?

EXERCISE 14-13   Chloral (CCl_3CHO) reacts rapidly with methanol to give the hemiacetal but only very slowly to give the corresponding acetal. Explain.

The fact that acetals are formed only in an acid-catalyzed reaction has the corollary that acetal groups are stable to base. This can be synthetically very useful, as illustrated by the following synthesis of glyceraldehyde from readily available acrolein (CH_2=$CHCHO$). Hydrogen chloride in ethanol adds in the anti-Markownikoff manner to acrolein to give 3-chloropropionaldehyde, which then reacts with the ethanol to give the acetal.

$$CH_2=CHCHO \ + \ HCl \ \longrightarrow \ ClCH_2CH_2CHO$$

$$ClCH_2CH_2CHO \ + \ 2 \ C_2H_5OH \ \longrightarrow \ ClCH_2CH_2CH(OC_2H_5)_2$$

The key step in the synthesis involves E2-type dehydrochlorination of the chloroacetal without destroying the acetal group, which is stable to base.

$$ClCH_2-CH_2-CH(OC_2H_5)_2 + KOH \xrightarrow{\text{E2}} CH_2=CH-CH(OC_2H_5)_2$$

Hydroxylation of the double bond with neutral permanganate then gives the diethyl acetal of glyceraldehyde. This kind of step would not be possible with acrolein itself because the aldehyde group reacts with permanganate as easily as the double bond.

$$CH_2=CH-CH(OC_2H_5)_2 \xrightarrow{\text{KMnO}_4} \underset{\underset{\displaystyle OH}{|}\,\underset{\displaystyle OH}{|}}{CH_2-CH}-CH(OC_2H_5)_2$$

Finally, mild acidic hydrolysis of the acetal function yields glyceraldehyde.

$$\underset{\underset{\displaystyle OH}{|}\,\underset{\displaystyle OH}{|}}{CH_2-CH}-CH(OC_2H_5)_2 + H_2O \xrightarrow{\text{H}^\oplus} \underset{\underset{\displaystyle OH}{|}\,\underset{\displaystyle OH}{|}}{CH_2-CH}-CHO + 2C_2H_5OH$$

glyceraldehyde

The position of equilibrium in acetal and hemiacetal formation is rather sensitive to steric hindrance. Large groups in either the aldehyde or the alcohol tend to make the reaction less favorable. Table 14-3 shows some typical conversions in acetal formation when 1 mole of aldehyde is allowed to come to equilibrium with 5 moles of alcohol.

Table 14-3   Conversions of Aldehydes to Acetals with Various Alcohols
(1 Mole of Aldehyde to 5 Moles of Alcohol)

Aldehyde	% Conversion to acetal			
	Ethanol	Cyclohexanol	Isopropyl alcohol	t-Butyl alcohol
CH_3CHO	78	56	43	23
$(CH_3)_2CHCHO$	71		23	
$(CH_3)_3CCHO$	56	16	11	
C_6H_5CHO	39	23	13	

D. Polymerization of Aldehydes

A reaction closely related to acetal formation is the polymerization of aldehydes. Both linear and cyclic polymers are obtained. For example, formaldehyde in water solution polymerizes to a solid long-chain polymer called paraformaldehyde or "polyoxymethylene."

$$n \cdot CH_2{=}O + H_2O \longrightarrow H{-}O{-}CH_2{-}\!\!\underbrace{(O{-}CH_2)}_{n-2}\!\!O{-}CH_2{-}O{-}H$$

paraformaldehyde

This material, when strongly heated, reverts to formaldehyde; it is therefore a convenient source of gaseous formaldehyde. When heated with dilute acid, paraformaldehyde yields the solid trimer trioxymethylene (m.p. 61°). The cyclic tetramer is also known.

trioxymethylene

Long-chain formaldehyde polymers have become very important as plastics in recent years. The low cost of paraformaldehyde ($0.12/lb) is highly favorable in this connection, but the instability of the material to elevated temperatures and dilute acids precludes its use in plastics. However, the "end-capping" of polyoxymethylene chains through formation of esters or acetals produces a remarkable increase in stability, and such modified polymers have excellent properties as plastics. Delrin (DuPont) is a stabilized formaldehyde polymer with exceptional strength and ease of molding.

EXERCISE 14-14   Write a reasonable mechanism for the polymerization of formaldehyde in water solution under the influence of a basic catalyst. Would you expect base catalysis to produce any trioxymethylene? Why?

14-4   CONDENSATIONS OF CARBONYL COMPOUNDS WITH RNH₂ DERIVATIVES

A wide variety of substances with —NH_2 groups condense with carbonyl compounds to give $\diagdown$C=N— compounds and water. These reactions usually require acid catalysts.

$$\diagdown\!\!\!{\underset{\diagup}{C}}{=}O + H_2N{-}R \xrightarrow{\;\;H^{\oplus}\;\;} \diagdown\!\!\!{\underset{\diagup}{C}}{=}N{-}R + H_2O$$

Table 14-4 summarizes a number of important reactions of this type and the nomenclature of the reactants and products.

Table 14-4   Condensation Reactions of Carbonyl Compounds with R—NH$_2$ Derivatives

Reactant	Typical product	Class of product
H$_2$N–R (R= alkyl, aryl or hydrogen) amine	CH$_3$CH=N–CH$_3$ acetaldehyde methylimine	imine[a] (Schiff's base)
NH$_2$–NH$_2$ hydrazine	$\begin{array}{c} CH_3 \\ \diagdown \\ C=N-NH_2 \\ \diagup \\ CH_3 \end{array}$ acetone hydrazone	hydrazone
	$\begin{array}{c} CH_3 \qquad\qquad CH_3 \\ \diagdown \qquad\qquad \diagup \\ C=N-N=C \\ \diagup \qquad\qquad \diagdown \\ CH_3 \qquad\qquad CH_3 \end{array}$ acetone azine	azine
H$_2$N–NHR (R=alkyl, aryl or hydrogen) substituted hydrazine	◻=N–NH–⬡ (NO$_2$, NO$_2$) cyclobutanone 2,4–dinitro-phenylhydrazone	substituted hydrazone[b]
$\overset{\displaystyle O}{\overset{\displaystyle \|}{H_2NNHCNH_2}}$ semicarbazide	⬡–CH=N–$\overset{H}{N}$–$\overset{O}{\overset{\|}{C}}$–NH$_2$ benzaldehyde semicarbazone	semicarbazone[b]
HO–NH$_2$ hydroxylamine	CH$_2$=N–OH formaldoxime	oxime[b]

[a] Most unsubstituted imines, i.e., R = H, are unstable and polymerize.

[b] Usually these derivatives are solids and are excellent for the isolation and characterization of aldehydes and ketones.

14-5 HYDROGEN HALIDE ADDITION AND REPLACEMENT BY HALOGEN

Addition of hydrogen halides to carbonyl groups is so easily reversible as to prevent isolation of the products.

$$
\underset{H}{\overset{CH_3}{\diagdown}}C=O \ + \ HCl \ \rightleftharpoons \ \underset{H}{\overset{CH_3}{\diagup}}\underset{OH}{\overset{Cl}{\diagdown}}C
$$

However, many aldehydes react with alcohols in the presence of an excess of hydrogen chloride to give α-chloro ethers.

$$
\underset{H}{\overset{CH_3}{\diagdown}}C=O \ + \ HCl \ + \ CH_3OH \ \rightleftharpoons \ \underset{H}{\overset{CH_3}{\diagup}}\underset{Cl}{\overset{O-CH_3}{\diagdown}}C \ + \ H_2O
$$

EXERCISE 14-15   Write a reasonable mechanism for the reaction of hydrogen chloride and methanol with formaldehyde to give methyl chloromethyl ether that is consistent with the fact that the reaction occurs under conditions where neither methylene chloride nor methyl chloride are formed.

Replacement of the carbonyl function by two chlorines occurs with phosphorus pentachloride in ether.

$$
\text{\Large$\bigcirc$}=O \ + \ PCl_5 \ \xrightarrow{\text{ether}} \ \text{\Large$\bigcirc$}\overset{Cl}{\underset{Cl}{<}} \ + \ POCl_3
$$

14-6 REDUCTION OF CARBONYL COMPOUNDS

A. Formation of Alcohols

The easiest large-scale reduction method for conversion of aldehydes and ketones to alcohols is by catalytic hydrogenation.

$$
\begin{array}{c} CH_2 \\ CH_2 \diagup \quad \diagdown \\ \ \qquad C=O \\ CH_2 \diagdown \quad \diagup \\ CH_2 \end{array} \quad \xrightarrow[\text{(Ni), } 50°]{\text{H}_2, \ 1000 \ \text{psi}} \quad \begin{array}{c} CH_2 \\ CH_2 \diagup \quad \diagdown \\ \ \qquad CHOH \\ CH_2 \diagdown \quad \diagup \\ CH_2 \end{array}
$$

$$95\text{--}100\%$$

The advantage over most chemical reduction schemes is that usually the product can be obtained simply by filtration from the catalyst followed by distillation. The usual catalysts are nickel, palladium, copper chromite, or platinum promoted with ferrous iron. Hydrogenation of aldehyde and ketone carbonyl groups is much slower than of carbon-carbon double bonds and rather more strenuous conditions are required. This is not surprising, since hydrogenation of carbonyl groups is calculated to be less exothermic than that of double bonds.

$$\text{C=C} + H_2 \longrightarrow -\underset{H}{\underset{|}{C}}-\underset{H}{\underset{|}{C}}- \qquad \Delta H = -30 \text{ kcal}$$

$$\text{C=O} + H_2 \longrightarrow -\underset{H}{\underset{|}{C}}-OH \qquad \Delta H = -12 \text{ kcal}$$

It follows that it is generally not possible to reduce a carbonyl group in the presence of a double bond without also saturating the double bond.

In recent years inorganic hydrides such as lithium aluminum hydride, LiAlH$_4$, and sodium borohydride, NaBH$_4$, have become extremely important as reducing agents of carbonyl compounds. These reagents have considerable utility, especially with sensitive and expensive carbonyl compounds. The reduction of cyclobutanone to cyclobutanol is a good example.

$$\text{cyclobutanone} \xrightarrow[\text{ether}]{\text{LiAlH}_4} \xrightarrow{H_2O, \; H^{\oplus}} \text{cyclobutanol}$$

90%

With the metal hydrides the key step is transfer of a hydride ion to the carbonyl carbon of the substance being reduced.

$$\underset{R}{\overset{R}{\underset{\delta\oplus}{C}}}\overset{\delta\ominus}{=}O \; + \; H:\overset{\oplus}{\underset{H}{\underset{|}{Al}}}-H \; \overset{\ominus}{Li} \longrightarrow \underset{R}{\overset{R}{C}}\overset{\ominus}{\underset{H}{\underset{}{O}}}AlH_3 \; \overset{\oplus}{Li}$$

Lithium aluminum hydride is best handled very much like a Grignard reagent, since it is soluble in ether and is sensitive to both oxygen and moisture. (Lithium hydride is insoluble in organic solvents and is not an effective reducing agent for organic compounds.) All four hydrogens on aluminum can be utilized.

$$\overset{\oplus}{Li} \; H:\overset{H}{\underset{H}{\underset{..}{Al}}}:H^{\ominus} + 4\,CH_2=O \longrightarrow \overset{\oplus}{Li} \; \overset{\ominus}{\underset{O-CH_3}{\underset{|}{CH_3-O-Al-O-CH_3}}} \xrightarrow{H_2O, \; H_2SO_4}$$

$$4\,CH_3OH \; + \; Al_2(SO_4)_3 \; + \; Li_2SO_4$$

The reaction products must be decomposed with water and acid as with the Grignard complexes. Any excess lithium aluminum hydride is decomposed by water and acid with evolution of hydrogen.

$$LiAlH_4 \; + \; 2\,H_2SO_4 \; \longrightarrow \; \tfrac{1}{2}\,Li_2SO_4 \; + \; \tfrac{1}{2}\,Al_2(SO_4)_3 \; + \; 4\,H_2$$

Lithium aluminum hydride usually reduces carbonyl groups without affecting carbon-carbon double bonds. It is, in addition, a strong reducing agent for carbonyl groups of carboxylic acids, esters, and other acid derivatives, as will be described in Chapter 16.

Sodium borohydride is a milder reducing agent than lithium aluminum hydride and will reduce aldehydes and ketones but not acids or esters. It reacts sufficiently slowly with water in neutral or alkaline solution, so that reductions which are reasonably rapid can be carried out in water solution without considerable hydrolysis of the reagent.

$$NaBH_4 \; + \; 4\,CH_2{=}O \; + \; 4\,H_2O \; \longrightarrow \; 4\,CH_3OH \; + \; NaB(OH)_4$$

B. Reduction of Carbonyl Compounds to Hydrocarbons

There are a number of methods of transforming $\diagdown \!\! C{=}O$ to $\diagdown \!\! CH_2$. In some cases, the following sequence of conventional reactions may be useful.

This route is long, requires a hydrogen α to the carbonyl function and may give rearrangement in the dehydration step (pp. 295–296).

More direct methods may be used depending on the character of the R groups of the carbonyl compound. If the R groups are such as to be stable to a variety of reagents there is no problem, but with sensitive R groups not all methods are equally applicable. When the R groups are stable to acid but unstable to base, the **Clemmensen** reduction with amalgamated zinc and hydrochloric acid is often very good. The mechanism of the Clemmensen reduction is not well

59%

understood. It is clear that in most cases, the alcohol is *not* an intermediate, since the Clemmensen conditions do not suffice to reduce most alcohols to hydrocarbons.

When the R groups of the carbonyl compound are stable to base but not to acid, the **Huang-Minlon modification of the Wolff-Kishner reduction** is often very convenient. This involves heating the carbonyl compound in a high-boiling polar solvent such as ethylene glycol with hydrazine and potassium hydroxide and driving the reaction to completion by distilling out the water formed.

$$\text{cyclopentanone} + NH_2-NH_2 \xrightarrow[\text{CH}_2\text{OHCH}_2\text{OH}]{KOH,\ 150°} \text{cyclopentane} + N_2 + H_2O$$

90%

14-7 OXIDATION OF CARBONYL COMPOUNDS

Aldehydes are easily oxidized by moist silver oxide or by potassium permanganate solution to the corresponding acids. The mechanism of the permanganate oxidation has some resemblance to the chromic acid oxidation of alcohols (pp. 296–297).

$$R-\underset{O}{C}H \xrightarrow{[O]} R-C\underset{OH}{\overset{O}{\|}}$$

Ketones are much more difficult to oxidize at the carbonyl group than aldehydes. Ketones with α-hydrogens can be oxidized in acidic or basic solutions because of enol formation, as will be described in Chapter 15. Thus,

$$CH_3-\underset{O}{\overset{\|}{C}}-CH_3 \underset{\xleftarrow{\hspace{1cm}}}{\overset{\overset{\ominus}{OH}\ (\text{or } H^{\oplus})}{\longrightarrow}} CH_3-\underset{OH}{\overset{}{C}}=CH_2$$

ketone   enol

Enols, being unsaturated, are easily attacked by reagents which oxidize unsaturated molecules.

14-8 THE CANNIZZARO REACTION

A characteristic reaction of aldehydes without α-hydrogens is the self oxidation-reduction that they undergo in the presence of strong base. Using formaldehyde as an example,

$$2\ CH_2{=}O + NaOH \xrightarrow[H_2O]{heat} CH_3OH + H-C\underset{ONa}{\overset{O}{\|}}$$

If the aldehyde has α-hydrogens, other reactions usually occur more rapidly.

The mechanism of the Cannizzaro reaction combines many features of other processes studied in this chapter. The first step is reversible addition of hydroxide ion to the carbonyl group.

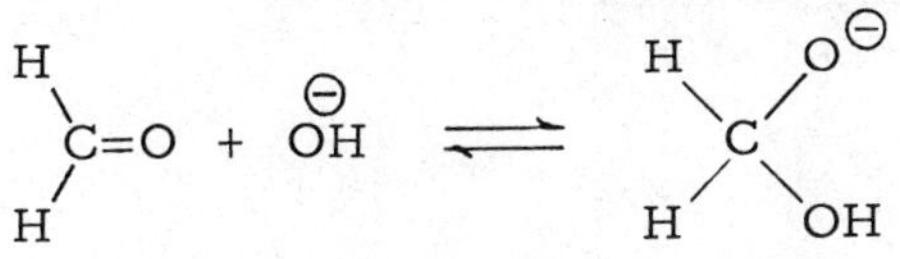

The hydroxyalkoxide ion so formed can act as a hydride-ion donor like lithium aluminum hydride and effect the reduction of a molecule of formaldehyde to methanol.

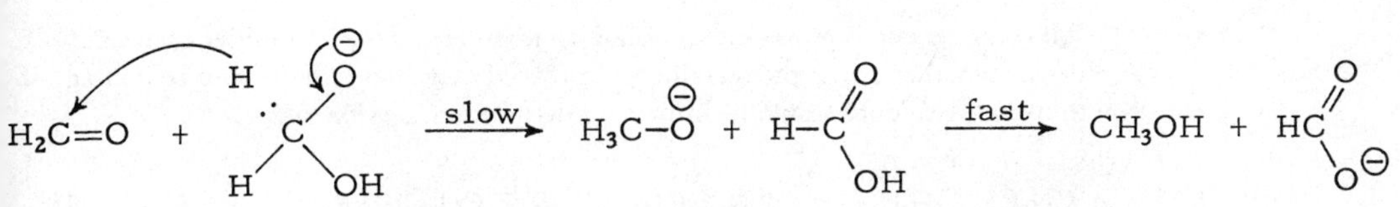

EXERCISE 14-16   Assume that an equimolar mixture of formaldehyde and trimethylacetaldehyde (each undergoes the Cannizzaro reaction by itself) is heated with sodium hydroxide solution. Write equations for the various possible combinations of Cannizzaro reactions which might occur. Would you expect formaldehyde used in excess to primarily reduce or oxidize trimethylacetaldehyde? Why?

SUPPLEMENTARY EXERCISES

14-17 Write equations for the synthesis of the following substances based on the indicated starting materials. Give the reaction conditions as accurately as possible.

a. $(CH_3)_2CHCHO$ from $(CH_3)_2CHCH_2CH_2OH$

b.

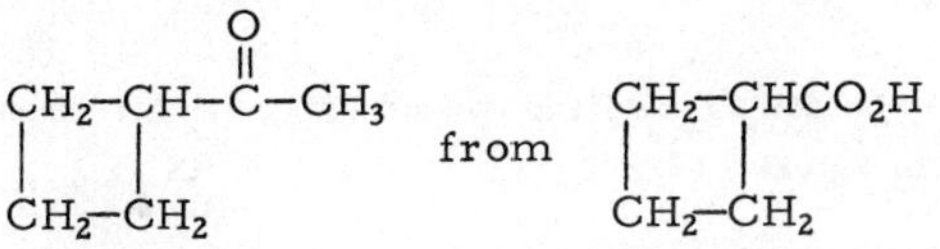

c.

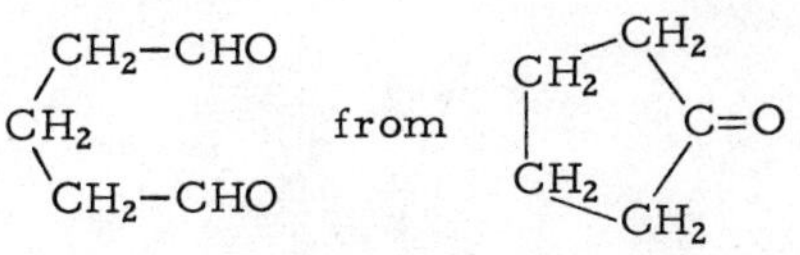

d.

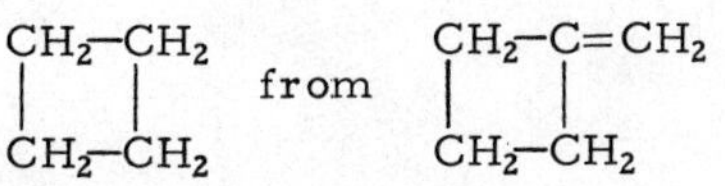

e. cyclopentene-1-carboxylic acid from cyclopentanone

14-18 Write reasonable mechanisms for each of the following reactions. Support your formulations with detailed analogies insofar as possible.

a. $\underset{\quad}{H-\overset{O}{\overset{\|}{C}}-\overset{O}{\overset{\|}{C}}-H}$ + NaOH $\xrightarrow{H_2O}$ $HOCH_2CO_2Na$

b. $CH_3-\underset{\underset{Br}{|}}{\overset{\overset{H}{|}}{C}}-\underset{\underset{OH}{|}}{\overset{\overset{H}{|}}{C}}-CH_3$ $\xrightarrow[H_2O]{Ag^{\oplus}}$ $CH_3-\overset{O}{\overset{\|}{C}}-CH_2-CH_3$

14-19 The following reactions represent "possible" synthetic reactions. Consider each carefully and decide whether or not the reaction will proceed as written. Show your reasoning. If you think side reactions would be important, write equations for each.

a. $CH_3CH(OC_2H_5)_2$ + $2\,NaOCH_3$ $\xrightarrow[50°]{\overset{\text{excess}}{CH_3OH}}$ $CH_3CH(OCH_3)_2$ + $2\,NaOC_2H_5$

b. $(CH_3)_3CCOCH_2CH_3$ + $KMnO_4$ $\xrightarrow[KOH]{H_2O}$ $(CH_3)_3COH$ + $CH_3CH_2CO_2K$

c. $CH_3CCl(CH_3)CH_2Cl$ + $2\,NaOCH_3$ $\xrightarrow[50°]{CH_3OH}$ $CH_3C(CH_3)(OCH_3)CH_2OCH_3$ + $2\,NaCl$

d. $O{=}CH-CO_2H$ + $NaBH_4$ $\xrightarrow{CH_3OH}$ $O{=}CH-CH_2OH$

e. $CH_2{=}O$ + $CH_3CO_2CH_3$ + NaOH $\rightarrow$ HCO_2Na + CH_3CH_2OH + CH_3OH

14-20 Name each of the following substances by an accepted system:

a. $CH_3OCH_2C(OCH_3)_3$ *d.* $[(CH_3)_3CO]_3Al$

b. $CH_3-\underset{\underset{OH}{|}}{CH}-SO_3Na$ *e.* $CH_3(CH_3CO_2)C(CN)(CH_3)$

          f. $(CH_3)_2C{=}N-N(CH_3)_2$

c. $CH_3C(OCH_3)_3$ *g.* $(CH_2)_2CHC(CH_3)NOH$

14-21 Show how structures may be deduced for the two substances with respective infrared and n.m.r. spectra as shown in Figure 14-2.

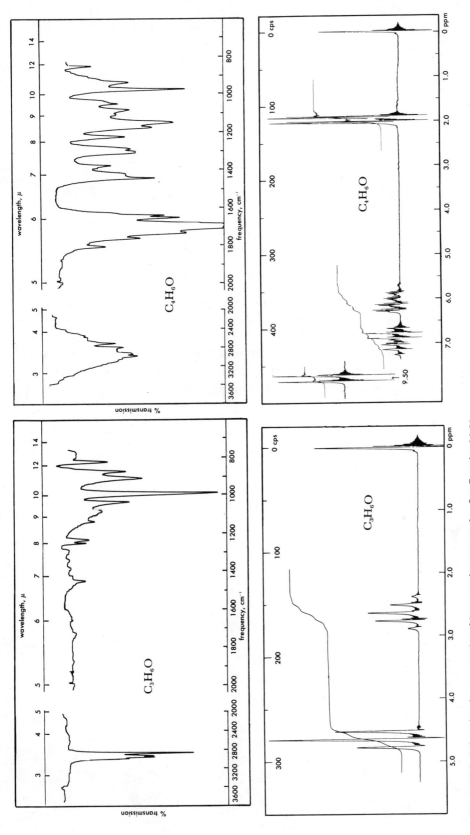

Figure 14-2 Infrared and n.m.r. spectra of two organic compounds.   See Exercise 14-21.

Aldehydes and Ketones.
Reactions Involving the Substituent Groups.
Unsaturated and Polycarbonyl Compounds.

*C*arbonyl groups often have a profound effect on the reactivity of their substituents. This is particularly evident when the substituents have hydrogen and halogen atoms on carbon alpha to the carbonyl groups, or when there is a double bond in the α,β position. In this chapter we shall consider, first, a number of very important synthetic reactions involving α hydrogens and, later, reactions of unsaturated and polycarbonyl compounds.

Aldehydes and Ketones. Reactions Involving the Substituent Groups. Unsaturated and Polycarbonyl Compounds

CHAPTER 15

15-1 HALOGENATION OF ALDEHYDES AND KETONES

Halogenation of saturated aldehydes and ketones usually occurs exclusively by replacement of hydrogens **alpha** to the carbonyl group.

$$CH_3\overset{O}{\overset{\|}{C}}CH_3 + Cl_2 \longrightarrow ClCH_2\overset{O}{\overset{\|}{C}}CH_3 + HCl$$

chloroacetone

2-bromocyclohexanone

The characteristics of such reactions are very different from those of the halo-genation of alkanes (Chapter 3). Acetone has been particularly well studied and reacts smoothly with chlorine, bromine, and iodine.

An important feature of the reaction is that acetone reacts at the *same* rate with each halogen. Indeed, the rate of formation of halogenated acetone is inde-pendent of the concentration of halogen, even at quite low halogen concentra-tions. Furthermore, halogenation of acetone is catalyzed by both acids and bases. The rate expressions for formation of halogenated acetone in water solu-tion are

$$v = k \, [CH_3COCH_3] \, [\overset{\ominus}{O}H] \qquad \text{at moderate concentrations of } OH^{\ominus}$$

$$v = k' \, [CH_3COCH_3] \, [H^{\oplus}] \qquad \text{at moderate concentrations of } H^{\oplus}$$

The ratio of k to k' is 12,000, which means that hydroxide ion is a much more effective catalyst than hydrogen ion.

EXERCISE 15-1   A detailed study of the rate of bromination of acetone in water, using acetic acid-acetate buffers, has shown that

$$v = \{6 \times 10^{-9} + 5.6 \times 10^{-4}[\overset{\oplus}{H_3O}] + 1.3 \times 10^{-6}[CH_3CO_2H] + 7[\overset{\ominus}{O}H] +$$
$$3.3 \times 10^{-6}[CH_3CO_2^{\ominus}] + 3.5 \times 10^{-6}[CH_3CO_2H][CH_3CO_2^{\ominus}]\}[CH_3COCH_3]$$

in which the rate is expressed in moles/liter/sec when the concentrations are in moles/liter.

a. Calculate the rate of the reaction for 1 M acetone in water at pH 7 in the absence of acetic acid or acetate ion.

b. Calculate the rate of the reaction for 1 M acetone in a solution made by neutralizing 1 M acetic acid with sufficient sodium hydroxide to give pH 5.0 (K_A of acetic acid = 1.75×10^{-5}).

To account for the role of the catalysts and the independence of the rate on the halogen concentration, the acetone must necessarily be slowly converted by the catalysts to an intermediate that reacts rapidly with halogen to give the prod-ucts. This intermediate is α-methylvinyl alcohol, which is the unstable enol form of acetone.

$$CH_3-\overset{\overset{\displaystyle O}{\|}}{C}-CH_3 \xrightarrow[\text{slow}]{H^{\oplus} \text{ (or } \overset{\ominus}{O}H)} CH_3-\overset{\overset{\displaystyle OH}{|}}{C}=CH_2 \xrightarrow[\text{fast}]{Br_2} CH_3-\overset{\overset{\displaystyle \overset{\oplus}{O}H}{\|}}{C}-CH_2-Br + \overset{\ominus}{Br}$$

enol

(α-methylvinyl alcohol)

$$\xrightarrow{\text{fast}} CH_3-\overset{\overset{\displaystyle O}{\|}}{C}-CH_2Br + H^{\oplus} + Br^{\ominus}$$

As long as the first step is slow compared with the second and third steps, the rate will be independent of both the concentration of halogen and its nature, whether chlorine, bromine, or iodine.

We shall now discuss each step in the reaction in more detail. First, there is the question of how the catalysts function to convert the ketone to its enol form.

A. Base-Catalyzed Enolization

With a basic catalyst, the first step is removal of a proton from the α position to give the enolate anion [1].

$$CH_3-\overset{\overset{\displaystyle O}{\|}}{C}-CH_2\!:\!H + \overset{\ominus}{O}H \underset{\text{}}{\overset{\text{slow}}{\rightleftharpoons}} \left[CH_3-\overset{\overset{\displaystyle \overset{\ominus}{O}}{|}}{C}=CH_2 \longleftrightarrow CH_3-\overset{\overset{\displaystyle O}{\|}}{C}-CH_2\!\!:^{\ominus} \right] + H_2O$$

[1]

Normally, C—H bonds are highly resistant to attack by basic reagents, but removal of a hydrogen, *alpha* to a carbonyl group, results in the formation of a considerably stabilized anion with a substantial proportion of the negative charge on oxygen. As a result, hydrogens, *alpha* to carbonyl groups, have acidic character and can be removed as protons. In contrast to the dissociation of many weak acids (e.g., CH_3CO_2H, H_3BO_3, HF, etc.), the acidic proton on carbon is removed *slowly* and equilibrium between the ketone and its enolate anion [1] is not established rapidly. This means, of course, that, if the proton is removed slowly from carbon, the reverse reaction must also be slow.[1] As a result, the enolate anion has ample time to add a proton to oxygen to form the enol (which process is at least 10^{10} times faster than conversion to the ketone).

$$\left[CH_3-\overset{\overset{\displaystyle O}{\|}}{C}=CH_2 \right]^{\ominus} + H^{\oplus} \underset{\text{}}{\overset{\text{fast}}{\rightleftharpoons}} CH_3-\overset{\overset{\displaystyle OH}{|}}{C}=CH_2$$

[1] At equilibrium, the rate of conversion of ketone to enol and the rate of the reverse reaction are equal.

Either the enol or the enolate anion can combine rapidly with halogen to give the α-halo ketone.

$$\left[CH_3 - \overset{\overset{\displaystyle O}{\|}}{C} \cdots CH_2 \right]^{\ominus} + Br_2 \quad \xrightarrow{\text{fast}} \quad CH_3 - \overset{\overset{\displaystyle O}{\|}}{C} - CH_2Br + Br^{\ominus}$$

$$CH_3 - \overset{\overset{\displaystyle OH}{|}}{C} = CH_2 + Br_2 \quad \xrightarrow{\text{fast}} \quad CH_3 - \overset{\overset{\displaystyle \oplus OH}{\|}}{C} - CH_2Br + Br^{\ominus} \quad \xrightarrow{(-HBr)} \quad CH_3 - \overset{\overset{\displaystyle O}{\|}}{C} - CH_2Br$$

The slowest step in the whole sequence is the formation of the enolate anion, and the over-all rate is thus independent of the halogen concentration.

B. Acid-Catalyzed Enolization

Catalysis of the enolization of acetone by acids involves, first, oxonium-salt formation and, second, removal of an α proton with water or other proton acceptors.

$$CH_3 - \overset{\overset{\displaystyle O}{\|}}{C} - CH_3 + H^{\oplus} \quad \xrightleftharpoons{\text{fast}} \quad CH_3 - \overset{\overset{\displaystyle \oplus OH}{\|}}{C} - CH_3$$

$$CH_3 - \overset{\overset{\displaystyle \oplus OH}{\|}}{C} - CH_2{:}H + H_2O \quad \xrightarrow{\text{slow}} \quad CH_3 - \overset{\overset{\displaystyle OH}{|}}{C} = CH_2 + H_3O^{\oplus}$$

This differs from base-catalyzed enolization in that the enol is formed directly and not subsequently to the formation of the enolate anion. Also, proton addition to the carbonyl oxygen greatly facilitates proton removal from the α carbon by the electron-attracting power of the positively charged oxygen. Nevertheless, the rate of enolization (or halogenation) is determined by this last step.

The characteristics of acid- and base-catalyzed enolization, as revealed by the halogenation of acetone, are displayed in a wide variety of other, and usually more complicated, reactions. For this reason the halogenation reaction has been considered in rather more detail than is consistent with its intrinsic importance as a synthetic reaction.

EXERCISE 15-2   Optically active s-butyl phenyl ketone is converted to the optically inactive ketone by dilute acid. If bromine is present, 2-bromo-2-butyl phenyl ketone is formed at the *same* rate. Explain.

C. Haloform Reaction

The above discussion on the halogenation of ketones is incomplete in one important respect concerning base-induced halogenation. That is, once an α-halo ketone is formed, the other hydrogens on the same carbon are rendered more acidic by the electron-attracting effect of the halogen and are replaced much more rapidly than the first hydrogen.

$$CH_3-\overset{\overset{\displaystyle O}{\|}}{C}-CH_3 \xrightarrow{\text{slow}} CH_3-\overset{\overset{\displaystyle O}{\|}}{C}-CH_2Br \xrightarrow{\text{fast}} CH_3-\overset{\overset{\displaystyle O}{\|}}{C}-CHBr_2 \xrightarrow{\text{fast}} CH_3-\overset{\overset{\displaystyle O}{\|}}{C}-CBr_3$$

The result is that, if the monobromo ketone is desired, the reaction is best carried out with an acidic catalyst rather than a basic catalyst. A further complication in the base-catalyzed halogenation of a methyl ketone is that the trihalo ketone formed is readily attacked by base with cleavage of a carbon-carbon bond.

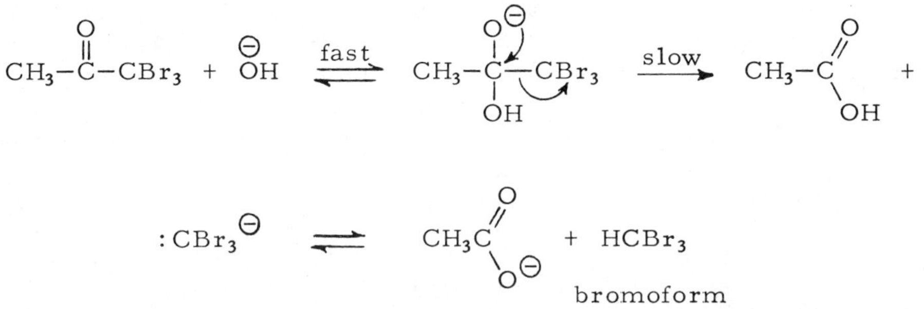

$$CH_3-\overset{\overset{\displaystyle O}{\|}}{C}-CBr_3 + \overset{\ominus}{OH} \underset{}{\overset{\text{fast}}{\rightleftharpoons}} CH_3-\overset{\overset{\displaystyle O^{\ominus}}{|}}{\underset{\overset{\displaystyle |}{OH}}{C}}-CBr_3 \xrightarrow{\text{slow}} CH_3-\overset{\overset{\displaystyle O}{/\!/}}{C}\underset{OH}{\diagdown} +$$

$$:CBr_3^{\ominus} \rightleftharpoons CH_3\overset{\overset{\displaystyle O}{/\!/}}{C}\underset{O^{\ominus}}{\diagdown} + HCBr_3$$

$$ \text{bromoform}$$

This sequence is often called the **haloform reaction** because it results in the production of chloroform, bromoform, or iodoform, depending upon the halogen used. The haloform reaction is a useful method for detection of methyl ketones, particularly when iodine is used because iodoform is a highly insoluble, bright-yellow solid. The reaction is also useful for the synthesis of carboxylic acids when the methyl ketone is more available than the corresponding acid.

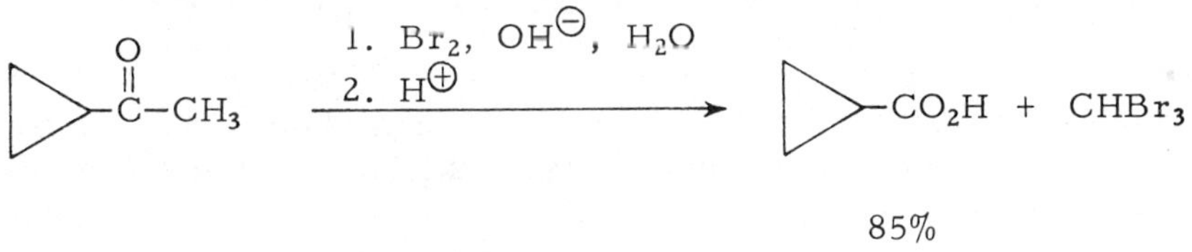

$$\triangleright\!\!-\overset{\overset{\displaystyle O}{\|}}{C}-CH_3 \quad \xrightarrow[\text{2. } H^{\oplus}]{\text{1. } Br_2,\ OH^{\ominus},\ H_2O} \quad \triangleright\!\!-CO_2H + CHBr_3$$

$$ 85\%$$

EXERCISE 15-3   Explain why many β-halo ketones undergo E2 elimination with considerable ease. What kinds of β-halo ketones might not undergo such elimination readily?

EXERCISE 15-4   The ΔH values calculated from bond energies for both of the following reactions in the vapor phase are equal (-9 kcal):

$$H_2O + CH_3-\overset{\overset{\displaystyle O}{\|}}{C}-CCl_3 \rightarrow CH_3-\overset{\overset{\displaystyle O}{\|}}{C}-OH + HCCl_3$$

$$H_2O + CCl_3-\overset{\overset{\displaystyle O}{\|}}{C}-CH_3 \rightarrow CCl_3-\overset{\overset{\displaystyle O}{\|}}{C}-OH + CH_4$$

Explain why the first, but not the second, reaction proceeds rapidly with the aid of sodium hydroxide. Would you expect acetic acid to undergo the haloform reaction? Explain.

15-2   REACTIONS OF ENOLATE ANIONS

A. The Aldol Addition

Many of the most important synthetic reactions of carbonyl compounds involve enolate anions, either as addends to suitably activated double bonds or as participants in nucleophilic substitutions. When the addition is to a carbonyl double bond, it is often called an **aldol addition.** S_N reactions of enolate anions will be considered in Chapter 16 with regard to synthetic applications.

The course of the aldol addition is typified by the reaction of acetaldehyde with base, and, if carried out under reasonably mild conditions, gives β-hydroxybutyraldehyde (acetaldol).

$$2\,CH_3CHO \xrightarrow{\text{dilute NaOH}} CH_3\overset{\overset{\displaystyle OH}{|}}{C}HCH_2CHO$$

If the mixture is heated, the product is dehydrated to crotonaldehyde (2-butenal).

$$CH_3-\overset{\overset{\displaystyle OH}{|}}{C}H-CH_2-CHO \xrightarrow{\overset{\ominus}{OH}\ \text{(or } H^{\oplus})} CH_3CH=CH-CHO$$

The ease of this dehydration, even under alkaline conditions, is in accord with the ease of related eliminations involving β-substituted carbonyl compounds (see Exercise 15-3).

Formation of the enolate anion by removal of an α hydrogen by base is the first step in the aldol addition.

The anion then adds to the carbonyl bond in a manner analogous to the addition of cyanide ion in cyanohydrin formation (pp. 317–320). It will be expected, from consideration of the two resonance forms of the enolate anion, that addition might take place in either of two ways: The anions may attack to form a carbon-carbon or a carbon-oxygen bond, leading ultimately to the aldol [2] or α-hydroxyethyl vinyl ether [3].

$$CH_3\overset{O}{\underset{||}{C}}-H + \left[\overset{O^{\ominus}}{\underset{|}{CH_2}}=\overset{}{C}-H \leftrightarrow :\overset{\ominus}{CH_2}-\overset{O}{\underset{||}{C}}-H \right]$$

$$\xrightarrow{} CH_3-\overset{O^{\ominus}}{\underset{|}{\underset{H}{C}}}-CH_2-\overset{O}{\underset{||}{C}}H \xrightarrow{H^{\oplus}} CH_3-\overset{OH}{\underset{|}{\underset{H}{C}}}-CH_2CHO \quad [2]$$

$$\xrightarrow{} CH_3-\overset{O^{\ominus}}{\underset{|}{\underset{H}{C}}}-O-CH=CH_2 \xrightarrow{H^{\oplus}} CH_3-\overset{OH}{\underset{|}{\underset{H}{C}}}-O-CH=CH_2 \quad [3]$$

Although the formation of [3] is mechanistically reasonable, it is much less so on thermodynamic grounds. Indeed, while the over-all ΔH (for the vapor) calculated from bond energies is -4 kcal for the formation of the aldol, it is $+20.4$ kcal[1] for the formation of [3].

EXERCISE 15-5   When the formation of acetaldol is carried on in D_2O containing $OD^{\ominus}$, using moderate concentrations of undeuterated acetaldehyde, the product formed in the early stages of the reaction contains no deuterium bound to carbon. Assuming the mechanism above to be correct, what can you conclude as to which step in the reaction is the slow step? What would then be the kinetic equation for the reaction? What would you expect to happen to the kinetics and the nature of the product formed in D_2O at *very low* concentrations of acetaldehyde?

EXERCISE 15-6   What would be the products expected from aldol additions involving propionaldehyde, trimethylacetaldehyde, and a mixture of the two aldehydes?

The equilibrium constant is favorable for the aldol addition of acetaldehyde, as in fact it is for most aldehydes. For ketones, however, the reaction is much less favorable. With acetone, only a few per cent of the addition product "diacetone alcohol" [4] is present at equilibrium. This is understandable on the basis of steric hindrance and the fact that the ketone-carbonyl bond is about 3

$$2\ CH_3\overset{O}{\underset{||}{C}}CH_3 \underset{\xrightarrow{}}{\overset{\overset{\ominus}{OH}}{\rightleftharpoons}} CH_3-\overset{OH}{\underset{|}{\underset{CH_3}{C}}}-CH_2-\overset{O}{\underset{||}{C}}-CH_3$$

$$[4]$$

kcal stronger than the aldehyde-carbonyl bond. Despite the unfavorable equilibrium constant, it is possible to prepare diacetone alcohol in good yield with the aid of an apparatus like that shown in Figure 15-1.

[1] This value probably is too large by 3 to 4 kcal, because vinyl ethers normally have stabilization energies of this magnitude.

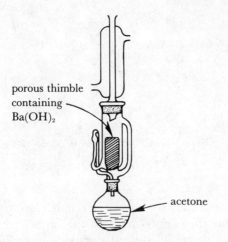

porous thimble
containing
Ba(OH)$_2$

acetone

Figure 15-1

Apparatus for preparation of diacetone
alcohol.

The acetone is boiled and the hot condensate from the reflux condenser flows
back through the porous thimble over the solid barium hydroxide contained
therein and comes to equilibrium with diacetone alcohol.   The barium hydroxide is retained by the porous thimble and the liquid phase is returned to the
boiler where the acetone (boiling 110° below diacetone alcohol) is selectively
vaporized and returned to the reaction zone to furnish more diacetone alcohol.

EXERCISE 15-7   At what point would the system shown in Figure 15-1 cease to produce more
diacetone alcohol?   What would happen if some barium hydroxide were to get
through a hole in the thimble and pass into the boiler?   Why is barium hydroxide
more suitable for the preparation than sodium hydroxide?

The ingredients in the key step in aldol addition are fundamentally an electron-pair donor and an electron-pair acceptor.   In the formation of acetaldol
and diacetone alcohol, both roles are played by one kind of molecule, but there
is no reason why this should be a necessary condition for reaction.   Many kinds
of mixed additions are possible.   Consider the combination of formaldehyde
and acetone: Formaldehyde cannot form an enolate anion because it has no α
hydrogens, but it is expected to be a particularly good electron-pair acceptor because of freedom from steric hindrance and the fact that it has an unusually
weak carbonyl bond (166 kcal vs. 179 kcal for acetone).   Acetone forms an enolate anion easily but is relatively poor as an acceptor.   Consequently, the addition of acetone to formaldehyde should and does occur readily.

$$CH_3-\overset{\overset{O}{\|}}{C}-CH_3 + CH_2{=}O \xrightarrow{\overset{\ominus}{OH}} CH_3-\overset{\overset{O}{\|}}{C}-CH_2CH_2OH$$

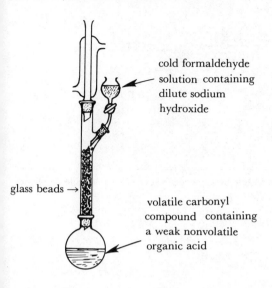

cold formaldehyde
solution containing
dilute sodium
hydroxide

glass beads →

volatile carbonyl
compound containing
a weak nonvolatile
organic acid

Figure 15-2

Apparatus for preparation of monohydroxymethylene aldol-addition products from formaldehyde and carbonyl
compounds with more than one α hydrogen.

The problem is not to get addition, but rather to keep it from going too far. Indeed, all six α hydrogens can be easily replaced by —CH₂OH groups.

$$CH_3-\overset{\overset{\displaystyle O}{\|}}{C}-CH_3 \;+\; 6\,CH_2O \;\xrightarrow{\;\ominus OH\;}\; (HOH_2C)_3C-\overset{\overset{\displaystyle O}{\|}}{C}-C(CH_2OH)_3$$

To obtain high yields of the monohydroxymethylene derivative, it is usually necessary to use an apparatus like that shown in Figure 15-2. The scheme here is to have the addition take place in the presence of a large excess of acetone so as to assure favorable formation of the monoadduct. The reaction is then quenched and the acetone separated and used again. This is achieved by boiling rapidly a solution of acetone containing an excess of a nonvolatile weak organic acid, such as succinic acid $(CH_2)_2(CO_2H)_2$. The vapor is condensed and then mixed with a very slow trickle of an alkaline formaldehyde solution. The addition then occurs while the mixture flows down over a column of glass beads, and gives the monoadduct because the acetone is present in great excess. The reaction stops and reversal is prevented when the alkali is neutralized by the acid in the boiler. The excess acetone is revaporized and sent up to react with more formaldehyde.

Aldol addition products can be converted to a variety of substances by reactions that have been discussed previously. Of particular importance is the dehydration of aldols to α,β-unsaturated carbonyl compounds, which is preferably achieved with an acidic catalyst. The formation of crotonaldehyde by dehydration of acetaldol has already been mentioned (p. 340). Another example is the dehydration of diacetone alcohol to mesityl oxide.

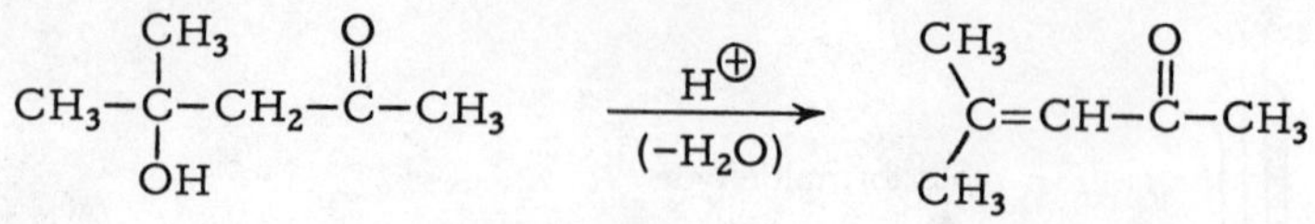

$$CH_3-\underset{\underset{OH}{|}}{\overset{\overset{CH_3}{|}}{C}}-CH_2-\overset{\overset{O}{\|}}{C}-CH_3 \xrightarrow[(-H_2O)]{H^{\oplus}} \underset{CH_3}{\overset{CH_3}{\diagup}}C=CH-\overset{\overset{O}{\|}}{C}-CH_3$$

4-methyl-3-penten-2-one
(mesityl oxide)

EXERCISE 15-8   Predict the principal products to be expected in each of the following reactions; give your reasoning:

a. $CH_3CHO + (CH_3)_2CO \xrightarrow{NaOH}$

b. $(CH_3)_2C(OH)CH_2COCH_3 \xrightarrow{NaOH}$

c. $CH_2O + (CH_3)_3CCHO \xrightarrow{NaOH}$

EXERCISE 15-9   Show how the following compounds can be synthesized from the indicated starting materials by way of aldol-addition products:

a. $CH_3-\underset{\underset{OH}{|}}{CH}-CH_2-\underset{\underset{OH}{|}}{CH_2}$ from acetaldehyde

b. $CH_3CH{=}CH-CH_2OH$ from acetaldehyde

c. $(CH_3)_2CHCH_2CH_2CH_3$ from acetone

d. $CH_3CH-\overset{\overset{O}{\|}}{C}-CH_2CH_3$ from propionaldehyde
   $\underset{\underset{CH_3}{|}}{}$

EXERCISE 15-10   Aldol additions also occur in the presence of acidic catalysts. For example, acetone with dry hydrogen chloride slowly yields $(CH_3)_2C{=}CHCOCH_3$ (mesityl oxide) and $(CH_3)_2C{=}CHCOCH{=}C(CH_3)_2$ (phorone). Write mechanisms for the formation of these products giving particular attention to the way in which the new carbon-carbon bonds are formed. Review pp. 154 and 320–323.

B. Nucleophilic Substitution Involving Enolate Anions

An enolate anion can be formed in good yield from a ketone and a powerfully basic reagent, such as sodium or potassium amide, provided that the ketone has an α hydrogen. The enolate anion so formed can theoretically undergo S_N reactions with an alkyl halide in two different ways. Thus, for *t*-butyl methyl ketone and methyl iodide, we could have the following reactions, which differ only in the position of attack at the enolate anion:

$$
\begin{array}{c}
\underset{\underset{CH_3}{|}}{CH_3-\overset{\overset{CH_3O}{|}}{C}-\overset{\overset{O}{||}}{C}-CH_3}
\quad \xrightarrow[(-NH_3)]{KNH_2} \quad
\left[
\underset{\underset{CH_3}{|}}{CH_3-\overset{\overset{CH_3O}{|}}{C}-\overset{\overset{O}{||}}{C}-CH_2:}{}^{\ominus}
\quad \longleftrightarrow \quad
\underset{\underset{CH_3}{|}}{CH_3-\overset{\overset{CH_3}{|}}{C}-\overset{\overset{O}{}}{C}=CH_2}{}^{\ominus}
\right] K^{\oplus}
\end{array}
$$

CH₃I   (−KI)

C−alkylation   O−alkylation

$$
\underset{\underset{CH_3}{|}}{CH_3-\overset{\overset{CH_3}{|}}{C}-\overset{\overset{O}{||}}{C}-CH_2-CH_3}
$$

$$
\underset{\underset{CH_3}{|}}{CH_3-\overset{\overset{CH_3}{|}}{C}-\overset{OCH_3}{\underset{CH_2}{C}}}
$$

The possibility of the enolate anion's acting as though its charge were effectively concentrated on carbon or on oxygen was discussed earlier in connection with aldol addition (p. 340). However, the situation there is actually quite different from the one here, because the reaction on oxygen was indicated to be quite thermodynamically unfavorable over-all ($\Delta H = +20$ kcal) compared to that on carbon ($\Delta H = -4$ kcal). However, O- and C-alkylation of the *anion* are *both* thermodynamically favorable. Furthermore, alkylation, unlike the aldol addition, is not reversible under ordinary conditions, and therefore the O-alkylation product is not expected to go over to the C-alkylation product, even if the latter is 24 kcal more stable.

EXERCISE 15-11   Vinyl ethers (enol ethers) are more stable to rearrangement than vinyl alcohols (enols). Why? What conditions would you expect to be favorable for rearrangement of a vinyl ether?

Whether C- or O-alkylation occurs often depends on the reactivity of the halide. A key factor appears to be the degree of formation of the new bond to the carbon of the halide in the transition state between reactant and products. If formation of the new bond is well advanced, as will usually be necessary in pushing out the leaving group from a halide of relatively low S_N2 reactivity, then C-alkylation is likely to be favored.

The alkylation of simple ketones with alkyl halides and sodium amide (**Haller-Bauer alkylation**) is not a very important synthetic reaction, except in the preparation of highly substituted ketones, such as hexamethylacetone, which are difficult to make in other ways.

$$(CH_3)_3C\overset{O}{\overset{||}{C}}-CH_3 + 3\ NaNH_2 + 3\ CH_3I \longrightarrow (CH_3)_3C\overset{O}{\overset{||}{C}}C(CH_3)_3 + 3\ NaI + 3\ NH_3$$

More useful alkylation procedures for the preparation of α-substituted ketones will be discussed below and in Chapter 16.

EXERCISE 15-12   *a.* The Haller-Bauer alkylation is much less successful for ethyl and higher primary halides than for methyl halides. Explain why competing reactions might be particularly important for such cases.

        b. What would you expect to happen to acetaldehyde under the Haller-Bauer conditions?

UNSATURATED CARBONYL COMPOUNDS

The combination of a carbonyl function and a double bond in the same molecule leads to exceptional properties only when the groups are close to one another. The cumulated and conjugated arrangements are of particular interest. We shall consider first the conjugated or α,β-unsaturated carbonyl compounds, because their chemistry is closely related to that of the substances already discussed in this chapter and in Chapter 14.

15-3 α,β-UNSATURATED ALDEHYDES AND KETONES

The most generally useful preparation of α,β-unsaturated carbonyl compounds is by dehydration of aldol addition products, as described on pp. 340 and 343. Conjugation of the carbonyl group and double bond has a marked influence on spectroscopic properties, particularly on ultraviolet spectra, as the result of stabilization of the excited electronic states which, for $\pi \rightarrow \pi^*$ transitions, can be described in terms of important contributions of polar-resonance structures (see also pp. 196–198).

$$\left[\overset{\backslash}{\underset{/}{C}}=\overset{|}{C}-\overset{|}{C}=O \quad\longleftrightarrow\quad \overset{\backslash}{\underset{/\oplus}{C}}-\overset{|}{\underset{\ominus}{C}}-\overset{|}{C}=O \quad\longleftrightarrow\quad \overset{\oplus\backslash}{\underset{/}{C}}-\overset{|}{C}=\overset{|}{C}-\overset{\ominus}{O} \right]$$

The effect of conjugation is also reflected in n.m.r. spectra. It is found that the protons on the β carbon of α,β-unsaturated carbonyl compounds usually come at 0.7 to 1.7 ppm lower than ordinary olefinic protons. The effect is smaller for the α protons.

EXERCISE 15-13   Interpret the proton n.m.r. spectra given in Figure 15-3 in terms of structures of compounds with the molecular formulas $C_6H_{10}O$ and C_9H_8O. The latter substance has a phenyl (C_6H_5) group.

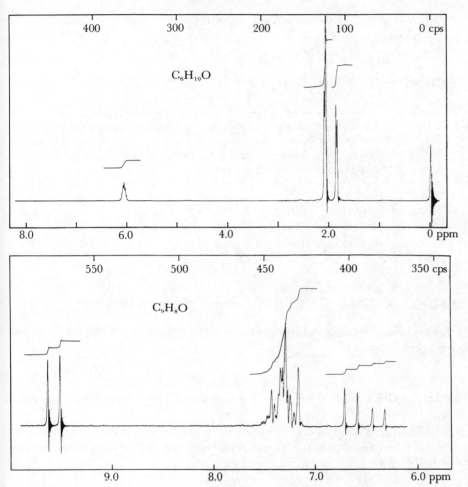

Figure 15-3   Proton n.m.r. spectra at 60 Mcps with TMS as standard.   See Exercise 15-21.

α,β-Unsaturated carbonyl compounds may undergo the usual addition and condensation reactions at the carbonyl group, such as cyanohydrin and hydrazone formation and addition of organometallic compounds. These reactions, however, may be complicated by, if not overshadowed by, "1,4-addition" (see pp. 188–189 and 206–207), which gives as the overall result 1,2-addition to the C—C double bond, see Exercise 15-14. The balance between the two modes of reaction is so delicate that relatively small changes in steric hindrance are sufficient to cause one or the other process to predominate.

With hydrogen cyanide, cyanohydrin formation is usually more rapid than 1,4-addition, and if the equilibrium is favorable, as with most aldehydes, only 1,2-addition is observed.

$$CH_3-CH=CH-CHO + HCN \xrightarrow{\overset{\ominus}{OH}} CH_3-CH=CH-\overset{\overset{\displaystyle OH}{|}}{\underset{\underset{\displaystyle C\equiv N}{|}}{C}}-H$$

With ketones, cyanohydrin formation is less favorable, and 1,4-addition results to give a β-cyano ketone.

$$CH_2=CH-\overset{\overset{\displaystyle O}{\|}}{C}-CH_3 \ + \ HCN \ \xrightarrow{\overset{\ominus}{OH}} \ N\equiv C-CH_2-CH_2-\overset{\overset{\displaystyle O}{\|}}{C}-CH_3$$

EXERCISE 15-14   Calculate ΔH for vapor-phase 1,2- and 1,4-additions of hydrogen cyanide to methyl vinyl ketone. Write a mechanism for 1,4-addition that is consistent with catalysis by bases and the fact that hydrogen cyanide does not add to an isolated carbon-carbon double bond.

Addition of hydrogen halides to α,β-unsaturated aldehydes and ketones places the halogen on the β carbon. With a vinyl group in conjugation with the carbonyl function, the product is opposite to that expected from Markownikoff's rule.

$$CH_2=CH-\overset{\overset{\displaystyle O}{\|}}{C}-H + HCl \ \longrightarrow \ ClCH_2-CH_2-\overset{\overset{\displaystyle O}{\|}}{C}-H$$

Similar additions occur to α,β-unsaturated acids and the products are those expected from 1,4-addition.

$$CH_2=CH-\overset{\overset{\displaystyle O}{\|}}{C}-OH + HCl \ \longrightarrow \ \left[ClCH_2-CH=\overset{\overset{\displaystyle OH}{|}}{C}-OH \right] \ \longrightarrow \ ClCH_2-CH_2\overset{\overset{\displaystyle O}{\|}}{C}-OH$$

β,γ-Unsaturated aldehydes and ketones are usually relatively difficult to synthesize and are found to rearrange readily to the α,β-unsaturated isomers, particularly in the presence of basic reagents.

$$CH_2=CH-CH_2-CHO \ \xrightarrow{\text{base}} \ CH_3-CH=CH-CHO$$

EXERCISE 15-15   Write a reasonable mechanism for the base-induced rearrangement of 3-butenal to 2-butenal. Why is 2-butenal the more stable isomer?

15-4 KETENES

Substances with cumulated carbonyl and carbon-carbon double bonds, $\overset{\diagdown}{\underset{\diagup}{C}}=C=O$, are called **ketenes** and, as might be expected, have interesting and unusual properties. Ketene itself, $CH_2=C=O$, and its monosubstitution products, $RCH=C=O$ with R = alkyl or aryl, are called **aldoketenes,** while disubstituted ketenes, $R_2C=C=O$, are called **ketoketenes.**

There are relatively few general methods for preparing ketenes. The simplest procedure is to treat an α-bromo acyl bromide with zinc, but the yields are not usually very good.

$$
\underset{\substack{| \\ Br}}{\overset{\substack{R \\ |}}{R-C}}-\underset{\substack{| \\ Br}}{C}\overset{\substack{O \\ \|}}{} + Zn \xrightarrow{\text{ether}} \underset{\substack{/ \\ R}}{\overset{\substack{R \\ \backslash}}{}} C=C=O + ZnBr_2
$$

Several special methods are available for ketene itself. The most convenient laboratory preparation is to pass acetone vapor over a coil of resistance wire heated electrically to a dull red heat. Air is excluded to avoid simple combustion.

$$
\underset{}{CH_3-\overset{\overset{\textstyle O}{\|}}{C}-CH_3} \xrightarrow{750°} CH_2=C=O + CH_4
$$

ketene
b. p. −56°

The weakest bonds in acetone are the C—C bonds and, at 750°, fragmentation yields a methyl radical and an acetyl radical.

$$
CH_3-\overset{\overset{\textstyle O}{\|}}{C}-CH_3 \longrightarrow CH_3\overset{\overset{\textstyle O}{\|}}{C}\cdot + \cdot CH_3 \longrightarrow CH_2=C=O + CH_4
$$

Transfer of a hydrogen atom (i.e., disproportionation) gives methane and ketene.

Ketene is a very useful acetylating agent for ROH and RNH$_2$ compounds. It reacts rapidly, and since the reactions involve additions, there are no by-products to be separated.

$$
CH_2=C=O
$$

$$
\xrightarrow{H_2O} CH_3-\overset{\overset{\textstyle O}{\|}}{C}\overset{\diagdown}{\underset{OH}{}}
$$

$$
\xrightarrow{CH_3CO_2H} CH_3-\overset{\overset{\textstyle O}{\|}}{C}-O-\overset{\overset{\textstyle O}{\|}}{C}-CH_3
$$

$$
\xrightarrow{CH_3CH_2OH} CH_3-\overset{\overset{\textstyle O}{\|}}{C}-O-CH_2CH_3
$$

$$
\xrightarrow{CH_3NH_2} CH_3-\overset{\overset{\textstyle O}{\|}}{C}-\overset{\overset{\textstyle H}{|}}{N}-CH_3
$$

EXERCISE 15-16   Write reasonable mechanisms for the reaction of ketene with alcohols and amines. Would you expect these reactions to be facilitated by acids and/or bases?

The considerable convenience of ketene as an acetylating agent should make it an excellent candidate for commercial sale in cylinders (b.p. −56°) except for the fact that the substance is unstable with respect to formation of a dimer known as diketene. The dimer is itself a highly reactive substance with such unusual characteristics that its structure was not firmly established until 1945 to 1955, some 38 to 48 years after it was first prepared.

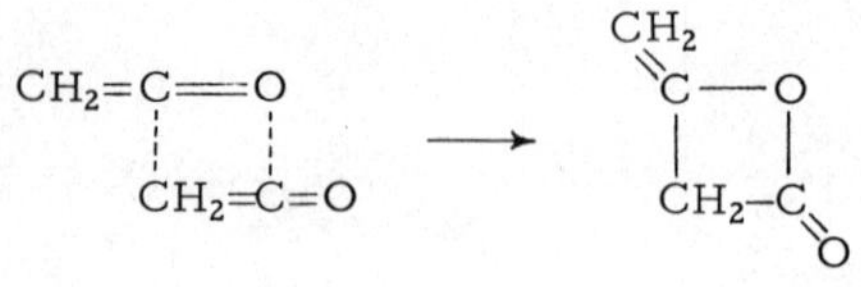

diketene

(vinylaceto–β–lactone)

EXERCISE 15-17   The following structures have been proposed or could be proposed for diketene. Show how infrared, ultraviolet, and n.m.r. spectroscopy might be used to distinguish between the possibilities (if necessary, review Chapter 2).

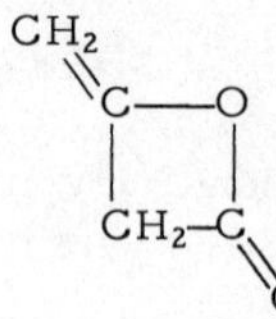

[i] 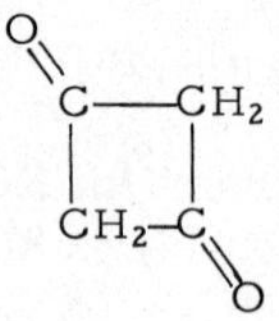   [ii] 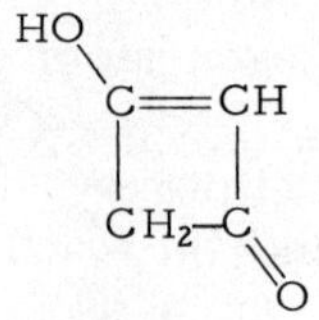   [iii] 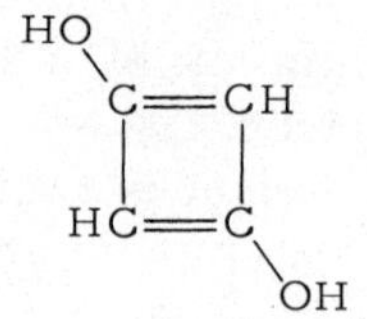   [iv]

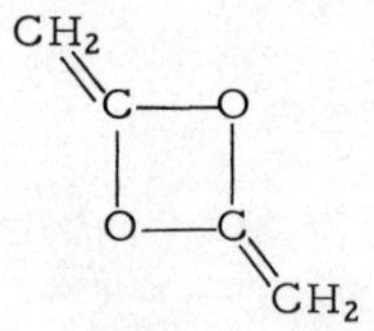

[v] 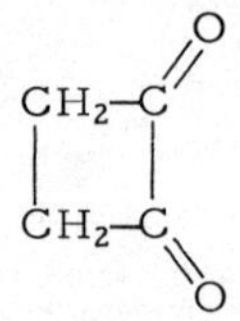   [vi] 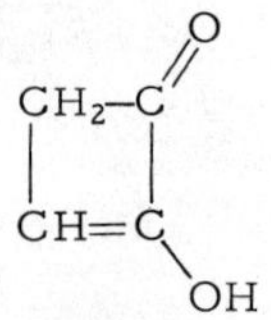   [vii] 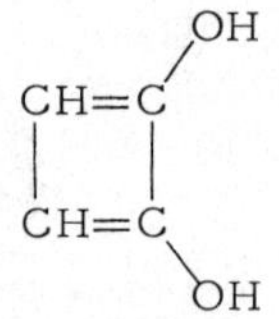   [viii]

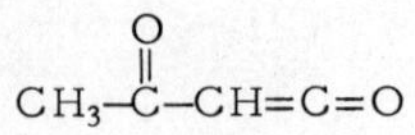

$$CH_3-\overset{\overset{\displaystyle O}{\|}}{C}-CH=C=O$$ (the favored structure for many years)

[ix]

POLYCARBONYL COMPOUNDS

15-5   1,2-DICARBONYL COMPOUNDS

Some typical and important members of this class have structures as follows:

$$H-\overset{\overset{\displaystyle O}{\|}}{C}-\overset{\overset{\displaystyle O}{\|}}{C}-H \qquad CH_3-\overset{\overset{\displaystyle O}{\|}}{C}-\overset{\overset{\displaystyle O}{\|}}{C}-CH_3 \qquad C_6H_5-\overset{\overset{\displaystyle O}{\|}}{C}-\overset{\overset{\displaystyle O}{\|}}{C}-C_6H_5$$

glyoxal	biacetyl	benzil
(ethanedial)	(2, 3–butanedione)	(diphenyl diketone)

Most of the 1,2-dicarbonyl compounds are yellow in color. Glyoxal is unusual in being yellow in the liquid state, but green in the vapor state. It has very reactive aldehyde groups.

Glyoxal undergoes an internal Cannizzaro reaction with alkali to give glycolic acid.

$$H-\overset{\overset{\displaystyle O}{\|}}{C}-\overset{\overset{\displaystyle O}{\|}}{C}-H \;+\; \overset{\ominus}{OH} \longrightarrow H-\underset{\underset{\displaystyle H}{|}}{\overset{\overset{\displaystyle OH}{|}}{C}}-\overset{\displaystyle O}{\underset{\underset{\displaystyle O}{|}}{C\hspace{-2pt}\diagup\hspace{-8pt}\diagdown}}{}^{\ominus} \xrightarrow{H^{\oplus}} H-\underset{\underset{\displaystyle H}{|}}{\overset{\overset{\displaystyle OH}{|}}{C}}-\overset{\displaystyle O}{C}\diagdown_{OH}$$

An analogous reaction occurs with benzil, which results in carbon skeleton rearrangement.   This is one of a very few carbon-skeleton rearrangements brought about by basic reagents, and is known as the **benzilic acid rearrangement.**

$$C_6H_5-\overset{\overset{\displaystyle O}{\|}}{C}-\overset{\overset{\displaystyle O}{\|}}{C}-C_6H_5 \;+\; \overset{\oplus}{Na}\;\overset{\ominus}{OH} \longrightarrow C_6H_5-\underset{\underset{\displaystyle C_6H_5}{|}}{\overset{\overset{\displaystyle OH}{|}}{C}}-\overset{\displaystyle O}{C}{}^{\ominus}\;{}^{\oplus}_{O\;Na} \xrightarrow{H^{\oplus}} C_6H_5-\underset{\underset{\displaystyle C_6H_5}{|}}{\overset{\overset{\displaystyle OH}{|}}{C}}-\overset{\displaystyle O}{C}\diagdown_{OH}$$

benzil   benzilic acid

EXERCISE 15-18   What experiments might be done to prove or disprove the following mechanism for rearrangement of glyoxal to glycolic acid?

$$\overset{\overset{\displaystyle O}{\|}}{HC}-\overset{\overset{\displaystyle O}{\|}}{CH} \;\underset{}{\overset{\overset{\ominus}{OH}}{\rightleftharpoons}}\; \left[H-\overset{\overset{\displaystyle O}{\|}}{C}-\overset{\ominus}{C}=O \;\leftrightarrow\; H-\overset{\overset{\displaystyle O}{|}^{\ominus}}{C}=C=O \right] \overset{H^{\oplus}}{\rightleftharpoons}$$

$$H-\overset{\overset{\displaystyle OH}{|}}{C}=C=O \xrightarrow{H_2O} H-\underset{\underset{\displaystyle H}{|}}{\overset{\overset{\displaystyle OH}{|}}{C}}-\overset{\displaystyle O}{C}\diagdown_{OH}$$

EXERCISE 15-19   Write a mechanism analogous to that for the Cannizzaro reaction for the benzil-benzilic acid transformation.   Would you expect the same type of reaction to occur with biacetyl?   Why or why not?

EXERCISE 15-20   1,2-Cyclopentanedione exists substantially as the monoenol, whereas biacetyl exists as the keto form. Suggest explanations for this behavior that take into account possible conformational differences between the two substances. How easily would you expect dione [5] to enolize? Why?

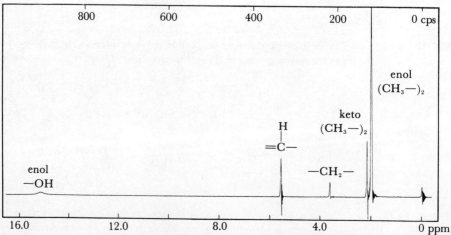

[5]

15-6   1,3-DICARBONYL COMPOUNDS

Most of the important properties of 1,3-dialdehydes, aldehyde ketones, and diketones that are characteristic of the 1,3-relationship are well illustrated by acetylacetone (2,4-pentanedione).

$$CH_3—\overset{\overset{O}{\|}}{C}—CH_2—\overset{\overset{O}{\|}}{C}—CH_3$$

acetyl acetone

This substance is unusual in existing to the extent of 85% as the enol form.

$$CH_3—\overset{\overset{O}{\|}}{C}—CH_2—\overset{\overset{O}{\|}}{C}—CH_3 \rightleftharpoons$$

15%   85%

| 800 | 600 | 400 | 200 | 0 cps |

enol (CH₃—)₂

keto (CH₃—)₂

H
|
=C—

—CH₂—

enol
—OH

16.0   12.0   8.0   4.0   0 ppm

Figure 15-4   N.m.r. spectrum of acetylacetone, $CH_3COCH_2COCH_3$, at 60 Mcps. Calibrations are relative to tetramethylsilane.

The n.m.r. spectrum of acetylacetone (Figure 15-4) is very informative about the species present in the pure liquid. Resonance lines for both the keto and enol forms can be readily distinguished. The keto form has its CH_2 resonance at 218 cps and its CH_3 resonances at 120 cps, whereas the enol form shows its CH_3 and vinyl-CH resonances at 110 cps and 334 cps, respectively. The enolic-OH proton comes at the very low field value of 910 cps with respect to tetramethylsilane. That each form may be observed separately indicates that the equilibrium between them is not established in less than 0.1 sec at room temperature (see pp. 43–45). However, when a basic catalyst is added, the lines broaden considerably; and when the mixture is heated, the lines coalesce to an average spectrum as expected for rapid equilibration.

The very large chemical shift of the enol-OH proton is the consequence of internal hydrogen bonding involving the carbonyl group.

This type of hydrogen bonding is also important in stabilizing the enol form, as evidenced by an increase in the percentage of enol in those solvents, such as hexane, that cannot effectively solvate the ketone groups of the keto form.

The enol form is also considerably stabilized by electron delocalization, as in the following resonance structures:

Such stabilization is, of course, not possible for the keto form.

The term **conformer** is often used to designate one of two or more stereochemical conformations that are in such rapid equilibrium as to not represent discrete isolable substances under ordinary conditions (cf. p. 130). The term **tautomer** is employed in exactly the same sense for structural isomers in rapid equilibrium, such as the keto and enol forms of acetylacetone. When tautomerization involves only the shift of a proton, it is sometimes called a **prototropic** change. While, in principle, the only difference between the interconversion of acetylacetone and its enol and 1,4-pentadiene and 1,3-pentadiene is a matter of relative reaction rate, rightly or wrongly, the term tautomeric change is usually applied exclusively to the more rapid process.

The enol of acetylacetone is moderately acidic with $K_A \sim 10^{-9}$ (compared with K_A of 10^{-5} for acetic acid and 10^{-16} for ethanol). Alkali metal salts of the enol can be alkylated with alkyl halides of good S_N2 reactivity and generally give C-alkylation. The yields are better than in the Haller-Bauer alkylation because the more weakly basic anions give less E2 elimination (see p. 239). A number of synthetically important alkylations of other 1,3-dicarbonyl compounds will be discussed in Chapter 16.

Polyvalent metal cations often form very stable and slightly polar enolate salts with acetylacetone, better known as metal chelates. Cupric ion is a particularly good chelating agent.

cupric acetylacetonate (dark blue)

Beryllium acetylacetonate is a further example of a metal chelate; it melts at 108°, boils at 270°, and is soluble in many organic solvents.

EXERCISE 15-21   2,6-Bicyclo[2.2.2]octanedione [6] exhibits no enolic properties. Explain.

[6]

EXERCISE 15-22   Account for the considerable K_A of the enol of acetylacetone with respect to ethyl alcohol. Arguing from the proportions of each at equilibrium, which is the stronger acid, the keto or the enol form of acetylacetone? Explain.

EXERCISE 15-23   Interpret the proton n.m.r. spectra shown in Figure 15-5 in terms of structure of the compounds with molecular formulas $C_{10}H_{10}O_2$ and $(CH_3CH=C=O)_2$. See also Exercise 15-17.

15-7 1,4-DICARBONYL COMPOUNDS

Most of the reactions of the 1,4-dicarbonyl compounds are the conventional reactions expected for isolated carbonyl groups. An important exception is

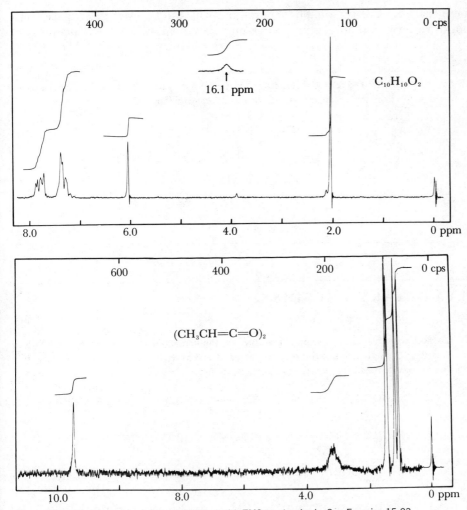

Figure 15-5   Proton n.m.r. spectra at 60 Mcps with TMS as standard.   See Exercise 15-23.

formation of pyrrole derivatives from 1,4-dicarbonyl compounds and ammonia or primary amines.

These reactions are reasonably general and can also be used to prepare compounds with oxygen and sulfur in five-membered rings.

EXERCISE 15-24   Write a reasonable mechanism, supported by analogy, for the acid-catalyzed dehydration of acetonylacetone to 2,5-dimethylfuran [7].

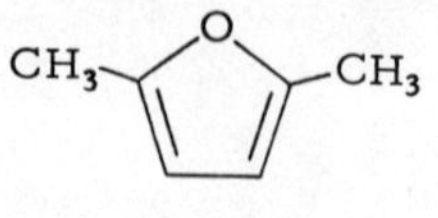

$$CH_3 \overset{O}{\diagup\!\!\!\diagdown} CH_3$$

2, 5–dimethylfuran

[7]

SUPPLEMENTARY EXERCISES

15-25 The following reactions represent "possible" synthetic reactions. Consider each carefully and decide whether or not the reaction will proceed as written. *Show your reasoning.* If you think side reactions would be important, write equations for each.

a. $CH_3COCH_3 + 6 Br_2 + 8 NaOH \longrightarrow 2 CHBr_3 + Na_2CO_3 + 6 NaBr + 6 H_2O$

b. $CH_3CHO + NaNH_2 + (CH_3)_3CCl \longrightarrow (CH_3)_3CCH_2CHO + NH_3 + NaCl$

c. $(CH_3)_2CHCOCH_3 + CH_2{=}O \xrightarrow{Ca(OH)_2} (CH_3)_2C(CH_2OH)COCH_3$

d. $CH_3CHO + CH_3CO_2C_2H_5 \xrightarrow{OH^{\ominus}} CH_3\underset{\underset{OH}{|}}{C}HCH_2CO_2C_2H_5$

15-26 Write equations for a practical laboratory synthesis of each of the following substances, *based* on the indicated starting materials (several steps may be required). Give reagents and conditions.

a. 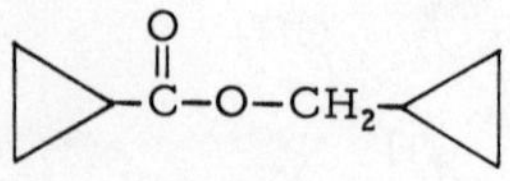 $\triangleright\!\!-\overset{O}{\overset{\|}{C}}-O-CH_2\!\!-\!\!\triangleleft$ from $\triangleright\!\!-\overset{O}{\overset{\|}{C}}-CH_3$

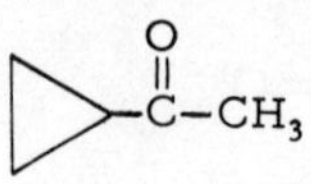

b. $CH_2{=}CHCOCH_3$ from CH_3COCH_3

c. $(CH_3)_3CCO_2H$ from $(CH_3)_2C(OH)C(CH_3)_2OH$

d. $(CH_3)_3CCOC(CH_3)_3$ from $CH_3CH_2COCH_2CH_3$

    e. $CH_3CH_2CH(OH)CN$ from CH_3CHO

    f. $(CH_3)_2CHCH_2CH(CH_3)_2$ from CH_3COCH_3

    g. $CH_3CH_2\overset{\overset{\displaystyle CH_3}{|}}{C}HCHO$ from $CH_3CH_2CH_2CHO$

    h. $(CH_3)_3CCH_2CH_2CH_3$ from $(CH_3)_3CCOCH_3$

15-27 Give for each of the following pairs of compounds a chemical test, preferably a test-tube reaction, that will distinguish between the two compounds:

    a. $CH_3COCH_2CH_2COCH_3$ and $CH_3COCH_2COCH_3$

    b. $(CH_3CH_2CH_2CH_2)_2CO$ and $[(CH_3)_3C]_2CO$

    c. $(CH_3)_2C(OH)CH_2COCH_3$ and $(CH_3)_2CHCH(OH)COCH_3$

    d. $C_6H_5COCOC_6H_5$ and $C_6H_5COCH_2COC_6H_5$

    e. $CH_3CH{=}C{=}O$ and $CH_2{=}CH{-}CH{=}O$

    f. $ClCH_2CH_2COCH_3$ and $CH_3\overset{\overset{\displaystyle }{|}}{C}HCOCH_3$ with Cl below

15-28 How might spectroscopic methods be used to distinguish between the two isomeric compounds in the following pairs:

    a. $CH_3CH{=}CHCOCH_3$ and $CH_2{=}CHCH_2COCH_3$

    b. $CH_3CH_2\overset{\overset{\displaystyle O}{\|}}{C}OH$ and CH_3COCH_2OH

    c.   and

    d. $C_6H_5COCH_2COC_6H_5$ and $p\text{-}CH_3C_6H_4COCOC_6H_5$

    e. $CH_3CH{=}C{=}O$ and $CH_2{=}CH{-}CHO$

    f.   and $CH_3COCH_2CH_3$

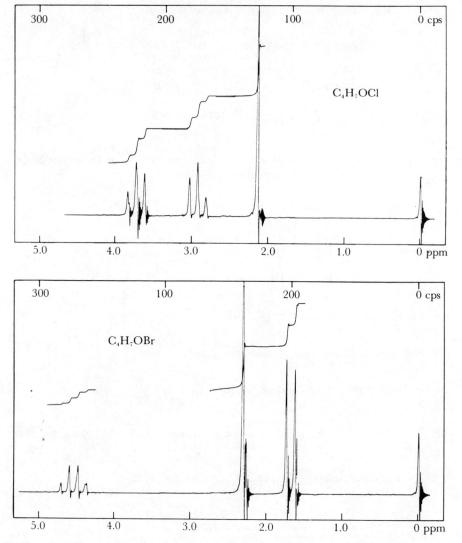

Figure 15-6   Proton n.m.r. spectra at 60 Mcps with TMS as standard.   See Exercise 15-30.

g.   CH$_3$COCHCOCH$_3$ and   CH$_3$COCH=CCH$_3$
          | |
          CH$_3$ OCH$_3$

15-29   a. Calculate the percentage of enol present in benzoylacetone from its n.m.r. spectrum, given in Figure 15-5.

b. Estimate the amount of enolization expected for each of the following compounds:

1. $C_6H_5COCH_2C_6H_5$

2. $CH_3COC(CH_3)_2COCH_3$

3.

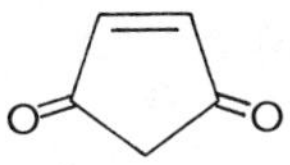

4.

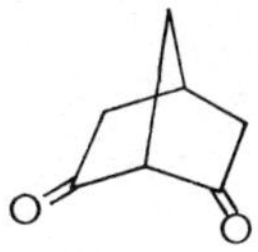

5.

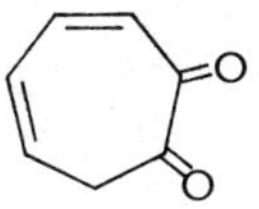

15-30 The n.m.r. spectra of two compounds of formulas C_4H_7OCl and C_4H_7OBr are shown in Figure 15-6. Assign to each compound a structure that is consistent with its spectrum. Show your reasoning. Give a concise description of the chemical properties to be expected for each compound.

Carboxylic Acids
and Derivatives

W_e *shall be concerned in this chapter with the chemistry of the carboxylic acids,* RCO_2H, *and some of their functional derivatives of the type RCOX.*

Although the carboxyl function $-C\overset{\displaystyle O}{\underset{\displaystyle O-H}{\diagup}}$ *is a combination of a hydroxyl and a carbonyl group, the combination is such a close one that neither group behaves independently of the other. Therefore, the properties of the hydroxyl and carbonyl groups of carboxylic acids are not expected to be typical of those of alcohols, aldehydes, or ketones. However, there is sufficient similarity and analogous behavior so that we shall be able to make a number of helpful comparisons of the behavior of the hydroxyl groups of alcohols and acids, and of the carbonyl groups of aldehydes, ketones, and acids.*

Carboxylic Acids and Derivatives

CHAPTER 16

The carboxyl group $-C\overset{\displaystyle O}{\underset{\displaystyle OH}{\diagup}}$ of carboxylic acids produces an acid reaction in water through ionization of the carboxyl hydrogen.

$$RCO_2H + H_2O \rightleftharpoons RCO_2^{\ominus} + H_3O^{\oplus}$$

Generally, carboxylic acids are weak acids so that ionization is far from complete, and the corresponding carboxylate salts are considerably hydrolyzed in aqueous solution.

$$CH_3CO_2H + Na^{\oplus}OH^{\ominus} \rightleftharpoons CH_3CO_2^{\ominus}Na^{\oplus} + H_2O$$

acetic acid   sodium acetate

Some representative carboxylic acids with different R groups are shown in Figure 16-1. The nomenclature of carboxylic acids was discussed previously (p. 221).

Carboxylic acids with R as an alkyl or alkenyl group are also called **fatty acids,**

$$CH_3CH_2CO_2H \qquad\qquad CH_2{=}CHCO_2H \qquad\qquad CH{\equiv}CCO_2H$$

propionic acid   acrylic acid   propiolic acid

(propanoic)   (propenoic)   (propynoic)

$$CH_3CH_2CH_2CH_2CH_2CO_2H \qquad \underset{H_2C}{\overset{H_2C}{\diagup}}CHCO_2H \qquad \text{⟨benzene⟩}{-}CO_2H$$

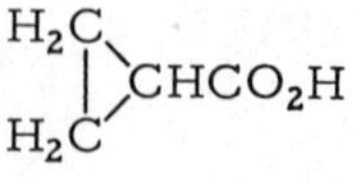

caproic acid   cyclopropane-   benzoic acid

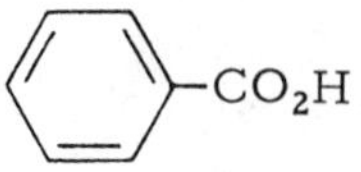

(hexanoic)   carboxylic acid

$$BrCH_2CO_2H \qquad\qquad \underset{\underset{OH}{|}}{CH_3CHCO_2H} \qquad\qquad NCCH_2CO_2H$$

bromoacetic acid   lactic acid   cyanoacetic acid

                              (α-hydroxypropionic)

$$\underset{\underset{NH_2}{|}}{CH_3CHCO_2H} \qquad\qquad CH_3\overset{O}{\overset{\|}{C}}CH_2CO_2H \qquad\qquad \underset{\underset{CH_2CO_2H}{|}}{CH_2CO_2H}$$

alanine   acetoacetic acid   succinic acid

(α-aminopropionic)   (butanedioic)

Figure 16-1   Representative carboxylic acids.

but this term applies more specifically to the naturally occurring straight-chain, saturated and unsaturated aliphatic acids, which, in the form of esters, are constitutents of the fats, waxes, and oils of plants and animals. The most abundant of the fatty acids are palmitic, stearic, oleic, and linoleic acids; they occur as glycerides, which are esters of the trihydric alcohol, glycerol.

$$CH_3(CH_2)_{14}CO_2H \qquad\qquad\qquad \text{palmitic acid}$$
$$CH_3(CH_2)_{16}CO_2H \qquad\qquad\qquad \text{stearic acid}$$
$$CH_3(CH_2)_7CH{=}CH(CH_2)_7CO_2H \qquad\qquad\qquad \text{oleic acid } (cis)$$
$$CH_3(CH_2)_4CH{=}CHCH_2CH{=}CH(CH_2)_7CO_2H \qquad\qquad \text{linoleic acid}$$

Alkaline hydrolysis of fats affords salts of the fatty acids, those of the alkali metals being useful as soaps.

$$
\begin{matrix}
\overset{\displaystyle O}{\underset{\displaystyle \|}{}} \\
CH_2O\overset{\|}{C}R \\
| \\
CHO\overset{\|}{C}R \\
| \\
CH_2O\overset{\|}{C}R
\end{matrix}
\quad \xrightarrow{\text{NaOH}} \quad
\begin{matrix}
CH_2OH \\
| \\
CHOH \\
| \\
CH_2OH
\end{matrix}
+ \; 3\,RCO_2{}^{\ominus}\,Na^{\oplus}
\quad \xrightarrow{\;H^{\oplus}\;} \quad
3\,RCO_2H
$$

     fat   glycerol   soap   fatty acid

(as a glyceride)

PHYSICAL PROPERTIES OF CARBOXYLIC ACIDS

16-1 HYDROGEN BONDING

The physical properties of carboxylic acids reflect a considerable degree of association through hydrogen bonding. We have encountered such bonding previously in the case of alcohols (pp. 280–284); however, acids form stronger hydrogen bonds than alcohols because their O—H bonds are more strongly polarized as $\overset{\delta\ominus}{\text{—O}}\overset{\delta\oplus}{\text{—H}}$. In addition, carboxylic acids have the possibility of forming hydrogen bonds to the rather negative oxygen of the carbonyl dipole rather than just to the oxygen of another hydroxyl group. Indeed, carboxylic acids in the solid and liquid states mostly exist as cyclic dimers.

$$
\begin{matrix}
& & \delta\ominus & & \\
& \overset{\delta\oplus}{O} \!\! \diagup\!\!\! \overset{\displaystyle O}{} \cdots H\!\!-\!\!O & & \\
R\!\!-\!\!C & & & C\!\!-\!\!R & \\
& O\!\!-\!\!H \cdots O & & \\
& & \delta\ominus & &
\end{matrix}
$$

These dimeric structures persist to some extent even in the vapor state and in dilute solution in hydrocarbon solvents.

The physical properties of some representative carboxylic acids are listed in Table 16-1. The notably high melting points and boiling points of acids relative to alcohols and chlorides can be attributed to the strength and degree of hydrogen bonding. These differences in volatility are shown more strikingly by Figure 16-2, which is a plot of boiling point versus n for the homologous series $CH_3(CH_2)_{n-2}X$, in which X is —CO_2H, —CH_2OH, and —CH_2Cl.

Hydrogen bonding is also responsible for the high water solubility of the simple aliphatic acids, formic, acetic, propionic, and butyric; water molecules can solvate the carbonyl group through hydrogen bonds. Nonetheless, as the hydrocarbon residue R increases in size (both in chain length and the degree of branching) the solubility decreases markedly.

Solvation of a carboxylic acid through hydrogen bonding

Table 16-1   Physical Properties of Representative Carboxylic Acids

Acid	Structure	Solubility g/100 g H_2O	m.p. °C	b.p. °C	K_a (H_2O) at 25°
formic	HCO_2H	∞	8.4	100.7	1.77×10^{-4}
acetic	CH_3CO_2H	∞	16.6	118.1	1.75×10^{-5}
propionic	$CH_3CH_2CO_2H$	∞	−22	141.1	1.3×10^{-5}
n-butyric	$CH_3CH_2CH_2CO_2H$	∞	−8	163.5	1.5×10^{-5}
isobutyric	$(CH_3)_2CHCO_2H$	20^{20}	−47	154.5	1.4×10^{-5}
n-valeric	$CH_3(CH_2)_3CO_2H$	3.3^{16}	−34.5	187	1.6×10^{-5}
palmitic	$CH_3(CH_2)_{14}CO_2H$	insol.	64	390	
stearic	$CH_3(CH_2)_{16}CO_2H$	0.034^{25}	69.4	360 d	
chloroacetic	$ClCH_2CO_2H$	sol.	63	189	1.4×10^{-3}
dichloroacetic	Cl_2CHCO_2H	8.63	5–6	194	5×10^{-2}
trichloroacetic	Cl_3CCO_2H	120^{25}	58	195.5	1×10^{-1}
trifluoroacetic	F_3CCO_2H	∞	−15	72.4	strong[a]
α-chlorobutyric (D,L)	$CH_3CH_2CHClCO_2H$	sol. hot		101^{15mm}	1.4×10^{-3}
β-chlorobutyric (D,L)	$CH_3CHClCH_2CO_2H$		44	116^{22mm}	8.9×10^{-5}
γ-chlorobutyric	$ClCH_2CH_2CH_2CO_2H$		16	196^{22mm}	3.0×10^{-5}
δ-chloro-*n*-valeric	$ClCH_2(CH_2)_3CO_2H$		18	130^{11mm}	2×10^{-5}
methoxyacetic	$CH_3OCH_2CO_2H$	sol.		203	3.3×10^{-4}
cyanoacetic	$N{\equiv}CCH_2CO_2H$	sol.	66	108^{15mm}	4×10^{-3}
vinylacetic	$CH_2{=}CHCH_2CO_2H$	sol.	−39	163	3.8×10^{-5}
benzoic	$C_6H_5CO_2H$	0.27^{18}	122	249	6.5×10^{-5}
phenylacetic	$C_6H_5CH_2CO_2H$	1.66^{20}	76.7	265	5.6×10^{-5}

[a] The term "strong" acid implies complete dissociation in aqueous solution.

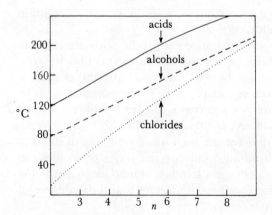

Figure 16-2

Boiling points of acids, $CH_3(CH_2)_{n-2}CO_2H$, alcohols, $CH_3(CH_2)_{n-2}CH_2OH$, and chlorides, $CH_3(CH_2)_{n-2}CH_2Cl$.

Table 16-2   Ultraviolet Absorption Properties of Carboxylic
Acids, Aldehydes, and Ketones

Compound	λ_{max}, mμ	ε_{max}	Solvent
acetic acid	204	40	water
acetic acid	197	60	hexane
acetaldehyde	293	12	hexane
acetone	270	16	alcohol
butyric acid	207	74	water
butyraldehyde	290	18	hexane

16-2   SPECTRA OF CARBOXYLIC ACIDS

The infrared spectra of carboxylic acids provide clear evidence of hydrogen bonding. This is illustrated in Figure 16-3, which shows the spectrum of acetic acid in carbon tetrachloride solution, together with those of ethanol and acetaldehyde for comparison. The spectrum of ethanol has two absorption bands, characteristic of the OH bond; one is a sharp band at 3640 cm^{-1}, corresponding to free or unassociated hydroxyl groups, and the other is a broad band centered on 3350 cm^{-1} due to hydrogen-bonded groups. The spectrum of acetic acid shows no absorption due to free hydroxyl groups but, like that of ethanol, has a very broad intense absorption ascribed to associated OH groups. However, the frequency of absorption, 3000 cm^{-1}, is shifted appreciably from that of ethanol and reflects a stronger type of hydrogen bonding than in ethanol. The absorption due to the carbonyl group of acetic acid (1740 cm^{-1}) is broad but not shifted significantly from the carbonyl absorption in acetaldehyde.

The carboxyl function does absorb ultraviolet radiation, but the wavelengths at which this occurs are appreciably shorter than for carbonyl compounds like aldehydes and ketones, and, in fact, are out of the range of most commercial ultraviolet spectrometers. Some idea of how the hydroxyl substituent modifies the absorption properties of the carbonyl group in carboxylic acids can be seen from Table 16-2 in which are listed the wavelengths of maximum light absorption (λ_{max}) and the extinction coefficients at maximum absorption (ϵ_{max}) of several carboxylic acids, aldehydes, and ketones.

In the nuclear magnetic resonance spectra of carboxylic acids, the carboxyl proton is found to absorb at unusually low magnetic fields. The chemical shift of carboxylic acid protons comes about 5.5 ppm toward lower magnetic fields than that of the hydroxyl proton of alcohols. This behavior parallels that of the enol hydrogens of 1,3-dicarbonyl compounds (pp. 353 and 385) and is probably similarly related to hydrogen-bond formation.

EXERCISE 16-1   Explain why the chemical shift of the acidic proton of a carboxylic acid, dissolved in a nonpolar solvent like carbon tetrachloride, varies less with concentration than that of the OH proton of an alcohol under the same conditions (see also p. 284).

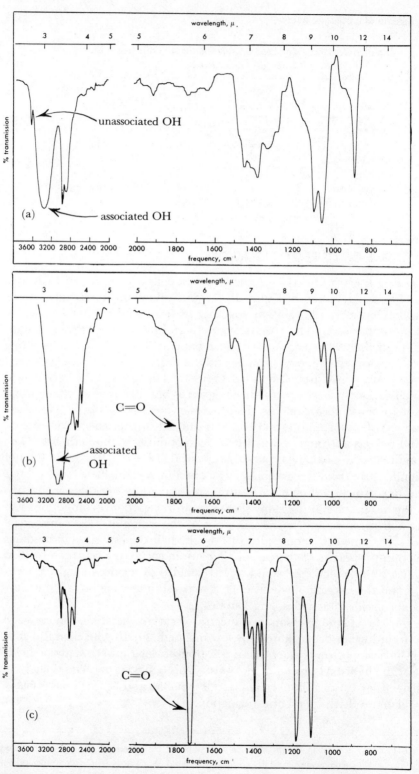

Figure 16-3 Infrared spectra of ethanol (a), acetic acid (b), and acetaldehyde (c); 10 per cent in carbon tetrachloride.

CHEMICAL PROPERTIES OF CARBOXYLIC ACIDS

Most of the reactions of carboxylic acids can be classified as belonging to one of four principal types.

a.

Reactions involving cleavage of the O—H bond — e.g., acid dissociation, solvolytic reactions.

b.

Reactions at the carbonyl carbon — most of which involve attack by a nucleophile :N on the carbonyl carbon with subsequent cleavage of a C—O bond, e.g., esterification, acid-chloride formation, and reduction by hydrides.

c.

Decarboxylation — e.g., Kolbe electrolysis.

d.

Reactions at the **α carbon** — e.g., the Hell-Volhard-Zelinsky reaction and reactions of α-substituted carboxylic acids.

In the ensuing discussion, the emphasis will be on showing how we can correlate the chemistry of carboxylic acids with the principles that have been outlined in earlier chapters.

16-3 DISSOCIATION OF CARBOXYLIC ACIDS

A. The Resonance Effect

Compared with mineral acids such as hydrochloric, perchloric, nitric, and sulfuric acids, the fatty acids, $CH_3(CH_2)_{n-2}CO_2H$, are weak. The extent of dissociation in aqueous solution is relatively small, the acidity constants, K_A, being approximately 10^{-5} (see Table 16-1).

$$RCO_2H + H_2O \rightleftharpoons RCO_2^{\ominus} + H_3O^{\oplus}$$

$$K_A = \frac{[RCO_2^{\ominus}][H_3O^{\oplus}]}{[RCO_2H]} \sim 10^{-5} \quad \text{for } R = CH_3(CH_2)_{\overline{n}}$$

Even though weak acids, the fatty acids are, however, many orders of magnitude stronger than the corresponding alcohols, $CH_3(CH_2)_{n-2}CH_2OH$. Thus, the K_A of acetic acid, CH_3CO_2H, is 10^{10} times larger than that of ethanol, CH_3CH_2OH.

The acidity of the carboxyl group stems, at least in part, from the polar nature of the carbonyl group, the polarity of which can be ascribed to contributions of the structures $\diagdown C{=}\overset{..}{\underset{..}{O}} \leftrightarrow \overset{\oplus}{\diagdown} C{-}\overset{..}{\underset{..}{O}}{:}^{\ominus}$. For a carboxyl group, these structures and an additional possibility are shown by [1a], [1b] and [1c].

[1a]   [1b]   [1c]   [1]

Although the uncharged structure [1a] is of major importance, structures [1b] and [1c] make significant contributions.

The stabilization energy of the carboxylate anion is expected to be greater than that of the acid, because the anion can be regarded as a resonance hybrid of two energetically equivalent structures [2a] and [2b], while the acid is repre-

[2a]   [2b]   [2]

sented by a hybrid of nonequivalent structures [1a] through [1c]. In discussing resonance in organic compounds (Chapter 9), it was stressed that the greatest stabilization is achieved when the contributing structures are energetically equivalent. Applied to the present case, we conclude that the resonance energy of the carboxylate anion should be greater than that of the acid; we therefore expect a driving force (a gain in stability) to promote the dissociation of carboxylic acids. The fact that alcohols are far weaker acids than carboxylic acids may be attributed to the lack of stabilization of alkoxide ions comparable to that of carboxylate anions. The energy difference corresponding to the dissociation of a carboxylic acid, as by Eq. (16-1), relative to that of an alcohol actually amounts to about 10 kcal.

$$CH_3-C \overset{\overset{\delta\ominus}{O}}{\underset{\underset{\delta\oplus}{O-H}}{}} \;+\; H_2O \;\rightleftharpoons\; CH_3-C \overset{\overset{\frac{1}{2}\ominus}{O}}{\underset{\underset{\frac{1}{2}\ominus}{O}}{}} \;+\; H_3O^{\oplus} \qquad (16\text{-}1)$$

B. The Inductive Effect

There are considerable differences between the strengths of some of the acids listed in Table 16-1. Formic acid and almost all the α-substituted acetic acids of Table 16-1 are stronger than acetic acid. Trifluoroacetic acid is in fact comparable in strength to hydrochloric acid. The nature of the groups which are close neighbors of the carboxyl carbon obviously has a profound effect on the acid strength—a phenomenon which is commonly called the **inductive effect,** symbolized as $\pm I$. The inductive effect is distinguished from resonance effects of the type discussed earlier by being associated with substitution on the saturated carbon atoms of the fatty acid chain. It is taken as negative ($-I$) if the substituent is acid-enhancing, and positive ($+I$) if the substituent is acid-weakening.

The high acid strength of α-halogen-substituted acids (e.g., chloroacetic), compared with acetic acid, results from the electron-attracting power (electronegativity) of the substituent halogen relative to the carbon to which it is attached. The electron-attracting power of three such halogen atoms is of course expected to be greater than that of one halogen—hence trichloroacetic acid (K_A, 3.0×10^{-1}) is a markedly stronger acid than chloroacetic acid (K_A, 1.4×10^{-3}). The polar effect of carbon-halogen bonds can be considered to be transmitted to the carboxyl group in two apparently different ways. One way, which is often taken to be the whole of the inductive effect, has the substituent causing shifts in the average distributions of the bonding electrons down the chain of intervening atoms. This produces a succession of electron shifts along the chain,

$$Cl \leftarrow CH_2 \leftarrow C \overset{\displaystyle O}{\underset{\displaystyle O-H}{\big\|}}$$

arrows show
movement of average
position of electrons
towards chlorine

which, for an electron-attracting substituent, increases dissociation by stabilizing the carboxylate anion.

As would be expected the inductive effect falls off rapidly with increasing distance of the substituent from the carboxyl group. This is readily seen by the significant difference between the K_A values of the α-, β-, and γ-chlorobutyric acids (see Table 16-1).

Many other groups besides halogen exhibit an acid-enhancing, electron-withdrawing ($-I$) effect. Among these are nitro ($-NO_2$); methoxyl (CH_3O-); carbonyl ($\diagdown C=O$, as in aldehydes, ketones, acids, esters, and amides); cyano or nitrile ($-C\equiv N$) and trialkylammonium ($R_3\overset{\oplus}{N}-$). Alkyl groups—methyl, ethyl, isopropyl, etc.—are the only substituents listed in Table 16-1 that are acid weakening relative to hydrogen (as can be seen by comparing their K_A's with those of formic and acetic acids). We may take this to mean that alkyl groups release electrons to the carboxyl group and thus exhibit a $+I$ effect. The magnitude of the electrical effects of alkyl groups does not appear to change greatly in going from methyl to ethyl to propyl, etc. (compare the K_A values of acetic, propionic, butyric, and valeric acids). The $+I$ effects of alkyl groups have been evoked ear-

$$CH_3 \rightarrow C \overset{O}{\underset{O-H}{\Bigg\Vert}}$$

the arrows represent shifts
in the average positions of the
bonding electrons from the
methyl group toward the carboxyl group (+*I* effect)

lier to account for the orientation observed in addition of unsymmetrical reagents to alkenes (p. 146).

In addition to their acidic properties, carboxylic acids also can act as weak
bases, the carbonyl oxygen accepting a proton from a strong acid like H_2SO_4
or $HClO_4$, Eq. (16-2). Such protonation is an important step in acid-catalyzed
esterification, as discussed on pp. 289–290. A proton can also add to the hydroxyl oxygen, Eq. (16-3). The resulting conjugate acid is normally less stable
than its isomer with the proton on the carbonyl group.

$$R\text{-}\overset{O}{\underset{}{\overset{\Vert}{C}}}\text{-}OH + H_2SO_4 \rightleftharpoons R\text{-}\overset{\overset{\oplus}{O}H}{\underset{}{\overset{\Vert}{C}}}\text{-}OH + HSO_4{}^{\ominus} \qquad (16\text{-}2)$$

$$R\text{-}\overset{O}{\underset{}{\overset{\Vert}{C}}}\text{-}OH + H_2SO_4 \rightleftharpoons R\text{-}\overset{O}{\underset{}{\overset{\Vert}{C}}}\text{-}\overset{\oplus}{O}H_2 + HSO_4{}^{\ominus} \qquad (16\text{-}3)$$

EXERCISE 16-2   Explain why the equilibrium of Eq. (16-2) is more favorable than that of Eq. (16-3).

16-4 REACTIONS AT THE CARBONYL CARBON OF CARBOXYLIC ACIDS

Many important reactions of carboxylic acids involve attack on carbon of the
carbonyl group by nucleophilic species. These reactions are frequently catalyzed
by acids, since addition of a proton or formation of a hydrogen bond to the carbonyl oxygen makes the carbonyl carbon more strongly electropositive and
hence more vulnerable to nucleophilic attack. The following equations illustrate
an acid-catalyzed reaction involving a negatively charged nucleophile (:N$^{\ominus}$):

$$R\text{-}\overset{O}{\overset{\Vert}{C}}\text{-}OH + H^{\oplus} \rightleftharpoons R\text{-}\overset{\oplus OH}{\overset{\Vert}{C}}\text{-}OH \quad :N^{\ominus} \rightleftharpoons R\text{-}\overset{OH}{\underset{N}{\overset{\vert}{C}}}\text{-}OH$$

Subsequent cleavage of a C—O bond and loss of a proton yields a displacement
product.

$$R\text{-}\overset{OH}{\underset{N}{\overset{\vert}{C}}}\text{-}OH \xrightarrow{-OH^{\ominus}} R\text{-}\overset{\oplus OH}{\overset{\Vert}{C}}\text{-}N \xrightarrow{-H^{\oplus}} R\text{-}\overset{O}{\overset{\Vert}{C}}\text{-}N$$

An important example of this type of reaction is the formation of esters as discussed on pp. 288–291. Similar addition-elimination mechanisms occur in many reactions at the carbonyl groups of acid derivatives. A less obvious example of addition to carboxyl groups involves hydride ion (H:$^{\ominus}$) and takes place in lithium aluminum hydride reduction of carboxylic acids (Sec. 16-4B).

EXERCISE 16-3   Use bond energies and the data of Table 9-3 (p. 194) to calculate ΔH for the addition of water to acetic acid to give 1,1,1-trihydroxyethane and compare it with ΔH for hydration of acetaldehyde in the vapor phase. Would you expect the rate, the equilibrium constant, or both for hydration of acetic acid in water solution to be increased in the presence of a strong acid such as sulfuric acid? Explain.

The usefulness of direct ester formation from alcohols and acids is of course limited to those alcohols or acids that do not undergo extensive side reactions in the presence of strong acids. Furthermore, if the alcohol is particularly bulky, the reaction will usually not proceed satisfactorily, since the intermediate stage (p. 290) is rendered unstable by crowding of the substituent groups.

A. Acid-Chloride Formation

Carboxylic acids react with phosphorus trichloride, phosphorus pentachloride, or thionyl chloride with replacement of OH by Cl to form acid (acyl) chlorides, RCOCl.

$$(CH_3)_2CHCH_2C \overset{O}{\underset{OH}{\big\|}} \quad \xrightarrow{SOCl_2} \quad (CH_3)_2CHCH_2C \overset{O}{\underset{Cl}{\big\|}} \quad + \; SO_2 \; + \; HCl$$

isovaleric acid   isovaleryl chloride

Formyl chloride, HCOCl, is unstable and decomposes rapidly to carbon monoxide and hydrogen chloride at ordinary temperatures.

B. Reduction of Carboxylic Acids

In general, carboxylic acids are difficult to reduce either by catalytic hydrogenation or by sodium and alcohol—nonetheless, reduction to primary alcohols proceeds smoothly with lithium aluminum hydride, LiAlH$_4$.

$$RCO_2H \quad \xrightarrow{LiAlH_4} \quad \xrightarrow{H^{\oplus}, \, H_2O} \quad RCH_2OH$$

$$CH_2{=}CHCH_2CO_2H \quad \xrightarrow{LiAlH_4} \quad \xrightarrow{H^{\oplus}, \, H_2O} \quad CH_2{=}CHCH_2CH_2OH$$

3–butenoic acid   3–butenol

(vinylacetic acid)   (allylcarbinol)

The first step in lithium aluminum hydride reduction of carboxylic acids is formation of a complex aluminum salt of the acid and liberation of 1 mole of hydrogen.

$$R-\overset{\displaystyle O}{\underset{\displaystyle OH}{C}} \ + \ LiAlH_4 \ \longrightarrow \ R-\overset{\displaystyle O}{\underset{\displaystyle OAlH_3}{C}}{}^{\ominus} \ \overset{\oplus}{Li} \ + \ H_2$$

Reduction then proceeds by successive transfers of hydride ion, $H{:}^{\ominus}$, from aluminum to carbon, as shown schematically in Eq. (16-4). The first such transfer reduces the acid salt to the oxidation level of the aldehyde; reduction does not stop at this point, however, but goes on rapidly to the alcohol stage.

$$RCOO^{\ominus} \ \xrightarrow{\ H{:}^{\ominus}\ } \ RCHO \ \xrightarrow{\ H{:}^{\ominus}\ } \ RCH_2OH \qquad (16\text{-}4)$$

salt   aldehyde   alcohol

Insufficient information is available to permit very specific structures to be written for the intermediates in the lithium aluminum hydride reduction of carboxylic acids. However, the product is a complex aluminum alkoxide, from which the alcohol is freed by hydrolysis.

$$4\,RCO_2H \ + \ 3\,LiAlH_4 \ \longrightarrow \ [(RCH_2O)_4Al]\,Li \ + \ 4\,H_2 \ + \ 2\,LiAlO_2$$

$$\downarrow H_2O, \ HCl$$

$$4\,RCH_2OH \ + \ AlCl_3 \ + \ LiCl$$

16-5 DECARBOXYLATION OF CARBOXYLIC ACIDS

The ease of loss of carbon dioxide from the carboxyl group varies greatly with the nature of the acid. Some acids require to be heated as their sodium salts in the presence of soda lime (in general, however, this is not a good preparative procedure).

$$CH_3{\dashv}\overset{\displaystyle O}{\underset{\displaystyle O}{C}}{}^{\ominus} \ Na^{\oplus} \ \xrightarrow{\ NaOH, \ CaO\ } \ CH_4 \ + \ CO_2$$

sodium acetate

Other acids lose carbon dioxide by simply heating.

$$\underset{\text{malonic acid}}{\overset{\displaystyle \overset{CO_2H}{\underset{\displaystyle CO_2H}{CH_2}}}{}} \quad \xrightarrow{\;140-160°\;} \quad \underset{\text{acetic acid}}{CH_3CO_2H} \;+\; CO_2$$

Thermal decarboxylation occurs most readily when the alpha carbon carries a strongly electron-attracting group (i.e., $-I$ substituent), as in the following examples:

O_2N-CH_2-COOH	nitroacetic acid	
$HOOC-CH_2-COOH$	malonic acid	decarboxylation occurs
$NC-CH_2-COOH$	cyanoacetic acid	readily at temperatures of 100–150°
CH_3CO-CH_2-COOH	acetoacetic acid	
CCl_3CO_2H	trichloracetic acid	
$CH_2=CH-CH_2-COOH$	vinylacetic acid	does not decarboxylate readily below 200°

The mechanisms of thermal decarboxylation are probably not the same in all cases, but decarboxylation of β,γ-unsaturated acids may be a cyclic process of elimination in which hydrogen bonding plays an important role.

$$\underset{\text{malonic acid}}{\overset{\displaystyle H}{\underset{\displaystyle CH_2}{HO-C \quad C=O}}} \quad \longrightarrow \quad \underset{\substack{\text{enol form of} \\ \text{acetic acid}}}{HO-C\overset{OH}{\underset{CH_2}{}}} \;+\; \underset{}{\overset{O}{\underset{O}{C}}} \quad \longrightarrow \quad \underset{\text{acetic acid}}{CH_3COOH \;+\; CO_2}$$

EXERCISE 16-4   Predict the product of decarboxylation of 2-methyl-3-butenoic acid.

EXERCISE 16-5   Explain why decarboxylation of α,α-dimethylacetoacetic acid, $CH_3COC(CH_3)_2CO_2H$, in the presence of bromine gives α-bromoisopropyl methyl ketone, $CH_3COC(CH_3)_2Br$.

Stepwise decarboxylation also occurs, particularly in reactions in which the carboxylate radical ($RCO_2\cdot$) is formed. This radical can degrade further to a hydrocarbon radical $R\cdot$ and CO_2. The over-all decarboxylation product is determined by what $R\cdot$ reacts with: If a good hydrogen atom donor is present, RH is formed; if a halogen donor like Br_2 is present, RBr is formed.

$$RCO_2 \cdot \quad\quad \longrightarrow \quad\quad R\cdot \; + \; CO_2$$

$$R\cdot \; + \; R'H \quad\quad \longrightarrow \quad\quad RH \; + \; R'\cdot$$

$$R\cdot \; + \; Br_2 \quad\quad \longrightarrow \quad\quad RBr \; + \; Br\cdot$$

<hr>

EXERCISE 16-6 What information would you need to calculate ΔH for $CH_3CO_2 \cdot \rightarrow CO_2 +$ $\cdot CH_3$?

<hr>

Carboxylate radicals can be generated in several ways. One is the thermal decomposition of diacyl peroxides, which are compounds with a rather weak O—O bond.

$$R-\overset{\overset{\displaystyle O}{\|}}{C}-O \;\vdots\; O-\overset{\overset{\displaystyle O}{\|}}{C}-R \quad\quad \longrightarrow \quad\quad 2\,R-\overset{\overset{\displaystyle O}{\|}}{C}-O\,\cdot$$

Another method involves electrolysis of sodium or potassium carboxylate solutions, known as **Kolbe electrolysis,** in which carboxylate radicals are formed by transfer of an electron from the carboxylate ion to the anode. Decarboxylation may occur simultaneously with, or subsequent to, the formation of carboxylate radicals, leading to hydrocarbon radicals, which subsequently dimerize.

$$RCO_2^{\ominus} \quad \longrightarrow \quad RCO_2\cdot \; + \; e \quad\quad \text{anode reaction}$$

$$K^{\oplus} \; + \; e \; + \; H_2O \quad \longrightarrow \quad KOH \; + \; \tfrac{1}{2}\,H_2 \quad\quad \text{cathode reaction}$$

$$RCO_2\cdot \quad \longrightarrow \quad R\cdot \; + \; CO_2$$

$$R\cdot \; + \; R\cdot \quad \longrightarrow \quad RR$$

<hr>

EXERCISE 16-7 Why does Kolbe electrolysis not give RH by the reactions $RCO_2\cdot \xrightarrow{-CO_2}$ $R\cdot \xrightarrow{H_2O} RH$?

EXERCISE 16-8 At high current densities, electrolysis of salts of carboxylic acids in hydroxylic solvents produce (at the anode) alcohols and esters of the type ROH and RCO_2R. Explain.

<hr>

16-6 REACTIONS AT THE ALPHA CARBONS OF CARBOXYLIC ACIDS

A. The Hell-Volhard-Zelinsky Reaction

Bromine reacts smoothly with carboxylic acids in the presence of small quantities of phosphorus to form *alpha*-bromocarboxylic acids.

$$CH_3COOH + Br_2 \xrightarrow{P} CH_2BrCOOH + HBr$$

α-bromoacetic acid

The reaction is slow in the absence of phosphorus, whose function appears to be to form phosphorus tribromide which reacts with the acid to give the acid bromide.

$$2\,P + 3\,Br_2 \rightarrow 2\,PBr_3$$

$$CH_3CO_2H + PBr_3 \rightarrow CH_3COBr + POBr + HBr \quad .$$

acetyl bromide

This speeds up the reaction because acid-catalyzed enolization of the acid bromide occurs much more readily than enolization of the parent acid. Bromine probably reacts with the enol of the acid bromide in the same way as it reacts with the enols of ketones (p. 338).

The Hell-Volhard-Zelinsky reaction results exclusively in alpha substitution and is therefore limited to carboxylic acids with α hydrogens. Chlorine with a trace of phosphorus reacts similarly but with less over-all specificity, since con-current free-radical chlorination can occur at all positions along the chain (as in hydrocarbon halogenation; see pp. 75–76).

$$CH_3CH_2CO_2H \begin{cases} \xrightarrow{Cl_2,\ P} & \underset{\underset{Cl}{|}}{CH_3CHCO_2H} \\[2em] \xrightarrow{Cl_2,\ h\nu} & \underset{\underset{Cl}{|}}{CH_3CHCO_2H} + ClCH_2CH_2CO_2H \end{cases}$$

α-chloropropionic   β-chloropropionic
acid   acid

EXERCISE 16-9   Use appropriate stabilization energies to show why the enol form of acetyl bromide is likely to be more stable relative to acetyl bromide than 1,1-dihydroxy-ethylene is relative to acetic acid.

B. Substitution Reactions of α-Halo Acids

The halogen of an α-halo acid is readily replaced by nucleophilic reagents such as $CN^{\ominus}$, $OH^{\ominus}$, $I^{\ominus}$, and NH_3. Thus, a variety of α-substituted carboxylic acids may be prepared by reactions that are analogous to S_N2 substitutions of alkyl halides.

$$CH_3\underset{\underset{I}{|}}{C}HCO_2H$$

α-iodopropionic acid

$$CH_3\underset{\underset{OH}{|}}{C}HCO_2{}^{\ominus} \xrightarrow{H^{\oplus}} CH_3\underset{\underset{OH}{|}}{C}HCO_2H$$

lactic acid

$$I^{\ominus} \qquad OH^{\ominus}$$

$$CH_3\underset{\underset{Br}{|}}{C}HCO_2H \xrightarrow[\text{excess}]{NH_3} CH_3\underset{\underset{NH_2}{|}}{C}HCO_2NH_4 \xrightarrow{H^{\oplus}} CH_3\underset{\underset{NH_2}{|}}{C}HCO_2H$$

α-bromopropionic acid

alanine

$$CN^{\ominus}$$

$$CH_3\underset{\underset{CN}{|}}{C}HCO_2H \xrightarrow{H_2O} CH_3\underset{\underset{CO_2H}{|}}{C}HCO_2H$$

α-cyanopropionic acid

methylmalonic acid

The reason for facile substitution reactions of halogen in the α position is at least partly related to the electron-attracting characteristics of the neighboring carboxyl function, which makes the α carbon slightly positive and more hospitable to the approach of an electron-sharing reagent.

Also, we expect enhanced S_N2 reactivity of halogen located next to a carbonyl group through analogy with allyl halides (cf. pp. 246–247).

The S_N1 reactivity of α-halo acids is particularly low. This is reasonable because formation of a carbonium ion at the α carbon should be difficult, owing to the positive character of the carbonyl carbon; and to the fact that little, if any, help could be expected through electron delocalization because the corresponding resonance structure has a positive, single-bonded oxygen.

$$\left[\begin{array}{c} \overset{|}{-}\overset{|}{C}\overset{\oplus}{-}\overset{\overset{\displaystyle O}{\displaystyle \parallel}}{C}\overset{\displaystyle \diagdown}{OH} \end{array} \longleftrightarrow \begin{array}{c} \overset{|}{-}C=\overset{\overset{\displaystyle \overset{\oplus}{O}}{\displaystyle \diagup}}{C}\overset{\displaystyle \diagdown}{OH} \end{array} \right]$$

Similar considerations apply to the S_N1 and S_N2 reactions of α haloaldehydes and ketones.

FUNCTIONAL DERIVATIVES OF CARBOXYLIC ACIDS

A functional derivative of a carboxylic acid is a substance formed by replacement of the hydroxyl group of the acid by some other group, X, that can be hydrolyzed back to the parent acid according to Eq. (16-5). By this definition, an amide $RCONH_2$, but not a ketone $RCOCH_3$, is a functional derivative of a

$$R-\overset{\overset{\displaystyle O}{\displaystyle \parallel}}{\underset{\displaystyle X}{C}} + H_2O \longrightarrow R-\overset{\overset{\displaystyle O}{\displaystyle \parallel}}{\underset{\displaystyle OH}{C}} + HX \qquad (16\text{-}5)$$

carboxylic acid. A number of types of acid derivatives are given in Table 16-3. The common structural feature of the compounds listed in Table 16-3 is the acyl group $R-\overset{\overset{\displaystyle O}{\displaystyle \diagup}}{C}\diagdown$. Nitriles, $RC{\equiv}N$, however, are often considered to be acid derivatives, even though the acyl group is not present as such, because hydrolysis of nitriles leads to carboxylic acids. The chemistry of nitriles will be discussed in Chapter 19.

$$CH_3C{\equiv}N \quad \xrightarrow{\quad H^{\oplus}, \ H_2O \quad} \quad CH_3COOH$$

acetonitrile   acetic acid

EXERCISE 16-10   Predict the relative volatility of acetic acid, acetic anhydride, ethyl acetate, and acetamide. Give your reasoning.

The carbonyl group plays a dominant role in the reactions of acid derivatives, just as it does for the parent acids. The two main types of reactions of acid derivatives with which we shall be concerned are the replacement of X by attack of a nucleophile $:N^{\ominus}$ at the carbonyl carbon with subsequent cleavage of the C—X bond, Eq. (16-6), and substitution at the α carbon facilitated by the carbonyl group, Eq. (16-7).

$$R-\overset{\overset{\displaystyle O}{\displaystyle \parallel}}{\underset{\displaystyle X}{C}} + :N^{\ominus} \longrightarrow R-\overset{\overset{\displaystyle \overset{\ominus}{O}}{\displaystyle |}}{\underset{\displaystyle N}{C}}{\overset{\curvearrowright}{-}}X \longrightarrow R-\overset{\overset{\displaystyle O}{\displaystyle \parallel}}{\underset{\displaystyle N}{C}} + :X^{\ominus} \qquad (16\text{-}6)$$

Table 16-3 Functional Derivatives of Carboxylic Acids

Derivative	Structure	Example Structure	Example Name
esters	R-C(=O)-OR'	CH₃-C(=O)-OC₂H₅	ethyl acetate
acid halides (acyl halides)	R-C(=O)-X, X=F, Cl, Br, I	C₆H₅-C(=O)-Br	benzoyl bromide
anhydrides	R-C(=O)-O-C(=O)-R	CH₃-C(=O)-O-C(=O)-CH₃	acetic anhydride
amides (primary)	R-C(=O)-NH₂	C₆H₅-C(=O)-NH₂	benzamide
amides (secondary and tertiary)	RCNHR' RCNR'R''	CH₃-C(=O)-NHCH₃; H-C(=O)-N(CH₃)₂	N-methyl-acetamide; N,N-dimethyl-formamide

Derivative	Structure	Example Structure	Example Name
imides	R-C(=O)-NH-C(=O)-R	succinimide ring (CH₂-CH₂ bridging two C=O with NH)	succinimide
acyl azides	R-C(=O)-N₃	CH₃-C(=O)-N₃	acetyl azide
hydrazides	R-C(=O)-NHNH₂	C₂H₅-C(=O)-NHNH₂	propiono-hydrazide
hydroxamic acids	R-C(=O)-NHOH	ClCH₂-C(=O)-NHOH	chloroacetyl-hydroxamic acid
lactones (cyclic esters)	cyclic (CH₂)ₙ ... O most stable with n = 3,4	γ-butyrolactone ring	γ-butyrolactone
lactams (cyclic amides)	cyclic (CH₂)ₙ ... NH most stable with n = 3,4	δ-caprolactam ring	δ-caprolactam

$$RCH_2-\overset{\overset{\displaystyle O}{\|}}{\underset{\underset{\displaystyle X}{|}}{C}} + YZ \longrightarrow RCH-\overset{\overset{\displaystyle O}{\|}}{\underset{\underset{\displaystyle X}{|}}{C}} + HZ \qquad (16\text{-}7)$$

16-7 REACTIONS AT THE CARBONYL CARBON

Displacement Reactions of Acid Derivatives

The more important displacement reactions include:

a. Hydrolysis of acid derivatives to the parent acids—usually acid- and base-catalyzed. Acid chlorides usually hydrolyze rapidly, though, without the agency of an acid or basic catalyst.

$$R-\overset{\overset{\displaystyle O}{\|}}{\underset{\underset{\displaystyle X}{\backslash}}{C}} + H_2O \xrightarrow{\;\;H^{\oplus}\; or\; OH^{\ominus}\;} R-\overset{\overset{\displaystyle O}{\|}}{\underset{\underset{\displaystyle OH}{\backslash}}{C}} + HX$$

$$X = -OR, \;\; halogen, \;\; -NH_2 \;\; and \;\; R-\overset{\overset{\displaystyle O}{\|}}{\underset{\underset{\displaystyle O-}{\backslash}}{C}}$$

b. Ester interchange—acid or base catalysts are usually required.

$$CH_3-\overset{\overset{\displaystyle O}{\|}}{\underset{\underset{\displaystyle OCH_3}{\backslash}}{C}} + CH_3CH_2OH \underset{\longleftarrow}{\overset{\;\;H^{\oplus}\; or\; OR^{\ominus}\;}{\rightleftharpoons}} CH_3-\overset{\overset{\displaystyle O}{\|}}{\underset{\underset{\displaystyle OCH_2CH_3}{\backslash}}{C}} + CH_3OH$$

methyl acetate   ethanol   ethyl acetate   methanol

c. Formation of esters from acid chlorides and anhydrides.

$$R-\overset{\overset{\displaystyle O}{\|}}{\underset{\underset{\displaystyle Cl}{\backslash}}{C}} + R'OH \longrightarrow R-\overset{\overset{\displaystyle O}{\|}}{\underset{\underset{\displaystyle OR'}{\backslash}}{C}} + HCl$$

$$\begin{matrix} R-\overset{\overset{\displaystyle O}{\|}}{C} \\ \quad\;\;\backslash \\ \qquad O \\ \quad\;\;/ \\ R-\underset{\underset{\displaystyle O}{\|}}{C} \end{matrix} + R'OH \longrightarrow R-\overset{\overset{\displaystyle O}{\|}}{\underset{\underset{\displaystyle OR'}{\backslash}}{C}} + R-\overset{\overset{\displaystyle O}{\|}}{\underset{\underset{\displaystyle OH}{\backslash}}{C}}$$

d. Formation of amides from esters, acid chlorides, and anhydrides.

$$
\begin{array}{ccc}
\underset{\text{OR}'}{\overset{\displaystyle\overset{O}{\|}}{\text{R—C}}} & \left.\right\}\quad\xrightarrow{\;\text{NH}_3\;}\quad\left.\right\{ & \underset{\text{NH}_2}{\overset{\displaystyle\overset{O}{\|}}{\text{R—C}}}\ +\ \text{R}'\text{OH}
\end{array}
$$

(scheme: esters, acid chlorides, and anhydrides reacting with NH_3 to form amides)

$$
\underset{\text{Cl}}{\overset{\overset{O}{\|}}{\text{R—C}}} \longrightarrow \underset{\text{NH}_2}{\overset{\overset{O}{\|}}{\text{R—C}}}\ +\ \text{NH}_4^{\oplus}\ \text{Cl}^{\ominus}
$$

$$
\overset{\overset{O}{\|}}{\text{R—C}}\diagdown\underset{\text{R—C}\diagup}{\overset{O}{}}\diagup\underset{\|}{}{O} \longrightarrow \underset{\text{NH}_2}{\overset{\overset{O}{\|}}{\text{R—C}}}\ +\ \text{RCO}_2^{\ominus}\ \text{NH}_4^{\oplus}
$$

All of these reactions are rather closely related, and we shall illustrate the principles involved mostly by the reactions of esters, since these have been particularly well studied. Acid-catalyzed hydrolysis of esters is the reverse of acid-catalyzed esterification discussed previously (pp. 288–291). In contrast, base-induced hydrolysis (saponification) is, in effect, an irreversible reaction. The initial step is the attack of hydroxide ion at the electron-deficient carbonyl carbon; the intermediate anion [3] so formed then has the choice of losing $OH^{\ominus}$ and reverting to the original ester, or of losing $CH_3O^{\ominus}$ to form the acid. The over-all reaction is irreversible since, once the acid is formed, it is immediately

$$
\underset{\underset{\displaystyle\text{OH}^{\ominus}}{(\delta\oplus}}{\overset{\overset{\displaystyle\delta\ominus}{\overset{O}{\|}}}{\text{CH}_3\text{—C—OCH}_3}} \ \rightleftharpoons\ \left[\ \underset{\text{OH}}{\overset{\overset{\displaystyle O^{\ominus}}{\|}}{\text{CH}_3\text{—C—OCH}_3}}\ \right]
$$

$$
[3]
$$

converted to the carboxylate anion, which is not further attacked by base. As a result, the reaction goes to completion in the direction of hydrolysis.

$$
\left[\ \underset{\text{OH}}{\overset{\overset{\displaystyle O^{\ominus}}{\|}}{\text{CH}_3\text{—C—OCH}_3}}\ \right] \ \rightleftharpoons\ \overset{\overset{O}{\|}}{\text{CH}_3\text{C—OH}}\ +\ \text{CH}_3\text{O}^{\ominus}\ \longrightarrow\ \underset{O^{\ominus}}{\overset{\overset{O}{\|}}{\text{CH}_3\text{—C}}}\ +\ \text{HOCH}_3
$$

$$
[3]
$$

EXERCISE 16-11   Why is a carboxylate anion more resistant to attack by nucleophilic agents, such as $CH_3O^{\ominus}$, than the corresponding ester?

Base-catalyzed ester interchange is analogous to the saponification reaction, except that an alkoxide base is used in catalytic amounts in place of hydroxide. The equilibrium constant is much nearer to unity, however, than for saponification, because the salt of the acid is not formed.

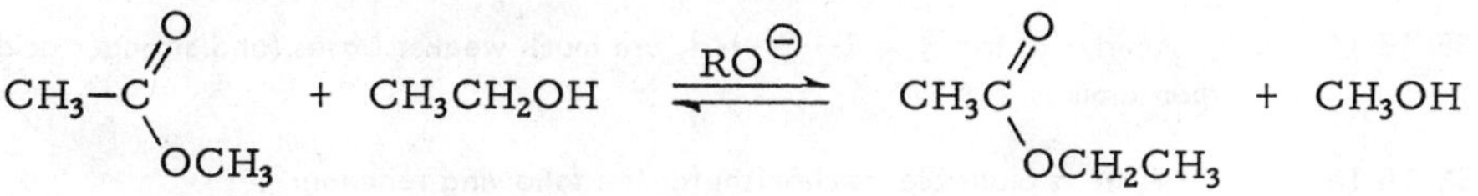

$$CH_3-C\overset{O}{\underset{OCH_3}{\diagdown}} \;+\; CH_3CH_2OH \;\underset{}{\overset{RO^{\ominus}}{\rightleftharpoons}}\; CH_3C\overset{O}{\underset{OCH_2CH_3}{\diagdown}} \;+\; CH_3OH$$

The mechanism is as shown in Eq. (16-8).

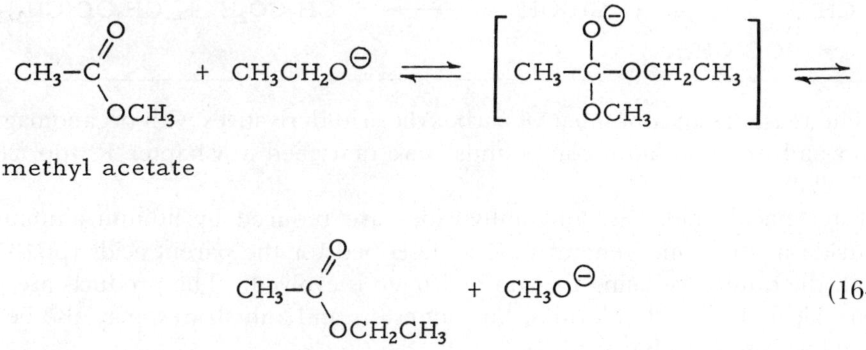

$$CH_3-C\overset{O}{\underset{OCH_3}{\diagdown}} \;+\; CH_3CH_2O^{\ominus} \;\rightleftharpoons\; \left[CH_3-\overset{O^{\ominus}}{\underset{OCH_3}{\overset{|}{C}}}-OCH_2CH_3 \right] \;\rightleftharpoons$$

methyl acetate

$$CH_3-C\overset{O}{\underset{OCH_2CH_3}{\diagdown}} \;+\; CH_3O^{\ominus} \qquad\qquad (16\text{-}8)$$

ethyl acetate

Either methoxide or ethoxide ion can be used as the catalyst since the equilibrium of Eq. (16-9) is rapidly established.

$$CH_3O^{\ominus} \;+\; CH_3CH_2OH \;\rightleftharpoons\; CH_3CH_2O^{\ominus} \;+\; CH_3OH \qquad (16\text{-}9)$$

Acid-catalyzed ester interchange is entirely analogous to acid-catalyzed esterification and hydrolysis and requires no further discussion.

EXERCISE 16-12   By analogy with ester hydrolysis, propose a mechanism for each of the following reactions:

a. $C_6H_5CO_2CH_3 \;+\; C_2H_5OH \;\overset{H^{\oplus}}{\longrightarrow}\; C_6H_5CO_2C_2H_5 \;+\; CH_3OH$

b. $CH_3COCl \;+\; CH_3CH_2OH \;\rightarrow\; CH_3CO_2CH_2CH_3 \;+\; HCl$

c. $(CH_3CO)_2O \;+\; CH_3OH \;\overset{H^{\oplus}}{\longrightarrow}\; CH_3CO_2CH_3 \;+\; CH_3COOH$

d. $CH_3CONH_2 \;+\; H_3O^{\oplus} \;\rightarrow\; CH_3CO_2H \;+\; NH_4^{\oplus}$

e. $CH_3CONH_2 \;+\; {}^{\ominus}OH \;\rightarrow\; CH_3CO_2^{\ominus} \;+\; NH_3$

f. $CH_3COCl \;+\; 2\,NH_3 \;\rightarrow\; CH_3CONH_2 \;+\; NH_4Cl$

EXERCISE 16-13   What can you conclude about the mechanism of acid-catalyzed hydrolysis of β-butyrolactone from the following equation:

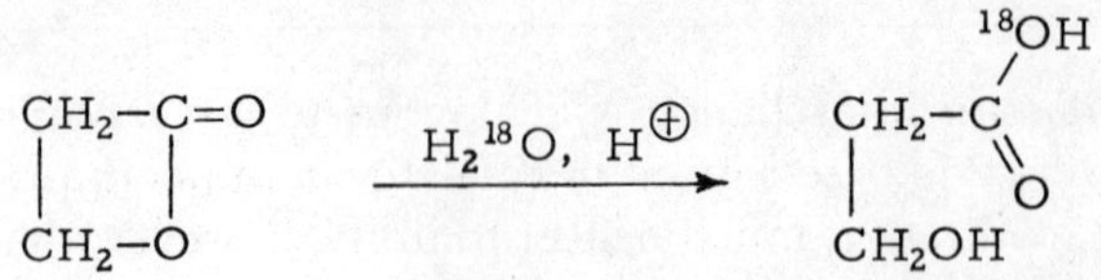

$$
\begin{array}{c}
\text{CH}_2\text{—C}{=}\text{O} \\
| \qquad | \\
\text{CH}_2\text{—O}
\end{array}
\quad \xrightarrow{\text{H}_2{}^{18}\text{O},\ \text{H}^{\oplus}} \quad
\begin{array}{c}
{}^{18}\text{OH} \\
\diagup \\
\text{CH}_2\text{—C} \\
| \qquad\ \ \diagdown \\
\text{CH}_2\text{OH}\ \ \ \text{O}
\end{array}
$$

EXERCISE 16-14   Amides of the type $R{-}\overset{\displaystyle O}{\overset{\displaystyle \|}{C}}{-}NH_2$ are much weaker bases (and stronger acids) than amines. Why?

EXERCISE 16-15   Write a plausible mechanism for the following reaction:

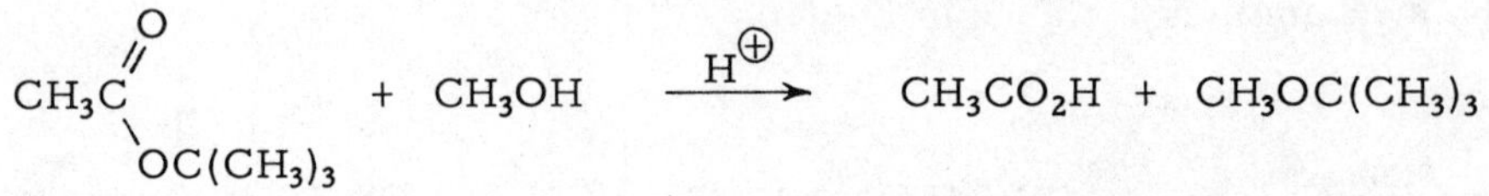

$$
\text{CH}_3\text{C}\underset{\text{OC(CH}_3)_3}{\overset{\displaystyle O}{\overset{\displaystyle \|}{\diagdown}}}
\quad +\ \text{CH}_3\text{OH} \quad \xrightarrow{\text{H}^{\oplus}} \quad
\text{CH}_3\text{CO}_2\text{H}\ +\ \text{CH}_3\text{OC(CH}_3)_3
$$

The reactions of a number of carboxylic-acid derivatives with organomagnesium and organolithium compounds were described in Chapter 12 (pp. 264–267, 270).

Esters, acid chlorides, and anhydrides are reduced by lithium aluminum hydride in the same general way as described for the parent acids (pp. 371–372), the difference being that no hydrogen is evolved. The products are primary alcohols. Acid chlorides, but not esters and anhydrides, may also be reduced with sodium borohydrides.

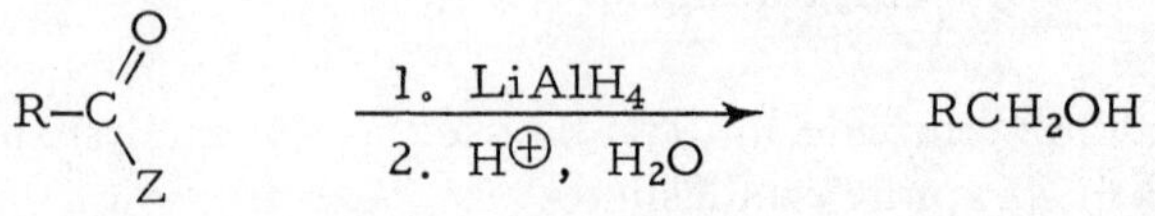

$$
\text{R—C}\underset{Z}{\overset{\displaystyle O}{\overset{\displaystyle \|}{\diagdown}}}
\quad \xrightarrow[\ 2.\ \text{H}^{\oplus},\ \text{H}_2\text{O}\ ]{\ 1.\ \text{LiAlH}_4\ }
\quad \text{RCH}_2\text{OH}
$$

$$
Z\ =\ \text{Cl, OR, RCO}_2
$$

Nitriles can be reduced to amines by lithium aluminum hydride. An imine salt is an intermediate product; if the reaction is carried out under the proper conditions, this salt is the major product and provides an aldehyde on hydrolysis (see p. 310).

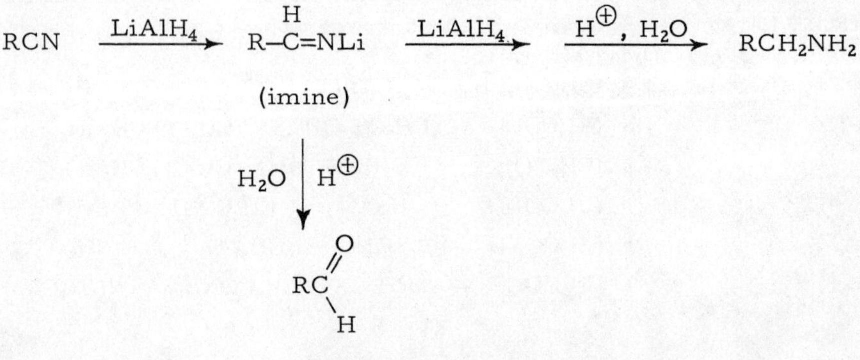

$$
\text{RCN} \xrightarrow{\text{LiAlH}_4} \overset{\displaystyle H}{R{-}C{=}NLi} \xrightarrow{\text{LiAlH}_4} \xrightarrow{\text{H}^{\oplus},\ \text{H}_2\text{O}} \text{RCH}_2\text{NH}_2
$$

(imine)

$$
\text{H}_2\text{O}\ \Big\downarrow\ \text{H}^{\oplus}
$$

$$
\text{RC}\underset{H}{\overset{\displaystyle O}{\overset{\displaystyle \|}{\diagdown}}}
$$

Amides can be reduced to primary amines, and N-substituted amides to secondary and tertiary amines.

$$
\left.\begin{array}{l} RCONH_2 \\ RCONHR' \\ RCONR_2' \end{array}\right\} \quad \xrightarrow[\ H^{\oplus}, \ H_2O\ ]{LiAlH_4} \quad \left\{\begin{array}{l} RCH_2NH_2 \\ RCH_2NHR' \\ RCH_2NR_2' \end{array}\right.
$$

Although lithium aluminum hydride is a very useful reagent, it is sometimes too expensive and impractical to be employed on a large scale. Other methods of reduction may then be necessary. Of these, the most important are reduction of esters with sodium and ethanol (acids do not react readily)

$$
RCO_2R' + 4\,Na + 4\,C_2H_5OH \xrightarrow{C_2H_5OH} RCH_2OH + R'OH + 4\,C_2H_5O^{\ominus}Na^{\oplus}
$$

and high-pressure hydrogenation over a copper chromite catalyst.

$$
RCO_2R' + 2\,H_2 \quad \xrightarrow[Cu(Cr)]{200°} \quad RCH_2OH + R'OH
$$

16-8 REACTIONS AT THE ALPHA CARBONS OF CARBOXYLIC ACID DERIVATIVES

A. The Acidic Properties of Esters with α Hydrogens

Many important synthetic reactions in which C—C bonds are formed involve esters and are brought about by basic reagents. This is possible because the alpha hydrogens of an ester such as $RCH_2CO_2C_2H_5$ are weakly acidic, and a strong base, such as sodium ethoxide, can produce a significant concentration of the ester anion at equilibrium.

$$
RCH_2CO_2C_2H_5 + C_2H_5O^{\ominus} \rightleftharpoons R\overset{\ominus}{C}HCO_2C_2H_5 + C_2H_5OH
$$

The acidity of α hydrogens is attributed partly to the $-I$-inductive effects of the ester oxygens, and partly to resonance stabilization of the resulting anion.

$$
\underset{\underset{H}{|}}{R-\overset{\ominus}{\underset{..}{C}}}-\overset{\overset{\textstyle ..O..}{\|}}{C}\diagdown_{OC_2H_5} \quad \longleftrightarrow \quad \underset{\underset{H}{|}}{R-C}=\overset{\overset{\textstyle ..\overset{\ominus}{O}.}{/}}{C}\diagdown_{OC_2H_5}
$$

When the alpha carbon of the ester carries a second strongly electron-attracting group, the acidity of α hydrogen is greatly enhanced. Examples of such compounds follow:

$$O_2NCH_2CO_2C_2H_5 \qquad \text{ethyl nitroacetate}$$

$$C_2H_5O_2CCH_2CO_2C_2H_5 \qquad \text{diethyl malonate}$$

$$NCCH_2CO_2C_2H_5 \qquad \text{ethyl cyanoacetate}$$

$$CH_3COCH_2CO_2C_2H_5 \qquad \text{ethyl acetoacetate}$$

The stabilization of the anions of these specially activated esters is greater than for simple esters because the negative charge can be distributed over more than two centers. Thus, for the anion of ethyl acetoacetate, we can regard all three of the resonance structures [4a] through [4c] as important contributors to the hybrid [4].

Since the anion [4] is relatively stable, the K_A of an α hydrogen of ethyl acetoacetate is about 10^{-11} in water solution.

Ethyl acetoacetate, like acetylacetone (pp. 352–353), ordinarily exists at room temperature as an equilibrium mixture of keto and enol tautomers in the ratio of 92.5 to 7.5. This can be shown by rapid titration with bromine but is more clearly evident from the n.m.r. spectrum (Figure 16-4), which shows absorptions of the hydroxyl, vinyl, and methyl protons of the enol form, in addition to absorptions expected for the keto form.

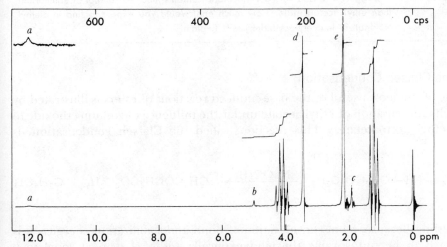

keto form, 92.5%   enol form, 7.5%

Figure 16-4   N.m.r. spectrum of ethyl acetoacetate at 60 Mcps; calibrations are relative to tetramethylsilane at 0.00 ppm.   Peaks marked a, b, and c are assigned respectively to
the protons of the enol form, whereas peaks d and e are assigned to the α-CH₂ and
methyl protons, respectively, of the keto form.   The quartet of lines at 4.2 ppm and
the triplet at 1.3 ppm result from the ethyl groups of both keto and enol forms.

Interconversion of the enol and keto forms of ethyl acetoacetate is powerfully
catalyzed by bases through the anion [4] and less so by acids through the conjugate acid of the keto form with a proton adding to the ketone oxygen.

Nonetheless, if contact with acidic and basic substances is rigidly excluded (to the extent of using quartz equipment in place of glass, glass normally having a slightly alkaline surface) then interconversion is slow enough that it is possible to separate the lower-boiling enol from the keto form by fractional distillation under reduced pressure. The separated tautomers are indefinitely stable when stored at $-80°$ in quartz vessels.

EXERCISE 16-16   Suggest a reason why acetylacetone contains much more enol at equilibrium than ethyl acetoacetate. How much enol would you expect to find in diethyl malonate? In acetylacetaldehyde? Explain.

B. The Claisen Condensation

One of the most useful of the base-induced reactions of esters is illustrated by the self-condensation of ethyl acetate under the influence of sodium ethoxide to give ethyl acetoacetate. This reaction, called the **Claisen condensation,** is

$$CH_3\overset{\overset{O}{\|}}{C}\!\!-\!\!OC_2H_5 \ + \ H\!-\!CH_2CO_2C_2H_5 \ \xrightarrow{\text{NaOC}_2H_5} \ CH_3COCH_2CO_2C_2H_5 \ + \ C_2H_5OH$$

interesting because, from consideration of bond and stabilization energies, it is expected to be unfavorable thermodynamically with ΔH (vapor) equal to 6 kcal/mole. This expectation is realized in practice, and much effort has been expended to determine conditions by which practical yields of the condensation product can be obtained.

The mechanism of the Claisen condensation has some of the flavor of both the aldol addition (pp. 340–343) and nucleophilic reactions of acid derivatives discussed earlier (pp. 370–372). The first step, as shown in Eq. (16-10), is the formation of the anion of ethyl acetate, which, being a powerful nucleophile, attacks the carbonyl carbon of a second ester molecule, Eq. (16-11). Elimination of ethoxide ion then leads to the β-keto ester, ethyl acetoacetate, Eq. (16-12).

$$C_2H_5O^\ominus \ + \ H\!-\!CH_2CO_2C_2H_5 \ \rightleftharpoons \ {}^\ominus\!:CH_2CO_2C_2H_5 \ + \ C_2H_5OH \qquad (16\text{-}10)$$

$$CH_3\!-\!\overset{\overset{O}{\|}}{C}\diagdown_{OC_2H_5} \ + \ :CH_2CO_2C_2H_5 \ \rightleftharpoons \ CH_3\!-\!\overset{\overset{O^\ominus}{|}}{\underset{OC_2H_5}{C}}\!\!-\!\!CH_2CO_2C_2H_5 \qquad (16\text{-}11)$$

$$CH_3\!-\!\overset{\overset{O^\ominus}{|}}{\underset{OC_2H_5}{C}}\!\!-\!\!CH_2CO_2C_2H_5 \ \rightleftharpoons \ CH_3\!-\!\overset{\overset{O}{\|}}{C}\!\!-\!\!CH_2CO_2C_2H_5 \ + \ C_2H_5O^\ominus \qquad (16\text{-}12)$$

The sum of these steps represents an unfavorable equilibrium, and satisfactory yields of the β-keto ester are obtained only if the equilibrium can be shifted by removal of one of the products. One simple way of doing this is to remove the ethyl alcohol by distillation as it is formed; this may be difficult, however, to carry to completion and, in any case, is self-defeating if the starting ester is low-boiling. Alternatively, one can use a large excess of sodium ethoxide. This is helpful because ethanol is a weaker acid than the ester enol, and excess ethoxide shifts the equilibrium to the right through conversion of the β-keto ester to the enolate salt.

$$CH_3\!-\!\overset{O}{\overset{\|}{C}}\!-\!CH_2CO_2C_2H_5 \; + \; C_2H_5O^{\ominus} \; \rightleftharpoons \; CH_3\!-\!\overset{O}{\overset{\|}{C}}\!-\!\overset{\ominus}{\underset{..}{C}}HCO_2C_2H_5 \; + \; C_2H_5OH$$

Obviously the condensation product must be recovered from the enol salt and isolated under conditions that avoid reversion to starting materials. The best procedure is to quench the reaction mixture by pouring it into an excess of cold dilute acid.

EXERCISE 16-17   Other conceivable products of the Claisen condensation of ethyl acetate are

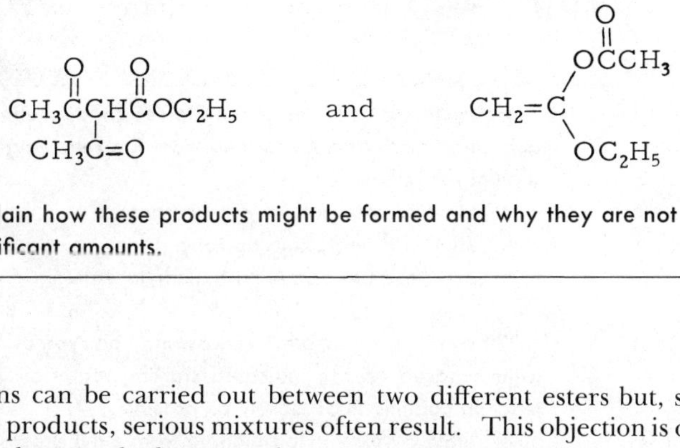

$$CH_3\overset{O}{\overset{\|}{C}}CH\overset{O}{\overset{\|}{C}}OC_2H_5 \qquad \text{and} \qquad CH_2=C\overset{\overset{\displaystyle O}{\overset{\|}{OCCH_3}}}{\underset{\displaystyle OC_2H_5}{}}$$
$$\underset{\displaystyle CH_3\overset{|}{C}=O}{}$$

Explain how these products might be formed and why they are not formed in significant amounts.

Claisen condensations can be carried out between two different esters but, since there are four possible products, serious mixtures often result. This objection is obviated if one of the esters has no α hydrogen and reacts readily with a carbanion according to Eqs. (16-11) and (16-12). The reaction then has considerable resemblance to the mixed aldol additions, discussed on pp. 342–343. Among the useful esters without α hydrogens, and with the requisite electrophilic reactivity, are those of benzoic, formic, oxalic, and carbonic acids. Several practical examples of mixed Claisen condensations are shown below.

$$C_6H_5CO_2C_2H_5 \; + \; CH_3CO_2C_2H_5 \; \xrightarrow[\text{2. }H^{\oplus}]{\text{1. }C_2H_5O^{\ominus}} \; C_6H_5COCH_2CO_2C_2H_5 \; + \; C_2H_5OH$$

ethyl benzoate   ethyl benzoylacetate

                                                                                    55%

$$HCO_2C_2H_5 \quad + \quad C_6H_5CH_2CO_2C_2H_5 \quad \xrightarrow[\text{2. } H^{\oplus}]{\text{1. } C_2H_5O^{\ominus}}$$

ethyl   ethyl
formate   phenylacetate

$$C_6H_5\underset{\underset{CHO}{|}}{C}HCO_2C_2H_5 \quad \rightleftharpoons \quad C_6H_5-\underset{\underset{CHOH}{\|}}{C}-CO_2C_2H_5$$

ethyl formylphenylacetate

90%

An important variation on the Claisen condensation is to use a ketone as the anionic reagent. This sometimes works well because ketones are usually more acidic than simple esters and the base-induced self-condensation of ketones (aldol addition) is thermodynamically unfavorable (p. 341). A typical example is the condensation of cyclohexanone with ethyl oxalate.

$$(CO_2C_2H_5)_2 \quad + \quad \text{[cyclohexanone]} \quad \xrightarrow[\text{2. } H^{\oplus}]{\text{1. } C_2H_5O^{\ominus}} \quad \text{[2-(ethyl oxalyl)-cyclohexanone]} \quad + \quad C_2H_5OH$$

ethyl oxalate   cyclohexanone   2-(ethyl oxalyl)-cyclohexanone

---

EXERCISE 16-18   Write structures for all of the Claisen condensation products that may reasonably be expected to be formed from the following mixtures of substances and sodium ethoxide:
  a. ethyl acetate and ethyl propionate
  b. ethyl carbonate and acetone
  c. ethyl oxalate and ethyl trimethylacetate

EXERCISE 16-19   Show how the substances below may be synthesized by Claisen-type condensations based on the indicated starting materials. Specify the reagents and reaction conditions as closely as possible.
  a. ethyl α-propionylpropionate from ethyl propionate
  b. ethyl 2,4-diketopentanoate from acetone
  c. diethyl phenylmalonate from ethyl phenylacetate
  d. acetylacetone from acetone
  e. 2,2,6,6-tetramethyl-3,5-heptanedione from pinacolone (*t*-butyl methyl ketone)

C. Alkylation of Acetoacetic and Malonic Esters

The anions of esters like ethyl acetoacetate and diethyl malonate can be alkylated with alkyl halides. These reactions are important for the synthesis of carboxylic acids and ketones and are similar in general character to the Haller-Bauer alkylation of ketones discussed earlier (pp. 344–346). The ester is converted by a strong base to the enolate anion, Eq. (16-13), and this is then alkylated in an S_N2 reaction with the alkyl halide, Eq. (16-14). Usually, C-alkylation predominates.

$$CH_3COCH_2CO_2C_2H_5 + C_2H_5O^{\ominus} \rightleftharpoons CH_3CO\overset{\ominus}{\ddot{C}}HCO_2C_2H_5 + C_2H_5OH \qquad (16\text{-}13)$$

$$CH_3I + CH_3CO\overset{\ominus}{\ddot{C}}HCO_2C_2H_5 \longrightarrow CH_3CO\underset{\substack{|\\ CH_3}}{C}HCO_2C_2H_5 + I^{\ominus} \qquad (16\text{-}14)$$

Esters of malonic acid can be alkylated in a similar fashion.

$$H_2C\begin{cases}CO_2C_2H_5\\CO_2C_2H_5\end{cases} \xrightarrow{NaOC_2H_5} \xrightarrow{CH_3CH_2Br} CH_3CH_2{-}CH\begin{cases}CO_2C_2H_5\\CO_2C_2H_5\end{cases}$$

Alkylacetoacetic and alkylmalonic esters can be hydrolyzed under acidic conditions to the corresponding acids and, when these are heated, they readily decarboxylate (see pp. 372–373). Alkylacetoacetic esters thus yield methyl alkyl ketones, while alkylmalonic esters produce carboxylic acids.

$$CH_3CO\overset{\substack{CH_3\\|}}{C}HCO_2C_2H_5 \xrightarrow{H^{\oplus},\ H_2O} CH_3CO\overset{\substack{CH_3\\|}}{C}HCO_2H \xrightarrow[-CO_2]{heat} \underset{\text{methyl ethyl ketone}}{CH_3COCH_2CH_3}$$

$$CH_3CH_2CH\begin{cases}CO_2C_2H_5\\CO_2C_2H_5\end{cases} \xrightarrow{H^{\oplus},\ H_2O} CH_3CH_2CH\begin{cases}CO_2H\\CO_2H\end{cases} \xrightarrow[-CO_2]{heat} \underset{n\text{-butyric acid}}{CH_3CH_2CH_2CO_2H}$$

EXERCISE 16-20 Why does the following reaction fail to give ethyl propionate?

$$CH_3CO_2C_2H_5 + CH_3I \xrightarrow{NaOC_2H_5}\!\!\!\!\!\!\!\!\!/\!\!/\quad CH_3CH_2CO_2C_2H_5$$

EXERCISE 16-21 Show how one could prepare cyclobutanecarboxylic acid starting from diethyl malonate and a suitable dihalide.

REACTIONS OF UNSATURATED CARBOXYLIC ACIDS AND THEIR DERIVATIVES

Unsaturated carboxylic acids of the type $RCH{=}CH(CH_2)_nCOOH$ usually exhibit the properties characteristic of isolated double bonds and isolated carboxyl groups when n is large and the functional groups are far apart. As expected, exceptional behavior is most commonly found when the groups are sufficiently close together to interact strongly — as in α,β-unsaturated acids, $R\overset{(\beta)}{C}H{=}\overset{(\omega)}{C}HCO_2H$. We shall emphasize those properties that are exceptional in the following discussion.

16-9 MIGRATION OF THE DOUBLE BOND

In the presence of strong base, α,β- and β,γ-unsaturated acids tend to interconvert by migration of the double bond.

$$RCH{=}CH{-}CH_2COOH \xrightleftharpoons{\quad NaOH \quad} RCH_2CH{=}CHCOOH$$

β, γ–unsaturated acid α, β–unsaturated acid

Ester derivatives, $RCH{=}CH{-}CH_2COOR'$, and the corresponding unsaturated aldehydes and ketones, $RCH{=}CH{-}CH_2COR'$, are even more prone to this type of rearrangement than are the acids.

EXERCISE 16-22   Write a mechanism for the base-catalyzed equilibration of α,β- and β,γ-unsaturated esters. Which isomer would you expect to predominate? Why is this type of isomerization less facile for the acids than for the esters? Would γ,δ-unsaturated esters rearrange readily to the α,β-unsaturated esters? Why or why not?

16-10 DOUBLE-BOND ADDITION REACTIONS

A. Hydration and Hydrogen-Bromide Addition

Like alkenes, the double bonds of α,β-unsaturated acids can be brominated, hydroxylated, hydrated, and hydrobrominated, although the reactions are often relatively slow. With unsymmetrical addends, the direction of addition is opposite to that observed for alkenes (anti-Markownikoff). Thus acrylic acid adds hydrogen bromide and water so that β-bromo- and β-hydroxypropionic acids are formed.

$$\text{CH}_2{=}\text{CHCOOH} \quad
\begin{array}{l}
\xrightarrow{\;\text{HBr}\;} \quad \text{BrCH}_2\text{CH}_2\text{COOH} \\[2pt]
\hspace{3.2em} \beta\text{–bromopropionic acid} \\[10pt]
\xrightarrow[\text{H}^{\oplus}]{\;\text{H}_2\text{O}\;} \quad \underset{\;\;\;\;\;\;|}{\text{CH}_2\text{CH}_2\text{COOH}} \\
\hspace{4.6em}\text{OH}
\end{array}$$

acrylic acid

These additions are closely analogous to the addition of halogens and halogen acids to butadiene (pp. 188–189 and 206–207).

B. Lactone Formation

When the double bond of an unsaturated acid lies farther down the carbon chain than between the alpha and beta positions, conjugate addition is not possible. Nonetheless, the double bond and carboxyl group frequently interact in the presence of acid catalysts because the carbonium ion that results from addition of a proton to the double bond has a built-in nucleophile (the carboxyl group), which may attack the cationic center to form a cyclic ester (i.e., a lactone). Lactone formation usually only occurs readily by this mechanism when a five- or six-membered ring can be formed.

$$CH_2=CHCH_2CH_2C\overset{O}{\underset{OH}{\big/}} \quad \xrightarrow{H^{\oplus}} \quad CH_3-\overset{\oplus}{C}HCH_2CH_2C\overset{O}{\underset{OH}{\big/}} \quad \xrightarrow{-H^{\oplus}} \quad$$

allylacetic acid   γ-valerolacetone

Five- and six-membered lactones are also formed by internal esterification when either γ- or δ-hydroxy acids are heated. Under similar conditions, β-hydroxy acids are dehydrated to α,β-unsaturated acids, while α-hydroxy acids undergo bimolecular esterification to substances with six-membered dilactone rings called **lactides.**

$$HOCH_2CH_2CH_2CO_2H \quad \xrightarrow{heat}$$

γ-hydroxybutyric acid   γ-butyrolactone

$$CH_3\underset{\underset{OH}{|}}{C}HCH_2CO_2H \quad \xrightarrow{heat} \quad CH_3CH=CHCO_2H \;+\; H_2O$$

β-hydroxybutyric acid

$$2\;CH_3\underset{\underset{OH}{|}}{C}HCO_2H \quad \xrightarrow{heat} \quad \qquad\qquad +\;2\,H_2O$$

α-hydroxypropionic acid   lactide
(lactic acid)

EXERCISE 16-23   Would you expect vinylacetic acid to form a lactone when heated with a
catalytic amount of sulfuric acid?

DICARBOXYLIC ACIDS

Acids in which there are two carboxyl groups separated by a chain of more
than five carbon atoms ($n > 5$) have, for the most part, unexceptional properties
—the carboxyl groups behaving more or less independently of one another.

Table 16-4   Dicarboxylic Acids

Acid	Formula	m.p. °C	$K_1 \times 10^5$ at 25°	$K_2 \times 10^5$ at 25°
oxalic (ethanedioic)	$\begin{array}{c} CO_2H \\ | \\ CO_2H \end{array}$	189	3500	5.3
malonic (propanedioic)	$CH_2 \begin{array}{c} CO_2H \\ CO_2H \end{array}$	136 dec.	171	0.22
succinic (butanedioic)	$(CH_2)_2 \begin{array}{c} CO_2H \\ CO_2H \end{array}$	185	6.6	0.25
glutaric (pentanedioic)	$(CH_2)_3 \begin{array}{c} CO_2H \\ CO_2H \end{array}$	98	4.7	0.29
adipic (hexanedioic)	$(CH_2)_4 \begin{array}{c} CO_2H \\ CO_2H \end{array}$	152	3.7	0.24
pimelic (heptanedioic)	$(CH_2)_5 \begin{array}{c} CO_2H \\ CO_2H \end{array}$	105	3.4	0.26
maleic (cis-butenedioic)	$\begin{array}{c} HCCO_2H \\ \| \\ HCCO_2H \end{array}$	130	1170	0.026
fumaric (trans-butenedioic)	$\begin{array}{c} HCCO_2H \\ \| \\ HO_2CCH \end{array}$	sub. 200	93	2.9
phthalic (o-benzene dicarboxylic)	$\begin{array}{c} CO_2H \\ CO_2H \end{array}$	231	130	0.39[18]

$$
\begin{array}{c}
CO_2H \\
/ \\
(CH_2)_n \\
\backslash \\
CO_2H
\end{array}
$$

When the carboxyl groups are closer together, however, the possibilities for interaction increase; we shall be primarily concerned with such acids. A number of important dicarboxylic acids are listed in Table 16-4.

16-11 ACIDIC PROPERTIES OF DICARBOXYLIC ACIDS

The inductive effect of one carboxyl group is expected to enhance the acidity of the other and, from Table 16-4, we see that the acid strength of the dicarboxylic acids, as measured by the first acid-dissociation constant, K_1, is higher than that of acetic acid (K_A, 1.5×10^{-5}) and falls off with increasing distance between the two carboxyl groups. The second acid-dissociation constant, K_2, is smaller than K_A for acetic acid (with the exception of oxalic acid) for the reason that it is more difficult to pull off a proton under the electrostatic attraction of the nearby carboxylate anion ($+I$ effect).

16-12 THERMAL BEHAVIOR OF DICARBOXYLIC ACIDS

The reactions that occur when diacids are heated depend critically upon the chain length separating the carboxyl groups. Cyclization is usually favored if a strainless five- or six-membered ring can be formed. Thus adipic and pimelic acids decarboxylate and cyclize to cyclopentanone and cyclohexanone, respectively.

$$
(CH_2)_4 \begin{array}{c} COOH \\ COOH \end{array} \xrightarrow{300°}
\begin{array}{c} CH_2 \\ | \\ CH_2 \end{array}
\begin{array}{c} CH_2 \\ \\ CH_2 \end{array} C=O \; + \; CO_2 \; + \; H_2O
$$

adipic acid   cyclopentanone

$$
(CH_2)_5 \begin{array}{c} COOH \\ COOH \end{array} \xrightarrow{300°}
\begin{array}{c} CH_2-CH_2 \\ CH_2 \quad\quad CH_2 \\ CH_2-CH_2 \end{array} C=O \; + \; CO_2 \; + \; H_2O
$$

pimelic acid   cyclohexanone

Succinic and glutaric acids take a different course. Rather than form the strained cyclic ketones, cyclopropanone (unknown) and cyclobutanone, both acids form cyclic anhydrides—succinic and glutaric anhydrides—having five- and six-membered rings, respectively. Phthalic and maleic acids behave similarly giving five-membered cyclic anhydrides.

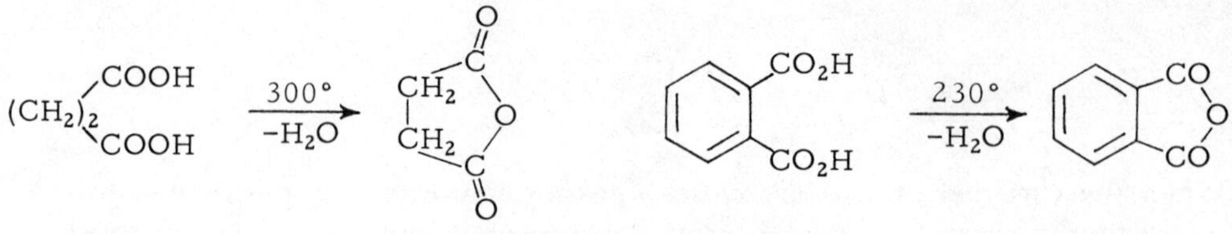

$$(CH_2)_2 \begin{matrix} COOH \\ COOH \end{matrix} \xrightarrow[-H_2O]{300°} \text{succinic anhydride}$$

succinic
acid

succinic
anhydride

phthalic
acid

$$\xrightarrow[-H_2O]{230°}$$

phthalic
anhydride

$$(CH_2)_3 \begin{matrix} COOH \\ COOH \end{matrix} \xrightarrow[-H_2O]{300°} \text{glutaric anhydride}$$

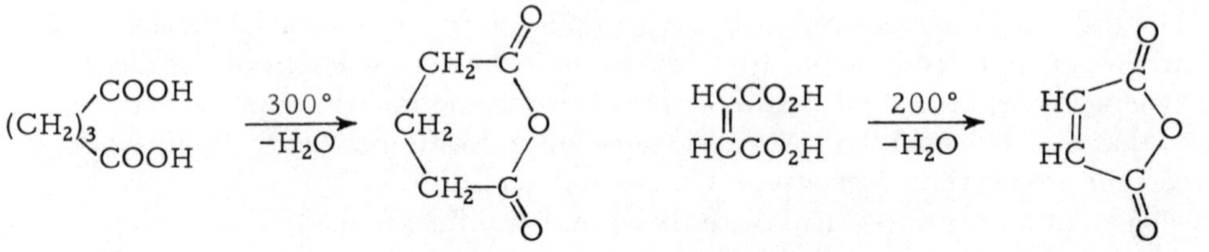

glutaric
acid

glutaric
anhydride

$$\begin{matrix} HCCO_2H \\ \| \\ HCCO_2H \end{matrix} \xrightarrow[-H_2O]{200°}$$

maleic
acid

maleic
anhydride

Malonic and oxalic acids behave still differently, each undergoing decarboxylation when heated (see pp. 372–373).

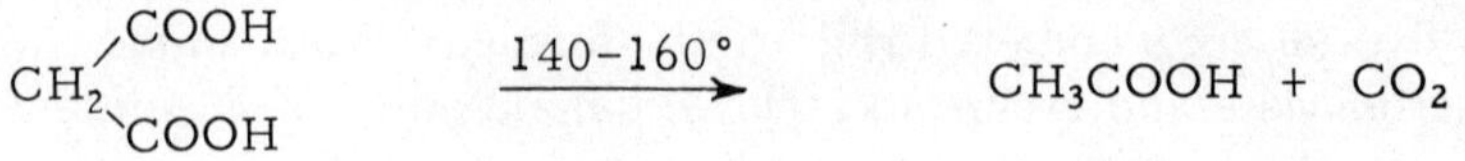

$$CH_2 \begin{matrix} COOH \\ COOH \end{matrix} \xrightarrow{140-160°} CH_3COOH + CO_2$$

malonic acid

$$\begin{matrix} COOH \\ | \\ COOH \end{matrix} \xrightarrow{160-180°} CO_2 + HCOOH$$

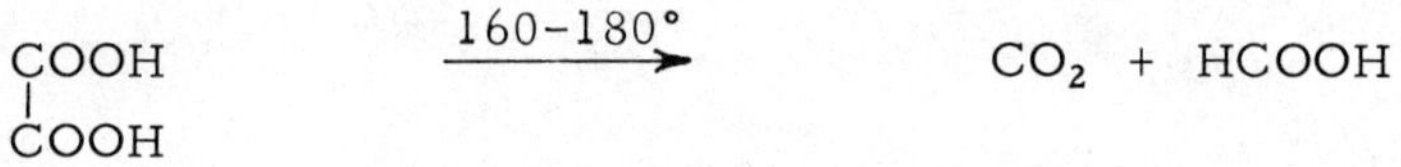

oxalic acid

EXERCISE 16-24   Fumaric and maleic acids give the same anhydride on heating, but fumaric
acid must be heated to much higher temperatures than maleic acid to effect the
same change. Explain. Write reasonable mechanisms for both reactions.

SUPPLEMENTARY EXERCISES

16-25   Write equations for a practical laboratory synthesis of each of the following substances
based on the indicated starting materials (several steps may be required). Give reagents
and conditions.

    a. *n*-butyric acid from *n*-propyl alcohol

    b. trimethylacetic acid from *t*-butyl chloride

    c. isobutyric acid from isobutylene

    d. α-bromo-α-*t*-butylacetic acid from *t*-butyl chloride

16-26 *t*-Butyl acetate is converted to methyl acetate by sodium methoxide in methanol about one-tenth as fast as ethyl acetate is converted to methyl acetate under the same conditions. With dilute hydrogen chloride in methanol, *t*-butyl acetate is rapidly converted to *t*-butyl methyl ether and acetic acid, whereas ethyl acetate goes more slowly to ethanol and methyl acetate.

    a. Write reasonable mechanisms for each of the reactions and show how the relative-rate data agree with your mechanisms.

    b. How could one use ^{18}O as a tracer to substantiate your mechanistic picture?

16-27 Write equations for a practical laboratory synthesis of each of the following substances *based* on the indicated starting materials (several steps may be required). Give reagents and conditions.

    a. β-chloroethyl bromoacetate from ethanol and/or acetic acid

    b. α-methoxyisobutyramide from isobutyric acid

    c. 3,5,5-trimethyl-3-hexanol from 2,4,4-trimethyl-1-pentene (commercially available)

    d. α-*t*-butylacetaldehyde from *t*-butylacetic acid

    e. 2,3,3-trimethyl-2-butanol from tetramethylethylene

    f. cyclopentanone diethylene ketal, , from adipic acid

16-28 Give for each of the following pairs of compounds a chemical test, preferably a test-tube reaction, that will distinguish between the two substances. Write an equation for each reaction.

    a. HCO_2H and CH_3CO_2H

    b. $CH_3CO_2C_2H_5$ and $CH_3OCH_2CO_2H$

    c. $CH_2{=}CHCO_2H$ and $CH_3CH_2CO_2H$

    d. CH_3COBr and $BrCH_2CO_2H$

    e. $BrCH_2CH_2CH_2CO_2CH_3$ and $CH_3CH_2CHBrCO_2CH_3$

    f. $(CH_3CH_2CO)_2O$ and

    g.   and

    h. $HC{\equiv}CCO_2CH_3$ and $CH_2{=}CHCO_2CH_3$

    i. $CH_3CO_2NH_4$ and CH_3CONH_2

    j. $CH_2{=}CH{-}CH_2CH_2CO_2H$ and $CH_3CH_2CH{=}CHCO_2H$

    k. $(CH_3CO)_2O$ and $CH_3CO_2CH_2CH_3$

16-29 Explain how you could distinguish between the pairs of compounds listed in Exercise 16-28 by spectroscopic means.

16-30 Suppose you were given four bottles, each containing a different isomer (α, β, γ, or δ) of hydroxypentanoic acid. Explain in detail how you could distinguish the various isomers by chemical reactions.

16-31 Compound A ($C_4H_8O_3$) was optically active, quite soluble in water (giving a solution acidic to litmus), and, on strong heating, yielded B ($C_4H_6O_2$), which was optically inactive, rather water-soluble (acidic to litmus), and reacted much more readily with $KMnO_4$ than A. When A was oxidized with dilute chromic acid solution, it was converted to a volatile liquid C (C_3H_6O), which did not react with $KMnO_4$ and gave a yellow precipitate with I_2 and NaOH solution.

Write *appropriate* structures for the lettered compounds and equations for *all* of the reactions mentioned. Is Compound A reasonably uniquely defined by the above description? Explain.

16-32 Name each of the following substances by an accepted system:

$$a. \quad \begin{array}{c} CH_2\!-\!CH_2 \quad CO_2CH_3 \\ \diagup \qquad \diagup \diagup \\ CH_2 \qquad C \\ \diagdown \qquad \diagup \diagdown \\ CH_2\!-\!CH_2 \quad CO_2CH_3 \end{array}$$

b. $CH_3COCH[CH(CH_3)_2]CO_2C_2H_5$

c. $CH_3CH_2COC(CH_3)_2CON(CH_3)_2$

d. $HOCH\!=\!CHCO_2C_2H_5$

e. $C_2H_5OCOCOCH_2CO_2C_2H_5$

f. $C_2H_5O_2CCH_2CH(CO_2C_2H_5)COCO_2C_2H_5$

$$g. \quad \begin{array}{c} \quad CH_2 \\ CH_2 \diagdown \\ | \qquad C\!=\!O \\ CH_2 \diagup \\ \quad C\!-\!CO_2CH_3 \\ \quad | \\ \quad CH_3 \end{array}$$

$$h. \quad \begin{array}{c} CH_2\!=\!CH\!-\!CH_2 \\ \diagdown \\ CHCO_2H \\ \diagup \\ CH_2\!=\!CH\!-\!CH_2 \end{array}$$

i. $CH_3CH_2COCH(CH_3)CH_2CH_2CH(CH_3$

j. $CH_3CH_2CH_2CH(CH_2CH\!=\!CH_2)CO_2H$

k. $CH_3COCH(CO_2C_2H_5)_2$

Optical Isomerism

*S*tereoisomerism in its broadest sense is isomerism of compounds having the same structural formula but different arrangements of groups in space. We usually recognize two main types of stereoisomers—geometrical (cis-trans) and optical isomers. The distinction between these types is straightforward for the optical isomers of s-butyl bromide (pp. 231–232) and the cis-trans isomers of 2-butene (pp. 129–130), but is less clear for compounds like 1,2-bromochlorocyclohexane, which have isomers that can differ by having the groups cis or trans and also by being nonidentical with their mirror images.

In this chapter we shall emphasize optical isomerism, which could be defined as isomerism associated with differences in rotation of the plane of polarized light. It is important to recognize, however, that optical isomerism is quite independent of the phenomenon of optical rotation—molecules can exist in right-handed or left-handed forms irrespective of their ability to exhibit optical rotation. We must commonly measure optical rotations to detect optical isomers, but there are, as we shall see, other and even more powerful methods for this purpose.

The whole subject of optical isomerism is of particular importance to bio-chemistry. Some of the reasons for this are discussed in this chapter and also later in Chapter 20.

Optical Isomerism

The simplest form of optical isomerism is where a compound can exist in two stereoisomeric forms whose molecular structures are nonsuperimposable reflections of one another. Apart from this difference in molecular arrangement, which is a difference of the same kind as between right- and left-handed gloves, the ordinary physical properties of such isomers are identical [1] except that they rotate the plane of plane-polarized light equally, but in *opposite* directions. The meaning of this statement may be better understood with the aid of the following brief explanation of plane-polarized light (see also p. 231).

17-1 PLANE-POLARIZED LIGHT AND THE ORIGIN OF OPTICAL ROTATION

Electromagnetic radiation, as the name implies, involves the propagation of both electric and magnetic forces. At each point in a light beam, there is a component electric field and a component magnetic field, both of which oscillate in all directions perpendicular to each other and to the direction in which the beam is propagated. In plane-polarized light, the component electric field oscillates as in ordinary light except that the direction of oscillation is contained within a plane. Likewise, the component magnetic field oscillates within a plane,

---

[1] This is strictly true only in the absence of other optically active substances.

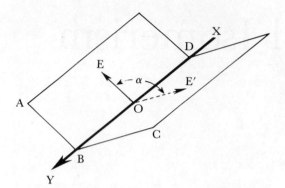

Figure 17-1

Schematic representation of the electrical component of plane-polarized light and optical rotation. The beam is assumed to travel from X toward Y.

the planes in question being perpendicular. A schematic representation of the electrical part of plane-polarized light and its interaction with an optical isomer is shown in Figure 17-1. The beam of polarized light XY has a component electric field which oscillates in the plane ABD. At the point O, the direction of oscillation is along OE. If now at O the beam passes through a transparent substance, which has the power to cause the direction of oscillation of the electrical field to rotate through an angle α to the new direction OE' in the plane CBD, the substance is said to be optically active.

A clockwise rotation, as the observer looks towards the beam, defines the substance as **dextrorotatory** (i.e., rotates to the right) and the angle α is taken as a positive (+) rotation. If the rotation is counterclockwise, the substance is described as **levorotatory** (i.e., rotates to the left) and the angle α is taken as a negative (−) rotation.

The question naturally arises as to why some substances interact with polarized light in this manner while others do not. We shall oversimplify the explanation since the subject is best treated rigorously with rather complex mathematics. However, it is not difficult to understand that the electric forces in a light beam impinging on a molecule will interact to some extent with the electrons within the molecule. Although radiant energy may not actually be absorbed by the molecule to promote it to higher excited electronic-energy states (see Chapter 2), a perturbation of the electronic configuration of the molecule can occur. One can visualize this process as a polarization of the electrons brought about by the oscillating electric field associated with the radiation. This kind of interaction is important to us here because it causes the electric field of the radiation to change its direction of oscillation. The effect produced by any one molecule is extremely small, but in the aggregate may be measurable as a net rotation of the plane-polarized light. Molecules like methane, ethylene and acetone, which have enough symmetry so that each is identical with its reflection, do not rotate plane-polarized light. This is because the symmetry of each is such that every optical rotation in one direction is cancelled by an equal rotation in the opposite direction. However, a molecule with its atoms so disposed in space that it is not symmetrical to the degree of being superimposable on its mirror image will have a net effect on the incident polarized light, since then the electromagnetic interactions do not average to zero; such substances we characterize as being optically active.

17-2 SPECIFIC ROTATION

The angle of rotation of the plane of polarized light α depends on the number and kind of molecules the light encounters — it is found that α varies with the concentration of a solution (or the density of a pure liquid) and on the distance through which the light travels. A third important variable is the wavelength of the incident light, which must always be specified even though the sodium D line (5893 A) is commonly used. To a lesser extent, α varies with the temperature and with the solvent (if used), which also should be specified. Thus, the **specific rotation** $[\alpha]$, of a substance is generally expressed by the following formulas:

For solutions:

$$[\alpha]_{\lambda}^{t^{\circ}} = \frac{100\ \alpha}{l \cdot c}$$

For neat liquids:

$$[\alpha]_{\lambda}^{t^{\circ}} = \frac{\alpha}{l \cdot d}$$

α = measured degree of rotation
t° = temperature
λ = wavelength of light
l = length in decimeters of light path through the solution
c = concentration in grams of sample/100 ml of solution
d = density of liquid in grams/ml

For example, when a compound is reported as having $[\alpha]_{D}^{25^{\circ}} = -100$ ($c = 2.5$, chloroform), this means that it has a specific levorotation of 100 degrees at a concentration of 2.5 grams per 100 ml of chloroform solution at 25°C when contained in a tube 1 decimeter long, the rotation being measured with sodium D light, which has a wavelength of 5893 A.

Frequently, molecular rotation $[M]$ is used in preference to specific rotation and is related to specific rotation by the following equation,

$$[M]_{\lambda}^{t^{\circ}} = \frac{[\alpha]_{\lambda}^{t^{\circ}} \cdot M}{100}$$

where M is the molecular weight of the optically active compound. Expressed in this form, optical rotations of different compounds are directly comparable since differences in rotation arising from differences in molecular weight are taken into account.

17-3 OPTICALLY ACTIVE COMPOUNDS WITH ASYMMETRIC CARBON ATOMS

A. One Asymmetric Carbon

Having discussed what is meant by optical activity, we shall now consider the conditions of asymmetry which are necessary for a compound to be optically active. The inflexible condition for optical activity is: *the geometric structure of a molecule must be such that it is nonsuperimposable on its mirror image.* Unless this condition holds, the molecule cannot exist in optically active forms.

EXERCISE 17-1   Many familiar objects, such as gloves, shoes, and screws, are nonidentical with
their mirror images.   Is it reasonable to expect such objects to be optically active
provided they are transparent to light, or are further conditions necessary?

There are a number of types of structural elements that can make a molecule
asymmetric and nonidentical with its mirror image.   The most common and important of these is the asymmetrically substituted carbon atom, which is a carbon
atom bonded to four *different* atoms or groups.   If a molecule has such an asymmetrically substituted atom, the molecule will be nonidentical with its mirror
image and will therefore be optically active.   A simple example is *s*-butyl alcohol
[1], the carbinyl carbon of which is said to be asymmetric since it carries four
different groups, hydrogen, hydroxyl, methyl, and ethyl.

$$CH_3 \quad\quad H$$
$$\diagdown \;\; \diagup$$
$$C$$
$$\diagup \;\; \diagdown$$
$$CH_3CH_2 \quad\quad OH$$

[1]

However, *s*-butyl alcohol, as prepared from optically inactive materials (e.g.,
by the reduction of methyl ethyl ketone with lithium aluminum hydride), is
optically inactive.

$$CH_3COCH_2CH_3 \xrightarrow{\text{LiAlH}_4} CH_3CH(OH)CH_2CH_3$$

It is a mixture of two isomeric forms, [2] and [3], which are related as object to
mirror image.

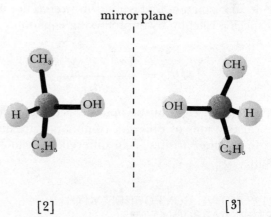

[2]   [3]

The chemical and physical properties of the two forms are identical, *except* they
rotate the plane of plane-polarized light equally but in opposite directions.
Mirror image forms of the same compound, such as [2] and [3], are called
enantiomers.   The *s*-butyl alcohol, as prepared by the reduction of inactive
methyl ethyl ketone, is optically inactive because it is a mixture of equal numbers
of molecules of each enantiomer; the net optical rotation is therefore zero.
Such a mixture is described as **racemic.**

Table 17-1   Physical Properties of Tartaric Acids

Tartaric acid	Specific rotation, $[\alpha]_D^{20}$ in H_2O	Melting point, °C	Specific gravity	Solubility in H_2O (g/100 g at 25°)
meso[a]		140	1.666	$120^{(15°)}$
(−)	−11.98°	170	1.760	147
(+)	+11.98°	170	1.760	147
(±)		205	1.687	25

[a] *meso*-Tartaric acid is discussed on pp. 406–408.

Separation of the enantiomers in a racemic mixture is known as **resolution,** and conversion of the molecules of one enantiomer into a racemic mixture of both is called **racemization.**

Although the ordinary physical properties of pure enantiomers (apart from their optical properties) are identical, they are frequently different from the physical properties of the racemic mixture. In such instances, a **racemic compound** or **racemate** is formed that has a crystal structure different from those of the pure enantiomers and will therefore differ in melting point, solubility, and density. Tartaric acid is one such example, and the physical properties of the various forms of tartaric acid are given in Table 17-1. The racemic tartaric acid has a noticeably higher melting point and lower solubility than the separate component enantiomers, which means that the racemic acid has the more stable crystal structure. In other words, the 1:1 mixture of enantiomers gives a stronger packing than either enantiomer separately. This is analogous to the observation that right- and left-handed objects usually can be packed in a box better than all right- or all left-handed objects.

B. Projection Formulas

We have distinguished the two enantiomers of s-butyl alcohol, [2] and [3], with a picture of a three-dimensional model to show the tetrahedral arrangement of the groups about the asymmetric carbon atom. Clearly it will be inconvenient to do this in every case, particularly for more complex examples. It is necessary therefore to have a simpler convention for distinguishing between optical isomers. The so-called Fischer projection formulas are widely used for this purpose and, by their use, the enantiomers of s-butyl alcohol are represented by [4] and [5].

$$
\begin{array}{ccc}
\text{CH}_3 & \text{CH}_3 & \uparrow \\
\text{H--C--OH} & \text{HO--C--H} & \\
\text{CH}_2\text{CH}_3 & \text{CH}_2\text{CH}_3 & \text{North} \\
\\
[4] & [5] &
\end{array}
$$

The convention of the Fischer projections is such that the east and west bonds of the asymmetric carbon are considered to extend *out* of the plane of the paper and the north and south bonds extend *behind* the plane of the paper. This is shown more explicitly in structures [6] and [7], or [8] and [9]. Structures [2], [4], [6], and [8] all correspond to one enantiomer while [3], [5], [7], and [9] correspond to the other.

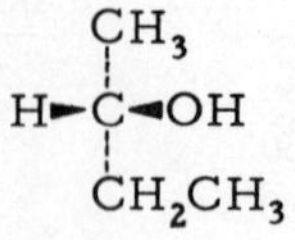

$$CH_3$$
$$H\!\!\rightarrow\!\!C\!\!\leftarrow\!\!OH$$
$$CH_2CH_3$$

[6]

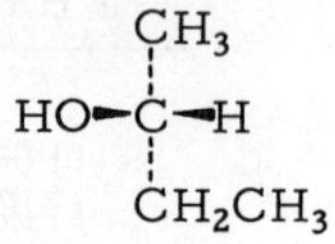

$$CH_3$$
$$HO\!\!\rightarrow\!\!C\!\!\leftarrow\!\!H$$
$$CH_2CH_3$$

[7]

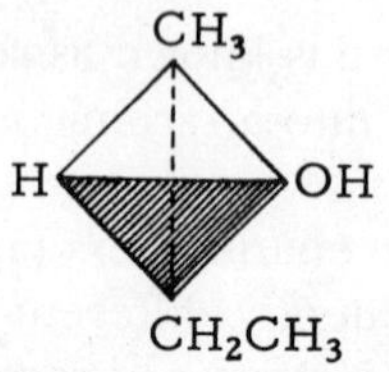

$$CH_3$$
$$H \quad OH$$
$$CH_2CH_3$$

[8]

$$CH_3$$
$$HO \quad H$$
$$CH_2CH_3$$

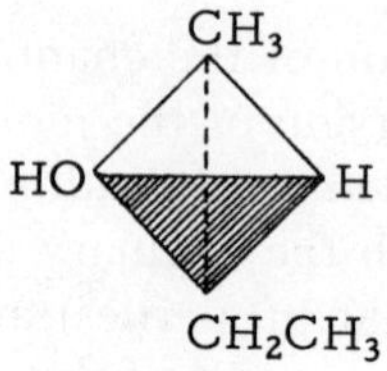

[9]

   With projection formulas, configuration is inverted (i.e., one enantiomer is changed into the other) each time two atoms or groups about the asymmetric atom (or asymmetric center as it is often called) are interchanged. Clearly, if we interchange hydrogen for hydroxyl in [4], we have the enantiomer [5]. Less obvious is the interchange of methyl and hydrogen in [4] to give [10], which by our convention is equivalent to [5]. (Inspection of models may be helpful if the results of these operations are not clear.)

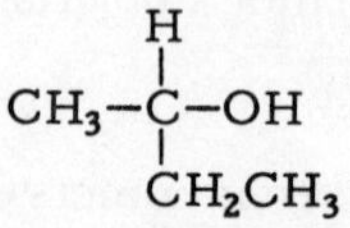

$$H$$
$$CH_3\!-\!C\!-\!OH$$
$$CH_2CH_3$$

[10]

   It should be noted that [10] is not strictly a Fischer projection formula because, by the Fischer convention, the carbon chain is always written vertically. Note also that rotation of a Fischer projection formula 180° in the plane of the paper leaves the configuration unchanged.

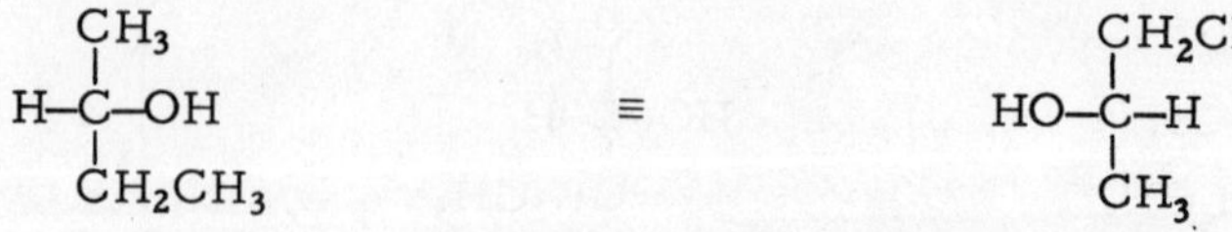

$$CH_3$$
$$H\!-\!C\!-\!OH$$
$$CH_2CH_3$$

$$\equiv$$

$$CH_2CH_3$$
$$HO\!-\!C\!-\!H$$
$$CH_3$$

C. Compounds with Two Asymmetric Carbon Atoms

   We have considered how a compound with one asymmetric carbon atom can exist in two optically active forms. However, it would be incorrect to infer from this that asymmetric carbon is a *necessary* condition for optical activity, since many compounds are known that have no asymmetric atoms but may still exhibit optical isomerism (see pp. 409–412). It would be no more correct to infer that, because a molecule has *two* or *more* asymmetric carbons, it will necessarily be optically active.

For example, consider a molecule with structure and conformation as in [11] with two asymmetric atoms, 1 and 2, the groups attached to atom 1 being the same as for atom 2, and the structure being so oriented that atom 1 is toward the front and atom 2 toward the rear. It can be seen that [11] is identical with its mirror image [12] by simply rotating [11] end for end to give [13], which, when turned 180° as shown by the arrow, superimposes on [12]. A molecule with this structure will be optically inactive, despite the presence of two asymmetric carbons, because it is superimposable on its mirror image.

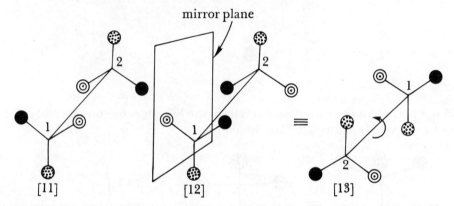

One could argue, however, that this condition does not hold for all conformations of [11]. Certainly, the conformation [14] is not superimposable on its mirror image [15].

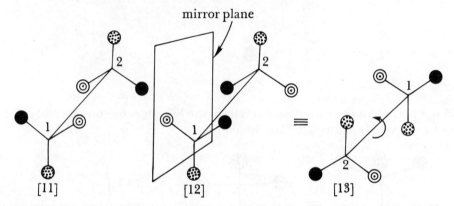

Nevertheless, the molecule represented by [14] will not be optically active, because the asymmetric conformation [14] is rapidly converted into its enantiomer [15] by rotation about the bond joining the two asymmetric centers. Optical activity would be possible only if it were possible to "freeze" the molecule in one of the asymmetric conformations.

It will be seen that the eclipsed conformation [16] of the same system has a plane of symmetry that bisects the molecule into two halves, each half being the mirror image of the other. Molecules that possess this sort of symmetry are frequently said to be internally compensated, since the optical rotations contributed by each asymmetric half are equal in degree but opposite in sign; the net rotation is therefore zero.

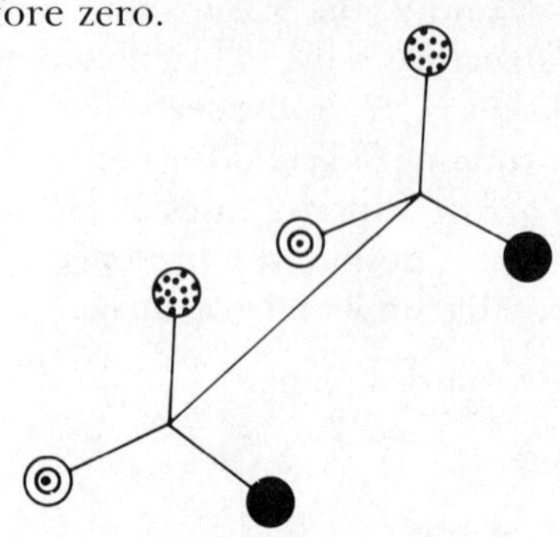

[16]

This is perhaps more easily visualized from the Fischer projection formula of the conformations [11] through [16], which follow:

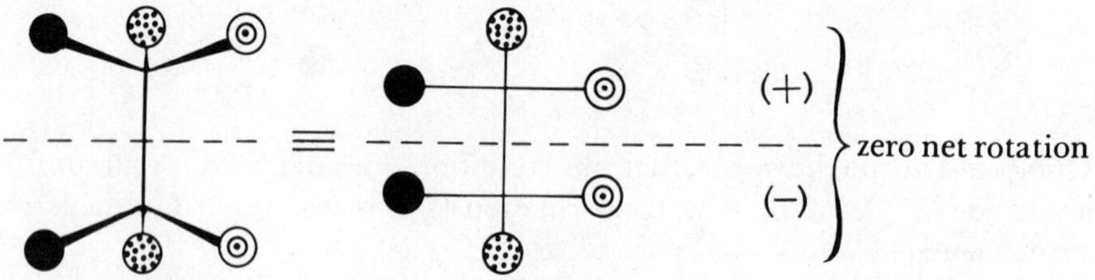

$(+)$
$(-)$ } zero net rotation

[16]

To generalize, if a substance has a plane of symmetry in at least one conformation, it will not be resolvable into optically active forms (provided that all of the possible optically active conformations are in reasonably rapid equilibrium with, or pass through, the symmetrical conformation).

Among the many examples of compounds that have two asymmetric carbon atoms, but that are optically inactive because their molecules are free to pass through a conformation with a plane of symmetry, are *meso*-tartaric acid [17], *meso*-2,3-dibromobutane [18], and *cis*-cyclohexane-1,2-dicarboxylic acid [19]. The asterisks in the formulas denote the asymmetric carbons.

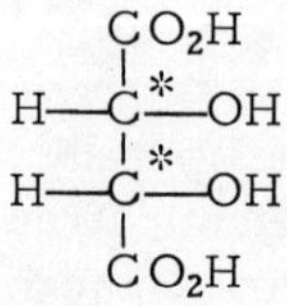

CO_2H
H—C*—OH
H—C*—OH
CO_2H

[17]

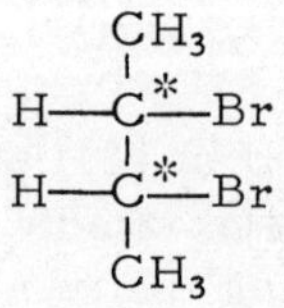

CH_3
H—C*—Br
H—C*—Br
CH_3

[18]

CH_2—CH_2 H
CH_2 C*
CH_2—C* CO_2H
              CO_2H

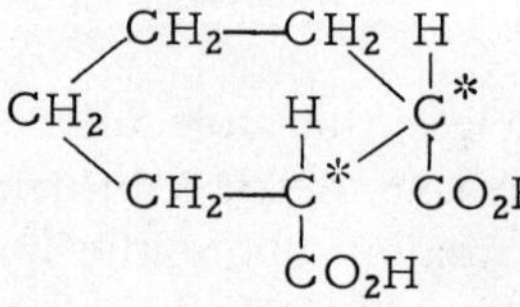

[19]

EXERCISE 17-2   Draw the chair form of cis-cyclohexane-1,2-dicarboxylic acid. Is it identical with its mirror image? Why is the compound not resolvable? How many stereoisomers are possible for cyclohexane-1,3-dicarboxylic acid and, of these, which are optical isomers and which are geometric isomers?

The prefix *meso* denotes an optically inactive optical isomer of a compound that can exist in other optically active modifications. Tartaric acid and 2,3-dibromobutane each have a total of three optical isomers, two optically active enantiomers and one optically inactive *meso* form. These are shown in structures [20a], [20b], and [17] for tartaric acid and [21a], [21b], and [18] for 2,3-dibromobutane.

| [20a] | [20b] | [21a] | [21b] |

EXERCISE 17-3   Draw structures similar to [11] through [15] for all the possible different staggered conformations of (+)-tartaric acid [20a]. Are any of these identical with their mirror images? How many optically active forms of tartaric acid could there be altogether if rotation were *not* possible about the 2,3-bond and only the staggered conformations were allowed?

Stereoisomeric structures that are not enantiomers and thus not mirror images are called **diastereomers.** *meso*-Tartaric acid [17] and either one of the optically active tartaric acids [20a or 20b] are therefore diastereomers. Only [20a] and [20b] are enantiomers. Diastereomers usually have substantially different physical properties, whereas enantiomers have identical properties apart from their optical properties. This is illustrated in Table 17-1 for the tartaric acids. The reason for the difference in physical properties between diastereomers can be seen very simply for a substance with two asymmetric centers by noting that a right shoe on a right foot can be a mirror image and nonidentical with a left shoe on a left foot, but is not expected to be a mirror image or have the same physical properties as a left shoe on a right foot or a right shoe on a left foot.

Many compounds have two asymmetric carbons but cannot exist in an internally compensated *meso* form. This situation occurs when the two asymmetric carbons are differently substituted so that there is no conformation in which any of the isomers has a plane of symmetry. As an example, consider the possible diastereomers of 2,3,4-trihydroxybutanal, [22] and [23], which are commonly known as erythrose and threose, respectively. They are represented below by the projection formulas [22a] and [23a], as well as by the conformational, or so-called "saw-horse," structures, [22b] and [23b].

$$\begin{array}{c} CHO \\ | \\ H-C-OH \\ | \\ H-C-OH \\ | \\ CH_2OH \end{array} \quad \text{or} \quad \begin{array}{c} OHC \diagup \diagdown OH \\ H \diagdown \diagup OH \\ | \\ CH_2OH \end{array} \qquad\qquad \begin{array}{c} CHO \\ | \\ HO-C-H \\ | \\ H-C-OH \\ | \\ CH_2OH \end{array} \quad \text{or} \quad \begin{array}{c} OH \\ OHC \diagup \diagdown H \\ H \diagdown \diagup OH \\ | \\ CH_2OH \end{array}$$

erythrose

[22a]   [22b]   [23a]   [23b]

Neither diastereomer has a plane of symmetry in any conformation, and consequently there are two pairs of enantiomers, or a total of four optical isomers. In general, a compound with n asymmetric carbons will have 2^n possible optical isomers, provided there are no isomers with a plane of symmetry arising from similarly substituted asymmetric carbons as in *meso* forms. The structures assigned to erythrose and threose have been established beyond question by the finding that (−)-erythrose, which is a naturally occurring sugar, on oxidation with nitric acid gives *meso*-tartaric acid, whereas (+)-threose, which does not occur naturally, gives (+)-tartaric acid.

$$\begin{array}{c} CHO \\ | \\ H-C-OH \\ | \\ HO-C-H \\ | \\ CH_2OH \end{array} \xrightarrow{HNO_3} \begin{array}{c} CO_2H \\ | \\ H-C-OH \\ | \\ HO-C-H \\ | \\ CO_2H \end{array} \qquad \begin{array}{c} CHO \\ | \\ H-C-OH \\ | \\ H-C-OH \\ | \\ CH_2OH \end{array} \xrightarrow{HNO_3} \begin{array}{c} CO_2H \\ | \\ H-C-OH \\ | \\ H-C-OH \\ | \\ CO_2H \end{array}$$

(+)-threose   (+)-tartaric acid   (−)-erythrose   *meso*-tartaric acid

---

EXERCISE 17-4   Write projection formulas for (+)-erythrose and (−)-threose. Which tartaric acids will they give on oxidation?

EXERCISE 17-5   Draw projection formulas for all of the possible optical isomers of 2,3,4-trihydroxypentanoic acid.

EXERCISE 17-6   Camphor has two asymmetric carbons, but only two optical isomers are known. Explain. (Models will be helpful.)

$$H-\left\langle\begin{array}{c} CH_3 \\ | \\ C \\ | \\ CH_3 \end{array}\right\rangle-CH_3 \qquad \text{camphor}$$

17-4 OPTICALLY ACTIVE COMPOUNDS HAVING NO ASYMMETRIC CARBON ATOMS

A. Allenes and Spiranes

Many compounds have no asymmetric carbon atoms, yet exhibit optical isomerism. This condition sometimes exists when there is a possibility for restricted rotation. For instance, in a molecule of allene, the two planes that contain the terminal methylene (CH_2) groups are mutually perpendicular because of the rigidity and directional character of the two cumulated double bonds.

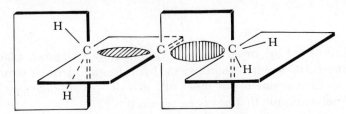

Consequently, an allene of the type $XYC=C=CXY$, in which X and Y are different, is asymmetric and can exist in two, nonsuperimposable, optically active forms.

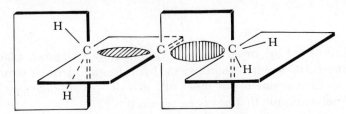

mirror plane

EXERCISE 17-7   Can the structures $CH_2=C=CBr_2$ and $BrHC=C=C=CHBr$ be optically active? Explain.

The optical isomerism of allenes was predicted by van't Hoff some sixty years before experiment proved him to be correct. The delay was mainly caused by practical difficulties in resolving asymmetric allenes. The first successful resolutions were achieved with the allenes, [24] and [25].

[24]   [25]

Other structures that can have the same type of asymmetry are the spiranes, which are bicyclic compounds with one atom (and only one) common to both rings. The simplest example is spiro[2.2]pentane [26].

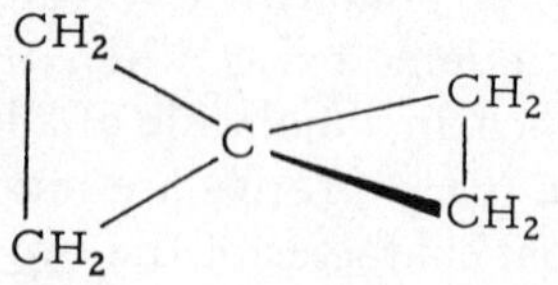

$$
\begin{array}{c}
CH_2 \\
| \qquad C \qquad CH_2 \\
CH_2 \qquad\qquad CH_2
\end{array}
$$

[26]

The two rings of [26], or any spirane, cannot lie in a common plane; hence, provided that each ring is substituted so that it has no plane of symmetry, the substance can exist as one or the other of a pair of optically active enantiomers. An example of a spirane that has been resolved is [27].

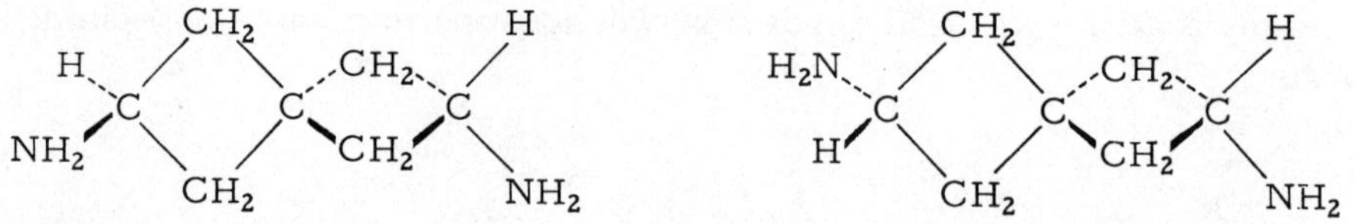

[27]

EXERCISE 17-8   Would the following structures be resolvable into optically active isomers? Show the structures of the possible isomers.

a.

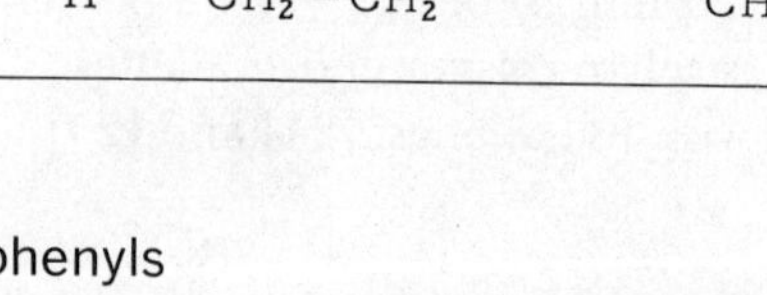

$$
\begin{array}{c}
CH_3 \qquad CH_2-CH_2 \qquad\qquad H \\
C \qquad\qquad\qquad C=C \\
H \qquad CH_2-CH_2 \qquad\qquad CO_2H
\end{array}
$$

b.

$$
\begin{array}{c}
CH_3 \qquad CH_2-CH_2 \qquad\qquad\qquad CH_2-CH_2 \qquad CH_3 \\
C \qquad\qquad\qquad C=C=C \qquad\qquad\qquad C \\
H \qquad CH_2-CH_2 \qquad\qquad\qquad CH_2-CH_2 \qquad H
\end{array}
$$

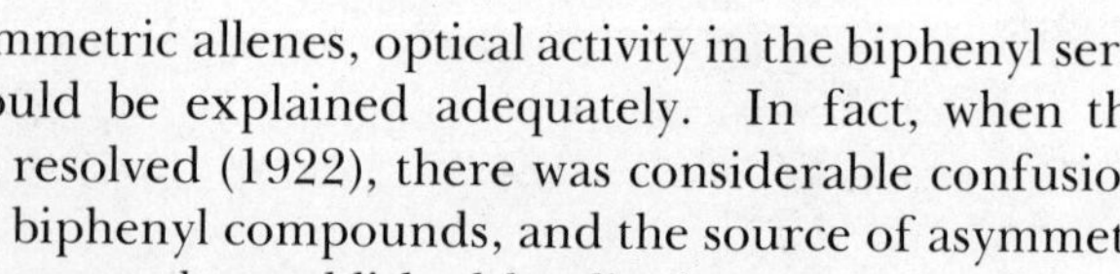

B. Optically Active Biphenyls

In contrast to the asymmetric allenes, optical activity in the biphenyl series was discovered before it could be explained adequately. In fact, when the first biphenyl derivative was resolved (1922), there was considerable confusion as to the correct structure of biphenyl compounds, and the source of asymmetry was not known. It was subsequently established by dipole-moment and X-ray diffraction data that the benzene rings in biphenyls are coaxial.

common
axis

With this information, the existence of stable optical isomers of o,o'-dinitro-diphenic acid [28] can be explained only if rotation about the central bond does not occur and, in addition, the two rings lie in different planes. A molecule of [28] fulfilling these requirements is not superimposable on its mirror image, and will therefore be optically active.

[28]

The lack of rotation about the pivot bond is caused by steric hindrance be-tween the bulky *ortho* substituents. Evidence for this stems from the failure to resolve any biphenyl derivatives that are not substituted in *ortho* positions. Also, resolution of *ortho*-substituted derivatives can be achieved only if the *ortho* sub-stituents are sufficiently large. Thus, o,o'-difluorodiphenic acid [29], like the corresponding dinitro derivative [28], is resolvable but is more easily racemized than [28]. This is due to the smaller size of the fluorine atom relative to the nitro group and, with less interference from the *ortho* substituents, the rings can more easily pivot about the central bond; once they pass through the planar con-formation, the asymmetry is lost and racemization results.

[29]   planar   [29]

It is not necessary that all four *ortho* positions be substituted. The prerequisite for optical activity is only that the substituent(s) be large enough to prevent free rotation and that each ring be unsymmetrically substituted. For example, com-pounds [30], [31], and [32] have been resolved. However, [33] is not resolvable since not only are the *ortho* substituents too small, but one ring is symmetrically substituted; therefore, the molecule has a plane of symmetry when the rings are mutually perpendicular.

[30]

[31]

[32]

[33]

EXERCISE 17-9 Which of the following biphenyl derivatives would you expect might give stable enantiomers? Show your reasoning.

a.

c.

b.

d.

C. Optically Active Cycloalkenes

One of the most interesting developments in the stereochemistry of organic compounds in recent years has been the demonstration that *trans*-(but not *cis*-)cyclooctene can be resolved into stable optically active forms. In general, a *trans*-cycloalkene would not be expected to be resolvable because of the possibility for a plane of symmetry passing through the double bond and the other ring carbons [Figure 17-2(a)]. When the chain connecting the ends of the double

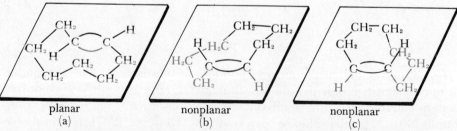

planar
(a)

nonplanar
(b)

nonplanar
(c)

Figure 17-2 Schematic representation of planar (a) and nonplanar (b) and (c) conformations of trans-cycloalkenes using cyclooctene as a specific example. For cyclooctene the planar state is very highly strained.

bond is short, as in cyclȯöctene, however, steric hindrance prevents ready formation of the planar conformation, and the two mirror image forms [Figure 17-2(b) and (c)] can be separately stable.

EXERCISE 17-10   Stuart models (p. 13) indicate that *trans*-cyclopentadecene is not likely to be optically stable. How and where might *trans*-cyclopentadecene be substituted so as to give stable mirror-image forms possessing no asymmetrically substituted carbon atoms?

17-5 ABSOLUTE AND RELATIVE CONFIGURATION

The sign of rotation of plane-polarized light by an enantiomer is not easily related to either its absolute or relative configuration. This is true even for substances with very similar structures, and we find that an optically active acid derivative having the same sign of rotation as the parent acid need not have the same configuration. Thus, given lactic acid, $CH_3CHOHCO_2H$, with a specific rotation $+3.82°$, and methyl lactate, $CH_3CHOHCO_2CH_3$, with a specific rotation $-8.25°$, we cannot tell from the rotations alone whether the acid and ester have the same or a different arrangement of groups about the asymmetric center. The relative configurations have to be obtained by other means.

If we convert (+)-lactic acid into its methyl ester, we can be reasonably certain that the ester will be related in configuration to the acid, since esterification should not affect the configuration about the asymmetric carbon atom. It happens that the methyl ester so obtained is levorotatory, so we know that (+)-lactic acid and (−)-methyl lactate have the same relative configuration at the asymmetric carbon, even if they possess opposite signs of optical rotation. However, we still do not know the *absolute* configuration; that is, we are unable to tell which of the two possible configurations of lactic acid, [34a] or [34b], corresponds to the dextro or (+)-acid and which to the levo or (−)-acid.

[34a]

[34b]

Until quite recently, the absolute configuration of no optically active compound was known with certainty. Instead, configurations were assigned relative to a standard, glyceraldehyde, which was originally chosen for the purpose of correlating the configurations of carbohydrates but has also been related to many other classes of compounds, including α-amino acids, terpenes, and steroids, as well as a variety of other biochemically important substances. Dextrorotatory glyceraldehyde was arbitrarily assigned the configuration [35] and is known as D-(+)-glyceraldehyde. The levorotatory enantiomer [36] is designated as L-(−)-glyceraldehyde. In these names, the sign in parentheses refers only to the direction of rotation, while the small capital letters D or L denote the absolute configuration. The sign of rotation is sometimes written as d for (+) and l for (−), or dl for (±).

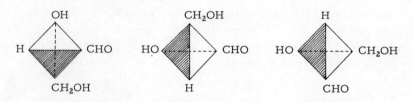

[35]   [36]

D-(+)-glyceraldehyde   L-(−)-glyceraldehyde

EXERCISE 17-11   Designate which of the following configurations of glyceraldehyde are D and which L:

In general, the absolute configuration of a substituent at an asymmetric center is specified by writing a projection formula with the carbon chain vertical and the lowest numbered carbon at the top. The D-configuration is then the one that has a specified substituent on the bond extending to the *right* of the asymmetric carbon; while the L-configuration has the substituent on the *left*.

$$R_2\text{--}\underset{\underset{R_3}{|}}{\overset{\overset{R_1}{|}}{C}}\text{--}X \qquad\qquad\qquad X\text{--}\underset{\underset{R_3}{|}}{\overset{\overset{R_1}{|}}{C}}\text{--}R_2$$

D-configuration   L-configuration

Compounds whose configurations are related to D-(+)-glyceraldehyde are taken to belong to the D-series, and those related to L-(−)-glyceraldehyde belong to the L-series. One method of relating configurations is illustrated in Figure 17-3, which shows how the configuration of (−)-lactic acid can be related to that of D-(+)-glyceraldehyde. Clearly, (−)-lactic acid belongs to the D series and has the configuration shown in structure [34a]. The other enantiomer is L-(+)-lactic acid with structure [34b].

Many of the naturally occurring α-amino acids have been correlated with glyceraldehyde by the type of transformations shown in Figure 17-4. Here, natural alanine is related to L-(+)-lactic acid and hence to L-(−)-glyceraldehyde. Alanine therefore belongs to the L-series, and by similar correlations, it has been shown that all of the α-amino acids which are also constituents of proteins are L-amino acids. Many D-amino acids are components of other biologically important substances.

When there are several asymmetric carbon atoms in a molecule, the configuration at one center is usually related directly or indirectly to glyceraldehyde, and the configurations at the other centers are determined relative to the first. Thus in the aldehyde form of the important sugar, (+)-glucose, there are four asymmetric centers, and so there are 2^4 = sixteen possible stereoisomers. The projection formula of the isomer which corresponds to natural glucose is [37]. By convention for sugars, the configuration of the *highest* numbered asymmetric carbon is referred to glyceraldehyde to determine the over-all configuration of the molecule. For glucose, this atom is C5, next to the CH_2OH group, and has the hydroxyl on the right. Therefore, naturally occurring glucose belongs to the D series and is properly called D-glucose (see also p. 436).

$$^1CHO$$
$$H-^2C^*-OH$$
$$HO-^3C^*-H$$
$$H-^4C^*-OH$$
$$H \quad ^5C^*-OH \qquad D$$
$$^6CH_2OH$$

[37]

On the other hand, the configurations of α-amino acids possessing more than one asymmetric center are determined by the *lowest* numbered asymmetric carbon, which is the carbon *alpha* to the carboxyl group. Thus, even though the natural α-amino acid, threonine, has exactly the same kind of arrangement of substituents as the natural sugar, threose, threonine by the amino acid convention belongs to the L-series, while threose by the sugar convention, belongs to the D-series.

$$CO_2H \qquad\qquad CHO$$
$$H_2N-C-H \quad L \qquad HO-C-H$$
$$H-C-OH \qquad H-C-OH \quad D$$
$$CH_3 \qquad\qquad CH_2OH$$
$$\text{L-threonine} \qquad \text{D-(−)-threose}$$

A serious ambiguity arises for compounds like the active tartaric acids. If the amino acid convention is used, (+)-tartaric acid [20a] falls in the D-series; while,

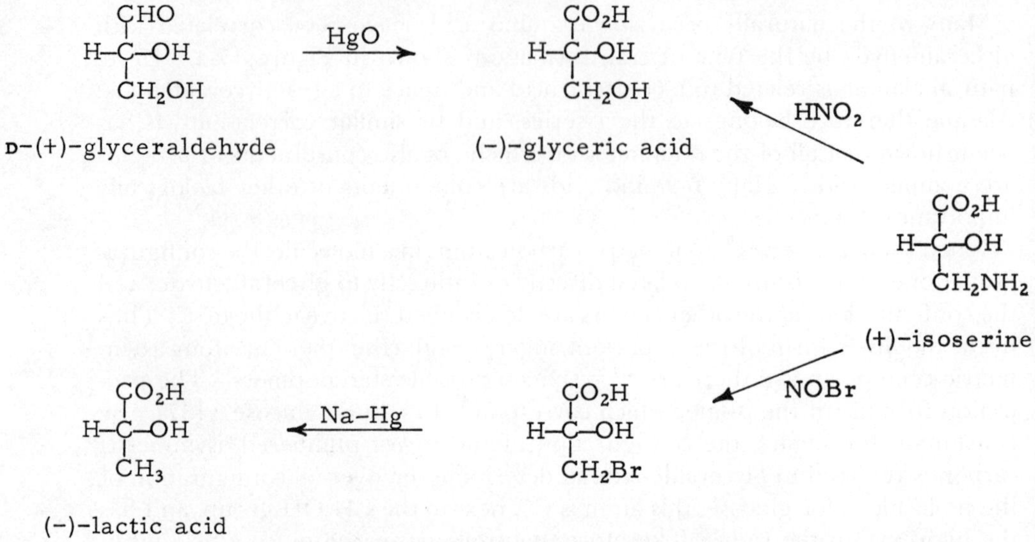

$$
\begin{array}{ccc}
\text{CHO} & & \text{CO}_2\text{H} \\
| & \xrightarrow{\;\;\text{HgO}\;\;} & | \\
\text{H--C--OH} & & \text{H--C--OH} \\
| & & | \\
\text{CH}_2\text{OH} & & \text{CH}_2\text{OH}
\end{array}
$$

D-(+)-glyceraldehyde   (−)-glyceric acid

(arrow labeled HNO$_2$)

$$
\begin{array}{c}
\text{CO}_2\text{H} \\
| \\
\text{H--C--OH} \\
| \\
\text{CH}_2\text{NH}_2
\end{array}
$$

(+)-isoserine

$$
\begin{array}{ccccc}
\text{CO}_2\text{H} & & \text{CO}_2\text{H} & & \\
| & \xleftarrow{\;\;\text{Na--Hg}\;\;} & | & \xleftarrow{\;\;\text{NOBr}\;\;} & \\
\text{H--C--OH} & & \text{H--C--OH} & & \\
| & & | & & \\
\text{CH}_3 & & \text{CH}_2\text{Br} & &
\end{array}
$$

(−)-lactic acid

Figure 17-3   Chemical transformations showing how the configuration of (−)-lactic acid has been related to D-(+)-glyceraldehyde. None of the transformations cause any change in configuration at the asymmetric carbon atom.

by the sugar convention, it has the L-configuration. One way out of this dilemma is to use the subscripts s and g to denote the amino acid or carbohydrate conventions, respectively. Then the absolute configuration of (+)-tartaric acid can be designated as either D$_s$-(+)-tartaric acid or L$_g$-(+)-tartaric acid.

At the time the choice of absolute configuration for glyceraldehyde was made, there was no way of knowing whether the configuration of (+)-glyceraldehyde was in reality [36] or [37]. However, the choice had a 50 per cent chance of being correct and we now know that [36], the D-configuration, is in fact the correct configuration of (+)-glyceraldehyde. This was established through use of a special X-ray crystallographic technique, which permitted determination of the absolute disposition of the atoms in space of sodium rubidium (+)-tartrate. The

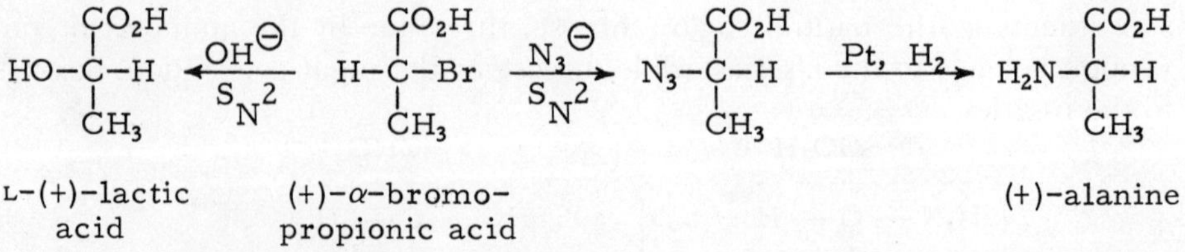

$$
\begin{array}{cccccccc}
\text{CO}_2\text{H} & & \text{CO}_2\text{H} & & \text{CO}_2\text{H} & & \text{CO}_2\text{H} \\
| & \xleftarrow[\text{S}_\text{N}2]{\text{OH}^\ominus} & | & \xrightarrow[\text{S}_\text{N}2]{\text{N}_3^\ominus} & | & \xrightarrow{\text{Pt, H}_2} & | \\
\text{HO--C--H} & & \text{H--C--Br} & & \text{N}_3\text{--C--H} & & \text{H}_2\text{N--C--H} \\
| & & | & & | & & | \\
\text{CH}_3 & & \text{CH}_3 & & \text{CH}_3 & & \text{CH}_3
\end{array}
$$

L-(+)-lactic   (+)-α-bromo-   (+)-alanine
acid   propionic acid

Figure 17-4   Chemical transformations showing how the configuration of natural (+)-alanine has been related to L-(+)-lactic acid and hence to L-(−)-glyceraldehyde (see Figure 17-3). The transformations shown involve two S$_\text{N}$2 reactions which are stereospecific and invert configuration (Chapter 11). Reduction of the azide group leaves the configuration unchanged.

configuration of (+)-tartaric acid [20a] had been previously shown by chemical means to be the same as that of (+)-glyceraldehyde. Consequently, the absolute configuration of any compound is now known once it has been correlated directly or indirectly with glyceraldehyde.

EXERCISE 17-12   Write Fischer projection formulas for each of the following substances, remembering, where necessary, that D and L isomers of substances with more than one asymmetric carbon are always enantiomers, not diastereomers. The glyceraldehyde convention is understood unless otherwise noted.

        a. L-alanine   d. L-glucose

        b. D-2,3-butanediol   e. D_s-threo-2,3-dihydroxybutyric acid

        c. D-threonine   f. L-erythro-2,3-butanediol monomethyl ether

---

17-6 SEPARATION OR RESOLUTION OF ENANTIOMERS

Since the physical properties of enantiomers are identical, they cannot usually be separated by physical methods, such as fractional crystallization or distillation. It is only in the presence of another optically active substance that the enantiomers behave differently, and almost all methods of resolution (and asymmetric synthesis) are based upon this fact.

Perhaps the most general resolution procedure is to form nonidentical derivatives of the enantiomers by converting them to diastereomers. For instance, if a racemic or D,L mixture of an acid is converted to a salt with an optically active base of the D-configuration, the salt will be a mixture of two diastereomers, (D-acid + D-base) and (L-acid + D-base). These diastereomeric salts are not identical and not mirror images and will therefore differ in their physical properties. Hence, separation by physical means, such as crystallization, is in principle possible. Once separated, the acid regenerated from each salt will be either the pure D- or L-enantiomer.

Resolution of optically active acids through formation of diastereomeric salts requires adequate supplies of suitable optically active bases. Brucine [38a], strychnine [38b], and quinine [39] are most frequently used because they are readily available, naturally occurring, optically active bases.

brucine, R=OCH₃ [38a]

strychnine, R=H [38b]

quinine [39]

For the resolution of a racemic base, optically active acids are used, such as (+)-tartaric acid, (−)-malic acid, (−)-mandelic acid, and (+)-camphor-10-sulfonic acid.

CH$_2$CO$_2$H
|
CHOH
|
CO$_2$H

malic acid

C$_6$H$_5$
|
CHOH
|
CO$_2$H

mandelic acid

camphor-10-sulfonic acid

To resolve an alcohol, an optically active acid may be used to convert the alcohol to a mixture of diastereomeric esters. High-molecular-weight acids (~400) are advantageous since they are likely to give crystalline esters, and these may usually be separated with fair ease by fractional crystallization.

Alternatively, the alcohol may be converted to a half-ester of a dicarboxylic acid, such as succinic or phthalic acid, by reaction with the corresponding anhydride. The resulting half-ester has a free carboxyl function and may then be resolved with an optically active base.

CH$_3$
|
*CHOH
|
CH$_2$
|
CH$_3$

D, L-s-butyl alcohol

+

CH$_2$
CH$_2$

succinic anhydride

→

CH$_3$ O
| ||
*CHO—C—CH$_2$
| |
CH$_2$ CH$_2$CO$_2$H
|
CH$_3$

half-ester of succinic acid

→

resolve with brucine

|hydrolysis

optically active alcohols

The method is of considerable generality and is limited only by the ease with which the particular diastereomers are separable and the ease of regenerating the pure enantiomer without concurrent racemization. Separation by physical methods is often tedious, and complete separation may not always be possible for a given set of diastereomers. In such cases, a second or third set may have to be prepared using different optically active resolving agents.

Other more specialized methods of resolution are also available. One procedure, which is excellent when applicable, takes advantage of differences in reaction rates of enantiomers with optically active substances. One enantiomer may react more rapidly, leaving an excess of the other enantiomer behind. As one example, racemic tartaric acid can be resolved with the aid of certain penicillin molds that consume the dextrorotatory enantiomer faster than the levorotatory enantiomer; as a result, almost pure (−)-tartaric acid can be recovered from the mixture.

(±)-tartaric acid + mold ⟶ (−)-tartaric acid + more mold

The crystallization procedure employed by Pasteur for his classical resolution of D,L-tartaric acid is limited to very few cases. It depends upon the formation of individual crystals of each enantiomer. Thus, if the crystallization of sodium ammonium tartrate is carried out below 27°, the usual racemate salt does not form; a mixture of crystals of the D- and L-salts forms instead. The two different kinds of crystals, which are related as object to mirror image, can be separated manually with the aid of a microscope and may be subsequently converted to the tartaric acid enantiomers by strong acid. A variation on this method of resolution is the seeding of a saturated solution of a D,L mixture with crystals of one pure enantiomer in the hope of causing immediate crystallization of that enantiomer, leaving the other in solution. Very few practical resolutions have been achieved in this way.

Chromatographic methods likewise have limited utility. The usual procedure is to pass a solution of the racemic substance over an optically active adsorbent to determine whether one enantiomer is adsorbed more strongly than the other. If so, careful elution may result in a partial or even complete resolution.

17-7 ASYMMETRIC SYNTHESIS AND ASYMMETRIC INDUCTION

If one could prepare α-hydroxypropionitrile from acetaldehyde and hydrogen cyanide in the absence of any optically active substance and produce an excess of one enantiomer over the other, this would constitute an **absolute asymmetric synthesis** — that is, creation of an optically active compound in a symmetrical environment from symmetrical reagents.

L-α-hydroxy-
propionitrile

D-α-hydroxy-
propionitrile

This is obviously unlikely for the given example because there is no reason for cyanide ion to have anything other than an exactly equal chance of attacking above or below the plane of the acetaldehyde molecule, thus producing equal numbers of molecules of each enantiomer.

However, when an asymmetric center is already present and a second center is created, an exactly 1:1 mixture of the two possible isomers (which are now diastereomers) is not expected. The optically active aldehyde [40] and methylmagnesium iodide can yield two diastereomeric alcohols, [41a] and [41b]. Indeed, both *are* formed, but [41b] dominates over [41a] by about 2:1.

[40]

[41a]   [41b]

The formation of unequal amounts of diastereomers when a second asymmetric center is created in the presence of a first is called **asymmetric induction.** The degree of stereochemical control displayed by the first asymmetric center usually depends on how close it is to the second — the more widely separated they are, the less steric control there is. Another factor is the degree of asymmetry at the first asymmetric center. If all the groups there are very much the same electrically and sterically, not much stereochemical control is to be expected.

Even when the asymmetric centers are close neighbors, asymmetric induction is seldom 100 per cent efficient in simple molecules. In biochemical systems, however, asymmetric synthesis is highly efficient. The photosynthesis of glucose [37] by plants from carbon dioxide and water gives the D-enantiomer only. The L-enantiomer is "unnatural" and, furthermore, is not even metabolized by animals. Similarly, all of the α-amino acids, which can be asymmetric and are constituents of proteins, have the L-configuration. The D-acids are usually regarded as "unnatural."

L-α-amino acid

The stereospecificity of biochemical reactions is a consequence of their being catalyzed in every case by enzymes, which are large protein molecules possessing many asymmetric centers and hence are themselves highly asymmetric. The stereospecificity of living organisms is imperative to their efficiency. The reason is that it is just not possible for an organism to be so constructed as to be able to deal with all of the theoretically possible isomers of molecules with many asymmetric centers. Thus, if a protein molecule has 100 different asymmetric centers (a not uncommon or, in fact, large number), it would have 2^{100} or 10^{30} possible optical isomers. A vessel with a capacity on the order of 10^7 liters would be required to hold all of the possible stereo-isomeric molecules of this structure if no two were identical. An organism so con-stituted as to be able to deal specifically with each one of these isomers would be very large indeed.

17-8 RACEMIZATION

Optically active biphenyl derivatives (see pp. 410–412) are racemized if the two aromatic rings at any time pass through a coplanar configuration by rotation about the central bond. This can be brought about more or less easily by heat, unless the *ortho*-substituents are very large.

The way in which compounds with asymmetric carbon atoms are race-mized is more complicated. Optically active carbonyl compounds of the type $\overset{*}{-}\text{CH}-\overset{|}{\text{C}}=\text{O}$, in which the *alpha* carbon is asymmetric, are racemized by both acids and bases, and from the discussion on pp. 336–338 of halogenation of carbonyl compounds, this is surely related to enolization. Formation of either the enol or the enolate anion will destroy the asymmetry at the α carbon so that, even if only trace amounts of enol are present at any given time, eventually all of the compound will be racemized. However, the mechanism requires both that there be an α hydrogen and also that the center of asymmetry be located at this α carbon. Otherwise acids and bases are ineffective in catalyzing race-mization.

Base-catalyzed enolization:

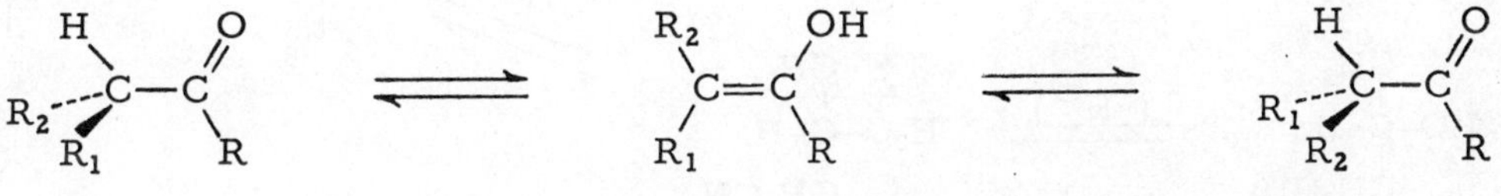

Acid-catalyzed enolization:

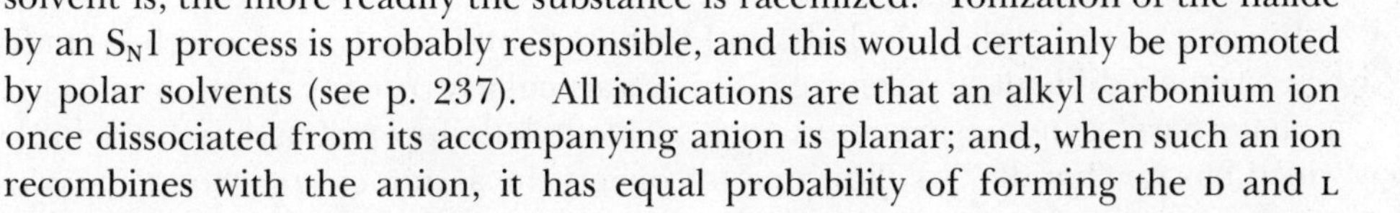

The racemization of an optically active secondary halide (e.g., *s*-butyl chlo-ride) may occur in solution and, usually, the more polar and better ionizing the solvent is, the more readily the substance is racemized. Ionization of the halide by an S_N1 process is probably responsible, and this would certainly be promoted by polar solvents (see p. 237). All indications are that an alkyl carbonium ion once dissociated from its accompanying anion is planar; and, when such an ion recombines with the anion, it has equal probability of forming the D and L enantiomers.

$$
\begin{array}{c} CH_3 \\ | \\ H-C-Cl \\ | \\ CH_2CH_3 \end{array}
\underset{\longleftarrow}{\overset{-Cl^{\ominus}}{\longrightarrow}}
\left[
\begin{array}{c} CH_3 \\ \overset{\oplus}{C} \\ H^{\diagup} \diagdown CH_2CH_3 \end{array}
\right]
\underset{\longleftarrow}{\overset{Cl^{\ominus}}{\longrightarrow}}
\begin{array}{c} CH_3 \\ | \\ Cl-C-H \\ | \\ CH_2CH_3 \end{array}
$$

D   L

Optically active halides can also be racemized by an S_N2 mechanism. A solution of active *s*-butyl chloride in acetone containing dissolved lithium chloride becomes racemic. Displacement of the chloride of the halide by chloride ion inverts configuration at the atom undergoing substitution (see pp. 230–232). A second substitution regenerates the original enantiomer. Eventually, this back-and-forth process produces equal numbers of the D- and L-forms; the substance is then racemic.

$$
\begin{array}{c} CH_3 \\ | \\ H-C-Cl \\ | \\ CH_2CH_3 \end{array}
\underset{Cl^{\ominus}}{\overset{Cl^{\ominus}}{\rightleftharpoons}}
\begin{array}{c} CH_3 \\ | \\ Cl-C-H \\ | \\ CH_2CH_3 \end{array}
$$

D   L

Asymmetric alcohols are often racemized by strong acids. Undoubtedly, ionization takes place, and recombination of the carbonium ion with water leads to either enantiomer.

$$
\begin{array}{c} CH_3 \\ | \\ H-C-OH \\ | \\ CH_2CH_3 \end{array}
\underset{\longleftarrow}{\overset{H^{\oplus}}{\longrightarrow}}
\begin{array}{c} CH_3 \overset{\oplus}{} \\ | \\ H-C-OH_2 \\ | \\ CH_2CH_3 \end{array}
\overset{(-H_2O)}{\diagdown}
$$

D

$$
\left[
\begin{array}{c} CH_3 \\ \overset{\oplus}{C} \\ H^{\diagup}\diagdown CH_2CH_3 \end{array}
\right]
$$

$$
\begin{array}{c} CH_3 \\ | \\ HO-C-H \\ | \\ CH_2CH_3 \end{array}
\underset{\longleftarrow}{\overset{(-H^{\oplus})}{\longrightarrow}}
\begin{array}{c} \overset{\oplus}{} CH_3 \\ | \\ H_2O-C-H \\ | \\ CH_2CH_3 \end{array}
\overset{H_2O}{\diagup}
$$

L

In contrast to halides, alcohols, and carbonyl compounds, hydrocarbons may be extremely difficult to racemize. This is particularly true for a compound with a quaternary asymmetric center, such as methylethylpropylbutylmethane [42], which has no "handle" to allow one to convert the asymmetric carbon to a symmetric condition by simple chemical means.

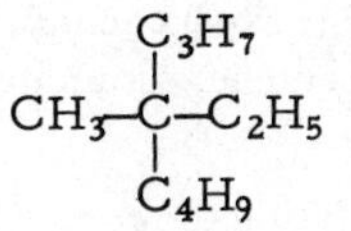

$$CH_3-\underset{\underset{C_4H_9}{|}}{\overset{\overset{C_3H_7}{|}}{C}}-C_2H_5$$

[42]

However, hydrocarbons that have a hydrogen atom at the asymmetric carbon may be racemized if they can be converted either to carbonium ions or else to carbanions. The ease of carbanion-type racemization will depend on the acidity of the attached hydrogen and on the stereochemical stability of the intermediate carbanion that is formed. If the configuration of the carbanion intermediate inverts, racemization will result.

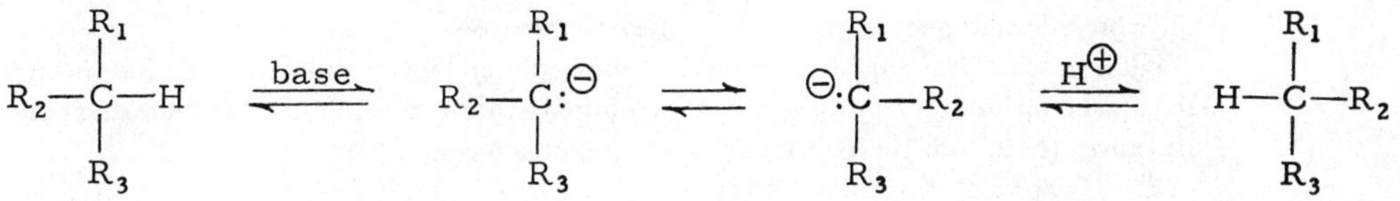

SUPPLEMENTARY EXERCISES

17-13 Which of the following projection formulas represent the same optical isomers? Write each in its proper form as a Fischer projection formula of 3-amino-2-butanol.

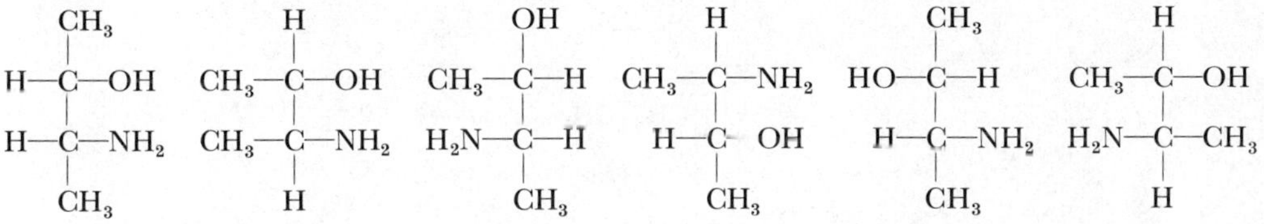

17-14 Draw Fischer projection formulas for all the possible different optical isomers of the following substances:

f.
$$\begin{array}{c} CO_2CH_3 \\ | \\ CHO \\ | \quad\quad CH_2 \\ CHO \\ | \\ CO_2CH_3 \end{array}$$

a. 1,2,3,4-tetrachlorobutane
b. methylethylpropylboron
c. 2,3-dibromopropionic acid
d. triisopropylmethane
e. 3-bromo-2,5-hexanediol

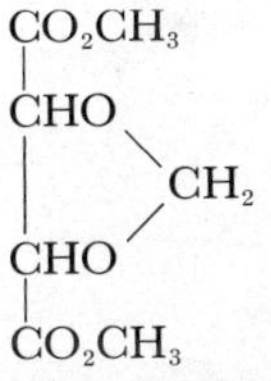

g. methyl hydrogen tartrate
h. s-butyl lactate

17-15 Predict the stereochemical configuration of the products from each of the following reactions. Write projection formulas for the starting materials and products.
   a. D-s-butyl alcohol with acetic anhydride
   b. D-methylethylisobutylcarbinol with hydrochloric acid
   c. D-glycerol monoacetate with aqueous sodium hydroxide
   d. D-s-butyl t-butyl ketone with bromine and dilute base

17-16 Explain how one could determine experimentally whether hydrogen peroxide in formic acid adds *cis* or *trans* to cyclopentene, assuming the possible addition products to be unknown.

17-17 Devise a reaction scheme for relating the configuration of (+)-2-butanol to glyceraldehyde. Think carefully about the reaction mechanisms involved in devising your scheme.

17-18 Discuss possible procedures for resolution of ethyl D,L-lactate (ethyl α-hydroxypropionate, b.p. 155°) into ethyl D-lactate and ethyl L-lactate.

17-19 How could you tell whether a chloroform solution of an optically active compound showing a rotation of − 100° was actually levorotatory by − 100° or dextrorotatory by +260°?

17-20 Solutions of optically active 2,2′-diiodobiphenyl-5,5′-dicarboxylic acid racemize at a measurable rate on heating. Racemization of active 2,3,2′,3′-tetraiodobiphenyl-5,5′-dicarboxylic acid goes many thousand times more slowly.

Make a scale drawing of the transition state (planar) for racemization; deduce from it the reason for the very slow racemization of the tetraiodo diacid. Use the following bond distances (note that the benzene ring is a regular hexagon):

C—C (benzene ring) = 1.40 A
C—C (between rings) = 1.47 A
C—H   = 1.07 A
C—I   = 1.63 A

The interference radii of iodine and hydrogen are 2.15 and 1.20 A, respectively.

17-21 Compounds of the type shown below have been found to be resolvable into two optically active forms. Explain.

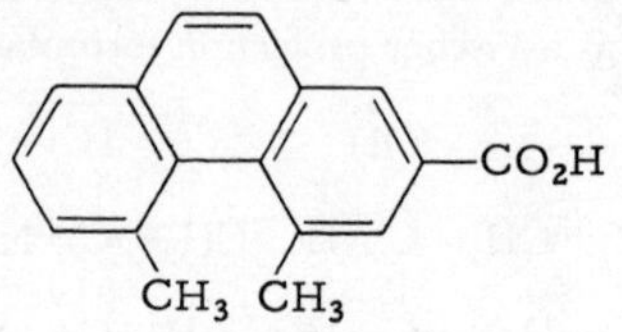

Carbohydrates

*C*arbohydrates are a major class of naturally occurring organic compounds which come by their name because they usually have, or approximate, the general formula $(C \cdot H_2O)_n$, with n equal to or greater than four. Among the well-known carbohydrates are the various sugars, starches, and cellulose, all of which are important for the maintenance of life in both plants and animals.

Although the structures of many carbohydrates appear to be quite complex, the chemistry of these substances usually involves only two basic kinds of functional groups—keto or aldehyde carbonyls and alcoholic hydroxyl groups. The carbonyl groups do not normally occur as such but are combined with the hydroxyl groups in the form of hemiacetal or acetal linkages of the kind discussed in Chapter 14.

An understanding of stereochemistry is particularly important to understanding the properties of carbohydrates. Optical isomerism, cis-trans isomerism, and axial-equatorial isomerism of cyclohexanes all play an important role.

Carbohydrates

Carbohydrates are formed in green plants as the result of **photosynthesis,** which is the chemical combination or "fixation" of carbon dioxide and water by utilization of energy gained through absorption of visible light.

$$x \ CO_2 + x \ H_2O \ \xrightarrow[\text{green plants}]{\text{light}} \ (CH_2O)_x + x \ O_2$$

carbohydrate

Although many aspects of photosynthesis are not yet well understood, the primary process is clearly the excitation of the green plant pigment chlorophyll-*a* (Figure 18-1) by absorption of light; the energy of the resulting activated chlorophyll-*a* molecules is used to oxidize water to oxygen and to reduce carbon dioxide. The first-formed carbon dioxide reduction product is not known with certainty but is probably closely related to D-glyceric acid.

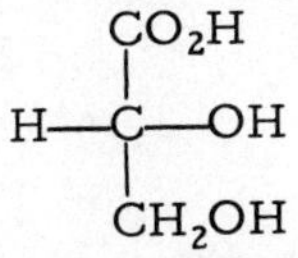

$$
\begin{array}{c}
CO_2H \\
| \\
H\text{---}C\text{---}OH \\
| \\
CH_2OH
\end{array}
\qquad \text{D-glyceric acid}
$$

From this compound, the plant carries out a series of enzyme-catalyzed reac-

427

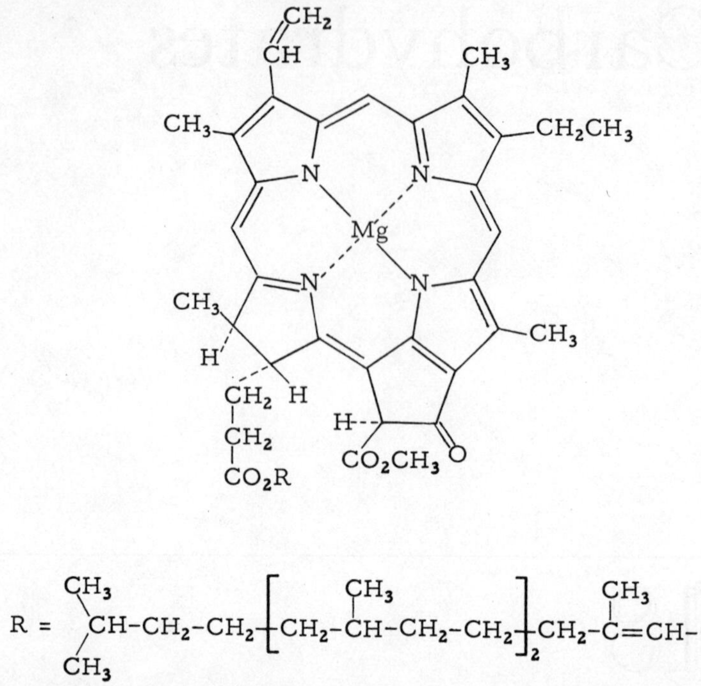

R = [structure] CH_3 / CH-CH$_2$-CH$_2$-[CH$_2$-CH-CH$_2$-CH$_2$]$_2$-CH$_2$-C=CH-CH$_2$-

Figure 18-1   The structure of chlorophyll-a showing *cis-trans* relationships of the substituents.

tions which result in the synthesis of simple sugars, such as glucose ($C_6H_{12}O_6$), and polymeric substances, such as the starches and cellulose ($C_6H_{10}O_5)_n$, with $n > 1000$.

18-1 CLASSIFICATION OF CARBOHYDRATES

The simple sugars or monosaccharides are the building blocks of carbohydrate chemistry. They are polyhydric alcohols of five, six, seven, or eight carbon atoms. They are also carbonyl compounds (aldehydes or ketones); however, the carbonyl group is not usually present as such but occurs combined with one of the hydroxyl groups in the same molecule to form a cyclic hemiacetal or hemiketal.

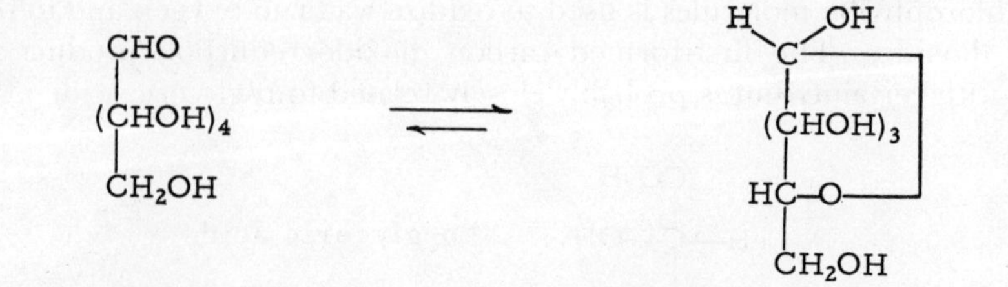

an aldohexose

(open-chain form)

a 1, 5-cyclic hemiacetal

of an aldohexose

Table 18-1   Typical Aldopentoses

Pentose and occurrence	Open-chain structure	Cyclic oxide structure[a]
L-arabinose free in many coniferous trees; combined as glycosides and polysaccharides	CHO H—C—OH HO—C—H HO—C—H CH$_2$OH	β–anomer
D-ribose found combined as N-glycosides in nucleic acids, several vitamins and coenzymes	CHO H—C—OH H—C—OH H—C—OH CH$_2$OH	α–anomer
2-deoxy-D-ribose found combined as N-glycosides in nucleic acids	CHO CH$_2$ H—C—OH H—C—OH CH$_2$OH	α–anomer
D-xylose combined as pentosan polysaccharides in woody materials	CHO H—C—OH HO—C—H H—C—OH CH$_2$OH	α–anomer

[a] The pyranose form is usually more stable than the furanose form for the free sugar. The furanose structure is shown for ribose and deoxyribose because this is the form in which these sugars occur in many important substances, such as the nucleic acids (Chapter 20).

The most abundant five-carbon sugars are L-arabinose, D-ribose, 2-deoxy-D-ribose, and D-xylose. They are classified as **pentoses** or, more correctly, as **aldopentoses,** since each has a potential aldehyde function. Both the open-chain and cyclic structures of some typical aldopentoses are shown in Table 18-1.

Table 18-2   Typical Six-carbon Sugars

Hexose	Open-chain structure	Cyclic oxide structure
D-glucose (see discussion)	CHO H—C—OH HO—C—H H—C—OH H—C—OH CH_2OH	α-anomer
D-fructose free in fruit juices and honey; combined as in sucrose and in polysaccharides	CH_2OH C=O HO—C—H H—C—OH H—C—OH CH_2OH	β-anomer
D-mannose constituent of polysaccharides	CHO HO—C—H HO—C—H H—C—OH H—C—OH CH_2OH	β-anomer
D-galactose constituent of oligosaccharides (lactose, melibiose, and raffinose) and polysaccharides (gums)	CHO H—C—OH HO—C—H HO—C—H H—C—OH CH_2OH	α-anomer

Table 18-3   Some Classes and Examples of Naturally Occurring Carbohydrates

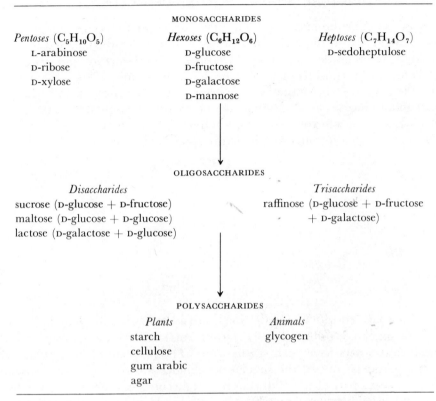

MONOSACCHARIDES

Pentoses ($C_5H_{10}O_5$)   *Hexoses* ($C_6H_{12}O_6$)   *Heptoses* ($C_7H_{14}O_7$)
   L-arabinose   D-glucose   D-sedoheptulose
   D-ribose   D-fructose
   D-xylose   D-galactose
                                        D-mannose

OLIGOSACCHARIDES

   Disaccharides   *Trisaccharides*
sucrose (D-glucose + D-fructose)   raffinose (D-glucose + D-fructose
maltose (D-glucose + D-glucose)   + D-galactose)
lactose (D-galactose + D-glucose)

POLYSACCHARIDES

   Plants   *Animals*
   starch   glycogen
   cellulose
   gum arabic
   agar

The common six-carbon sugars (hexoses) are D-glucose, D-fructose, D-galactose, and D-mannose.   They are all **aldohexoses,** except D-fructose, which is a **ketohexose.**   The structures of these hexoses are shown in Table 18-2.

The term **oligosaccharide** describes low-molecular-weight condensation polymers containing from two to nine monosaccharide units (most often hexoses). Many **disaccharides** (containing two monosaccharide units) are known, and, of these, sucrose is particularly important.

$$(C_6H_{11}O_5)O(C_6H_{11}O_5) \ + \ H_2O \ \longrightarrow \ C_6H_{12}O_6 \ + \ C_6H_{12}O_6$$

sucrose   D-glucose + D-fructose

Polysaccharides are high-molecular-weight polymers built up by repeated condensations of monosaccharides.   Examples are starches, glycogen, cellulose, and carbohydrate gums.   The relationship between the various classes of carbohydrates is summarized in Table 18-3.

Sugars are also found in nature in combination with nonsugars, usually hydroxy compounds or nitrogen bases.   Sugar derivatives of this kind are called **glycosides.**

18-2 THE STRUCTURE AND PROPERTIES OF D-GLUCOSE

Glucose is by far the most abundant monosaccharide; it occurs free in fruits, plants, honey, and in the blood and urine of animals, and combined in many glycosides, disaccharides, and polysaccharides. The structure and properties of glucose will be considered in greater detail than those of the other monosaccharides, not only because of its importance, but because much of what can be said about glucose can also be said about the other monosaccharides.

Glucose is an **aldohexose** — the name inferring that the compound is a six-carbon sugar with a terminal aldehyde group as in [1].

$$
\begin{array}{l}
\text{CHO} \\
^*\text{CHOH} \\
^*\text{CHOH} \\
^*\text{CHOH} \\
^*\text{CHOH} \\
\text{CH}_2\text{OH}
\end{array}
$$

[1]

The carbons labeled with an asterisk in [1] are asymmetric, and there are therefore 2^4, or sixteen, possible optically active forms. All are known — some occur naturally and others have been synthesized. The problem of identifying glucose as a particular one of the sixteen possibilities was solved by Emil Fischer during the latter part of the 19th century. The configurations he deduced for each of the asymmetric carbons, C2–C5, are shown in the projection formula [2].

$$
\begin{array}{l}
^1\text{CHO} \\
\text{H}-^2\text{C}-\text{OH} \\
\text{HO}-^3\text{C}-\text{H} \\
\text{H}-^4\text{C}-\text{OH} \\
\text{H}-^5\text{C}-\text{OH} \\
^6\text{CH}_2\text{OH}
\end{array}
$$

[2]

Although he was well aware that natural glucose could be the enantiomer of structure [2], his original guess at the absolute configuration proved to be correct; for the configuration at C5 is related to the configuration of the simplest "sugar," D-(+)-glyceraldehyde, which was arbitrarily assigned as [3] and later

$$
\begin{array}{l}
\text{CHO} \\
\text{H}-\text{C}-\text{OH} \\
\text{CH}_2\text{OH}
\end{array}
$$

[3]

shown to be correct (see pp. 413–417).   Therefore, natural glucose is specifically D-glucose.

EXERCISE 18-1   The logic necessary to solve this problem is essentially that used by Fischer in
his classic work which established the configurations of glucose, arabinose, and
mannose.

a. Write projection formulas for all the theoretically possible D-aldopentoses,
   $HOH_2C(CHOH)_3CHO$.

b. One of the D-aldopentoses is the naturally occurring D-arabinose, enantiomeric with the more abundant L-arabinose. Oxidation of D-arabinose
   with nitric acid gives an *optically active* five-carbon trihydroxydicarboxylic
   acid. Which of the D-aldopentoses could be D-arabinose?

c. D-Arabinose is converted by the following transformations into D-glucose
   and D-mannose. (This is the classic **Kiliani-Fischer cyanohydrin synthesis**
   of sugars.)   What do these transformations tell about the relationship
   between the configurations of mannose and glucose?

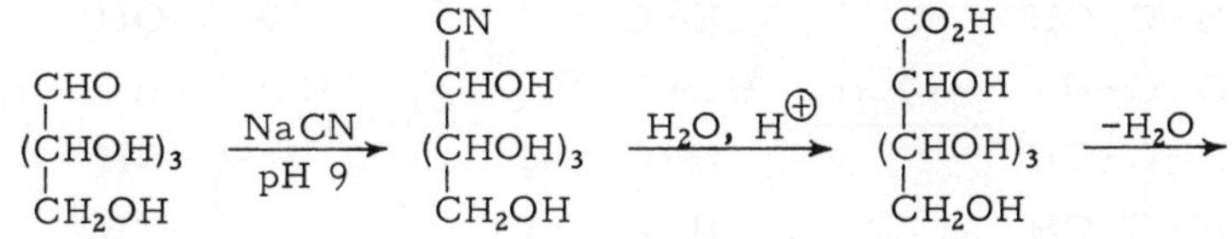

$$
\begin{array}{c}
CHO \\
(CHOH)_3 \\
CH_2OH
\end{array}
\xrightarrow[\text{pH 9}]{NaCN}
\begin{array}{c}
CN \\
CHOH \\
(CHOH)_3 \\
CH_2OH
\end{array}
\xrightarrow{H_2O,\ H^{\oplus}}
\begin{array}{c}
CO_2H \\
CHOH \\
(CHOH)_3 \\
CH_2OH
\end{array}
\xrightarrow{-H_2O}
$$

D–arabinose

$$
\begin{array}{c}
O=C\!\!\rule{0.6cm}{0.4pt} \\
CHOH \\
CHOH \\
CH\!\!\rule{0.6cm}{0.4pt}\!\!O \\
CHOH \\
CH_2OH
\end{array}
\xrightarrow[\text{pH 3}]{Na-Hg}
\begin{array}{c}
CHO \\
(CHOH)_4 \\
CH_2OH
\end{array}
$$

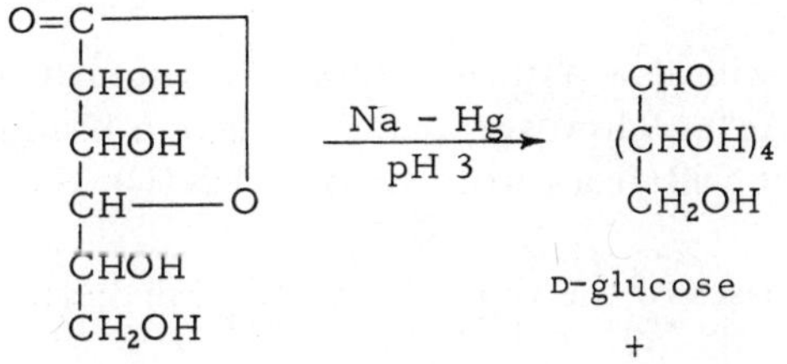

γ–lactone   D–glucose

+

D–mannose

d. Oxidation of D-glucose and D-mannose gives the six-carbon, tetrahydroxy-
   dicarboxylic acids, glucaric and mannaric acids, respectively. Both are
   optically active. What then are the configurations of the D- and L-arabi-
   noses?

e. D-Glucaric acid can form two different γ-monolactones, whereas D-mannaric
   acid can form only one monolactone. What then is the configuration of
   D-glucose and D-mannose?

EXERCISE 18-2   Deduce possible configurations of natural galactose from the following:

a. The **Wohl degradation** is a means of reducing the chain length of a sugar
   by one carbon through the following reaction sequence:

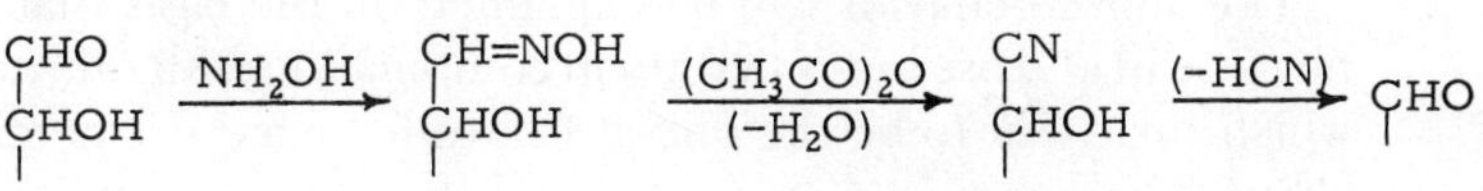

$$
\begin{array}{c}
CHO \\
CHOH
\end{array}
\xrightarrow{NH_2OH}
\begin{array}{c}
CH=NOH \\
CHOH
\end{array}
\xrightarrow[(-H_2O)]{(CH_3CO)_2O}
\begin{array}{c}
CN \\
CHOH
\end{array}
\xrightarrow{(-HCN)}
CHO
$$

D-Galactose gives a pentose by one Wohl degradation. This pentose on nitric acid oxidation gives an optically active, five-carbon, trihydroxydicarboxylic acid.

   b. The pentose by a second Wohl degradation followed by nitric acid oxidation gives D-tartaric acid.
   c. Write reasonable mechanisms for the reactions involved in the Wohl degradation.

Although glucose has some of the properties expected of an aldehyde, it lacks others. For example, it forms certain carbonyl derivatives (e.g., oxime, phenylhydrazone, and cyanohydrin); it can be reduced to the hexahydric alcohol, sorbitol, and oxidized with bromine to gluconic acid (a monocarboxylic acid). With nitric acid, oxidation proceeds further to give the dicarboxylic acid, D-glucaric acid.

$$
\begin{array}{ccccccc}
\text{CH}_2\text{OH} & & \text{CHO} & & \text{CO}_2\text{H} & & \text{CO}_2\text{H} \\
\text{H}-\text{C}-\text{OH} & & \text{H}-\text{C}-\text{OH} & & \text{H}-\text{C}-\text{OH} & & \text{H}-\text{C}-\text{OH} \\
\text{HO}-\text{C}-\text{H} & \xleftarrow{\text{Na-Hg}} & \text{HO}-\text{C}-\text{H} & \xrightarrow{\text{Br}_2} & \text{HO}-\text{C}-\text{H} & \xrightarrow{\text{HNO}_3} & \text{HO}-\text{C}-\text{H} \\
\text{H}-\text{C}-\text{OH} & & \text{H}-\text{C}-\text{OH} & & \text{H}-\text{C}-\text{OH} & & \text{H}-\text{C}-\text{OH} \\
\text{H}-\text{C}-\text{OH} & & \text{H}-\text{C}-\text{OH} & & \text{H}-\text{C}-\text{OH} & & \text{H}-\text{C}-\text{OH} \\
\text{CH}_2\text{OH} & & \text{CH}_2\text{OH} & & \text{CH}_2\text{OH} & & \text{CO}_2\text{H}
\end{array}
$$

  sorbitol   D-glucose   D-gluconic acid   D-glucaric acid

Glucose will also reduce Fehling's solution ($Cu^{II} \rightarrow Cu^{I}$) and Tollen's reagent ($Ag^{I} \rightarrow Ag^{0}$). However, it fails to give a bisulfite addition compound and, although it will react with amines (RNH_2), the products are not the expected

Schiff's bases of the type $\diagdown C{=}NR$. Furthermore, glucose forms two different

monomethyl derivatives (called methyl α-D-glucoside and methyl β-D-glucoside) under conditions which normally convert an aldehyde to a dimethyl acetal.

$$
\text{R}-\underset{\underset{O}{\|}}{\overset{\diagup H}{C}} + 2\,\text{CH}_3\text{OH} \xrightarrow{\text{H}^{\oplus}} \text{R}-\underset{\underset{\text{OCH}_3}{|}}{\overset{\overset{H}{|}}{\text{C}}}-\text{OCH}_3 + \text{H}_2\text{O}
$$

$$
\text{C}_6\text{H}_{12}\text{O}_6 + \text{CH}_3\text{OH} \xrightarrow{\text{H}^{\oplus}} (\text{C}_6\text{H}_{11}\text{O}_5)\text{OCH}_3 + \text{H}_2\text{O}
$$

                                        methyl α- and β-D-glucoside

The above behavior can be explained on the basis that the carbonyl group is not free in glucose but is tied up in combination with one of the hydroxyl groups, which turns out to be the one at C5, to form a cyclic hemiacetal represented by [4].

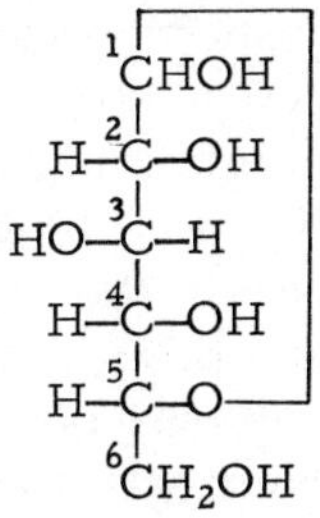

$$
\begin{array}{c}
\overset{1}{C}HOH \\
H\overset{2}{-}C-OH \\
HO\overset{3}{-}C-H \\
H\overset{4}{-}C-OH \\
H\overset{5}{-}C-O \\
\overset{6}{C}H_2OH
\end{array}
$$

[4]

A new asymmetric center is created at C1 by hemiacetal formation, and there are therefore two steroisomeric forms of D-glucose, both of which are known; they are α-D-glucose and β-D-glucose. A specific term is used to describe carbohydrate stereoisomers differing only in configuration at the hemiacetal carbon; they are called **anomers.**

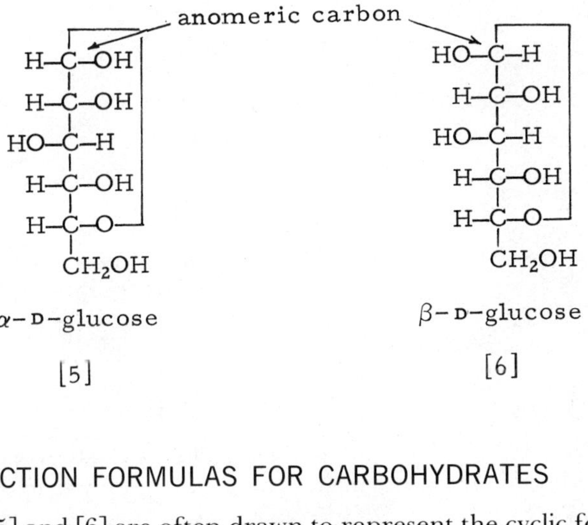

anomeric carbon

$$
\begin{array}{c}
H-C-OH \\
H-C-OH \\
HO-C-H \\
H-C-OH \\
H-C-O \\
CH_2OH
\end{array}
\qquad
\begin{array}{c}
HO-C-H \\
H-C-OH \\
HO-C-H \\
H-C-OH \\
H-C-O \\
CH_2OH
\end{array}
$$

α-D-glucose   β-D-glucose

[5]   [6]

18-3 PROJECTION FORMULAS FOR CARBOHYDRATES

Structures [5] and [6] are often drawn to represent the cyclic form of glucose, but they are not realistic of the molecular shapes; the Haworth projection formulas [7] and [8] are much superior in this respect.

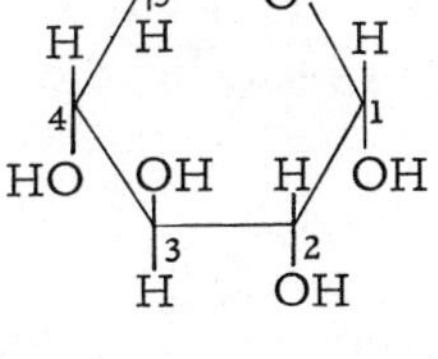

α-D-glucose

[7]

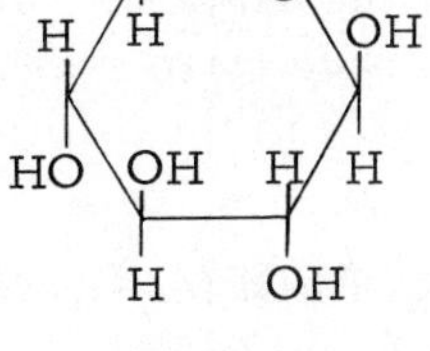

β-D-glucose

[8]

It may not be obvious from inspection that the projection formula [5] of α-D-glucose corresponds to the cyclic structure [7]. In fact, formula [5] is misleading because it appears to imply that the oxide link extends from the back of C1 to the front of C5. However, by simply rotating C5 about the C4–C5 bond (which readily takes place in the open-chain aldehyde form) we get structure [5a], in which the oxide bridge more clearly extends from the back of C1 to the back of C5. (The configuration at C5 is of course not altered by simple rotation about the single bond.) Structure [5a] is easier to recognize as being the same as [7].

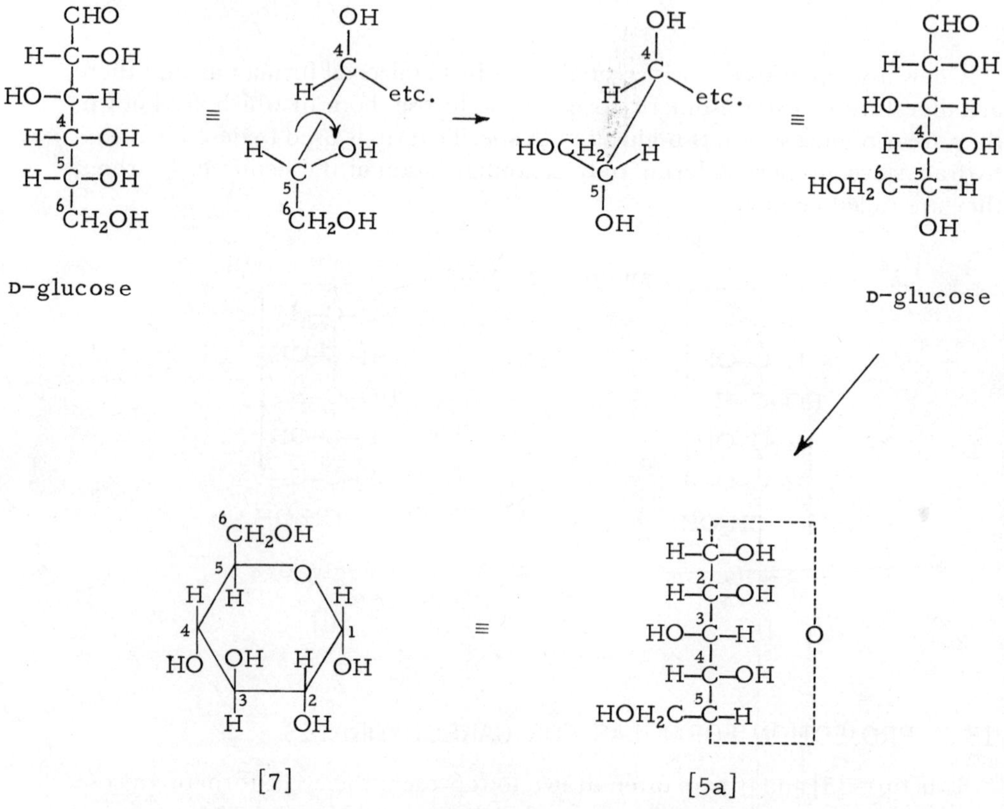

D-glucose

D-glucose

[7]   [5a]

The rules for writing the configurations of α- and β-D-glucose follow in summary and may of course be extrapolated to include other sugars.

1. In the chain-like representations [5] and [6], the OH group at C1 is to the *right* of the chain in the α-form and to the left in the β-form.

2. In the Haworth projection formulas [7] and [8], the CH₂OH group is written as *up* for D-sugars and *down* for L-sugars. For D-sugars, the OH at C1 will be *down* in the α-form and *up* in the β-form.

18-4 CONFORMATIONS OF CARBOHYDRATES

Ideally, we should draw conformational structures for glucose rather than projection formulas, and, by analogy with cyclohexane, we expect the six-membered cyclic oxide structure of glucose to exist preferentially in a chair form. X-ray studies have in fact determined that crystalline α-D-glucose has the chair structure [9], and presumably crystalline β-D-glucose has structure [10], which is particularly interesting because all the substituents can be seen to occupy equatorial positions.

[9]   [10]

Whether these conformational preferences are preserved when the sugar goes into solution is uncertain, because there is likely to be less difference in energy between the boat and chair forms of the oxide ring than a correspondingly substituted cyclohexane ring. However, when the hydroxyl groups are esterified, as in α- and β-D-glucose 2,3,4,6-tetraacetate, it has been found that a chair conformation is preferred, with the largest number of bulky substituents occupying equatorial positions. The Cl-OH is axial in the α-form of glucose tetraacetate and equatorial in the β-form.

$\alpha-$ $\beta-$

D-glucose 2, 3, 4, 6-tetraacetate (Ac = $CH_3\overset{\overset{O}{\|}}{C}-$)

18-5 CONVENTIONS FOR INDICATING RING SIZE OF MONOSACCHARIDES

Since the oxide ring is six-membered in some sugars and five-membered in others, it is helpful to use names that indicate the ring size. The five- and six-membered oxide rings bear a formal relationship to the cyclic oxides, furan and pyran.

pyran   furan

Hence, the terms **furanose** and **pyranose** have been coined to denote five- and six-membered rings in cyclic sugars. The two forms of glucose are appropriately identified by the names α-D-glucopyranose and β-D-glucopyranose. Likewise, L-arabinose, D-xylose, D-galactose, and D-mannose occur naturally as pyranoses—but D-ribose (in combined form) and D fructose occur as furanoses (see Tables 18-1 and 18-2).

18-6 MUTAROTATION

Although the crystalline forms of α- and β-D-glucose are quite stable, in solution each form slowly changes into an equilibrium mixture of both. The process can be readily observed as a decrease in the optical rotation of the α-anomer (+112°) or an increase for the β-anomer (+18.7°) to the equilibrium value of 52.5°. The phenomenon is known as mutarotation and is commonly observed for reducing sugars (i.e., sugars with a carbonyl function in the form of a hemiacetal). Both acids and bases catalyze mutarotation, and are particularly effective if both are present in the same solution. The generally accepted mechanism is shown in Eq. (18-1) and is virtually the same as described for acid- and base-catalyzed hemiacetal and hemiketal formation of aldehydes and ketones (see pp. 320–323).

$$(18\text{-}1)$$

β-D-glucose   aldehyde form   α-D-glucose

At equilibrium, there is present some 64 per cent of the β-anomer and 30 per cent of the α-anomer. The amount of the free aldehyde form present at equilibrium is very small (some 0.024 mole per cent in neutral solution). Preponderance of the β-anomer is to be expected if glucose exists in solution mostly in the chair conformation. In this conformation, the hydroxyl substituent at C1 is equatorial in the β-anomer [10] and axial in the α-anomer [9]; hence the β-anomer should be more stable.

18-7   REACTIONS OF GLUCOSE WITH AMINES — OSAZONE FORMATION

As stated earlier, glucose forms some, but not all, of the common carbonyl derivatives. The amount of free aldehyde present in solution is so small that it is not surprising that no bisulfite derivative forms. With amines, the product is not a Schiff's base but a glucosylamine of cyclic structure analogous to the hemiacetal structure of glucose, Eq. (18-2). The Schiff's base may be an intermediate which rapidly cyclizes to the glucosylamine, but this is uncertain.

aldehyde form of   Schiff's base   anomers of N-phenyl-
   D-glucose   D-glucosylamine

The reaction of glucose with an excess of phenylhydrazine is particularly interesting since two phenylhydrazine molecules are incorporated into one of glucose. Subsequent to phenylhydrazone formation, and in a manner that is not entirely clear, the —CHOH group adjacent to the original aldehyde function is oxidized to a carbonyl group, which then consumes more phenylhydrazine to form a crystalline derivative called an **osazone,** or specifically **glucose phenylosazone.**

glucose   glucose   glucose
                              phenylhydrazone   phenylosazone

The sugar osazones have some utility for characterization and identification of sugars. Fischer employed the reaction in his work which established configuration of the sugars. The kind of information that can be obtained is illustrated by the following example.

glucose and   phenylosazone from glucose,   fructose
   mannose   mannose and fructose

Since the *same* phenylosazone is obtainable from glucose, mannose, and fructose, the configurations of C3, C4, and C5 must be the same for all three sugars. Further, glucose and mannose differ only in configuration at C2; they are said to be **epimers.**

EXERCISE 18-3   D-Arabinose and D-ribose give the same phenylosazone. D-Ribose is reduced to the optically inactive pentahydric alcohol, ribitol. D-Arabinose can be degraded by the **Ruff** method, which involves the following reactions:

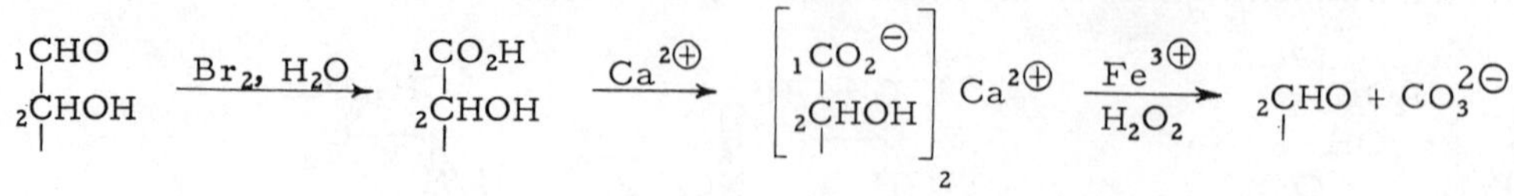

$$\begin{array}{c} {}_1CHO \\ | \\ {}_2CHOH \\ | \end{array} \xrightarrow{Br_2,\ H_2O} \begin{array}{c} {}_1CO_2H \\ | \\ {}_2CHOH \\ | \end{array} \xrightarrow{Ca^{2\oplus}} \left[\begin{array}{c} {}_1CO_2^{\ominus} \\ | \\ {}_2CHOH \\ | \end{array}\right]_2 Ca^{2\oplus} \xrightarrow[H_2O_2]{Fe^{3\oplus}} \begin{array}{c} {}_2CHO + CO_3^{2\ominus} \\ | \end{array}$$

The tetrose, D-erythrose, so obtained can be oxidized with nitric acid to *meso*-tartaric acid. What are the configurations of D-arabinose, D-ribose, ribitol, and D-erythrose?

18-8 GLYCOSIDES

Although abundant quantities of glucose and fructose are found in the free state, they and less common sugars occur widely in plants and animals combined with various hydroxy compounds. Structurally, these substances are related to the simple α- and β-methyl glucosides, since the nonsugar component (called the **aglycone** group R) is bonded through oxygen to the hemiacetal or hemiketal carbon. The generic name for this type of compound is **glycoside,** or, more specifically, O-glycoside, to denote that the linkage is through oxygen.

$$H-\underset{|}{\overset{|}{C}}-OR \qquad RO-\underset{|}{\overset{|}{C}}-H$$

       α–O–glycoside β–O–glycoside

If the sugar residue is glucose, the derivative is a glucoside; if fructose, a fructoside; if galactose, a galactoside. In the special case where R is another sugar residue, the glycosides are disaccharides; or if R is already a disaccharide, the glycoside is a trisaccharide, and so on.

Of particular importance biologically are the N-glycosides, in which the sugar residue is D-ribose or 2-deoxy-D-ribose [1] and the aglycone is attached to the sugar by a C—N bond involving a derivative of a nitrogen base, usually pyrimidine or purine.

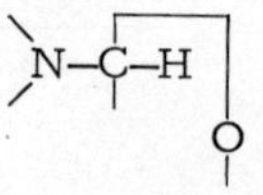

$$\underset{/}{\overset{\backslash}{N}}-\underset{|}{\overset{|}{C}}-H \qquad \beta\text{–N–glycoside}$$

[1] The prefix "deoxy" means "without oxygen." Thus, 2-deoxy-D-ribose is D-ribose, in which the 2-hydroxyl group is replaced with hydrogen.

These glycosides are better known as ribonucleosides and deoxyribonucleosides.

ribonucleoside   deoxyribonucleoside   pyrimidine   purine
(partial structure)   (partial structure)

Adenosine is one example of a purine ribonucleoside, and when esterified at the 5′-position with the triphosphoryl group (a phosphoric acid anhydride)

$$-\overset{OH}{\underset{O}{\overset{|}{P}}}-O-\overset{OH}{\underset{O}{\overset{|}{P}}}-O-\overset{OH}{\underset{O}{\overset{|}{P}}}-OH,$$

it is known as adenosine triphosphate (ATP), a so-called "energy-rich" compound present in muscle tissue.

adenosine   adenosine triphosphate (ATP)

18-9 DISACCHARIDES

The simplest and most important oligosaccharides are disaccharides. These, on acid or enzymatic hydrolysis, give the component monosaccharides which are frequently hexoses. The bond between the hexoses is an O-glycoside linkage, but only one hemiacetal hydroxyl need be involved. In fact, many disaccharides have reducing properties indicating that one of the sugar residues has the easily opened hemiacetal function. However, when both hexoses are joined through their anomeric carbons, as in sucrose, the sugar resembles a methyl glycoside (an acetal) in that it has no reducing properties, and forms no phenylosazone or other carbonyl derivatives (provided that the experimental conditions do not effect hydrolysis of the acetal function).

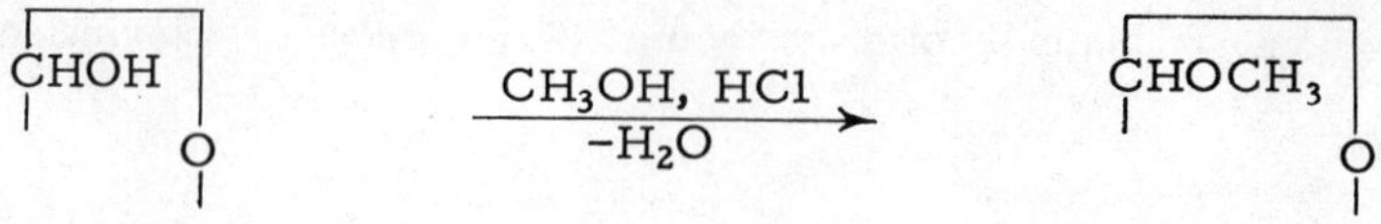

$$\begin{array}{c} \overset{|}{\underset{|}{\text{CHOH}}} \quad \Big| \\ \qquad\qquad O \\ \overset{|}{} \end{array} \quad \xrightarrow[-H_2O]{CH_3OH,\ HCl} \quad \begin{array}{c} \overset{|}{\underset{|}{\text{CHOCH}_3}} \quad \Big| \\ \qquad\qquad O \\ \overset{|}{} \end{array}$$

a methyl O–glycoside
(non–reducing)

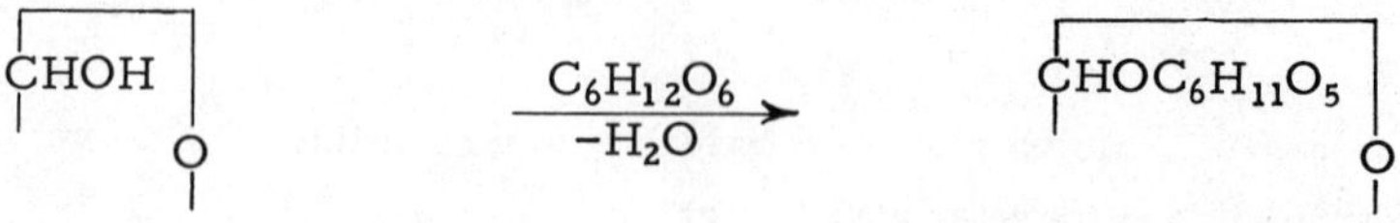

$$\begin{array}{c} \overset{|}{\underset{|}{\text{CHOH}}} \quad \Big| \\ \qquad\qquad O \\ \overset{|}{} \end{array} \quad \xrightarrow[-H_2O]{C_6H_{12}O_6} \quad \begin{array}{c} \overset{|}{\underset{|}{\text{CHOC}_6H_{11}O_5}} \quad \Big| \\ \qquad\qquad O \\ \overset{|}{} \end{array}$$

disaccharide

(reducing if monosaccharides
are not linked through their
anomeric carbons)

   Among the more important disaccharides are sucrose [11], maltose [12], cellobiose [13], and lactose [14]. Sucrose and lactose occur widely as the free sugars, lactose in the milk of mammals and sucrose in plants, fruit, and honey (principally in sugar cane and sugar beet). Maltose is the product of enzymatic hydrolysis of starch, and cellobiose is a product of hydrolysis of cellulose.

   To fully establish the structure of a disaccharide we must know (1) the identity of the component monosaccharides; (2) the type of ring junction, furanose or pyranose, in each monosaccharide, as it exists in the disaccharide; (3) the positions which link one monosaccharide with the other; and (4) the anomeric configuration (α or β) of this linkage.

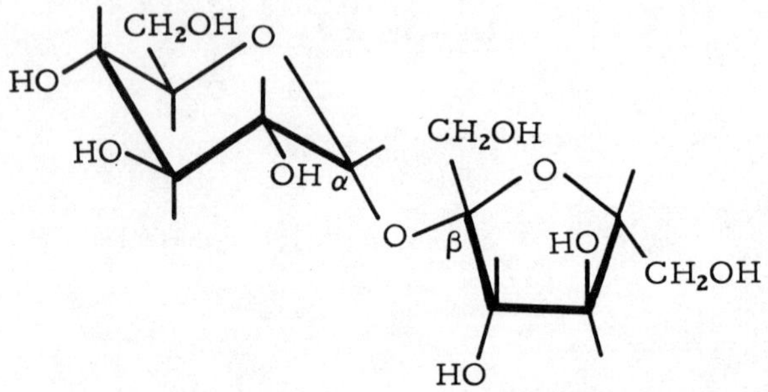

sucrose

[11]

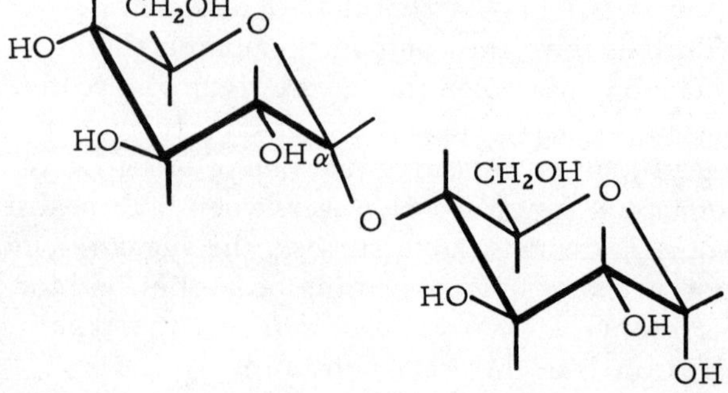

maltose

[12]

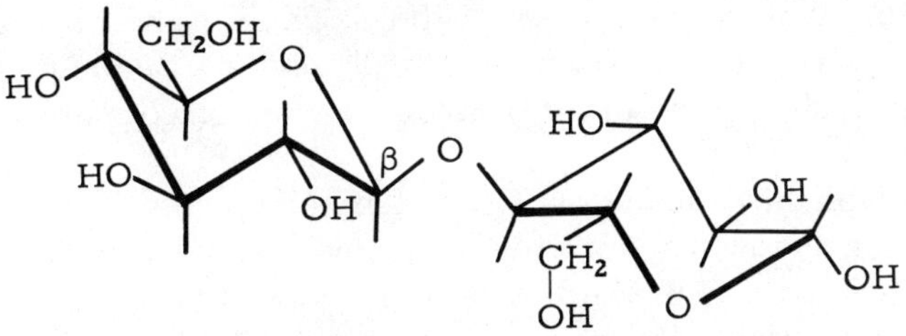

cellobiose

[13]

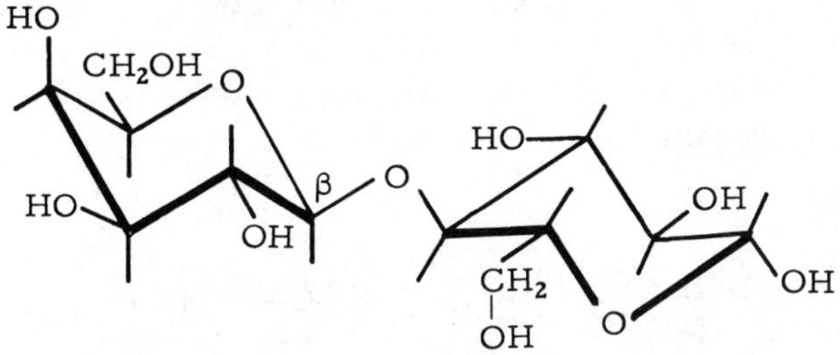

lactose

[14]

EXERCISE 18-4   Draw Haworth and conformation structures for each of the following disaccharides:

 a. 6-O-β-D-glucopyranosyl-β-D-glucopyranose
 b. 4-O-β-D-galactopyranosyl-α-D-glucopyranose
 c. 4-O-β-D-xylopyranosyl-β-L-arabinopyranose
 d. 6-O-α-D-galactopyranosyl-β-D-fructofuranose

18-10 POLYSACCHARIDES

The fibrous tissue in the cell walls of plants and trees contains the polysaccharide **cellulose,** which consists of long chains of glucose units, each of which is combined by a β-glucoside link to the C4 hydroxyl of another glucose unit as in the disaccharide **cellobiose.**

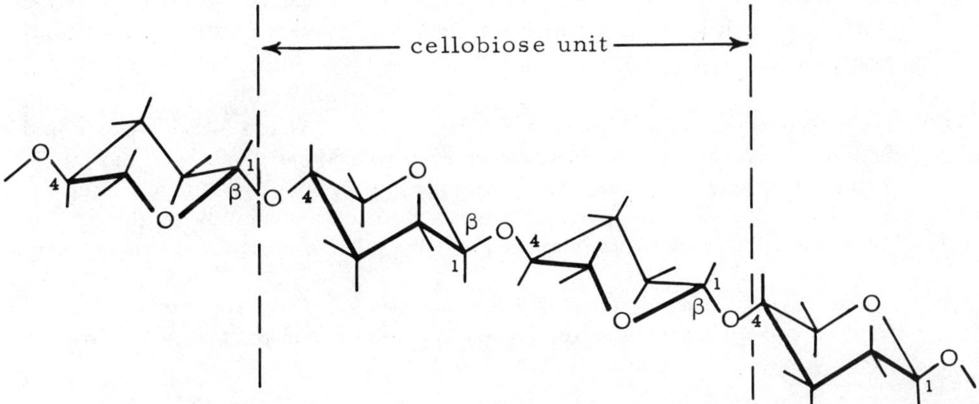

cellobiose unit

Indeed, enzymatic hydrolysis of cellulose leads to cellobiose. The molecular weight of cellulose varies with the source but is usually high, as can be judged from cotton cellulose, which appears to consist of some 3000 glucose units per molecule.

The natural fibers obtained from cotton, wood, flax, hemp, and jute are all cellulose fibers and serve as raw materials for the textile and paper industries. In addition to its use as a natural fiber and in those industries which depend on wood as a construction material, cellulose is used to make cellulose acetate (for making rayon acetate yarn, photographic film, and cellulose acetate butyrate plastics), nitric acid esters (gun cotton and celluloid [1]), and cellulose xanthate (for making viscose rayon fibers). The process by which viscose rayon is manufactured involves converting wood pulp or cotton linters into cellulose xanthate by reaction with carbon disulfide and sodium hydroxide.

$$-\overset{|}{\underset{|}{C}}-OH \quad \xrightarrow[(-H_2O)]{CS_2,\ NaOH} \quad -\overset{|}{\underset{|}{C}}-O-\overset{\overset{S}{\|}}{C}-S^{\ominus}\ Na^{\oplus}$$

cellulose xanthate

The degree of polymerization of the original cellulose generally falls to around 300 monomer units in this process. At this degree of polymerization, the cellulose is regenerated in the form of fine filaments by forcing the xanthate solution through a spinneret into an acid bath.

$$-\overset{|}{\underset{|}{C}}-O-\overset{\overset{S}{\|}}{C}-S^{\ominus} \quad \xrightarrow{H^{\oplus}} \quad -\overset{|}{\underset{|}{C}}-OH\ +\ CS_2$$

A few creatures (e.g., ruminants and termites) are able to metabolize cellulose with the aid of appropriate microorganisms in their intestinal tracts; but man cannot utilize cellulose as food because he lacks the necessary hydrolytic enzymes. However, such enzymes are widely distributed in nature. In fact, the deterioration of cellulosic materials, either textiles, paper, or wood, by enzymatic degradation (such as by dry rot) is an economic problem which is not yet adequately solved.

The second very widely distributed polysaccharide is **starch,** which is stored in the seeds, roots, and fibers of plants as a food reserve — a potential source of glucose. The chemical composition of starch varies with the source, but in any one starch there are two structurally different polysaccharides. Both consist entirely of glucose units, but one is a linear structure (**amylose**) and the other is a branched structure (**amylopectin**).

The amylose form of starch consists of repeating 1,4-glucopyranose links as in cellulose, but unlike cellulose the linkage is α rather than β. Hydrolysis by the enzyme diastase leads to maltose.

[1] Celluloid is partially nitrated cellulose (known as pyroxylin) plasticized with camphor.

maltose unit

In amylopectin, amylose-like chains are apparently branched by 1,6-linkages.

Animals also store glucose in the form of starchlike substances called glycogens. These resemble amylopectin more than amylose, in that they are branched chains of glucose units with 1,4- and 1,6-glucoside links.

EXERCISE 18-5   How can the β-D-glucoside units of cellulose produce a polymer with a stronger, more compact physical structure than the α-D-glucose units of starch? Models will be helpful.

18-11   VITAMIN C

The "antiscorbutic" factor of fresh fruits which prevents the development of the typical symptoms of scurvy in humans is a carbohydrate derivative known as vitamin C or ascorbic acid. This substance is actually not a carboxylic acid but a lactone and owes its acidic properties (and ease of oxidation) to the presence of an enediol grouping. It belongs to the L series by the glyceraldehyde convention.

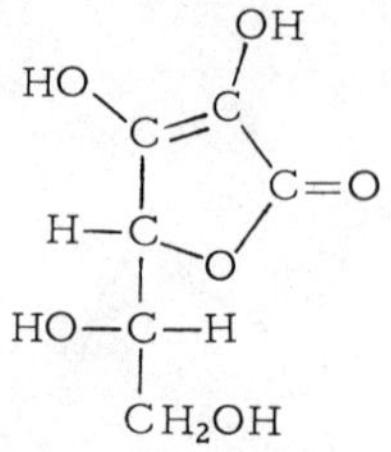

L–ascorbic acid

SUPPLEMENTARY EXERCISES

18-6   A naturally occurring optically active pentose ($C_5H_{10}O_5$) reduces Tollen's reagent and forms a tetraacetate with acetic anhydride. It gives an optically *inactive* phenylosazone. Write all the possible structures for this pentose which are in accord with all the experimental facts.

18-7   A hexose, $C_6H_{12}O_6$, which we shall call X-ose, on reduction with sodium amalgam gives pure D-sorbitol, and, upon treatment with phenylhydrazine, gives an osazone different from that of D-glucose. Write a projection formula for X-ose and equations for its reactions.

18-8   Draw Haworth- and conformation-type formulas for each of the following:
   a. methyl 2,3,4,6-O-tetramethyl-α-D-glucopyranoside
   b. β-D-arabinofuranosyl α-L-arabinofuranoside
   c. L-sucrose

18-9   Sugars condense with anhydrous acetone in the presence of an acid catalyst to form isopropylidene derivatives.

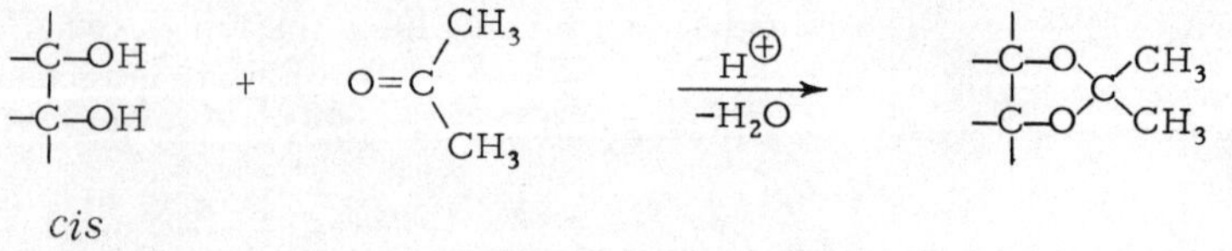

Predict the products of reaction of α-D-galactopyranose, α-D-glucopyranose, and α-D-glucofuranose with acetone and an acid catalyst.

18-10   Complete the following sequence of reactions, writing structures for all the products, $A-\mathcal{J}$:

a.   α-D-glucofuranose $\xrightarrow[\text{HCl}]{\substack{\text{acetone}\\ \text{(1 mole)}}}$ A (see Exercise 18-9)

b. A $\xrightarrow{\text{NaIO}_4}$ B

c. B $\xrightarrow{\text{Na}^{14}\text{CN}}$ $C + D$

d. $C + D$ $\xrightarrow[\text{2. H}^{\oplus},\,\text{H}_2\text{O}]{\text{1. H}_2\text{O, OH}^{\ominus}}$ $E + F +$ acetone

e. $E + F$ $\xrightarrow[(-\text{H}_2\text{O})]{\Delta}$ $G + H$

f. $G + H$ $\xrightarrow[\text{H}_2\text{O}]{\text{NaBH}_4}$ $I + $ D-glucose-6-^{14}C

Organic Nitrogen Compounds.
Amines, Amides, Nitriles.
Nitro, Azo, Diazo, and Related Compounds

A very wide variety of organic compounds contain nitrogen, but for the purposes of this chapter we shall take organic nitrogen compounds as substances having carbon-nitrogen bonds. We shall consider first the chemistry of ammonia derivatives and then the chemistry of substances having nitrogen at a higher level of oxidation. Finally, the properties of a number of interesting and important compounds with C—N—N groups will be discussed. Throughout we shall pay particular attention to the way that nitrogen influences the chemistry of the organic groups to which it is attached.

Organic Nitrogen Compounds.
Amines, Amides, Nitriles.
Nitro, Azo, Diazo, and Related Compounds

The chemistry of organic nitrogen substances is quite variegated, as indeed is the chemistry of inorganic nitrogen compounds, because of the variety of oxidation levels available to this element. Consequently, it may be helpful to review Table 19-1, wherein are listed some important types of inorganic nitrogen compounds in order of increasing oxidation level of nitrogen. Several simple carbon-nitrogen derivatives are also included, which for practical purposes can be regarded as being as inorganic in nature as carbon dioxide or metal carbonates.

Table 19-1   Inorganic Nitrogen Compounds

increasing average oxidation state of nitrogen[a]			
-3	NH_3 *ammonia*	$NH_4^{\oplus}$ *ammonium ion*	$H\!-\!C\!\equiv\!N$ *hydrocyanic acid*
	$HOC\!\equiv\!N$ ⇌ *cyanic acid*	$O\!=\!C\!=\!NH$ *isocyanic acid*	$HO\!-\!\overset{\displaystyle O}{\overset{\|}{C}}\!-\!NH_2$ *carbamic acid*
-2	$H_2N\!-\!NH_2$ *hydrazine*		
-1	$HN\!=\!NH$ *diimide* *(unstable)*	NH_2Cl *chloramine*	NH_2OH *hydroxylamine*
$-\frac{1}{3}$	$H\!-\!\overset{\oplus}{N}\!=\!N\!=\!\overset{\ominus}{N}$ *hydrazoic acid*	$Na\overset{\oplus}{N}\!=\!\overset{\ominus}{N}\!=\!\overset{\oplus}{N}\!=\!\overset{\ominus}{N}$ *sodium azide*	
0	$N\!\equiv\!N$ *nitrogen*		
$+\frac{1}{3}$	$Cl\!-\!\overset{\oplus}{N}\!=\!N\!=\!\overset{\ominus}{N}$ *chlorine azide*		
$+1$	$\overset{\ominus}{N}\!=\!\overset{\oplus}{N}\!=\!O$ *nitrous oxide*	$H_2N_2O_2$ *hyponitrous acid* *(unstable)*	$F\!-\!N\!=\!N\!-\!F$ *difluorodiazine*
$+2$	$\cdot N\!=\!O$ *nitric oxide*	$F_2N\!-\!NF_2$ *tetrafluorohydrazine*	
$+3$	$O\!=\!N\!-\!O\!-\!N\!=\!O$ *dinitrogen trioxide* *(nitrous acid anhydride)*	HNO_2 *nitrous acid*	$O\!=\!N\!-\!Cl$ *nitrosyl chloride*
$+4$	$\cdot NO_2$ ⇌ *nitrogen dioxide*	$O_2N\!-\!NO_2$ *dinitrogen tetroxide*	
$+5$	$O_2N\!-\!O\!-\!NO_2$ *dinitrogen pentoxide* *(nitric acid anhydride)*	HNO_3 *nitric acid*	O_2NCl *nitryl chloride*

[a] The numbers in the left-hand column refer to the conventional oxidation state of nitrogen in the compounds listed.

DERIVATIVES OF AMMONIA

19-1   TYPES AND NOMENCLATURE OF AMINES

The nomenclature of alkyl-substituted ammonias or amines was considered briefly in Chapter 11. We shall give a short review here in order to focus attention on the types of substitution which are commonly encountered. Classification is made according to the number of alkyl or aryl groups attached to nitrogen, since this number is important in determining the chemical reactions that are possible at the nitrogen atom.

$$RNH_2 \qquad R_2NH \qquad R_3N \qquad R_4\overset{\oplus}{N}\ \overset{\ominus}{X}$$

primary   secondary   tertiary   quaternary
amine   amine   amine   ammonium salt

Amino compounds can be named either as derivatives of ammonia or as amino-substituted compounds. Thus, $HOCH_2CH_2NH_2$ can be named almost equally well as 2-hydroxyethylamine or as 2-aminoethanol, although by convention 2-aminoethanol is favored, since hydroxyl normally takes precedence over amino. With halogens the situation is reversed, and 2-chloroethylamine would be favored over 2-aminoethyl chloride. Some typical amines with the names which they have in common use are listed in Table 19-2 together with their physical properties.

Salts of amines with inorganic or organic acids are usually best named as substituted ammonium salts.

Table 19-2   Typical Amines and Their Properties

Amine	Name	B.p., °C	M.p., °C	Water solubility, g/100 ml	K_B in water[a]
NH_3	ammonia	-33	-77.7	90^0	1.8×10^{-5}
CH_3NH_2	methylamine	-6.5	-92.5	1156	4.4×10^{-4}
$CH_3CH_2NH_2$	ethylamine	16.6	-80.6	∞	5.6×10^{-4}
$(CH_3)_3CNH_2$	t-butylamine	46	-67.5	∞	2.8×10^{-4}
$(CH_3CH_2)_2NH$	diethylamine	55.5	-50	v. sol.	9.6×10^{-4}
$(CH_3CH_2)_3N$	triethylamine	89.5	-115	1.5^{20}	4.4×10^{-4}
$(CH_3CH_2CH_2CH_2)_3N$	tri-n-butylamine	214		sl. sol.	
⟨ ⟩NH	piperidine	106	-9	∞	1.6×10^{-3}
⟨ ⟩N	pyridine	115	-42	∞	1.7×10^{-9}
⟨ ⟩—NH₂	cyclohexylamine	134		sl. sol.	4.4×10^{-4}
⟨ ⟩—NH₂	aniline	184.4	-6.2	3.4^{20}	3.8×10^{-10}
$H_2NCH_2CH_2NH_2$	ethylenediamine	116	8.5	sol.	8.5×10^{-5}

[a] Usually at 20–25°C.

$$\overset{\oplus}{CH_3NH_3} \quad Cl^{\ominus}$$

$$CH_2=CH-CH_2-\overset{\overset{\displaystyle H}{\underset{\displaystyle |}{\oplus}}}{\underset{\overset{\displaystyle |}{\displaystyle CH_3}}{N}}-CH_3 \quad \overset{\ominus}{O_2CCH_3}$$

methylammonium chloride   allyldimethylammonium
acetate

However, such names are sometimes unwieldy, and it is not uncommon to use the name of the corresponding amine in conjunction with the name of the acid, i.e., methylamine hydrochloride for methylammonium chloride. With quaternary salts an extension of the same system leads to trimethylamine methiodide for tetramethylammonium iodide.

EXERCISE 19-1   Name the following substances by an accepted system.

a. $CH_2=CH-\overset{\oplus}{N}(CH_3)_3 \quad Br^{\ominus}$

b. $(HOCH_2CH_2)_3N$

c. $H_2NCH_2CO_2H$

d. $H_2NCH_2CH_2\overset{\oplus}{N}H_3\overset{\ominus}{Cl}$

e.   [phenyl]$-N\overset{\diagup CH_3}{\diagdown CH_2CH_3}$

f.   [pyridinium]$\overset{\oplus}{N}-CH_3 \quad I^{\ominus}$

19-2 PHYSICAL AND SPECTROSCOPIC PROPERTIES OF AMINES

The properties of amines depend in an important way on the degree of substitution at nitrogen. For example, tertiary amines have no N—H bonds and are thus unable to form hydrogen bonds of the type N—H----N. In general, N—H----N bonds are somewhat weaker than those of corresponding types, O—H----O and F—H----F, because the electronegativity of nitrogen is less than that of oxygen or fluorine. Even so, association of the molecules of primary and secondary amines (but not tertiary amines) through hydrogen bonding is significant and decreases their volatility relative to hydrocarbons of similar size, weight, and shape, as the following examples show.

$CH_3CH_2CH_2CH_2CH_2NH_2$ $CH_3CH_2CH_2CH_2CH_2CH_3$

n-pentylamine   *n*-hexane

M.W. 87; b.p. 130°   M.W. 86; b.p. 69°

$CH_3CH_2NHCH_2CH_3$ $CH_3CH_2CH_2CH_2CH_3$

diethylamine   *n*-pentane

M.W. 73; b.p. 55.5°   M.W. 72; b.p. 36°

$$\underset{\text{triethylamine}}{\overset{\overset{\displaystyle CH_2CH_3}{|}}{CH_3CH_2-N-CH_2CH_3}}$$

M. W. 101; b. p. 89. 5°

$$\underset{\text{3-ethylpentane}}{\overset{\overset{\displaystyle CH_2CH_3}{|}}{CH_3CH_2CHCH_2CH_3}}$$

M. W. 100; b. p. 93. 3°

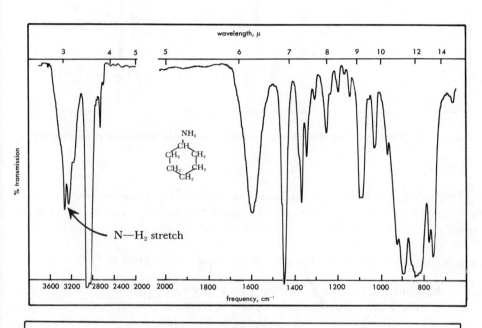

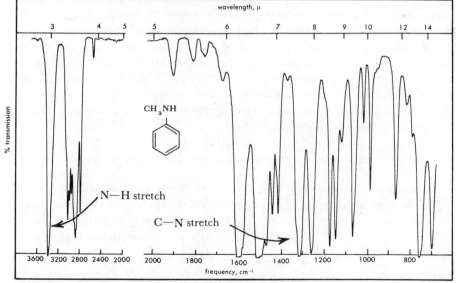

Figure 19-1   Infrared spectra of cyclohexylamine and N-methylaniline.

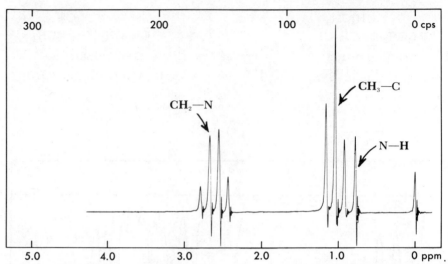

Figure 19-2   N.m.r. spectrum of diethylamine at 60 Mcps relative to tetramethylsilane (0.00 ppm).

The water solubilities of the lower-molecular-weight amines are generally greater than those of alcohols of comparable molecular weights. This is the result of hydrogen-bonding between the amine and water, which leads to hydrogen bonds of considerable strength, of the type $-\overset{|}{\underset{|}{N}}$:---H—O—H.

A characteristic feature of the infrared spectra of primary and secondary amines is the moderately weak absorption at 3500 to 3300 cm^{-1}, corresponding to N—H stretching vibrations. Primary amines have two such bands in this region, whereas secondary amines generally show only one band. Absorption is shifted to lower frequencies on hydrogen bonding of the amine, but since NH---N hydrogen bonding is weaker than OH---O hydrogen bonding, the shift is not as great and the bands are not as intense as are the absorption bands of hydrogen-bonded O—H groups (see pp. 281–282). Absorptions corresponding to C—N vibrations are less easily identifiable—except in the case of aromatic amines, which absorb fairly strongly near 1300 cm^{-1}. Spectra that illustrate these effects are shown in Figure 19-1.

The n.m.r. spectra of amines show characteristic absorptions for H—$\overset{|}{\underset{|}{C}}$—N protons around 2.7 ppm. The resonances of N—H protons are not so easily identifiable; considerable variability arises from differences in degree of hydrogen bonding and matters are further complicated when, as with diethylamine (Figure 19-2), the N—H resonance has nearly the same chemical shift as the resonances of CH$_3$—C protons.

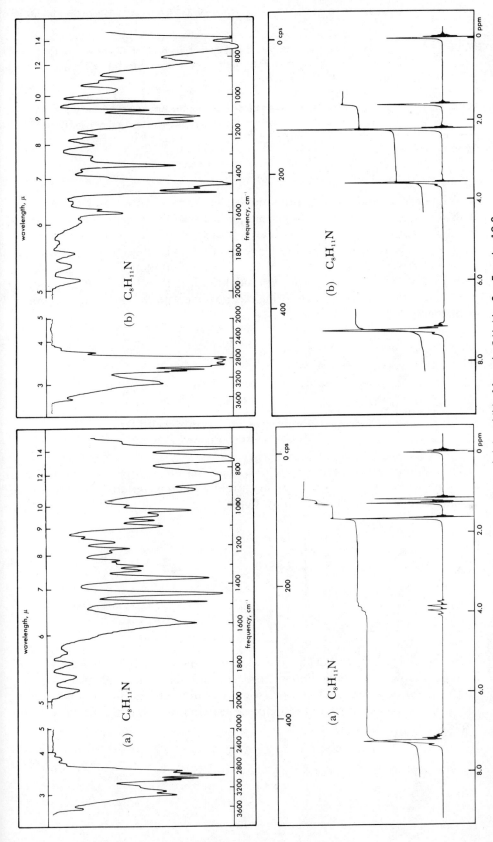

Figure 19-3 Infrared and n.m.r. spectra of two isomeric organic compounds (a) and (b) of formula $C_8H_{11}N$. See Exercise 19-3.

EXERCISE 19-2   How could one show with certainty that the peak at 47 cps with reference to tetramethylsilane in the n.m.r. spectrum of diethylamine (Figure 19-2) is actually due to the N—H resonance?

EXERCISE 19-3   Show how structures can be deduced for the substances (a) and (b) of molecular formulas $C_8H_{11}N$, whose n.m.r. and infrared spectra are shown in Figure 19-3.

19-3 STEREOCHEMISTRY OF AMINES

The bond angles of nitrogen in amines and ammonia are closer to the tetrahedral value of 109.5° than to the 90°, which would be expected for pure p bonds. That the angles are less than tetrahedral may be taken to be a consequence of electrostatic repulsion between the bonding electrons and the unshared electron pair (cf. pp. 117–118). The configuration of a nitrogen which forms bonds at these angles is pyramidal, and, if three different groups are attached, optical isomers are, in principle, possible with the center of asymmetry at nitrogen.

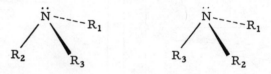

optical isomers of an asymmetrically
substituted amine

The resolution of such a mixture of isomers has not as yet been achieved, and it appears that such isomers are very rapidly interconverted by an inversion process involving a planar transition state.

planar transition
state

With ammonia, inversion of this type occurs at about 4×10^{10} times per second at room temperature; with aliphatic tertiary amines, the rate is likely to be more on the order of 10^3 to 10^5 times per second. Such rates of inversion are much too great to permit resolution of optical isomers by presently available techniques.

19-4 AMINES AS ACIDS AND BASES

Although perhaps the most characteristic chemical property of amines is their ability to act as bases by accepting protons from a variety of acids, it should not be forgotten that primary and secondary amines are also able to act as acids, albeit, very weak acids. The lithium salts of such amines are readily preparable in ether solution by treatment of the amine with phenyllithium.

$$(C_2H_5)_2NH + C_6H_5Li \xrightarrow{\text{ether}} (C_2H_5)_2\overset{\ominus}{N} \overset{\oplus}{Li} + C_6H_6$$

lithium diethylamide

The salts of aliphatic amines, which correspond to acids with K_A values of about 10^{-33}, are powerfully basic reagents and are particularly effective in causing dehydrohalogenation by the E2 mechanism.

The base strengths of saturated aliphatic amines, as corresponds to the equilibrium constant K_B of the following reaction, are usually about 10^{-4} in water solu-

$$RNH_2 + H_2O \xrightleftharpoons{K_B} \overset{\oplus}{R}NH_3 + \overset{\ominus}{O}H$$

tion. Ammonia and primary, secondary, and tertiary amines have the same base strengths within perhaps a factor of 10, as can be seen from the data in Table 19-2. There is no evidence for formation of undissociated amine hydroxides such as R_3NHOH, except insofar as these are equivalent to a hydrogen-bonded complex between amine and water, $R_3N\text{---}H\text{—}O\text{—}H$.

Substantial differences in base strength are found for unsaturated amines having the groupings $-\overset{|}{C}=\overset{..}{N}-$ or $-\overset{|}{C}=\overset{|}{C}-\overset{..}{N}-$. An example of the first of these is pyridine, C_5H_5N, which is a nitrogen analog of benzene, often called a **heterocycle** because not all of the atoms in the ring are of the same element.

 **pyridine**

Relative to aliphatic amines, pyridine is a weak base with $K_B = 1.7 \times 10^{-9}$.

EXERCISE 19-4   Draw atomic orbital models for pyridine, pyridinium ion, trimethylamine, and trimethylammonium ion. Show clearly the hybridization to be expected for nitrogen (review p. 116) in each species.

Vinylamines or enamines, $R\text{—}CH\text{=}CHNH_2$, are not usually stable and rearrange readily to imines (pp. 325–326). An exception of a particular sort is aniline (phenylamine, $C_6H_5NH_2$) which has an amino group attached to a ben-

zene ring. Here, the imine structure is less favorable by virtue of the considerable stabilization energy of the aromatic ring.

It will be noted from the table of stabilization energies (p. 193) that aniline is
about 3 kcal more stable than expected for a compound with just a benzene ring.
This can be ascribed in either resonance or molecular-orbital theory to delocalization of the unshared pair of electrons on nitrogen over the benzene ring.
The resonance structures are

[1a]   [1b]   [1c]

The extra 3-kcal stabilization energy can be accounted for in terms of the structures [1a] to [1c].

The K_B of aniline is 10^{-10}, which is 10^6 less than that of cyclohexylamine.
Most, if not all, of the difference can be accounted for by the decrease in stabilization associated with forming a bond to the unshared electron pair of nitrogen
and hence preventing it from being delocalized over the benzene ring.

S.E. = 41 kcal   S.E. = 38 kcal

S.E. = 0 kcal   S.E. = 0 kcal

EXERCISE 19-5   Guanidine ($K_B \sim 1$) is a very strong base and an exception to the generalization that unsaturated amines are weaker bases than saturated amines. Consider
various ways of adding a proton to guanidine and the kind of changes in stabilization energies which would be expected for each.

guanidine

19-5 METHODS FOR THE PREPARATION OF AMINES

A. Alkylation

We discussed the reactions of ammonia and amines with alkyl halides in Chapter 11. Such processes appear to provide straightforward syntheses of amines — at least with those halides which undergo S_N2 but not E2 reactions readily. For example,

$$CH_3I + NH_3 \longrightarrow CH_3\overset{\oplus}{N}H_3 \; \overset{\ominus}{I}$$

The methylamine is recoverable by neutralization of the hydriodic acid salt with a strong base, such as sodium hydroxide.

$$CH_3\overset{\oplus}{N}H_3 \overset{\ominus}{I} + \overset{\oplus}{N}a\overset{\ominus}{O}H \longrightarrow CH_3NH_2 + NaI + H_2O$$

In practice, such reactions lead to serious mixtures of products because of equilibria of the following kind and subsequent reactions to give more than monoalkylation.

$$CH_3\overset{\oplus}{N}H_3 \; \overset{\ominus}{I} + NH_3 \rightleftharpoons CH_3NH_2 + \overset{\oplus}{N}H_4 \; \overset{\ominus}{I}$$

$$CH_3NH_2 + CH_3I \longrightarrow (CH_3)_2\overset{\oplus}{N}H_2 \; \overset{\ominus}{I}$$

Actually, we would expect the reaction of ammonia with methyl iodide to give mono-, di-, and trimethylamine, as well as tetramethylammonium iodide.

$$(CH_3)_3N + CH_3I \longrightarrow (CH_3)_4\overset{\oplus}{N} \; \overset{\ominus}{I}$$

The latter product is, of course, not readily converted to an amine by treatment with base.

Nevertheless, the alkylation reaction is by no means hopeless as a practical method for the preparation of amines because usually the starting materials are readily available and the boiling-point differences between mono-, di-, and trialkylamines are sufficiently large to make for easy separations by fractional distillation. Separations may also be achieved by chemical means.

Concerning the tetraalkylammonium halide salts formed by exhaustive alkylation of amines, they resemble alkali salts and, with moist silver oxide, can be converted to tetraalkylammonium hydroxides, which are strong bases.

$$(CH_3)_4N^{\oplus} I^{\ominus} \xrightarrow[\text{(}-AgI\text{)}]{Ag_2O, \; H_2O} (CH_3)_4N^{\oplus} OH^{\ominus}$$

Tetramethylammonium hydroxide, when heated, decomposes slowly according to the following equation:

$$(CH_3)_4 \overset{\oplus}{N} \ \overset{\ominus}{OH} \longrightarrow CH_3OH + (CH_3)_3N$$

With a higher alkylammonium hydroxide, thermal decomposition leads to the formation of an alkene. The reaction is a standard method for the preparation of alkenes.

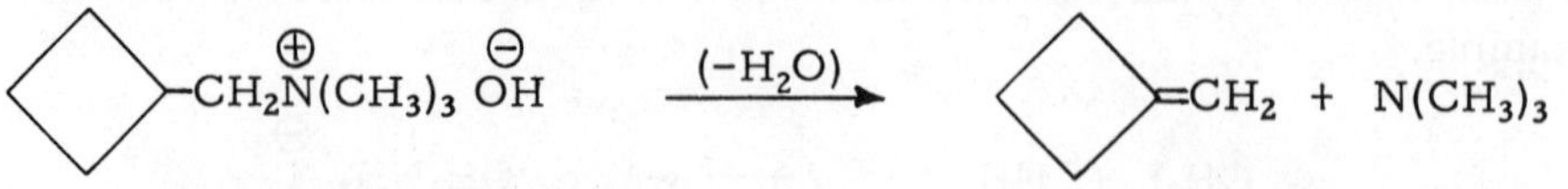

Amines may also be prepared by alkylation of ammonia with primary alcohols at high temperatures and pressures. Acid catalysts are beneficial, indicating S_N2 attack on the oxonium salt of the alcohol.

$$CH_3OH + NH_3 \xrightarrow[300°C]{ZnCl_2, \ NH_4Cl} CH_3NH_2 + H_2O$$

These reactions also give mixtures of products.

For the preparation of primary amines of the type R_3CNH_2 having a tertiary alkyl group bonded to nitrogen, the **Ritter reaction** of an alcohol or alkene with a nitrile or hydrogen cyanide is often highly advantageous. This reaction involves formation of a carbonium ion by action of strong sulfuric acid on an alkene, Eq. (19-1); combination of the carbonium ion with the unshared electrons on nitrogen of RCN:, Eq. (19-2); and then hydrolysis, first to the corresponding amide and finally to the amine, Eq. (19-3). We use here the preparation of t-butylamine as an example; $RC\equiv N$ can be an alkyl cyanide such as acetonitrile or hydrogen cyanide itself.

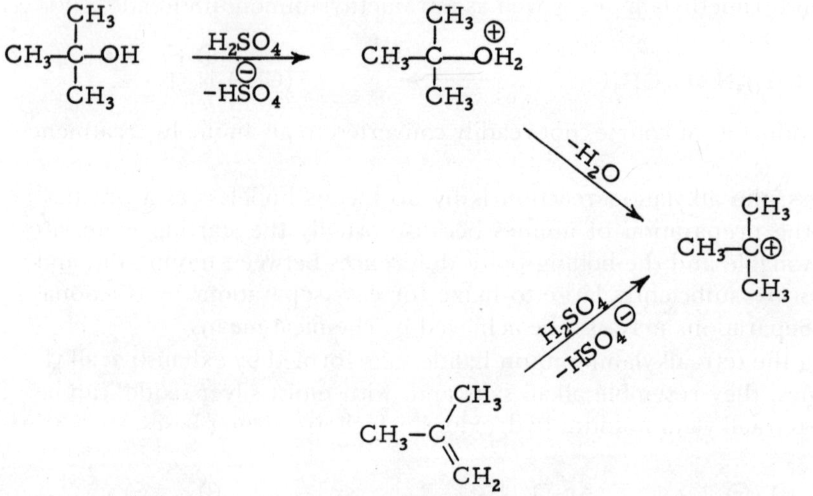

(19-1)

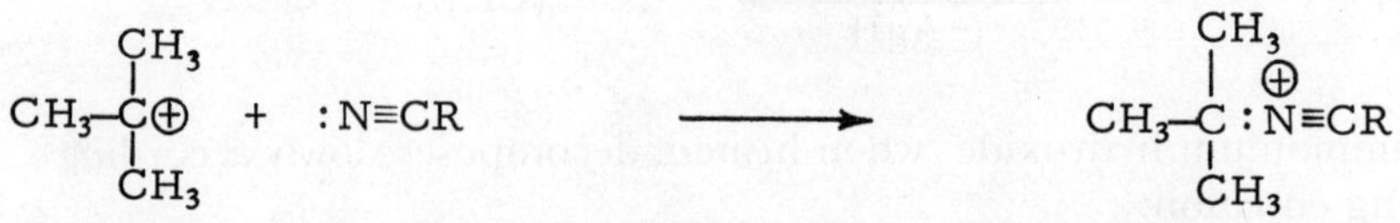

(19-2)

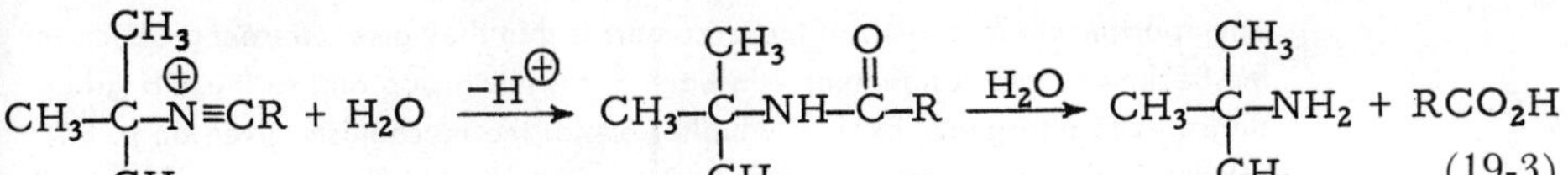

$$CH_3-\underset{\underset{CH_3}{|}}{\overset{\overset{CH_3}{|}}{C}}-\overset{\oplus}{N}\equiv CR + H_2O \xrightarrow{-H^{\oplus}} CH_3-\underset{\underset{CH_3}{|}}{\overset{\overset{CH_3}{|}}{C}}-NH-\overset{\overset{O}{\|}}{C}-R \xrightarrow{H_2O} CH_3-\underset{\underset{CH_3}{|}}{\overset{\overset{CH_3}{|}}{C}}-NH_2 + RCO_2H \qquad (19\text{-}3)$$

EXERCISE 19-6   Explain why in the Ritter reaction with hydrogen cyanide and *t*-butyl alcohol, the product is *t*-butylamine and not *t*-butyl cyanide (or trimethylacetic acid).

EXERCISE 19-7   Would you expect the Ritter reaction to occur well between methanol and acetonitrile? Explain.

B. The Beckmann Rearrangement

Rearrangement of oximes of ketones (p. 326) often provides a useful synthesis of amines through formation of intermediates with positive nitrogen analogous to carbonium ions — this is the **Beckmann rearrangement.**

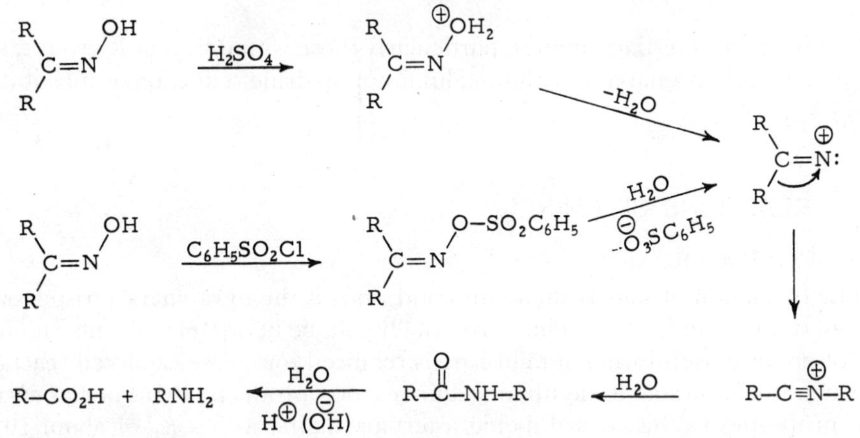

The last stages of the reaction are seen to be closely allied to the Ritter reaction (see above). The amide is not usually hydrolyzed under the conditions of the reaction and, if the amine is desired, a separate hydrolysis step has to be carried out. Phosphorus pentachloride is often used to cause the Beckmann rearrangement of oximes.

EXERCISE 19-8   It is usually possible to obtain two different stable oximes from an unsymmetrical ketone. These so-called *syn-* and *anti-*isomers are related to *cis-trans* isomers of alkenes.

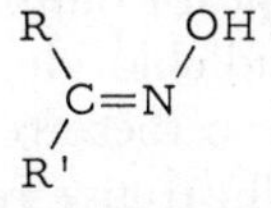

(*syn* to R, *anti* to R′) 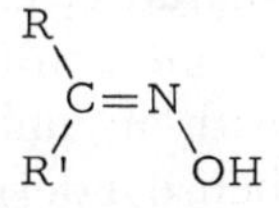   (*syn* to R′, *anti* to R)

An important characteristic of these isomers is that they give *different* products in the Beckmann rearrangement. In each case, the group *anti* to the OH group migrates to nitrogen. Explain whether or not the mechanism given on p. 461 for the Beckmann rearrangement can account for this fact and, if not, how it might be modified to do so. What products might be expected from the *syn-* and *anti-*forms of benzaldehyde oxime?

C. Formation of Amines by Reduction

Excellent procedures are available for preparation of primary, secondary, and tertiary amines by the reduction of a variety of types of nitrogen compounds. Primary amines can be obtained by hydrogenation or lithium aluminum hydride reduction of nitro compounds, azides, oximes, nitriles, and unsubstituted amides. Some care has to be exercised in the reduction of nitro compounds since reduction is highly exothermic. For example, the reaction of 1 mole (61 g) of nitromethane with hydrogen to give methylamine liberates sufficient heat to raise the temperature of a 25-lb iron bomb 100°.

$$CH_3NO_2 + 3\,H_2 \longrightarrow CH_3NH_2 + 2\,H_2O \qquad \Delta H = -85 \text{ kcal}$$

Secondary and tertiary amines, particularly those with different R groups, are advantageously prepared by lithium aluminum hydride reduction of substituted amides (p. 383).

19-6 REACTIONS OF AMINES

A. Salt Formation

The formation of salts from amines and acids is the most characteristic reaction of amines, and, since amines are usually soluble in organic solvents, amines are often very useful when a mild base is required for a base-catalyzed reaction or when it is desirable to tie up an acidic reaction product. Pyridine has excellent properties in this regard, being a tertiary amine with a K_B of about 10^{-9}, reasonably volatile (b.p. 115°), and soluble in both water and hydrocarbons. When a stronger base is required, triethylamine is commonly used. The strengths of various amines as bases was considered in Section 19-4.

B. Acylation of Amines

The unshared electrons on nitrogen play a key role in many other reactions of amines besides salt formation. In fact, almost all reactions of amines at the nitrogen atom have, as a first step, the formation of a bond involving the unshared electron pair on nitrogen. A typical example is acylation, wherein an amine is formed by the reaction of an acid chloride, an anhydride, or an ester with an amine (p. 380). The initial step in these reactions is as follows, using benzoyl derivatives and methylamine as illustrative reactants.

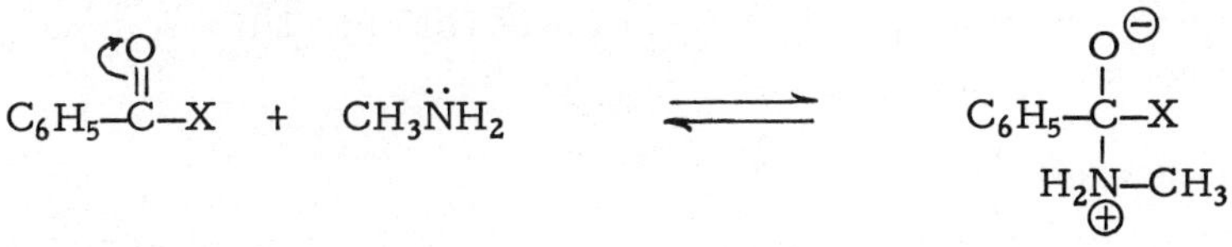

$$C_6H_5-\overset{\overset{O}{\|}}{C}-X \;+\; CH_3\ddot{N}H_2 \;\;\; \rightleftharpoons \;\;\; C_6H_5-\overset{\overset{O^{\ominus}}{|}}{\underset{\underset{\oplus}{H_2N-CH_3}}{C}}-X$$

$$X \;=\; \text{halogen,} \;\; -O-\overset{\overset{O}{\|}}{C}-C_6H_5 \;\; \text{or} \;\; -OR$$

The reaction is completed by loss of a proton and elimination of $X^{\ominus}$.

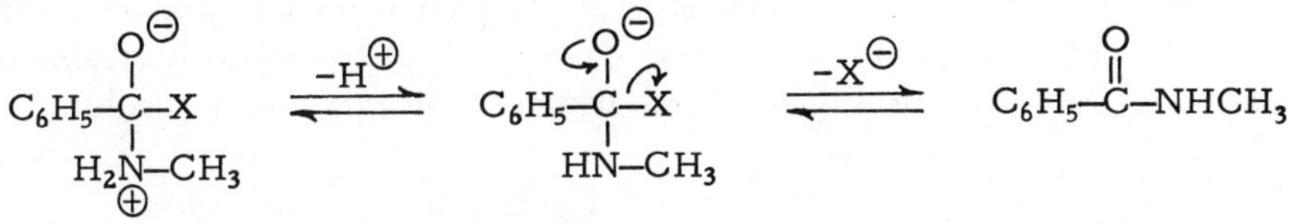

$$C_6H_5-\overset{\overset{O^{\ominus}}{|}}{\underset{\underset{\oplus}{H_2N-CH_3}}{C}}-X \;\;\underset{}{\overset{-H^{\oplus}}{\rightleftharpoons}}\;\; C_6H_5-\overset{\overset{O^{\ominus}}{|}}{\underset{\underset{}{HN-CH_3}}{C}}-X \;\;\underset{}{\overset{-X^{\ominus}}{\rightleftharpoons}}\;\; C_6H_5-\overset{\overset{O}{\|}}{C}-NHCH_3$$

EXERCISE 19-9   Calculate ΔH values for the following reactions in the vapor phase using appropriate stabilization energies (see p. 194).

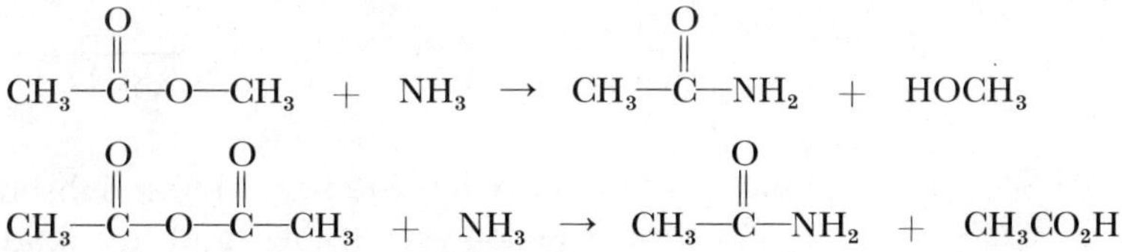

$$CH_3-\overset{\overset{O}{\|}}{C}-O-CH_3 \;+\; NH_3 \;\rightarrow\; CH_3-\overset{\overset{O}{\|}}{C}-NH_2 \;+\; HOCH_3$$

$$CH_3-\overset{\overset{O}{\|}}{C}-O-\overset{\overset{O}{\|}}{C}-CH_3 \;+\; NH_3 \;\rightarrow\; CH_3-\overset{\overset{O}{\|}}{C}-NH_2 \;+\; CH_3CO_2H$$

Which of these reactions would you expect to be the more rapid—(a) if the rate-determining step is the addition of NH_3 to the carbonyl group, (b) if the rate-determining step is loss of $X^{\ominus}$? Show your reasoning.

A serious disadvantage to the preparation of amides through the reaction of an amine with an acyl chloride (or anhydride) is the formation of 1 mole of amine salt for each mole of amide.

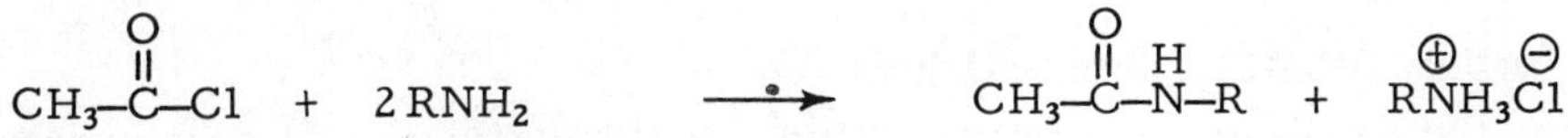

$$CH_3-\overset{\overset{O}{\|}}{C}-Cl \;+\; 2\,RNH_2 \;\;\longrightarrow\;\; CH_3-\overset{\overset{O}{\|}}{C}-\overset{H}{\underset{}{N}}-R \;+\; R\overset{\oplus}{N}H_3\overset{\ominus}{C}l$$

This is especially serious if the amine is the expensive ingredient in the reaction. In such circumstances, the reaction is usually carried on in a two-phase system with the acid chloride and amine in the nonaqueous phase and sodium hydroxide in the aqueous phase. As the amine salt is formed and dissolves in the water, it is converted back to amine by the sodium hydroxide and extracted back into the nonaqueous phase.

$$R\overset{\oplus}{N}H_3\overset{\ominus}{C}l \;+\; Na\overset{\oplus}{}O\overset{\ominus}{}H \;\;\longrightarrow\;\; RNH_2 \;+\; Na\overset{\oplus}{}C\overset{\ominus}{}l \;+\; H_2O$$

This procedure requires an excess of acid chloride, since some of it is wasted by hydrolysis.

C. Amines with Nitrous Acid

Some of the most important and interesting reactions of amines are brought about by nitrous acid (HONO). The character of the products depends very much on whether the amine is primary, secondary, or tertiary. Indeed, nitrous acid is a useful reagent to determine whether a particular amine is primary, secondary, or tertiary. Thus, with primary amines, nitrous acid results in evolution of nitrogen gas; with secondary amines an insoluble yellow liquid or solid N-nitroso compound, R_2N—N=O, separates; whereas tertiary amines (at least those which are not aniline derivatives) dissolve in and react with nitrous acid solutions, without evolution of nitrogen, usually to give complex products.

D. Halogenation

Primary amines in the presence of base react with hypochlorous acid [or *t*-butyl hypochlorite, $(CH_3)_3C$—OCl] to produce both mono- and di-substitution products.

$$RNH_2 \quad \xrightarrow[\text{OH}^\ominus]{\text{Cl}_2} \quad R\text{—}\overset{\overset{\text{H}}{|}}{\text{N}}\text{—}Cl \quad \xrightarrow[\text{OH}^\ominus]{\text{Cl}_2} \quad R\text{—}\overset{\overset{\text{Cl}}{|}}{\text{N}}\text{—}Cl$$

Secondary amines give mono-N-haloamines. These substances are rather weak bases, $K_B \sim 10^{-13}$; they are not very stable, and are oxidizing agents. They hydrolyze in water, particularly in acid solution, to regenerate the halogen.

$$R_2NCl + HCl \longrightarrow R_2NH + Cl_2$$

Compounds with N—F bonds have potential uses as oxidizing agents in rocket fuels by virtue of the possibility of yielding H—F and N_2, each of which has very strong bonds.

19-7 OXIDATION OF AMINES

A. Tertiary Amines. Amine Oxides

For the oxidation of a tertiary amine by those reagents such as hydrogen peroxide, H_2O_2, or percarboxylic acids, $RC\overset{\displaystyle\nearrow^{\text{O}}}{\underset{\searrow_{\text{O—O—H}}}{}}$, which can supply an oxygen atom with six electrons, the expected product is an amine oxide. Thus, triethylamine can be oxidized to triethylamine oxide.

$$\begin{matrix} CH_3CH_2 \\ CH_3CH_2\text{—N:} \\ CH_3CH_2 \end{matrix} \qquad \xrightarrow{[\,\text{:}\overset{..}{\text{O}}\text{:}\,]} \qquad \begin{matrix} CH_3CH_2 \\ CH_3CH_2\text{—}\overset{\oplus}{\text{N}}\text{—}\overset{\ominus}{\text{O}} \\ CH_3CH_2 \end{matrix}$$

Amine oxides are interesting to us in two connections. Amine oxides decompose when strongly heated, and this reaction provides a useful preparation of alkenes. With triethylamine oxide, ethylene is formed.

$$CH_3-CH_2 \overset{\ominus}{\underset{O}{\overset{\oplus}{N}}} \text{...} \quad \longrightarrow \quad CH_3-CH_2 \underset{CH_3-CH_2}{\overset{}{N}} OH \quad + \quad CH_2=CH_2$$

N, N-diethylhydroxylamine

The second interesting point about amine oxides is that, unlike amines, they would not be expected to undergo inversion at the nitrogen atom, and the oxides from amines with three different R groups should be resolvable into optically active forms. This has been realized for several amine oxides, including the one from methylethylallylamine.

EXERCISE 19-10   Show how one could synthesize and resolve methylethylallylamine oxide from allylamine, with the knowledge that amine oxides are somewhat basic substances having K_B values of about 10^{-11}.

B. Oxidation of Primary and Secondary Amines

Addition of an oxygen atom from hydrogen peroxide or a peracid to a primary or secondary amine would be expected to lead to amine oxide-type intermediates, which then could rearrange to hydroxylamines.

$$CH_3CH_2NH_2 \xrightarrow{[:\ddot{O}:]} \left[CH_3-CH_2-\overset{O^{\ominus}}{\underset{H}{\overset{\oplus}{N}}}-H \right] \longrightarrow CH_3-CH_2-\overset{OH}{\underset{}{N}}-H$$

N-ethylhydroxylamine

$$CH_3CH_2 \underset{CH_3CH_2}{\overset{}{N}}-H \longrightarrow \left[CH_3-CH_2 \underset{CH_3-CH_2}{\overset{\oplus}{N}} \overset{O^{\ominus}}{\underset{H}{}} \right] \longrightarrow CH_3-CH_2 \underset{CH_3-CH_2}{\overset{}{N}} OH$$

N, N-diethylhydroxylamine

These oxidations take a complicated course, because the hydroxylamines are themselves easily oxidized and, in the case of primary amines, oxidation occurs all the way to nitro compounds, in fair-to-good yields.

$$CH_3(CH_2)_5NH_2 \xrightarrow{\text{CH}_3\text{CO}_3\text{H}} CH_3(CH_2)_5NO_2$$

33%

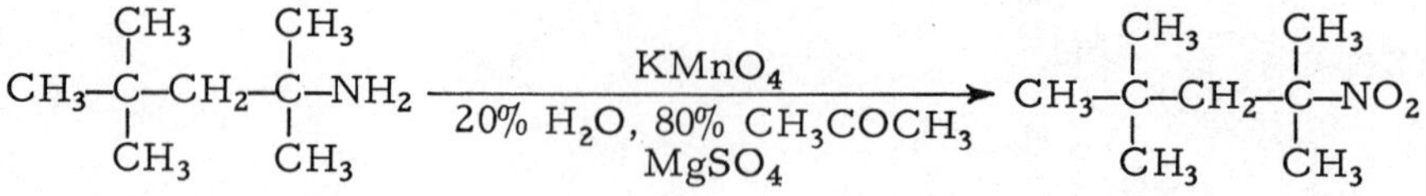

$$CH_3-\underset{\underset{CH_3}{|}}{\overset{\overset{CH_3}{|}}{C}}-CH_2-\underset{\underset{CH_3}{|}}{\overset{\overset{CH_3}{|}}{C}}-NH_2 \xrightarrow[\substack{20\% \ H_2O, \ 80\% \ CH_3COCH_3 \\ MgSO_4}]{\text{KMnO}_4} CH_3-\underset{\underset{CH_3}{|}}{\overset{\overset{CH_3}{|}}{C}}-CH_2-\underset{\underset{CH_3}{|}}{\overset{\overset{CH_3}{|}}{C}}-NO_2$$

77%

EXERCISE 19-11   Show how 2-methyl-2-nitropropane might be synthesized from (a) t-butyl alcohol, (b) pinacolone.

AMIDES

19-8 PHYSICAL AND SPECTRAL CHARACTERISTICS OF AMIDES

The properties of the simple amides are particularly important in their relevance to the chemistry of peptides and proteins, substances that are fundamental to all life as we know it—their characteristics being primarily due to their polyamide structures. The structural parameters of the amide group have been carefully determined, and the following diagram gives a reasonable idea of what is to be expected for most amides.

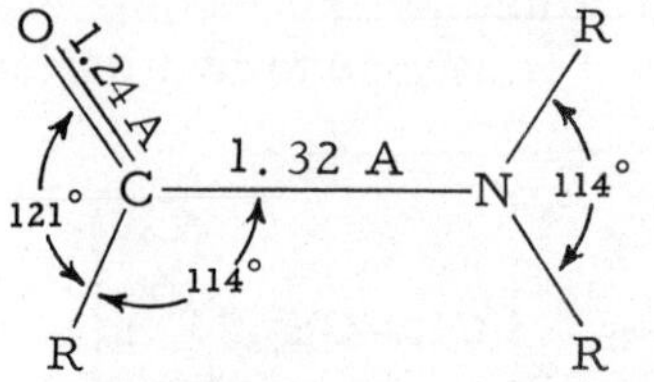

An important feature of the group is that it is planar—the carbon, oxygen, nitrogen, and the first atoms of the R groups lying in the same plane. This is anticipated on the basis of either the resonance or the molecular-orbital methods. The important resonance structures of the amide group are as follows.

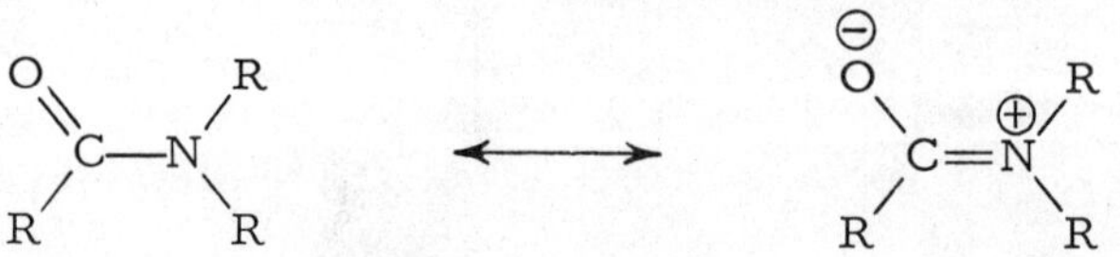

Coplanarity is required if the dipolar structure is to be significant. The stabilization energy of acetamide is 11 kcal/mole, and this is likely to be typical of most amides.

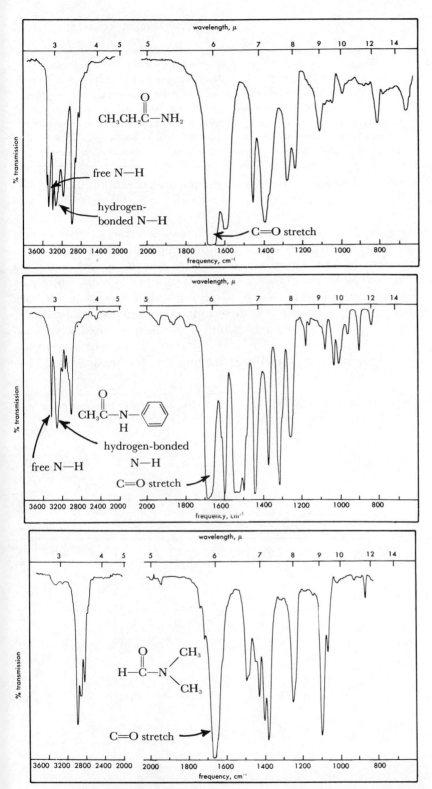

Figure 19-4   Infrared spectra of propionamide, acetanilide, and N,N-dimethylformamide in chloroform solution. Note the appearance of both free NH bands (sharp, 3300–3500 cm⁻¹)
and hydrogen-bonded N—H bands (broad, 3100–3300 cm⁻¹) for unsubstituted and
monosubstituted amides.

EXERCISE 19-12   The proton n.m.r. spectrum of N,N-dimethylformamide shows a single proton resonance at 8.06 ppm and two separate three-proton resonances at 2.78 and 2.95 ppm at room temperature. At 150°, the two three-proton lines are found to have coalesced to a single six-proton line, while the single-proton line is unchanged. Explain the n.m.r. spectrum of this compound and its behavior with temperature. What would you predict the energy barrier would be for the process by which the lines are caused to coalesce at elevated temperatures?

Considerable information is available on the infrared spectra of amides. By way of example, the spectra of three typical amides with different degrees of substitution on nitrogen are shown in Figure 19-4.

As we might expect, a strong carbonyl absorption is evident in the spectra of all amides, although the frequency of absorption varies slightly with the structure of the amide. Thus unsubstituted amides generally absorb near 1690 cm^{-1}, whereas mono-N-substituted and di-N-substituted amides absorb at slightly lower frequencies. The N—H stretching frequencies of amides are closely similar to those of amines and show shifts of 100 to 200 cm^{-1} to lower frequencies as the result of hydrogen bonding. Unsubstituted amides have two N—H bands of medium intensity near 3500 and 3400 cm^{-1}, whereas monosubstituted amides, to a first approximation, have only one N—H band near 3440 cm^{-1}.

EXERCISE 19-13   Amides with structures like the following are difficult to prepare and are relatively unstable. Explain.

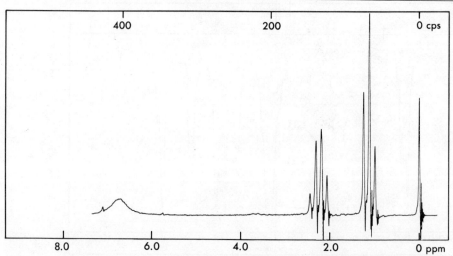

Figure 19-5   N.m.r. spectrum of propionamide, $CH_3CH_2CONH_2$, in chloroform solution (solvent not shown) at 60 Mcps relative to TMS at 0.00 ppm.

The n.m.r. resonances of the N—H protons of amides are usually somewhat different from any we have discussed so far. Customarily, these will appear as a quite broad ragged singlet absorption which may turn to a broad triplet at high temperatures. A typical example is afforded by propionamide (Figure 19-5).

EXERCISE 19-14   Show how structures can be deduced for the two substances with the molecular formula $C_5H_9NO_3$ and $C_{10}H_{13}NO$ from their infrared and n.m.r. spectra, as given in Figure 19-6.

In general, the amide group is reasonably polar and the lower-molecular-weight amides are reasonably high-melting and water-soluble, as compared to esters, amines, alcohols, and the like. N,N-Dimethylformamide and N-methyl-pyrrolidone have excellent solvent properties for both polar and nonpolar substances.

$$H-\overset{\overset{\displaystyle O}{\|}}{C}-N(CH_3)_2$$

N, N–dimethylformamide

N–methylpyrrolidone
(N–methyl–γ–butyrolactam)

Amides with N—H bonds are weakly acidic, the usual K_A being about 10^{-16}.

$$CH_3-\overset{\overset{\displaystyle O}{\|}}{\underset{NH_2}{C}} \quad \rightleftharpoons \quad \left[CH_3-\overset{\overset{\displaystyle O}{\|}}{\underset{\overset{|}{NH}}{C}}{}^{\ominus} \quad \longleftrightarrow \quad CH_3-\overset{\overset{\displaystyle O^{\ominus}}{|}}{\underset{NH}{C}} \right] + H^{\oplus}$$

Amides then are far more acidic than ammonia with $K_A \sim 10^{-33}$, and this reflects a very substantial degree of stabilization of the amide anion. However, amides are still very weak acids and, for practical purposes, are to be regarded as essentially nonacidic in aqueous solutions.

The degree of basicity of amides is very much less than that of aliphatic amines. For acetamide, K_B is about 10^{-15}.

$$CH_3-\overset{\overset{\displaystyle O}{\|}}{C} + H_2O \quad \rightleftharpoons$$
$$\underset{NH_2}{}$$

$$CH_3-\overset{\overset{\displaystyle O}{\|}}{\underset{\overset{\oplus}{NH_3}}{C}} + {}^{\ominus}OH$$

$$CH_3-\overset{\overset{\displaystyle OH}{|}}{\underset{\overset{NH_2}{\oplus}}{C}} + {}^{\ominus}OH$$

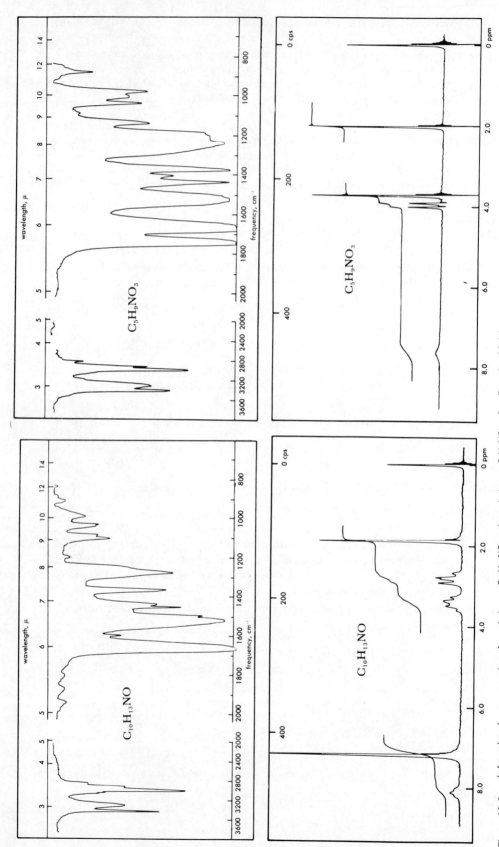

Figure 19-6   Infrared and n.m.r. spectra of a substance C₁₀H₁₃NO and a substance C₅H₉NO₃.   See Exercise 19-14.

The proton can become attached either to nitrogen or to oxygen, and the choice between the assignments is not an easy one. Nitrogen is, of course, intrinsically more basic than oxygen; but formation of the N-conjugate acid would cause loss of all the stabilization energy of the amide, whereas addition to oxygen would enhance its stabilization energy. Even though addition to oxygen seems to be favorable, amides are far from strong bases in water solution.

19-9 SYNTHESES OF AMIDES

Several general methods for preparation of amides have already been discussed in some detail (see Chap. 16). The principal routes are from the carboxylic acids and derivatives; the Ritter reaction (pp. 460–461) and the Beckmann rearrangement (p. 461) also are very useful for the preparation of amides. The hydrolysis of nitriles is a satisfactory method for preparation of unsubstituted amides and is particularly convenient in a variant wherein hydrolysis is induced under mildly basic conditions by hydrogen peroxide (see Exercise 19-15).

EXERCISE 19-15   Nitriles are converted readily to amides with hydrogen peroxide in dilute sodium hydroxide solution. The reaction is

$$RC{\equiv}N \ + \ 2H_2O_2 \quad \xrightarrow{\overset{\ominus}{OH}} \quad RC{\overset{O}{\underset{NH_2}{\big\backslash}}} \quad | \ O_2 \ + \ H_2O$$

The rate equation is

$$\nu = k\,[H_2O_2][\overset{\ominus}{OH}][RC{\equiv}N]$$

When hydrogen peroxide labeled with ^{18}O ($H_2{}^{18}O_2$) is used in ordinary water ($H_2{}^{16}O$), the resulting amide is labeled with ^{18}O ($RC^{18}ONH_2$).

Write a mechanism for this reaction which is consistent with *all* the experimental facts. Note that hydrogen peroxide is a weak acid ($K_A \sim 10^{-12}$) and, in the absence of hydrogen peroxide, dilute sodium hydroxide attacks nitriles only very slowly.

19-10 HYDROLYSIS OF AMIDES

In general, amides can be hydrolyzed in either acid or basic solutions. However, these reactions are usually slow. The mechanisms are much like that of ester hydrolysis (p. 380).

19-11   NITRILES

The carbon-nitrogen triple bond differs considerably from the carbon-carbon triple bond by being stronger (212 kcal vs. 200 kcal) and much more polar. The degree of polarity of the carbon-nitrogen triple bond corresponds to about 70 per cent of the dipole moment expected if *one* of the bonds of the triple bond were fully ionic. With this knowledge it is not surprising that liquid nitriles have rather high dielectric constants compared to most organic liquids and are reasonably soluble in water.

Nitriles absorb with variable strength in the infrared in the region 2000 to 2300 cm^{-1}, owing to stretching vibrations of the carbon-nitrogen triple bond.

The preparation of nitriles by S_N2 reactions between alkyl or allyl halides with cyanide ion has been mentioned before (p. 224), and this is the method of choice where the halide is available and reacts satisfactorily. Other useful syntheses involve cyanohydrin formation (pp. 317–320) or dehydration of the corresponding amide.

70%

The reduction of nitriles to amines and the hydrolysis of nitriles to amides have been discussed earlier (see pp. 382 and 462, 377 and 471).

Hydrogens on the *alpha* carbons of nitriles are about as acidic as the hydrogens *alpha* to carbonyl groups; accordingly, esters of cyanoacetic acid undergo many reactions similar to those of the esters of malonic and acetoacetic acids (pp. 386–389). It is possible to alkylate the α-positions of nitriles with alkyl halides by a process which is typified in the following example.

66%

EXERCISE 19-16   Nitriles of the type RCH_2CN undergo an addition reaction analogous to the aldol addition in the presence of strong bases such as lithium amide. Hydrolysis of the initial reaction product with dilute acid yields a cyanoketone,

$$RCH_2-\underset{O}{\overset{\parallel}{C}}-\underset{CN}{\overset{|}{C}}H-R.$$ Show the steps that are involved in the mechanism of the over-all reaction and outline a scheme for its use to synthesize large-ring ketones of the type $(CH_2)_nC=O$ from dinitriles of the type $NC(CH_2)_nCN$.

NITROSO AND NITRO COMPOUNDS

19-12 NITROSO COMPOUNDS

Although nitroso compounds, R—N=O, have no special synthetic importance
at present, they do possess some interesting properties.   Primary and secondary
nitroso compounds are unstable and rearrange to oximes.

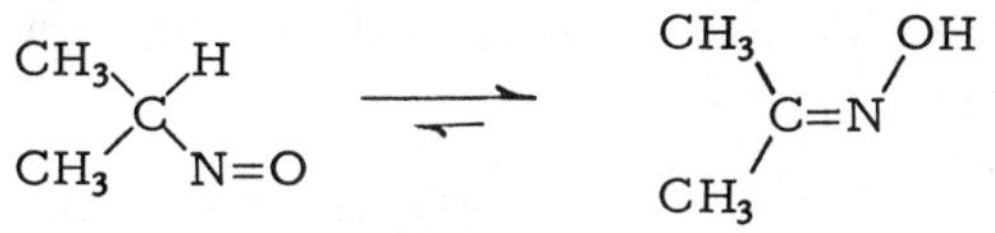

2-nitrosopropane

Tertiary and aromatic nitroso compounds are reasonably stable substances,
which, although usually blue or green in the gas phase or in dilute solution,
may be isolated as colorless or yellow solids or liquids.   The color changes are
due to dimerization, which apparently occurs through nitrogen-nitrogen bonding.

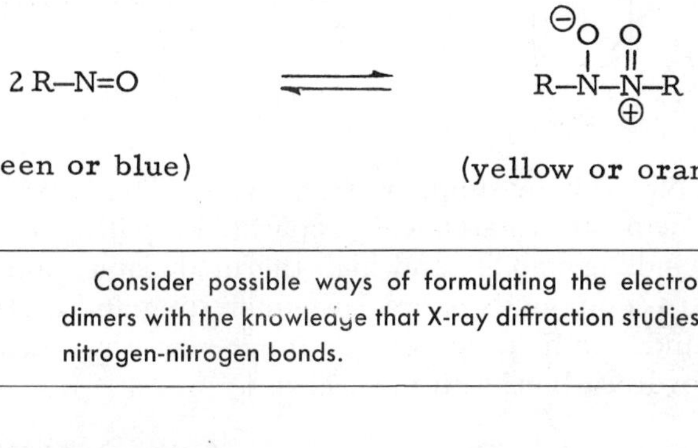

2 R—N=O   ⇌   R—N—N—R

(green or blue)   (yellow or orange)

19-13 NITRO COMPOUNDS

Nitro compounds make up a very important class of nitrogen derivatives.
The nitro group ($-NO_2$) like the carboxylate anion, is well formulated as a
hybrid of two equivalent resonance structures.

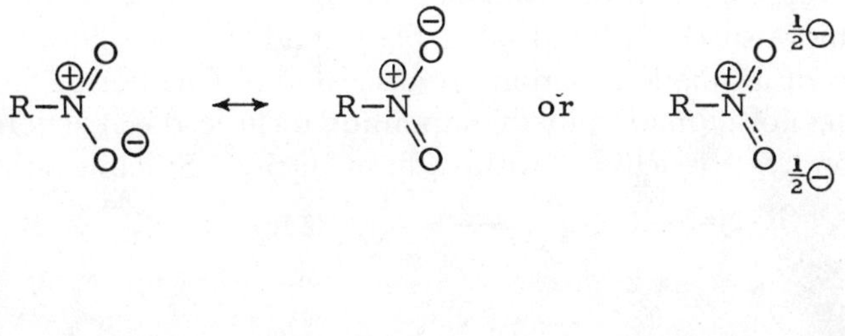

The hybrid structure is seen to have a full positive charge on nitrogen and a half-negative charge on oxygen. The polar character of the nitro group results in lower volatility of nitro compounds than ketones of about the same molecular weight; thus the boiling point of nitromethane (M.W. 61) is 101°, whereas acetone (M.W. 58) has a boiling point of 56°. Surprisingly, the water solubility is low; a saturated solution of nitromethane in water is less than 10 per cent by weight, whereas acetone is infinitely miscible with water.

Nitro groups of nitroalkanes can be identified by strong infrared bands at about 1580 and 1375 cm^{-1}, whereas the corresponding bands in the spectra of aromatic nitro compounds occur at slightly lower frequencies. A weak transition occurs in the electronic spectra of nitroalkanes at around 2700 A; aromatic nitro compounds, such as nitrobenzene, have extended conjugation and absorb at longer wavelengths (~3300 A).

Nitro compounds are quite unstable in the thermodynamic sense and the heat of decomposition of nitromethane, according to the following stoichiometry, is 67.4 kcal/mole.

$$CH_3NO_2 \longrightarrow \tfrac{1}{2}N_2 + CO_2 + \tfrac{3}{2}H_2 \qquad \Delta H = -67.4 \text{ kcal}$$

Advantage is taken of the considerable energies and rapid rates of processes such as this in the commercial use of nitro compounds as explosives. With some nitro compounds such as 2,4,6-trinitrotoluene (TNT), there is a further advantage of low shock sensitivity.

2, 4, 6-trinitrotoluene

TNT is not set off easily by simple impact and even burns without exploding. However, once detonation starts, it is propagated rapidly. The characteristics of reasonable handling stability and high thermodynamic potential makes the chemistry of nitro compounds particularly interesting and useful.

Nitro compounds can be prepared in a number of ways, including the direct substitution of hydrocarbons with nitric acid.

$$RH + HONO_2 \longrightarrow RNO_2 + H_2O$$

This reaction was discussed earlier (p. 77) in connection with the nitration of alkanes, and it was there noted that reaction is successful only when conducted at high temperatures in the vapor phase. Mixtures of products are invariably obtained. Direct nitration of aromatic compounds such as benzene is, in contrast, much more successful and takes place readily in the liquid phase. The characteristics of aromatic nitration are discussed in Chapter 22.

Other routes to aliphatic nitro compounds include the reaction of an alkyl halide (of good S_N2 reactivity) with sodium nitrite. Suitable solvents are di-

$$R-N=N-R \longrightarrow 2R\cdot + N_2$$

methyl sulfoxide $(CH_3)_2SO$ and dimethylformamide. As will be seen from Eq. (19-4), formation of the nitrite ester by O- instead of N-alkylation is a competing reaction.

$$CH_3(CH_2)_6Br + NaNO_2 \xrightarrow[(-NaBr)]{HCON(CH_3)_2} CH_3(CH_2)_6NO_2 + CH_3(CH_2)_6ONO$$

$$60\% \qquad\qquad 30\%$$

$$(19\text{-}4)$$

Silver nitrite is frequently used in preference to sodium nitrite as the nitrating agent, usually in diethyl ether as solvent.

$$ICH_2CO_2C_2H_5 + AgNO_2 \xrightarrow{0°, \text{ ether}} O_2NCH_2CO_2C_2H_5 + AgI$$

$$\text{ethyl nitroacetate}$$

$$77\%$$

Tertiary nitro compounds may be prepared by the oxidation of the corresponding amine with aqueous potassium permanganate solution (p. 466).

EXERCISE 19-19   Show from the electronic structure of nitrite ion how it could react with an alkyl halide in the S_N2 manner to give either a nitrite ester or a nitro compound. What kind of properties would you expect for a nitrite ester and how could they be removed from the reaction products?

Nitro compounds are readily reduced to amines (p. 462) and this affords a particularly useful synthesis of aromatic amines, as will be discussed in Chapter 24. Most aliphatic amines are more easily prepared in other ways.

SOME COMPOUNDS WITH N—N BONDS

Among the organic nitrogen compounds having nitrogen above the oxidation level of ammonia are a wide variety of substances with N—N bonds. We shall mention only a very few of the more important of these substances, namely hydrazines, azo and diazo compounds, and azides.

19-14 HYDRAZINES

Organic hydrazines are substitution products of NH_2—NH_2 and have many properties similar to those of amines in forming salts and acyl derivatives (p. 378) as well as undergoing alkylation and condensations with carbonyl compounds (p. 326 and p. 439). Unsymmetrical hydrazines can be prepared by careful reduction of N-nitrosoamines. Dimethylhydrazine is prepared in this way for use as a rocket fuel.

$$\underset{CH_3}{\overset{CH_3}{\diagdown}} NH \;+\; HONO \;\longrightarrow\; \underset{CH_3}{\overset{CH_3}{\diagdown}} N\text{--}NO \;\xrightarrow{2\,H_2}\; \underset{CH_3}{\overset{CH_3}{\diagdown}} N\text{--}NH_2$$

Aromatic hydrazines are best prepared by reduction of aromatic diazonium salts (Chapter 24).

Hydrazines of the type $R\text{---}\overset{H}{N}\text{---}\overset{H}{N}\text{---}R$ are usually easily oxidized to the corresponding azo compounds, $R\text{---}N{=}N\text{---}R$.

19-15 AZO COMPOUNDS

Azo compounds possess the —N=N— grouping. Aliphatic azo compounds of the type R—N=N—H appear to be highly unstable and decompose to R—H and nitrogen. Derivatives of the type R—N=N—R are much more stable and can be prepared as mentioned above by oxidation of the corresponding hydrazines. Aromatic azo compounds are available in considerable profusion from diazonium coupling reactions (Chapter 24) and are of commercial importance as dyes and coloring materials.

A prime characteristic of azo compounds is their tendency to decompose into organic free radicals and liberate nitrogen.

The ease of these reactions is usually a fairly reasonable guide to the stabilities of the free radicals that result. For instance, it is found that azomethane $(CH_3N{=}NCH_3)$ is stable to about 400°C, and azobenzene $(C_6H_5N{=}NC_6H_5)$ is also resistant to thermal decomposition; but, when the azo compound decomposes to radicals that are stabilized by resonance, the decomposition temperature is greatly reduced. Thus α,α'-azobisisobutyronitrile decomposes to radicals at moderate temperatures (60 to 100°), and for this reason is a very useful agent for generating radicals, such as are required for the initiation of polymerization of vinyl compounds.

$$\underset{CH_3}{\overset{CN}{\underset{|}{\overset{|}{CH_3{-}C{-}}}}}N{=}N\underset{CH_3}{\overset{CN}{\underset{|}{\overset{|}{{-}C{-}CH_3}}}} \xrightarrow{60\text{--}100°} 2\,\underset{CH_3}{\overset{CN}{\underset{|}{\overset{|}{CH_3{-}C\cdot}}}} \;+\; N_2$$

α, α'–azobisisobutyronitrile

EXERCISE 19-20   Arrange the following azo substances in order of their expected rates of thermal decomposition to produce nitrogen. Give your reasoning.

a. $\langle\!\!\!\!\!\!\!\bigcirc\!\!\!\!\!\!\!\rangle$—CH₂—N=N—CH₂—$\langle\!\!\!\!\!\!\!\bigcirc\!\!\!\!\!\!\!\rangle$ b. $(CH_3)_3C\text{--}N{=}N\text{--}C(CH_3)_3$

c. [structure: cyclohexyl–N=N–cyclohexyl]

e. [structure: benzene ring with fused N=N=N group]

d. $CH_3-N=N-CH_3$

19-16 DIAZO COMPOUNDS

The parent of the diazo compounds, diazomethane $CH_2{=}\overset{\oplus}{N}{=}\overset{\ominus}{N}$, has been mentioned before in connection with formation of carbenes (p. 249). It is one of the most versatile and useful reagents in organic chemistry, despite the fact that it is highly toxic, dangerously explosive, and cannot be stored without decomposition.

Diazomethane is an intensely yellow gas, b.p. $-23°$, which is customarily prepared and used in diethyl ether or methylene chloride solution. It can be synthesized in a number of ways, the most useful of which employs the action of base on an N-nitroso-N-methylamide.

$$R-\overset{\overset{O}{\|}}{\underset{\underset{NO}{|}}{\underset{N-CH_3}{C}}} + NaOH \xrightarrow{\text{ether}} R-CO_2Na + CH_2N_2 + H_2O$$

As a methylating agent of reasonably acidic substances, diazomethane has nearly ideal properties. It can be used in organic solvents; reacts very rapidly without need for a catalyst; the coproduct is nitrogen which offers no separation problem; it gives essentially quantitative yields; and it acts as its own indicator to show when reaction is complete. With acids it gives esters and with enols it gives O-alkylation.

[reaction: benzoic acid (C₆H₅–CO–OH) + CH_2N_2 → methyl benzoate (C₆H₅–CO–OCH₃) + N_2]

[reaction: $CH_3-C(\overset{H\cdots}{O})=CH-C(=O)-CH_3$ enol form + CH_2N_2 → $CH_3-C(OCH_3)=CH-C(=O)-CH_3$ + N_2]

Diazomethane was originally believed to possess the three-membered, *diazirine* ring structure, but this was disproved by electron-diffraction studies, which showed the linear structure to be correct.

$$CH_2\underset{\diagdown N}{\overset{\diagup N}{\|}}$$

diazirine

$$CH_2{=}\overset{\oplus}{N}{=}\overset{\ominus}{N}$$

diazomethane

Recently, a variety of authentic "cyclodiazomethanes," or more properly diazirines, have been prepared, and these have been found to have very different
properties from the diazoalkanes.   The simple diazirines are colorless and do
not react with dilute acids, bases, or even bromine.   The syntheses of these substances are relatively simple.   One of several possible routes follows.

$$\begin{matrix} R \\ \diagdown \\ C=O \\ \diagup \\ R \end{matrix} + NH_3 + NH_2Cl \longrightarrow \begin{matrix} R \diagdown \quad NH \\ \quad C \diagdown | \\ R \diagup \quad NH \end{matrix} \xrightarrow{CrO_3} \begin{matrix} R \diagdown \quad N \\ \quad C \parallel \\ R \diagup \quad N \end{matrix}$$

"isohydrazone"

SUPPLEMENTARY EXERCISES

19-21   Write equations for a practical laboratory synthesis of each of the following compounds
based on the indicated starting materials.   Give reagents and conditions.
a. dimethyl-*t*-amylamine from *t*-amyl chloride
b. $(CH_3)_3CCH_2NH_2$ from $(CH_3)_3CCO_2H$
c. 1,6-diaminohexane from butadiene
d. isobutyronitrile from isobutyl alcohol
e. $(CH_3CO_2CH_2)_3C-NO_2$ from nitromethane
f. N-*t*-butylacetamide from *t*-butyl alcohol
g. methylethyl-*n*-butylamine oxide from *n*-butylamine

19-22   *a.* Make a chart of the m.p., b.p., and solubilities in water, ether, dilute acid, and
dilute base of each of the following compounds:

     n-octylamine   N,N-dimethylacetamide
     di-*n*-butylamine   1-nitrobutane
     tri-*n*-propylamine   2-nitro-2-methylbutane

    b. Outline a practical procedure for separation of an equimolal mixture of each of the
above compounds into the *pure components*.   Note that selective reactions are *not*
suitable unless the reaction product can be reconverted to the starting material.
Fractional distillation will not be accepted here as a practical means of separation
of compounds boiling less than 25° apart.

19-23   Give for each of the following pairs of compounds a chemical test, preferably a test-tube
reaction which will distinguish between the two compounds.
a. $(CH_3)_3CNH_2$ and $(CH_3)_2NC_2H_5$
b. $CH_3CH_2NO_2$ and CH_3CONH_2
c. $CH_3CH_2C\equiv N$ and $CH\equiv C-CH_2NH_2$
d. CH_3CH_2NHCl and $CH_3CH_2NH_3Cl$
e. $CH_3NHCOCH_3$ and $CH_3NHCO_2CH_3$
f. $CH_3OCH_2CH_2NH_2$ and $CH_3NHCH_2CH_2OH$

g. $CH_3CH_2C\begin{matrix} \overset{O}{\diagup\!\!\diagup} \\ \diagdown \\ NH_2 \end{matrix}$ and $CH_3OCH_2CH_2NH_2$

19-24 Arrange the following pairs of substances in order of expected base strengths. Show your reasoning.

    a. $(CH_3)_3N$ and $(CF_3)_3N$

    b.   ⬡—CH_2NH_2 and CH_3—⬡—NH_2

    c. $CH_3C{\equiv}N:$ and   ⬡N:

    d.   H—C⟨$\overset{NH}{NH_2}$ and   H—C⟨$\overset{O}{NH_2}$ (review Exercise 19-5)

    e.   (pyrrole with N—CH_3)   and   (azepine with N—CH_3)   (review pp. 190, 457–458)

19-25 Using spectroscopic methods, how could you distinguish one isomer from the other in the following pairs.

    a.   ⬡$\overset{CH_3}{—NH_2}$ and   ⬡—$NHCH_3$

    b. $CH_3CH_2\overset{O}{\overset{\|}{—C}}—NH_2$ and $H\overset{O}{\overset{\|}{—C}}—N(CH_3)_2$

    c. $CH_3CH_2—NO_2$ and $CH_3CH_2—ONO$

Amino Acids, Peptides, Proteins, and Enzymes

The chemistry of life is largely the chemistry of polyfunctional organic compounds. The functional groups are usually of types which interact rather strongly and are often so located with respect to one another that both intra- and intermolecular interactions can be important. One example is afforded by carbohydrates, and we have seen how the alcohol and carbonyl functions interact in these substances leading both to the cyclization of the simple sugars and to the formation of bonds between sugar molecules to give polysaccharides. The present chapter is devoted to the chemistry of substances which feature interaction between amine and carboxylic acid functions with particular emphasis on examples which are of physiological importance. This will be done in three stages. First, the chemistry of some simple α-amino acids will be considered with the intention of illustrating how the respective properties of amine and acid functions are modified in molecules which possess both groups. Then we shall discuss a few important properties of peptides and proteins, substances made up of amino acids linked together by amide bonds. Brief attention will also be given to the chemical problems presented by enzymes, which are protein molecules able to act as efficient catalysts for specific chemical reactions and, finally, to the molecular basis of genetics.

Amino Acids, Peptides, Proteins, and Enzymes

CHAPTER 20

20-1 TYPES OF BIOLOGICALLY IMPORTANT AMINO ACIDS

Most of the amino acids involved in biochemical reactions have a primary amino group in the α-position with respect to the carboxylic acid function. All the natural amino acids that occur as constituents of proteins (with the exception of glycine) have a center of asymmetry at the α-position and belong to the L series—as corresponds to the projection formula shown below (see also pp. 414–415).

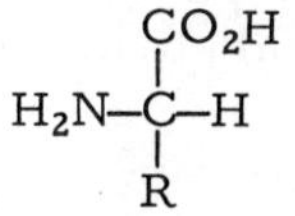

$$\begin{array}{c} CO_2H \\ | \\ H_2N-C-H \\ | \\ R \end{array} \qquad \text{L–amino acid}$$

The structures and names of some particularly important α-amino acids are shown in Table 20-1. It will be seen that the names in common use for amino acids are not very descriptive of their structural formulas; but at least they have the advantage of being shorter than the systematic names. As will be seen later, the abbreviations Gly, Glu, etc., that are listed in Table 20-1 are particularly useful in designating the sequences of amino acids in proteins and peptides. Amino acids that have an excess of amine over acid groups are called *basic* amino acids (e.g., lysine and arginine), whereas those with an excess of acid groups are called *acidic* amino acids (e.g., aspartic and glutamic acids). Three of the amino acids listed in Table 20-1, cysteine, cystine, and methionine, contain sulfur, and the making and breaking of S—S linkages in the interconversion of cysteine and cystine are important processes in the biochemistry of sulfur-containing peptides and proteins. Further characteristics of the general reaction $2\,RSH \underset{2[H]}{\overset{[O]}{\rightleftarrows}} R—S—S—R$ will be considered in Chapter 21.

The fact that all of the more important naturally occurring amino acids have α-hydrogens suggests that biosynthesis and degradation of amino acids occur by way of α-keto acids and α-imino acids.

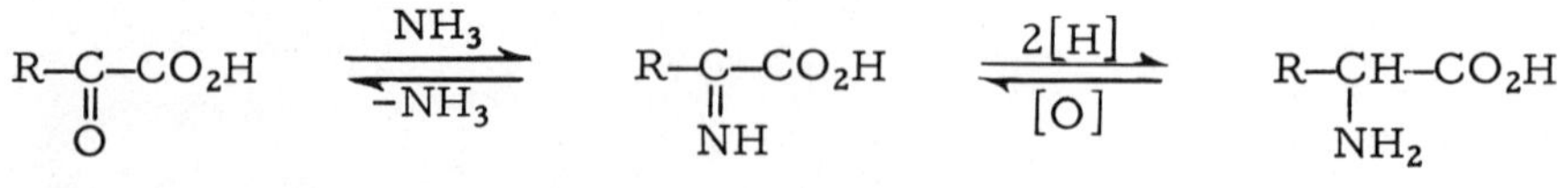

$$R\underset{O}{\overset{\|}{-C}}-CO_2H \underset{-NH_3}{\overset{NH_3}{\rightleftarrows}} R\underset{NH}{\overset{\|}{-C}}-CO_2H \underset{[O]}{\overset{2[H]}{\rightleftarrows}} R\underset{NH_2}{\overset{|}{-CH}}-CO_2H$$

α-keto acid   α-imino acid

Organisms differ considerably in their ability to synthesize amino acids; the acids that are indispensable for maintenance of proper nitrogen balance in the human body, yet which the body cannot synthesize, are often called "essential" amino acids and are marked with asterisks in Table 20-1.

EXERCISE 20-1   Pick out the amino acids in Table 20-1 which have more than one asymmetric center and draw projection formulas for all the possible stereoisomers of each which possess the L configuration for the α-carbon.

EXERCISE 20-2   Which of the amino acids in Table 20-1 are "acidic" amino acids and which "basic" amino acids? Which of the structures shown would have the most basic nitrogen? The least basic amino nitrogen? The most acidic and least acidic carboxyl group? Give the reasons for your choices.

20-2 SYNTHESIS OF α-AMINO ACIDS

Many of the types of reactions which are useful for the preparation of amino acids have been discussed earlier in connection with separate syntheses of carboxylic acids (Chapter 16) and amino compounds (Chapter 19). Examples include amination of chloroacetic acid to yield glycine, which works best with a large excess of ammonia,

$$3\,NH_3 + ClCH_2CO_2H \xrightarrow{50°} NH_2CH_2CO_2^{\ominus}\,\overset{\oplus}{NH_4} + \overset{\oplus}{NH_4}\overset{\ominus}{Cl}$$

$$\Big\downarrow H^{\oplus}$$

$$NH_2CH_2CO_2H$$

glycine

and the **Strecker synthesis,** which, in its first step, bears a close relationship to cyanohydrin formation.

Table 20-1 Amino Acids Important as Constituents of Proteins

Name	Abbreviation	Formula	$[M]_D$ of L$_s$-isomer, H_2O, 25°[a]	Isoelectric point, pH units	Water solubility at isoelectric point,[b] g/100 g/20°C
glycine	Gly	$NH_2CH_2CO_2H$		6.0	22.5
alanine	Ala	CH_3CHCO_2H $\underset{}{NH_2}$	+1.6°	6.0	15.8
valine*	Val	$(CH_3)_2CHCHCO_2H$ $\underset{}{NH_2}$	+6.6°	6.0	6.8
leucine*	Leu	$(CH_3)_2CHCH_2CHCO_2H$ $\underset{}{NH_2}$	−14.4°	6.0	2.4
isoleucine*	Ileu	$CH_3CH_2CH-CHCO_2H$ $CH_3\ NH_2$	+16.3°	6.0	2.1
phenylalanine*	Phe	$C_6H_5CH_2CHCO_2H$ $\underset{}{NH_2}$	−57.0°	5.5	2.7
serine	Ser	$HOCH_2CHCO_2H$ $\underset{}{NH_2}$	−7.9°	5.7	4.3
threonine*	Thr	$CH_3CH-CHCO_2H$ $OH\ NH_2$	−33.9°	5.6	1.6

Continued on p. 484

Table 20-1   Amino Acids Important as Constituents of Proteins (Continued)

Name	Abbreviation	Formula	$[M]_D$ of L_S-isomer, H_2O, 25°[a]	Isoelectric point, pH units	Water solubility at isoelectric point,[b] g/100 g/20°C
lysine*	Lys	$NH_2(CH_2)_4\underset{\underset{NH_2}{\mid}}{C}HCO_2H$	+19.7°	9.6	very sol.
δ-hydroxylysine	Lys-OH	$NH_2CH_2\underset{\underset{OH}{\mid}}{C}H(CH_2)_2\underset{\underset{NH_2}{\mid}}{C}HCO_2H$	+14.9°	9.15	very sol.
arginine	Arg	$\underset{\underset{NH_2}{\mid}}{\overset{\overset{NH}{\parallel}}{C}}-NH(CH_2)_3\underset{\underset{NH_2}{\mid}}{C}HCO_2H$	+21.8°	11.2	very sol.
aspartic acid	Asp	$HO_2CCH_2\underset{\underset{NH_2}{\mid}}{C}HCO_2H$	+6.7°	2.8	0.4
asparagine	Asp-NH₂	$NH_2COCH_2\underset{\underset{NH_2}{\mid}}{C}HCO_2H$	-7.4°	5.4	2.4
glutamic acid	Glu	$HO_2C(CH_2)_2\underset{\underset{NH_2}{\mid}}{C}HCO_2H$	+17.7°	3.2	0.7
glutamine	Glu-NH₂	$NH_2CO(CH_2)_2\underset{\underset{NH_2}{\mid}}{C}HCO_2H$	+9.2°	5.7	3.6[18]
cysteine	CySH	$HSCH_2\underset{\underset{NH_2}{\mid}}{C}HCO_2H$ [H] ↑↓ [O]	-20.0°	5.1	very sol.
cystine	CyS—CyS	$S-CH_2\underset{\underset{NH_2}{\mid}}{C}HCO_2H$ $\mid$ $S-CH_2\underset{\underset{NH_2}{\mid}}{C}HCO_2H$	-509° (1 N HCl)	5.0	0.009

		Structure	$[M]_D$ [a]		g [?]
methionine*	Met	$CH_3S(CH_2)_2\overset{\underset{\displaystyle NH_2}{\mid}}{C}HCO_2H$	$-14.9°$	5.7	3.0
tyrosine	Tyr	HO-$\langle\bigcirc\rangle$-$CH_2\overset{\underset{\displaystyle NH_2}{\mid}}{C}HCO_2H$	$-18°$	5.7	0.04
thyroxine	Thy	(thyroxine structure)	-3.8[c]		
proline	Pro	(proline structure)	$-99.2°$	6.3	154.5
hydroxyproline	Hypro	(hydroxyproline structure)	$-99.6°$	5.7	34.5
tryptophan*	Try	(tryptophan structure)	$-68.8°$	5.9	1.1
histidine	His	(histidine structure)	$-59.8°$	7.5	4.0

[a] For definition of $[M]_D$ see p. 401. Usually, the concentration $c = 1$–2 g per 100 ml of solution. For slightly soluble amino acids, the rotations are given for HCl solutions.

[b] Refers to the L isomer. The D, L mixtures are usually less soluble (see p. 403).

[c] In ethanolic sodium hydroxide solution.

* Must be included in diet for maintenance of proper nitrogen equilibrium in normal adult humans.

$$\text{C}_6\text{H}_5\text{-CHO} + \text{NH}_3 + \text{HCN} \longrightarrow \text{C}_6\text{H}_5\text{-CH-C}\equiv\text{N} \xrightarrow{\text{H}^{\oplus}, \text{H}_2\text{O}} \text{C}_6\text{H}_5\text{-CH-CO}_2\text{H}$$
$$\underset{\text{NH}_2}{\qquad\qquad\qquad\qquad} \qquad \underset{\text{NH}_2}{\qquad}$$

With those amino acids which are very soluble in water, it is usually necessary to isolate the product either by evaporation of an aqueous solution or by precipitation induced by addition of an organic solvent like alcohol. Difficulties may be encountered in obtaining a pure product if inorganic salts are coproducts of the synthesis.

EXERCISE 20-3   Show the sequence of steps involved in the Strecker synthesis of α-amino acids.

EXERCISE 20-4   Show how the following amino acids can be prepared from the indicated starting materials by the methods described above or earlier.
a. leucine from isobutyl alcohol
b. lysine from 1,4-dibromobutane
c. proline from adipic acid
d. glutamic acid from α-ketoglutaric acid

20-3   THE ACID-BASE PROPERTIES OF AMINO ACIDS

The behavior of glycine is reasonably typical of that of the simple amino acids. Since glycine is neither a very strong acid nor a very strong base, we shall expect a solution of glycine in water to contain four species in rapid equilibrium.

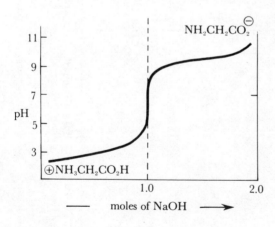

Figure 20-1

Titration curve of glycine, $\text{NH}_2\text{CH}_2\text{CO}_2\text{H}$.

$$\overset{\oplus}{\text{N}}\text{H}_3\text{CH}_2\text{CO}_2\text{H} \underset{+\text{H}^{\oplus}}{\overset{-\text{H}^{\oplus}}{\rightleftharpoons}} \text{NH}_2\text{CH}_2\text{CO}_2\text{H} \rightleftharpoons \overset{\oplus}{\text{N}}\text{H}_3\text{CH}_2\overset{\ominus}{\text{CO}}_2 \underset{+\text{H}^{\oplus}}{\overset{-\text{H}^{\oplus}}{\rightleftharpoons}} \text{NH}_2\text{CH}_2\overset{\ominus}{\text{CO}}_2$$

conjugate acid   neutral glycine   dipolar ion   conjugate base
of glycine   of glycine

The proportions of these species is expected to change with pH — the conjugate acid being the predominant form at low pH values and the conjugate base being favored at high pH values. Since the establishment of equilibrium between the neutral molecule and the dipolar ion (sometimes called the "inner salt" or "zwitterion") involves no net change in hydrogen or hydroxide ion concentrations, the *ratio* of these two substances is to a good approximation independent of pH.

$$\text{NH}_2\text{CH}_2\text{CO}_2\text{H} \quad \rightleftharpoons \quad \overset{\oplus}{\text{NH}}_3\text{CH}_2\overset{\ominus}{\text{CO}}_2$$

EXERCISE 20-5   Devise physical or chemical ways to determine directly or calculate the equilibrium constant between neutral glycine and its dipolar ion. Arguing from substituent effects on the ionization of carboxylic acids and amines, would you expect the equilibrium constant to be closer to 0.1, 1.0, or 10? Explain.

A titration curve starting with glycine hydrochloride is shown in Figure 20-1. Two equivalents of base are required to convert $\overset{\oplus}{\text{NH}}_3\text{CH}_2\text{CO}_2\text{H}$ to $\text{NH}_2\text{CH}_2\text{CO}_2^{\ominus}$. The pH of half-neutralization during addition of the first equivalent of base corresponds to an acid with K_A of 5×10^{-3}, whereas the pH of half-neutralization during the addition of the second equivalent of base corresponds to $K_A = 2 \times 10^{-10}$. There will be a pH on the titration curve where the concentration of $\overset{\oplus}{\text{NH}}_3\text{CH}_2\text{CO}_2\text{H}$ will be just equal to the concentration of $\text{NH}_2\text{CH}_2\text{CO}_2^{\ominus}$. If these two ions conduct electric current equally well, then, in an electrolytic experiment, there will be no net migration of the ions at this particular pH, which is called the **isoelectric point**. Generally, the isoelectric point corresponds also to the pH at which the amino acid has minimum water solubility. Isoelectric points are listed for most of the amino acids shown in Table 20-1.

EXERCISE 20-6   Suppose one were to titrate an equimolal mixture of ammonium chloride and acetic acid with two equivalents of sodium hydroxide. How would the titration curve be expected to differ from that of glycine hydrochloride shown in Figure 20-1? Take K_A for acetic acid equal to 2×10^{-5} and K_A for ammonium ion to be 5×10^{-10}.

20-4   ANALYSIS OF AMINO ACIDS

A. Nitrous Acid Reactions

The action of nitrous acid on amino acids proceeds in a manner similar to that discussed earlier for ordinary amines (p. 464). Primary amino groups are lost as nitrogen; secondary amino groups are nitrosated whereas tertiary amino functions do not usually react. Measurement of the nitrogen evolved on treatment of amino acids or their derivatives with nitrous acid provides a useful analysis for free —NH₂ groups in such materials (**Van Slyke amino-nitrogen**

determination). With amino acids, as with amines, the nitrous acid reaction is not to be regarded as a generally satisfactory preparative method for conversion of RNH_2 to ROH.

B. The Ninhydrin Test

In many kinds of research it is important to have simple and sensitive means for analysis of amino acids, particularly in small quantities. Detection of α-amino acids of the type $R—\underset{\underset{NH_2}{|}}{CH}—CO_2H$ is readily achieved by the "ninhydrin color test," wherein heating of an alcoholic solution of the triketone, "ninhydrin," with a solution containing an amino acid produces a blue-violet color. The sensitivity and reliability of this test is such that 0.1 micromole of amino acid gives a color intensity which is reproducible to a few per cent, provided that a reducing agent such as stannous chloride is present to prevent oxidation of the colored salt by dissolved oxygen.

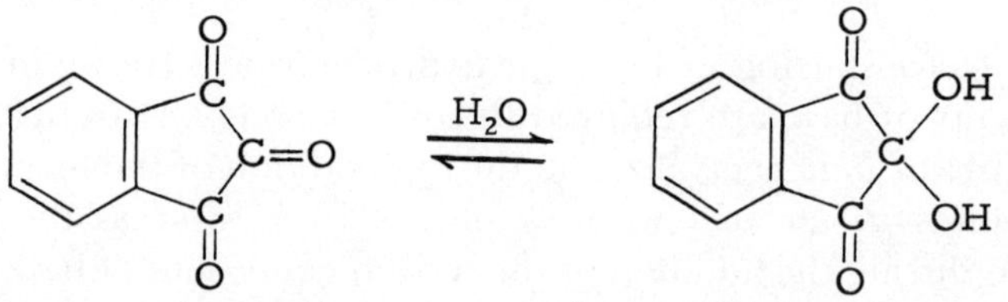

      indane-1, 2, 3-trione   "ninhydrin"

The color-forming reaction is interesting because most α-amino acids give the same color irrespective of their structure. The sequence of steps that leads to the color is shown below.

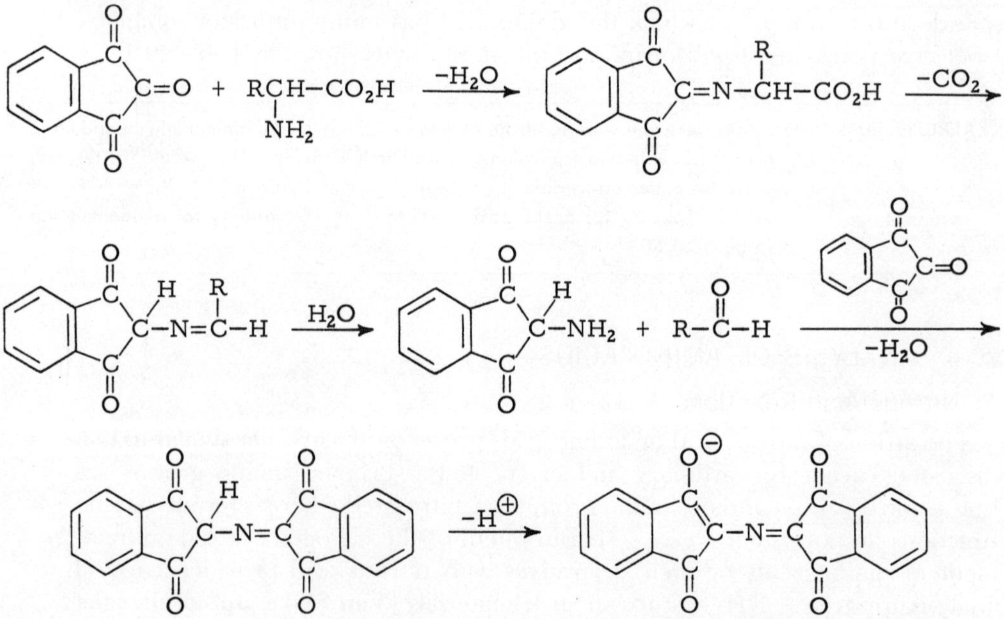

blue

EXERCISE 20-7   Write mechanisms based insofar as possible on analogy for each of the steps involved in the ninhydrin test using glycine as an example.   Would you expect ammonia or methylamine to give the blue color?

C. Chromatography

   Ninhydrin is very useful in two chromatographic methods for the analysis of amino acids.   One of these is paper chromatography, wherein amino acids are separated as the consequence of differences in their partition coefficients between water and an organic solvent.   The aqueous phase is held stationary in the microporous structure of the paper.   The differences in partition coefficients show up as differences in rates of migration on the surface of moist (but not wet) filter paper over which is passed a slow flow of a water-saturated organic solvent. We shall discuss one of several useful modes of operation.   In this, a drop of the solution to be analyzed is placed on the corner of a sheet of moist filter paper, which is then placed in an apparatus like that of Figure 20-2, arranged so that the organic solvent can migrate upward by capillarity across the paper, carrying the amino acids with it along one edge.   The acids that have the greatest solubility in the organic solvent move most rapidly and, before the fastest moving acid reaches the top of the paper, the paper is removed, dried, then turned side-

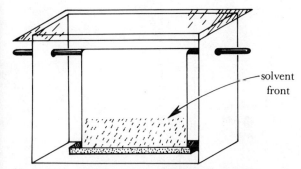

solvent front

Figure 20-2   Diagram of apparatus used to develop a paper chromatogram.   Paper is suspended from its top edge within an airtight container, here a glass box closed with a glass plate, having an atmosphere saturated with solvent vapor; the lower edge of paper dips into a trough containing the liquid solvent.

wise, and a different solvent allowed to diffuse across the width.   This double migration process gives a better separation of the amino acids than a single migration and results in concentration of the different amino acids in rather well-defined zones or spots.   These spots can be made visible by first drying and then spraying the paper with ninhydrin solution.   The final result is as shown in Figure 20-3 and is usually quite reproducible under a given set of conditions.   The identities of the amino acids that produce the various spots are established by comparison with the behavior of known mixtures.

EXERCISE 20-8   Arrange the following amino acids in the order in which you would expect each to move in a paper chromatogram with the weak organic base, 2,4,6-collidine, as the organic phase; glycine, phenylalanine, arginine, and glutamic acid. Show your reasoning.

$$CH_3$$

2, 4, 6–collidine

$$CH_3 \quad N \quad CH_3$$

Paper chromatography has proved very useful in following the mechanisms of biological processes using radioactive tracers. For example, in the study of the fixation of carbon dioxide in photosynthesis it was found possible to determine the rate of incorporation of radioactive carbon as carbon dioxide into various sugars, amino acids, and the like, by separating the products of photosynthesis at a succession of time intervals on paper chromatograms and analyzing their radioactivities by scanning the paper with a Geiger counter or by simply measuring the degree of fogging of an X-ray film laid over the chromatograms.

A quantitative method of analysis of amino acids can be achieved by passing the solution to be analyzed through columns packed with an ion-exchange resin whereby the acids are separated in accord to their ability to be complexed with

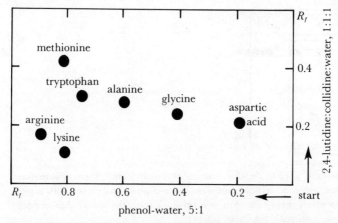

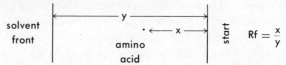

Figure 20-3   Idealized two-dimensional paper chromatogram of a mixture of amino acids. The horizontal and vertical scales represent the distance of travel of a component of the mixture in a given solvent in a given time relative to that of the solvent itself. This is known as the Rf value and is fairly constant for a particular compound in a given solvent. A rough identification of the amino acids present in the mixture may therefore be made on the basis of their Rf values.

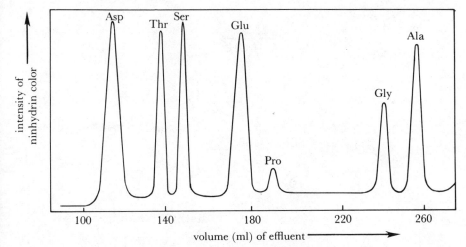

intensity of
ninhydrin color

volume (ml) of effluent ⟶

Figure 20-4   Section of amino acid chromatogram obtained by the method of automatic amino acid analysis from a hydrolyzed sample of the enzyme ribonuclease. The component amino acids listed are present in the ratio Asp:Thr:Ser:Glu:Pro:Gly:Ala = 15:10:15:12:4:3:12, as determined by peak intensity.

the highly polar sites of the resin. The effluent from the column is mixed with ninhydrin solution and the intensity of the blue color developed is measured with a photoelectric colorimeter and plotted as a function of time at constant flow rates. A typical analysis of a mixture of amino acids by this method is shown in Figure 20-4.

20-5 LACTAMS

The cyclization of hydroxy acids through lactone formation has been discussed in Chapter 16. The corresponding cyclization of amino acids leads to **lactams.**

$$CH_2\!-\!C\overset{O}{\diagup} \qquad CH_2\!-\!C\overset{O}{\diagup}$$

γ–butyrolactone   γ–butyrolactam

Formation of α- and β-lactams is expected to generate considerable ring strain, and other more favorable reactions usually intervene. Thus, while γ-butyrolactam can be prepared by heating ethyl γ-aminobutyrate, the corresponding α-lactam is not formed from ethyl α-aminobutyrate but, instead, the dimeric diethyldiketopiperazine [1] with a six-membered ring results.

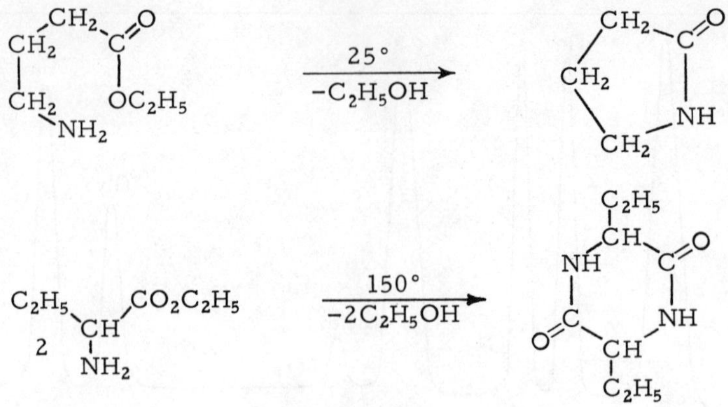

[1]

diethyldiketopiperazine

β-Lactams have been rather intensively investigated following the discovery that the important antibiotic penicillin G [2], produced by fermentation with *Pencillium notatum*, possesses a β-lactam ring.

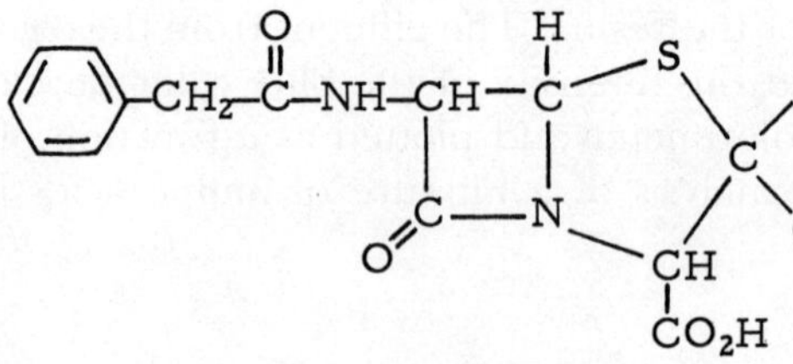

penicillin G (benzylpenicillin)

[2]

The problem of determining the correct structure of penicillin was an extraordinarily difficult one because the molecule is very labile and undergoes extensive rearrangements to biologically inactive products even under very mild conditions. The β-lactam structure was finally established by X-ray diffraction analysis. Penicillin G and many closely related compounds with different groups in place of the benzyl group have been synthesized.

20-6 PEPTIDES AND PROTEINS

The characteristic structural feature of peptides and proteins is a chain or ring of amino acids joined together by amide linkages. Peptides are classified by the number of amino acid groups in the chain and are named as derivatives of the amino acid, which terminates the chain at the carboxyl end. This acid is called the "C-terminal acid." The acid that furnishes the α-amino group at the other end of the chain is called the "N-terminal acid."

$$\underset{\text{ycylalanine (H} \cdot \text{Gly} \cdot \text{Ala} \cdot \text{OH)}}{\text{H}_2\text{N}-\text{CH}_2-\overset{\overset{\text{O}}{\|}}{\text{C}}-\text{NH}-\overset{\overset{\text{CH}_3}{|}}{\text{CH}}-\text{CO}_2\text{H}}$$

ycylalanine (H · Gly · Ala · OH)

a dipeptide

alanylcysteinylserine (H · Ala · CySH · Ser · OH)

a tripeptide

EXERCISE 20-9   Draw out the complete structure (using projection formulas) of the important hormonal peptide, oxytocin.

H · CyS · Tyr · Ileu · Glu—NH₂ · Asp—NH₂ · CyS · Pro · Leu · Gly · NH₂

The distinction between a protein and a peptide is not completely clear. One arbitrary choice is to call proteins only those substances with molecular weights greater than 10,000. The distinction might also be made in terms of differences in physical properties, particularly hydration and conformation. The naturally occurring peptides have relatively short flexible chains and, although hydrated in aqueous solution, are reversibly so; proteins, on the other hand, have very long chains which appear to be coiled and folded in rather particular ways, with water molecules helping to fill the interstices. Under the influence of heat, organic solvents, salts, etc., protein molecules undergo more or less irreversible changes, called **denaturation,** in which both the conformations of the chains and the degree of hydration are altered. The result is usually a decrease in solubility and loss of ability to crystallize. The essence of the distinction emphasized here between a protein and a peptide is that if one were to duplicate the sequence of amino acids in a naturally occurring peptide, the synthetic and natural materials would be identical in their chemical and physiological properties. On the other hand, synthesis of a natural protein would involve not only duplication of the constituent peptide chains but also duplication of the conformations and manner of hydration of the chains. We shall discuss some of the available evidence on the conformations assumed by peptide chains later.

A. Peptide Structures

A wide variety of peptides occur naturally—however, of those whose structures have been determined, a considerable proportion contain one or more amino acids which are not found as constituents of proteins. Indeed, many peptides are cyclic and, in some, even D-amino acids occur. Most of the well-characterized peptides contain three to ten amino acid units.

The properties of peptides and of proteins are a critical function of not only the number and kind of their constituent amino acids but also the sequence in which the amino acids are linked together. Analyses for amino acid content can be made by complete hydrolysis and ion-exchange separations, as described earlier. Establishment of the sequence of amino acids is much more difficult but has been carried through to completion on peptide chains having even more than 100 amino acid units.

The general procedure for determining amino acid sequences is to establish the nature of the end groups and then, by a variety of hydrolytic or oxidative methods, break the chain up into peptides having two to five amino acid units. The idea in using a variety of ways of cutting the chains is to obtain fragments with common units which can be matched up to one another to obtain the overall sequence.

EXERCISE 20-10   A pentapeptide on complete hydrolysis yields 3 moles of glycine, 1 mole of alanine, and 1 mole of phenylalanine. Among the products of partial hydrolysis are found H · Ala · Gly · OH and H · Gly · Ala · OH. What structures are possible for this substance on the basis of its giving *no* nitrogen in the Van Slyke determination?

Determination of the amino acid that supplies the terminal amino group in a peptide chain (the N-terminal acid) is best made by treatment of the acid with 2,4-dinitrofluorobenzene, a substance very reactive in nucleophilic displacements with amines but not amides. The product is an N-2,4-dinitrophenyl derivative of the peptide which, after hydrolysis of the amide linkages, yields an N-2,4-dinitrophenylamino acid.

$$O_2N\text{—}\langle\rangle\text{—F} + NH_2CH_2\overset{O}{\underset{\|}{C}}\text{—R} \xrightarrow{-HF} O_2N\text{—}\langle\rangle\text{—NH—CH}_2\overset{O}{\underset{\|}{C}}\text{—R}$$

(with NO$_2$ on each ring)

2,4-dinitrofluorobenzene   peptide

$$\xrightarrow[H^{\oplus}]{H_2O} O_2N\text{—}\langle\rangle\text{—N—CH}_2\text{—CO}_2H + \text{amino acids.}$$

(with NO$_2$ and H on ring)

N–2,4-dinitrophenylglycine

(low solubility)

This substance can be separated from the ordinary amino acids resulting from hydrolysis of the peptide, owing to the low basicity of the 2,4-dinitrophenyl-substituted nitrogen, which greatly reduces the solubility of the compound in acid solution and alters its chromatographic behavior.

EXERCISE 20-11   Would the 2,4-dinitrofluorobenzene method for determination of end groups work satisfactorily on glycylglutamylalanine? Explain.

B. Peptide Synthesis

The problem of synthesizing peptides is of great importance and has received considerable attention. The major difficulty in putting together a chain of say 100 amino acids in a particular order is one of over-all yield. At least 100 separate synthetic steps would be required and, if the yields in each step are all equal to $n \times 100$ per cent, the over-all yield is ($n^{100} \times 100\%$). Thus, if each yield is 90 per cent, the over-all yield is only 0.003 per cent. Obviously, a laboratory synthesis of a peptide chain comparable to those which occur in proteins must be a highly efficient process. The extraordinary ability of living cells in achieving syntheses of this nature, not of just one, but of a wide variety of such substances is truly impressive.

Several methods for the formation of amide bonds have been discussed in Chapters 16 and 19. The most generally useful reactions are of the type where X is halogen, alkoxyl, and acyloxy, as corresponds to acyl halides, esters, and

$$
\underset{X}{\overset{O}{R-C}} \; + \; NH_2-R' \quad \longrightarrow \quad \underset{NHR'}{\overset{O}{R-C}} \; + \; HX
$$

acid anhydrides. When applied to joining up two different amino acids, difficulty is to be expected, because these same reactions can link together two amino acids of the same kind.

$$
\underset{}{\overset{O}{NH_2CH_2C-OH}} \quad \xrightarrow{PCl_3} \quad \underset{}{\overset{O}{NH_2CH_2C-Cl}}
$$

$$
2 \; \underset{}{\overset{O}{NH_2CH_2C-Cl}} \quad \xrightarrow{-HCl} \quad \underset{}{\overset{O \quad\quad O}{NH_2CH_2CNHCH_2C-Cl,}} \quad \text{etc.}
$$

To avoid such reactions, a "protecting group" is substituted on the amino function of the acid that is to act as the acylating agent. The requirements for a good protecting group are that it be easily attachable to the amino group without causing racemization of an optically active acid; be inert in the reactions whereby the peptide bonds are formed; and be easily removable without affecting the peptide linkages or sensitive functional groups on the amino acid side chains, such as the sulfur-containing groups of cysteine, cystine, and methionine.

One of the more satisfactory protecting substituents is the carbobenzyloxy

$$
\overset{O}{\underset{}{}}
$$

($C_6H_5CH_2OC-$) group. The carbobenzyloxy protecting group is introduced with benzyl chloroformate, which is prepared by the reaction of phosgene ($COCl_2$) with benzyl alcohol in toluene as solvent.

$$\text{C}_6\text{H}_5\text{—CH}_2\text{OH} + \text{COCl}_2 \xrightarrow{-20°} \text{C}_6\text{H}_5\text{—CH}_2\text{O}\overset{\overset{\displaystyle O}{\|}}{\text{C}}\text{—Cl} + \text{HCl}$$

benzyl chloroformate

95%

$$\text{C}_6\text{H}_5\text{—CH}_2\text{—O}\overset{\overset{\displaystyle O}{\|}}{\text{C}}\text{—Cl} + \text{NH}_2\text{CH}_2\text{CO}_2\text{H} \xrightarrow[\text{2. HCl}]{\text{1. dil. NaOH, 5°}}$$

$$\text{C}_6\text{H}_5\text{—CH}_2\text{—O}\overset{\overset{\displaystyle O}{\|}}{\text{C}}\overset{\overset{\displaystyle H}{\,}}{\text{—N}}\text{—CH}_2\text{CO}_2\text{H}$$

75%

The next step in peptide synthesis is to activate the carboxyl function of the protected amino acid. This can be done in several ways. The obvious method is to make the acid chloride, but this requires rather strong reagents and the acid chloride is often more reactive than is desirable. Appropriate mixed anhydrides are generally more useful—one of the best being easily prepared from ethyl (or isobutyl) chloroformate ($\text{ClCO}_2\text{C}_2\text{H}_5$) as follows.

$$\text{C}_6\text{H}_5\text{—CH}_2\text{—O}\overset{\overset{\displaystyle O}{\|}}{\text{C}}\overset{\overset{\displaystyle H}{\,}}{\text{—N}}\text{—CH}_2\text{CO}_2\text{H} \xrightarrow[\text{2. ClCO}_2\text{C}_2\text{H}_5]{\text{1. (C}_2\text{H}_5)_3\text{N}}$$

$$\text{C}_6\text{H}_5\text{—CH}_2\text{—O}\overset{\overset{\displaystyle O}{\|}}{\text{C}}\overset{\overset{\displaystyle H}{\,}}{\text{—N}}\text{—CH}_2\overset{\overset{\displaystyle O}{\|}}{\text{C}}\text{—O}\overset{\overset{\displaystyle O}{\|}}{\text{—C}}\text{—O—C}_2\text{H}_5$$

Acylation of another amino acid with the mixed anhydride forms a peptide bond. The carboxyl group of the new peptide can be activated and still another amino acid linked on.

$$\text{C}_6\text{H}_5\text{—CH}_2\text{—O}\overset{\overset{\displaystyle O}{\|}}{\text{C}}\overset{\overset{\displaystyle H}{\,}}{\text{—N}}\text{—CH}_2\overset{\overset{\displaystyle O}{\|}}{\text{C}}\text{—O}\overset{\overset{\displaystyle O}{\|}}{\text{—C}}\text{—O—C}_2\text{H}_5 + \text{H}_2\text{N}\overset{\overset{\displaystyle CH_3}{\,}}{\text{—CH}}\text{CO}_2\text{CH}_3 \longrightarrow$$

$$\text{C}_6\text{H}_5\text{—CH}_2\text{—O}\overset{\overset{\displaystyle O}{\|}}{\text{C}}\overset{\overset{\displaystyle H}{\,}}{\text{—N}}\text{—CH}_2\overset{\overset{\displaystyle O}{\|}}{\text{—C}}\text{—NH}\overset{\overset{\displaystyle CH_3}{\,}}{\text{—CH}}\text{—CO}_2\text{CH}_3 + \text{CO}_2 + \text{C}_2\text{H}_5\text{OH}$$

EXERCISE 20-12   Explain why the mixed anhydride of N-carbobenzyloxyglycine and ethyl acid carbonate reacts with alanine to give N-carbobenzyloxyglycylalanine and not N-carbo-
ethoxyalanine.

After formation of the desired number of peptide bonds in the synthesis of a
polypeptide by methods such as those described on the preceding pages, the protecting groups must be removed to give the final product.   The carbobenzyloxy
group is normally removed by reduction.   It is a characteristic of benzyl ether
and ester groups to undergo **hydrogenolysis** with formation of toluene and a
hydroxyl group.   The usual reagents are hydrogen over palladium, but this
combination has the disadvantage of being inapplicable to sulfur-containing
systems, which poison the catalyst.

$$\text{C}_6\text{H}_5\text{—CH}_2\text{—O—}\overset{\text{O}}{\overset{\|}{\text{C}}}\text{—}\overset{\text{H}}{\text{N}}\text{—CH}_2\text{—}\overset{\text{O}}{\overset{\|}{\text{C}}}\text{—peptide} \xrightarrow{\text{H}_2,\ \text{Pd}}$$

$$\text{C}_6\text{H}_5\text{—CH}_3 + \text{CO}_2 + \text{NH}_2\text{CH}_2\text{—}\overset{\text{O}}{\overset{\|}{\text{C}}}\text{—peptide}$$

Alternative reducing systems for carbobenzyloxy groups employ (1) sodium
metal in liquid ammonia at $-40°$ or (2) triethylsilane and palladium chloride.
The over-all result is the same, but now the reaction can be carried out on sulfur
compounds.   However, sodium in liquid ammonia reduces cystine to cysteine.

EXERCISE 20-13   On what theoretical grounds can we expect the C—O bonds of benzyloxy
groups to undergo hydrogenolysis more readily than ethoxy groups?

EXERCISE 20-14   Show how each of the following substances can be synthesized starting with
the individual amino acids.
a. glycylalanylcysteine
b. $HO_2C(CH_2)_2CH(NH_2)CONHCH_2CO_2H$
c. glutamine from glutamic acid

20-7   PROTEIN STRUCTURES

The special character of proteins derives not just from the length and complexity of their peptide chains but also from the way living organisms are able to
synthesize them in special, frequently metastable, conformations and degrees of
hydration.   In this connection the familiar, rapid and irreversible changes that
occur when the white of an egg is heated provide a vivid example of the character of protein denaturation reactions.

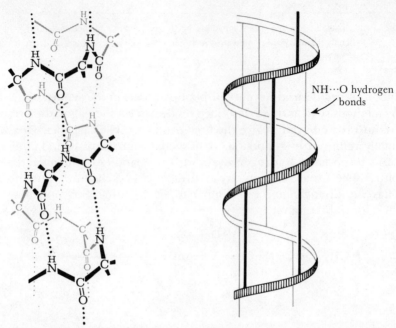

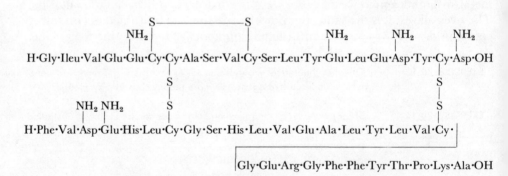

NH···O hydrogen bonds

Figure 20-5   Peptide chain of a protein coiled to form an alpha helix.   Configuration of the helix is maintained by hydrogen bonds, shown as vertical dotted (or solid) lines.   The helix on the left shows the detailed atom structure of the peptide chain (the side-chain groups are not shown).   The helix on the right is a schematic representation without structural detail.

$$
\begin{array}{c}
\text{S}\!\!-\!\!-\!\!-\!\!-\!\!-\!\!-\!\!-\!\!-\!\!\text{S}\\
\text{NH}_2| \qquad\qquad |\qquad\qquad\qquad\text{NH}_2\qquad\text{NH}_2\qquad\quad\text{NH}_2\\
\text{H·Gly·Ileu·Val·Glu·Glu·Cy·Cy·Ala·Ser·Val·Cy·Ser·Leu·Tyr·Glu·Leu·Glu·Asp·Tyr·Cy·Asp·OH}\\
|\qquad\qquad\qquad\qquad\qquad\qquad\qquad\qquad\qquad\qquad|\\
\text{S}\qquad\qquad\qquad\qquad\qquad\qquad\qquad\qquad\qquad\text{S}
\end{array}
$$

NH₂ NH₂   S   S

H·Phe·Val·Asp·Glu·His·Leu·Cy·Gly·Ser·His·Leu·Val·Glu·Ala·Leu·Tyr·Leu·Val·Cy·|

|Gly·Glu·Arg·Gly·Phe·Phe·Tyr·Thr·Pro·Lys·Ala·OH

Figure 20-6   Amino acid sequence in beef insulin.

Considerable attention has been given to the possible ways in which peptide chains can be arranged so as to give stable conformations.   An especially favorable arrangement that is found to occur in many peptides and proteins is the **α-helix.**   The principal feature of the α-helix is the coiling of peptide chains in such a way as to form hydrogen bonds between the amide hydrogens and carbonyl groups that are four peptide bonds apart.   The hydrogen bonds are nearly parallel to the long axis of the coil and the spacing between the turns is about 5.4 A (see Figure 20-5).   The amino acid side chains lie outside the coil of the α-helix. However, proteins are not perfect α-helices, since steric hindrance between certain of the amino acid side chains or the lack of hydrogen bonding is sometimes sufficient to reduce the stability of the normal α-helix and allow the chain to fold. The amino acids, proline and hydroxyproline, are particularly important in this connection.

Three levels of complexity therefore exist in any one protein structure. The *primary structure* is the specific sequence of amino acids in the polypeptide chain; the *secondary structure* is the way in which the chain is coiled — perhaps to form an α-helix; and the *tertiary structure* is the way in which the coiled chain(s) is folded and hydrated in the natural state.

The primary structure of the antidiabetic hormone, insulin, has been deduced by chemical degradation and synthesis. The sequence of the 51 amino acids in beef insulin is shown in Figure 20-6. Sheep and hog insulin have been found to have slightly different structures. Disulfide linkages hold the two peptide chains together and play an important role in determining the conformation and the physiological properties of insulin.

The bewildering and almost random-appearing sequences of amino acids in the peptide chains of proteins, such as insulin, probably play several roles in influencing the properties of proteins. In the first place, the electrical behavior of proteins and their isoelectric points are determined by the number and location of acidic and basic amino acids. Second, the steric effects of substituent groups determine the stabilities and positions of folds in the peptide helices. The nature of the amino acid sequences may also influence the degree of intermolecular interactions and protein solubilities. Peptides of one kind of amino acid are often highly insoluble, partly because of strong intermolecular forces. If the regularity of the chain is broken up by having different amino acids therein, the intermolecular forces are expected to be diminished.

Proteins are found to occur in a very wide variety of sizes and shapes. Determination of the molecular weights and dimensions of proteins has been made with the aid of an impressive array of physical techniques. Molecular weights can be obtained by analysis for particular constituents (see Exercise 20-15), determination of diffusion rates, sedimentation velocities in the ultracentrifuge, light scattering, and even measurements of the sizes of individual, very large protein molecules by electron microscopy. The shapes are deduced from measurements of rates of molecular relaxation after electric polarization; changes in optical properties (double refraction) resulting from streaming in liquid flow, directly by electron microscopy, and perhaps most importantly by the intensities of light or X-ray scattering as a function of scattering angle. The application of all these methods is often rendered difficult by the high degree of hydration of proteins and by the fact that many proteins undergo reversible association reactions to give dimers, trimers, etc. The molecular weights, molecular dimensions, and isoelectric points of a few important proteins are compared in Table 20-2.

It is found that many proteins contain metals such as iron, zinc, and copper, and these metal atoms turn out to be intimately involved in the biological functions of the molecules to which they are bound. The well-known oxygen-carrying property of hemoglobin and the hemocyanins is a case in point.

Table 20-2   Some Typical Proteins

Name	Mol. wt.	Shape	Axial ratio[a]	Isoelectric point	Occurrence	Function
insulin[b,c]	6,000	associates in solution		5.4	pancreas	regulation of blood sugar levels
ribonuclease[b,c]	13,000			7.8	pancreas	hydrolysis of ribonucleic acids
myoglobin (horse)[c]	17,500	platelets	~1:3:5.5		horse heart	respiratory protein
lysozyme[c]	14,600	prolate ellipsoid	2.3	10.7	egg white	breaks down the cell walls of bacteria by hydrolysis of $\beta(1{\rightarrow}4)$ glucose linkages
α-chymotrypsin[c]	25,000	associates in solution		8.4	pancreas	hydrolysis of ester and peptide linkages
papain	21,000			8.8	latex of papaya melons	hydrolysis of peptide linkages
hemoglobin[c]	66,700	nearly spherical	1.2	6.7	red-blood corpuscles	respiratory protein
catalase	250,000	blocks[d]			liver and kidney	destroys H_2O_2
fibrogenin	330,000	elongated	18	6.8	blood plasma	blood clotting
tobacco mosaic virus (protein part)[b]	41,000,000	hexagonal prisms or rods[d]		4.1	infected tobacco or tomato plants	plant virus

[a] Ratio of molecular axial lengths as determined by physical methods of various types.
[b] Complete sequence of amino acids has been established.
[c] Structure investigated by X-ray diffraction methods.
[d] From electron-microscope photographs.

EXERCISE 20-15   Hemoglobin, the protein responsible for carrying oxygen from the lungs to the body tissues, contains 0.355 per cent of iron. Hydrolysis of 100 g of hemoglobin gives 1.48 g of tryptophan; calculate the minimum molecular weight of hemoglobin which is consistent with these results.

A number of proteins form well-defined crystals which, in principle at least, makes possible complete determination of their structures by X-ray diffraction. The problems involved are far from simple, there being even in a small protein, such as insulin, on the order of 700 atoms (not counting hydrogens) to be located. The X-ray diffraction work which has so far been successful in providing structural information about proteins has proceeded with stepwise improvements in resolution of the structural details. For example, in the early stages of the determination of the structure of iron-containing protein myoglobin, the resolution achieved was 6 A, which did not permit the individual atoms to be seen but did show the peptide chains twisting and turning through a matrix of water molecules (i.e., tertiary structure). Improvement of the resolution to 2 A has enabled identification of most of the individual amino acids by virtue of the shapes of their substituent groups (primary and secondary structure).

The biological functions of proteins are extremely diverse. Some act as hormones regulating various metabolic processes (e.g., insulin is responsible for the maintenance of blood sugar levels); some act as catalysts (enzymes) for biological reactions, and others as biological structural materials (e.g., collagen in connective tissue and keratin in hair). The oxygen-carrying properties of hemoglobin in mammals (and the copper-containing proteins called hemocyanins, which function similarly for shellfish) have been mentioned already. Some blood proteins function to form antibodies, which provide resistance to disease, while the so-called nucleoproteins are important constituents of the genes that supply and transmit genetic information in cell division. The viruses, such as tobacco mosaic virus, are made up of nucleoproteins encased in a protein "coat." The structures of many viruses are so regular that they can be obtained in nicely crystalline form. Viruses function by invading the cells of the host and by supplying a genetic pattern that destroys the normal functions of the cells and sets the cellular enzymes to work synthesizing more virus particles.

20-8 ENZYMES

A very large group of proteins display enzymic activity—which is to say that they have the ability to catalyze specific organic or even inorganic reactions. The catalytic power and specificity of most enzymes is extraordinarily high, and practically all biochemical reactions are carried on through the agency of enzymes—each usually quite specific for its purpose. Nothing seems to be left to chance; even the equilibration of carbon dioxide with water is achieved with the aid of an enzyme known as carbonic anhydrase.[1] Further, sensitive biochemical materials are protected from oxidation (by hydrogen peroxide) by highly efficient enzymes (such as catalase, which converts hydrogen peroxide to water). Many enzymes are very well defined substances which can be crystallized and have highly reproducible physical properties and catalytic activities. Almost all are denatured and become inactive when heated strongly. Rather than attempt to catalog enzymes and their functions, we shall consider first the problems presented by a typical proteolytic (protein-splitting) enzyme, α-chymotrypsin; we shall then consider enzyme-coenzyme combinations, and, finally, the genetic code that is used in the replication of cells.

α-Chymotrypsin is a proteolytic enzyme of molecular weight 25,000, which has a quite general power of effecting the hydrolysis of carboxyl derivatives, amides, esters, hydrazides, etc. It works on ordinary esters such as p-nitrophenyl acetate but is particularly effective for derivatives of acylated α-amino acids. Chymotrypsin can attack the middle of peptide chains in contrast to various **aminopeptidases** and **carboxypeptidases,** which cause hydrolysis of

[1] Many enzymes are named by adding the suffix -ase to a word or words descriptive of the type of enzymatic activity. Thus, esterases hydrolyze esters, reductases achieve reductions, etc.

only N-terminal acids and C-terminal acids, respectively. Chymotrypsin is formed in the pancreas and plays an important role in digestion by assisting in the hydrolysis of proteins in the intestinal tract. An interesting feature of chymotrypsin is the way that it is produced in an inactive form by the pancreas cells—presumably to prevent it from attacking surrounding proteins. The precursor, called chymotrypsinogen, is converted to chymotrypsin by hydrolytic splitting off of two dipeptides under the influence of other enzymes, for example, trypsin or pepsin. One might well ask how the proteolytic enzyme molecules like chymotrypsin keep from causing the hydrolysis of each other. The fact is that although chymotrypsin molecules form association complexes with one another, because of steric hindrance or some other structural factor, hydrolytic cleavage does not occur. In this connection, it is significant that chymotrypsin attacks denatured proteins more rapidly than the natural proteins with their precisely folded chains, and it is probably this factor which limits self-destruction.

The sequence of amino acids in chymotrypsin has been determined in the manner described for insulin, and presumably the way in which the chains are coiled and folded will eventually be obtained by X-ray diffraction studies as has been done for myoglobin.

The mechanism by which chymotrypsin catalyzes the hydrolysis of peptides and other carboxyl derivatives is still unknown. However, much important information has come from studies of reaction rates using different substrates, particularly in the presence of compounds that inhibit catalytic activity by complexing with the active site and thus preventing the approach of authentic reactants.

EXERCISE 20-16   What might one conclude about the active site of α-chymotrypsin from the fact that negatively charged inhibitors are less effective in reducing catalytic activity than neutral molecules of the same type of structure?

It is clear that catalysis by chymotrypsin (like that of many other enzymes) proceeds first by complex formation (enzyme-substrate complex) and second by a bond-cleaving step. From studies with p-nitrophenyl acetate, it appears that the complex produces hydrolysis in two steps. First, p-nitrophenol is liberated with the formation of an acetylated chymotrypsin, which then has to react with water to give acetic acid before hydrolysis of another molecule of p-nitrophenyl acetate can start.

Chymotrypsin contains sulfur, and the part that is in the form of cystine linkages does not seem to be directly implicated at the active site. However, the cystine linkages probably do play an important role in determining the folding of the enzyme around the substrate. Recent evidence suggests that one of the two methionine residues in chymotrypsin may be involved at the active site, possibly in a secondary step.

20-9 COENZYMES

Certain enzymes react with their substrates only when they are combined with another substance called a coenzyme. A coenzyme is not usually a protein; it is a much simpler organic molecule than an enzyme, and the enzyme-coenzyme complex is formed reversibly. A given coenzyme may function with more than one enzyme to operate on different substrates.

A typical coenzyme is nicotinamide-adenine nucleotide[1] (NAD$^\oplus$), which, in conjunction with the enzyme, alcohol dehydrogenase (ADH), oxidizes ethanol to acetaldehyde with the formation of the reduced coenzyme (NADH) and acetaldehyde.

(NAD$^\oplus$)   (NADH)

For the coenzyme to participate in the oxidation of additional alcohol molecules, it must dissociate from the ADH and combine with another enzyme and be converted back to NAD$^\oplus$ by a suitable oxidizing agent. A sequence of oxidations and reductions of similar type ultimately goes back to utilization of oxygen from the air as the primary oxidizing agent. The R group of NAD$^\oplus$ is a combination of the five-carbon sugar, D-ribose, with adenine and pyrophosphoric acid— the complete structure is shown in [3].

nicotinamide–adenine nucleotide (NAD$^\oplus$)

[3]

[1] This substance is often called "diphosphopyridine nucleotide" (DPN$^\oplus$). The name used here has been approved by the International Union of Biochemistry.

The mode of attachment of the coenzyme to the enzyme is not known.

Many enzymes utilize the B vitamins as coenzymes. An especially simple system is provided by carboxylase which, in conjunction with thiamine pyrophosphate, catalyzes the decarboxylation of α-keto acids such as pyruvic acid.

$$2\ CH_3-\overset{O}{\underset{\|}{C}}-\overset{O}{\underset{\|}{C}}-OH \xrightarrow{\ (-2CO_2)\ } CH_3\overset{O}{\underset{\|}{C}}-\overset{OH}{\underset{|}{C}}HCH_3$$

   pyruvic acid   acetoin

Thiamine [4], which is essential to human nutrition (vitamin B_1), has a variety of functional groups, and it is not immediately obvious just how thiamine can act to assist the decarboxylation of pyruvic acid to give acetoin. Surprisingly, the important step appears to be ionization of the hydrogen at the 2-position of the thiazolium (sulfur- and nitrogen-containing) ring.

thiamine, R=H

thiamine pyrophosphate

thiamine conjugate

base

$$(R\ =\ -\overset{OH}{\underset{\underset{O}{\|}}{P}}-O-\overset{OH}{\underset{\underset{O}{\|}}{P}}-OH)$$

[4]

EXERCISE 20-17   Explain how the conjugate base of thiamine might react with pyruvic acid to produce an intermediate which could easily decarboxylate (see p. 373). Complete the reaction sequence leading to the formation of acetoin.

20-10 BIOSYNTHESIS OF PROTEINS

One of the most interesting and basic problems connected with the synthesis of proteins in living cells is how the component amino acids are induced to link together in the sequences which are specific for each type of protein. There is also the related problem of how the information as to the amino acid sequences is perpetuated in each new generation of cells. We now know that the substances responsible for genetic control in plants and animals are present in and originate from the chromosomes of cell nuclei. Chemical analysis of the chromosomes has revealed them to be composed of giant molecules of deoxyribonucleoproteins, which are deoxyribonucleic acids (DNA) bonded to proteins. Since it is known that DNA rather than the protein component of a nucleoprotein contains the genetic information for the biosynthesis of enzymes

and other proteins, we shall be interested mainly in DNA and will first discuss
its structure.   Note that part or perhaps all of a particular DNA is the chemical
equivalent of the Mendelian gene—the unit of inheritance.

20-11 THE STRUCTURE OF DNA

The role of DNA in living cells is analogous to that of a punched tape used for
controlling the operation of an automatic turret lathe—DNA supplies the information for the development of the cells, including synthesis of the necessary
enzymes and such replicas of itself as are required for reproduction by cell division.   Obviously, we would not expect the DNA of one kind of organism to be
exactly the same as DNA of another kind of organism.   It is therefore impossible
to be very specific about the structure of DNA without being specific about the
organism from which it is derived.   Nonetheless, the basic structural features of
DNA have been found to be the same for many kinds of cells, and we shall be
mainly concerned with these basic features in the following discussion.

In the first place, DNA molecules are quite large—sufficiently so as to permit
them to be seen individually in photographs taken with electron microscopes.
The molecular weights vary considerably, but values of 1,000,000 to 4,000,000,-
000 are typical.   X-ray diffraction indicates that DNA is made up of two long-
chain molecules twisted around each other to form a double-stranded helix
about 20 A in diameter.

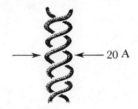

$\longrightarrow$ $\longleftarrow$ 20 A

As we shall see, the components of the chains are such that the strands can be held
together efficiently by hydrogen bonds.   In agreement with the proposed structure, it
has been found that, when DNA is heated to about 80° under proper conditions, the
strands of the helix untwist and dissociate to two randomly coiled fragments.   Furthermore, when the dissociated material is allowed to cool slowly under the proper
conditions, the fragments recombine and regenerate the helical structure.

Chemical studies show that the strands of DNA have the structure of a long-chain
polymer made of alternating phosphate and nitrogen base-substituted sugar residues [5].

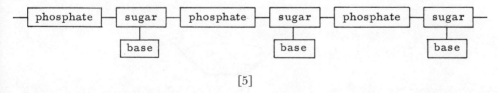

[5]

The sugar is D-2-deoxyribofuranose [6], and each sugar residue is bonded to two
phosphate groups by way of ester links involving the 3- and 5-hydroxyl groups.

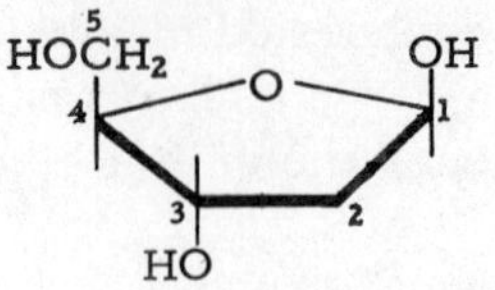

2–deoxyribofuranose

[6]

The backbone of DNA is thus a polyphosphate ester of a 1,3-glycol.

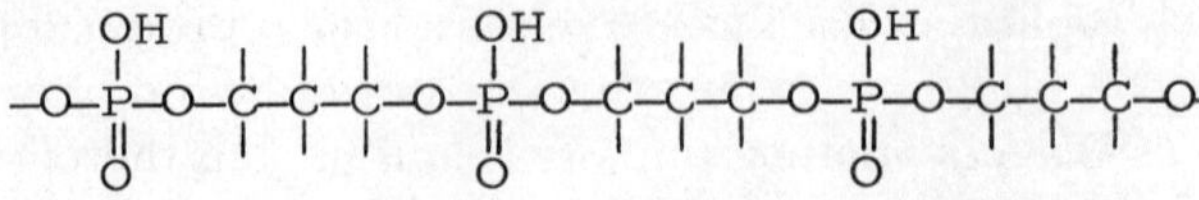

With inclusion of the details of the sugar residue, the structure of DNA becomes as shown in Figure 20-7.

Each of the sugar residues of DNA is bonded at the 1-position to one of four bases, adenine [7], guanine [8], cytosine [9], and thymine [10], through an N-glycosidic linkage. The four bases are derivatives of either pyrimidine or purine, both of which are heterocyclic nitrogen bases.

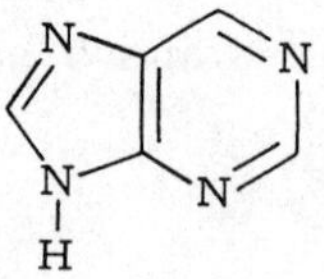

purine 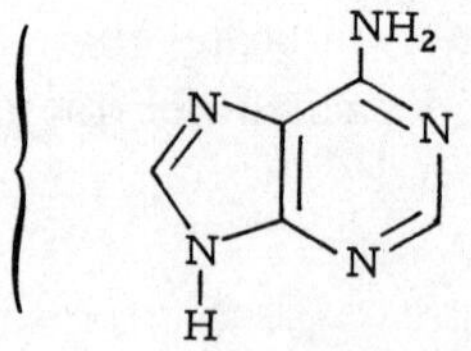   adenine   guanine

                          [7]   [8]

R = nitrogen base; adenine, guanine, cytosine or thymine.

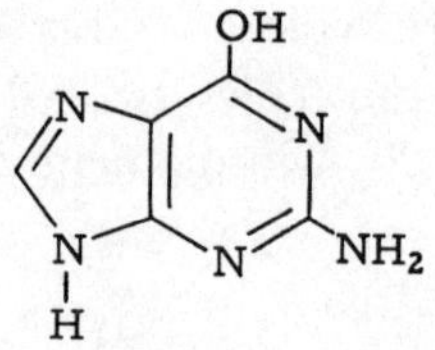

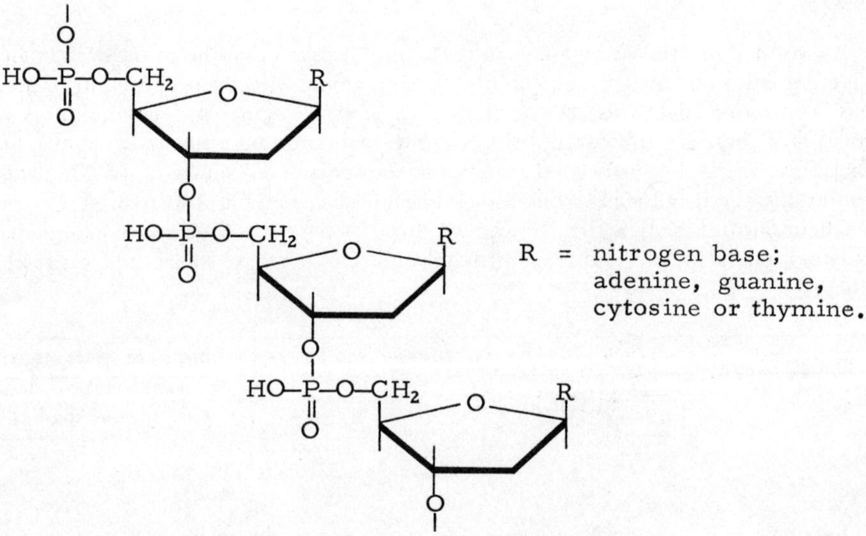

Figure 20-7   Structure of the strands of deoxyribonucleic acid (DNA).

2-hydroxypyrimidine   cytosine   thymine
                                [9]   [10]

For the sake of simplicity in illustrating N-glycoside formation in DNA, we shall show the type of bonding involved for the sugar and base components only (i.e., the deoxyribose **nucleoside** structure). Attachment of 2-deoxyribose to the purines, adenine and guanine, is easily envisoned as involving the NH group of the five-membered ring (see also p. 439). The union is always that of a β-N-deoxyribofuranoside.

2-deoxyribofuranose   adenine   adenine deoxyriboside
                                                        (β)

However, an analogous process with the pyrimidines, cytosine and thymine, has to involve tautomerization of the base to an amide-type structure.

cytosine   cytosine deoxyriboside
                                          (furanoside)
                                              (β)

Esterification of the 5-hydroxyl group of deoxyribose nucleosides, such as cytosine deoxyriboside with phosphoric acid, gives the corresponding **nucleotides.**

cytosine deoxyribonucleotide

Thus DNA may be considered to be built up from nucleotide monomers by esterification of the 3-hydroxyl group of one nucleotide with the phosphate group of another. Enzymes are available which hydrolyze DNA to cleave the linkage at C3 and give the 5-phosphorylated nucleotides. There are other enzymes which cleave DNA at C5 to give the 3-phosphorylated nucleotides.

The number of nucleotide units in a DNA chain varies from about 3000 to 10,000,000. Although the sequence of the purine and pyrimidine bases in the chains are not known, there is a striking equivalence between certain of the bases regardless of the origin of DNA. Thus the number of adenine groups equals the number of thymine groups, and the number of guanine groups equals the number of cytosine groups (i.e., $A = T$ and $G = C$). Also, the over-all percentage composition of the bases is constant in a given species but varies widely from one species to another.

The equivalence between the purine and pyrimidine bases in DNA has been accounted for by Watson and Crick (1953) through the suggestion that the two strands are constructed so that, when twisted together in the helical structure, hydrogen bonds are formed involving adenine in one chain and thymine in the other or cytosine in one chain and guanine in the other. Thus, each adenine occurs paired with a thymine and each cytosine with a guanine and the strands are said to have **complementary** structures. The postulated hydrogen bonds are shown in Figure 20-8, and the relation of the bases to the strands in Figure 20-9.

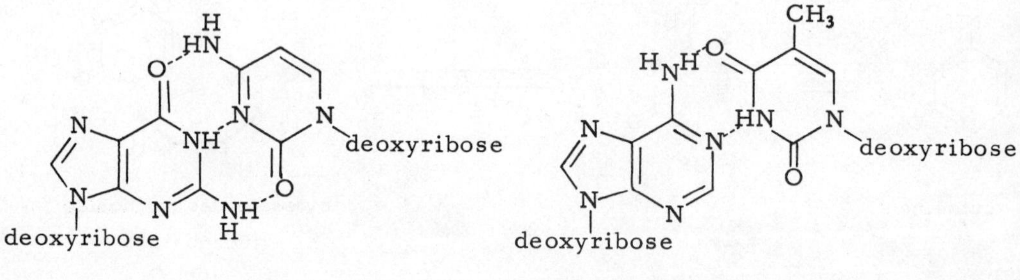

guanine–cytosine   adenine–thymine

Figure 20-8   Hydrogen bonding postulated between DNA strands involving guanine-cytosine and adenine-thymine. In each case, the distance between the Cl of the two deoxyribose units is 11 A and the favored geometry has the rings coplanar.

EXERCISE 20-18   Write equations for the steps involved in hydrolysis of adenine deoxyribonucleoside to deoxyribose and adenine. Would you expect the reaction to occur more readily in acidic or basic solution?

EXERCISE 20-19   The following steps have been used in the synthesis of 1-D-glucosylcytosine.

$$\text{D-glucose} \xrightarrow[\text{(CH}_3\text{CO)}_2\text{O}]{\text{HBr}} \text{1-bromoglucose tetraacetate}$$

$$\xrightarrow{\text{2,4-diethoxypyrimidine}} \text{4-ethoxy-1-(tetraacetyl-D-glucosyl)-pyrimid-2-one}$$

$$\xrightarrow{\text{NH}_3 \text{ (excess)}} \text{1-D-glucosylcytosine}$$

Write out the structures of the various substances given and the mechanism of the reaction with 2,4-diethoxypyrimidine. Why does the reaction of 1-bromo-glucose tetraacetate with 2,4-diethoxypyrimidine not yield 6-ethoxy-1-(tetra-acetyl-D-glucosyl)-pyrimid-2-one?

20-12 GENETIC CONTROL AND THE REPLICATION OF DNA

It is now clear the DNA provides the genetic recipe that permits cell division to produce identical cells. In reproducing itself, it perpetuates the information necessary to regulate the synthesis of specific enzymes and other proteins of the cell structure. The genetic information inherent in DNA appears to depend on the arrangement of the bases (symbolized as A, T, G, and C) along the phosphate-carbohydrate backbone—that is, on the arrangement of the four nucleotides specific to DNA. Thus the sequence A–G–C at some point may convey a dif-

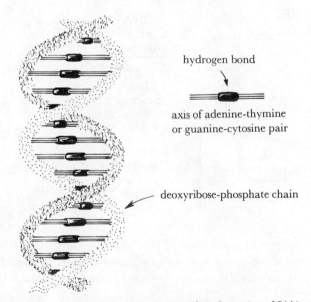

hydrogen bond

axis of adenine-thymine
or guanine-cytosine pair

deoxyribose-phosphate chain

Figure 20-9   Schematic representation of configuration of DNA, showing the relation between the axes of hydrogen-bonded purine and pyrimidine bases and the deoxyribose-phosphate strands. There are 10 pairs of bases per complete 360° twist of the chain. The spacing between the strands is such that there is a wide and a narrow helical "groove" which goes around the molecule. Apparently in the combination of DNA with protein, the protein is wound around the helix filling one or the other of the grooves.

ferent message than would G–A–C.   Indeed, the base sequence in DNA can be modified chemically by treatment of DNA *in vitro* (outside the cell) or *in vivo* (inside the cell) with nitrous acid, which can convert the primary amino groups of adenine, cytosine, and guanine to OH groups, and this clearly changes the genetic message, since DNA modified in this way leads to mutations in the organisms from which it was originally obtained.   A drastic change may occur when the DNA of a bacteriophage (which is no more than a bundle of DNA enclosed in a protein coat) is introduced into a bacterium.   The bacteriophage DNA acts as a primer for the synthesis of DNA and proteins of its own kind, finally causing dissolution of the host cell and liberation of new bacteriophage particles.

Other important experiments which indicate that a given organism manufactures DNA of its own kind are based on the synthesis of DNA *in vitro*.   A mixture of the four DNA nucleotides, A, G, C, and T, with triphosphate groups in the 5-position can be polymerized to DNA in the presence of the enzyme, DNA-polymerase, magnesium ions, and a DNA primer.   The latter can come from a variety of sources, but the synthetic DNA has the composition of the primer DNA, even if the relative concentrations of the nucleotides are varied.   The role of magnesium is not clear, but it behaves as a type of inorganic coenzyme, since the enzyme apparently does not function in its absence.   The triphosphate grouping on the nucleotides is necessary as a source of energy to drive the reaction forward; some 12 kcal/mole are liberated in the cleavage of the triphosphoryl group to pyrophosphate.

Precise details of the mechanism of replication of DNA are not known, but it is very likely that the DNA double helix unwinds into two complementary chains, and, during the unwinding process, each chain serves as a template on which is built the complement of itself.

EXERCISE 20-20   *Escherichia coli* bacteria grown in a medium containing ^{15}N-labeled ammonium chloride produce ^{15}N-containing DNA.   This can be distinguished from ordinary ^{14}N–DNA by ultracentrifugation in concentrated cesium chloride solution—the heavier ^{15}N-labeled DNA undergoing sedimentation more rapidly.   When the bacteria grown in an ^{15}N medium are transferred to an ^{14}N medium, DNA replication continues but, after one generation, all the DNA present appears to be of one kind, containing equal amounts of ^{15}N and ^{14}N; after two generations, the DNA is now of two kinds present in equal amounts—all ^{14}N–DNA and $^{14}N,^{15}N$–DNA.   What do these results tell about the replication of DNA and its stability in the cell?[1]

EXERCISE 20-21   An enzyme is known which converts nucleotide diphosphates into polyribonucleotides. Polyuridylic acid (uridylic acid $=$ uracil riboside 5′-monophosphate) synthesized with the aid of this enzyme combines readily with polyadenylic acid in a 1:1 ratio to give a rodlike structure.   Account for these observations in terms of possible structural formulas.

---

[1] An account of this experiment and its significance is given by M. Meselson and F. N. Stahl, *Proc. Natl. Acad. Sci.*, **44,** 671 (1958).

Organosulfur
Compounds

Sulfur is just below oxygen in Group VI of the periodic classification of the elements. Therefore, we might predict the chemistry of organosulfur compounds (herein taken to be substances having carbon-sulfur bonds) to parallel the chemistry of their oxygen analogs to the degree that the chemistry of hydrogen sulfide parallels that of water. This prediction is not fully realized, for several factors operate to make sulfur different from oxygen. In this chapter we shall attempt to correlate where possible the chemistry of organosulfur compounds with that of corresponding oxygen compounds, with emphasis on showing how and why differences arise.

Organosulfur Compounds

CHAPTER 21

One of the important reasons that organosulfur compounds have properties which differ from analogously constituted oxygen compounds is that sulfur is substantially less electron-attracting than oxygen and, in this respect, lies between nitrogen and carbon. Another marked difference between oxygen and sulfur is that sulfur, like most of the elements in the second and higher rows of the periodic table, is reluctant to form double bonds. Thus, thiocarbonyl compounds with $\diagdown \mathrm{C}{=}\mathrm{S}$ linkages are relatively uncommon and are often unstable with respect to polymerization. This can be ascribed to low effectiveness of π-type overlap (often designated as p_π-p_π overlap) involving $3p$ orbitals. In this connection we may note that S_2, unlike O_2, is highly unstable and that elemental sulfur is most stable in the cyclic S_8 form. The reluctance of sulfur to form double bonds to carbon is also exhibited by phosphorus and silicon, and no stable compounds are known with $\mathrm{C}{=}\mathrm{Si}$ or $\mathrm{C}{=}\mathrm{P}$ bonds (at least where silicon and phosphorus are to be taken as utilizing $3p$ orbitals in π-type overlap).

After the above discussion of the lack of normal π bonding by sulfur, it may come as a surprise that the chemistry of sulfur compounds is in many instances influenced by π-type bonding which arises through overlap involving d orbitals. The d orbitals of sulfur are normally vacant. However, the possibility of π-d

513

bonding arises when sulfur is bonded to an atom like oxygen; here, in addition to a σ bond between the sulfur and oxygen atoms, a π bond may form by utilizing an unshared electron pair of oxygen and the vacant sulfur d orbitals. This kind of π bond is properly described as involving p_π-d_π overlap. The result is a "double bond" which differs from an ordinary p-π double bond because it occurs by virtue of expansion of the valence shell of sulfur to hold more than eight electrons. A characteristic substance of this type is dimethyl sulfoxide, $(CH_3)_2SO$, which we can regard as a resonance hybrid of the following electronic structures.

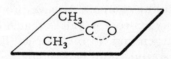

Both structures seem to be important—as judged by the high polarity of the S—O bond, and also by the S—O bond distances and infrared stretching frequencies, which indicate some double-bond character. The question of whether to denote the S—O bonds of sulfoxides and similar substances as $\overset{\oplus}{S}$—$\overset{\ominus}{O}$ or S=O is mainly a matter of personal preference. It is no argument against the double-bond structure to doubt that sulfur can expand its valence shell to hold more than eight electrons because compounds like $:SF_4$ and SF_6 are well-known, stable substances. We shall henceforth use the double-bond formulas, but it must be remembered that these do not imply any necessary correspondence to carbon-oxygen or nitrogen-oxygen double bonds. Indeed, an important difference between ordinary double bonds with p_π-p_π overlap and sulfur-oxygen double bonds with p_π-d_π overlap is the absence of any requirement for the groups attached to sulfur to lie in one plane. Thus dimethyl sulfoxide differs from acetone in having a nonplanar configuration.

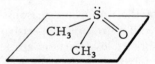

EXERCISE 21-1   Formulate each of the following substances in terms of electronic structure, types of bonds (i.e., σ and π) and probable molecular geometry (i.e., linear, angular, planar, pyramidal, etc.) with rough estimates of bond angles.

a. H_2S f. S_6 (six-membered ring)
b. SO_2 g. CS_2
c. SF_4 h. $SOCl_2$
d. H_2SO_4 i. S_8 (eight-membered ring)
e. Na_2SO_3

21-1 TYPES AND NOMENCLATURE OF ORGANOSULFUR COMPOUNDS

A number of typical sulfur compounds with their common and IUPAC names are listed in Table 21-1. It is often convenient to classify sulfur compounds according to whether the sulfur therein is bivalent or more than bivalent. As will be seen from Table 21-1, the bivalent sulfur derivatives are structurally analogous to oxygen compounds of types discussed in earlier chapters. These sulfur derivatives are often named by using the prefix *thio* in conjunction with the name of the corresponding oxygen analog.

CH_3CH_2SH

ethanethiol

$CH_3-\overset{\overset{S}{\|}}{C}\underset{S-H}{}$

dithioacetic acid
(ethanethionthioic acid)

thiophenol

The prefix *thia* is occasionally used when sulfur replaces carbon in an organic compound.

$\begin{matrix} CH_2-CH_2 \\ | \quad\quad | \\ S——CH_2 \end{matrix}$

thiacyclobutane
(trimethylene sulfide)
(thietane)

1, 2, 4, 6–tetraphenylthiabenzene

EXERCISE 21-2   Write structural formulas for the following substances:

a. di-*t*-butyl thioketone
b. ethylene sulfide
c. methyl thioacetate
d. β,β'-dichloroethyl sulfide (mustard gas)

e. tris-(methylsulfonyl)-methane
f. cis-1,4-dithiacyclohexane dioxide
g. trimethylene disulfide
h. 5-thia-1,3-cyclopentadiene (thiophene)

21-2 THIOLS

The thiols (or mercaptans) are derivatives of hydrogen sulfide in the same way that alcohols are derivatives of water. The volatile thiols, both aliphatic and aromatic, are like hydrogen sulfide in possessing characteristically disagreeable odors.

A variety of thiols occurs along with other sulfur compounds to the extent of several per cent in crude petroleum. Besides their odors, these substances cause difficulties in petroleum refining, particularly by poisoning metal catalysts.

Thiols also have animal and vegetable origins; notably, butanethiol is a component of skunk secretion; propanethiol is evolved from freshly chopped onions, and, as we have seen in Chapter 20, the thiol groups of cysteine are important to the chemistry of proteins and enzymes.

In many respects, the chemistry of thiols is like that of alcohols. Thus thiols can be readily prepared by the reaction of sodium hydrosulfide (NaSH) with

Table 21-1 Typical Organosulfur Compounds

Compound	Oxygen analog	Common name	IUPAC name
		A. Bivalent sulfur	
CH_3SH	ROH	methyl mercaptan	methanethiol
$C_2H_5SC_2H_5$	ROR	diethyl sulfide diethyl thioether	ethylthioethane
$C_6H_5SSC_6H_5$	$R\!-\!O\!-\!O\!-\!R$	diphenyl disulfide	phenyldithiobenzene
$(CH_3)_3\overset{\oplus}{S}\ \overset{\ominus}{Br}$	$R_3\overset{\oplus}{O}\ \overset{\ominus}{X}$	trimethylsulfonium bromide	
$(C_6H_5)_2C\!=\!S$	$R_2C\!=\!O$	thiobenzophenone	
	ROCl	2,4-dinitrobenzenesulfenyl chloride	2,4-dinitrobenzenesulfenyl chloride

B. *Sulfur greater than bivalent*[a]

Structure		
$C_2H_5\text{—}\overset{\text{O}}{\underset{..}{S}}\text{—OH}$	ethanesulfinic acid	ethanesulfinic acid
$CH_3\text{—}\overset{\text{O}}{\underset{\text{O}}{S}}\text{—OH}$	methanesulfonic acid	methanesulfonic acid
$CH_3\text{—}\overset{\text{O}}{\underset{\text{O}}{S}}\text{—Cl}$	methanesulfonyl chloride	methanesulfonyl chloride
$CH_3\text{—}\overset{\text{O}}{\underset{..}{S}}\text{—}C_2H_5$	ethyl methyl sulfoxide	methylsulfinylethane
$C_6H_5\text{—}\overset{\text{O}}{\underset{\text{O}}{S}}\text{—}C_6H_5$	diphenyl sulfone	phenylsulfonylbenzene

[a] Substances such as dimethyl sulfite $(CH_3O)_2SO$ and dimethyl sulfate $(CH_3O)_2SO_2$ are excluded from this table, since they do not have carbon-sulfur bonds.

those alkyl halides, sulfates, or sulfonates which undergo S_N2 displacements—this synthesis paralleling the preparation of alcohols from similar substances and hydroxide ion (Chapter 11).

$$C_2H_5Br + NaSH \longrightarrow C_2H_5SH + NaBr$$

Since thiols are acids of comparable strength to hydrogen sulfide ($K_A = 6 \times 10^{-8}$), more or less of the thioether may be produced by the following sequence of reactions, unless the sodium hydrosulfide is used in large excess.

$$C_2H_5SH + NaSH \rightleftharpoons C_2H_5SNa + H_2S$$

$$C_2H_5SNa + C_2H_5Br \longrightarrow (C_2H_5)_2S + NaBr$$

Thiols can also be prepared by the reaction of Grignard reagents with sulfur (p. 264).

cyclohexyl
bromide

cyclohexane-
thiol

Thiols do not form as strong intermolecular hydrogen bonds as do alcohols, and consequently the low-molecular-weight thiols have lower boiling points than alcohols; thus ethanethiol boils at 35° compared to 78.5° for ethanol. The difference in boiling points diminishes with increasing chain length.

The lack of extensive hydrogen-bonding is also evident from the infrared spectra of thiols, wherein a weak band appears in the region 2600 to 2550 cm^{-1}, which is characteristic of S—H linkages. In contrast to the O—H absorption of alcohols, the frequency of this band does not shift significantly with concentration, physical state (gas, solid, or liquid), or the nature of the solvent; the —SH group is therefore probably not extensively hydrogen-bonded.

Perhaps surprisingly, in view of the smaller electronegativity of sulfur than oxygen, thiols are considerably stronger acids than the corresponding alcohols. Thus the K_A of ethanethiol is about 10^{-11}, compared to 10^{-17} for ethanol. However, this behavior is not unusual, in that H_2O is a weaker acid than H_2S, HF is weaker than HCl, and NH_3 is a weaker acid than PH_3. Apparently, the important factor is that, for the first-row elements, the bonds to hydrogen are stronger and considerably *shorter* than for higher-row elements. Consequently, the energy for ionic dissociation is greater for the hydrides of the first-row elements, even though the bonds have greater ionic character to begin with.[1]

Thiols form insoluble salts with heavy metals, particularly mercury. This behavior is the origin of the common (but now disfavored) name, **mercaptan,** for thiols. The salts are thus called mercaptides. As mentioned above, alkali-metal salts of thiols react readily in S_N2-type displacements to yield thioethers,

[1] See L. Pauling, *J. Chem. Ed.,* **33,** 16 (1956).

and this provides a general method of synthesis of these substances. The pronounced nucleophilicity of sulfur combined with its relatively low basicity makes for rapid reaction with little competition from elimination, except for those compounds where S_N2-type displacement is quite unfavorable and E2-type elimination is favorable.

Thiols react with carboxylic acids and acid chlorides to yield thioesters and with aldehydes and ketones to yield dithioacetals and dithioketals, respectively.

$$CH_3CH_2SH \ + \ CH_3\overset{\overset{\displaystyle O}{\|}}{C}-Cl \quad \longrightarrow \quad CH_3\overset{\overset{\displaystyle O}{\|}}{C}-S-C_2H_5 \ + \ HCl$$

ethyl thioacetate

$$HSCH_2CH_2CH_2SH \ + \ CH_3\overset{\overset{\displaystyle O}{\|}}{C}-CH_3 \quad \xrightarrow{\ HCl\ }$$

1, 3-propanedithiol

acetone trimethylene
dithioketal

EXERCISE 21-3   Thiols are unlike alcohols in that they do not react readily with hydrogen bromide to yield bromides. Explain how a difference in behavior in this respect might be expected.

An important point of difference between thiols and alcohols is their behavior toward oxidizing agents. In general, oxidation of alcohols occurs with increase of the oxidation level of carbon rather than that of oxygen; carbonyl groups, but not peroxides, are formed (cf. pp. 296–297). This is because O—H bonds are strong bonds, which means that it takes a powerful oxidizing agent to achieve one-electron oxidation of oxygen by removing a hydrogen atom from the hydroxyl group of an alcohol.

$$R-O-H \ + \ \cdot X \quad \longrightarrow \quad RO\cdot \ + \ HX$$

(a generally
unfavorable
reaction)

$$2 RO\cdot \quad \longrightarrow \quad ROOR$$

In addition, the hydroxyl oxygen of an alcohol does not accept an oxygen atom from reagents like hydrogen peroxide, although these same reagents readily donate an oxygen atom to nitrogen of amines to form amine oxides (see p. 464).

$$R\ddot{O}H \ + \ H_2O_2 \quad \xrightarrow{\ \ //\ \ } \quad R\overset{\oplus}{\underset{}{\ddot{O}}}:H \quad \longrightarrow \quad R-O-O-H$$

$$R\ddot{N}(CH_3)_2 \ + \ H_2O_2 \quad \xrightarrow{(-H_2O)} \quad R\overset{\oplus}{N}(CH_3)_2$$

Oxidation of thiols takes a different course than the oxidation of alcohols because sulfur is much more easily oxidized than carbon and the compounds in which sulfur is in a higher oxidation state are frequently quite stable. Furthermore, because the strength of S—H bonds (83 kcal) is considerably less than that of O—H bonds (111 kcal), there is good reason to expect that reaction mechanisms that are unfavorable with alcohols might well be more favorable with sulfur. Thus we find that oxidation of thiols with a variety of mild oxidizing agents, such as atmospheric oxygen, halogens, sulfuric acid, etc., produces disulfides, probably by way of thioxy radicals.

$$R\text{–}S\text{–}H + [O] \longrightarrow R\text{–}S\cdot + H[O]$$

$$2\,RS\cdot \longrightarrow RS\text{–}SR$$

$$\text{disulfide}$$

EXERCISE 21-4   Write mechanisms for the conversion of a thiol to a disulfide by oxidation with air or iodine which are in accord with the observation that the reaction with either oxidizing agent is accelerated by alkali.

Vigorous oxidation of thiols with nitric acid, permanganate, or hydrogen peroxide gives sulfonic acids, possibly by way of the disulfide, or else through intermediate formation of the sulfenic and sulfinic acids, which are themselves too readily oxidized to be isolated.

R–S–S–R $\longrightarrow$ $\underset{\overset{\|}{O}}{\overset{\overset{O}{\|}}{R\text{–}S\text{–}S\text{–}R}}$ $\longrightarrow$ $\underset{\overset{\|\;\|}{O\;O}}{\overset{\overset{O\;O}{\|\;\|}}{R\text{–}S\text{–}S\text{–}R}}$

disulfide   thiosulfonate ester   disulfone

R–SH

R–S–OH $\overset{\overset{O}{\|}}{R\text{–}S\text{–}OH}$

sulfenic acid   sulfinic acid

RSO_3H

sulfonic acid

21-3 ALKYL SULFIDES

Organic sulfides or thioethers, R—S—R′, are readily obtained by displacement reactions between alkyl compounds and salts of thiols (p. 518) or by addition of thiols to alkenes. The addition reactions proceed most readily with free-radical catalysts and such catalysts lead to anti-Markownikoff addition.

$$\text{HOCH}_2\text{CH}_2\text{SH} + (\text{CH}_3)_2\text{SO}_4 \xrightarrow[\text{60--70}°]{\text{aq. 25\% NaOH}} \text{HOCH}_2\text{CH}_2\text{SCH}_3$$

ethan-2-ol-1-thiol   2-(methylthio)-ethanol

$$\text{CH}_3\text{SH} + \text{CH}_2\text{=CHCH}_2\text{CN} \xrightarrow[h\nu,\ 24\ \text{hr.}]{(\text{C}_6\text{H}_5\text{CO}_2)_2} \text{CH}_3\text{SCH}_2\text{CH}_2\text{CH}_2\text{CN}$$

methanethiol   allyl cyanide   4-(methylthio)-butyronitrile

Sulfides undergo two important reactions involving the electron pairs on sulfur. Thus, they act as nucleophilic agents toward substances that undergo nucleophilic displacement readily to give sulfonium salts, and they are rather easily oxidized to sulfoxides and sulfones.

trimethylsulfonium iodide

dimethyl sulfoxide   dimethyl sulfone

The formation of sulfonium salts from alkyl halides is reversible, and heating of the salt causes dissociation into its components. Sulfonium salts are analogous in structure and properties to quaternary ammonium salts, and their hydroxides form strongly basic water solutions. In contrast, oxonium salts are generally much more reactive (p. 302).

A noteworthy feature of sulfonium salts is that, when substituted with three different groups, they can usually be separated into optical enantiomers. Thus the reaction of methyl ethyl sulfide with bromoacetic acid gives a sulfonium salt which has been separated into dextro- and levorotatory forms by crystallization as the salt of an optically active amine. The asymmetry of these ions stems from the nonplanar configuration of the bonds formed by sulfonium sulfur.

enantiomers of methylethyl(carboxymethyl)-sulfonium ion

The optically active forms of unsymmetrically substituted sulfonium ions are quite stable—surprisingly so in view of the very low configurational stability of analogously constituted amines. Apparently, nonplanar compounds of the type $R_3Y:$, where Y is an element in the second horizontal row of the periodic table, undergo inversion much less readily than similar compounds for which Y is a first-row element. Thus phosphorus compounds resemble sulfur compounds in this respect, and several asymmetric phosphines $(R_1R_2R_3P:)$ have been successfully resolved into enantiomeric forms (see Chapter 31).

EXERCISE 21-5   When a solution of methyldiethylsulfonium bromide is heated, a mixture of sulfonium salts is formed, including trimethyl- and triethylsulfonium bromides. Explain.

EXERCISE 21-6   Dimethyl sulfide reacts with bromine in the absence of water to produce a crystalline addition compound which reacts with water to produce dimethyl sulfoxide. What is the likely structure of the addition compound and the mechanism of its formation and reaction with water?

EXERCISE 21-7   How many and what kind of stereoisomers would you expect for each of the following compounds:

a. methylethyl-s-butylsulfonium bromide

b. $[CH_3(C_2H_5)SCH_2CH_2S(CH_3)C_2H_5]^{2\oplus}$ 2 Br$^\ominus$

$$\begin{array}{c} CH_2-CH_2 \\ \stackrel{\oplus}{/} \qquad \stackrel{\oplus}{\backslash} \\ c. \quad CH_3S \qquad SCH_3 \quad 2Br^\ominus \\ \backslash \qquad / \\ CH_2-CH_2 \end{array}$$

21-4 SULFOXIDES AND SULFONES

Oxidation of sulfides, preferably with hydrogen peroxide in acetic acid, yields sulfoxides and sulfones. The degree of oxidation is determined by the ratio of the reagents, and either the sulfoxide or sulfone can be obtained in good yield.

$$\begin{array}{c} \xrightarrow[\text{CH}_3\text{CO}_2\text{H}]{1.5 \text{ moles, } 30\% \text{ H}_2\text{O}_2} \quad \overset{O}{\underset{\|}{CH_3}}S CH_2CH_2\overset{NH_2}{\underset{|}{C}}HCO_2H \end{array}$$

methionine sulfoxide

$$CH_3SCH_2CH_2\overset{NH_2}{\underset{|}{C}}HCO_2H$$

methionine

$$\xrightarrow[\text{CH}_3\text{CO}_2\text{H}]{3.2 \text{ moles, } 30\% \text{ H}_2\text{O}_2} \quad \overset{O}{\underset{\overset{\|}{S}}{CH_3}}\underset{\underset{\|}{O}}{\overset{\|}{S}}-CH_2CH_2\overset{NH_2}{\underset{|}{C}}HCO_2H$$

methionine sulfone

Dimethyl sulfoxide, b.p. 86° (25 mm), is a versatile solvent which provides a particularly useful medium for reactions between polar and nonpolar reagents. One such example is the formation of nitriles from organic halides and sodium cyanide. However, dimethyl sulfoxide is not to be regarded as an inert solvent in all circumstances; in fact, it reacts rapidly with halides as active as α-bromo-ketones and more slowly with sulfonate esters at elevated temperatures. Furthermore, it tends to decompose at temperatures above 80°. Sulfones are also good solvents but are higher-boiling and may be solid at room temperature; dimethyl sulfone has m.p. 110° and b.p. 238°, whereas tetramethylene sulfone has m.p. 10° and b.p. 288°. The value of sulfoxides and sulfones as solvents for salts and saltlike substances stems in part from the fact that they are particularly efficient for solvating cations (see p. 237).

EXERCISE 21-8   Unsymmetrically substituted sulfoxides, but not the corresponding sulfones, exhibit optical isomerism. Write structures for the stereoisomers you would expect for
   a. methyl ethyl sulfoxide
   b. the disulfoxide of 1,3-dithiacyclohexane
   c. di-s-butyl sulfoxide
   It has been stated that the existence of stable optical enantiomers of a sulfoxide *precludes* formulation of such substances with oxygen-sulfur double bonds, RR'S=O. Is this statement correct? Why?

21-5 SULFENIC, SULFINIC, AND SULFONIC ACIDS

The sulfenic acids, RSOH, are unstable with respect to self-oxidation and reduction and generally cannot be isolated. However, certain derivatives of sulfenic acids are relatively stable, notably the acid halides RSCl, esters RSOR', amides RSNH$_2$, and anhydrides (RS)$_2$O. A general reaction of alkyl- and aryl-sulfenyl halides is addition to alkenes and alkynes—in fact, 2,4-dinitrobenzenesulfenyl chloride has some use for the preparation of solid derivatives of alkenes through addition to give chloroalkyl 2,4-dinitrophenyl sulfides.

$$CH_3(CH_2)_5CH=CH_2 \ + \ O_2N-\!\!\!\!\bigcirc\!\!\!\!-SCl \ \longrightarrow \ CH_3(CH_2)_5-\!\!\underset{Cl}{\overset{}{C}}\!H-CH_2-S-\!\!\!\!\bigcirc\!\!\!\!-NO_2$$

Sulfinic acids, RSO$_2$H, are more stable than sulfenic acids but are nonetheless easily oxidized to sulfonic acids, RSO$_3$H. They are moderately strong acids with K_A values comparable to the first ionization of sulfurous acid ($K_A \sim 10^{-2}$).

EXERCISE 21-9   Ethyl phenylsulfinate but not phenylsulfinic acid has been obtained optically active. Explain.

Many sulfonic acids, RSO$_3$H, have considerable commercial importance as detergents in the form of their sodium salts, RSO$_3$Na. For optimum detergency, R should be a group which, in the form of RH, is highly oil and grease soluble. Many commercial detergents are sodium alkylarylsulfonates of types which are readily synthesized from petroleum by reactions discussed in Chapter 22.

$$C_{9-15}H_{19-31}-\langle\!\!\bigcirc\!\!\rangle-\overset{\ominus}{S}\overset{\oplus}{O_3Na}$$

The resistance of highly branched alkyl chains of arylalkylsulfonates to bio-chemical degradation and the water pollution that results has led to a reduction in the use of such substances as detergents for domestic purposes. Sodium aryl-alkylsulfonates with nonbranched side chains or sodium alkylsulfonates derived from long-chain alcohols are more easily degraded by bacteria. The principal advantage that sodium sulfonates have as detergents over the sodium salts of fatty acids (p. 363) used in ordinary soaps is that the corresponding calcium and magnesium salts are much more soluble, and hence the sulfonates do not pro-duce scum when used in hard water.

Sulfonic acid groups are often introduced into organic molecules to increase water solubility.   This is particularly important in the dye industry, where it is desired to solubilize colored organic molecules for use in aqueous dye baths (see Chapter 28).

Aliphatic sulfonic acids can be prepared in several ways.   The most generally useful being (1) the oxidation of thiols (p. 520), (2) the reaction of sodium sulfite with alkyl halides that react well by the S_N2 mechanism, and (3) the oxygen-induced, anti-Markownikoff addition of sodium bisulfite to alkenes.

$$\underset{\overset{|}{CH_3}}{\overset{\overset{CH_3}{|}}{ClCH_2CH_2C-SH}} + 3H_2O_2 \xrightarrow{CH_3CO_2H} \underset{\overset{|}{CH_3}}{\overset{\overset{CH_3}{|}}{ClCH_2CH_2C-SO_3H}} + 3H_2O$$

4-chloro-2-methyl-   4-chloro-2-methyl
2-butanethiol   butane-2-sulfonic acid

92%

$$\langle\!\!\bigcirc\!\!\rangle-OCH_2CH_2Cl \xrightarrow[\text{(reflux)}]{\text{aq. } Na_2SO_3} \langle\!\!\bigcirc\!\!\rangle-OCH_2CH_2SO_3Na$$

β-phenoxyethyl chloride   sodium phenoxy-
ethanesulfonate

100%

$$CH_3CH=CH_2 + NaHSO_3 \xrightarrow[\text{H}_2\text{O, } 25°]{O_2} CH_3CH_2CH_2SO_3Na$$

sodium propanesulfonate

Arylsulfonic acids are almost always prepared by sulfonation of the correspond-ing hydrocarbon (pp. 544 and 551).

Sulfonic acids are strong acids, comparable in strength to sulfuric and per-chloric acids.   Furthermore, the sulfonate group is an excellent leaving group from carbon in nucleophilic displacement reactions (see, for example, Exercise 11-4), and, in consequence, conversion of an alcohol to a sulfonate ester is a very important way to activate alcohols for replacement of the hydroxyl group by a variety of nucleophilic reagents. A sulfonate ester is best prepared from a sulfonyl chloride and an alcohol, and many sulfonyl chlorides are available commercially which can be used for this purpose (methanesulfonyl chloride, benzenesulfonyl chloride, p-toluenesulfonyl chloride, p-bromobenzenesulfonyl chloride, etc.); other sulfonyl chlorides can be made by treatment of the salt of the sulfonic acid with phosphorus pentachloride.

$$3\,RSO_3Na \ + \ PCl_5 \quad \longrightarrow \quad 3RSO_2Cl \ + \ 2NaCl \ + \ NaOPO_2$$

A number of important antibiotic drugs, the so-called sulfa drugs, are sulfonamide derivatives.

sulfadiazine   sulfaguanidine

EXERCISE 21-10   Write a mechanism for the oxygen-induced addition of sodium bisulfite to alkenes. Would the reaction be expected to proceed more efficiently or less efficiently at pH values greater than 8? Why?

SUPPLEMENTARY EXERCISES

21-11 Write equations for a practical synthesis of each of the following substances based on the specified starting materials. Give reagents and approximate reaction conditions.

  a. $CH_3-\overset{\overset{\displaystyle O}{\|}}{C}-S-CH_2CH_2CH_3$ from n-propyl alcohol
  b. optically active methylethyl-n-butylsulfonium bromide from n-butyl alcohol

  c. from trimethylene dibromide

  d. neopentanethiol from neopentyl chloride

21-12 Write projection formulas for the possible stereoisomers of the following substances.
  a. methylethyl-2-butenylsulfonium bromide
  b. methyl α-bromopropanesulfonate
  c. bis-(methylsulfinyl)-methane

  d. $CH_3-\overset{\overset{\displaystyle O}{\|}}{\underset{\underset{\displaystyle O}{\|}}{S}}-N=\overset{}{\underset{\underset{\displaystyle CH_3}{|}}{S}}-$

  e. methyl ethyl sulfite

21-13 Give for each of the following pairs of compounds a chemical test, preferably a test-tube reaction, which would serve to distinguish one from the other.

    a. CH_3CH_2SH and CH_3SCH_3

    b. $(CH_3CH_2S)_2$ and $(CH_3CH_2)_2S$

    c. $CH_3S(O)OCH_3$ and $CH_3CH_2SO_3H$

    d. $CH_3S(O)OCH_3$ and $CH_3S(O)_2CH_3$

    e. $CH_3SCH_2CH_2OH$ and $CH_3OCH_2CH_2SH$

    f. optically active *s*-butyldiethylsulfonium bromide and optically active *s*-butyl-carbinyldimethylsulfonium bromide

    g. optically active (D-*s*-butyl)-methylethylsulfonium bromide and optically active (D,L-*s*-butyl)-methylethylsulfonium bromide

21-14 Suppose it were desired to study the addition of bromine to an alkene double bond in water in the absence of organic solvents. A possible substrate for this purpose would be $CH_2{=}CHCH_2CH_2CH_2CH_2{-}X$, where $-X$ is a solubilizing group. What would be the merits of having $-X$ as $-SO_3Na$ over $X = -OH$, $-NH_2$, $-CO_2Na$, $-\overset{\oplus}{N}(CH_3)_3Br^{\ominus}$? How could you synthesize $CH_2{=}CHCH_2CH_2CH_2CH_2SO_3Na$ from allyl bromide?

Arenes. Electrophilic
Aromatic Substitution

*B*enzene and the other aromatic hydrocarbons usually have such strikingly different properties from typical open-chain conjugated polyenes, such as 1,3,5-hexatriene, that it is convenient to consider them as a separate class of compounds called arenes. In this chapter, we shall outline the salient features of the chemistry of arenes and, in subsequent chapters, we shall discuss the chemistry of various kinds of substituted arenes, particularly the halogen, oxygen, and nitrogen derivatives.

Arenes.
Electrophilic
Aromatic
Substitution

Some of the important properties of benzene were discussed in Chapter 9 in connection with the resonance method. Most noteworthy is the fact that benzene has a planar hexagonal structure in which all six carbon-carbon bonds are of equal length (1.397 A), and each carbon is bonded to one hydrogen. Considering each carbon to form sp^2-σ bonds to its hydrogen and neighboring carbons, there remain six electrons, one for each carbon atom, which are termed π electrons. These electrons are not to be taken as localized in pairs between alternate carbon nuclei to form three conventional conjugated bonds. Rather, they should be regarded as delocalized symmetrically through the p_z orbitals of all six carbons (p. 182). The bonds between the carbons are therefore neither single nor double bonds, and, in fact, their lengths are such as to be intermediate between single and double bonds. However, there is more to the bonding than just the simple average of C—C single and double bonds, because benzene C—C bonds are substantially stronger than the average of the strengths of single and double bonds. This is reflected in the heat of combustion of benzene, which is substantially less than expected on the basis of bond energies; and the extra stability of benzene by virtue of its stronger bonds is what we have called its **stabilization energy.** A large part of this stabilization energy can be ascribed to delocalization or **resonance energy** of the six carbon π electrons.

The choice of a suitable and convenient graphical formula to represent the structure of benzene presents a problem, since the best way to indicate delocalized bonding electrons is by dotted lines, which are quite time-consuming to draw.   Dotted-line structural formulas are preferred when it is necessary to show the fine details of an aromatic structure — as when the degree of bonding is *not* equal between different pairs of carbons, e.g., phenanthrene, etc.   Short-hand notations are usually desirable, however, and we shall most often use the conventional hexagon with alternating single and double bonds (i.e., Kekulé cyclohexatriene) despite the fact that benzene does not possess ordinary double bonds.   Another and widely used notation for benzene is a hexagon with an inscribed circle to represent a closed shell of π electrons.   However, as we have mentioned before (p. 184), this is fine for benzene but possibly misleading for other aromatic hydrocarbons, e.g., phenanthrene.

22-1   NOMENCLATURE OF ARENES

A. Benzene Derivatives

A variety of substituted benzenes are known with one or more of the hydrogen atoms of the ring replaced with other atoms or groups; and, in almost all of these compounds, the special stability associated with the benzene nucleus is retained.   A few examples of "benzenoid" hydrocarbons follow, and it will be noticed that the hydrocarbon substituents include alkyl, alkenyl, alkynyl, and aryl groups.

toluene
(methylbenzene)

ethylbenzene

cumene
(isopropylbenzene)

styrene
(vinylbenzene)

phenylacetylene
(ethynylbenzene)

biphenyl
(phenylbenzene)

diphenylmethane

The naming of the hydrocarbons listed above is fairly straightforward. Each is named as an alkyl, alkenyl, or arylbenzene, unless for some reason the compound has a trivial name. The hydrocarbon group (C_6H_5—) from benzene itself is called a phenyl group and is sometimes abbreviated as the symbol ϕ or as Ph. Aryl groups in general are often abbreviated as Ar.

Other groups which have trivial names include the following:

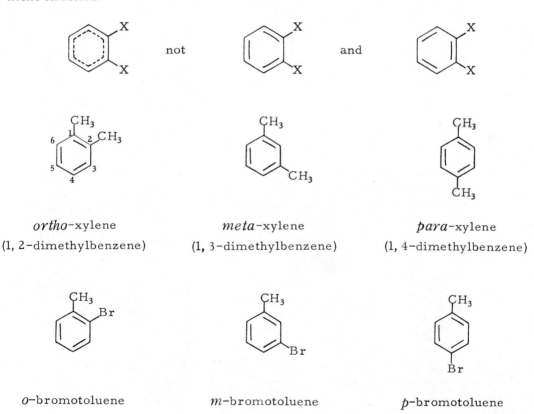

benzyl   benzal   benzo   benzhydryl

When there are two or more substituents on a benzene ring, position isomerism arises. Thus, there are three possible isomeric disubstituted benzene derivatives according to whether the substituents have the 1,2, 1,3, or 1,4 relationship. The isomers are commonly designated as *ortho*, *meta*, and *para* (or *o*, *m*, and *p*) for the 1,2-, 1,3- and 1,4-isomers respectively. The actual symmetry of the benzene ring is such that only one 1,2-disubstitution product is found despite the fact that two would be predicted if benzene had the 1,3,5-cyclohexatriene structure.

ortho-xylene
(1, 2–dimethylbenzene)

meta-xylene
(1, 3–dimethylbenzene)

para-xylene
(1, 4–dimethylbenzene)

o–bromotoluene

m–bromotoluene

p–bromotoluene

EXERCISE 22-1   How many isomeric products could each of the xylenes give on introduction of a third substituent? Name each isomer using chlorine as the third substituent.

EXERCISE 22-2   Name each of the following compounds by an accepted system:

a. $(C_6H_5)_2CHCl$ b. $C_6H_5CHCl_2$ c. $C_6H_5CCl_3$

d.

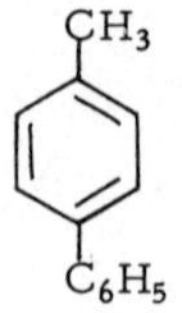

e.

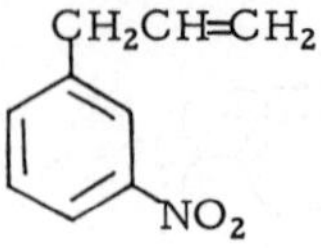

f.

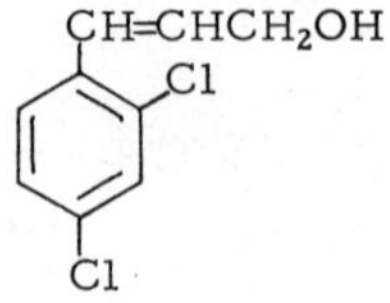

B. Polynuclear Aromatic Hydrocarbons

A wide range of polycyclic aromatic compounds are known that have benzene rings with common *ortho* positions. The parent compounds of this type are usually called **polynuclear** aromatic hydrocarbons. Three important examples are naphthalene, anthracene, and phenanthrene. In anthracene, the rings are connected in a *linear* manner, while in phenanthrene they are connected *angularly.*

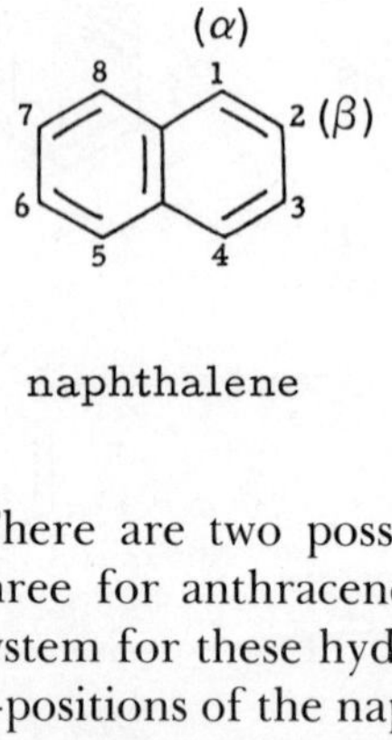

naphthalene 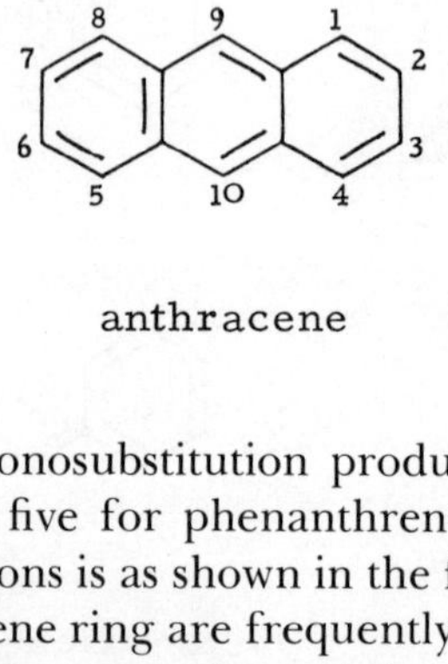   anthracene 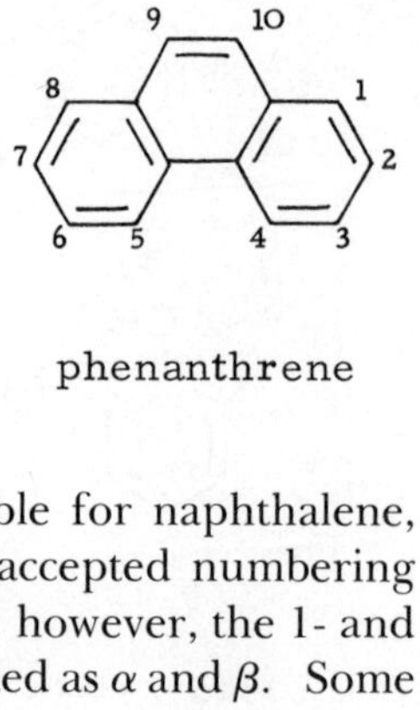   phenanthrene

There are two possible monosubstitution products possible for naphthalene, three for anthracene, and five for phenanthrene. The accepted numbering system for these hydrocarbons is as shown in the formulas; however, the 1- and 2-positions of the naphthalene ring are frequently designated as α and β. Some illustrative substitution products are shown below.

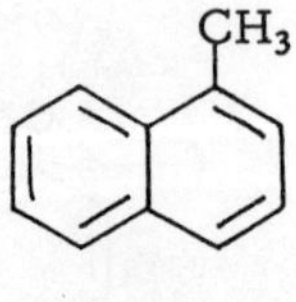

1-methylnaphthalene   2-methylnaphthalene   1-methylanthracene
(α-methylnaphthalene)   (β-methylnaphthalene)

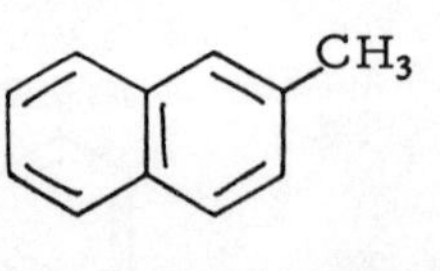

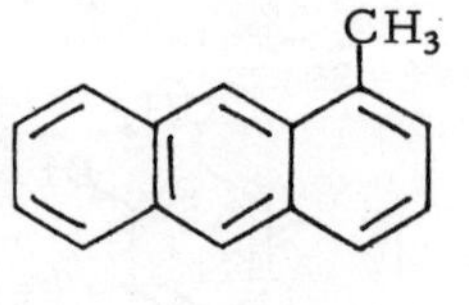

How many possible disubstitution (X,X and X,Y) products are there for naphthalene, phenanthrene, anthracene, and biphenyl? Name each of the possible dimethyl derivatives.

Substances which can be regarded as partial or complete reduction products of aromatic compounds are often named as *hydro* derivatives of the parent system — the completely reduced derivatives being known as *perhydro* compounds. Thus,

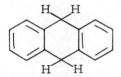

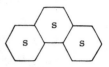

9, 10–dihydro-anthracene

1, 2, 3, 4–tetrahydro-naphthalene

(tetralin)

perhydro-phenanthrene

Note that when a simple hexagon is used to represent a saturated cyclohexane ring, it is sometimes labeled with the letter *s* to avoid any possible confusion with a benzene ring.

The names that have been given to the more elaborate types of polynuclear aromatic hydrocarbons are for the most part distressingly uninformative in relation to their structures.   A thorough summary of names and numbering systems has been published by A. M. Patterson, L. T. Capell, and D. F. Walker, "Ring Index," 2nd Ed., American Chemical Society, 1960.

22-2 PHYSICAL PROPERTIES OF ARENES

The pleasant odors of the derivatives of many arenes are the reason they are often called **aromatic hydrocarbons.**   The arenes themselves, however, are generally quite toxic; some are even carcinogenic and inhalation of their vapors should be avoided.   The volatile arenes are highly flammable and burn with a luminous sooty flame in contrast to alkanes and alkenes, which burn with a bluish flame leaving little carbon residue.

A list of the more common arenes and their physical properties is given in Table 22-1.   They are less dense than water and are highly insoluble.   Boiling points are found to increase fairly regularly with molecular weight, but there is little correlation between melting point and molecular weight.   The melting point is highly dependent on the symmetry of the compound; thus benzene melts 100° higher than toluene, and the more symmetrical *p*-xylene has a higher melting point than either the *o*- or the *m*-isomer.

Table 22-1   *Physical Properties of Arenes*

Compound	M.p., °C	B.p., °C	Density, d_4^{20}
benzene	5.5	80	0.8790
toluene	−95	111	0.866
ethylbenzene	−94	136	0.8669
n-propylbenzene	−99	159	0.8617
isopropylbenzene (cumene)	−96	152	0.8620
t-butylbenzene	−58	168	0.8658
o-xylene	−25	144	0.8968
m-xylene	−47	139	0.8811
p-xylene	13	138	0.8541
mesitylene (1,3,5-trimethylbenzene)	−50	165	0.8634
durene (1,2,4,5-tetramethylbenzene)	80	191	
naphthalene	80	218	
anthracene	216	340	
phenanthrene	101	340	

22-3 SPECTROSCOPIC PROPERTIES OF ARENES

A. Infrared Spectra

The presence of a phenyl group in a compound can be ascertained with a fair degree of certainty from its infrared spectrum. Furthermore, the number and positions of substituent groups on the ring can also be determined from the spectrum. For example, in Figure 22-1, we see the individual infrared spectra of four compounds, toluene, *o*-, *m*-, and *p*-xylene. That each spectrum is of a benzene derivative is apparent from certain common features, notably the two bands near 1600 cm^{-1} and 1500 cm^{-1} which, although of variable intensity, have been correlated with the stretching vibrations of the carbon-carbon bonds of the aromatic ring; in some compounds, there is an additional band around 1580 cm^{-1}. The sharp bands near 3030 cm^{-1} are characteristic of aromatic C—H bonds. Other bands in the spectra, especially those between 1650 and 2000 cm^{-1}, between 1225 and 950 cm^{-1}, and below 900 cm^{-1}, have been correlated with the number and positions of ring substituents. Although we shall not document all these various bands in detail, each of the spectra in Figure 22-1 is marked to show some of the types of correlations that have been made.

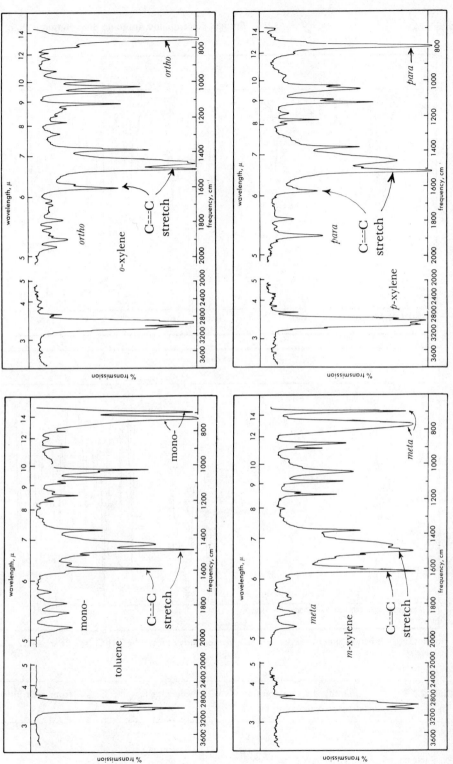

Figure 22-1 Infrared spectra of toluene, o-, m-, and p-xylenes. The number and positions of ring substituents determine the pattern of the low-intensity bands in the region 2000 to 1650 cm⁻¹ and the positions of the stronger bands in the region 800 to 690 cm⁻¹.

535

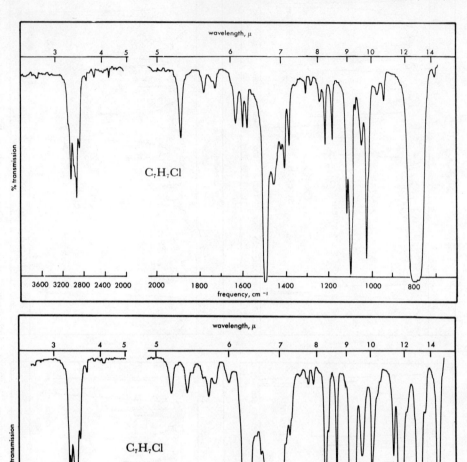

Figure 22-2   Infrared spectra of two isomeric compounds of formula C_7H_7Cl (see Exercise 22-4).

EXERCISE 22-4   Identify the two compounds with molecular formula C_7H_7Cl from their infrared spectra shown in Figure 22-2.

B. Electronic Absorption Spectra

Compared to straight-chain conjugated polyenes, aromatic compounds have relatively complex absorption spectra with several bands in the ultraviolet region.

Benzene and the alkylbenzenes possess two bands in which we shall be primarily interested, one lying near 2000 A and the other near 2600 A.

The 2000 A band is of fairly high intensity and corresponds to excitation of a π electron of the conjugated system to a π^* orbital (i.e., a $\pi \rightarrow \pi^*$ transition). The excited state has significant contributions from dipolar structures such as [1].

[1]

This is analogous to the absorption bands of conjugated dienes (pp. 196–197) except that the wavelength of absorption of benzene is shorter. In fact, benzene and the alkylbenzenes absorb just beyond the range of most commercial quartz spectrometers. However, this band (which we say is due to the benzene **chromophore**) is intensified and shifted to longer wavelengths when the conjugated system is extended by replacement of the ring hydrogens by unsaturated groups (e.g., —HC=CH$_2$, —C≡CH, —HC=O, and —C≡N; see Table 22-2). The absorbing chromophore now embraces the electrons of the unsaturated substituent as well as those of the ring. In the specific case of styrene, the excited state is a hybrid structure composite of [2a] and [2b] and other related dipolar structures.

[2a]   [2b]

Similar effects are observed for benzene derivatives in which the substituent has unshared electron pairs in conjugation with the benzene ring (e.g., —N̈H$_2$, —ÖH, —C̈l:). An unshared electron pair is to some extent delocalized to be-

Table 22-2   Effect of Conjugation on the Ultraviolet Spectrum of the Benzene Chromophore

	Benzene	Styrene	Benzaldehyde	Biphenyl	Stilbene
λ_{max}, A	1,980	2,440	2,440	2,500	2,950
ε_{max}	8,000	12,000	15,000	18,000	27,000

come a part of the aromatic π-electron system in both the ground and excited states, but more importantly in the excited state. This may be illustrated for aniline by the following structures, which can be regarded as contributing to the hybrid structure of aniline.

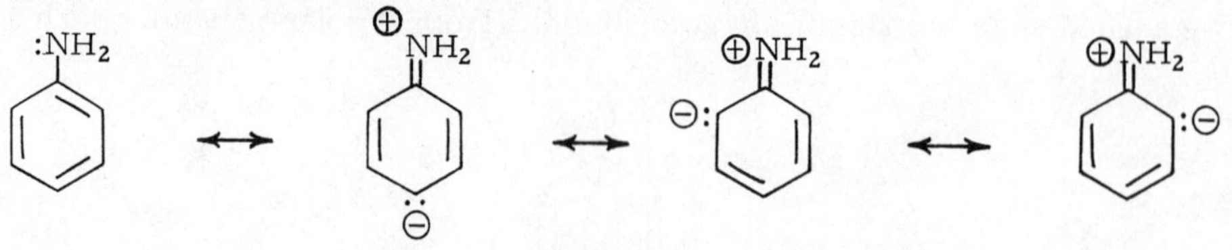

The data of Table 22-3 show the effect on the benzene chromophore of this type of substituent.

EXERCISE 22-5   Predict the effect on the ultraviolet spectrum of a solution of aniline in water when hydrochloric acid is added. Explain why a solution of sodium phenoxide absorbs at longer wavelengths than a solution of phenol (see Table 22-3).

Table 22-3   Effect of Substituents on the Ultraviolet Spectrum of the Benzene Chromophore

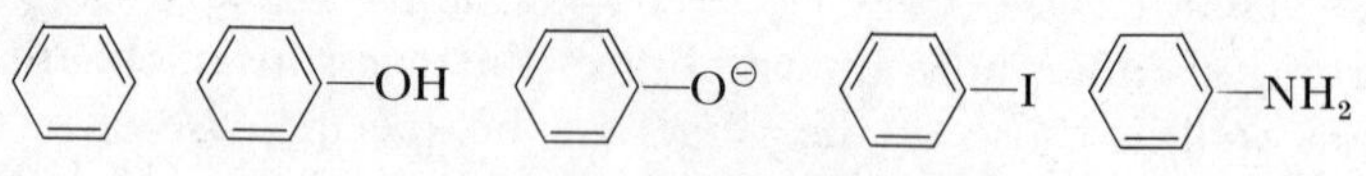

	Benzene	Phenol	Phenoxide ion	Iodobenzene	Aniline
λ_{max}, A	1,980	2,100	2,350	2,260	2,300
ε_{max}	8,000	6,200	9,400	13,000	8,600

As already mentioned, the benzene chromophore gives rise to a second band at longer wavelengths, and this is shown for benzene in Figure 22-3. This band is of relatively low intensity and is found to be a composite of several equally spaced (1000 cm^{-1}) narrow peaks. It appears to be remarkably characteristic of aromatic hydrocarbons, for no analogous band is found in the spectra of conjugated polyenes. For this reason, it is often called the *benzenoid band*. The position and intensity of this band, like the one at shorter wavelengths, is affected by the nature of the ring substituents, particularly by those which extend the conjugated system, as may be seen from the data in Table 22-4 and Table 22-5.

Table 22-4   The Effect of Substituents on Absorption corresponding to the Benzenoid Band

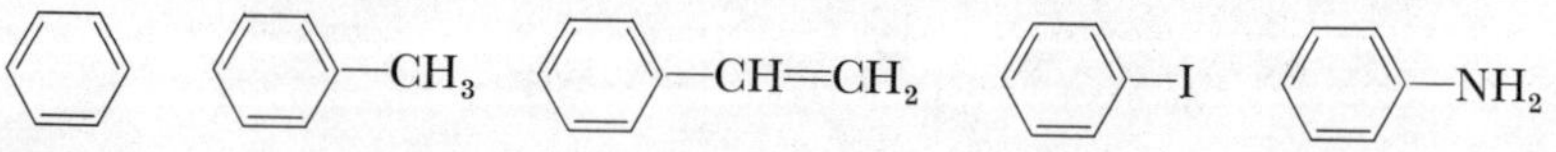

	Benzene	Toluene	Styrene	Iodobenzene	Aniline
λ_{max}, A	2,550	2,610	2,820	2,560	2,800
ε_{max}	230	300	450	800	1,430

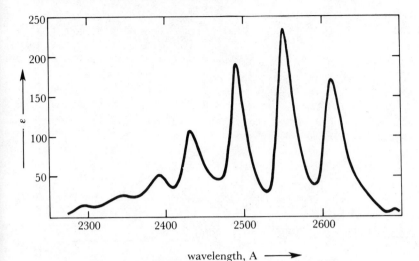

Figure 22-3 Ultraviolet absorption spectrum of benzene (in cyclohexane) showing the "benzenoid" band.

C. Nuclear Magnetic Resonance Spectra

The chemical shifts of aromatic protons (6.5 to 8.0 ppm) are characteristically toward lower magnetic fields than those of protons attached to ordinary double bonds (4.6 to 6.9 ppm). The difference is usually on the order of 2 ppm and has special interest because we have already formulated the hydrogens in both types of systems as being bonded to carbon through sp^2-σ bonds.

In general, the spin-spin splittings observed for phenyl derivatives are extremely complex. An example is afforded by nitrobenzene (Figure 22-4), which has different chemical shifts for its *ortho*, *meta*, and *para* hydrogens and six *different* spin-spin interaction constants: J_{23}, J_{24}, J_{25}, J_{26}, J_{34}, J_{35} (the subscripts correspond to position numbers of the protons).

$$
\begin{array}{c}
\text{NO}_2 \\
\text{H}_6 \quad 1 \quad 2 \quad \text{H} \\
\text{H}_5 \quad \quad 3 \quad \text{H} \\
4 \\
\text{H}
\end{array}
$$

Table 22-5   Benzenoid Band of Linear Polycyclic Aromatics

	Benzene	Naphthalene	Anthracene	Naphthacene	Pentacene
λ_{max}, A	2,550	3,140	3,800	4,800	5,800
ε_{max}	230	316	7,900	11,000	12,600

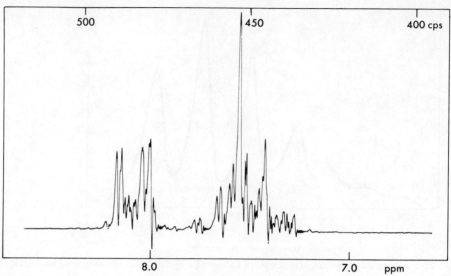

Figure 22-4   N.m.r. spectrum of nitrobenzene at 60 Mcps with reference to tetramethylsilane as 0.00 ppm.

Such a spectrum is much too complex to be analyzed by any very simple procedure. Nonetheless, as will be seen from Exercise 22-6, nuclear magnetic resonance can be useful in assigning structures to aromatic derivatives, particularly in conjunction with integrated line intensities and approximate values of the coupling constants between the ring hydrogens, as shown below.

EXERCISE 22-6   Establish the structures of the following benzene derivatives on the basis of their empirical formulas and n.m.r. spectra as shown in Figure 22-5. Remember that equivalent protons do not normally split each other's resonances (p. 40).

        a. C_8H_{10} c. $C_9H_{10}O_2$
        b. C_8H_7OCl d. C_9H_{12}

REACTIONS OF AROMATIC HYDROCARBONS

22-4 ELECTROPHILIC AROMATIC SUBSTITUTION

In this section we shall be mainly interested in the reactions of arenes that involve attack on the aromatic ring. We shall not at this point elaborate on the reactions of substituent groups around the ring, although, as we shall see later, these and reactions at the ring are not always independent.

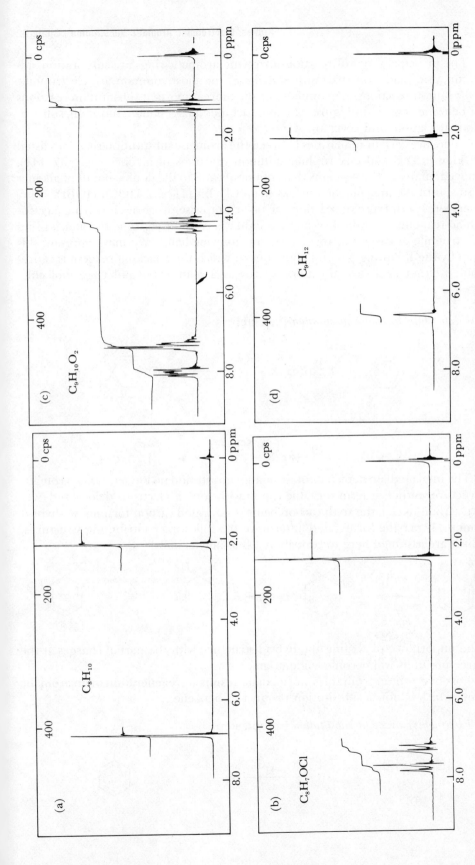

Figure 22-5 Proton n.m.r. spectra of some benzene derivatives at 60 Mcps with reference to TMS at 0 ppm (see Exercise 22-6).

The principal types of reactions involving aromatic rings are substitution, addition, and oxidation reactions. Of these, the most common are electrophilic substitution reactions. A summary of the more important substitution reactions of benzene is given in Figure 22-6 and includes halogenation, nitration, sulfonation, alkylation, and acylation.

There are certain similarities between the aromatic substitution reactions listed in Figure 22-6 and electrophilic addition reactions of alkenes (pp. 137–141). Indeed, many of the reagents that commonly add to the double bonds of alkenes also substitute an aromatic nucleus (e.g., Cl_2, Br_2, H_2SO_4, HOCl, HOBr). Furthermore, both types of reaction are polar, stepwise processes involving electrophilic reagents, and the key step for either is considered to be the attack of an electrophile at carbon to form a cationic intermediate. We may represent this step by the following general equations in which the attacking reagent is represented either as a formal cation, $X^{\oplus}$, or as a neutral but polarized molecule, $\overset{\delta\oplus}{X}\text{—}\overset{\delta\ominus}{Y}$:

Electrophilic aromatic substitution (first step)

Electrophilic addition to alkenes (first step)

The intermediate depicted for aromatic substitution no longer has an aromatic structure; rather, it is an unstable cation with four π electrons delocalized over five carbon nuclei, the sixth carbon being a saturated carbon forming sp^3-hybrid bonds. It may be formulated in terms of the following contributing structures, which are assumed here to contribute essentially equally.

The importance of writing the hybrid structure with the partial charges at the three positions will become evident later.

Loss of a proton from this intermediate results in regeneration of an aromatic ring, which is now a substitution product of benzene.

Electrophilic aromatic substitution (second step)

The gain in stabilization attendant on regeneration of the aromatic ring is sufficiently advantageous that this, rather than combination of the cation with $Y^\ominus$, is the chosen course of reaction. Herein lies the difference between aromatic substitution and alkene addition. In the case of alkenes, there is usually no substantial resonance energy to be gained by loss of a proton from the intermediate, which tends instead to react by combination with a nucleophilic reagent.

Electrophilic addition to alkenes (second step)

$$\overset{\oplus}{C}H_2\text{--}CH_2X \ + \ Y^\ominus \quad\longrightarrow\quad YCH_2\text{--}CH_2X$$

EXERCISE 22-7   Calculate from appropriate bond and stabilization energies the heats of reaction of chlorine with benzene to give (a) chlorobenzene and (b) 1,2-dichloro-3,5-cyclohexadiene. Your answer should indicate that substitution is energetically more favorable than addition.

EXERCISE 22-8   On what basis (other than the thermodynamic one suggested in Exercise 22-7) could we decide whether or not the following addition-elimination mechanism for bromination of benzene actually takes place?

EXERCISE 22-9   Explain with the aid of an energy diagram for aromatic nitration how one can account for the fact that hexadeuterobenzene undergoes nitration with nitric acid ul the same rate as ordinary benzene.

A. Nature of the Substituting Agent

It is important to realize that in aromatic substitution the electrophilic substituting agent, $X^\oplus$ or $\overset{\delta\oplus\ \ \delta\ominus}{X\text{--}Y}$, is not necessarily the reagent that is initially added to the reaction mixture. For example, nitration in mixtures of nitric and sulfuric acids is not usually brought about by attack of the nitric acid molecule on the aromatic compound, but by attack of a more electrophilic species, the *nitronium ion*, $NO_2^\oplus$. There is good evidence to show that this ion is formed from nitric acid and sulfuric acid according to the following equation:

$$HNO_3 \ + \ 2\,H_2SO_4 \quad\rightleftharpoons\quad NO_2^\oplus \ + \ H_3O^\oplus \ + \ 2\,HSO_4^\ominus$$

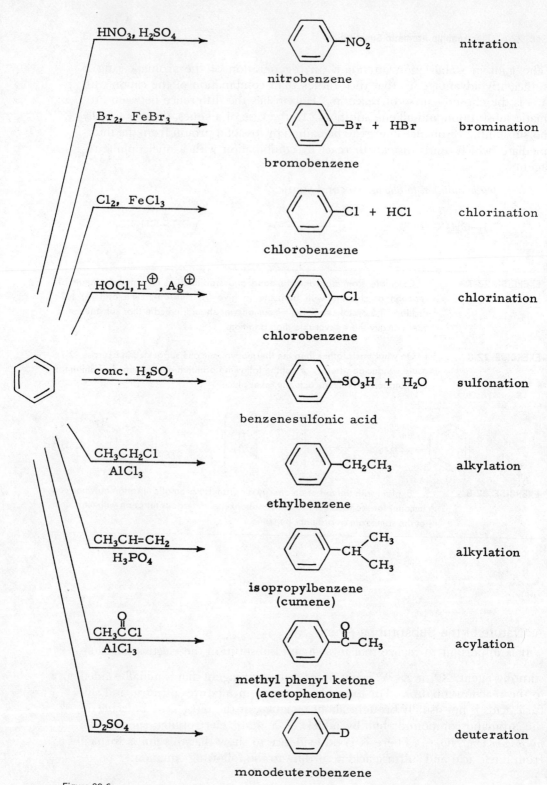

Figure 22-6

Typical benzene substitution reactions.

The nitronium ion so formed then attacks the aromatic ring to give an aromatic nitro compound.

nitrobenzene

In general, the function of a catalyst (which is so often necessary to promote aromatic substitution) is to generate an electrophilic substituting agent from the given reagents. Thus, it is necessary to consider carefully for each substitution reaction what the actual substituting agent might be.

B. Nitration

We have already mentioned that the nitronium ion, $NO_2^{\oplus}$, is the active nitrating agent in nitric acid–sulfuric acid mixtures. The nitration of toluene is a fairly typical example of a nitration that proceeds well using nitric acid in a $1:2$ mixture with sulfuric acid. The nitration product is a mixture of o-, m-, and p-nitrotoluenes.

| 62% | 5% | 33% |

The presence of any appreciable concentration of water in the reaction mixture is deleterious since water tends to reverse the reaction by which nitronium ion is formed.

$$NO_2^{\oplus} + H_2O \rightleftharpoons H_2NO_3^{\oplus} \xrightarrow{HSO_4^{\ominus}} HNO_3 + H_2SO_4$$

It follows that the potency of the mixed acids can be increased by using fuming nitric and fuming sulfuric acids, which have almost negligible water contents. With such mixtures, nitration of relatively unreactive compounds can be achieved. For example, p-nitrotoluene is far less reactive than toluene, but, when heated with an excess of nitric acid in fuming sulfuric acid, it can be converted successively to 2,4-dinitrotoluene and to 2,4,6-trinitrotoluene (TNT).

CH₃   CH₃   CH₃

[structure: p-nitrotoluene] → [structure: 2,4-dinitrotoluene] → [structure: 2,4,6-trinitrotoluene]

      HNO₃, 120°   HNO₃, 120°
    ─────────────   ─────────────
      SO₃, H₂SO₄   SO₃, H₂SO₄

NO₂   NO₂   NO₂

p-nitrotoluene   2, 4-dinitrotoluene   2, 4, 6-trinitrotoluene

There are several interesting features about the nitration reactions thus far discussed. In the first place, the conditions required for nitration of *p*-nitro-toluene would, in contrast, rapidly oxidize an alkene by cleavage of the double bond.

[structure: cyclohexene]   HNO₃
                           ─────────→   [structure of adipic acid]

adipic acid

We may also note that the nitration of toluene does not lead to equal amounts of the three possible mononitrotoluenes. The methyl substituent apparently orients the entering substituent preferentially to the *ortho* and *para* positions. This aspect of aromatic substitution will be discussed later in the chapter in conjunction with the effect of substituents on the reactivity of aromatic compounds.

EXERCISE 22-10   From the fact that nitrations in concentrated nitric acid are strongly retarded by added nitrate ions and strongly accelerated by small amounts of sulfuric acid, deduce the nature of the actual nitrating agent.

EXERCISE 22-11   Account for the fact that fairly reactive arenes (e.g., benzene, toluene, and ethylbenzene) are nitrated with excess nitric acid in nitromethane solution at a rate that is *independent* of the concentration of the arene (i.e., zeroth order). Does this mean that nitration of an equimolal mixture of benzene and toluene would necessarily give an equimolal mixture of nitrobenzene and nitrotoluenes? Why or why not?

C. Halogenation

The mechanism of halogenation is complicated by the fact that molecular halogens, Cl_2, Br_2, and I_2, form complexes with aromatic hydrocarbons. Although complex formation assists substitution by bringing the reactants in close proximity, it does not always follow that a substitution reaction will occur. A catalyst is usually necessary, and the catalysts most frequently used are metal halides that are capable of accepting electrons ($FeBr_3$, $AlCl_3$, and $ZnCl_2$). Their catalytic activity may be attributed to their ability to polarize the halogen-halogen bond in the following way:

$$\overset{\delta\oplus}{Br}\text{---}\overset{\delta\ominus}{Br}\text{----}FeBr_3$$

The positive end of the halogen dipole attacks the aromatic compound while the negative end is complexed with the catalyst. We may then represent the reaction sequence as follows, with the slow step being formation of a σ bond between $Br^{\oplus}$ and the aromatic ring:

$$C_6H_6 + Br_2 \rightleftharpoons \overset{\pi\text{-complex}}{\underset{}{\bigcirc}} \underset{\longleftarrow}{\overset{FeBr_3}{\longrightarrow}} \bigcirc$$

The order of reactivity of the halogens is $F_2 > Cl_2 > Br_2 > I_2$. Fluorine is too reactive to be of practical use for the preparation of aromatic fluorine compounds and indirect methods are necessary (see Chapter 23). Iodine is usually unreactive in most cases. It is sometimes stated that iodination fails because the reaction is reversed as the result of the reducing properties of the hydrogen iodide that is formed.

$$C_6H_6 + I_2 \quad \underset{\longleftarrow}{\longrightarrow} \quad C_6H_5I + HI$$

This view is not correct because, as Kekulé himself showed, iodobenzene is not reduced by hydriodic acid except at rather high temperatures. One way of achieving direct iodination is to convert molecular iodine to some more active species (perhaps $I^{\oplus}$) with an oxidizing agent such as nitric acid; with combinations of this kind, good yields of iodination products are obtained.

$$\text{(toluene)} \quad + \quad I_2 \quad \xrightarrow{\text{HNO}_3} \quad \text{o-iodotoluene} \quad + \quad \text{p-iodotoluene}$$

o-iodotoluene   p-iodotoluene

D. Alkylation

An important method of synthesis of alkylbenzenes utilizes an alkyl halide as the alkylating agent together with a metal halide catalyst, usually aluminum chloride.

$$\text{benzene} \quad + \quad CH_3CH_2Br \quad \xrightarrow[80°]{AlCl_3} \quad \text{ethylbenzene}$$

benzene   ethyl bromide   ethylbenzene
(large excess)

83%

The class of reaction is familiarly known as **Friedel-Crafts alkylation.** The metal-halide catalyst functions much as it does in halogenation reactions; that is, it provides a source (real or potential) of a positive substituting agent, which in this case is a carbonium ion.

$$\begin{array}{c}CH_3\\ \diagdown\\ \quad CH-Cl\\ \diagup\\ CH_3\end{array} + AlCl_3 \rightleftharpoons \begin{array}{c}CH_3\\ \diagdown \oplus\\ \quad CH---Cl-AlCl_3\\ \diagup \quad\quad\quad \ominus\\ CH_3\end{array}$$

$$\text{benzene} + \begin{array}{c}CH_3\\ \diagdown \oplus\\ \quad CH---Cl-AlCl_3\\ \diagup \quad\quad\quad \ominus\\ CH_3\end{array} \rightarrow \overset{\frac{1}{3}\oplus}{\underset{\frac{1}{3}\oplus}{\bigcirc}} \overset{H \quad CH(CH_3)_2}{}\; \overset{\frac{1}{3}\oplus}{}\; \overset{\ominus}{AlCl_4} \rightarrow \text{cumene} + AlCl_3 + HCl$$

cumene

(isopropylbenzene)

Alkylation is not restricted to alkyl halides; alcohols and alkenes may be used to advantage in the presence of acidic catalysts, such as H_3PO_4, H_2SO_4, HF, BF_3, or HF—BF_3. Ethylbenzene is made commercially from benzene and ethylene using phosphoric acid as the catalyst. Cumene is made similarly from benzene and propylene.

Under these conditions, the carbonium ion, which is the active substituting agent, is generated by protonation of the alkene.

$$CH_2=CH_2 \quad + \quad H^\oplus \quad \rightleftharpoons \quad CH_3CH_2^\oplus$$

$$CH_3CH=CH_2 \quad + \quad H^\oplus \quad \rightleftharpoons \quad CH_3\overset{\oplus}{C}HCH_3$$

EXERCISE 22-12 Write a mechanism for the alkylation of benzene with isopropyl alcohol catalyzed by boron trifluoride.

E. Acylation

Acylation and alkylation of arenes are closely related. The reaction effectively introduces an acyl group, RCO—, into an aromatic ring, and the product is an aryl ketone. The acylating reagents commonly used are acid halides, RCOCl, or anhydrides, (RCO)$_2$O. The catalyst is usually aluminum chloride, and its function is to generate the active substituting agent, which potentially is an acyl cation.

$$CH_3COCl \quad + \quad AlCl_3 \quad \rightleftharpoons \quad CH_3\overset{\oplus}{C}O \text{---} \overset{\ominus}{Cl}\text{--}AlCl_3$$

methyl phenyl ketone
(acetophenone)

Acylation differs from alkylation in that reaction is usually carried out in a solvent, commonly carbon disulfide or nitrobenzene. Furthermore, acylation requires more catalyst than alkylation since much of the catalyst is effectively removed by complex formation with the product ketone.

$$C_6H_5COCH_3 \ + \ AlCl_3 \ \rightleftharpoons \ \begin{array}{c} C_6H_5 \\ \diagdown \\ CH_3 \diagup \end{array} C{=}O\text{---}AlCl_3$$

1:1-complex

When an acylating reagent such as carboxylic anhydride is used, still more catalyst is required since some is consumed in converting the acyl compound to the acyl cation.

$$(RCO)_2O \ + \ 2AlCl_3 \ \longrightarrow \ R\overset{\oplus}{C}O \ \ \overset{\ominus}{AlCl_4} \ + \ RCO_2AlCl_2$$

Unlike alkylation, acylation is easily controlled to give monosubstitution because, once an acyl group is attached to a benzene ring, it is not possible to introduce a second acyl group into the same ring. For this reason, arenes are sometimes best prepared by acylation, followed by reduction of the carbonyl group with zinc and hydrochloric acid (p. 329). For example, n-propylbenzene is best prepared by this two-step route since, as we have noted, the direct alkylation of benzene with n-propyl chloride may give considerable cumene and polysubstitution products.

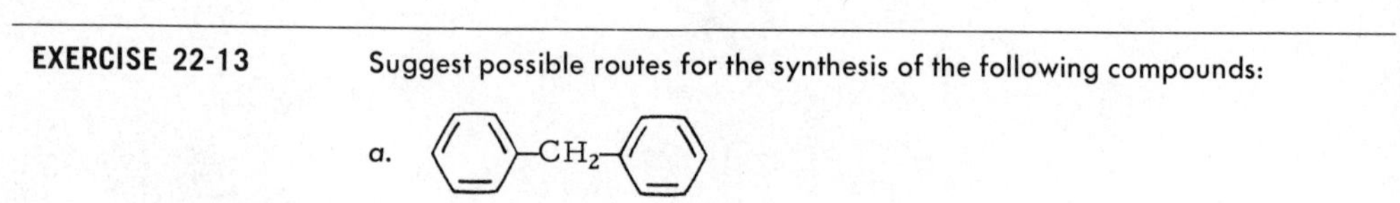

propionyl chloride   n-propylbenzene

EXERCISE 22-13   Suggest possible routes for the synthesis of the following compounds:

a.

b.

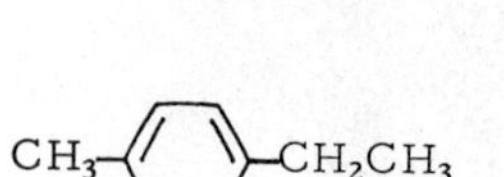

c.

F. Sulfonation

Substitution of the sulfonic acid (—SO₃H) group for a hydrogen of an aromatic hydrocarbon is usually carried out by heating the hydrocarbon with a slight excess of concentrated or fuming sulfuric acid.

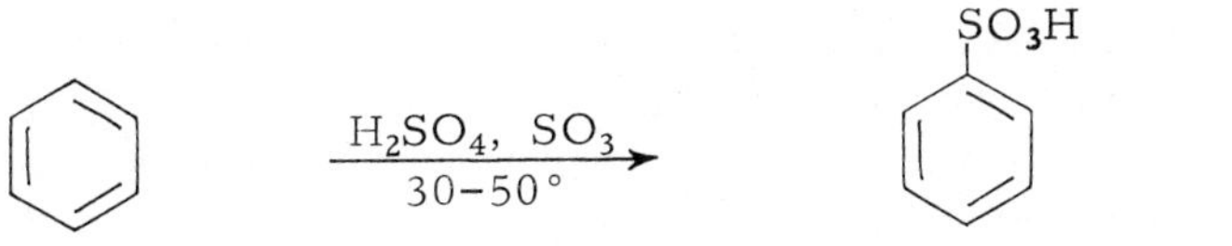

benzenesulfonic acid

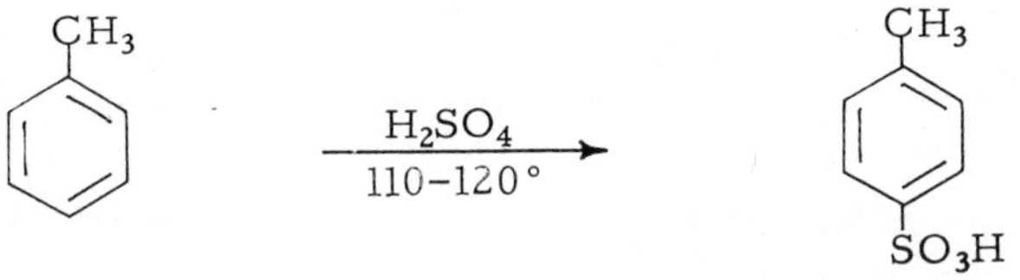

p-toluenesulfonic acid

The actual sulfonating agent is normally the SO_3 molecule, which, although it is a neutral reagent, has a powerfully electrophilic sulfur atom.

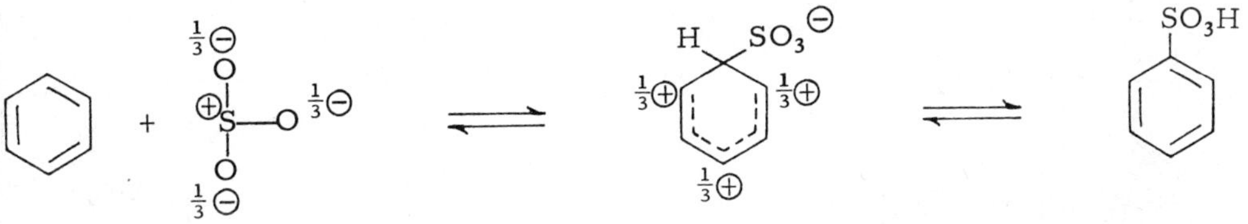

G. Deuteration

It is possible to replace the ring hydrogens of many aromatic compounds by exchange with deuterosulfuric acid. The mechanism is analogous to other electrophilic substitutions.

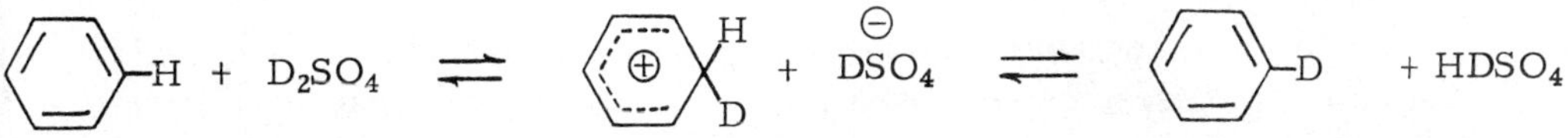

Perdeuterobenzene can be made from benzene in good yield if a sufficiently large excess of deuterosulfuric acid is used. Deuteration might appear to be competitive with sulfonation but actually deuteration occurs under much milder conditions.

22-5   EFFECT OF SUBSTITUENTS ON REACTIVITY AND ORIENTATION IN ELECTROPHILIC AROMATIC SUBSTITUTION

In planning syntheses based on substitution reactions of mono- or polysubstituted benzenes, it is imperative to be able to predict in advance which of the available positions of the ring are most likely to be substituted. This is now possible with a rather high degree of certainty, thanks to the work of many chemists over the last 100 years. Few, if any other, problems in organic chemistry have received so much attention, and there is now accumulated enough data on the orienting and reactivity effects of ring substituents in electrophilic substitution to permit the formulation of some very valuable generalizations.

Basically, three problems are involved in the substitution reactions of aromatic compounds: (*a*) proof of the structures of the possible isomers, *o*, *m*, and *p*, that are formed; (*b*) the percentage of each isomer formed, if the product is a mixture; and (*c*) the reactivity of the compound being substituted relative to some standard substance, usually benzene. Originally, the identity of each isomer formed was established by **Körner's absolute method,** which involves determining how many isomers each will give on further substitution, this number being diagnostic of the particular isomer (see Exercise 22-1). In practice, Körner's method is often very tedious and lengthy, and it is now primarily of historical interest except in its application to substitution reactions of unusual types of aromatic systems. For benzenoid compounds, structures can usually be established with the aid of correlations between spectroscopic properties and positions of substitution, as we have indicated earlier in this chapter. Also, it is often possible to convert the isomers to compounds of known structure by reactions that do not lead to rearrangement. For example, trifluoromethylbenzene on nitration gives only one product, which has been shown to be the *meta*-nitro derivative by conversion to the known *m*-nitrobenzoic acid.

A. The Pattern of Orientation in Aromatic Substitution

The reaction most studied in connection with the orientation problem is nitration, but the principles established also apply for the most part to the related reactions of halogenation, sulfonation, alkylation, and acetylation. Some illustrative data for the nitration of a number of mono-substituted benzene derivatives are given in Table 22-6. The orientation data are here expressed as the percentage of *ortho*, *meta*, and *para* isomers formed, and the rate data are over-all rates relative to benzene. Rates are also expressed as **partial rate factors,** symbolized as f_o, f_m, and f_p, which are respectively the rate of substitution at *one* of the *ortho*, *meta*, and *para* positions relative to *one* of the six equivalent positions in benzene. Consideration of the partial rate factors is particularly useful, since it permits one to tell at a glance if, for example, a substituent gives *ortho-para* substitution with activation ($f_o, f_p > 1$), but *meta* substitution with deactivation ($f_m < 1$).

EXERCISE 22-14 Calculate the partial-rate factors for each different position in the mononitration of biphenyl, given that the over-all reaction rate relative to benzene is 40, and the products are 68% o-, 1% m- and 31% p-nitrobiphenyl. (Remember, there are *two* benzene rings in biphenyl).

Inspection of the data in Table 22-6 shows that each substituent falls into one of three categories:

1. Those substituents [e.g., CH_3 and —$C(CH_3)_3$] which **activate all** the ring positions relative to benzene ($f > 1$), but are more activating for the *ortho* and *para* positions than for the *meta* position. These substituents lead to predominance of the *ortho* and *para* isomers. As a class, they give *o,p*-**orientation with activation.** Other examples, in addition to those included in Table 22-6, are —OH, —OCH_3, —NR_2, and —$NHCOCH_3$.

2. Those substituents (e.g., Cl, Br, and CH_2Cl) which **deactivate all** of the ring positions ($f < 1$) but deactivate the *ortho* and *para* positions less than the *meta* position so that formation of the *ortho* and *para* isomers is favored. These substituents are classified as giving *o,p*-**orientation with deactivation.**

Table 22-6 Orientation and Rate Data for Nitration of Some Monosubstituted Benzene Derivatives

Substituent, R	Orientation			Relative reactivity	Partial rate factors		
	$\% \, o$	$\% \, m$	$\% \, p$		f_o	f_m	f_p
—CH_3	56.5	3.5	40	24	42	2.5	58
—$C(CH_3)_3$	12.0	8.5	79.5	15.7	5.5	4.0	75
—CH_2Cl	32.0	15.5	52.5	0.302	0.29	0.14	0.951
—Cl	29.6	0.9	68.9	0.033	0.029	0.0009	0.137
—Br	36.5	1.2	62.4	0.030	0.033	0.0011	0.112
—NO_2	6.4	93.2	0.3	$\sim 10^{-7}$	1.8×10^{-6}	2.8×10^{-5}	2×10^{-7}
—$CO_2C_2H_5$	28.3	68.4	3.3	0.0003	2.5×10^{-4}	6×10^{-4}	5×10^{-5}
—CF_3		100					
—$\overset{\oplus}{N}(CH_3)_3$		89	11				

3. Those substituents [e.g., —NO$_2$, —CO$_2$C$_2$H$_5$, —$\overset{\oplus}{N}$(CH$_3$)$_3$, and —CF$_3$] that
   deactivate **all** the ring positions ($f < 1$) but deactivate the *ortho* and *para*
   positions more than the *meta* position. Hence, mostly the *meta* isomer is
   formed. These substituents give *meta* **orientation with deactivation.**

There is no known example of a substituent that activates the ring and, at the
same time, directs an electrophilic reagent preferentially to the *meta* position.

A more comprehensive list of substituents which fall into one of the three main
categories is given in Table 22-7 and it may be convenient to refer to this table
when in doubt as to the orientation characteristics of particular substituents.
An explanation of these substituent effects follows, which should make clear the
criteria whereby predictions of the behavior of other substituents can be made
with considerable confidence.

Table 22-7   Orientation and Reactivity Effects of Ring Substituents

o,p-Orientation with activation	*o,p*-Orientation with deactivation	*m*-Orientation with deactivation
—OH	—CH$_2$Cl	—NO$_2$
—O$^{\ominus}$	—F	—$\overset{\oplus}{N}$H$_3$
—OR	—Cl	—$\overset{\oplus}{N}$R$_3$
—OC$_6$H$_5$	—Br	—$\overset{\oplus}{P}$R$_3$
—NH$_2$	—I	—$\overset{\oplus}{S}$R$_2$
—NR$_2$	—CH=CHNO$_2$	—$\overset{\oplus}{I}$C$_6$H$_5$
—NHCOCH$_3$		—CF$_3$
—alkyl (e.g., CH$_3$)		—CCl$_3$
—aryl (e.g., C$_6$H$_5$)		—SO$_3$H
		—SO$_2$R
		—CO$_2$H
		—CO$_2$R
		—CONH$_2$
		—CHO
		—COR
		—C≡N

B. Electrical Effects

One very important effect of substituent groups on aromatic substitution is
the inductive effect which we have encountered previously in connection with
the ionization of carboxylic acids (pp. 369–370). An electron-attracting group
($-I$ effect) will exert an electrostatic effect such as to destabilize a positively
charged intermediate, while an electron-donating group ($+I$ effect) will have

the opposite effect. We shall illustrate this simple principle, using the $(CH_3)_3\overset{\oplus}{N}$— group as an example. This group is strongly electron-attracting and, if we write the hybrid structure of the substitution intermediate with the group X representing some electrophilic substituting agent, we see at once that the charge produced in the ring is unfavorable when the $(CH_3)_3\overset{\oplus}{N}$— substituent is present, particularly for substitution at the *ortho* and *para* positions where adjacent atoms would carry *like* charges. Thus, although all three intermediates should then be less stable than the corresponding intermediate for benzene, the *ortho* and *para* intermediates should be less favorable than the one for *meta* substitution. This should lead to *m*-orientation with deactivation, as indeed is observed.

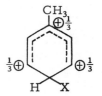

ortho substitution   *meta* substitution   *para* substitution

Other substituents that are strongly electron-attracting and that also orient *meta* with deactivation include —NO_2, —CF_3, —$\overset{\oplus}{P}(CH_3)_3$, —$SO_3H$, —$CO_2H$, —$CO_2CH_3$, —$CONH_2$, —CHO, —$COC_6H_5$, and —C≡N.

EXERCISE 22-15   Explain why the —CF_3, —NO_2, and —CHO groups should be *meta*-orienting with deactivation.

The activating and *o,p* orienting influence of alkyl substituents can be also rationalized on the basis of inductive effects. Thus, the substitution intermediates for *o*-, *p*-, and *m*-substitution of toluene are stabilized by the capacity of a methyl group to release electrons ($+I$ effect) and partially compensate for the positive charge.

ortho substitution   *meta* substitution   *para* substitution

Furthermore, the stabilization is most effective in *ortho* and *para* substitution where part of the positive charge is adjacent to the methyl substituent. (For other examples of stabilization of positive carbon by alkyl groups see p. 146.) The result is *o,p*-orientation with activation.

In addition to the inductive effects of substituents, conjugation effects may be a factor in orientation and are frequently decisive. This is especially true of substituents that carry one or more pairs of unshared electron pairs on the atom immediately attached to the ring (e.g., —ÖH, —Ö:$^{\ominus}$, —ÖCH$_3$, —ṄH$_2$, —ṄHCOCH$_3$, —Cl̈:). An electron pair so situated helps to stabilize the positive charge of the substitution intermediate, as the following resonance forms will indicate for *ortho* and *para* substitution of anisole (methyl phenyl ether).

[3]   *ortho* substitution

[4]   *para* substitution

In *meta* substitution, however, the charge is not similarly stabilized as no resonance structures analogous to [3] or [4] can be written. Accordingly, the favored orientation is *ortho-para;* but whether substitution proceeds with activation or deactivation depends on the strength of the inductive effect of the substituent. For example, halogen substituents are strongly electronegative and deactivate the ring at all positions; yet they strongly orient *ortho* and *para* through conjugation of the unshared electron pairs. Apparently the inductive effect is strong enough to reduce the over-all reactivity, but not powerful enough to determine the orientation. Thus for *para* substitution of chlorobenzene the intermediate stage is formed less readily than in the substitution of benzene itself.

(unfavorable, since electropositive
carbon is next to chlorine)

Other groups such as —NH$_2$, —NHCOCH$_3$, and —OCH$_3$ are electron-at-tracting but much less so than the halogens, and the inductive effect is com-pletely overshadowed by the conjugation effect. Therefore, substitution pro-ceeds with *o,p*-orientation and activation. The most activating common sub-stituent is —$\ddot{\text{O}}$:$^\ominus$, which combines a large electron-donating inductive effect with a conjugation effect.

EXERCISE 22-16   Explain why the nitration and halogenation of biphenyl goes with activation at the *ortho* and *para* positions but with deactivation at the *meta* position. Suggest a reason why biphenyl is more reactive than 2,2'-dimethylbiphenyl in nitration.

EXERCISE 22-17   Explain why the bromination of aniline gives 2,4,6-tribromoaniline, whereas the nitration of aniline with mixed acids gives *m*-nitroaniline.

C. Orientation in Disubstituted Benzenes

The orientation and reactivity effects of substituents discussed for the sub-stitution of monosubstituted benzenes also hold for disubstituted benzenes ex-cept that the directing influence now comes from two groups. Qualitatively, the effects of both substituents are additive. We would therefore expect *p*-nitrotoluene to be less reactive than toluene because of the deactivating effect of a nitro group. Also, the most likely position of substitution should be, and is, *ortho* to the methyl group and *meta* to the nitro group.

When the two substituents have opposed orientation effects, it is not always easy to predict what products will be obtained. For example 2-methoxy-acet-anilide has two powerful *o,p*-directing substituents, —OCH$_3$ and —NHCOCH$_3$. Nitration of this compound gives mainly the 4-nitro derivative, which indicates that the —NHCOCH$_3$ exerts a stronger influence than OCH$_3$.

EXERCISE 22-18   Predict the favored positions of substitution in the nitration of the following compounds:

a.

b.

c.

d.

e.

f.

g.

(consider the character of the various resonance structures for substitution in the 1- and 2-positions).

22-6 SUBSTITUTION REACTIONS OF POLYNUCLEAR AROMATIC HYDROCARBONS

Although naphthalene, phenanthrene, and anthracene resemble benzene in many respects, they are more reactive than benzene in both substitution and addition reactions. This is expected theoretically because quantum mechanical calculations show that the loss in stabilization energy for the first step in electrophilic substitution or addition decreases progressively from benzene to anthracene; therefore the reactivity in substitution and addition reactions should increase from benzene to anthracene.

EXERCISE 22-19   *a.* Calculate from the data of Table 9-2 (p. 193) the over-all loss in stabilization energy for the addition of chlorine to the 1,4-positions of naphthalene and to the 9,10-positions of phenanthrene. Which is likely to be the more favorable reaction?

b. Predict whether anthracene is more likely to undergo electrophilic substitution at the 1-, 2-, or 9-position. Show your reasoning.

In considering the properties of the polynuclear hydrocarbons relative to benzene, it is important to recognize that we neither expect nor find that all of the carbon-carbon bonds in polynuclear hydrocarbons are alike or correspond to benzene bonds in being halfway between single and double bonds. This we may predict from the hybrid structures of these molecules, derived by considering all of the electron-pairing schemes without formal bonds, there being three such structures for naphthalene, four for anthracene, and five for phenanthrene.

Naphthalene:

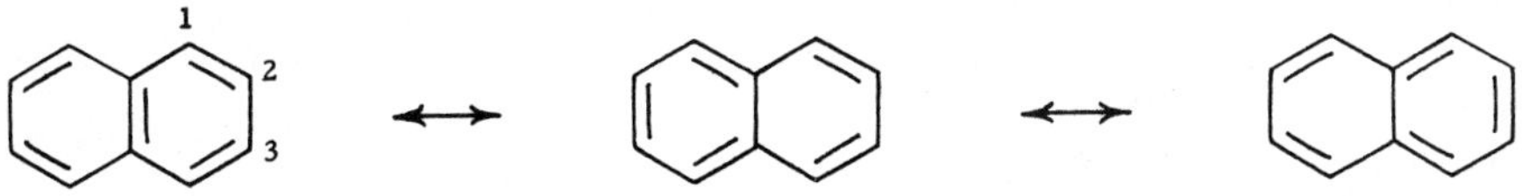

Anthracene:

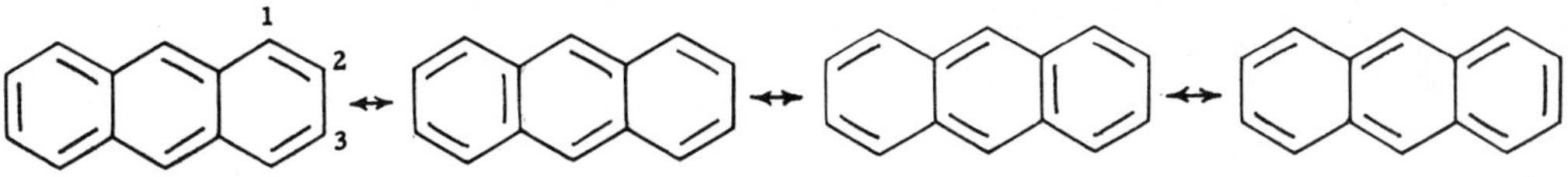

Phenanthrene:

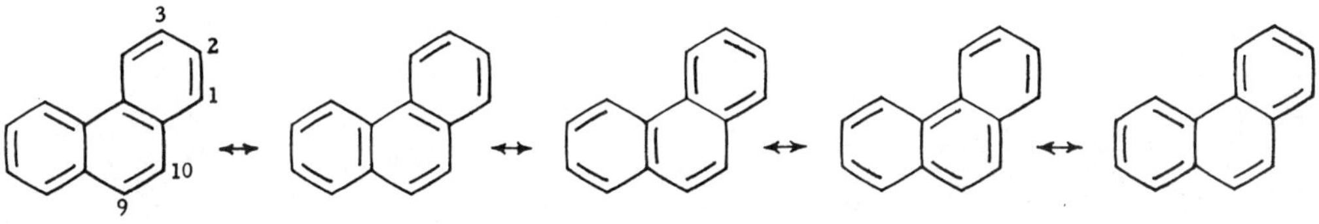

If we assume that each structure contributes equally to its resonance hybrid, then, in the case of naphthalene, the 1,2 and 2,3 bonds have $\frac{2}{3}$ and $\frac{1}{3}$ double-bond character, respectively. Accordingly, the 1,2-bond should be shorter than the 2,3-bond, and this has been verified by X-ray diffraction studies of crystalline naphthalene.

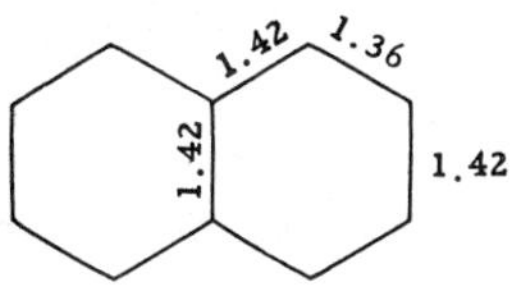

bond lengths of naphthalene, A units

Similarly, the 1,2-bond of anthracene should have $\frac{3}{4}$ double-bond character and should be shorter than the 2,3-bond, which has only $\frac{1}{4}$ double-bond character. The 1,2-bond is indeed shorter than the 2,3-bond.

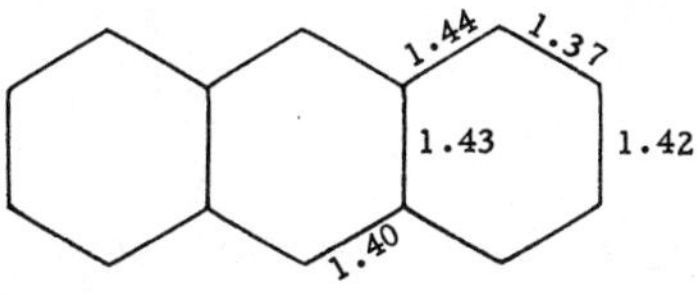

bond lengths of anthracene, A units

The trend towards greater inequality of the carbon-carbon bonds in polynuclear hydrocarbons is very pronounced in phenanthrene. Here, the 9,10-
bond is predicted to have $\frac{4}{5}$ double-bond character, and experiment verifies that
this bond does resemble an alkene double bond, as we shall see in subsequent
discussions.

A. Naphthalene

In connection with orientation in the substitution of naphthalene, the picture
is often complex, although the 1-position is most reactive.

$$\xrightarrow{\text{HNO}_3,\ \text{H}_2\text{SO}_4}$$

1-nitronaphthalene

$$\xrightarrow[\text{50\% CH}_3\text{CO}_2\text{H–H}_2\text{O}]{\text{Br}_2}$$

1-bromonaphthalene   2-bromonaphthalene
        99%   1%

$$\xrightarrow[\text{CS}_2\ -15°]{\text{CH}_3\text{COCl–AlCl}_3}$$

1-acetonaphthalene   2-acetonaphthalene
        75%   25%

$$\xrightarrow[\substack{\text{C}_6\text{H}_5\text{NO}_2,\ \text{AlCl}_3 \\ 25°}]{\text{CH}_3\text{COCl}}$$

Sometimes, relatively small changes in the reagents and conditions change the
pattern of orientation. One example is sulfonation which is a reversible reaction
leading to 1-naphthalene sulfonic acid at 120° but to the 2-isomer on prolonged

reaction or at temperatures above 160°C. Another example is supplied by Friedel-Crafts acylation, in which, in carbon disulfide, the major product is the 1-isomer while in nitrobenzene the major product is the 2-isomer.

EXERCISE 22-20　　　How would you go about proving that the acylation of naphthalene in the 2-position in nitrobenzene solution is not the result of thermodynamic control?

Normally, substitution of naphthalene occurs more readily at the 1-position than at the 2-position. This may be accounted for on the basis that the most favorable resonance structures for either the 1- or the 2-substituted intermediate are those which have one ring fully aromatic. We see then that 1-substitution is more favorable than 2-substitution since the positive charge in the 1-intermediate can be distributed over two positions, leaving one aromatic ring unchanged; but this is not possible for the 2-intermediate without affecting the benzenoid structure of both rings.

1-substitution:

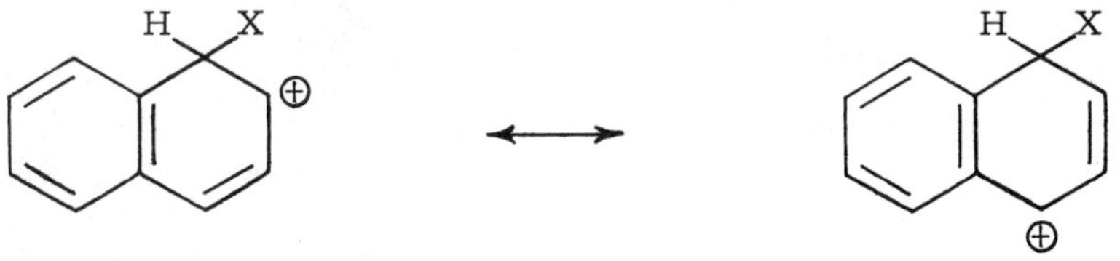

2-substitution:

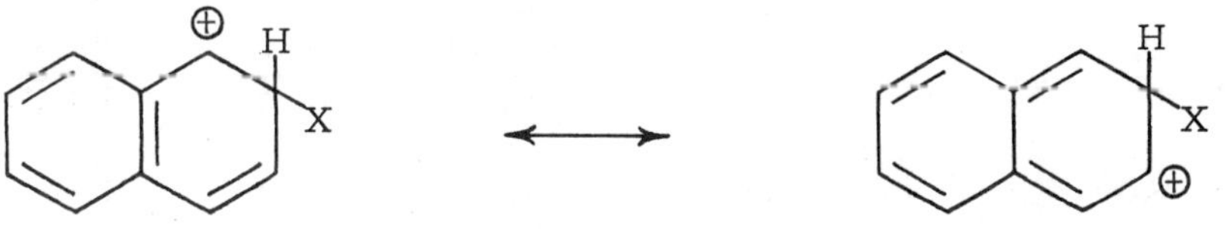

EXERCISE 22-21　　　Predict the orientation in the following reactions:
a. 1-methylnaphthalene + Br_2
b. 2-methylnaphthalene + HNO_3
c. 2-naphthoic acid + HNO_2

B. Phenanthrene

The substitution characteristics of the higher hydrocarbons are more complex than for naphthalene. For example, phenanthrene can be nitrated and sulfonated, but the products are mixtures of 1-, 2-, 3-, 4-, and 9-substituted phenanthrenes.

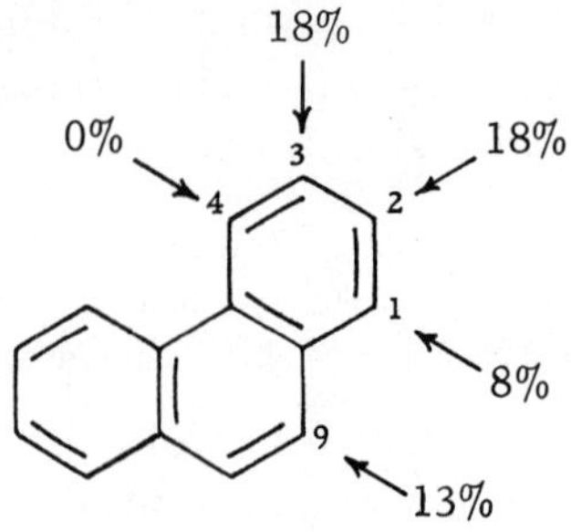

sulfonation

nitration

(percentages are yields of sulfonic acids with H_2SO_4 at 60°. At 120°, mostly the 2- and 3-sulfonic acids are obtained)

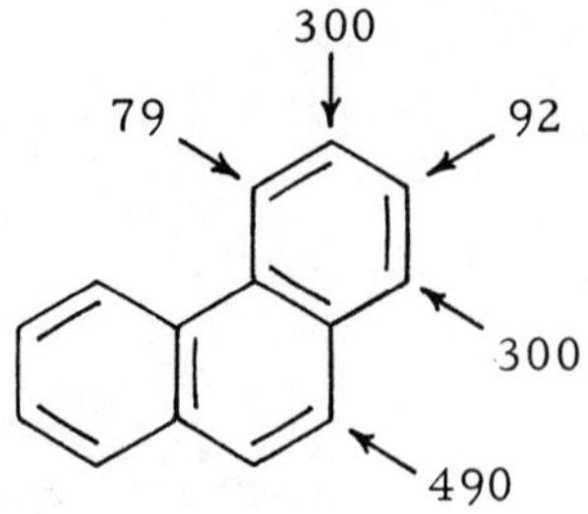

(figures at the 9, 1, 2, 3 and 4 positions are partial rate factors)

The 9,10-bond in phenanthrene is quite reactive; in fact, almost as much so as an alkene double bond. Addition therefore occurs fairly readily; in fact halogenation can give both 9,10-addition and 9-substitution products by the following scheme:

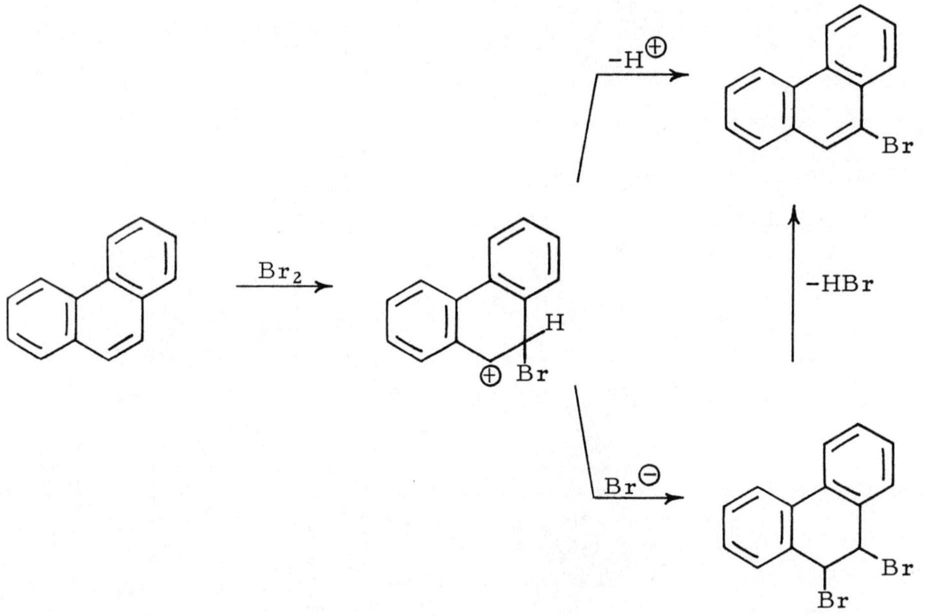

C. Anthracene

It is found that anthracene is even more reactive than phenanthrene and has a greater tendency to add to the 9,10-positions than to substitute. However, the addition products of nitration and halogenation readily give the 9-substitution products.

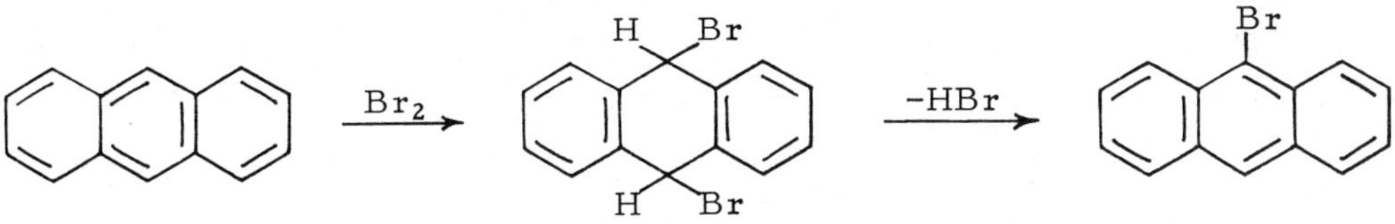

EXERCISE 22-22   Show how one can predict qualitatively the character of the 1,2-bond in acenaphthylene.

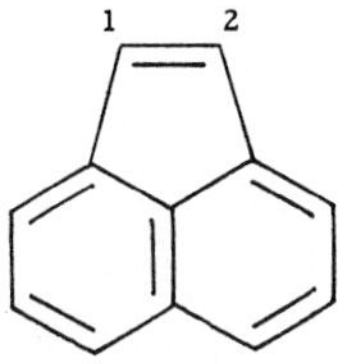

22-7   NONBENZENOID AROMATIC COMPOUNDS

A. Azulene

There are a number of compounds that possess some measure of aromatic character typical of benzene, but that do not possess a benzenoid ring. Appropriately, they are classified as nonbenzenoid aromatic compounds. One example of interest is azulene, which is isomeric with naphthalene and has a five- and a seven-membered ring fused through adjacent carbons.

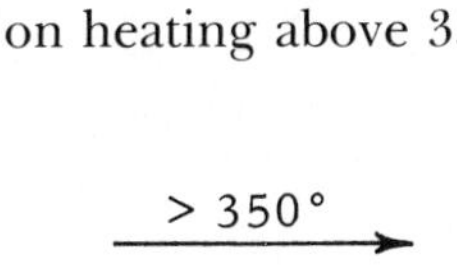

azulene

As the name implies, it is deep blue in color. It is less stable than naphthalene and isomerizes quantitatively on heating above 350° in the absence of air.

Azulene can be represented as a hybrid of neutral and ionic structures.

The postulated direction of polarization is the one that corresponds to putting greater weight on those ionic structures having six electrons in both the five- and seven-membered rings (see p. 190).

B. Cycloöctatetraene

Of equal interest to azulene is cycloöctatetraene, which is a bright-yellow, non-benzenoid, *nonaromatic* compound with alternating single and double bonds. If the carbons of cycloöctatetraene were to occupy the corners of a regular planar octagon, the C—C—C bond angles would have to be 135°. Apparently the resonance energy gained in the planar structure is not sufficient to overcome the unfavorable angle strain and cycloöctatetraene exists in a "tub" structure with alternating single and double bonds (see pp. 192–195).

planar   tub

There is, however, n.m.r. evidence that indicates that the tub form is in quite rapid equilibrium with a very small amount of the planar form at room temperature. Probably there is not much more than 10-kcal energy difference between the two forms.

Cycloöctatetraene can be readily prepared by polymerization of acetylene in the presence of nickel cyanide.

$$4HC\equiv CH \xrightarrow[50°]{Ni(CN)_2}$$

80–90%

With this reaction, cycloöctatetraene could be manufactured easily on a large scale; however, no profitable commercial uses of the substance have as yet been developed.

The chemistry of cycloöctatetraene is very interesting and unusual. Particularly noteworthy is the way in which it undergoes addition reactions with formation of bridged-ring products such as might be expected on the basis of "valence tautomerism" to bicyclo[4.2.0]2,4,7-octatriene.

Treatment of the bridged dichloride with strong bases causes elimination of hydrogen chloride and formation of chlorocycloöctatetraene.

C. Annulenes

There has been considerable interest for many years in the synthesis of conjugated cyclic polyalkenes with a large enough number of carbons in the ring to permit attainment of a strainless planar structure. Inspection of models shows that a strainless structure can only be achieved with two or more of the double bonds in *trans* configurations, and then only with a large enough ring that the "inside" hydrogens do not interfere with one another.

In discussing compounds of this type, it will be convenient to use the name **[n] annulene** to designate the simple conjugated cyclic polyalkenes, with *n* referring to the number of carbons in the ring—benzene being [6]annulene. The simplest conjugated cyclic polyolefin that could have a strainless planar ring

containing *trans* double bonds, except for interferences between the inside
hydrogens, is [10]annulene. Inside-hydrogen interferences are likely to be of

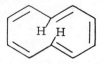

[10] annulene

at least some importance in all annulenes up to [30]annulene.

Several annulenes have now been synthesized (Sondheimer, 1959) and found
to be reasonably stable — at least much more so than could possibly be expected
for the corresponding open-chain conjugated polyenes. An elegant synthesis
of [18]annulene provides an excellent illustration of some of the more useful
steps for preparation of annulenes. The key reaction is oxidative coupling of
acetylenes by cupric acetate in pyridine solution.

$$2\,RC\equiv CH \quad \xrightarrow[\text{C}_5\text{H}_5\text{N}]{\text{Cu}^{II}} \quad RC\equiv C\text{--}C\equiv CR$$

This type of oxidative coupling with 1,5-hexadiyne gives a 6 per cent yield of
the cyclic trimer [5], which rearranges in the presence of potassium *t*-butoxide
to the brown, fully conjugated 1,2,7,8,13,14-tridehydro [18]annulene [6].

$$3\,HC\equiv C\text{--}CH_2\text{--}CH_2\text{--}C\equiv CH \quad \xrightarrow[\text{C}_5\text{H}_5\text{N}]{\text{Cu}^{II}}$$

[5]

$$K^{\oplus}\ {}^{\ominus}OC(CH_3)_3 \longrightarrow$$

[6]

$$\xrightarrow[\text{Pd(Pb)}]{\text{H}_2}$$

[18] annulene

Hydrogenation of [6] over a lead-poisoned palladium on calcium carbonate catalyst (the Lindlar catalyst, of general utility for hydrogenation of alkynes to alkenes) gives [18]annulene as a brown-red crystalline solid, reasonably stable in the presence of oxygen and light.

EXERCISE 22-24   Work out a synthesis of [20]annulene from the coupling product of allylmagnesium bromide with 1,4-dibromo-2-butene, which is reported to be 1,5,9-decatriene.

SUPPLEMENTARY EXERCISES

22-25   Write structural formulas for all of the possible isomers of C_8H_{10} containing one benzene ring. Show how many different mononitration products each could give if no carbon skeleton rearrangements occur but nitration is considered possible either in the ring or side chain. Name all of the mononitration products by an accepted system.

22-26   Write structural formulas (more than one might be possible) for aromatic substances that fit the following descriptions:
  a. C_8H_{10}, which can give only one theoretically possible ring nitration product
  b. $C_6H_3Br_3$, which can give three theoretically possible nitration products
  c. $C_6H_3Br_2Cl$, which can give two theoretically possible nitration products
  d. $C_8H_8(NO_2)_2$, which can give only two theoretically possible different ring mono-bromosubstitution products

22-27   1,3-Cyclohexadiene cannot be isolated from reduction of benzene by hydrogen over nickel. The isolable reduction product is always cyclohexane.
  a. Explain why the hydrogenation of benzene is difficult to stop at the 1,3-cyclohexadiene stage, even though 1,3-butadiene is relatively easy to reduce to butenes.
  b. How could an apparatus for determining heats of hydrogenation be used to obtain an accurate ΔH value for the reaction?

  c. Calculate a ΔH of combustion for benzene as 1,3,5-cyclohexatriene (no resonance) from bond energies and compare it with a calculated value for heat of combustion of benzene obtained from the experimental ΔH, $+5.9$ kcal, for the hydrogenation in (b).

22-28   Predict the most favorable position for mononitration for each of the following substances. Indicate whether the rate is greater or less than for the nitration of benzene. Give your reasoning in each case.
  a. fluorobenzene
  b. trifluoromethylbenzene
  c. acetophenone
  d. nitrosobenzene
  e. benzyldimethylamine
      oxide
  f. diphenylmethane

  g. p-methoxybromobenzene
  h. diphenyl sulfone
  i. p-t-butyltoluene
  j. $(C_6H_5)_2\overset{\oplus\ominus}{I}NO_3$
  k. m-diphenylbenzene (m-terphenyl)
  l. 4-acetylaminobiphenyl

22-29 Predict which of the following compounds may have some aromatic character. Give your reasons.

tropylium bromide

tropolone

[16] annulene

aceplieadylene

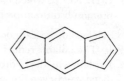

Aryl Halogen Compounds.
Nucleophilic Aromatic Substitution

The chemical behavior of aromatic halogen compounds depends largely upon whether the halogen is attached to carbon of the aromatic ring, as in bromo-benzene, or to carbon of an alkyl substituent, as in benzyl bromide. Compounds of the former type are referred to as aryl halides, and those of the latter type are called arylalkyl halides. In this chapter, we shall confine our attention to the preparation and reactions of aryl halides, with emphasis on the similarities and differences in properties of aryl halides and halides of types we have discussed in earlier chapters.

Aryl Halogen Compounds. Nucleophilic Aromatic Substitution

The general behavior of aryl halides is expected to be more like that of the vinyl halides than of other halides. Consequently it is no surprise to find that most aryl halides are usually much less reactive than alkyl or allyl halides toward nucleophilic reagents in either S_N1- or S_N2-type reactions. Thus, whereas ethyl bromide reacts easily with sodium methoxide in methanol to form methyl ethyl ether, vinyl bromide and bromobenzene completely fail to undergo nucleophilic displacement under similar conditions. Also, neither bromobenzene nor vinyl bromide reacts appreciably with boiling alcoholic silver nitrate solution even after many hours.

In contrast to phenyl halides, benzyl halides are quite reactive. In fact, they are analogous in reactivity to allyl halides (pp. 244–247) and are readily attacked by nucleophilic reagents in both S_N1- and S_N2-displacement reactions. The ability of benzyl halides to undergo S_N1 reactions is clearly related to the stability of the benzyl cation, the positive charge of which is expected, on the basis of the resonance structures [1a] through [1d], to be extensively delocalized.

[1a]   [1b]   [1c]   [1d]

When the halogen substituent is located two or more carbons from the aromatic ring, as in 2-phenylethyl bromide, $C_6H_5CH_2CH_2Br$, the pronounced activating effect evident in benzyl halides disappears, and the reactivity of the halide is essentially that of a primary alkyl halide (e.g., $CH_3CH_2CH_2Br$). Since, in general, the chemistry of arylalkyl halides is related more closely to that of aliphatic derivatives than to aryl halides, we shall defer further discussion of arylalkyl halides to Chapter 26, which is concerned with the chemistry of aromatic side-chain derivatives.

23-1 PHYSICAL PROPERTIES OF ARYL HALOGEN COMPOUNDS

There is nothing very unexpected about most of the physical properties of aryl halides. They are slightly polar substances and accordingly have boiling points approximating those of hydrocarbons of the same molecular weights; their solubility in water is very low, whereas their solubility in nonpolar organic solvents is high. In general, they are colorless, oily, highly refractive liquids with characteristic aromatic odors and with densities greater than that of water. A representative list of halides and their physical properties is given in Table 23-1.

With respect to the infrared spectra of aryl halides, correlations between structure and absorption bands of aromatic carbon-halogen bonds have not proved to be useful.

Table 23-1   Physical Properties of Aryl Halides

Name	B.p., °C	M.p., °C	$d^{20/4}$	n_D^{25}
fluorobenzene	85	−42	1.024	1.4646 [22.8]
chlorobenzene	132	−45	1.1066	1.5248
bromobenzene	155	−31	1.4991 [15/15]	1.5598
iodobenzene	189	−31	1.832	1.6214 [18.5]
o-chlorotoluene	159	−34	1.0817	1.5238
m-chlorotoluene	162	−48	1.0732	1.5214 [19]
p-chlorotoluene	162	7.5	1.0697	1.5199 [19]
1-chloronaphthalene	263		1.1938	1.6332 [20]
2-chloronaphthalene	265	55		

23-2 PREPARATION OF ARYL HALIDES

Many of the methods that are commonly used for the preparation of alkyl halides simply do not work when applied to the preparation of aryl halides. Thus, it is not possible to convert phenol to chlorobenzene by reagents such as HCl—ZnCl$_2$, SOCl$_2$, and PCl$_3$, which convert ethanol to ethyl chloride. In fact, there is no very practical route at all for conversion of phenol to chlorobenzene. In this situation, it is not surprising that some of the methods by which aryl halides are prepared are not often applicable to the preparation of alkyl halides. One of these methods is direct halogenation of benzene or its derivatives with chlorine or bromine in the presence of a metal halide catalyst, as discussed in Chapter 22, pp. 546–548.

Direct halogenation of monosubstituted benzene derivatives often gives a mixture of products, which may or may not contain practical amounts of the desired isomer. A more useful method of introducing a halogen substituent into a particular position of an aromatic ring involves the reaction of an aromatic primary amine with nitrous acid under conditions that lead to the formation of an aryldiazonium salt. Decomposition of the diazonium salt to an aryl chloride or bromide is effected by warming a solution of the diazonium salt with cuprous chloride or bromide in excess of the corresponding halogen acid. The method

is known as the **Sandmeyer reaction.**

For the formation of aryl iodides from diazonium salts, the cuprous catalyst is not necessary since iodide ion is sufficient to cause decomposition of the diazonium salt. However, oxidation and reduction are probably involved here also since considerable iodine is liberated during the reaction.

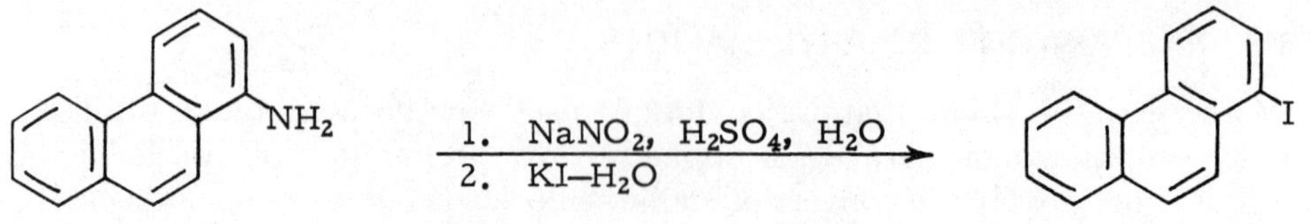

1-phenanthrylamine

1. NaNO$_2$, H$_2$SO$_4$, H$_2$O
2. KI–H$_2$O

1-iodophenanthrene
53%

Aryl fluorides may also be prepared from diazonium salts if the procedure is slightly modified. The amine is diazotized in the usual way; then fluoboric acid or a fluoborate salt is added, which usually causes precipitation of a sparingly soluble diazonium fluoborate. The salt is collected and thoroughly dried, then carefully heated to the decomposition point, the products being an aryl fluoride, nitrogen, and boron trifluoride.

$$C_6H_5N_2^{\oplus}\ BF_4^{\ominus} \xrightarrow{\text{heat}} C_6H_5F\ +\ N_2\ +\ BF_3$$

The reaction is known as the **Schiemann reaction.** An example (which gives a rather better than usual yield) follows:

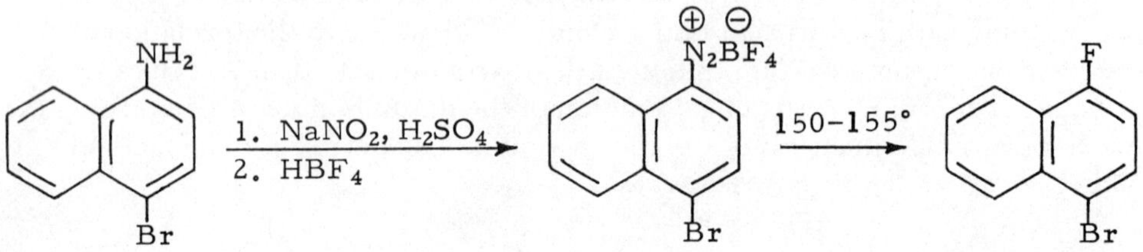

4-bromo-1-
naphthylamine

1. NaNO$_2$, H$_2$SO$_4$
2. HBF$_4$

4-bromonaphthalene
–1-diazonium fluoroborate

150–155°

1-fluoro-4-
bromonaphthalene
97%

The arylamines necessary for the preparation of aryl halides by the Sandmeyer and Schiemann reactions are usually prepared by reduction of the corresponding nitro compounds (see Chapter 24), which in turn are obtained by direct nitration of an aromatic compound. For example, although *m*-dichlorobenzene cannot be prepared conveniently by direct chlorination of benzene, it can be made by dinitration of benzene followed by reduction and the Sandmeyer reaction. In connection with this synthesis, it should be noted that tetrazotization (double diazotization) of 1,2- and 1,4-diaminobenzene derivatives is not as easy to achieve as with the 1,3-compound, because the 1,2- and 1,4-diaminobenzenes are very easily oxidized.

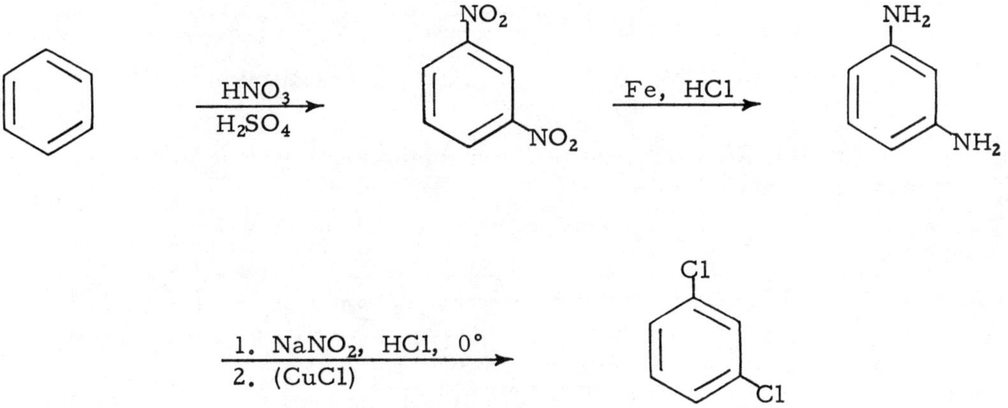

EXERCISE 23-1 Suggest a feasible synthesis of each of the following compounds based on benzene as the starting material:

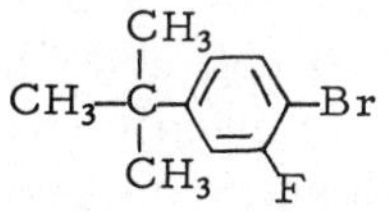

23-3 REACTIONS OF ARYL HALIDES

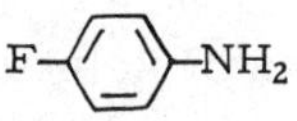

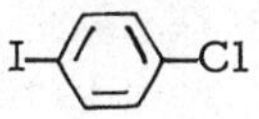

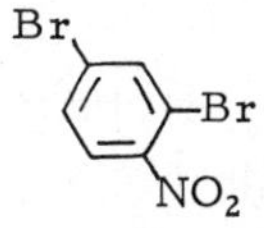

A. Organometallic Compounds from Aryl Halides

Grignard reagents can be prepared with fair ease from aryl bromides or iodides and magnesium metal.

$$C_6H_5Br + Mg \xrightarrow{\text{ether}} C_6H_5MgBr$$

phenylmagnesium bromide

Chlorobenzene and other aryl chlorides are usually unreactive unless added to the magnesium admixed with a more reactive halide. Ethylene dibromide is particularly useful as the second halide because it is converted to ethylene, which does not then contaminate the products, and it continually produces a fresh magnesium surface, which is sufficiently active to be able to react with the aryl chloride.

The reactions of arylmagnesium halides are analogous to those of alkylmagnesium halides (see Chapter 12) and require little further comment.

Aryllithiums can usually be prepared by direct reaction of lithium metal with chloro or bromo compounds.

$$C_6H_5Cl + 2 Li \xrightarrow{\text{ether}} C_6H_5Li + LiCl$$

phenyllithium

As with the Grignard reagents, aryllithiums react as one might expect by analogy with alkyllithiums.

EXERCISE 23-2   Suggest a method for preparing the following compounds from the indicated starting materials and any other necessary reagents:

a. p-ClC$_6$H$_4$C(CH$_3$)$_2$OH from benzene
b. 1-naphthoic acid from naphthalene

c. HO$_2$C—⟨benzene ring⟩—D from toluene

B. Nucleophilic Displacement Reactions of Activated Aryl Halides

While the simple aryl halides are inert to the usual nucleophilic reagents, considerable activation is produced by strongly electron-attracting substituents—provided these are located in either the *ortho* or *para* positions, or both. As one example, the displacement of chloride ion from 1-chloro-2,4-dinitrobenzene by dimethylamine occurs measurably fast in ethanol solution at room temperature. Under the same conditions, chlorobenzene completely fails to react; thus, the activating influence of the two nitro groups easily amounts to a factor of at least 10^8.

A related reaction is that of 2,4-dinitrofluorobenzene with peptides and proteins, which is used for analysis of the N-terminal amino acids in polypeptide chains. (See Chapter 20, p. 494.)

In general, the reactions of activated aryl halides bear a close resemblance to S$_N$2-displacement reactions of aliphatic halides. The same nucleophilic reagents are effective (e.g., CH$_3$O$^\ominus$, HO$^\ominus$, and RNH$_2$); the reactions are second order over-all—first order in halide and first order in nucleophile; and, for a given halide, the more nucleophilic the attacking reagent, the faster is the reaction. There must be more than a subtle difference in mechanism, however, since an aryl halide is unable to pass through the same type of transition state as an alkyl halide in S$_N$2 displacements.

EXERCISE 23-3   Why is the following mechanism of S_N2 substitution of an alkyl halide unlikely for aryl halides?

$$\overset{\ominus}{X}: \;+\; \overset{}{{>}}C{-}Y \;\rightleftharpoons\; \overset{\delta\ominus}{X}{-}{-}{-}{-}\overset{|}{\underset{/\backslash}{C}}{-}{-}{-}{-}\overset{\delta\ominus}{Y} \;\rightleftharpoons\; X{-}C{\overset{}{\diagdown}} \;+\; \overset{\ominus}{Y}:$$

transition state

A generally accepted mechanism of nucleophilic aromatic substitution visualizes the reaction as proceeding in two steps closely analogous to those postulated for electrophilic substitution (Chapter 22). The first step involves attack of the nucleophile $Y:^{\ominus}$ at the carbon bearing the halogen substituent to form an intermediate anion [2]. The aromatic system is of course destroyed on forming the anion, and the hybridization of carbon at the reaction site changes from sp^2 to sp^3.

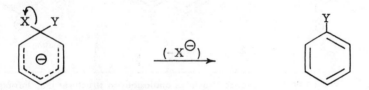

In the second step, loss of an anion, $X^{\ominus}$ or $Y^{\ominus}$, regenerates an aromatic system, and, if $X^{\ominus}$ is lost, the reaction is one of over-all nucleophilic displacement of X for Y.

In the case of a neutral nucleophilic reagent, Y or HY, the reaction sequence would be the same except for the necessary adjustments in charge of the intermediate.

Formation of [2] is highly unfavorable for the simple phenyl halides, even with the most powerful nucleophilic reagents. It should be clear how electron-attracting groups, such as $-NO_2$, $-NO$, $-C{\equiv}N$, $-N_2{}^{\oplus}$, etc., can facilitate nucleophilic substitution by this mechanism through stabilization of the intermediate. The effect of such substituents can be illustrated in the case of *p*-bromonitrobenzene and its reaction with methoxide ion. The structure of the reaction intermediate can be described in terms of the resonance structures [3a] through [3d]. Of these [3d] is especially important since it provides an extra degree of localization of the anionic charge over what would be expected if the NO_2 group were not present.

The reason that substituents in the *meta* positions have much less effect on the reactivity of an aryl halide is the substituent's inability to contribute directly to the delocalization of the negative charge in the ring; no structures can be written analogous to [3c] and [3d].

EXERCISE 23-4   *a.* Write resonance structures analogous to structures [3a] through [3d] to show the activating effect of —C≡N, —SO_2R, and —CF_3 groups in nucleophilic substitution of the corresponding p-substituted chlorobenzenes.

b. How would you expect the introduction of methyl groups *ortho* to the activating group to effect the reactivity of p-bromonitrobenzene and p-bromocyanobenzene toward ethoxide ion?

EXERCISE 23-5   Would you expect p-bromonitrobenzene or (p-bromophenyl)-trimethyl-ammonium chloride to be more reactive in bimolecular replacement of bromine by ethoxide ion? Why?

EXERCISE 23-6   Would you expect p-chloroanisole to be more or less reactive than chlorobenzene toward methoxide ion? Explain.

EXERCISE 23-7   Devise a synthesis of each of the following compounds from the indicated starting materials:

a. H_2N—⟨ ⟩—O—C_2H_5 from   *p*—nitrochlorobenzene

b. [structure: benzene ring with CCl$_3$, NO$_2$, OCH$_3$ substituents]   from   toluene

c. O$_2$N—[benzene ring]—N[piperidine ring], NO$_2$ from   benzene

A second possible mechanism of nucleophilic aromatic substitution resembles the S$_N$1 reactions of alkyl halides. It would involve the slow ionization of the aryl compound to an aryl cation, which may then react with a nucleophile to give the products.

$$C_6H_5-X \; \underset{slow}{\xrightarrow{-X^{\ominus}}} \; C_6H_5^{\oplus} \; \xrightarrow[fast]{H_2O} \; C_6H_5OH \; + \; H^{\oplus}$$

However, evidence for such an S$_N$1 reaction involving an aryl cation intermediate in the displacement reactions of aryl halides has thus far *not* been demonstrated.

C. Elimination-Addition Mechanism of Nucleophilic Aromatic Substitution

The reactivity of aryl halides such as the halobenzenes and halotoluenes is exceedingly low toward nucleophilic reagents that normally effect smooth displacements with alkyl halides and activated aryl halides. Substitutions, however, do occur under sufficiently forcing conditions involving either high temperatures or very strong bases. For example, the reaction of chlorobenzene with sodium hydroxide solution at temperatures around 340° has been an important commercial process for the production of phenol.

[structure: chlorobenzene] $\xrightarrow[340°]{aq. \; NaOH}$ [structure: phenol] + NaCl

Also, aryl chlorides, bromides, and iodides can be converted to arylamines by alkali salts of amines, which are very strong bases. In fact, the reaction of potassium amide with bromobenzene is extremely rapid, even at temperatures as low as −33°, with liquid ammonia as solvent.

[structure: bromobenzene] + K$^{\oplus}$ $\overset{\ominus}{N}$H$_2$ $\xrightarrow[-33°]{NH_3}$ [structure: aniline] + KBr

Displacement reactions of this type, however, differ from the previously discussed displacements of activated aryl halides in that rearrangement often occurs. That is to say, the entering group does not always take up the same position on the ring as that vacated by the halogen substituent. For example, the hydrolysis of *p*-chlorotoluene at 340° gives an equimolar mixture of *m*- and *p*-cresols.

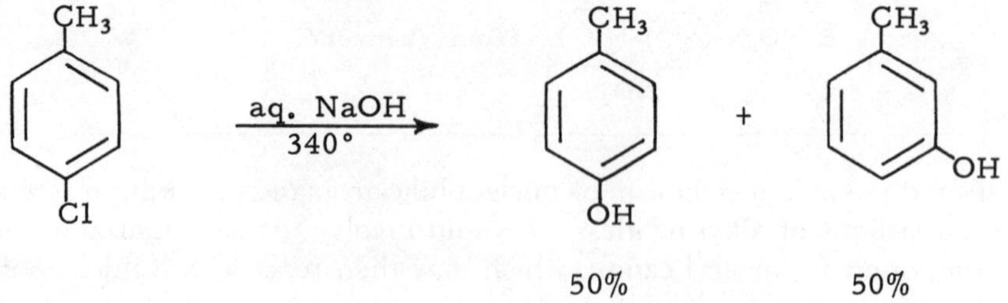

Even more striking is the exclusive formation of *m*-aminoanisole in the amination of *o*-chloroanisole.

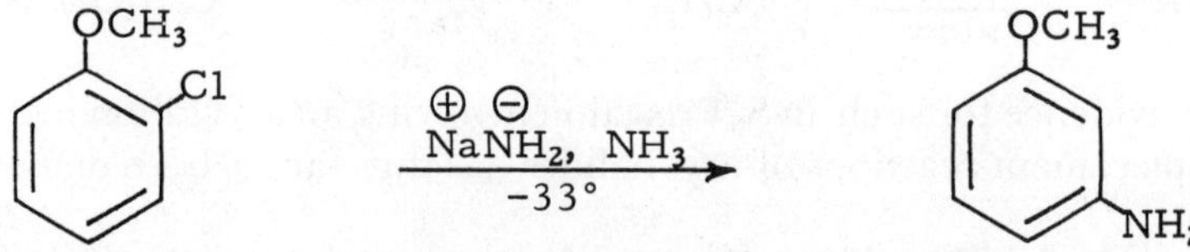

The mechanisms of this type of reaction have been widely studied, and much evidence has accumulated in support of a stepwise process, which proceeds first by base-catalyzed elimination of hydrogen halide (HX) from the aryl halide. In its gross aspects, this first reaction closely resembles the E2-elimination reactions of alkyl halides discussed earlier (Chapter 11, pp. 238–240) and is illustrated below for the amination of bromobenzene.

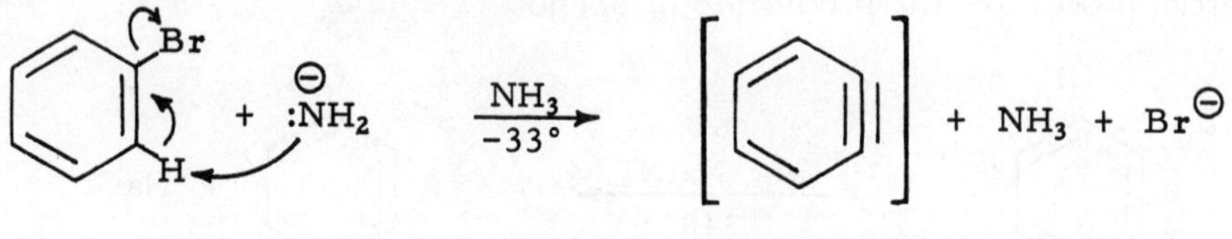

The product of the elimination reaction is a highly reactive intermediate [4] called **benzyne,** or **dehydrobenzene,** which differs from benzene in having an extra bond between two *ortho* carbons. Benzyne reacts rapidly with any available nucleophile, in this case the solvent ammonia, to give an addition product.

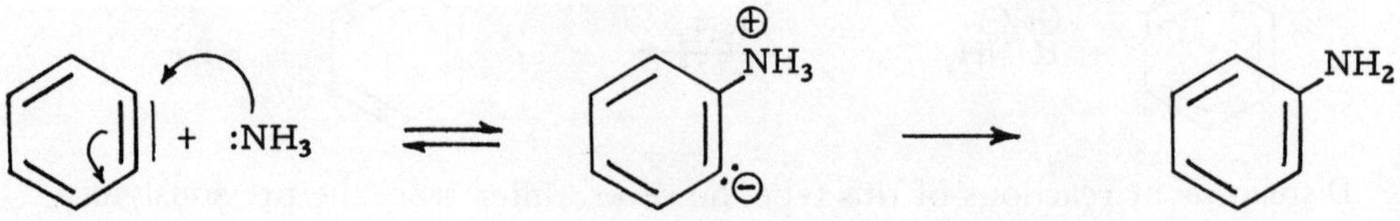

The occurrence of rearrangements in these reactions follows from the possibility of the nucleophile's attacking the intermediate at one or other of the carbons of the extra bond; with benzyne itself, the symmetry of the molecule is such that no rearrangement would be detected. However, this symmetry is destroyed if one of the ring carbons is labeled with ^{14}C isotope, so that two isotopically different products can be found. Studies of the amination of halobenzenes labeled with ^{14}C at the 1-position have demonstrated that essentially equal amounts of 1- and 2-^{14}C-labeled anilines are produced—as predicted by the elimination-addition mechanism.

50%   50%

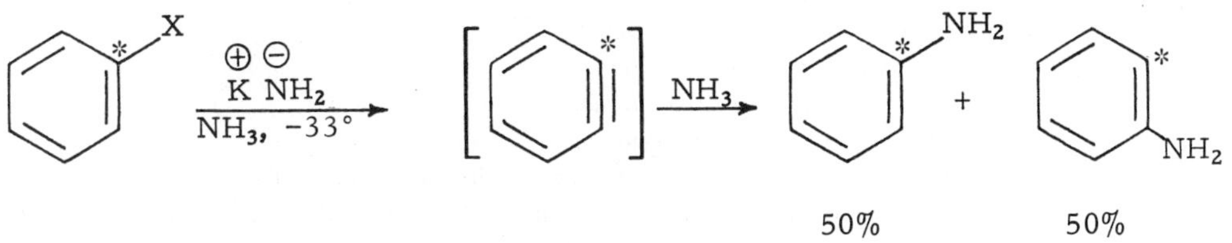

X = Cl, Br, I

* = ^{14}C

EXERCISE 23-8   In the hydrolysis of chlorobenzene-1-^{14}C with 4M aqueous sodium hydroxide at 340°, the products are 58 per cent phenol-1-^{14}C and 42 per cent phenol-2-^{14}C. Calculate the percentage of reaction proceeding (a) by an elimination-addition mechanism, and (b) by direct nucleophilic displacement. Would you expect the amount of direct displacement to increase or decrease if the reaction were carried out (a) at 240°, and (b) in aqueous sodium acetate in place of aqueous sodium hydroxide? Give the reasons on which you base your answers.

EXERCISE 23-9   Explain the following observations:
a. 2,6-Dimethylchlorobenzene does not react with potassium amide in liquid ammonia.
b. Fluorobenzene, labeled with deuterium in the 2- and 6-positions, undergoes rapid exchange of deuterium for hydrogen in the presence of potassium amide in liquid ammonia, but does not form aniline.

EXERCISE 23-10   Predict the principal product of the following reaction.

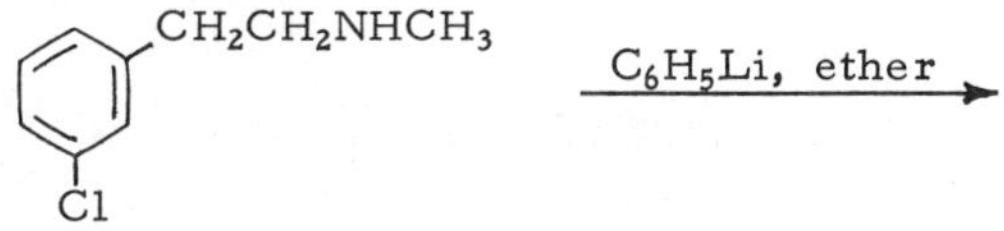

C_6H_5Li, ether ⟶

SUPPLEMENTARY EXERCISES

23-11   Give for each of the following pairs of compounds a chemical test, preferably a test-tube reaction, that will distinguish between the two compounds. Write a structural formula for each compound and equations for the reactions involved.

a. chlorobenzene and benzyl chloride

       b. *p*-nitrochlorobenzene and *m*-nitrochlorobenzene

       c. *p*-chloroacetophenone and α-chloroacetophenone

       d. *p*-ethylbenzenesulfonyl chloride and ethyl *p*-chlorobenzenesulfonate

       e. *p*-bromoaniline hydrochloride and *p*-chloroaniline hydrobromide

23-12 Show by means of equations how each of the following substances might be synthesized starting from the indicated materials. Specify reagents and approximate reaction conditions. Several steps may be required.

       a. 1,3,5-tribromobenzene from benzene

       b. *p*-fluorobenzoic acid from toluene

       c. *m*-bromoaniline from benzene

       d. *p*-nitrobenzoic acid from toluene

       e. *m*-dibromobenzene from benzene

       f. *m*-nitroacetophenone from benzene

       g. 2,4,6-trinitrobenzoic acid from toluene

       h. benzyl *m*-nitrobenzoate from toluene

23-13 Write a structural formula for a compound that fits the following description:

       a. an aromatic halogen compound that reacts with sodium iodide in acetone but not with aqueous silver nitrate solution

       b. an aryl bromide that cannot undergo substitution by the elimination-addition (benzyne) mechanism

       c. the least reactive of the monobromomononitronaphthalenes toward ethoxide ion in ethanol

23-14 Explain why the substitution reactions of α-halonaphthalenes in Eqs. (23-1) through (23-3) show no significant variation in the percentage of α- and β-naphthyl derivatives produced either with the nature of the halogen substituent or with the nucleophilic reagent.

$$\text{(23-1)}$$

$$38\% \quad\quad 62\%$$

$$\text{(23-2)}$$

$$32\% \quad\quad 68\%$$

$$\text{(23-3)}$$

$$33\% \quad\quad 67\%$$

Aryl Nitrogen Compounds

In this chapter, we shall consider the chemistry of aryl nitrogen compounds, starting with aromatic nitro compounds and continuing with aromatic amines and diazonium compounds. This sequence is opposite to the order in which we discussed the corresponding aliphatic nitrogen compounds but, as will be seen, the sequence is logical from the standpoint of synthesis.

Our interest in these compounds, besides their many practical uses, stems to a considerable degree from the way in which the typical properties of the aromatic ring and the substituents are modified by their mutual interactions. Aryl nitrogen compounds are expected to show a broad spectrum of behavior in this respect, nitro and diazonium groups being strongly electron attracting in contrast to amino groups, which are relatively strongly electron donating.

Aryl Nitrogen Compounds

Many of the properties of aryl halides, such as their lack of reactivity in nucleo-philic substitution reactions, are closely related to the properties of vinyl halides. Attempts to make similar comparisons between vinyl oxygen and nitrogen com-pounds and the related aryl oxygen and nitrogen compounds are often thwarted by the unavailability of suitable vinyl analogs. Thus, while vinyl ethers are easily accessible, most vinyl alcohols and primary or secondary amines are unstable with respect to their tautomers with $C{=}O$ and $C{=}N$ bonds. (1,3-Dicarbonyl compounds are a notable exception, see pp. 352–353.)

$$\overset{\backslash}{C}{=}\overset{/}{C}\overset{\backslash}{\underset{\diagdown}{N{-}H}} \longrightarrow -\overset{H}{\underset{|}{C}}{-}\overset{N}{\underset{|}{C}}{-} \qquad \Delta H = -16 \text{ kcal}$$

$$\overset{\backslash}{C}{=}\overset{/}{C}\overset{O{-}H}{\diagup} \longrightarrow -\overset{H}{\underset{|}{C}}{-}\overset{O}{\underset{||}{C}}{-} \qquad \Delta H = -18 \text{ kcal}$$

That the same situation does not hold for most aromatic amino and hydroxy compounds is a consequence of the stability of the benzene ring, which stability would be almost completely lost by tautomerization. For aniline, the stabiliza-tion energy corresponding to the heat of combustion is 41 kcal/mole (p. 193), and we can expect a stabilization energy of about 5 kcal/mole for its tautomer, 2,4-cyclohexadienimine.   Thus the ΔH of tautomerization is unfavorable by $(41 - 16 - 5) = 20$ kcal/mole.

$$\text{NH}_2 \rightleftharpoons \text{NH} \qquad \Delta H(\text{calc.}) = 20 \text{ kcal}$$

S. E. = 41 kcal   S. E. ~ 5 kcal

Phenol is similarly more stable than the corresponding ketone by about 17 kcal/mole.

$$\text{OH} \rightleftharpoons \text{O} \qquad \Delta H(\text{calc.}) = 17 \text{ kcal}$$

S. E. = 40 kcal   S. E. ~ 5 kcal

   Since aromatic amino and hydroxy compounds have special stabilization as enamines and enols, their behavior is not expected to parallel in all respects that of the less stable vinylamines and vinyl alcohols.   Nonetheless, similar reactions are often encountered.   Both enols and phenols react readily with halogens, and their salts can undergo either C or O alkylation with organic halides.   The qualitative differences observed in these reactions will be considered in more detail later (see also Chapter 25); but, as already indicated, such differences can usually be accounted for in terms of the stabilization of the aromatic ring.

AROMATIC NITRO COMPOUNDS

24-1 SYNTHESIS OF NITRO COMPOUNDS

   The most generally useful way to introduce a nitro group into an aromatic nucleus is by direct nitration, as previously discussed (pp. 545-546).   This method is obviously unsatisfactory when the orientation determined by substituent groups does not lead to the desired isomer.   Thus, p-dinitrobenzene and p-nitrobenzoic acid cannot be prepared by direct nitration, since nitrations of nitrobenzene and benzoic acid give practically exclusively m-dinitrobenzene and m-nitrobenzoic acid, respectively.   To prepare the *para* isomers, less direct routes are necessary—the usual stratagem being to use benzene derivatives with substituent groups that produce the desired orientation on nitration and then to make the necessary modifications in these groups to produce the final product. Thus, *p*-dinitrobenzene can be prepared from aniline by nitration of acetanilide (acetylaminobenzene), followed by hydrolysis to *p*-nitroaniline and replacement of amino by nitro through the action of nitrite ion, in the presence of cuprous salts, on the corresponding diazonium salt (see p. 600). Alternatively, the amino group of *p*-nitroaniline can be oxidized to a nitro group by trifluoroperacetic acid. In this synthesis, acetanilide is nitrated in preference to aniline itself, since not only is aniline easily oxidized by nitric acid, but the reaction leads to extensive *m*-substitution by nitration involving the anilinium ion. Another route to *p*-nitroaniline is to nitrate chlorobenzene and subsequently replace the chlorine with ammonia.

The nitrations mentioned give mixtures of *ortho* and *para* isomers, but these are usually easy to separate by distillation or crystallization. The same approach can be used to synthesize *p*-nitrobenzoic acid. The methyl group of toluene directs nitration preferentially to the *para* position, and subsequent oxidation with chromic acid yields *p*-nitrobenzoic acid.

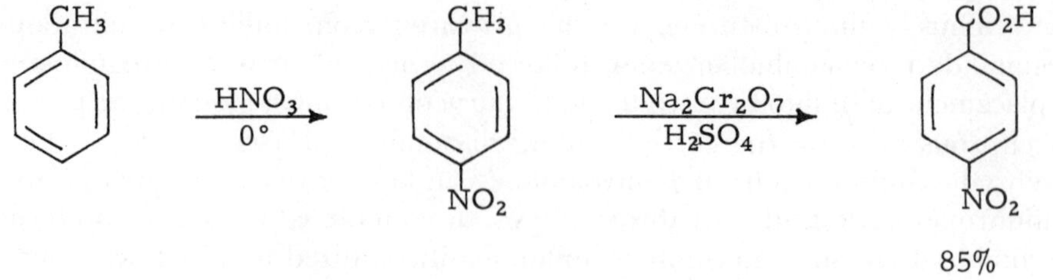

85%

In some cases, it may be necessary to have an activating group to facilitate substitution, which would otherwise be very difficult. The preparation of 1,3,5-trinitrobenzene provides a good example — direct substitution of *m*-dinitrobenzene requires long heating with nitric acid in fuming sulfuric acid. However, toluene is more readily converted to the trinitro derivative and this substance, on oxidation (p. 627) and decarboxylation (p. 372), yields 1,3,5-trinitrobenzene.

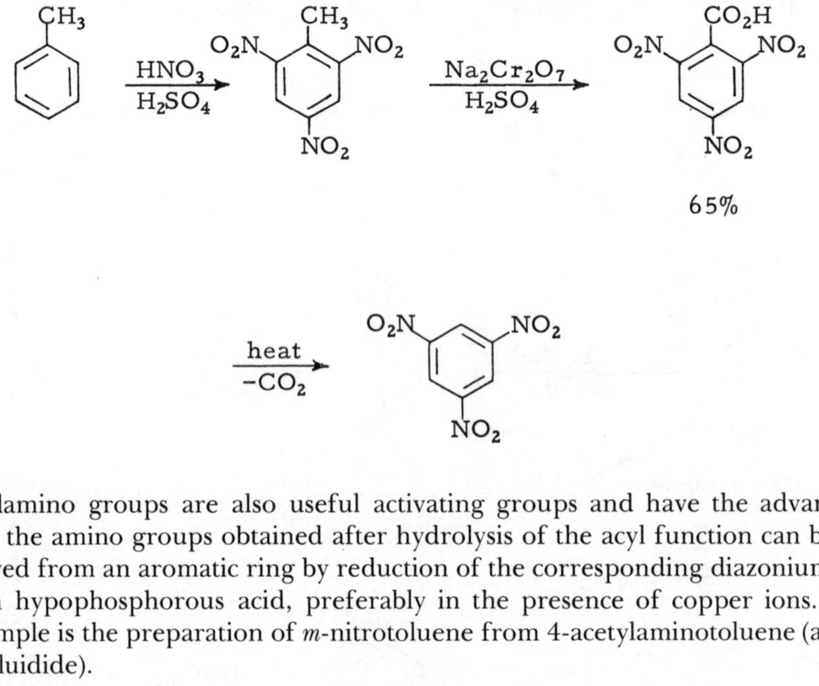

65%

Acylamino groups are also useful activating groups and have the advantage that the amino groups obtained after hydrolysis of the acyl function can be removed from an aromatic ring by reduction of the corresponding diazonium salt with hypophosphorous acid, preferably in the presence of copper ions. An example is the preparation of *m*-nitrotoluene from 4-acetylaminotoluene (aceto-*p*-toluidide).

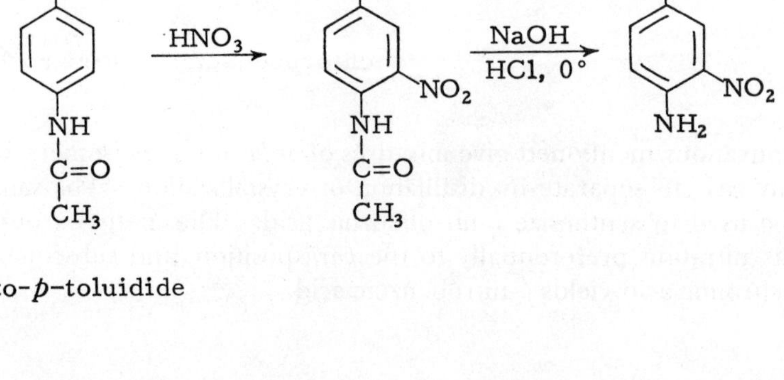

aceto-*p*-toluidide

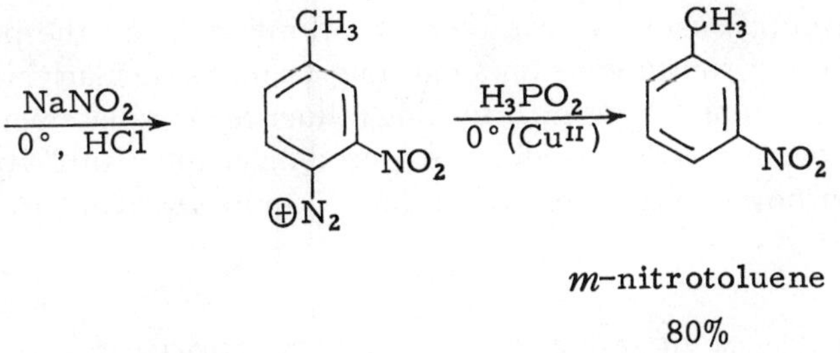

$$\xrightarrow[\text{0°, HCl}]{\text{NaNO}_2}$$

CH$_3$

NO$_2$

$\oplus$N$_2$

$$\xrightarrow[\text{0° (Cu}^{II}\text{)}]{\text{H}_3\text{PO}_2}$$

CH$_3$

NO$_2$

m-nitrotoluene

80%

The acetylamino derivatives of the amines are usually used in the nitration step in preference to the amines themselves because, as mentioned in connection with the formation of *p*-nitroaniline, they are less susceptible to oxidation by nitric acid and give the desired orientation.

EXERCISE 24-1   Show how the following compounds could be synthesized from the indicated starting materials. (It may be necessary to review parts of Chapters 22 and 23 to work this exercise.)

a. 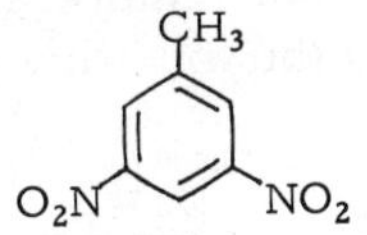   from   toluene

b. 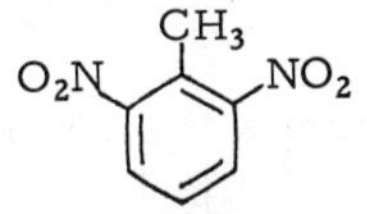   from   *p*-toluenesulfonic acid

c. 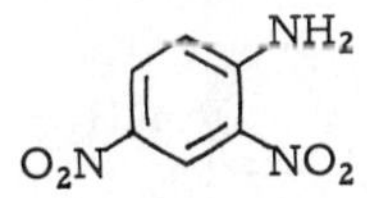   from   chlorobenzene

d. 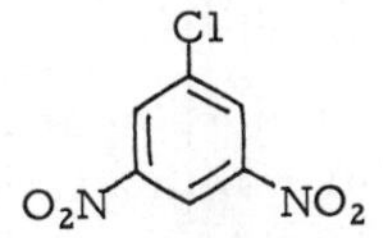   from   chlorobenzene

e. 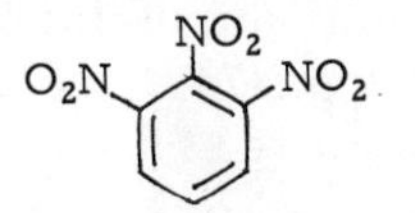   from   *p*-chlorobenzenesulfonic acid

---

The physical properties and spectra of aliphatic and aromatic nitro compounds were touched on briefly (p. 474). Nitrobenzene itself is a pale-yellow liquid (b.p. 210°), which should be handled with care since it has a considerable toxicity both by inhalation and by absorption through the skin.

A nitro group usually has a rather strong influence on the properties and reactions of other substituents on an aromatic ring, particularly when it is in an *ortho* or *para* position. A strong activating influence in displacement reactions of aromatic halogens was discussed in the preceding chapter (pp. 576-578), and we shall see later how nitro groups make aromatic amines weaker bases and phenols stronger acids.

24-2 REDUCTION OF AROMATIC NITRO COMPOUNDS

The most important synthetic reactions of nitro groups involve reduction, particularly to the amine level. In fact, aromatic amines are normally prepared by nitration followed by reduction. They may also be prepared by halogenation followed by amination, but since amination of halides requires the use of either amide salts or ammonia, and high temperatures, which often lead to rearrangements (pp. 579-581), the nitration-reduction sequence is usually preferred. Direct amination of aromatic compounds is not generally feasible.

A. Reduction of Nitro Compounds to Amines

The reduction of nitrobenzene to aniline requires six equivalents of reducing agent and appears to proceed through the following principal stages:

nitrobenzene   nitrosobenzene   N-phenylhydroxylamine

aniline

Despite the complexity of the reaction, reduction of aromatic nitro compounds to amines occurs smoothly in *acid* solution with a variety of reducing agents of which tin metal and hydrochloric acid or stannous chloride are often favored on a laboratory scale. Hydrogenation is also useful but is strongly exothermic and must be carried out with care (see p. 474).

Ammonium (or sodium) sulfide has the interesting property of reducing one nitro group in a dinitro compound much faster than the other.

$$\text{2,4-dinitroaniline} \xrightarrow[\text{C}_2\text{H}_5\text{OH}-\text{H}_2\text{O}]{\text{NH}_3,\ \text{H}_2\text{S},\ 50°} \text{product}$$

60%

It is not always easy to predict which of two nitro groups will be reduced most readily. In contrast to the reduction of 2,4-dinitroaniline, reduction of 2,4-dinitrotoluene leads to preferential reduction of the 4-nitro group.

$$\xrightarrow{\text{NH}_3,\ \text{H}_2\text{S}}$$

B. Reduction of Nitro Compounds in Neutral and Alkaline Solution

In neutral or alkaline solution, the reducing power of some of the usual reducing agents towards nitrobenzene is less than in acid solution. A typical example is afforded by zinc, which gives aniline in the presence of excess acid, but produces N-phenylhydroxylamine when buffered with ammonium chloride.

$$\text{C}_6\text{H}_5\text{-NO}_2 + 3\,\text{Zn} + 6\,\text{HCl} \xrightarrow{\text{H}_2\text{O}} \text{C}_6\text{H}_5\text{-NH}_2 + 3\,\text{ZnCl}_2 + 2\,\text{H}_2\text{O}$$

$$\text{C}_6\text{H}_5\text{-NO}_2 + 2\,\text{Zn} + 4\,\text{NH}_4\text{Cl} \xrightarrow{\text{H}_2\text{O}} \text{C}_6\text{H}_5\text{-NHOH} + 2\,\text{Zn(NH}_3)_2\text{Cl}_2 + \text{H}_2\text{O}$$

Nitrosobenzene is too easily reduced to be formed by direct reduction of nitrobenzene and is usually prepared by oxidation of N-phenylhydroxylamine with chromic acid.

$$\xrightarrow[\text{H}_2\text{SO}_4,\ 0°]{\text{K}_2\text{Cr}_2\text{O}_7}$$

Nitrosobenzene exists as a colorless dimer in the crystalline state. When the solid is melted or dissolved in organic solvents, the dimer undergoes reversible dissociation to the green monomer (see p. 473).

24-3 POLYNITRO COMPOUNDS

A number of aromatic polynitro compounds have important uses as high explosives. Of these, 2,4,6-trinitrotoluene (TNT), 2,4,6-trinitrophenol (picric acid), and N,2,4,6-tetranitro-N-methylaniline (tetryl) are particularly important. 1,3,5-Trinitrobenzene has excellent properties as an explosive but is difficult to prepare by direct nitration of benzene (p. 588).

2, 4, 6–trinitrotoluene   2, 4, 6–trinitrophenol   N, 2, 4, 6–tetranitro-
                                                N–methylaniline

(TNT)   (picric acid)   (tetryl)

The trinitro derivatives of m-t-butyltoluene and 1,3-dimethyl-5-t-butylbenzene possess musklike odors and have been used as ingredients of cheap perfumes and soaps.

1–methyl–3–t–butyl–   1, 3–dimethyl–5–t–butyl–
2, 4, 6–trinitrobenzene   2, 4, 6–trinitrobenzene

24-4 CHARGE-TRANSFER (π) COMPLEXES

An important characteristic of polynitro compounds is their ability to form more or less stable complexes with aromatic hydrocarbons, especially those that are substituted with alkyl groups or are otherwise expected to have electron-donating properties. The behavior is very commonly observed with picric acid, and the complexes therefrom are often nicely crystalline solids, which are useful for the separation, purification, and identification of aromatic hydrocarbons. These substances are often called "hydrocarbon picrates" but the name is misleading since they are not ordinary salts; furthermore, similar complexes are formed between aromatic hydrocarbons and trinitrobenzene, which shows that the nitro groups rather than the hydroxyl group are essential to complex formation. The binding in these complexes results from attractive forces between electron-rich and electron-poor substances. The designation **charge-transfer complex** originates from a resonance description in which the structure of the complex receives contributions from resonance forms involving transfer of an electron from the donor (electron-rich) molecule to the acceptor (electron-poor) molecule. However, the name π complex is also used because usually at least one component of the complex has a π-electron system. Charge-transfer complexes between polynitro compounds and aromatic hydrocarbons appear to have sandwich-type structures with the aromatic rings in parallel planes, although not necessarily coaxial.

formulation of charge–transfer complex between 1, 3, 5–trinitro–
benzene (acceptor) and 1, 3, 5–trimethylbenzene (donor)

Charge-transfer complexes are almost always more highly colored than their individual components. A spectacular example is afforded by benzene and tetracyanoethylene, each of which separately is colorless, but which give a bright-orange complex when mixed. A shift toward longer wavelengths of absorption is to be expected for charge-transfer complexes relative to their components because of the enhanced possibility for resonance stabilization of the excited state involving both components (see pp. 196-197 and 682-687).

EXERCISE 24-2   Tetracyanoethylene in benzene forms an orange solution, but when this solution is mixed with a solution of anthracene in benzene, a brilliant blue-green color is produced, which fades rapidly; colorless crystals of a compound of composition $C_{14}H_{10} \cdot C_2(CN)_4$ are then deposited. Explain the color changes that occur and write a structure for the crystalline product.

EXERCISE 24-3   Anthracene (m.p. 217°) forms a red crystalline complex (m.p. 164°) with 1,3,5-trinitrobenzene (m.p. 121°). If you were to purify anthracene as this complex, how could you regenerate the anthracene free of trinitrobenzene?

AROMATIC AMINES

24-5 GENERAL PROPERTIES

The physical properties of some representative aromatic amines are given in Table 24-1. Included in this table are the wavelengths and intensities of maximum absorption of ultraviolet radiation by the benzene chromophore (see pp. 537-538).

The chemical properties of the aromatic amines are in many ways similar to those of aliphatic amines—alkylation and acylation, for example, occur in the normal manner (pp. 459 and 462-463). We have noted before (p. 458) that aniline $C_6H_5NH_2$ is 10^6 times weaker as a base than cyclohexylamine, at least partly for the reason that, in the form of the salt, the 3-kcal extra stabilization energy, which can be ascribed to delocalization of the unshared electron pair over the aromatic ring, is lost because the electron pair must be *localized* when the nitrogen-proton bond is formed. The changes that occur in terms of the principal electron-pairing schemes for the aniline and anilinium ion are shown in structures [1a] through [1e], |2a] and [2b].

[1a]   [1b]   [1c]   [1d]   [1e]

38 kcal stabilization   3 kcal extra stabilization attributed
                                 to delocalization of unshared electron pair

[2a]   [2b]   38 kcal stabilization of
                                        benzene ring

A hybrid structure [3] for aniline, deduced from the structures [1a] through [1e], has some degree of double-bond character between the nitrogen and the ring, and some degree of negative charge at the *ortho* and *para* positions.

[3]

Accordingly, the ability of the amine nitrogen to add a proton should be particularly sensitive to the electrical effects of substituent groups on the aromatic ring, when such are present.   For example, substituents like nitro, cyano, and carbethoxy, which have the ability to stabilize an electron pair on an adjacent carbon (see pp. 577-578), are expected to substantially reduce the base strength of the amine nitrogen, when substituted in the *ortho* or *para* position, through extra stabilization of the aniline (but not the anilinium ion) by contributions of electron-pairing schemes such as [4].

$$\overset{\oplus}{NH_2}$$

[4]

To gain some idea of the magnitude of this effect, we first note that *m*-nitroaniline is 90 times weaker as a base than aniline, whereas *p*-nitroaniline is 35 times weaker than *m*-nitroaniline.   In contrast, *m*-nitrobenzoic acid is only 5.1 times stronger as an acid than benzoic acid, and only 1.2 times weaker than *p*-nitrobenzoic acid.   Clearly, the nitro groups in the nitroanilines exert a more powerful electrical effect than in the nitrobenzoic acids, and this is reasonable because the site at which ionization occurs is closer to the benzene ring in the anilines than in the acids.   Even when this factor is taken into account, however, *p*-nitroaniline is 30 times weaker than might otherwise be expected, unless forms like [4] are important.

The contribution made by the polar form [4] becomes much more important on excitation of *p*-nitroaniline by ultraviolet radiation (see pp. 196-197).   The necessary excitation energies are therefore lower than for aniline, with the result that the absorption bands in the electronic spectrum of *p*-nitroaniline are shifted to much longer wavelengths and are of higher intensity than are those of aniline (cf. Table 24-1).   Since no counterpart to [4] can be written for *m*-nitroaniline, the absorption bands of *m*-nitroaniline are not as intense and occur at shorter wavelengths than those of *p*-nitroaniline.

EXERCISE 24-4   N,N,4-Trimethylaniline has K_B of 3×10^{-9}, quinuclidine has $K_B = 4 \times 10^{-4}$, and benzoquinuclidine has $K_B = 6 \times 10^{-7}$.   What conclusions may be drawn from these results as to the cause(s) of the reduced base strength of aromatic amines relative to saturated aliphatic or alicyclic amines?   Explain.

quinuclidine   benzoquinuclidine

Table 24-1 Physical Properties of Some Representative Aromatic Amines

Name	Formula	M.p., °C	B.p., °C	K_B H$_2$O, 25°C	λ_{max}	ε	λ_{max}	ε
aniline	$C_6H_5NH_2$	−6	184	4.6×10^{-10}	2300	8,600	2800	1430
N-methylaniline	$C_6H_5NHCH_3$	−57	196	2.5×10^{-10}[b]	2450	11,600	2950	1800
N,N-dimethylaniline	$C_6H_5N(CH_3)_2$	2.5	193	2.42×10^{-10}[b]	2510	14,000	2980	1900
p-toluidine	![CH$_3$–C$_6$H$_4$–NH$_2$]	42	200	1.48×10^{-9}	2320	8,900	2860	1600
m-nitroaniline	![O$_2$N–C$_6$H$_4$–NH$_2$]	114	>285	4.0×10^{-13}	2800	4,800	3580	1450
p-nitroaniline	![O$_2$N–C$_6$H$_4$–NH$_2$]	148		1.1×10^{-12}	3810	13,500		
p-phenylenediamine	![H$_2$N–C$_6$H$_4$–NH$_2$]	140	267				3210	1550
benzidine	![H$_2$N–C$_6$H$_4$–C$_6$H$_4$–NH$_2$]	128[a]	400	1.4×10^{-12}	2840	24,500		
diphenylamine	$(C_6H_5)_2NH$	54	302	$\sim 10^{-14}$	2850	20,600		

triphenylamine	$(C_6H_5)_3N$	127	365	—[c]	2950	23,000
1-naphthylamine	NH₂ structure (1-naphthylamine)	50	301	9.9×10^{-11}	3200	5000
2-naphthylamine	NH₂ structure (2-naphthylamine)	113	294	2.0×10^{-10}	3400	2000

[a] Two metastable forms have m.p. 122 and 125°C.
[b] At 18°C.
[c] Not measurably basic in water solution.

597

Would you expect a nitro group *meta* or *para* to the nitrogen in benzoquinuclidine to have as large an effect on the base strength of benzoquinuclidine as the
corresponding substitution in aniline?

The negative character of the aromatic ring in aniline, expected on the basis
of the hybrid structure [3], is in accord with its ease of substitution by electrophilic agents and its general reactivity towards oxidizing agents. For example,
bromine reacts rapidly with aniline in water solution to give 2,4,6-tribromoani-
line in good yield. Introduction of the second and third bromines are so fast
that it is difficult to obtain the monosubstitution products in aqueous solution.

Other facets of the substitution of aromatic amines were discussed in connection
with the orientation effects of substituents (see p. 551 ff.).

24-6 AROMATIC AMINES WITH NITROUS ACID

Primary aromatic amines react with nitrous acid at 0° in a different way than
aliphatic amines in that the intermediate diazonium salts are much more stable
and can, in most cases, be isolated as nicely crystalline fluoborate salts (p. 574).
Other salts can often be isolated, but some of these, such as benzenediazonium
chloride, are not very stable and may decompose with considerable violence.

benzenediazonium	benzenediazonium
chloride	fluoborate
(water soluble)	(water insoluble)

The reason for the greater stability of aryldiazonium salts compared with
alkyldiazonium salts seems to be related to the difficulty of achieving S_N1-type
reactions with aryl compounds (p. 579). Even the gain in energy, associated with
formation of nitrogen by decomposition of a diazonium ion, is not sufficient to
make production of aryl cations occur readily at less than 100°.

This reaction has considerable general utility for replacement of aromatic amino groups by hydroxyl groups. In contrast to the behavior of aliphatic amines, no rearrangements occur.

Secondary aromatic amines react with nitrous acid to form N-nitroso compounds in the same way as do aliphatic amines (p. 464).

Tertiary aromatic amines normally behave differently from aliphatic tertiary amines with nitrous acid in that they undergo C-nitrosation, preferably in the *para* position. It is possible that an N-nitroso compound is formed first, which subsequently isomerizes to the *p*-nitroso derivative.

p-nitroso-N, N-dimethylaniline

EXERCISE 24-5   Pure secondary aliphatic amines can often be prepared free of primary and tertiary amines by cleavage of a p-nitroso-N,N-dialkylaniline with strong alkali to p-nitrosophenol and the dialkylamine. Why does this cleavage occur readily? Show how the synthesis might be used for preparation of di-*n*-butyl-amine starting with aniline and *n*-butyl bromide.

DIAZONIUM SALTS

24-7 PREPARATION AND GENERAL PROPERTIES

The procedure for formation of diazonium salts from amines and nitrous acid have been discussed earlier (p. 573). Most aromatic amines react readily, unless strong electron-withdrawing groups are present.

Tetrazotization of aromatic diamines is usually straightforward if the amino groups are located on different rings, as with benzidine, or are *meta* to each other on the same ring. Tetrazotization of amino groups *para* to one another, or diazotization of *p*-aminophenols, has to be conducted carefully to avoid oxidation.

Diazonium salts are normally stable only if the anion is one derived from a reasonably strong acid. Diazonium salts of weak acids usually convert to covalent forms from which the salts can usually be regenerated by strong acid. Benzenediazonium cyanide provides a good example in being unstable and forming two isomeric covalent benzenediazocyanides, one with the N=N bond *trans* and the other with the N=N bond *cis*. Of these, the *trans* isomer is the more stable.

$$C_6H_5\overset{\oplus}{N}{\equiv}\overset{\ominus}{N}{:}\ CN \quad \rightleftharpoons \quad \underset{N=N}{C_6H_5} \diagdown CN \quad + \quad \underset{N=\ddot{N}}{C_6H_5} \diagdown CN$$

$$\textit{cis}\text{-benzenediazocyanide} \quad \textbf{\textit{trans}}\text{-benzenediazocyanide}$$

In strong acid, the covalent diazocyanides are unstable with respect to benzene-diazonium ion and hydrogen cyanide.

The covalent forms are sometimes significant in the reactions of diazonium salts, since they offer a convenient path for the formation of free radicals (see pp. 476 and 721).

$$C_6H_5\overset{\oplus}{N}{\equiv}N \ + \ \overset{\ominus}{O_2}CCH_3 \quad \rightleftharpoons \quad C_6H_5N=N-O-\overset{\overset{\textstyle O}{\|}}{C}-CH_3$$

$$\xrightarrow{\text{slow}} \quad C_6H_5\cdot \ + \ N_2 \ + \ \cdot O-\overset{\overset{\textstyle O}{\|}}{C}-CH_3$$

24-8   REPLACEMENT REACTIONS OF DIAZONIUM SALTS

The utility of diazonium salts in synthesis is largely due to the fact that they provide the only readily accessible substances that undergo nucleophilic substitution reactions on the aromatic ring under mild conditions without the necessity of having activating groups, such as nitro or cyano, in the *ortho* or *para* position.

A. The Sandmeyer Reaction

The replacement of diazonium groups by halogen is the most important reaction of this type and some of its uses for the synthesis of aryl halides were discussed previously (pp. 573-575). Two helpful variations on the Sandmeyer reaction employ sodium nitrite with cuprous ion as catalyst for the synthesis of nitro compounds (p. 587), and cuprous cyanide for the synthesis of cyano compounds.

B. The Schiemann Reaction

The replacement of diazonium groups by fluorine was also discussed earlier (p. 574). This reaction, like the replacement of the diazonium group by hydroxyl (p. 598), may well involve aromatic cations as intermediates. One strong piece of evidence for this is the fact that benzenediazonium fluoborate yields 3-nitrobiphenyl along with fluorobenzene when heated in nitrobenzene.

Formation of 3-nitrobiphenyl is indicative of an electrophilic attack on nitrobenzene.

24-9 REACTIONS OF DIAZONIUM COMPOUNDS THAT OCCUR WITHOUT LOSS OF NITROGEN

A. Reduction to Hydrazines

Reduction of diazonium salts to arylhydrazines can be carried out smoothly with sodium sulfite or stannous chloride, or by electrolysis.

B. Diazo Coupling

A very important group of reactions of diazonium ions involve aromatic substitution by the diazonium salt acting as an electrophilic agent to yield azo compounds.

This reaction is highly sensitive to the nature of the substituent (X), and coupling to benzene derivatives normally occurs only when X is a strongly activating group such as —O$^\ominus$, —N(CH$_3$)$_2$, and —OH; however, coupling with X = OCH$_3$ may take place with particularly active diazonium compounds. Diazo coupling has considerable technical value, because the azo compounds that are produced are colored and often useful as dyes and coloring matters. A typical example of diazo coupling is afforded by formation of p-dimethylaminoazobenzene from benzenediazonium chloride and N,N-dimethylaniline.

p-dimethylaminoazobenzene

(yellow)

The product was once used to color edible fats and was therefore known as "Butter Yellow"; but its use as a food color is undesirable because it is reported to be quite carcinogenic.

Azo compounds can be made with practically any color in the visible spectrum, and the nature of some of these substances, which are employed as dyes for textiles, will be considered briefly in Chapter 28.

EXERCISE 24-6   N,N-Dimethylaniline, but not N,N,2,6-tetramethylaniline, couples readily with diazonium salts in neutral solution. Explain the low reactivity of N,N,2,6-tetramethylaniline by consideration of the geometry of the transition state for the reaction.

EXERCISE 24-7   Some very reactive unsaturated hydrocarbons, such as azulene (p. 563) couple with diazonium salts. At which position would you expect azulene to couple most readily? Explain.

EXERCISE 24-8   1-Naphthol couples with benzenediazonium chloride in the 2-position, 2-methyl-1-naphthol in the 4-position, and 2-naphthol in the 1-position. However, 1-methyl-2-naphthol does not couple at all under the same conditions. Why?

SUPPLEMENTARY EXERCISES

24-9   Give for each of the following pairs of compounds a chemical test, preferably a test-tube reaction, that will distinguish the two compounds. Write a structural formula for each compound and equations for the reactions involved:

    a. p-nitrotoluene and benzamide

    b. aniline and cyclohexylamine

    c. N-methylaniline and p-toluidine

    d. N-nitroso-N-methylaniline and p-nitroso-N-methylaniline

24-10 Show by equations how each of the following substances might be synthesized starting from the indicated materials. Specify reagents and approximate reaction conditions.

    a. *o*-dinitrobenzene from benzene

    b. 2,6-dinitrophenol from benzene

    c. 2-amino-4-chlorotoluene from toluene

    d. *p*-cyanonitrobenzene from benzene

    e. 2-amino-4-nitrophenol from phenol

    f. *m*-cyanotoluene from toluene

24-11 Write structural formulas for substances (one for each part) that fit the following descriptions:

    a. an aromatic amine that is a stronger base than aniline

    b. a substituted phenol that would not be expected to couple with benzenediazonium chloride in acid, alkaline, or neutral solution

    c. a substituted benzenediazonium chloride that would be a more active coupling agent than benzenediazonium chloride itself

24-12 Explain why triphenylamine is a much weaker base than aniline and why its electronic absorption spectrum is shifted to longer wavelengths compared with the spectrum of aniline (see Table 24-1). Would you expect N-phenylcarbazole to be a stronger or weaker base than triphenylamine? Explain.

Aryl Oxygen Compounds

*I*n *the previous chapter, we indicated that, although there are considerable structural similarities between vinyl alcohols (enols) and aromatic alcohols (phenols), and between vinylamines (enamines) and aromatic amines, the enols and enamines are generally unstable with respect to their keto and imine tautomeric forms, whereas the reverse is true of phenols and aromatic amines because of the stability associated with the aromatic ring.*

In the following discussion, after considering some of the more general procedures for the preparation of phenols, we shall take up the effect of the aromatic ring on the reactivity and reactions of the hydroxyl group of phenols and the effect of the hydroxyl group on the properties of the aromatic ring. Oxidation of the mono- and dihydric phenols is both of theoretical and practical importance and will be considered in some detail. The chapter concludes with discussions of the chemistry of quinones and of some nonbenzenoid seven-membered ring substances with aromatic properties.

Aryl Oxygen
Compounds

25-1 SYNTHESIS AND PHYSICAL PROPERTIES OF PHENOLS

Considerable amounts of phenol and the cresols (*o*-, *m*-, and *p*-methylphenols) can be isolated from coal tar. Phenol itself is used commercially in such large quantities that alternate methods of synthesis are necessary. Direct oxidation of benzene is unsatisfactory because phenol is much more readily oxidized than is benzene. The more usual procedures are to sulfonate or chlorinate benzene and then introduce the hydroxyl group by nucleophilic substitution using strong alkali.

These reactions are general for introduction of hydroxyl substituents on aromatic rings; however, in some cases, they proceed by way of benzyne intermediates (pp. 579-580) and may lead to rearrangement.

Table 25-1 Physical Properties of Some Representative Phenols

Name	Formula	M.p., °C	B.p., °C	K_A H$_2$O, 25°C	λ_{max}	ϵ	λ_{max}	ϵ
phenol	C$_6$H$_5$OH	43	182	1.3×10^{-10}	2105	6,200	2700	1450
p-cresol	CH$_3$—⟨⟩—OH	34	203	1.5×10^{-10}	2250	7,400	2800	1995
p-nitrophenol	O$_2$N—⟨⟩—OH	114		6.5×10^{-8}	3175	10,000		
picric acid	O$_2$N—⟨NO$_2$⟩—OH, NO$_2$	123			3800	13,450		
catechol	⟨OH⟩—OH	105	240	3.3×10^{-10a}	2140	6,300	2755	2300
resorcinol	HO—⟨⟩—OH	110	273	3.6×10^{-10a}	2160	6,800	2735	1900
hydroquinone	HO—⟨⟩—OH	170	285	1×10^{-10}			2900	2800
p-aminophenol	H$_2$N—⟨⟩—OH	186		6.6×10^{-9a}	2330	8,000	2800	3200
salicylaldehyde	⟨OH⟩—CHO	−7	197		2560	12,600	3240	3400

p-hydroxybenzaldehyde		115		2.2×10^{-8}	2835	16,000
1-naphthol		94	278	1×10^{-8}		
2-naphthol		123	285			

[a] At 18°C.

More recent commercial syntheses of phenol involve oxidation of toluene or isopropylbenzene. Oxidation of isopropylbenzene is economically feasible for the production of phenol because acetone is also an important product.

The physical properties of some representative phenols are summarized in Table 25-1. In general, phenols are rather more polar in character than the corresponding saturated alcohols. The magnitudes of the differences are well illustrated by comparison of the physical properties of phenol and cyclohexanol shown in Table 25-2.

The determining factor here appears to be the greater acidity of the phenolic hydroxyl group, which means that, in the undissociated form, the O—H bond is more strongly polarized as $\overset{\delta\ominus}{O}$—$\overset{\delta\oplus}{H}$ than for alcohols. We therefore expect phenols to be able to form stronger hydrogen bonds than alcohols, resulting in higher boiling points, higher water solubility, and increased ability to act as solvents for reasonably polar organic molecules. These expectations are verified in practice.

Table 25-2   Comparative Physical Properties of Phenol and Cyclohexanol

	Phenol	Cyclohexanol
m.p.	43°	25.5°
b.p.	181°	161°
water solubility, g/100 g, 20°	9.3	3.6
K_A	1.0×10^{-10}	$\sim 10^{-18}$

The ultraviolet absorption maxima of the phenols shown in Table 25-1 indicate a considerable effect of substituents on the wavelength and intensity of absorption.

25-2 SOME CHEMICAL PROPERTIES OF PHENOLS

A. Reactions Involving O—H Bonds

The acidity of phenols compared to alcohols can be accounted for by an argument similar to that used to explain the acidity of carboxylic acids (pp. 367-368). In the first place, we note that phenol has a stabilization energy of 40 kcal/mole, of which 38 kcal can be ascribed to the benzene ring (p. 193). The excess of 2 kcal appears to be due to delocalization of one of the unshared electron pairs on oxygen over the aromatic ring, as can be described in terms of the resonance structures [1a] through [1c].

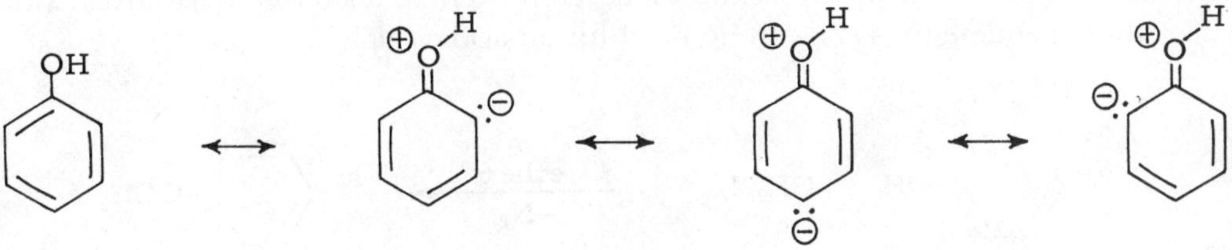

[1a] [1b] [1c]

Conversion of phenol by loss of the hydroxyl proton to phenoxide anion is expected to lead to substantially greater delocalization of the unshared pair because, as can be seen from the resonance structures [2a] through [2c], no charge separation is involved of the type apparent in [1a] through [1c].

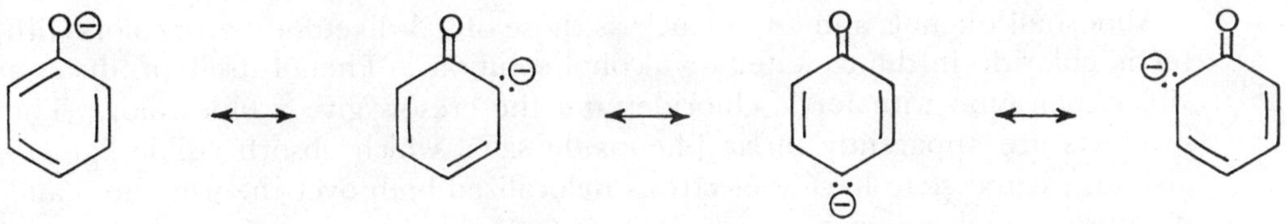

[2a] [2b] [2c]

The stabilization energy of the anion is therefore expected to be greater than 40 kcal and the ionization process energetically more favorable than for a saturated alcohol such as cyclohexanol.

The reactions of the hydroxyl groups of phenols, which involve breaking the O—H bonds and formation of new bonds from oxygen to carbon, are generally similar to those of alcohols. It is possible to prepare esters with carboxylic acid anhydrides, and to prepare ethers by reaction of phenoxide anions with halides, sulfate esters, sulfonates, etc., which react well by S_N2-type mechanisms.

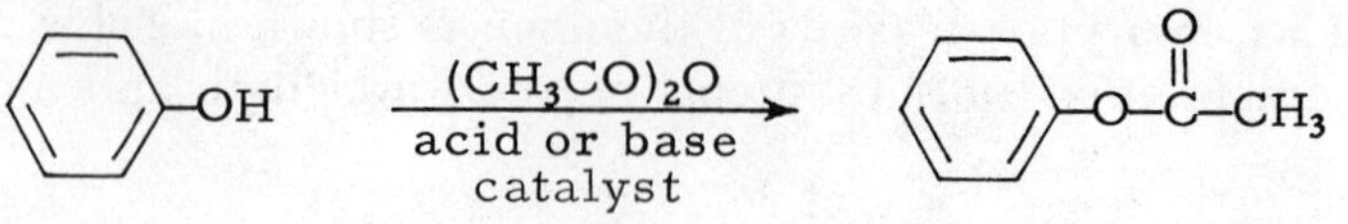

phenyl acetate

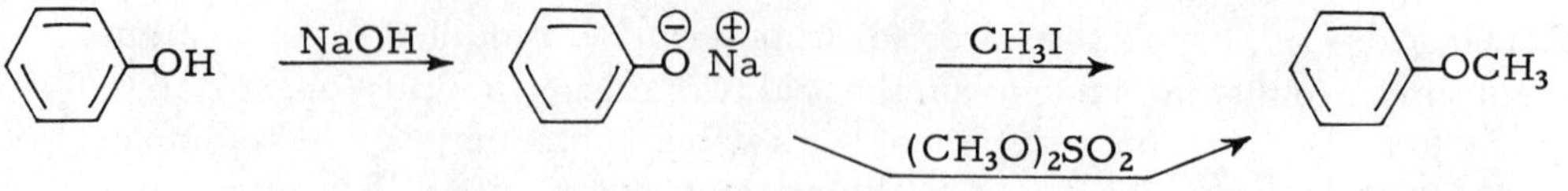

methoxybenzene
(anisole)

Phenols are sufficiently acidic to be converted to methoxy derivatives with diazomethane (p. 477) with no need for an acidic catalyst.

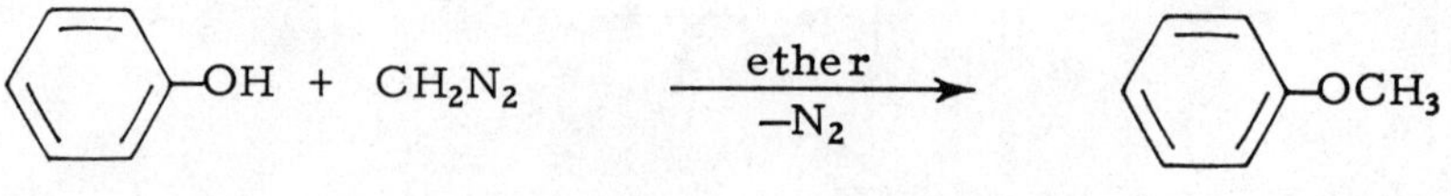

EXERCISE 25-1   Would you expect phenyl acetate to be hydrolyzed more readily or less readily than cyclohexyl acetate in alkaline solution?   Use reasoning based on the mechanism of ester hydrolysis (p. 380).

Almost all phenols and enols (such as those of 1,3-diketones) give colors with ferric chloride in dilute water or alcohol solutions. Phenol itself produces a violet coloration with ferric chloride, and the cresols give a blue color. The products are apparently ferric phenoxide salts, which absorb visible light to give an excited state having electrons delocalized both over the iron atom and the unsaturated system.

B. C- vs. O-Alkylation of Phenols

The same type of problem with respect to O- and C-alkylation is encountered with phenoxide salts as with enolate anions (pp. 344-345). Normally, only O-alkylation is observed. However, with allyl halides, either reaction can be made essentially the exclusive reaction by proper choice of solvent. With sodium phenoxide, the more polar solvents such as acetone tend to lead to phenyl allyl ether whereas in nonpolar solvents, such as benzene, *o*-allylphenol is the favored product.

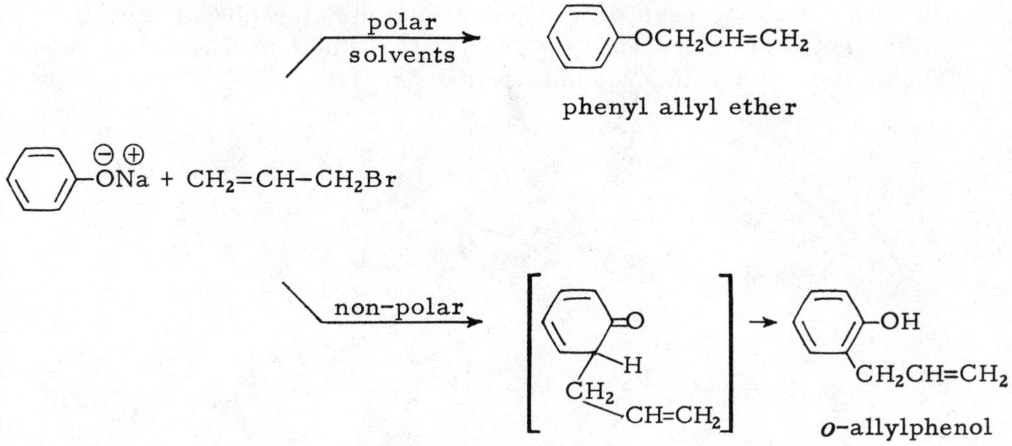

phenyl allyl ether

o-allylphenol

Apparently, in nonpolar solvents, the lack of dissociation of the —ONa part of the phenoxide salts tends to increase the steric hindrance at oxygen and makes attack on the ring more favorable.

The C-allylation product is thermodynamically more stable than the O-allylation product, as is shown by the fact that phenyl allyl ether rearranges to *o*-allyl phenol above 200°. Such rearrangements are quite general and are called **Claisen rearrangements.**

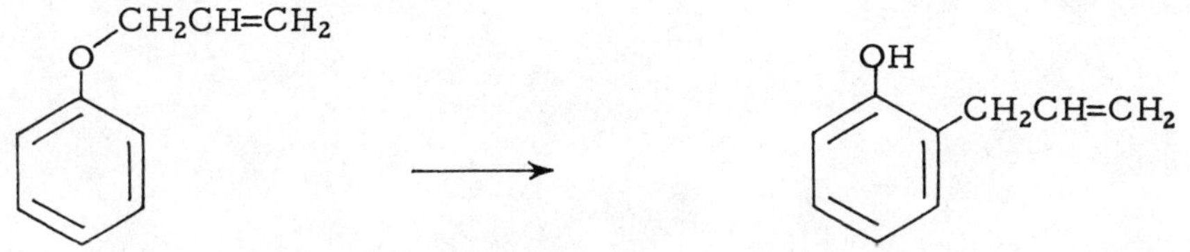

It should be noted that C-allylation of sodium phenoxide as observed in non-polar solvents is not the result of O-allylation followed by rearrangement, because the temperature of the allylation reaction is far too low to obtain the observed yield of *o*-allylphenol by rearrangement.

EXERCISE 25-2   Rearrangement of phenyl allyl-3-^{14}C ether at 200° gives o-allyl-1-^{14}C-phenol. What does this tell you about the rearrangement mechanism? Can it be a dissociation-recombination process? What product(s) would you expect from a *para* Claisen rearrangement of 2,6-dimethylphenyl allyl-3-^{14}C ether? From 2,6-diallylphenyl allyl-3-^{14}C ether?

C. Reactions Involving the C—O Bonds

In general, it is very difficult to break the aromatic C—O bond in reactions involving phenols or phenol derivatives. Thus, concentrated halogen acids do not convert phenols to aryl halides, and cleavage of phenyl alkyl ethers with hydrogen bromide or hydrogen iodide produces the phenol and an alkyl halide, not an aryl halide and an alcohol. Diaryl ethers, such as diphenyl ether, do not react with hydrogen iodide even at 200°.

Such behavior is very much in line with the difficulty of breaking aromatic halogen bonds in nucleophilic reactions (Chapter 23). There is no very suitable way for converting phenols to aryl halides, except when activation is provided by *ortho* or *para* nitro groups. Thus, 2,4-dinitrophenol is smoothly converted to 2,4-dinitrochlorobenzene with phosphorus pentachloride.

D. Reactions of the Aromatic Ring

The excess of electrons in the π-orbital systems of both phenol and phenoxide ion, predicted through consideration of the resonance forms such as lead to the hybrids [1] and [2], should make these compounds very susceptible to electrophilic substitution. [The situation here is very like that in aniline (see p. 598).] This is indeed the case, and phenols typically react rapidly with bromine in aqueous solution to substitute the positions *ortho* or *para* to the hydroxyl group — phenol itself giving 2,4,6-tribromophenol in high yield.

Other aspects of electrophilic substitution reactions of phenols are discussed in Chapter 22.

EXERCISE 25-3   Explain why phenol with bromine gives tribromophenol readily in water solution and o- and p-monobromophenols in nonpolar solvents. Note that 2,4,6-tribromophenol is at least a 300-fold stronger acid than phenol in water solution.

EXERCISE 25-4   The herbicide "2,4-D" is (2,4-dichlorophenoxy)-acetic acid. Show how this substance might be synthesized starting from phenol and acetic acid.

A number of important reactions of phenols involve electrophilic aromatic substitution of phenoxide ions. One example, which we have discussed in the previous chapter, is the diazo coupling reaction (pp. 601-602). Another example, which looks quite unrelated, is the **Kolbe reaction** wherein carbon dioxide reacts with sodium phenoxide at 125° to give the sodium salt of o-hydroxybenzoic acid (salicylic acid).

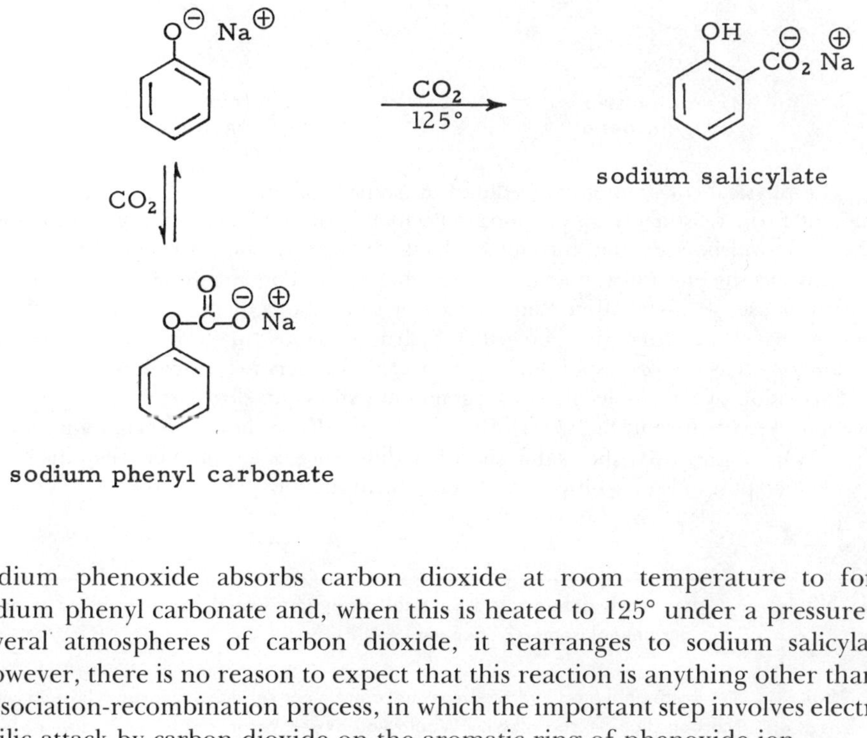

sodium salicylate

sodium phenyl carbonate

Sodium phenoxide absorbs carbon dioxide at room temperature to form sodium phenyl carbonate and, when this is heated to 125° under a pressure of several atmospheres of carbon dioxide, it rearranges to sodium salicylate. However, there is no reason to expect that this reaction is anything other than a dissociation-recombination process, in which the important step involves electrophilic attack by carbon dioxide on the aromatic ring of phenoxide ion.

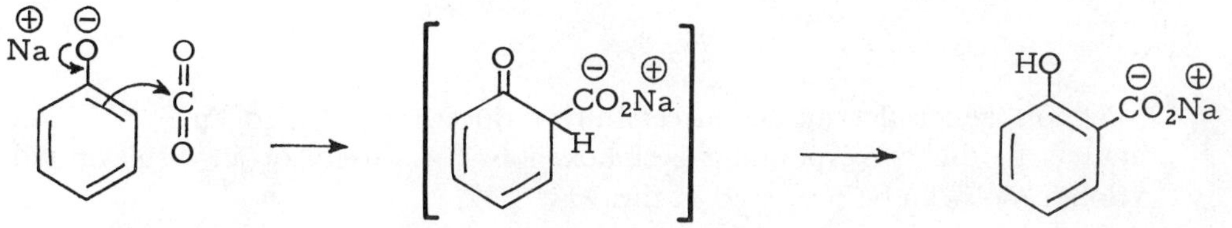

With sodium phenoxide and temperatures of 125 to 150°, *ortho* substitution occurs; at higher temperatures (250 to 300°) and particularly with the potassium salt, the *para* isomer is favored.

Many substances like salicylaldehyde, salicylic acid, *o*-nitrophenol, etc., that have hydroxyl groups *ortho* to some substituent to which they can form hydrogen bonds often have exceptional physical properties compared with the *meta* or *para* isomers. This is because formation of intra- rather than intermolecular hydrogen bonds reduces intermolecular attraction, thus reducing boiling points and increasing solubility in nonpolar solvents, etc. Compounds with intramolecular hydrogen bonds are often said to be **chelated** (Gk. *chele*, claw) and the resulting ring is called a **chelate ring.**

intramolecular
hydrogen bond

only intermolecular
hydrogen bonds

The physical constants for the different isomers of some substances that can and cannot form reasonably strong intramolecular hydrogen bonds are given in Table 25-3. It will be seen that intramolecular hydrogen bonding between suitable *ortho* groups has the effect of reducing both the melting and boiling points. An important practical use of this is often made in isomer separations, because many of the substances which can form intramolecular hydrogen bonds turn out to be volatile with steam, whereas the corresponding *meta* and *para* isomers are much less so.

Formation of intramolecular hydrogen bonds shows up clearly in n.m.r. spectra, as we have seen before in the case of the enol forms of 1,3-dicarbonyl compounds (pp. 352-353). Figure 25-1 shows that there is a difference of 2.3 ppm between the O—H resonance positions of *o*-nitrophenol and *p*-nitrophenol.

EXERCISE 25-5   How much difference in physical properties would you expect for o- and p-cyanophenol isomers? Explain.

EXERCISE 25-6   Resorcinol (*m*-dihydroxybenzene) can be converted to a carboxylic acid with carbon dioxide and alkali. Would you expect resorcinol to react more or less readily than phenol? Why? Which is the most likely point of monosubstitution? Explain.

Phenols generally can be successfully reduced with hydrogen over nickel catalysts to the corresponding cyclohexanols. A variety of alkyl-substituted cyclohexanols can be prepared in this way.

Table 25-3   Physical Properties of Some o, m, and p Disubstituted-Benzene Derivatives

Compound		B.p., °C	M.p., °C	Volatility with steam
OH / CH₃	ortho	191	31	++
	meta	203	12	++
	para	202	35	++
OH / CHO	ortho	196.5	−7	+
	meta	240	108	−
	para		117	−
OCH₃ / CHO	ortho	244	38	+
	meta	230		+
	para	248	2.5	+
OH / CO₂H	ortho	211²⁰mm	158	+
	meta		201	−
	para		215	−
OH / NO₂	ortho	216	45	+
	meta	194⁷⁰mm	97	−
	para		114	−

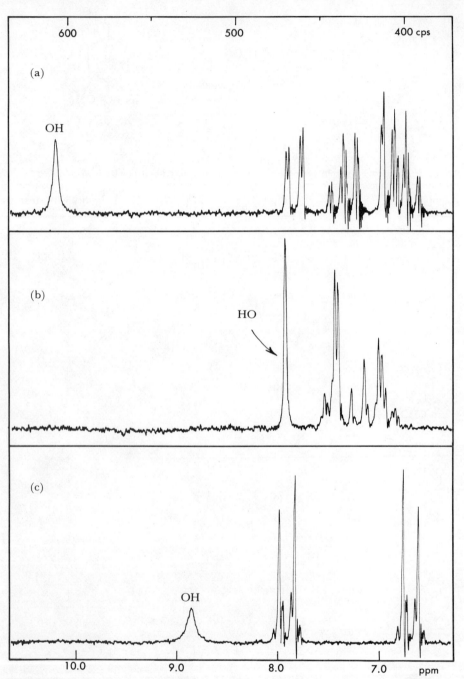

Figure 25-1

Nuclear magnetic resonance spectra at
60 Mcps of o-nitrophenol (a), m-nitro-
phenol (b), and p-nitrophenol (c) in
diethyl ether solution (the solvent bands
are not shown).

25-3 POLYHYDRIC PHENOLS

A number of important aromatic compounds have more than one phenolic hydroxyl group. These are most often derivatives of the following dihydric and trihydric phenols, all of which have commonly used but poorly descriptive names.

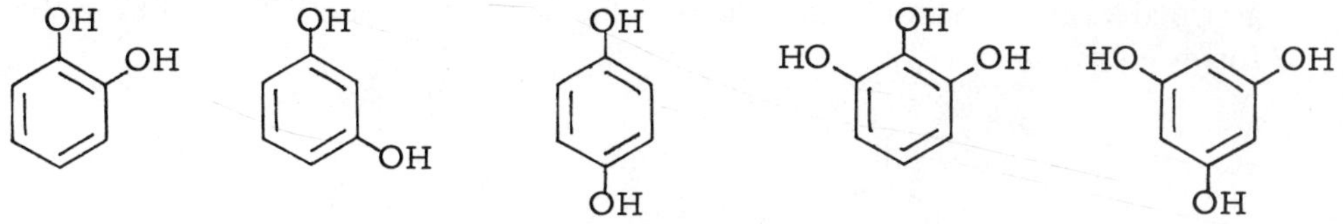

catechol   resorcinol   hydroquinone   pyrogallol   phloroglucinol

The polyhydric phenols with the hydroxyls in the *ortho* or *para* relationship are normally easily oxidized to quinones — the chemistry of which substances will be discussed shortly.

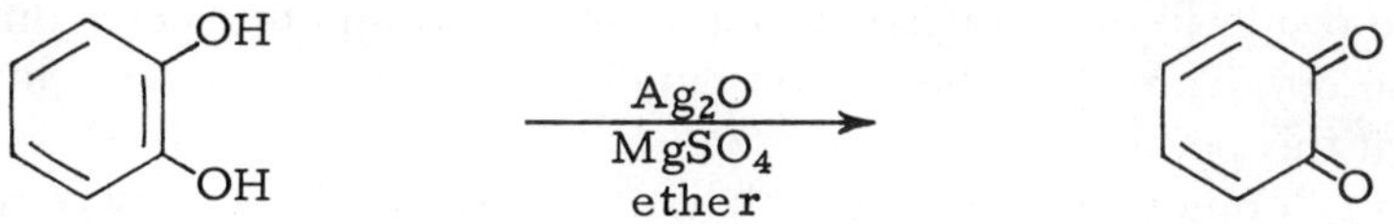

o-benzoquinone

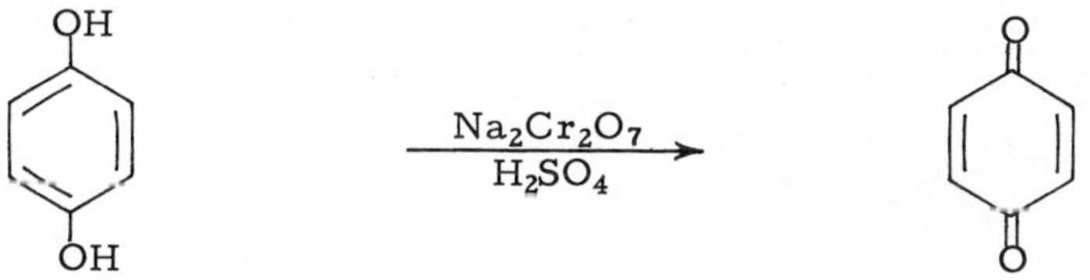

p-benzoquinone

The *m*-dihydroxybenzenes undergo oxidation but do not give *m*-quinones, since these are substances for which no single unstrained planar structure can be written. Oxidation of resorcinol gives complex products — probably by way of attack at the 4-position, which is activated by being *ortho* to one hydroxyl and *para* to the other. The use of hydroquinone and related substances as reducing agents for silver bromide in photography will be discussed later.

Substitution of more than one hydroxyl group on an aromatic ring tends to make the ring particularly susceptible to electrophilic substitution, especially when the hydroxyls are *meta* to one another, in which circumstance, their activating influences reinforce one another. For this reason, resorcinol and phloroglucinol are exceptionally reactive toward electrophilic reagents, particularly in alkaline solution.

QUINONES

Strictly speaking, quinones are conjugated cyclic diketones rather than aromatic compounds; hence a discussion of the properties of quinones is, to a degree, out of place in a chapter covering aromatic oxygen compounds, even though quinones have more stability than expected on the basis of bond energies alone. Thus, *p*-benzoquinone has a stabilization energy of 5 kcal, which can be ascribed largely to resonance structures like [3], there being a total of four polar forms equivalent to [3].

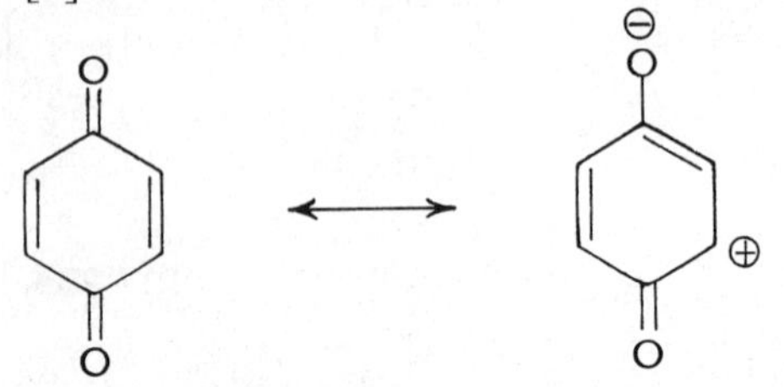

[3]

The fact that quinones and polyhydric phenols are normally very readily interconvertible results in the chemistry of either class of compound being difficult to disentangle one from the other. Consequently, it will be profitable to discuss quinones at this point.

A variety of quinone-like structures have been prepared, the most common of which are the 1,2- and 1,4-quinones as exemplified by *o*-benzoquinone and *p*-benzoquinone. Usually the 1,2-quinones are more difficult to make and are more reactive than the 1,4-quinones. A few 1,6- and 1,8-quinones are also known.

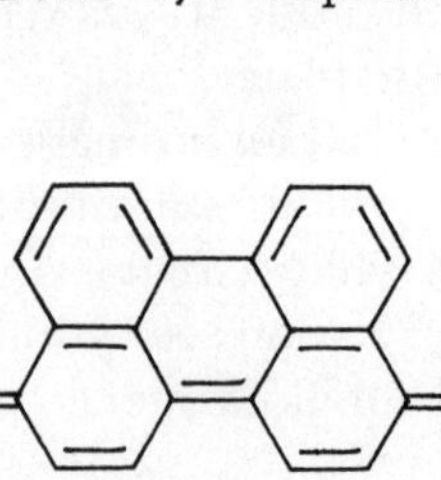

1, 5–dichloro–2, 6–naphthoquinone

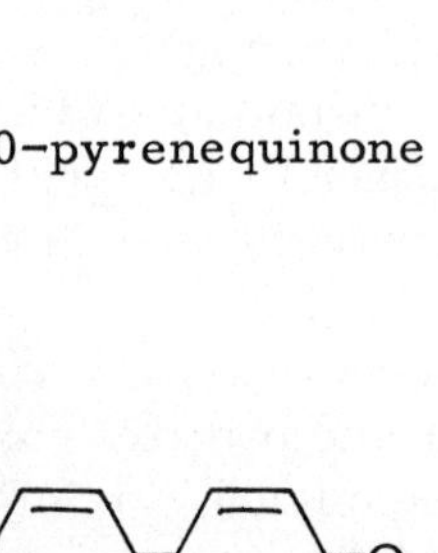

3, 10–pyrenequinone

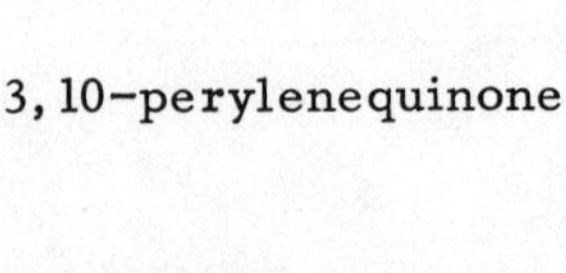

3, 10–perylenequinone

4, 4'–diphenoquinone

25-4 REDUCTION OF QUINONES

The most characteristic and important reaction of quinones is reduction to the corresponding dihydroxyaromatic compounds.

$$+ \ 2\,H^{\oplus} \quad \underset{-2e}{\overset{2e}{\rightleftarrows}} \quad \qquad\qquad (25\text{-}1)$$

Such reductions are unusual among organic reactions in being sufficiently rapid and reversible to give easily reproducible electrode potentials in an electrolytic cell. The position of the quinone-hydroquinone equilibrium, Eq. (25-1), is proportional to the square of the hydrogen-ion concentration; the electrode potential is therefore sensitive to pH, a change of one unit of pH in water solution changing the potential by 0.059 volt. Before the invention of the glass electrode pH meter, the half-cell potential developed by the quinone-hydroquinone equilibrium was widely used to determine pH values of aqueous solutions. The method is not very good above pH 9 to 10 because quinone reacts irreversibly with alkali.

Numerous studies have been made of half-cell potentials for the reduction of quinones. As might be expected, the potentials are greatest when the greatest gain in resonance stabilization is associated with formation of the aromatic ring.

EXERCISE 25-7   Arrange the following quinones in order of increasing half-cell potential expected for reduction: p-benzoquinone, 4,4'-diphenoquinone, cis-2,2'-diphenoquinone, 9,10-anthraquinone, and 1,4-naphthoquinone. Your reasoning should be based on differences in stabilization of the quinones and the hydroquinones, including steric factors (if any).

The hydroquinone-quinone oxidation-reduction system is actually somewhat more complicated than presented on the preceding page. This is evident in one way from the fact that mixing alcoholic solutions of hydroquinone and quinone gives a brown-red solution, which then deposits a crystalline green-black 1:1 complex known as **quinhydrone.** This substance is apparently a charge-transfer complex (of the type discussed on pp. 592-593) with the hydroquinone acting as the electron donor and the quinone as the electron acceptor. Quinhydrone is not very soluble and dissociates considerably to its components in solution.

The reduction of quinone requires two electrons, and it is of course possible that these electrons could either be transferred together or one at a time. The product of a single electron transfer leads to what is appropriately called a **semiquinone** [4] with both a negative charge and an odd electron.

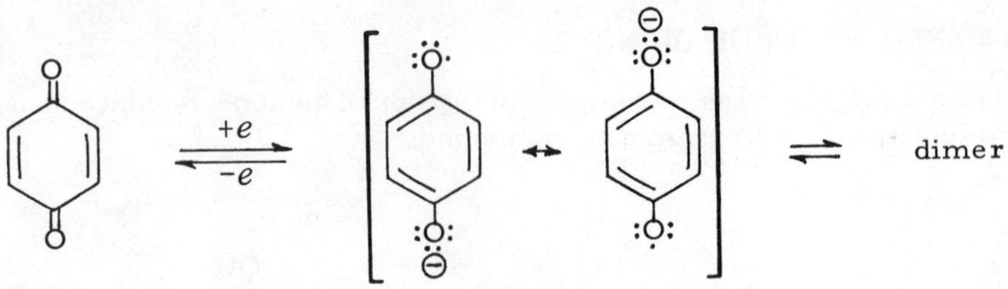

semiquinone

[4]

The formation of relatively stable semiquinone radicals by electrolytic reduction of quinones has been established by a variety of methods. Some semiquinone radicals undergo reversible dimerization reactions to form peroxides.

25-5 PHOTOGRAPHIC DEVELOPERS

A particularly important practical use of the hydroquinone-quinone oxidation-reduction system is in photography. Exposure of the minute grains of silver bromide in a photographic emulsion to blue light (or any visible light in the presence of suitable sensitizing dyes, see Chapter 28) produces a stable activated form of silver bromide, the activation probably involving generation of some sort of crystal defect. Subsequently, when the emulsion is brought into contact with a developer, which may be an alkaline aqueous solution of hydroquinone and sodium sulfite, the particles of activated silver bromide are reduced to silver metal much more rapidly than the ordinary silver bromide. Removal of the unreduced silver bromide with sodium thiosulfate ("fixing") leaves a suspension of finely divided silver in the emulsion in the form of the familiar photographic negative.

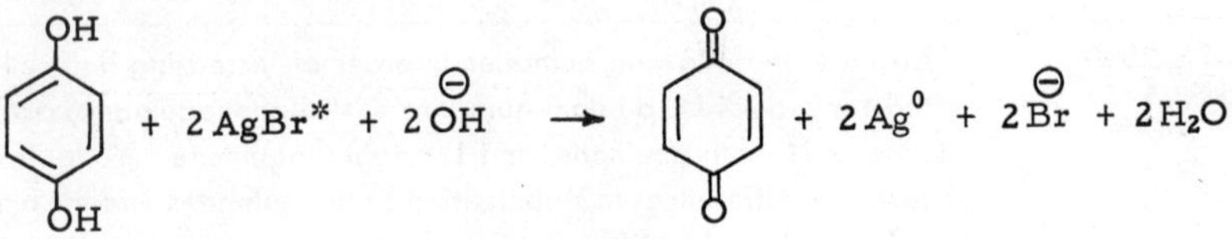

$AgBr^*$ = activated silver bromide

A variety of compounds related to hydroquinone are used as photographic developing agents. Structural formulas and commercial names for several important developers are shown below.

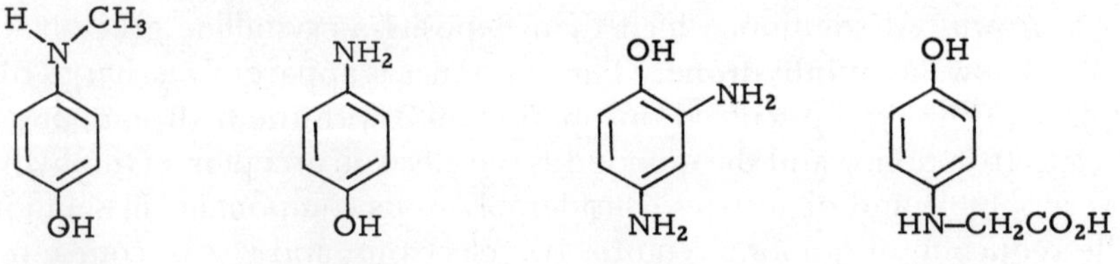

metol   rodinal   amidol   glycin

(elon)

p-Phenylenediamine is an effective developing agent but may cause dermatitis in sensitive individuals.

25-6 ADDITION REACTIONS OF QUINONES

Being α,β-unsaturated ketones, quinones are expected to have the possibility of forming 1,4-addition products in the same way as their open-chain analogs (p. 347). p-Benzoquinone itself undergoes such additions rather readily. Two examples are provided by the addition of hydrogen chloride and the acid-catalyzed addition of acetic anhydride.

In the second reaction, the hydroxyl groups of the hydroquinone are acetylated by the acetic anhydride. Hydrolysis of the product affords hydroxyhydroquinone.

Quinones with one double bond that is not part of an aromatic ring usually undergo Diels-Alder additions readily. With p-benzoquinone and butadiene, either the mono- or diadduct can be obtained. The monoadduct tautomerizes under the influence of acid or base to a hydroquinone derivative.

25-7   VITAMIN K₁

Many naturally occurring substances have quinone-type structures, one of the most important being the blood antihemmorrhagic factor, vitamin K₁, which occurs in green plants and is a substituted 1,4-naphthoquinone.

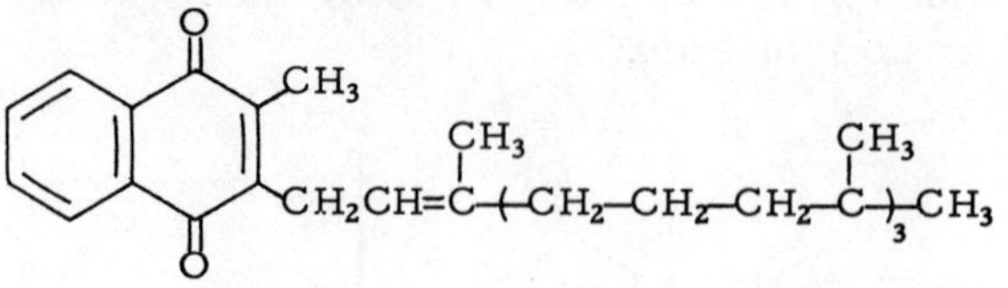

vitamin K₁

The structure of vitamin K₁ has been established by degradation and by synthesis. Surprisingly, the long alkyl side chain of vitamin K₁ is not necessary for its action in aiding blood clotting because 2-methyl-1,4-naphthoquinone is almost equally active on a molar basis.

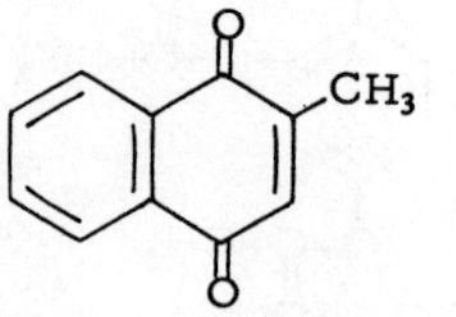

2-methyl-1, 4-naphthoquinone

(menadione)

25-8   TROPOLONES AND RELATED COMPOUNDS

The tropolones make up a very interesting class of nonbenzenoid aromatic compounds which were first encountered in several quite different kinds of natural products.   As one example of a naturally occurring tropolone, the substance called β-thujaplicin or hinokitiol has been isolated from the oil of the Formosan cedar and is 4-isopropyltropolone.

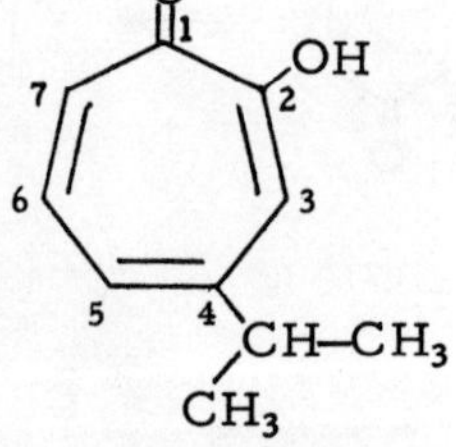

β-thujaplicin

(4-isopropyltropolone)

Tropolone itself can be prepared in a number of ways, the most convenient of which involves oxidation of 1,3,5-cycloheptatriene ("tropilidene") with alkaline potassium permanganate.   The yield is low but the product is readily isolated as the copper salt.

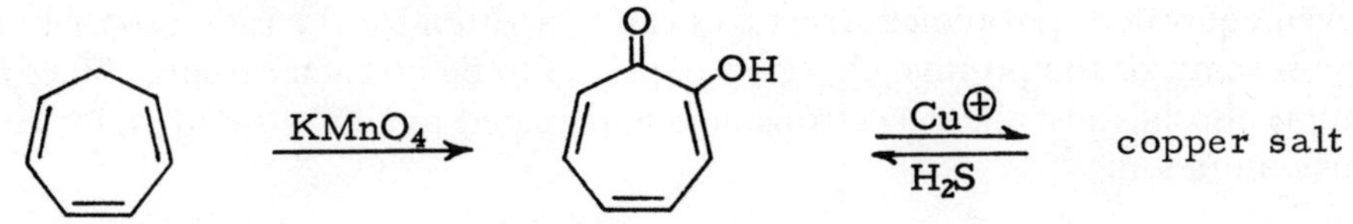

tropilidene   tropolone

Tropolone is an acid with an ionization constant of 10^{-7} which is intermediate between that of acetic acid and that of phenol. Like phenols, tropolones form colored complexes with ferric chloride solution. Tropolone has many properties which attest to its aromatic character. Thus, it resists hydrogenation, undergoes diazo coupling, and can be nitrated, sulfonated, and substituted with halogens. The aromaticity of tropolone can be attributed to resonance involving the two nonequivalent structures [5] and [6] and to the several structures such as [7] and [8] which correspond to the stable tropylium cation with six π electrons (p. 190).

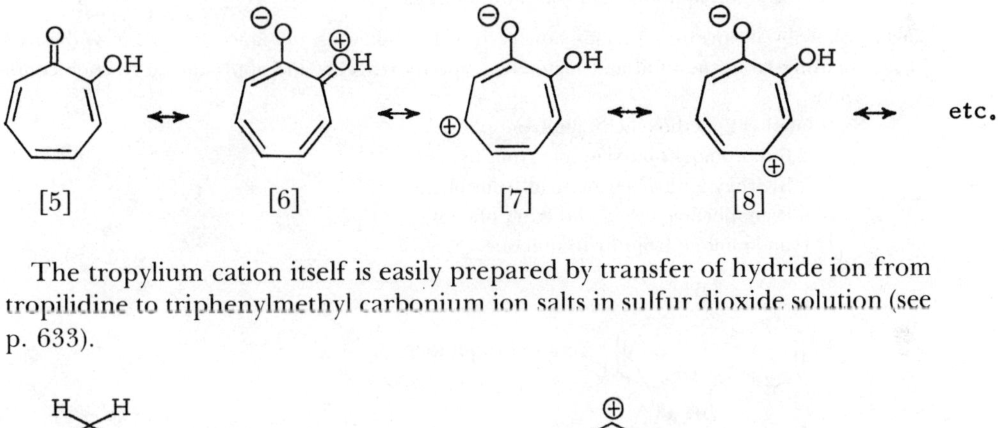

[5]   [6]   [7]   [8]

The tropylium cation itself is easily prepared by transfer of hydride ion from tropilidine to triphenylmethyl carbonium ion salts in sulfur dioxide solution (see p. 633).

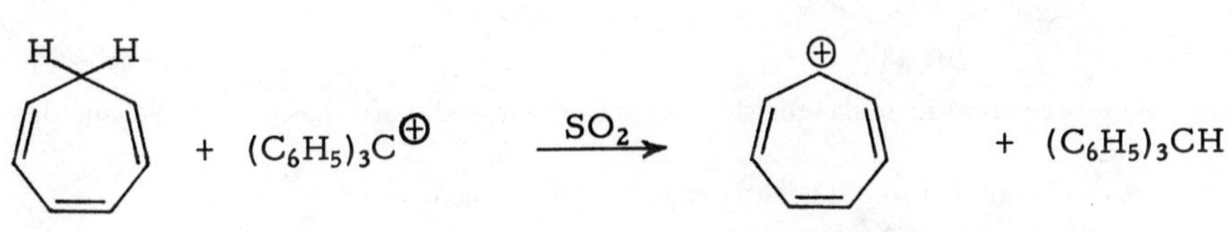

tropylium cation

EXERCISE 25-8   Tropone (2,4,6-cycloheptatrienone) is an exceptionally strong base for a ketone. Explain.

EXERCISE 25-9   At which position would you expect tropolone to substitute most readily with nitric acid? Explain.

Seven equivalent resonance structures can be written for the cation so that only one-seventh of the positive charge is expected to be on each carbon. Since the cation also has just six π electrons, it is anticipated to be unusually stable for a carbonium ion.

hybrid structure for
tropylium ion

SUPPLEMENTARY EXERCISES

25-10 Give for each of the following pairs of compounds a chemical test, preferably a test-tube reaction, that will distinguish between the two compounds. Write a structural formula for each compound and equations for the reactions involved.

   a. phenol and cyclohexanol
   b. methyl *p*-hydroxybenzoate and *p*-methoxybenzoic acid
   c. hydroquinone and resorcinol
   d. hydroquinone and tropolone
   e. 9,10-anthraquinone and 1,4-anthraquinone

25-11 Show by means of equations how each of the following substances might be synthesized, starting from the indicated materials. Specify reagents and approximate reaction conditions.

   a. methyl 2-methoxybenzoate from phenol
   b. 2,6-dibromo-4-*t*-butylanisole from phenol
   c. 2-hydroxy-5-nitrobenzoic acid from phenol
   d. 4-cyanophenoxyacetic acid from phenol
   e. cyanoquinone from hydroquinone

   f. [structure] from hydroquinone

25-12 Write structural formulas for substances (one for each part) that fit the following descriptions:

   a. a phenol that would be a stronger acid than phenol itself
   b. that isomer of dichlorophenol that is the strongest acid
   c. the Claisen rearrangement product from α-methylallyl-2,6-dimethylphenyl ether
   d. the Claisen-type rearrangement product from allyl 2,6-dimethyl-4-(β-methylvinyl)-phenyl ether
   e. a quinone which does not undergo Diels-Alder addition
   f. a quinone that would be a better charge-transfer agent than quinone itself
   g. the expected product from addition of hydrogen cyanide to monocyanoquinone
   h. a nonbenzenoid, quinone-like substance with its carbonyl groups in a 1,3-relationship

25-13 Calculate ΔH values for the following reactions in the gas phase, taking resonance energies into account as best you can:

   a. hydroquinone to quinone and hydrogen
   b. phenol to 2,5-cyclohexadienone

      c. 1,3,5-trihydroxybenzene to 1,3,5-cyclohexanetrione

      d. phenol with carbon dioxide to salicylic acid

25-14 Reduction of 9,10-anthraquinone with tin and hydrochloric acid in acetic acid produces a solid, light-yellow ketone, m.p. 156°, which has the formula $C_{14}H_{10}O$. This ketone is not soluble in cold alkali but does dissolve when heated with alkali. Acidification of cooled alkaline solutions of the ketone precipitate a brown-yellow isomer of the ketone of m.p. 120°, which gives a color with ferric chloride, couples with diazonium salts, reacts with bromine, and slowly is reconverted to the ketone.

      What are the structures of the ketone and its isomer? Write equations for the reactions described and calculate ΔH for interconversion of the isomers in the vapor phase.

25-15 Devise syntheses of each of the following photographic developing agents based on benzene as the aromatic starting material. Give approximate reaction conditions and reagents.

      a. hydroquinone

      b. *p*-aminophenol

      c. *p*-amino-N,N-diethylaniline

      d. (*p*-hydroxyphenyl)-aminoacetic acid

      e. 2,4-diaminophenol

25-16 Addition of hydrogen chloride to *p*-benzoquinone yields some 2,3,5,6-tetrachloroquinone. Explain how the latter could be formed in the absence of an external oxidizing agent.

25-17 Consider the possibility of benzilic acid-type rearrangements of 9,10-phenanthrenequinone and anthraquinone. Give your reasoning.

25-18 When quinone is treated with hydroxylamine and phenol is treated with nitrous acid, the same compound of formula $C_6H_5O_2N$ is produced. What is the likely structure of this compound and how would you establish its correctness?

25-19 How would you expect the properties of 3- and 4-hydroxy-2,4,6-cycloheptatrienone to compare with those of tropolone? Explain.

25-20 Make an atomic orbital model of phenol, showing in special detail the orbitals and electrons at the oxygen atom (it may be desirable to review Chapter 5 in connection with this problem). From your model, would you expect one or both pairs of unshared electrons on oxygen to be delocalized over the ring? What would be the most favorable orientation of the hydrogen of the hydroxyl group for maximum delocalization of an unshared electron pair?

Aromatic Side-Chain Derivatives

The pronounced modification in the reactivity of halogen, amino, and hydroxyl substituents when linked to aromatic carbon rather than saturated carbon was discussed in Chapters 23, 24, and 25. Other substituents, particularly those linked to an aromatic ring through a carbon-carbon bond, are also influenced by the ring, although usually to a lesser degree. Examples include $—CH_2OH$, $—CH_2OCH_3$, $—CH_2Cl$, $—CHO$, $—COCH_3$, $—CO_2H$, *and* $—CN$, *and we shall refer to aromatic compounds containing substituents of this type as* **aromatic side-chain derivatives.** *Our interest in them will be directed mainly to reactions at the side chain with particular reference to the effect of the aromatic ring on reactivity. In this connection, we shall discuss the relatively stable triarylmethyl cations, anions, and free radicals. Finally, the principles of electron resonance (e.p.r.) spectroscopy and its uses in studies of organic free radicals are considered briefly.*

Aromatic Side-Chain Derivatives

CHAPTER 26

There is a very wide variety of aromatic side-chain derivatives. However, we shall be largely concerned in this chapter with arylmethyl halides, aromatic aldehydes, ketones, and carboxylic acids, with emphasis on the aspects of their chemistry that differ from those of their saturated counterparts.

PREPARATION OF AROMATIC SIDE-CHAIN COMPOUNDS

Since the utility of any method of synthesis is limited by the accessibility of the starting materials, we may anticipate that the most practical methods for the preparation of benzenoid side-chain compounds will start from benzene or an alkylbenzene. These methods may be divided into two categories—those that modify an existing side chain, and those by which a side chain is introduced through substitution of the aromatic ring. We shall consider first the reactions that modify a side chain, and for which the obvious starting materials are the alkylbenzenes, especially toluene and the xylenes.

26-1 AROMATIC CARBOXYLIC ACIDS

Most alkylbenzenes can be converted to carboxylic acids by oxidation of the side chain with reagents such as potassium permanganate, potassium dichromate, or nitric acid.

627

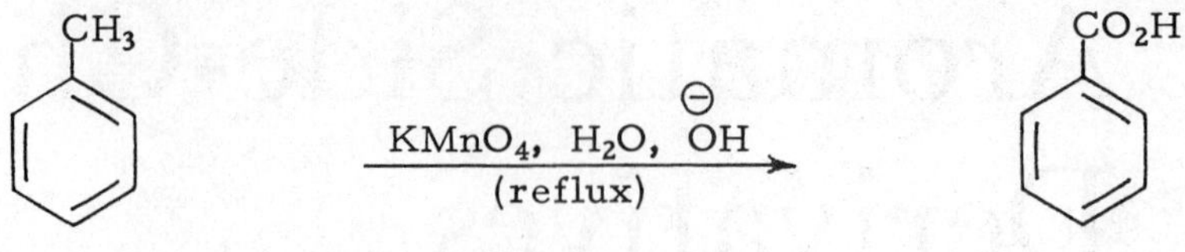

benzoic acid

Under the conditions of oxidation, higher alkyl or alkenyl groups are degraded and ring substituents, other than halogen and nitro groups, often fail to survive. As an example, oxidation of 5-nitro-2-indanone with dilute nitric acid leads to 4-nitrophthalic acid.

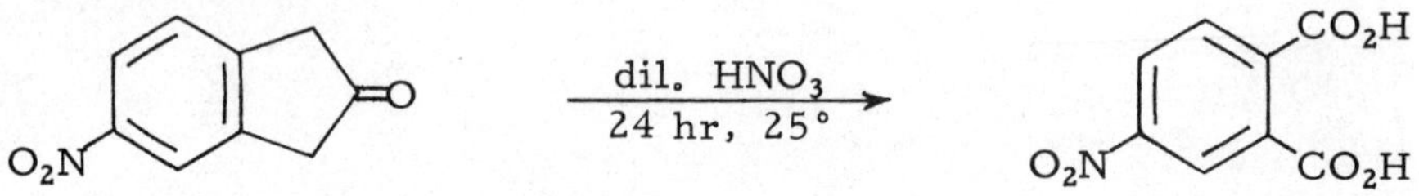

5-nitro-2-indanone   4-nitrophthalic acid

In order to retain a side-chain substituent, selective methods of oxidation are required. For example, *p*-toluic acid may be prepared from *p*-tolyl methyl ketone by the haloform reaction (pp. 338-339).

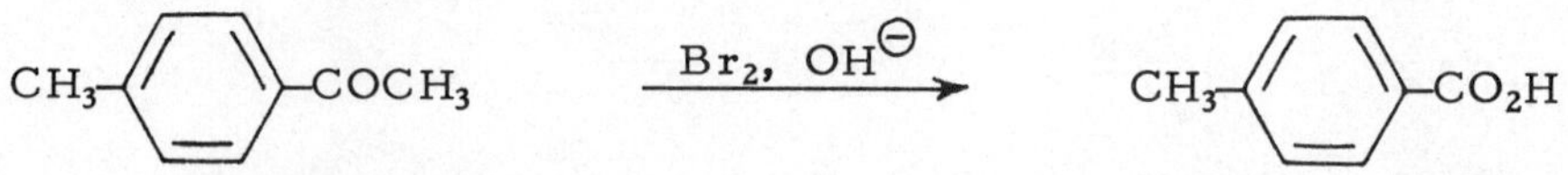

The Cannizzaro reaction (p. 330) is sometimes useful for the preparation of substituted benzoic acids and/or benzyl alcohols, provided that the starting aldehyde is available.

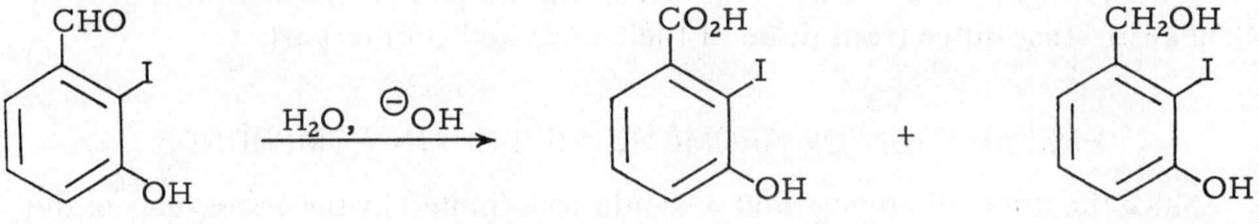

2-iodo-3-hydroxy-benzaldehyde	2-iodo-3-hydroxy-benzoic acid	2-iodo-3-hydroxy-benzyl alcohol
	80%	80%

EXERCISE 26-1   Suggest a practical synthesis of each of the following compounds from a readily available aromatic hydrocarbon:

a. 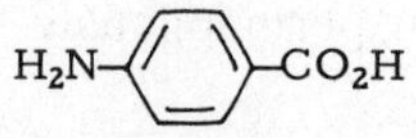 H_2N—⟨⟩—CO_2H b. 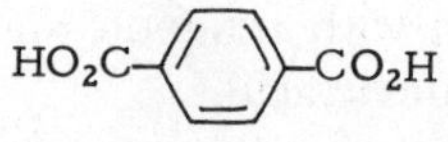 HO_2C—⟨⟩—CO_2H

c.

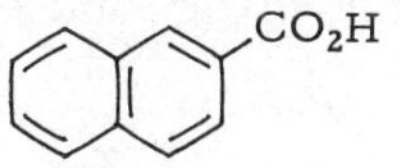

d.

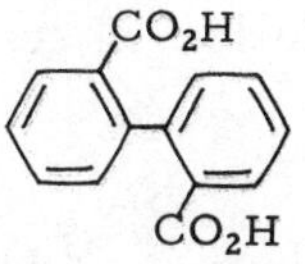

26-2 PREPARATION OF SIDE-CHAIN AROMATIC HALOGEN COMPOUNDS

   Although many side-chain halogen compounds can be synthesized by reactions that are also applicable to alkyl halides, there are several other methods especially useful for the preparation of arylmethyl halides. The most important of these are free-radical halogenation of alkylbenzenes and chloromethylation of aromatic compounds (p. 630).

   Light-induced, free-radical chlorination or bromination of alkylbenzenes with molecular chlorine or bromine gives substitution on the side chain rather than on the ring. Thus, toluene reacts with chlorine to give successively benzyl chloride, benzal chloride, and benzotrichloride.

$$C_6H_5CH_3 \xrightarrow[h\nu]{Cl_2} C_6H_5CH_2Cl \xrightarrow[h\nu]{Cl_2} C_6H_5CHCl_2 \xrightarrow[h\nu]{Cl_2} C_6H_5CCl_3$$

| toluene | benzyl chloride | benzal chloride | benzo-trichloride |

EXERCISE 26-2   Write a mechanism for the formation of benzyl chloride by the above reaction. What other products would you anticipate to be formed? At what position would you expect ethylbenzene to substitute under similar conditions?

26-3 SIDE-CHAIN COMPOUNDS DERIVED FROM ARYLMETHYL HALIDES

   Since arylmethyl halides, like benzyl and benzal chlorides, are quite reactive compounds that are readily available or easily prepared, they are useful intermediates for the synthesis of other side-chain derivatives. For example:

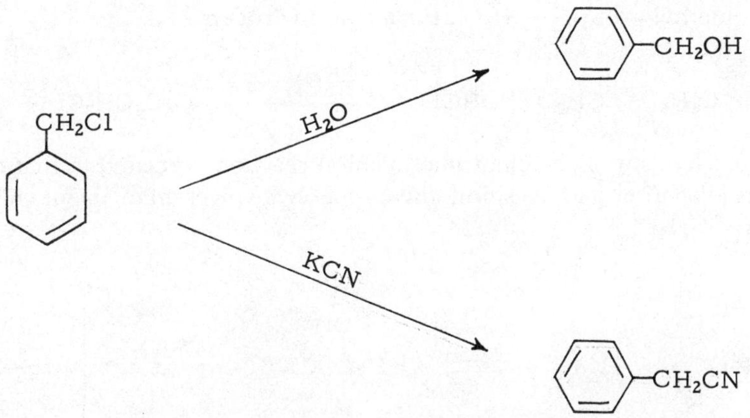

Benzal chloride hydrolyzes readily to benzaldehyde, and benzotrichloride to benzoic acid.

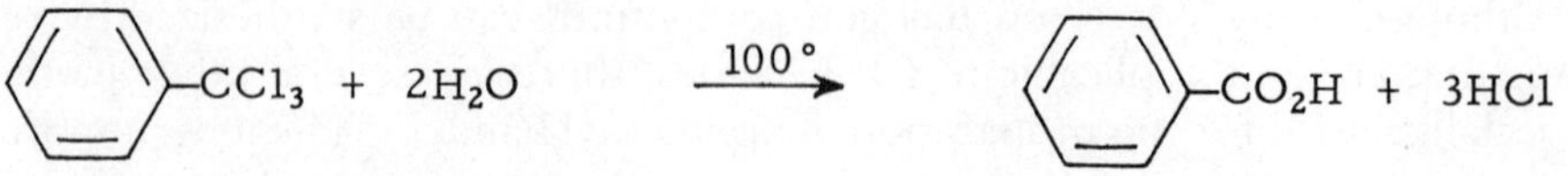

EXERCISE 26-3   Outline a suitable synthesis of each of the following compounds, starting with benzene:

    a. $C_6H_5CH_2COC_6H_5$

    b. 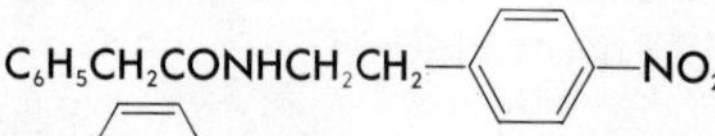 $C_6H_5CH_2CONHCH_2CH_2$—⟨ ⟩—NO_2

    c. Cl—⟨ ⟩—CHO

26-4 PREPARATION OF AROMATIC SIDE-CHAIN COMPOUNDS BY RING SUBSTITUTION

Turning now to introduction of a carbon side chain by direct substitution for aromatic hydrogen, we note that two such reactions have already been discussed, namely, Friedel-Crafts alkylation and acylation (see pp. 548-550). These will not be mentioned further here.

A. Chloromethylation

The reaction of an aromatic compound with formaldehyde and hydrogen chloride in the presence of zinc chloride as catalyst results in the substitution of a chloromethyl group, —CH_2Cl, for a ring hydrogen.

$$C_6H_6 + CH_2O + HCl \xrightarrow{\ ZnCl_2\ } C_6H_5CH_2Cl + H_2O$$

The mechanism of the chloromethylation reaction is related to that of Friedel-Crafts alkylation and acylation and probably involves an incipient chloromethyl cation, $^{\oplus}CH_2Cl$.

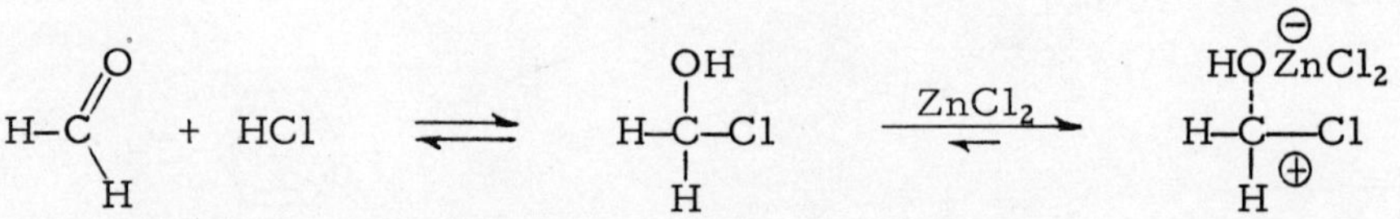

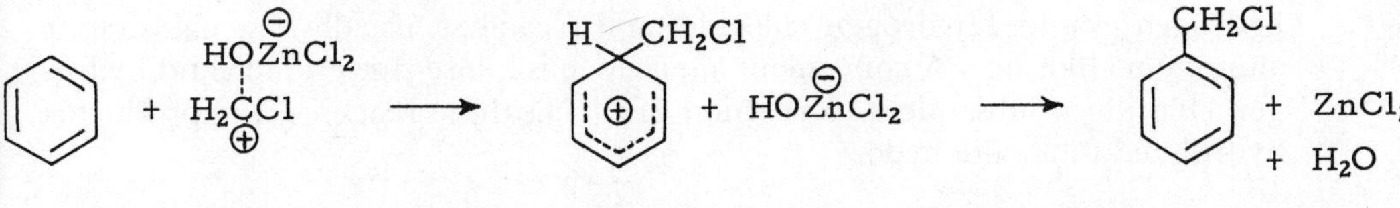

EXERCISE 26-4   Suggest a reason why zinc chloride is used in preference to aluminum chloride as a catalyst for chloromethylation reactions.

EXERCISE 26-5   Give the principal product(s) of chloromethylation of the following compounds:
a. 1-methylnaphthalene   c. p-methoxybenzaldehyde
b. 1-nitronaphthalene   d. anisole (using acetaldehyde in place of formaldehyde)

B. Aldehydes by Formylation

Substitution of the carboxaldehyde group (—CHO) into an aromatic ring is known as **formylation.** In the **Gattermann-Koch reaction,** this is accomplished by reaction of an aromatic hydrocarbon with carbon monoxide in the presence of hydrogen chloride and aluminum chloride. Cuprous chloride is also required for reactions proceeding at atmospheric pressure but is not necessary for reactions at elevated pressures.

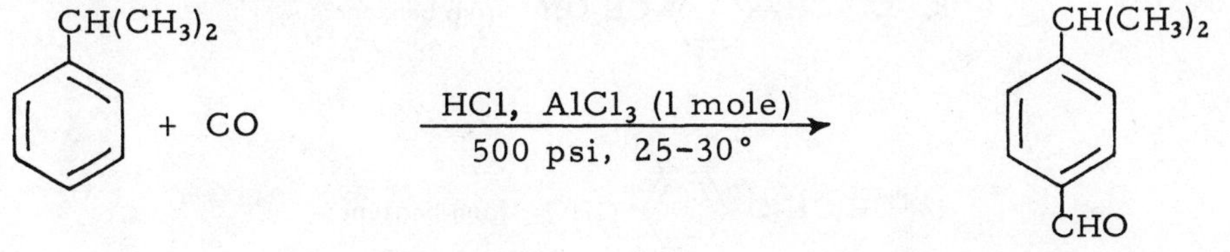

p-isopropylbenzaldehyde
60%

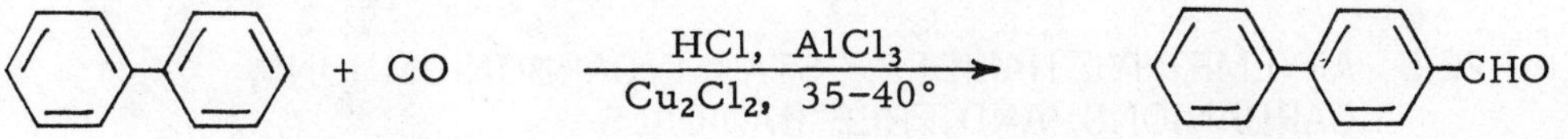

p-phenylbenzaldehyde
73%

EXERCISE 26-6   Suggest a possible mechanism for the Gattermann-Koch reaction.

Formylation by the **Gattermann reaction** (not to be confused with the Gattermann-Koch reaction) is restricted to reactive aromatic compounds like phenols, phenolic ethers, and certain hydrocarbons. The necessary reagents include hydrogen cyanide, hydrogen chloride, and a catalyst, usually zinc chloride or aluminum chloride. A convenient alternative is to use zinc cyanide and hydrogen chloride. Subsequent to reaction involving these reagents, the product is hydrolyzed to an aldehyde.

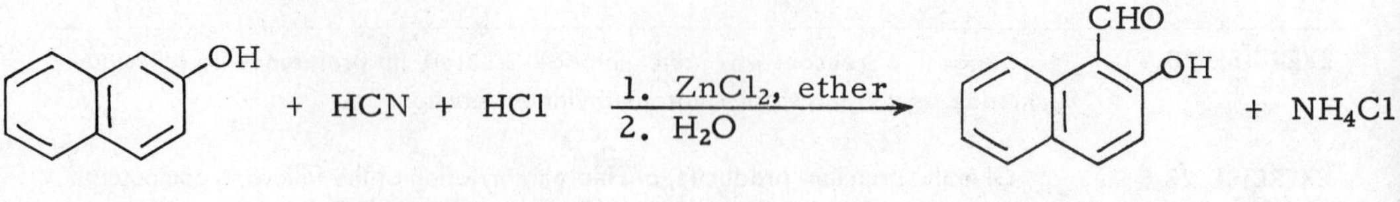
OH
+ HCN + HCl
1. $ZnCl_2$, ether
2. H_2O
CHO
OH
+ NH_4Cl

2-naphthol 2-hydroxy-1-naphthaldehyde

EXERCISE 26-7 Formulate the steps that are probably involved in the formylation of a phenol by the Gattermann reaction.

EXERCISE 26-8 How would you synthesize the following compounds from the indicated starting materials?

a. 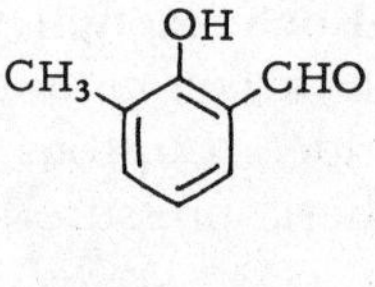
OH
CH_3
CHO
from toluene

b. 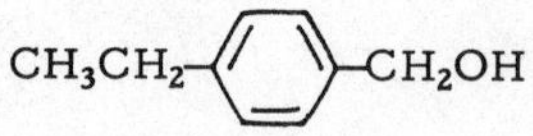
CH_3CH_2
CH_2OH
from benzene

c. 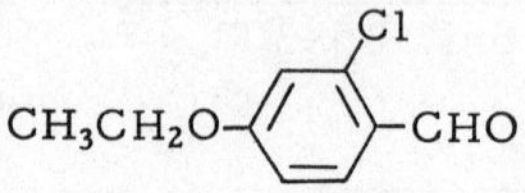
Cl
CH_3CH_2O
CHO
from benzene

PROPERTIES OF AROMATIC SIDE-CHAIN DERIVATIVES

26-5 ARYLMETHYL HALIDES. STABLE CARBONIUM IONS, CARBANIONS, AND FREE RADICALS

The arylmethyl halides of particular interest are those having both halogen and aryl substituents bonded to the same saturated carbon. Typical examples and their physical properties are listed in Table 26-1.

We noted in Chapter 23 that benzyl halides are comparable in both S_N1 and S_N2 reactivity to allyl halides and, because high reactivity in S_N1 reactions is associated primarily with exceptional carbonium-ion stability, the reactivity of benzyl derivatives can be ascribed mainly to resonance stabilization of the benzyl cation (p. 572). Diphenylmethyl or benzhydryl halides, $(C_6H_5)_2CHX$, are still more reactive than benzyl halides in S_N1 reactions, and this is reasonable because the

Table 26-1   Physical Properties of Arylmethyl Halides

Compound	Formula	B.p., °C	M.p., °C	$d^{20/4}$, g/ml
benzyl fluoride	$C_6H_5CH_2F$	140	-35	$1.0228^{25.3}$
benzyl chloride	$C_6H_5CH_2Cl$	179	-43	$1.1026^{18/4}$
benzyl bromide	$C_6H_5CH_2Br$	198	-4.0	$1.438^{22/0}$
benzyl iodide	$C_6H_5CH_2I$	93^{10mm}	24	$1.733^{25/4}$
benzal chloride	$C_6H_5CHCl_2$	207	-16	1.2557^{14}
benzotrichloride	$C_6H_5CCl_3$	214	-22	1.38
benzotrifluoride	$C_6H_5CF_3$	103	-29.1	1.1886^{20}
benzhydryl chloride (diphenylmethyl chloride)	$(C_6H_5)_2CHCl$	173^{19mm}	20.5	
triphenylmethyl chloride (trityl chloride)	$(C_6H_5)_3CCl$		112.3	

diphenylmethyl cation has two phenyl groups over which the positive charge can be delocalized and is, therefore, more stable relative to the starting halide than is the benzyl cation.

diphenylmethyl cation

Accordingly, we might expect triphenylmethyl or trityl halides, $(C_6H_5)_3C{-}X$, to be more reactive yet. In fact, the C—X bonds of such compounds are sufficiently labile that reversible ionization occurs in solvents that have reasonably high dielectric constants but do not react irreversibly with the carbonium ion. An example of such a solvent is liquid sulfur dioxide, and the degrees of ionization of a number of triarylmethyl halides in this solvent have been determined by electrical-conductance measurements, although the equilibria are complicated by ion-pair association.

$$(C_6H_5)_3C{-}Cl \; \xrightarrow[\;]{SO_2,\,0°} \; (C_6H_5)_3C^{\oplus}Cl^{\ominus} \; \rightleftharpoons \; (C_6H_5)_3C^{\oplus} + Cl^{\ominus}$$

ion pair   dissociated ions

Triarylmethyl cations are among the most stable carbonium ions known. They are intensely colored and are readily formed when the corresponding triaryl-carbinol is dissolved in strong acids.

$(C_6H_5)_3C{-}OH$ $\xrightleftharpoons{\;H_2SO_4\;}$ $(C_6H_5)_3C{-}\overset{\oplus}{O}H_2$ $\xrightleftharpoons{\;(-H_2O)\;}$ $(C_6H_5)_3C^{\oplus}$

triphenylcarbinol   triphenylmethyl cation

(colorless)   (orange-yellow)

EXERCISE 26-9   *a.* Suggest why the extent of ionic dissociation of triarylmethyl chlorides in liquid sulfur dioxide decreases for compounds [1], [2], and [3] in the order [1] > [2] > [3]. Use of models may be helpful here.

$(C_6H_5)_3C{-}Cl$

[1]   [2]   [3]

b. Which alcohol would you expect to give the more stable carbonium ion in sulfuric acid, 9-fluorenol [4] or 2,3,6,7-dibenzotropyl alcohol[1] [5]? Explain.

[4]   [5]

c. When triphenylcarbinol is dissolved in 100 per cent sulfuric acid, it gives a freezing-point depression that corresponds to formation of 4 moles of particles per mole of carbinol. Explain.

In addition to stable cations, triarylmethyl compounds form stable carbanions. Because of this, the corresponding hydrocarbons are relatively acidic compared to simple alkanes. They react readily with strong bases such as sodamide, and the resulting carbanions are usually intensely colored.

$(C_6H_5)_3CH \;+\; Na^{\oplus}\overset{\ominus}{N}H_2 \;\;\xrightleftharpoons{\;\;ether\;\;}\;\; (C_6H_5)_3C{:}^{\ominus} \; Na^{\oplus} \;+\; NH_3$

triphenylmethane   sodium triphenylmethide

(colorless)   (blood red)

EXERCISE 26-10   How many structures of comparable energy are there that may be considered as contributing to the hybrid of the resonance-stabilized triphenylmethide ion?

Triarylmethyl compounds also form stable triarylmethyl free radicals, and indeed, the first stable, carbon free radical to be reported was the triphenyl-

[1] According to the IUPAC rules for naming polycyclic compounds, when a benzene ring is "*ortho-*fused" to another ring, the prefix "benzo" is attached to the name of the parent ring compound. This prefix becomes "benz" when preceding a vowel (e.g., benzanthracene).

methyl radical, $(C_6H_5)_3C\cdot$, prepared inadvertently by Gomberg in 1900. Gomberg's objective was to prepare hexaphenylethane by a Wurtz coupling reaction of triphenylmethyl chloride with metallic silver; but he found that no hydrocarbon was formed unless air was carefully excluded from the system.

$$2(C_6H_5)_3C\text{—Cl} + 2Ag \xrightarrow{\text{benzene}} (C_6H_5)_3C\text{—}C(C_6H_5)_3 + 2AgCl$$

hexaphenylethane

In the presence of atmospheric oxygen, the product is triphenylmethyl peroxide, $(C_6H_5)_3COOC(C_6H_5)_3$, rather than hexaphenylethane. Although at first Gomberg believed that the product from the reaction of triphenylmethyl chloride with silver was the triphenylmethyl radical because of its avidity toward oxygen and chlorine, subsequent investigations showed that hexaphenylethane dissociates only slightly to triphenylmethyl radicals at room temperature in inert solvents ($K = 2.2 \times 10^{-4}$ at 24° in benzene). However, equilibrium between hexaphenylethane and triphenylmethyl radicals is rapidly established so that oxygen readily converts the ethane into the relatively stable triphenylmethyl peroxide.

$$(C_6H_5)_3C\text{—}C(C_6H_5)_3 \underset{K = 2.2 \times 10^{-4}}{\overset{\text{benzene } 24°}{\rightleftharpoons}} 2(C_6H_5)_3C\cdot$$

hexaphenylethane   triphenylmethyl radical

$$(C_6H_5)_3C\cdot + O_2 \rightleftharpoons (C_6H_5)_3COO\cdot \xrightarrow{(C_6H_5)_3C\cdot} (C_6H_5)_3COOC(C_6H_5)_3$$

triphenylmethyl
peroxide

While the above reactions involving the triphenylmethyl radical may seem entirely reasonable, at the time they were discovered, Gomberg's suggestion that the triphenylmethyl radical could exist as a fairly stable species was not well received. Today, the stability of the radical has been established beyond question by a variety of methods such as electron paramagnetic resonance (e.p.r.) spectroscopy, which is discussed briefly at the end of this chapter (pp. 640-641), and this stability can be attributed to stabilization of the odd electron by the attached phenyl groups.

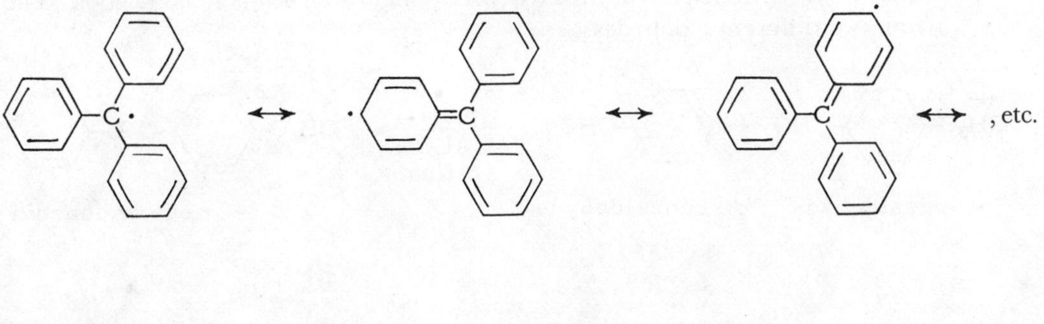

Although the slight dissociation of hexaphenylethane into triphenylmethyl radicals is mainly due to the electronic stability of the radicals formed, it is also due in part to relief of strain in going from the bulky ethane to the less hindered triphenylmethyl radical.

The stability of a carbon free radical, $R_3C\cdot$, is reflected in the ease with which the C—H bond of the corresponding hydrocarbon, R_3CH, is broken homolytically. For example, hydrogen bonded to a tertiary carbon is replaced in free-radical chlorination faster than hydrogen at a secondary or primary position (see p. 76) showing that the order of stability of the resulting carbon radicals is tertiary > secondary > primary. Hydrogen-abstraction reactions by radicals other than chlorine atoms have been investigated to obtain some measure of hydrocarbon reactivity and radical stability.

EXERCISE 26-11   Which of the following pairs of compounds would you expect to be the more reactive under the specified conditions? Give your reasons and write equations for the reactions involved.

a. $p\text{-}NO_2C_6H_4CH_2Br$ or $p\text{-}CH_3OC_6H_4CH_2Br$ on hydrolysis in aqueous acetone

b. $(C_6H_5)_3CH$ or $C_6H_5CH_3$ in the presence of phenyllithium

c. $(C_6H_5)_3C\text{—}C(C_6H_5)_3$ or $(C_6H_5)_2CH\text{—}CH(C_6H_5)_2$ on heating

d. $(C_6H_5)_2N\text{—}N(C_6H_5)_2$ or $(C_6H_5)_2CH\text{—}CH(C_6H_5)_2$ on heating

---

26-6 AROMATIC ALDEHYDES

Most of the reactions of aromatic aldehydes involve nothing new or surprising in view of our earlier discussion on the reactions of aldehydes (Chapters 14 and 15). One reaction, which is rather different and is usually regarded as being characteristic of aromatic aldehydes (although, in fact, it does occur with other aldehydes having no α hydrogens), is known as the **benzoin condensation** and is essentially a dimerization of two aldehyde molecules through the catalytic action of sodium or potassium cyanide.

benzoin

90%

The dimer so formed from benzaldehyde is an α-hydroxy ketone and is called benzoin. Unsymmetrical or mixed benzoins may often be obtained in good yield from two different aldehydes.

anisaldehyde   benzaldehyde   4-methoxybenzoin

In naming an unsymmetrical benzoin, substituents in the ring attached to the carbonyl group are numbered in the usual way while primes are used to number substituents in the ring attached to the carbinol carbon. For example:

$$\text{(3-NO}_2\text{-C}_6\text{H}_4\text{)}-\overset{\text{O}}{\overset{\|}{\text{C}}}-\overset{\text{OH}}{\overset{|}{\text{CH}}}-(\text{4-Cl-C}_6\text{H}_4)$$

3-nitro-4'-chlorobenzoin

EXERCISE 26-12 Draw structures and name all the possible benzoins that could be formed from a mixture of (a) p-tolualdehyde and o-ethoxybenzaldehyde, and (b) 8-methyl-1-naphthaldehyde and anisaldehyde. An unsymmetrical benzoin such as 4-methoxybenzoin is rather readily equilibrated with its isomer, 4'-methoxybenzoin, under the influence of bases. Explain.

Concerning the mechanism of benzoin formation, an alkali cyanide should and does react with the aldehyde to form a cyanohydrin. However, the cyanohydrin [6] thus formed has a relatively acidic α hydrogen because the resulting carbanion is stabilized by both a phenyl and a nitrile group. At the pH of a cyanide solution, a benzyl-type carbanion [7] is readily formed and, in a subsequent slow step, attacks the carbonyl carbon of a second aldehyde molecule. Loss of HCN from the addition product [8] leads to benzoin.

$$C_6H_5\overset{O}{\overset{\diagup}{C}}-H + HCN \underset{\longleftarrow}{\overset{\text{base}}{\longrightarrow}} C_6H_5-\underset{\underset{C\equiv N}{|}}{\overset{\overset{OH}{|}}{C}}-H \underset{\longleftarrow}{\overset{-H^{\oplus}}{\longrightarrow}} C_6H_5-\underset{\underset{C\equiv N}{|}}{\overset{\overset{OH}{|}}{C}}:^{\ominus}$$

[6]   [7]

$$C_6H_5-\underset{\underset{C\equiv N}{|}}{\overset{\overset{OH}{|}}{C}}:^{\ominus} + \overset{O}{\overset{\|}{C}}-C_6H_5 \overset{H^{\oplus}}{\longrightarrow} C_6H_5-\underset{\underset{CN}{|}}{\overset{\overset{OH}{|}}{C}}-\underset{\underset{H}{|}}{\overset{\overset{OH}{|}}{C}}-C_6H_5 \overset{-HCN}{\longrightarrow} C_6H_5-\overset{O}{\overset{\|}{C}}-\overset{OH}{\overset{|}{CH}}-C_6H_5$$

[8]   benzoin

Benzoins in general are sometimes useful intermediates for the synthesis of other compounds, since they can be oxidized to α-diketones and reduced in stages to various products depending upon the reaction conditions.

26-7 NATURAL OCCURRENCE AND USES OF AROMATIC SIDE-CHAIN DERIVATIVES

Derivatives of aromatic aldehydes occur naturally in the seeds of plants. For example, amygdalin is a substance occurring in the seeds of the bitter almond; it is a derivative of gentiobiose, which is a disaccharide made up of two glucose units; one of the glucose units is bonded through the OH group of benzaldehyde cyanohydrin by a β-glucoside linkage.

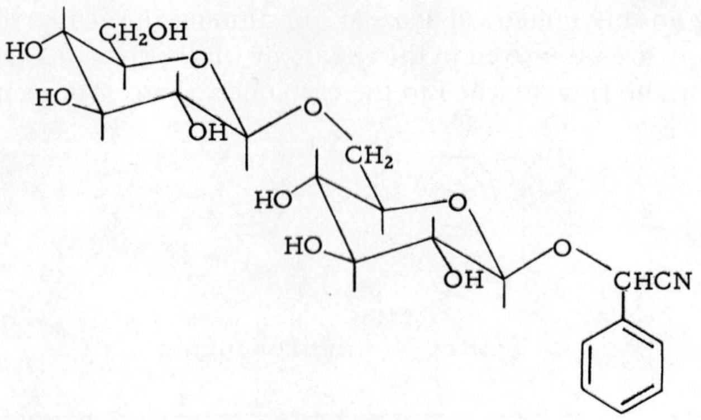

amygdalin

The flavoring vanillin occurs naturally as glucovanillin (a glucoside) in the vanilla bean, although it is also obtained commercially by oxidation of eugenol, which itself is a constituent of several essential oils.

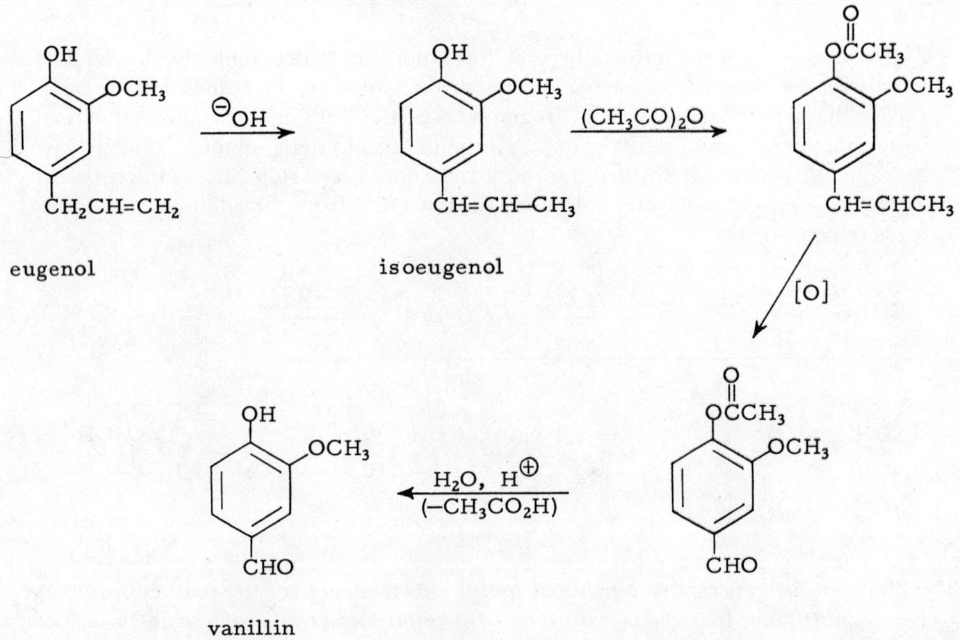

eugenol   isoeugenol

vanillin

Methyl salicylate, or oil of wintergreen, occurs in many plants, but it is also readily prepared synthetically by esterification of salicylic acid, which in turn is made from phenol (see p. 613).

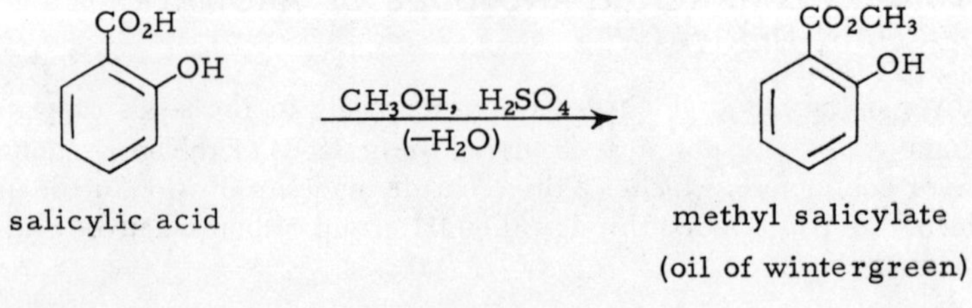

salicylic acid

$$\xrightarrow[(-H_2O)]{CH_3OH, \ H_2SO_4}$$

methyl salicylate

(oil of wintergreen)

The acetyl derivative of salicylic acid is better known as aspirin and is prepared from the acid with acetic anhydride using sulfuric acid as catalyst.

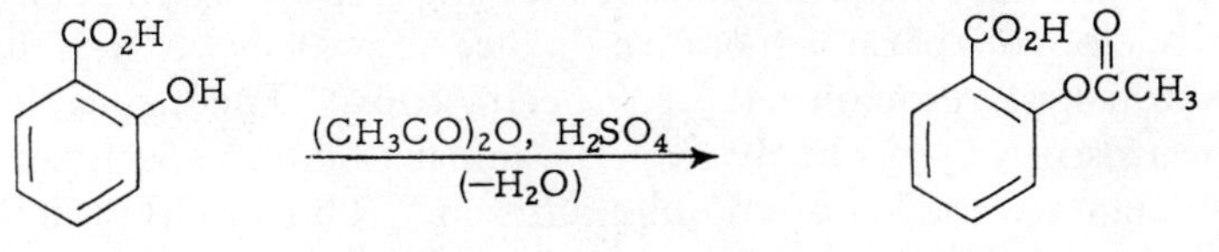

$$\xrightarrow[(-H_2O)]{(CH_3CO)_2O,\ H_2SO_4}$$

acetylsalicyclic acid

(aspirin)

The structures of several other side-chain compounds that have direct use as flavorings, perfumes, therapeutic drugs, or insecticides follow:

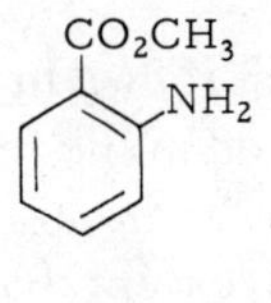

methyl anthranilate

(grape flavoring and perfume)

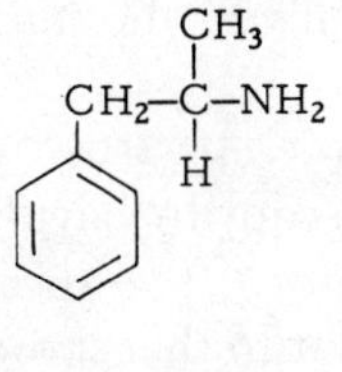

benzedrine

(central nervous system stimulant; decongestant)

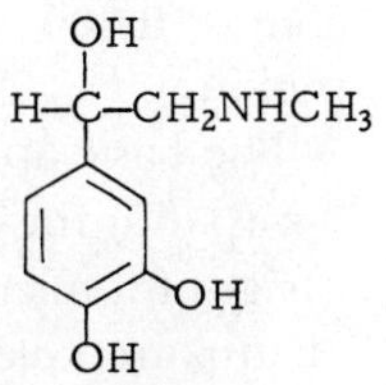

adrenaline (epinephrine)

(central nervous system stimulant; blood pressure raising principle of adrenal glands)

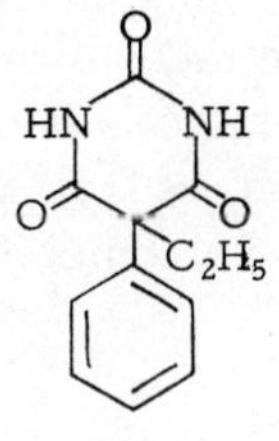

phenobarbital

(sedative)

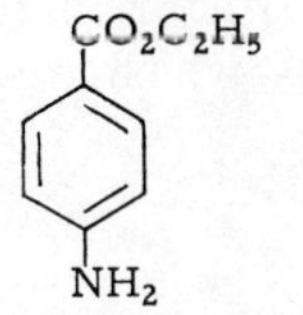

benzocaine

(local anesthetic)

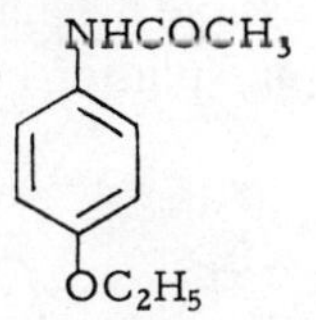

phenacetin

(analgesic)

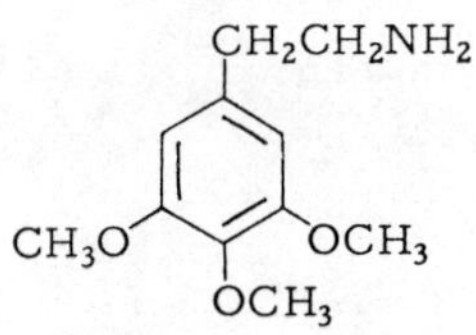

mescaline

(produces euphoria)

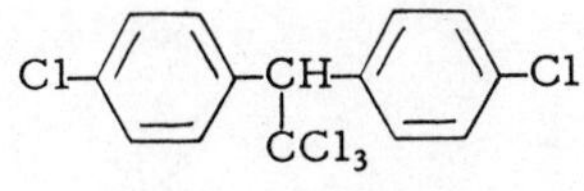

DDT

(insecticide)

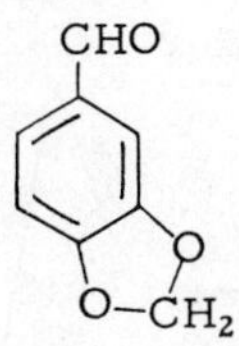

piperonal

(perfume ingredient)

26-8   ELECTRON PARAMAGNETIC RESONANCE (e.p.r.) SPECTROSCOPY

One of the most important methods of studying free radicals that has yet been developed is electron paramagnetic resonance (e.p.r.) or, as it is sometimes called, electron-spin resonance (e.s.r.) spectroscopy.   The principles of this form of spectroscopy are in many respects similar to n.m.r. spectroscopy, even though the language used is often quite different.   The important point is that an *unpaired* electron, like a proton, has a spin and a magnetic moment such that it has two possible orientations in a magnetic field corresponding to magnetic quantum numbers $+\frac{1}{2}$ and $-\frac{1}{2}$.   The two orientations define two energy states, which differ in energy by about 1000 times the energy difference between corresponding states for protons and, therefore, the frequency of absorption of electrons is about 1000 times that of protons at the same magnetic field.   At magnetic fields of 3600 gauss, the absorption frequency of free electrons is about 10,000 Mcps, which falls in the microwave, rather than the radiowave, region.

The basic apparatus for e.p.r. spectroscopy differs from that shown in Figure 2-6 (p. 35) for n.m.r. spectroscopy by having the sample located in the resonant cavity of a microwave generator.   The spectrum produced by e.p.r. absorption of unpaired electrons is similar to that shown in Figure 26-1a, except that e.p.r. spectrometers are normally so arranged as to yield a plot of the first derivative of the curve of absorption against magnetic field, rather than the absorption curve itself, as shown in Figure 26-1b.   This arrangement is used because it gives a better signal-to-noise ratio than a simple plot of absorption against magnetic field.

The sensitivity of e.p.r. spectroscopy for detection of radicals is high.   Under favorable conditions, a concentration as low as 10^{-12} M of free radicals can be readily detected.   Identification of simple hydrocarbon free radicals is often possible by analysis of the fine structure in their spectra, which arises from spin-spin splittings involving protons, which are reasonably close to the centers over

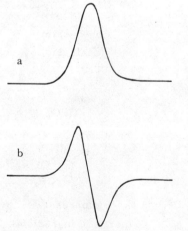

Figure 26-1

Plots of absorption and derivative e.p.r. curves, a and b respectively.

which the unpaired electron is distributed. The multiplicity of hydrogens and their location in the *ortho, meta,* and *para* positions of the triphenylmethyl radical produces an extremely complex e.p.r. spectrum with at least 21 observable absorption lines. Other radicals may give simpler spectra. Methyl radicals generated by X-ray bombardment of methyl iodide at $-196°\,C$ show four $(n + 1)$ resonance lines, as expected, for interaction of the electron with three (n) protons (see pp. 38-41).

One of the most exciting uses of e.p.r. is in the study of free-radical intermediates in organic reactions. Thus, in the oxidation of hydroquinone in alkaline solution by oxygen, the formation of the semiquinone radical (pp. 619-620) can be detected by e.p.r. The identity of the intermediate is shown by the fact that its electron spectrum is split into five equally spaced lines, which correspond to the four equivalent ring protons. The radical disappears by disproportionation reactions and has a half-life of about three seconds.

Similar studies have shown that free radicals are generated and decay in oxidations brought about by enzymes. Free radicals have been detected by e.p.r. measurements in algae "fixing" carbon dioxide in photosynthesis. The character of the radicals formed has been found to depend upon the wavelength of the light supplied for photosynthesis.

EXERCISE 26-13   The e.p.r. spectrum shown in Figure 26-2 is of a first-derivative curve of the absorption of a free radical produced by X irradiation of 1,3,5-cycloheptatriene present as an impurity in crystals of naphthalene.   Make a sketch of this spectrum as it would look as as *absorption* spectrum and show the structure of the radical to which it corresponds. Show how at least one isomeric structure for the radical can be eliminated by the observed character of the spectrum.

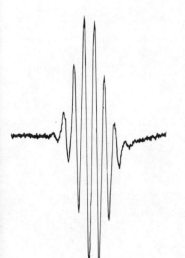

Figure 26-2

Electron paramagnetic resonance spectrum of cycloheptatrienyl radical produced by X irradiation of 1,3,5-cyclo-heptatriene.

Heterocyclic Aromatic Compounds

*H*eterocyclic organic compounds have cyclic structures in which one or more of the ring atoms are of elements other than carbon. Heterocycles having nitrogen, oxygen, and sulfur as hetero atoms have been studied more thoroughly than those involving other elements, such as phosphorus, boron, tin, and silicon. In this chapter we shall confine our attention to a discussion of the chemistry of heterocyclic nitrogen, oxygen, and sulfur compounds and, of these, we shall be concerned primarily with the aromatic heterocycles rather than their saturated analogs. The chemistry of saturated heterocycles like ethylene oxide, tetrahydrofuran, dioxane, pyrrolidine, piperidine, lactones, and lactams has been dealt with in earlier chapters, and, in general, the properties of such substances can be correlated with those of their open-chain analogs, provided appropriate account is taken of the strain and conformational effects that are associated with ring compounds. The variety of known heterocyclic compounds is so large as to make any comprehensive survey quite out of the question; instead, we shall try to emphasize the principles that are important to an understanding of the chemistry associated with the basic ring systems most frequently encountered in practice.

Heterocyclic Aromatic Compounds

The importance of heterocyclic compounds is apparent from the wealth and variety of such compounds that occur naturally or are prepared on a commercial scale by the dye and drug industries. Many of these compounds fulfill important physiological functions in plants and animals. We have already encountered some of the important naturally occurring heterocycles in earlier chapters. Thus, the carbohydrates may be classified as oxygen heterocycles, whereas the nucleic acids and some amino acids, peptides, and proteins possess nitrogen-containing ring systems.

We shall begin with a discussion of the five- and six-membered ring compounds containing only one hetero atom, namely, pyrrole, furan, thiophene, and pyridine. The properties of most of the important condensed or polycyclic

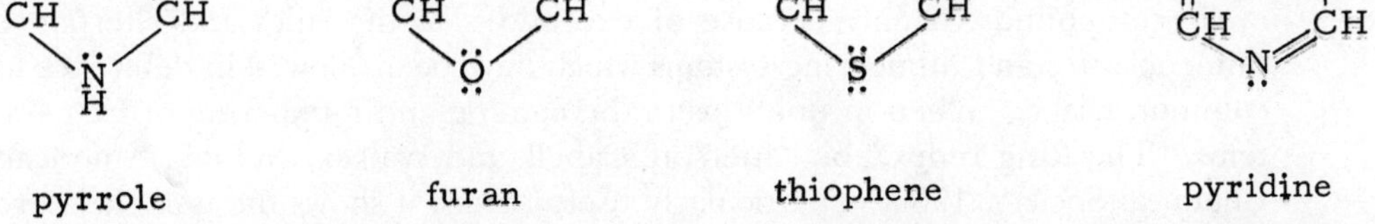

pyrrole
(azole)

furan
(oxole)

thiophene
(thiole)

pyridine
(azine)

derivatives, such as indole, benzofuran, benzothiophene, quinoline, isoquinoline, carbazole, and acridine usually turn out to be quite analogous to those of
the monocyclic systems when proper account is taken of the stabilizing effects of
the aromatic rings.

indole   benzofuran   benzothiophene   quinoline

isoquinoline   carbazole   acridine

We shall also discuss some aspects of the chemistry of those heterocycles of importance which have more than one hetero atom. Several examples follow.

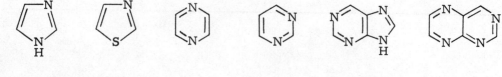

imidazole   thiazole   pyrazine   pyrimidine   purine   pteridine

Finally, a brief summary will be given of a few important naturally occurring
heterocyclic compounds. First, it will be necessary to consider systems for naming of heterocycles.

27-1 NOMENCLATURE OF HETEROCYCLIC RING SYSTEMS

Many common heterocyclic compounds including those already mentioned
have, over the years, acquired trivial names which are quite unlikely to be replaced by more systematic names. However, the need for systematic nomenclature still remains. We shall therefore describe briefly some of the rules
adopted by the IUPAC for the naming of monocyclic ring systems possessing
one or more hetero atoms. The system is simple and straightforward when applied to monocyclic compounds, but complications sometimes arise for polycyclic compounds, mainly because of exceptions to the rules and alternative
nomenclature and numbering systems which have been allowed in deference to
common usage. When in doubt as to the naming and numbering of ring systems, "The Ring Index," by Patterson, Capell, and Walker, 2nd ed., American
Chemical Society, 1960, is particularly useful, since it shows the nomenclature
for all known types of ring systems. Without this book, which was first published

in 1940, it would be hard to exaggerate the confusion that would now exist in the chemical literature over the naming of ring compounds.

A system has been devised whereby, in any given monocyclic compound, the size of the ring, the number, kind, and positions of the hetero atoms present and the degree of unsaturation are unambiguously specified in a short and simple name. This is done by adding an appropriate suffix and prefix to a given stem according to the following rules.

1. Ring size is denoted by the stem, *ir*, *et*, *ol*, *in*, *ep*, *oc*, *on*, or *ec* for 3-, 4-, 5-, 6-, 7-, 8-, 9-, or 10-membered rings, respectively.

2. The kind of hetero atom present is indicated by the prefix, *oxa*, *thia*, *aza* for oxygen, sulfur, or nitrogen, respectively; the prefixes *dioxa*, *dithia*, and *diaza* connote two oxygen, sulfur, or nitrogen atoms. When two or more different hetero atoms are present, they are cited in order of preference: oxygen before sulfur before nitrogen, as in the prefixes *oxaza* for one oxygen and one nitrogen, and *thiaza* for one sulfur and one nitrogen.

3. The degree of unsaturation is usually specified in the suffix, and a list of appropriate suffixes and their stems according to ring size is given in Table 27-1. It will be noted that the suffix changes slightly according to whether or not the ring contains nitrogen.

4. Numbering of the ring starts with the hetero atom and proceeds around the ring so as to give substituents (or other hetero atoms) the lowest numbered positions. When two or more different hetero atoms are present, oxygen takes precedence over sulfur and sulfur over nitrogen for the number one position. This rule is illustrated in the following examples.

Table 27-1   Stems, Suffix, and Ring Size of Heterocyclic Compounds

		Stem + suffix			
		Ring contains nitrogen		Ring contains no nitrogen	
Ring size	Stem	Unsaturated[a]	Saturated	Unsaturated[a]	Saturated
3	-ir-	-irine	-iridine	-irene	-irane
4	-et-	-ete	-etidine	-ete	-etane
5	-ol-	-ole	-olidine	-ole	-olane
6	-in-	-ine	[b]	-in	-ane
7	-ep-	-epine	[b]	-epin	-epane
8	-oc-	-ocine	[b]	-ocin	-ocane
9	-on-	-onine	[b]	-onin	-onane
10	-ec-	-ecine	[b]	-ecin	-ecane

[a] Corresponding to maximum number of double bonds, excluding cumulative double bonds.

[b] The prefix "perhydro" is attached to the stem and suffix of the parent unsaturated compound.

azine

(pyridine)

1, 3–thiazole

5–amino–1, 3–diazine

(5–aminopyrimidine)

5. Partially reduced ring compounds are often referred to as dihydro or tetra-hydro derivatives of the parent unsaturated compound. Saturation is also indicated by attaching the symbol H together with the number denoting position of saturation to the name of the parent unsaturated compound.

2, 3–dihydropyrrole

(2, 3–dihydrazole)

2, 5–dihydrofuran

(2, 5–dihydroxole)

2H–pyran

(2H–oxine,
α–pyran)

3H–pyrazole

(3H–1, 2–diazole)

Applying these basic rules to specific examples is rather like putting together the pieces of a jigsaw puzzle. Some simple examples follow and, where the chosen example has a commonly used trivial name, both trivial and systematic names are given, the latter being in parentheses. It will be noticed that when two vowels come together, then "a" of the prefix is omitted. For example ethylene oxide is called oxirane by the IUPAC system, rather than oxairane.

ethylenimine

(aziridine)

ethylene oxide

(oxirane)

azetidine

oxetane

thietane

pyrrole

(azole)

pyrrolidine

(azolidine)

furan

(oxole)

tetrahydrofuran

(oxolane)

thiophene
(thiole)

imidazole
(1, 3–diazole)

oxazole
(1, 3–oxazole)

isoxazole
(1, 2–oxazole)

pyridine
(azine)

piperidine
(perhydroazine)

pyridazine
(1, 2–diazine)

azepine

EXERCISE 27-1   Name the following compounds by an accepted system:

a. H₃C–S–CH₃

b. (structure with CH₃ on aziridine ring, N–CH₃)

c. S–NH (six-membered ring)

d. N–N / N (triazine ring)

e. (oxazolium structure) ⊕N–CH₃ Br⊖

f. (pyridine attached to N-methylpyrrolidine)

g. (pyrimidine with H₃C, OH, OH substituents)

h. H₃C–N(H)–CH₃ (pyrroline ring with two CH₃ groups)

EXERCISE 27-2   Draw structures for the following compounds, giving each its trivial name if
it has one:

a. diazirine
b. oxetan-2-one
c. azolidin-2-one
d. 3-azinecarboxylic acid
e. 2,5-furandione

f. 2-oxolecarboxaldehyde
g. 1,3-oxathiole
h. 4H-1,3-diazole
i. 2H-1,3-diazepine
j. 4H-1,4-oxazine

MONOHETERO RING SYSTEMS

27-2   SOME DERIVATIVES OF FURAN, PYRROLE, THIOPHENE, AND PYRIDINE

The physical properties of pyrrole, furan, thiophene, pyridine, and some of their more important polycyclic derivatives are summarized in Table 27-2. A striking feature of this table is the very large difference between the boiling points of pyrrole and furan or thiophene. The higher boiling point of pyrrole is attributed to association through hydrogen bonding. Other properties of these heterocycles will be mentioned in the ensuing discussion.

27-3   AROMATIC CHARACTER OF UNSATURATED HETEROCYCLES

A. Pyrrole, Furan, and Thiophene

The five-membered heterocyclic compounds, pyrrole, furan, and thiophene, are not as reactive as their diene-like structures (as commonly written) might suggest. Rather, each possesses considerable aromatic character arising from the delocalization of *four* carbon π electrons and *two* paired electrons donated by the hetero atom. This combination forms a sextet of delocalized electrons — a number which we have seen in the case of conjugated carbocyclic structures, such as benzene, cyclopentadienate anion, and cycloheptatrienyl (tropylium) cation, is usually quite favorable (p. 190).

The structure of each heterocycle can be described as a hybrid of several electron-pairing schemes, as shown below for pyrrole. We shall have more to say later about the degree of contribution of the dipolar resonance forms, [1b] to [1e].

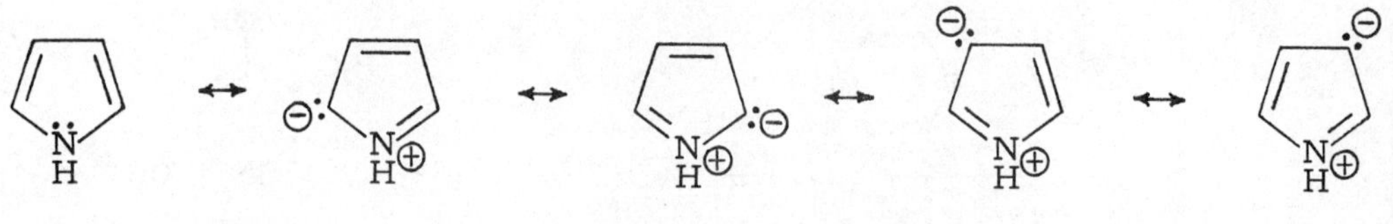

[1a]   [1b]   [1c]   [1d]   [1e]

or

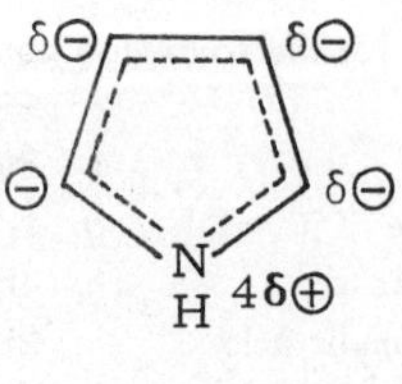

[1]

In terms of atomic orbitals, the structure of each of these heterocycles may be regarded as a planar pentagonal framework of C—H, C—C, and C—X σ bonds (X being the hetero atom) made up with sp^2-hybridized ring carbon atoms. There remain four carbon p-orbitals with one π electron, each to overlap with a doubly filled p-orbital of the hetero atom. This formulation is illustrated in Figure 27-1 for pyrrole.

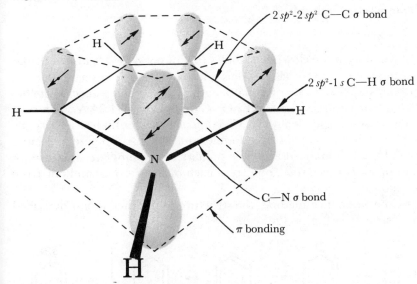

Figure 27-1   Atomic orbital description of pyrrole.

The stabilization energies of pyrrole, furan, and thiophene obtained from experimental and calculated heats of combustion (see Table 27-2) are only about

Table 27-2   Physical Properties, Heats of Combustion, and Stabilization Energies of Some Common Heterocycles

Compound	M.p., °C.	B.p., °C.	ΔH expt., kcal/mole	ΔH calc.,[b] kcal/mole	S.E.
benzene [a]	5.5	80	789	827	37.9
furan	—	32	507	523	16
pyrrole	—	130-131	578	594	16
thiophene	−38	84	612	623	11
pyridine	−42	115-116	675	696	21
naphthalene [a]	80	218	1250	1321	71
indole	52	253-254	1040	1088	48
quinoline	15	238	1137	1192	55
anthracene [a]	216	340	1712	1816	104
carbazole	245	355	1500	1583	83
acridine	110	346	1578	1685	107

[a] Included in the table for purposes of comparison.
[b] Calculated from bond energies, Table 3-4.

half of the stabilization energy of benzene. However, the heterocycles differ from benzene in that each has only one resonance structure, with no formal bonds or charge separation. Furthermore, on the basis of relative electronegativities of sulfur, nitrogen, and oxygen, we may anticipate that the structures analogous to [1b] to [1e] should be important in the order thiophene > pyrrole >furan. As a result, it is reasonable to expect furan to be the least aromatic of the three heterocycles, and indeed it is.

B. Pyridine

The structure of pyridine closely resembles that of benzene. Within a planar hexagonal framework of five carbon atoms and one nitrogen atom, all the carbon-carbon bonds appear to be of equal length (1.39 A) and intermediate between a C—C single bond (1.54 A) and a C=C double bond (1.34 A). The two C—N bonds are also of equal length (1.37 A) and are shorter than a C—N single bond (1.47 A) and longer than a C=N double bond (1.28 A). These molecular dimensions and the pronounced aromatic stability of pyridine are the result of delocalization of six p-π electrons, one from each of five carbons and one from the nitrogen atom.

In terms of the resonance method, the structure of pyridine is best described as a hybrid of structures [2a] to [2e].

[2a]   [2b]   [2c]   [2d]   [2e]   [2]

EXERCISE 27-3   Draw an atomic-orbital model for pyridine considering the unshared electron pair on nitrogen to be in a 2s orbital (see pp. 116-117).

27-4 CHEMICAL PROPERTIES OF PYRROLE, FURAN, THIOPHENE, AND PYRIDINE

In discussing the reactivity of these heterocycles, we shall be interested primarily in their degree of aromatic character, as typified by their ability to exhibit electrophilic and nucleophilic substitution reactions rather than undergo addition reactions. First, however, we shall consider their acidic and basic properties.

A. Basic Properties

In principle, each heterocycle can act as a base by accepting a proton or uniting with a Lewis acid at the hetero atom. Pyridine is weakly basic, forming pyridinium salts with strong acids; thiophene is virtually nonbasic, since it shows no tendency to form salts, whereas the base strengths of pyrrole and furan cannot be estimated accurately, because they polymerize in acid solution.

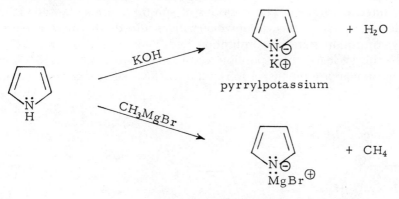

pyridinium bromide

EXERCISE 27-4   Would you expect pyrrole to add a proton to nitrogen more readily or less readily than aniline?

EXERCISE 27-5   Would you expect 1,3-diazole to be a weaker or stronger base than pyridine or pyrrole? Explain. What about 1,2-diazole?

B. Acidic Character

Pyrrole is weakly acidic and forms alkali-metal salts. There is also evidence that it forms saltlike Grignard reagents.

pyrrylpotassium

+ H_2O

+ CH_4

pyrrylmagnesium bromide

Although a precise value of the acid dissociation constant of pyrrole is not available, it is estimated at about 10^{-15}. Pyrrole is therefore a stronger acid than ammonia or the aliphatic amines by a factor of about 10^{18}. There are two reasons for the acidic character of pyrrole. Stability of the π-electron system of the resultant anion [3] may be an important factor, for there is no charge separation in the pyrryl anion such as there is in pyrrole.

[3a]   [3b]   [3c]   [3d]   [3e]

C. Electrophilic Substitution Reactions

The contrast between the reactivity of pyrrole and furan and that of pyridine is very striking; whereas pyridine is singularly unreactive toward reagents that normally effect electrophilic substitution of benzene, pyrrole and furan are extremely reactive—comparable in fact to the reactivity of aromatic amines and phenols. Thiophene is less reactive than pyrrole and furan, but more so than benzene.

Inspection of the hybrid structures of these heterocycles will indicate the main reason for the observed differences in reactivity. For example, pyrrole [1] is activated toward electrophilic attack as the result of its unsymmetrical charge distribution, which makes the ring carbons carry more negative charge than in benzene. However, with pyridine [2] the reverse is true, since the ring carbons are relatively electropositive and hence are deactivated toward positive or electrophilic reagents.

Electrophilic substitution of pyrrole, furan, and thiophene occurs preferentially at the 2-position, although the 3-position is attacked when the 2-positions are blocked. Pyridine, in its rare instances of electrophilic substitution, affords 3-substituted pyridines. The positions of substitution may be rationalized by considering which of the various alternatives affords the most stable (lowest energy) transition state or substitution intermediate (see pp. 554-557). For pyrrole, this is clearly the 2-position (compare structures [4] and [5]); for pyridine, by similar arguments, 3-substitution is favored (compare structures [6] and [7]).

2-substitution of pyrrole:

[4a]   [4b]   [4c]

3-substitution of pyrrole:

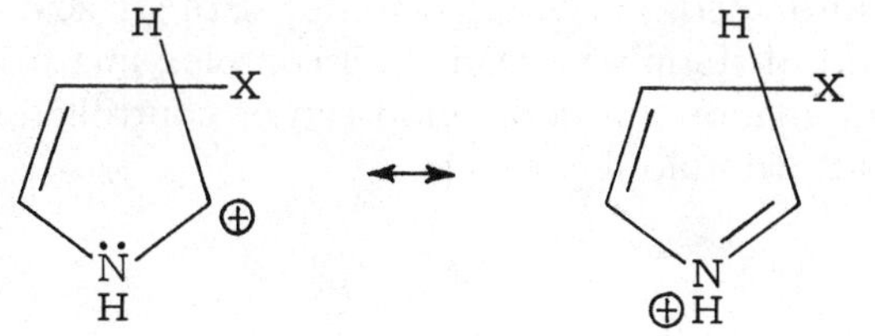

[5a]   [5b]

3-substitution of pyridine:

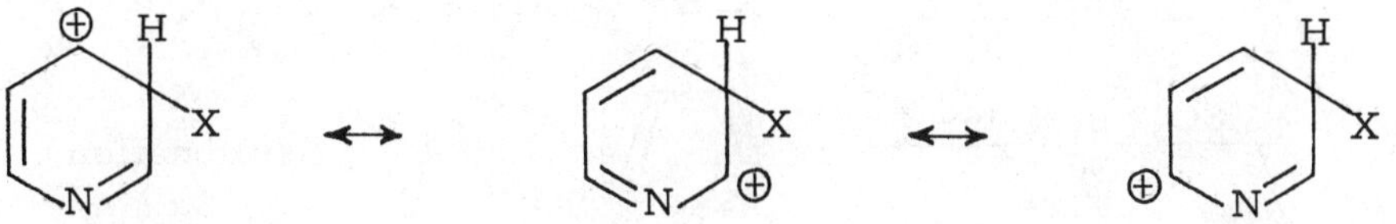

[6a]   [6b]   [6c]

2- or 4-substitution of pyridine:

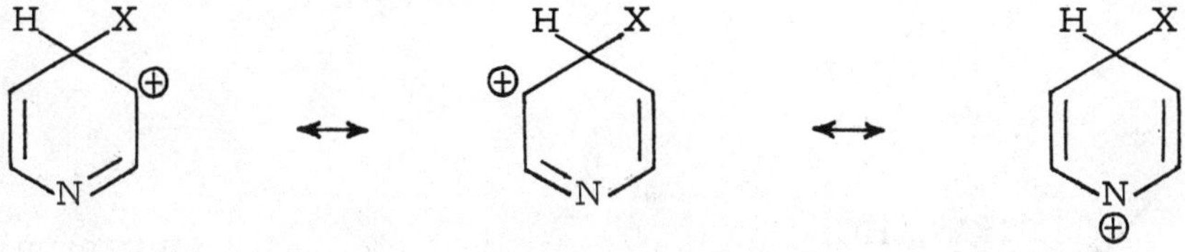

[7a]   [7b]   [7c]

(unfavorable)

The principal electrophilic substitution reactions of pyrrole are summarized in Figure 27-2. The important points to note, besides the fact that 2-substitution predominates, are: first, that nitration and sulfonation of pyrrole are possible, but only if strongly acidic conditions which would lead to polymerization are avoided; second, that pyrrole is sufficiently reactive for halogenation and Friedel-Crafts acylation to proceed without need for a catalyst. However, substituted pyrroles carrying electron-attracting substituents (e.g., —NO$_2$, —CO$_2$H) are less reactive than pyrrole and may require catalysts to effect substitution.

Furan resembles pyrrole in its behavior toward electrophilic reagents, and its principal reactions of this type are summarized in Figure 27-3. Furan is in fact slightly more reactive than pyrrole; for example, direct chlorination and bromination are hard to control and can lead to violent reaction—possibly caused by the halogen acid that is formed.

Related reactions of thiophene are summarized in Figure 27-4. Since thiophene is less reactive, particularly toward strong acids, than either pyrrole or furan, it can be sulfonated and nitrated under strongly acidic conditions. Although chlorination of thiophene leads to a complex mixture of polysubstitution products, bromination and iodination can be controlled to give 2-bromo-, 2,4-dibromo-, and 2-iodothiophenes.

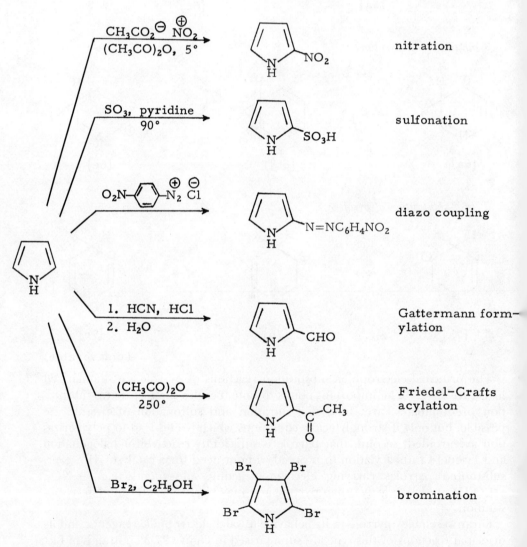

Figure 27-2

Electrophilic substitution reactions of pyrrole.

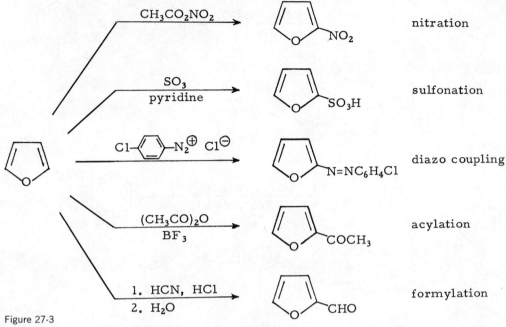

Figure 27-3

Electrophilic substitution reactions of furan.

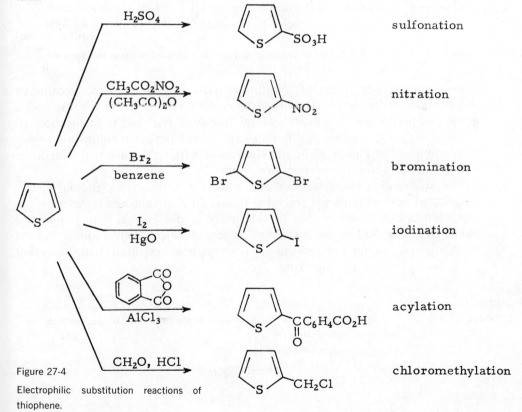

Figure 27-4

Electrophilic substitution reactions of thiophene.

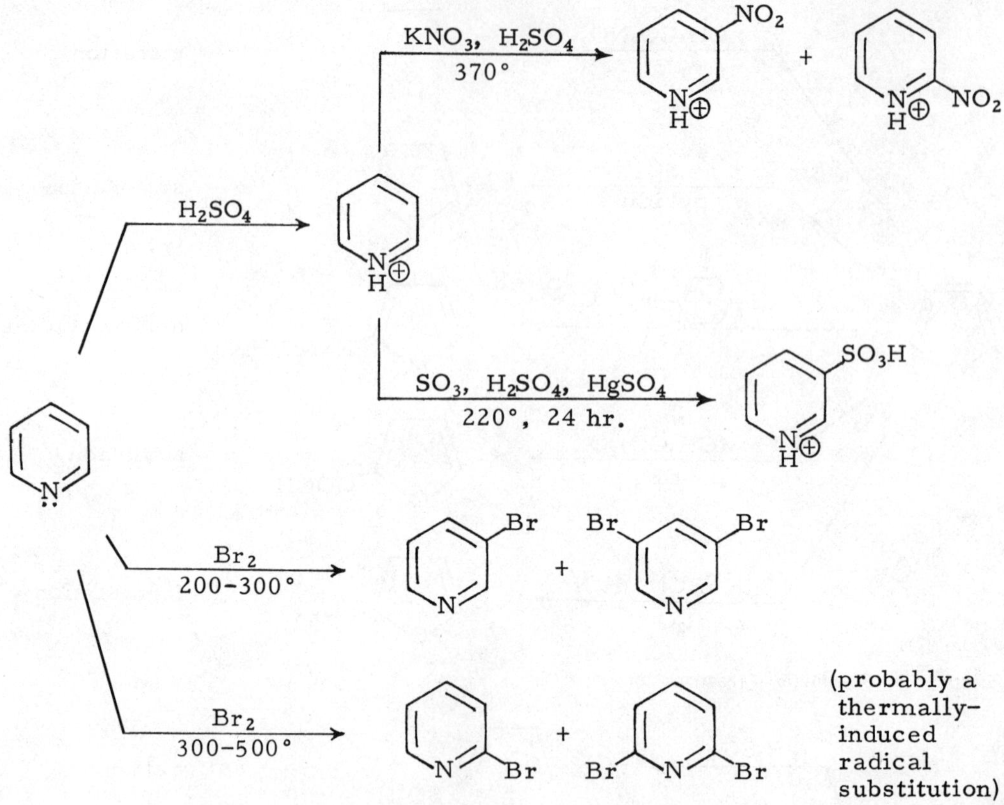

Figure 27-5   Electrophilic substitution reactions of pyridine. In most of these reactions the yields are low.

Electrophilic substitution of pyridine is hard to achieve, partly because of deactivation of the ring by the hetero atom (p. 650) and partly because under acidic conditions, as in sulfonation and nitration, the ring is further deactivated by formation of the pyridinium ion. Three pertinent substitution reactions are listed in Figure 27-5, and their most striking feature is the vigorous conditions necessary for successful reaction.

The substitution characteristics of the bicyclic heterocycles, indole, benzofuran, and benzothiophene, resemble those of the parent heterocycles except that electrophilic attack occurs preferentially at the 3-position in indole and benzothiophene and at the 2-position in benzofuran. Electrophilic attack on quinoline and isoquinoline takes place, as we might expect, at the benzenoid ring in preference to the pyridine ring.

EXERCISE 27-6   Suggest a feasible synthesis of each of the following compounds from the indicated starting material:

a. 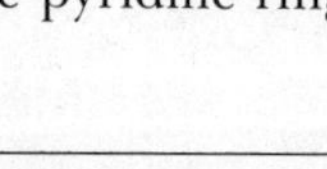   from thiophene

b. 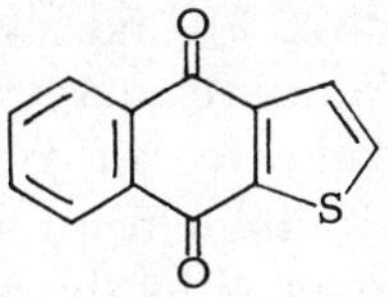   from thiophene

c. 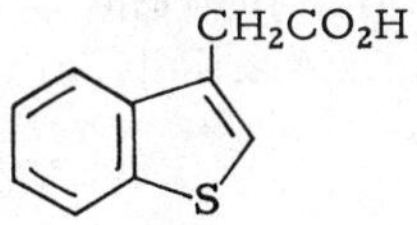   from benzothiophene

d. 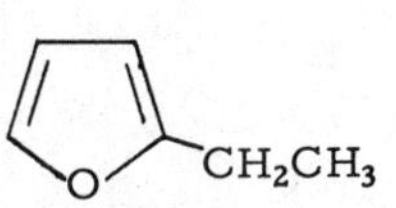   from furan

D. Nucleophilic Substitution Reactions

The most important substitution reactions of the pyridine ring are effected by nucleophilic reagents. Thus, pyridine can be aminated on heating with so-

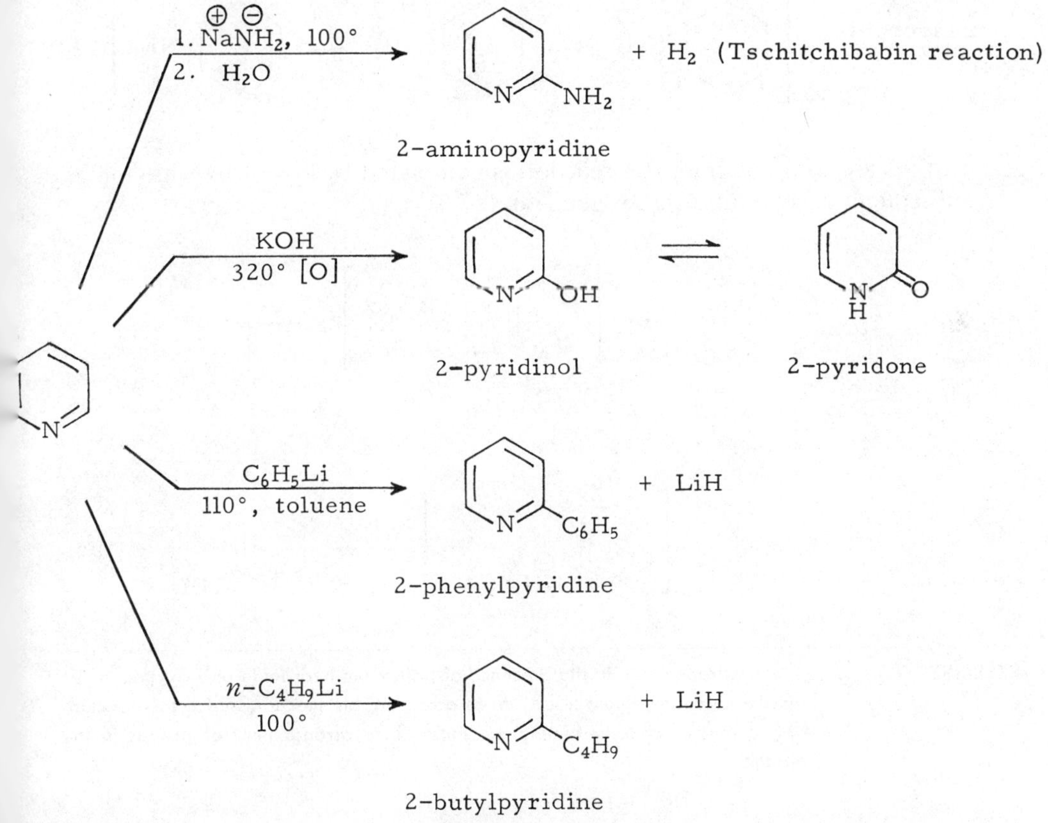

Figure 27-6   Nucleophilic substitution reactions of pyridine.

damide, hydroxylated with potassium hydroxide, and alkylated and arylated with alkyl- and aryllithiums (Figure 27-6). Since related reactions with benzene either do not occur or are relatively difficult, we can conclude that the ring nitrogen in pyridine has a pronounced activating effect for nucleophilic attack at the ring analogous to the activation produced by the nitro group in nitrobenzenes. The reason for this is that addition to the 2- or 4- but not the 3-position permits the charge to reside at least partially on nitrogen rather than on carbon [see Eqs. (27-1) and (27-2)].

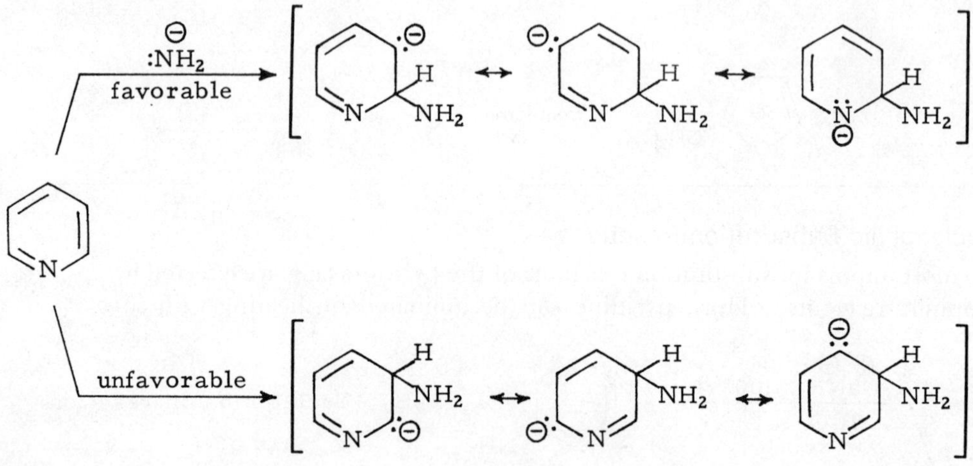

$$(27\text{-}1)$$

$$(27\text{-}2)$$

In the case of amination, the reaction is completed by loss of hydride ion and subsequent formation of hydrogen [Eq. (27-3)].

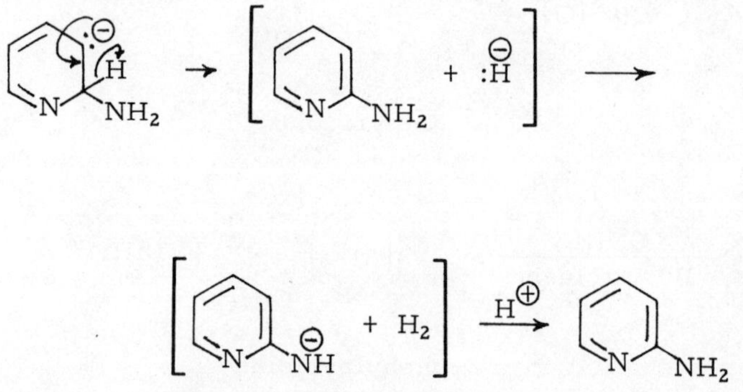

$$(27\text{-}3)$$

EXERCISE 27-7   *m*-Dinitrobenzene in the presence of potassium hydroxide and oxygen yields potassium dinitrophenoxide. Write a reasonable mechanism for this reaction with emphasis on determining the most likely arrangement of groups in the product.

EXERCISE 27-8   Predict the product(s) of the following reactions:

a. 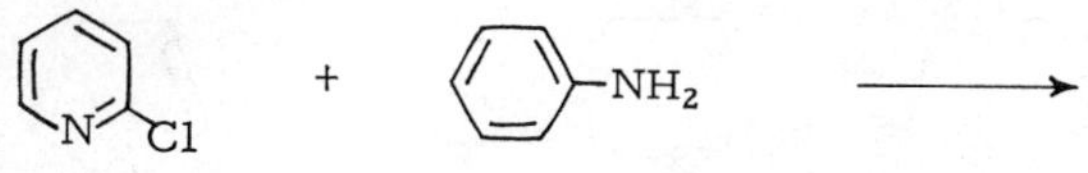 +   ⟶

b. 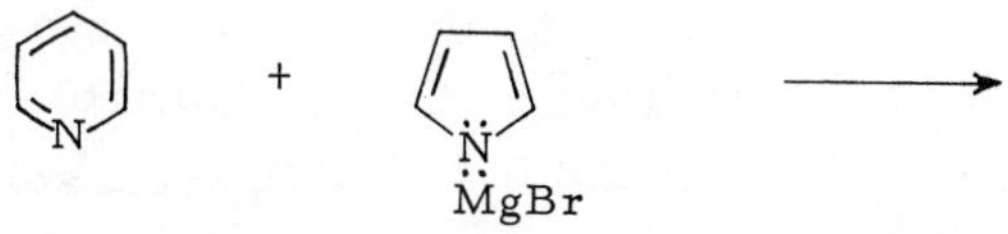 +   ⟶

c. indole $\xrightarrow{\text{KOH}}$ $\xrightarrow{\text{CH}_3\text{I}}$

d. quinoline $\xrightarrow{\text{KNH}_2}$

e. isoquinoline $\xrightarrow{\text{KNH}_2}$

f. acridine $\xrightarrow{\text{KNH}_2}$

E. Addition Reactions

Like other aromatic compounds, furan, pyrrole, thiophene, and pyridine can be hydrogenated relatively easily, and, with the exception of thiophene, which may act as a poison for some catalysts, give the fully saturated heterocycles on catalytic reduction.

Aromatic character in the five-membered ring heterocycles is least evident with furan, which clearly resembles a conjugated diene in the facility with which it reacts by 1,4-addition. Thus it readily forms adducts with reactive dienophiles in the Diels-Alder reaction (pp. 206-210).

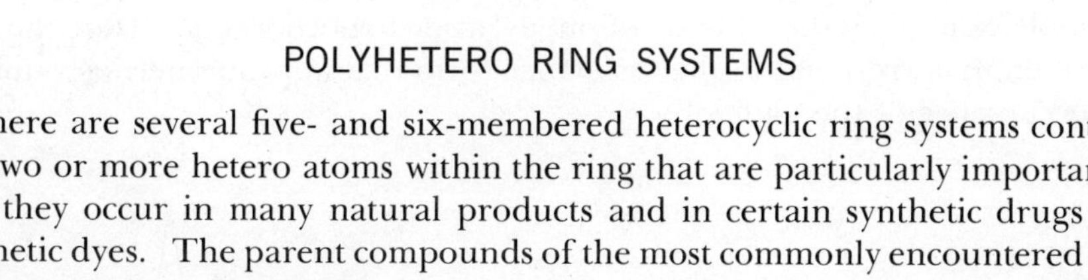

POLYHETERO RING SYSTEMS

There are several five- and six-membered heterocyclic ring systems containing two or more hetero atoms within the ring that are particularly important in that they occur in many natural products and in certain synthetic drugs and synthetic dyes. The parent compounds of the most commonly encountered ring systems are shown on p. 660.

A detailed description of the chemistry of these compounds will not be given. Their properties for the most part can be readily deduced from those of the monohetero ring systems just discussed, and we shall indicate here only their main characteristics. Each heterocycle can be classified as an aromatic compound, since each five- and six-membered ring compound has a delocalized

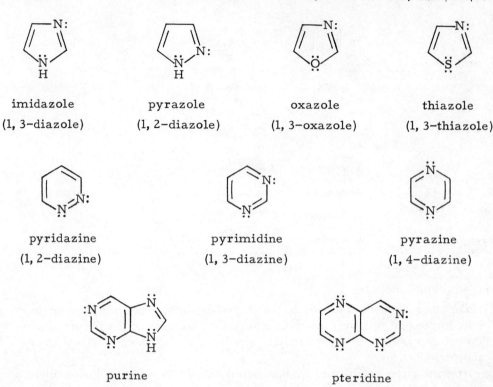

imidazole
(1, 3–diazole)

pyrazole
(1, 2–diazole)

oxazole
(1, 3–oxazole)

thiazole
(1, 3–thiazole)

pyridazine
(1, 2–diazine)

pyrimidine
(1, 3–diazine)

pyrazine
(1, 4–diazine)

purine

pteridine

sextet of π electrons; the bicyclic compounds, purine and pteridine, resemble naphthalene in having ten delocalized π electrons.

27-5 SYNTHESIS OF POLYHETERO RING SYSTEMS BY 1,3-CYCLOADDITION

Recent research has led to a number of very elegant syntheses of heterocyclic compounds by 1,3-cycloaddition (see also pp. 149-150). In this type of reaction a 1,3-"dipolar" compound (e.g., ozone, phenyl azide) adds to a multiple bond (e.g., C=C, C≡C, C=O, C≡N, etc.) to form a five-membered ring compound. A simple example is the addition of phenyl azide to norbornene. Here the azide is written to correspond to the resonance form that appropriately accounts for the occurrence of the addition.

norbornene

phenyl azide

There is an obvious similarity between the above reaction and the 1,1-, 1,2-, and 1,4-cycloaddition reactions discussed earlier (pp. 249, 207-210).

The resemblance is more than just superficial; for, like the Diels-Alder reaction, 1,3-cycloadditions are stereospecific and highly sensitive to the size of substituent groups in both components. Furthermore, there is the same uncertainty in the timing of reaction—that is, whether it is concerted or stepwise; but the evidence indicates that the reaction, if stepwise, does *not* involve ionic intermediates of sufficient stability to be trapped by external reagents.

In effect, the compounds that behave as 1,3-dipoles appear to be so only insofar as electron-pairing schemes may be written which place formal positive and negative charges at the 1- and 3-positions. Several 1,3-dipolar systems are listed in Table 27-3 together with the type of heterocyclic ring system each produces on reaction with a multiple bond. Although some of these compounds, such as ozone and organic azides, are comparatively stable, others are much too reactive to be isolated, and the existence of these as intermediates is inferred principally by the nature of the cyclic reaction products.

The versatility of the reaction should be apparent from the many different ring systems that may be synthesized, many of which have not yet been prepared by any other route.

EXERCISE 27-9   Write structures for the products of the following reactions:

a. C_6H_5N—N, N=N, C—C_6H_5 $\xrightarrow[-N_2]{150°}$ $\xrightarrow{C_6H_5CHO}$

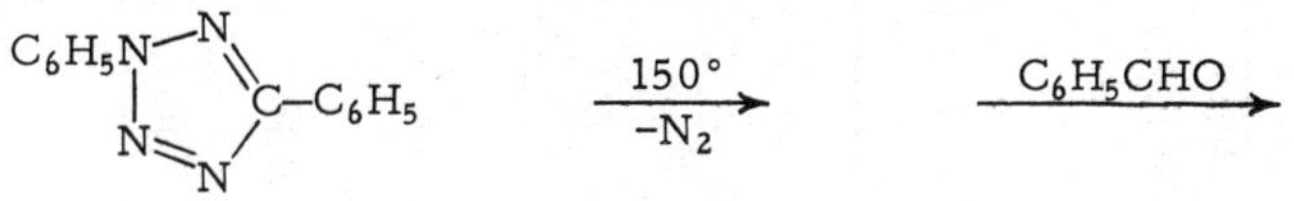

b. 2 $\overset{C_6H_5}{\underset{Cl}{>}}C$=N—NH$C_6H_5$ $\xrightarrow[-HCl]{(C_2H_5)_3N}$ $\xrightarrow{CS_2}$

c. $\overset{C_6H_5}{\underset{Cl}{>}}C$=N—OH $\xrightarrow[-HCl]{(C_2H_5)_3N}$ $\xrightarrow{C_6H_5CN}$

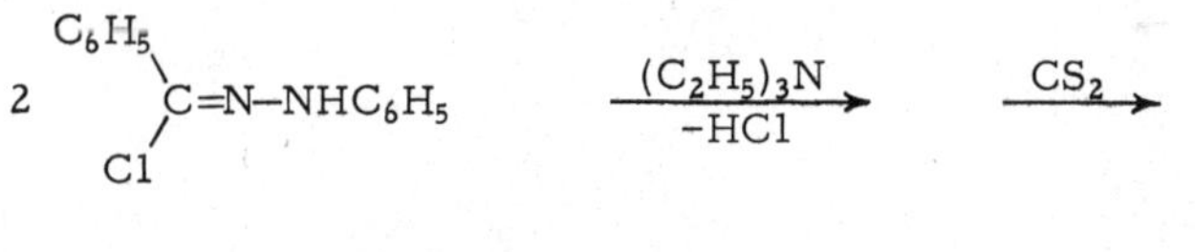

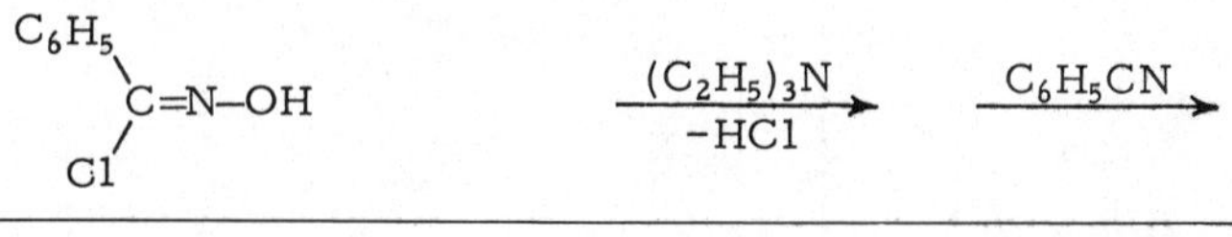

Table 27-3   1,3-Dipoles and Products of 1,3-Cycloaddition to Multiple Bonds

	1,3-Dipole	Heterocycle from C=C	Heterocycle from C=O
azides	$\overset{\oplus}{\ddot{N}}=\overset{\ominus}{\ddot{N}}-\ddot{N}-R$ ↔ $\ddot{N}\equiv\overset{\oplus}{N}-\overset{\ominus}{\ddot{N}}-R$	1,2,3-triazolines	—
nitrile ylides[a]	$R-\overset{\oplus}{C}=\ddot{N}-\overset{\ominus}{\overset{\displaystyle R'}{\underset{\displaystyle R'}{C}}}$ ↔ $R-C\equiv\overset{\oplus}{N}-\overset{\ominus}{\overset{\displaystyle R'}{\underset{\displaystyle R'}{C}}}$	pyrrolines	oxazolines
nitrilimines[a]	$R-\overset{\oplus}{C}=\ddot{N}-\ddot{N}-R'$ ↔ $R-C\equiv\overset{\oplus}{N}-\overset{\ominus}{\ddot{N}}-R'$	pyrazolines	1,3,4-oxadiazolidines

662

nitrile oxides[a]   isoxazolines   1,3,4-dioxazoles

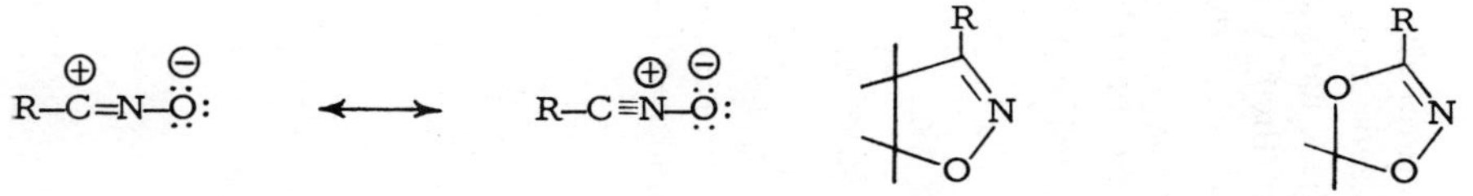

$$R-C\equiv\overset{\oplus}{N}-\overset{\ominus}{\underset{..}{O}}: \quad\longleftrightarrow\quad R-C\equiv\overset{\oplus}{N}-\overset{\ominus}{\underset{..}{O}}:$$

azomethine imines[b]   pyrazolidines

$$\overset{R}{\underset{R'}{C}}\overset{\oplus}{=}\overset{\ominus}{\underset{..}{N}}-\overset{..}{\underset{..}{N}}-R'' \quad\longleftrightarrow\quad \overset{R}{\underset{R'}{C}}\overset{\oplus}{-}\overset{\ominus}{\underset{..}{N}}-\overset{..}{\underset{..}{N}}-R''$$

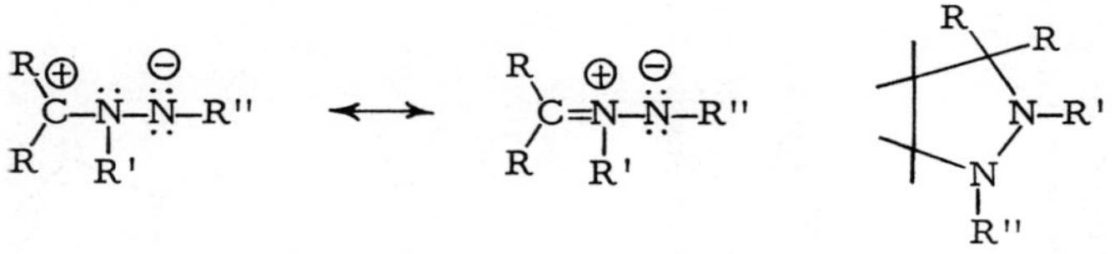

nitrilimine

$$\overset{R}{\underset{Cl}{\underset{R'}{C}}}=\overset{..}{N}-CH\overset{R'}{\underset{R'}{}} \quad\xrightarrow[-HCl]{(C_2H_5)_3N}\quad R-C\equiv\overset{\oplus}{N}-\overset{\ominus}{\underset{..}{C}}\overset{R'}{\underset{R'}{}} \;;\; \overset{R}{\underset{Cl}{C}}\overset{\oplus}{=}\overset{..}{N}-\overset{..}{N}H-R' \quad\xrightarrow[-HCl]{(C_2H_5)_3N}\quad R-C\equiv\overset{\oplus}{N}-\overset{\ominus}{\underset{..}{N}}-R'$$

nitrile ylide

$$\overset{R}{\underset{Cl}{C}}=\overset{..}{N}-OH \quad\xrightarrow[-HCl]{(C_2H_5)_3N}\quad R-C\equiv\overset{\oplus}{N}-\overset{\ominus}{\underset{..}{O}}:$$

nitrile oxide

[a] Prepared by elimination of HCl from appropriate carboxylic acid derivative.

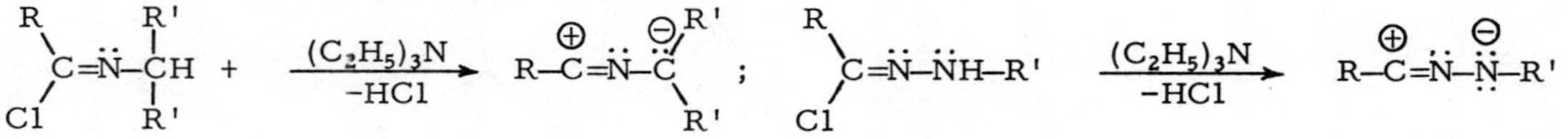

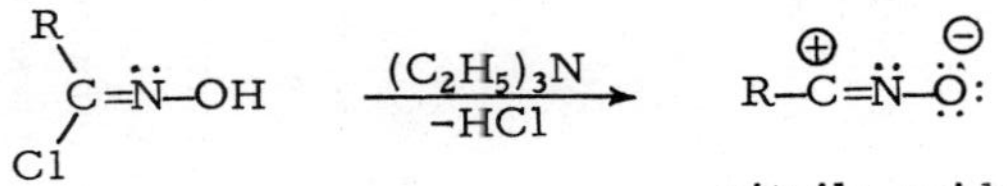

$$\overset{R}{\underset{R}{C}}=\overset{\oplus}{N}=\overset{\ominus}{\underset{..}{N}}: \;+\; R'-N=N-CN \quad\xrightarrow{-N_2}\quad \overset{R}{\underset{R}{C}}\overset{\oplus}{-}\overset{\ominus}{\underset{..}{N}}-\overset{..}{\underset{R'}{N}}-CN$$

[b] Prepared by reaction of a diazocyanide with a diazoalkane.

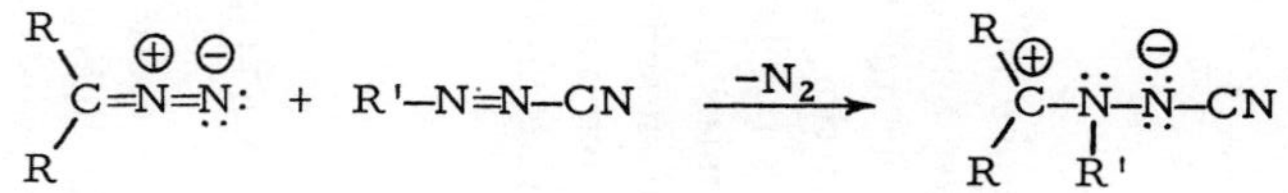

663

HETEROCYCLIC NATURAL PRODUCTS

Some of the heterocyclic ring systems mentioned in this chapter are of special interest and importance because certain of their derivatives are synthesized naturally as part of the life cycles of plants and animals. The structures of these naturally occurring compounds are often extremely complex, and elucidation of their structures has been and continues to be a major challenge to organic chemists and biochemists alike. The approach to solving the structure of a complex natural product is discussed in some detail in Chapter 30; at this point we shall briefly describe only a few natural products of known structure which can be classified as heterocyclic compounds and which are of some biological or physiological importance.

27-6 NATURAL PRODUCTS RELATED TO PYRROLE

An interesting compound having a fully conjugated cyclic structure of four pyrrole rings linked together through their 2- and 5-positions by four methine (═CH─) bridges is known as *porphyrin* [8].

[8]

Although porphyrin itself does not exist in nature, the porphyrin or related ring system is found in several very important natural products, notably hemoglobin, chlorophyll, and vitamin B_{12}.

Hemoglobin is present in the red corpuscles of blood and functions to carry oxygen from the lungs to the body tissue; it consists of a protein called *globin* bound to an iron-containing prosthetic group called *heme*. Acid hydrolysis of hemoglobin liberates the prosthetic group as a complex ferric salt called *hemin* [9]. The structure of hemin was established by 1929 after years of work, notably by W. Küster, R. Willstätter, and H. Fischer. A complete synthesis of hemin was achieved by Fischer in 1929, and his contributions were rewarded with a Nobel Prize (1930). The structure of hemin on p. 665 shows that the iron (as Fe^{III}) is complexed to all four of the pyrrole nitrogens.

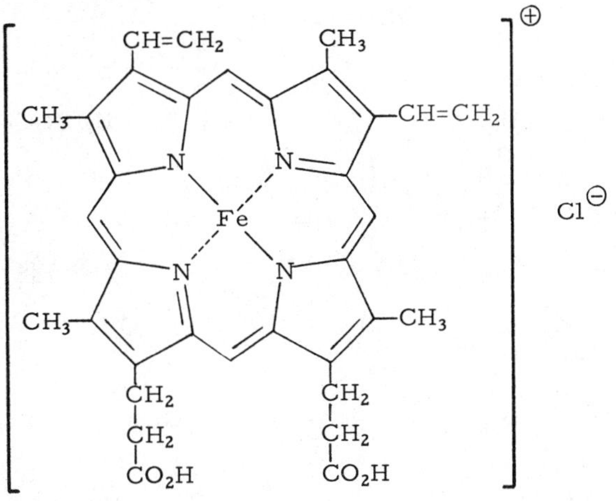

hemin

[9]

EXERCISE 27-10 Would you anticipate porphyrin to possess aromatic character? Explain.

Certain pigments in the bile of mammals, the so-called **bile pigments,** are pyrrole derivatives. They contain four pyrrole rings linked in a chain through a methine bridge between the 2-position of one ring and the 5-position of another. As one might suspect, bile pigments are degradation products of hemoglobin.

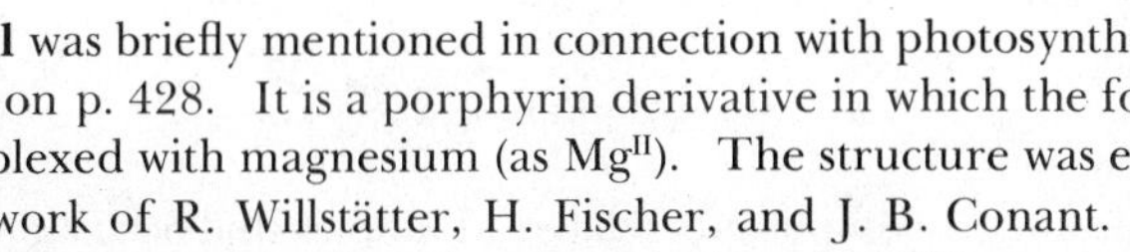

basic structure of a bile pigment

Chlorophyll was briefly mentioned in connection with photosynthesis, and its structure is shown on p. 428. It is a porphyrin derivative in which the four pyrrole nitrogens are complexed with magnesium (as Mg^{II}). The structure was established largely through the work of R. Willstätter, H. Fischer, and J. B. Conant. A total synthesis was completed by R. B. Woodward and co-workers in 1960.

The structure of **vitamin B_{12}** [10], known also as the antipernicious anemia factor and as cyanocobalamin, was finally established in 1955 as the result of both X-ray diffraction and chemical studies. The vitamin has a reduced porphyrin ring in which one methine bridge is absent and the nitrogen hetero atoms are complexed with a cyanocobalt group. It also has a ribofuranoside ring and a benzimidazole ring.

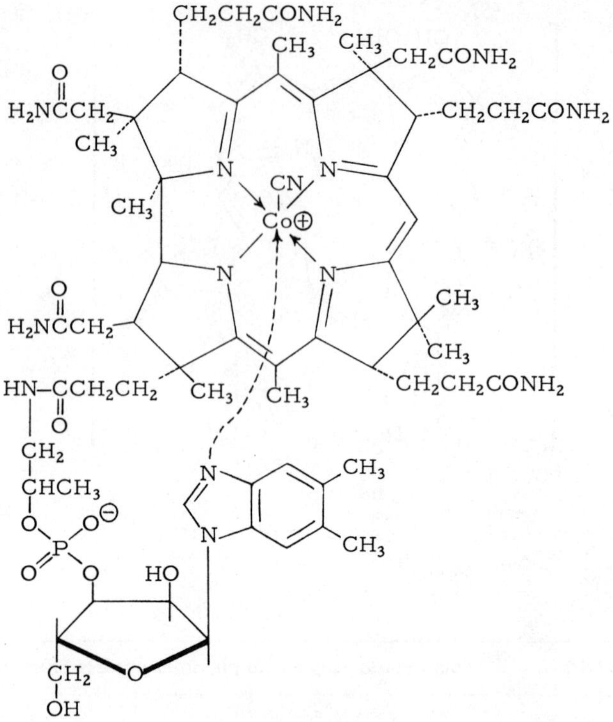

vitamin B_{12}

[10]

27-7 NATURAL PRODUCTS RELATED TO INDOLES

The indole ring system is common to many naturally occurring compounds, as for example the essential amino acid, tryptophan, which is a constituent of almost all proteins (p. 485).

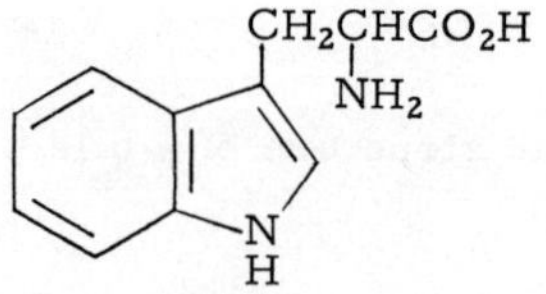

tryptophan

There are also many compounds related to indoles that occur in plants. They are part of a class of natural products known as **alkaloids** — the term being used to designate nitrogen-containing compounds of vegetable origin commonly having heterocyclic ring systems and one or more basic nitrogen atoms; their physiological activity is often pronounced and their structures complex. Alkaloids related to indole are called **indole alkaloids,** and these are commonly classified into subgroups such as (1) the Simple alkaloids, (2) the Ergot alkaloids, (3) the Harmala alkaloids,

(4) the Yohimbe alkaloids, and (5) the Strychnos alkaloids. We shall briefly describe one or more examples from each group.

Many of *the Simple alkaloids* resemble tryptophan in structure. Two such examples are gramine and tryptamine.

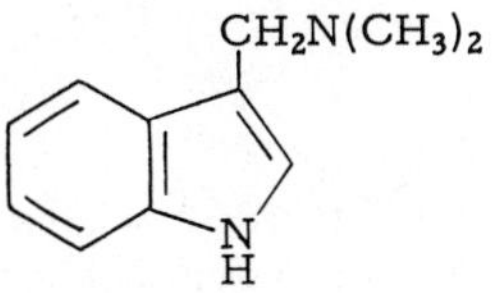

gramine

(from barley leaves)

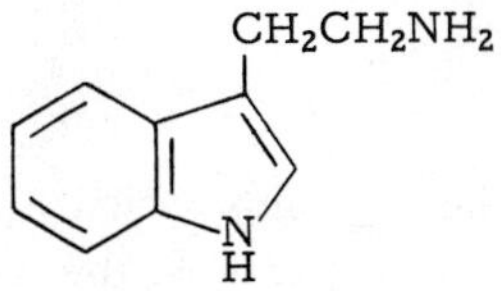

tryptamine

(from acacia trees)

An indole derivative commonly known as serotonin, which is actually 5-hydroxytryptamine, is of interest because of its apparent connection with mental processes. It occurs widely in plant and animal life, but its presence in the brain, and the schizophrenic state that ensues when its normal concentration is disturbed, indicates that it may have an important function in establishing a stable pattern of mental activity.

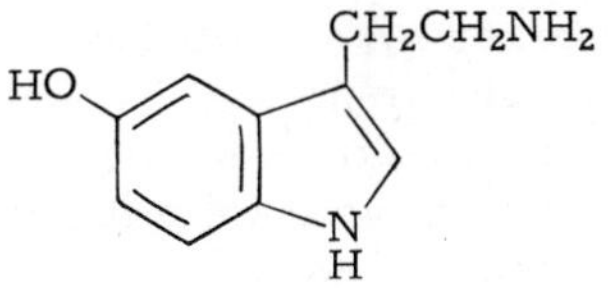

serotonin

The Ergot alkaloids are produced by a fungus known as ergot, which grows as a parasite on cereals, particularly rye. There are six such alkaloids, each of which is a complex of a levorotatory and a dextrorotatory form. Only the levorotatory form is physiologically active, causing contraction of muscle tissue. The levorotatory alkaloids are amides of the indole derivative known as lysergic acid.

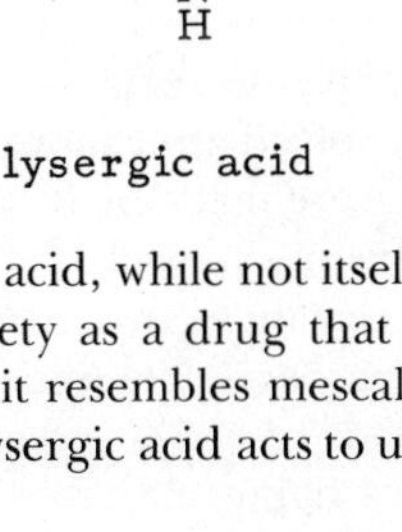

lysergic acid

The diethylamide of lysergic acid, while not itself a naturally occurring compound, has achieved fame and notoriety as a drug that can produce a temporary schizophrenic state. In this respect, it resembles mescaline (p. 639). Current theory suggests that the diethylamide of lysergic acid acts to upset the balance of serotonin in the brain.

EXERCISE 27-11   The dextrorotatory ergot alkaloids are amides of *isolysergic* acid.   Hydrolysis
of these amides with aqueous alkali gives lysergic acid.   What is the most likely
structure of isolysergic acid?   Why does rearrangement occur on basic hydrolysis?

The Harmala alkaloids have in common a linear tricyclic structure related both to
indole and to pyridine; the parent compound with this ring system is known as β-
carboline.

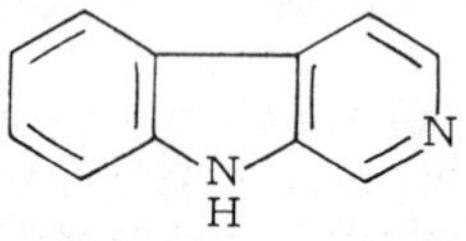

β-carboline

More important and of related structure are *the Yohimbe alkaloids,* the most important example being reserpine.   This compound has important clinical use in the
treatment of high blood pressure (hypertension) and also as a tranquilizer for the
emotionally disturbed.   The tranquilizing action is thought to be the result of a reduction in the concentration of brain serotonin.

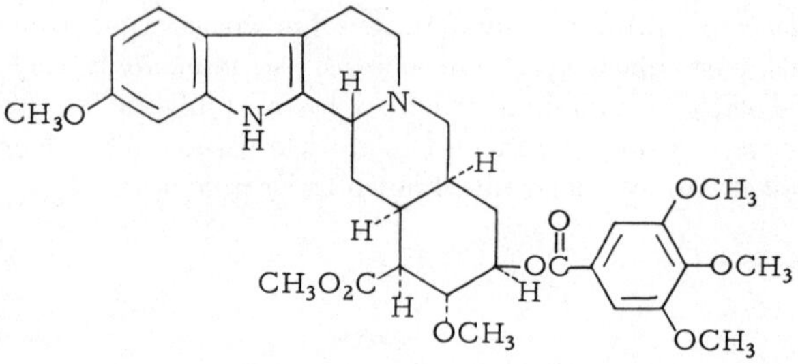

reserpine

Two outstanding examples of *the Strychnos alkaloids* are strychnine and brucine.
They occur in the seeds of *strychnos* plants; their structures are shown on p. 417,
from which it is evident they are derivatives of 2,3-dihydroindole.   The problem of
elucidating their structures was only solved after more than a century of research; the
major contributions in recent years were made by R. Robinson and R. B. Woodward.
A total synthesis of strychnine has been achieved.

Also occurring in the leaves of certain plants is an indole derivative known as
indican, which is a glucoside of 3-hydroxyindole (indoxyl).   Hydrolysis of indican to
indoxyl followed by air oxidation leads to *indigo*, a dark-blue substance that has been
used for centuries as a dyestuff (see Chapter 28).

indican   indoxyl   + glucose

indigo

27-8 NATURAL PRODUCTS RELATED TO PYRIDINE, QUINOLINE, AND ISOQUINOLINE

Among the natural products related to pyridine, we have already mentioned the alkaloid nicotine (pp. 19-20) and nicotinamide-adenine dinucleotide (NAD$^{\oplus}$, p. 503). Other important pyridine derivatives include nicotinic acid (niacin, antipellagra factor) and pyridoxine (vitamin B$_6$). Coniine is a toxic alkaloid which occurs in the shrub poison hemlock; it has a reduced pyridine (piperidine) ring.

nicotine   nicotinic acid   pyridoxine   coniine

(from tobacco)   (niacin)   (poisonous component
                                                              of hemlock)

A group of related and rather poisonous compounds known as *the Tropane alkaloids* are derivatives of reduced pyrroles and reduced pyridines. Two of the more important tropanes are atropine and cocaine.

atropine

(from Atropa belladonna plant,
"deadly nightshade")

(−)−cocaine

(from coca plant)

The Cinchona alkaloids are quinoline derivatives which occur in cinchona bark and have medicinal value as antimalarials. The most notable example is quinine, the structure of which is shown on p. 417.

Many alkaloids have isoquinoline and reduced isoquinoline ring systems. *The Opium alkaloids* are prime examples, and include the compounds narcotine, papaverine, morphine, codeine, and several others; all of which occur in the seed of the opium poppy.

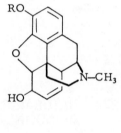

papaverine

narcotine

morphine, R=H

codeine, R=CH₃

27-9   NATURAL PRODUCTS RELATED TO PYRIMIDINE

The pyrimidine ring system occurs in thymine and cytosine (p. 507), which are component structures of the nucleic acids and certain coenzymes. A detailed account of the structures of nucleic acids are given on pages 505-508. We have also discussed one biological function of thiamine (p. 504), which is both a pyrimidine and a 1,3-thiazole derivative. The pyrophosphate of thiamine is the coenzyme of carboxylase — the enzyme that decarboxylates α-ketoacids; thiamine is also known as vitamin B_1, and a deficiency of it in the diet is responsible for the disease known as beri-beri.

There are, in addition to the above-mentioned naturally occurring pyrimidine derivatives, many pyrimidines of synthetic origin which are widely used as therapeutic drugs. Of these, we have already mentioned the sulfonamide drug, sulfadiazine (see p. 525). Another large class of pyrimidine medicinals is based on 2,4,6-tri-hydroxypyrimidine. Most of these substances are 5-alkyl or aryl derivatives of 2,4,6-trihydroxypyrimidine — which is better known as barbituric acid and can exist in several tautomeric forms.

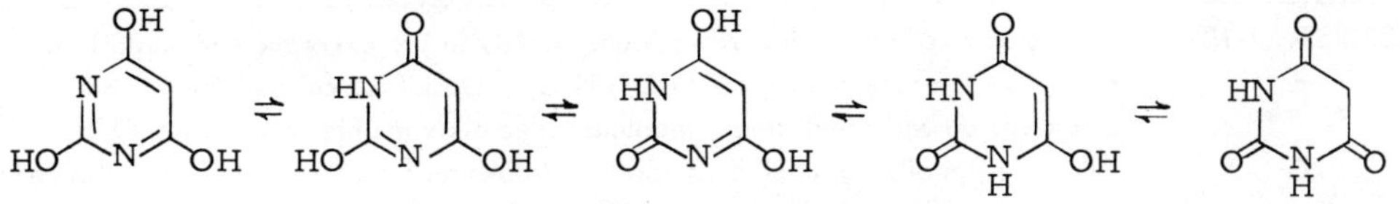

barbituric acid

(predominant form)

For simplicity we shall represent barbituric acid as the triketo tautomer. Two of the more important barbituric acids are known as veronal (5,5-diethylbarbituric acid) and phenobarbital (5-ethyl-5-phenylbarbituric acid).

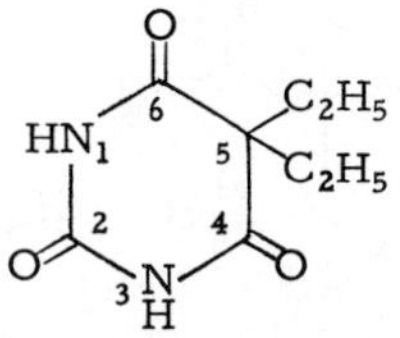

veronal

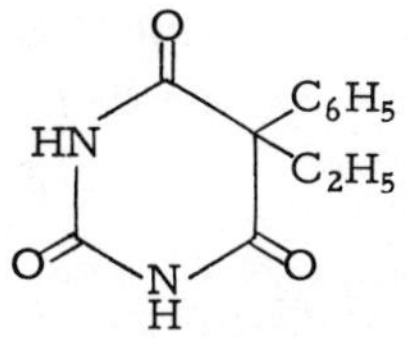

phenobarbital

Barbituric acids are readily synthesized by the reaction of urea with substituted malonic esters.

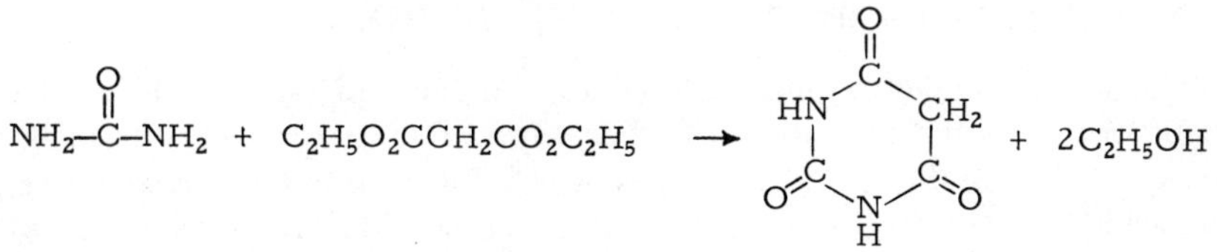

$$NH_2-\overset{O}{\overset{\|}{C}}-NH_2 \ + \ C_2H_5O_2CCH_2CO_2C_2H_5 \ \longrightarrow \ + \ 2C_2H_5OH$$

27-10 NATURAL PRODUCTS RELATED TO PURINE

Heterocyclic nitrogen bases (other than pyrimidines) present in nucleic acids are the purine derivatives, adenine and guanine (p. 506). Adenine is also a component of the trinucleotide, adenosine triphosphate (ATP), whose structure is shown on page 441. Nicotinamide-adenine dinucleotide ($NAD^{\oplus}$, p. 503) is also a derivative of adenine.

A number of alkaloids are purine derivatives. Examples include caffeine, which occurs in the tea plant and coffee bean, and theobromine, which occurs in the cocoa bean. The physiological stimulation derived from beverages such as tea, coffee, and many soft drinks, is due to the presence of caffeine.

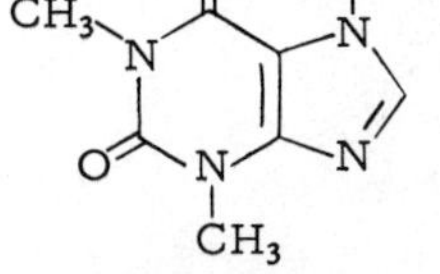

caffeine

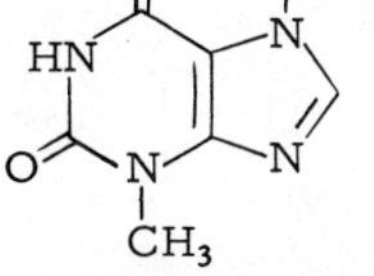

theobromine

Uric acid, a purine derivative found mainly in the excrement of snakes and birds, has the molecular formula $C_5H_4N_4O_3$. On nitric acid oxidation it breaks down to urea and a hydrated compound called alloxan of formula $C_4H_2N_2O_4 \cdot H_2O$. Alloxan is readily obtained by oxidation of barbituric acid. What is the probable structure of alloxan and uric acid? Why is alloxan hydrated?

27-11 NATURAL PRODUCTS RELATED TO PTERIDINE

An important naturally occurring pteridine derivative is folic acid (vitamin B_{10}).

folic acid

The pteridine structure also occurs in the wing pigments of butterflies and other insects.

27-12 NATURAL PRODUCTS RELATED TO PYRAN

The six-membered oxygen heterocycles, α-pyran and γ-pyran, do not have aromatic structures and they are not in themselves of any great interest to us here. Of more interest are the α- and γ-pyrones, which differ from the corresponding pyrans in having a carbonyl group at the α- and γ-ring positions, respectively.

α-pyran γ-pyran α-pyrone γ-pyrone

The pyrones may be regarded as pseudo-aromatic compounds—they are expected to have considerable electron delocalization through π overlap of orbitals of the double bond, the ring oxygen, and the carbonyl group. Thus, γ-pyrone is expected to have at least some stabilization associated with contributions of the electron-pairing schemes [11a] to [11e].

[11a]   [11b]   [11c]   [11d]   [11e]

It is significant in this connection that γ-pyrone behaves quite differently than might be expected from consideration of structure [11a] alone. For example, it does not readily undergo those additions characteristic of α,β-unsaturated ketones and does not form carbonyl derivatives.

EXERCISE 27-13   2,6-Dimethyl-γ-pyrone is converted by treatment with dimethyl sulfate and then with perchloric acid to $[C_8H_{11}O_2]^{\oplus}ClO_4^{\ominus}$. Simple recrystallization of this salt from ethanol converts it to $[C_9H_{13}O_2]^{\oplus}ClO_4^{\ominus}$. What are the structures of these salts, and why does the reaction with ethanol occur so readily?

The benzo derivatives of the pyrones are known as *coumarin* for benzo-α-pyrone and *chromone* for benzo-γ-pyrone.

coumarin

chromone

They are important in that many of their derivatives occur naturally. Thus, coumarins occur in grasses, citrus peel, and the leaves of certain vegetables. Coumarin itself occurs in clover and is widely used as a perfume and a flavoring agent; it can be prepared by condensation of salicylaldehyde with acetic anhydride.

EXERCISE 27-14   Show the probable mechanistic steps involved in the preparation of coumarin by the condensation of acetic anhydride with salicylaldehyde in the presence of sodium acetate as catalyst.

Chromones or benzo-γ-pyrones are widely distributed in plant life, mostly as pigments in plant leaves and flowers. Particularly widespread are the flavones (2-phenylchromones)—quercetin being the flavone most commonly found.

flavone

quercetin

The beautiful and varied colors of many flowers, fruits, and berries are due to the pigments known as *anthocyanins*. Their structures are closely related to the flavones, although they occur as glycosides, from which they are obtained as salts on hydrolysis with hydrochloric acid.   The salts are called *anthocyanidins*.   Two examples follow:

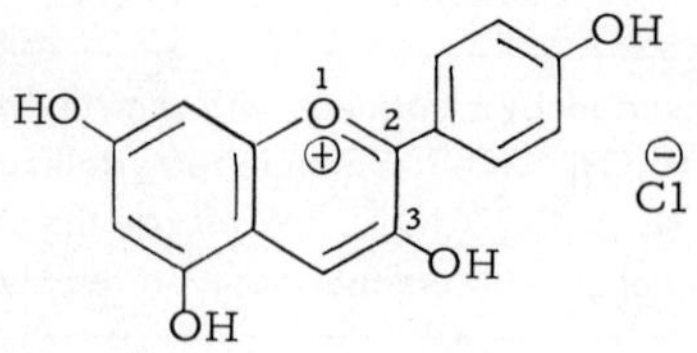

pelargonidin chloride

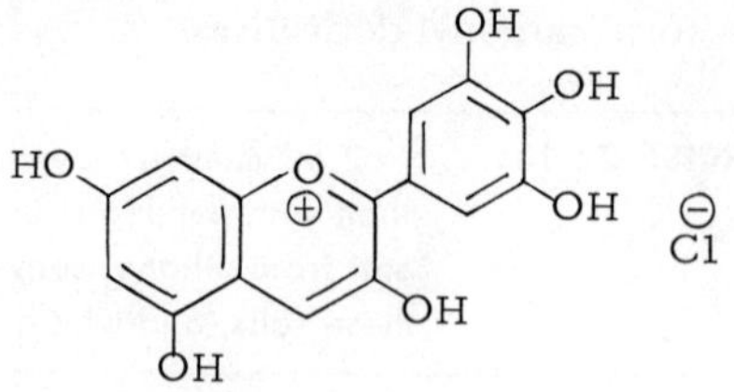

delphinidin chloride
(delphinium)

Glycoside formation is through the 3-hydroxy group of the anthocyanidin.

27-13 POLYHETERO NATURAL PRODUCTS

Of the many important polyhetero natural products with two or more different hetero atoms in one ring we have already mentioned penicillin (p. 492), peptides such as insulin (p. 498), and thiamine (p. 504).   Another interesting example is luciferin, the enzymatic oxidation of which produces the characteristic luminescence of the firefly.   Luciferin has been shown to be a benzothiazole derivative.

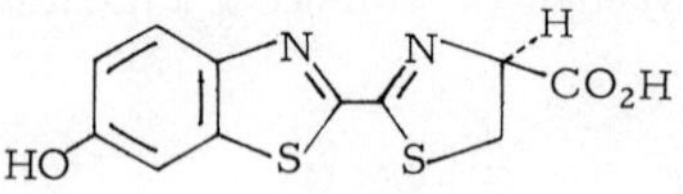

luciferin

Dyes and Photochemistry

The chemistry of dyes and dyeing processes has very great technical importance, but strong emphasis on this aspect of the subject would be quite out of place in a book such as this one. That dyes are of interest to us here at all is partly historical, because the first really important practical applications of synthetic organic chemistry were made in the dye industry. In addition, dyes are colored substances—the relation between color and chemical constitution presents a very important fundamental problem. The endless striving for better colors by dye chemists has contributed much to the solution of this fundamental problem, by providing many excellent examples on which to base and test theories of color in organic molecules. It is important to realize there is more to a successful dye than just an attractive color. If it is to be useful, say for coloring fabrics, some simple means must be available for introducing the color into the fiber and then, and usually of greater difficulty and importance, the color must be reasonably permanent—that is, resistant to normal laundry or cleaning procedures (wash-fast) and stable to light (light-fast). Here again fundamentally important problems are involved. The scientific approach to improving wash-fastness of fabric dyes has to be based on a knowledge of the structural factors bearing on the intermolecular forces that determine solubilities. Light-fastness is connected with the important area of the photochemistry of organic compounds which is currently an extraordinarily active field of research.

Progress in the dye industry has been largely empirical for many years. A very good reason for this is the staggering amount of experimental information available on dyes, many of which are exceptionally complex substances, so that only some sort of a relatively empirical approach could be employed. In our discussion we shall consider certain aspects of the process of light absorption which will help in relating color to structure, then a very few important types of dyes and the way they are applied to fabrics; we shall then turn to a brief discussion of organic photochemistry.

Dyes and Photochemistry

Visible light is electromagnetic radiation falling in a rather narrow range of wavelengths (4000 to 8000 A, 1 A $= 10^{-8}$ cm) of the very broad spectrum of electromagnetic waves of chemical interest. The sensation of color is the result of an extremely complex sequence of physiological and psychological changes triggered by light striking the retina of the eye. The sensations that persons with normal color vision identify with particular wavelengths are shown in Table 28-1. Intermediate wavelengths give intermediate colors; thus light of 5000 A gives the sensation of blue-green, 5600 A yellow-green, etc.

The sensation of white light has to be a more complicated one than that of color—at least, that sensation of color produced by light of a narrow band of wavelengths which, if sufficiently narrow, is usually called monochromatic light. The continuum of wavelengths from the sun produces the psychological response that we call white light, but the same response can also be produced by the superposition of many pairs of wavelengths with proper relative intensities. The colors of these pairs are said to be **complementary.**

The properties of complementary colors can be seen as follows. If we pass a beam of white light through a substance which absorbs essentially all blue light at 4800 ± 300 A, the emergent beam appears to be yellow, which is the color complementary to blue. We might also call this the **subtraction** color, since it is

Table 28-1   Color and Wavelength

Wavelength, A	Observed color	Complementary (subtraction) color
4000	violet	green-yellow
4800	blue	yellow
5300	green	purple (magenta)
5800	yellow	blue
6100	orange	green-blue
6600	red	blue-green (cyan)
7200	purple-red	green

the color that is produced when blue light is subtracted from a beam of white light. The complementary colors for each wavelength are listed in Table 28-1, and these will be important in permitting us to judge the color produced when a substance subtracts light of a particular color from white light.

EXERCISE 28-1   What color would you expect to perceive if white light were passed through a solution containing a substance that absorbed very strongly but only within the band 4800 ± 0.5 A?

COLOR AND CONSTITUTION

28-1   LIGHT ABSORPTION, FLUORESCENCE, AND PHOSPHORESCENCE

Whatever the mechanism for psychological response to color, the color of a substance that does not emit light itself is due to the light it transmits or reflects. The color of a solid and a solution of the same solid need not be identical or even similar, because of the difference in environment of the molecules in the solid and in solution. As might be expected, different solvents may produce different colored solutions with the same solute. In most cases the absorption spectrum of a crystal will depend on the way the crystal axes are oriented with respect to the light beam. In discussions of spectra we shall be concerned primarily with the colors of substances in solution. However, the colors of the same substances as dyes and pigments will often depend on their absorption characteristics as solids.

It is important to recognize that visible color will not necessarily depend on having the wavelength for maximum absorption (λ_{max}) in the visible region. Many substances with broad absorption bands will have λ_{max} below 4000 A and yet appear strongly colored because their absorption bands extend into the visible spectrum. This is illustrated in Figure 28-1.

The absorptions of electromagnetic radiation that produce visible colors correspond to changes in electronic states of molecules. At 4000 and 8000 A, absorption of 1 einstein of light (p. 26) is equivalent to excitation by energy amounting to 71 and 36 kcal/mole, respectively. The way that light energy is absorbed is worthy of brief comment.

The absorption process is not to be regarded as equivalent to simple excitation

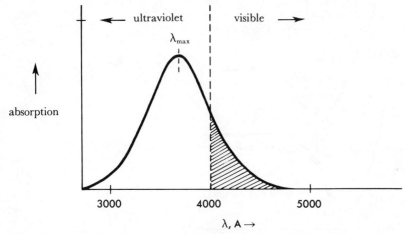

Figure 28-1   Absorption in the visible region by a substance that has λ_{max} in the ultraviolet.

by thermal energy of 36 to 71 kcal.   Instead, all the energy of the light quantum is taken up in excitation of an electron to a high-energy, usually antibonding orbital (pp. 32-34, 107-108, and 196-197).   An important point about such processes is that they occur more rapidly than the atoms vibrate in the bonds (Franck-Condon principle).   The short transition time of an electron between ground and excited states is in complete contrast to what happens during absorption of a quantum of radiofrequency energy in n.m.r. spectroscopy, wherein the absorption process may be slow compared to chemical reactions (pp. 43-46).   An electronically excited molecule is, therefore, in the first instant that it is produced ($<10^{-13}$ sec) just like the ground-state molecule as far as positions and kinetic energies of the atoms go, but has a very different electronic configuration.   What happens at this point depends on several factors, some of which can be best illustrated by energy diagrams of the type used earlier (p. 178).   We shall talk in terms of diatomic molecules, but the argument is easily extended to more complicated systems.

Consider the diagram of Figure 28-2, which shows schematic potential energy curves for a molecule A-B in the ground state (A-B) and in an excited electronic state (A-B*).   It should be obvious that these curves are not expected to have identical shapes—the weaker bonding in the excited state tending to make the average distance r_e between the nuclei at the bottom of the "potential well" greater in the excited state than in the ground state.

The transition marked 1 in Figure 28-2 corresponds to absorption of energy by an A-B molecule existing in a relatively high vibrational level.   The energy change occurs with no change in r (Franck-Condon principle), and the electronic energy of the A-B* molecule so produced is seen to be *above* the level required for dissociation of A-B*.   The vibration of the excited molecule therefore has no restoring force and leads to dissociation to A and B atoms.   On the other hand, the transition marked 2 leads to an excited vibrational state of A-B*, which is not expected to dissociate but can lose vibrational energy to the surroundings and come down to a lower vibrational state.   This is called "vibrational relaxation" and usually requires about 10^{-12} sec.   The vibrationally "re-

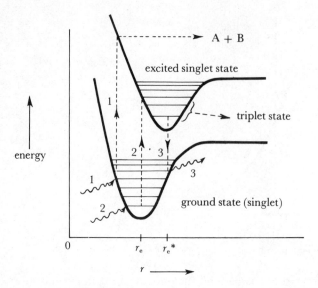

Figure 28-2   Schematic potential energy diagram for ground and excited electronic singlet states of a
diatomic molecule, A-B and A-B *, respectively. The horizontal lines represent vibrational energy levels (see p. 33). The wavy lines represent the arrival or departure of light quanta. It is
important to recognize that the curves shown here are schematic and, for actual systems, the
positions and shapes of the curves may be quite different from those shown.

laxed" excited state can now undergo several processes.   It can return to ground
state with emission of radiation (transition 3); this is known as **fluorescence,** the
wavelength of fluorescence being different from the original light absorbed.
Normally, fluorescence, if it occurs at all, occurs in 10^{-9} to 10^{-7} sec after absorption of the original radiation.   In many cases, the excited state can also return to
the ground state by nonradiative processes, the electronic excited state being
converted to a vibrationally excited ground state of the original molecule which
by vibrational relaxation proceeds to the ground state.   Among the possible nonradiative ways for the excited state to return to some sort of a ground state are
through conversion to a high-energy isomeric form, by chemical reactions with
surrounding molecules, by transfer of excess electronic energy to other molecules, or by decay through a lower energy **triplet** state.

   The latter type of process, involving a triplet state, is of particular chemical
interest because triplet states, even though of high energy, are often relatively
long-lived, up to a second or so, and can lead to important reaction products.
To explain, we must consider in more detail the nature of singlet and triplet
electronic states.

   We have already noted that in the ground states of ordinary molecules all the
electrons are paired; we can also have excited states with all electrons paired.
Such states with paired electrons are called **singlet** states.   A schematic representation of the ground state (S_0) and lowest excited singlet (S_1) electronic configurations of a molecule with four electrons and two bonding and two antibonding molecular orbitals are shown in Figure 28-3.   The π-electron system of
butadiene (p. 199) provides a concrete example of this type of system.

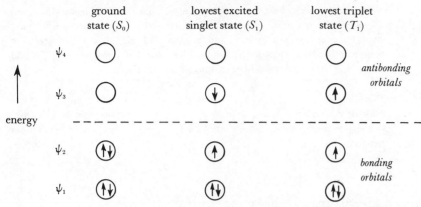

Figure 28-3   Schematic representation of the electronic configurations of ground and lowest excited singlet and triplet states of a molecule with four electrons and four molecular orbitals (ψ_1, ψ_2, ψ_3, and ψ_4).

A triplet state has two *unpaired* electrons and is normally more stable than the corresponding singlet state because, by Hund's rule (p. 106), less interelectronic repulsion is expected with unpaired than paired electrons. An example of a triplet electronic configuration (T_1) is shown in Figure 28-3. The name "triplet" arises from the fact that two unpaired electrons turn out to have *three* possible energy states in an applied magnetic field. "Singlet" means that there is only one possible energy state in a magnetic field.

Conversion of a singlet excited state to a triplet state ($S_1 \rightarrow T_1$) is energetically favorable but usually occurs rather slowly, in accord with the so-called spectroscopic selection rules, which predict that spontaneous changes of electronic configuration of this type should have very low probabilities. Nonetheless, if the singlet state is sufficiently long-lived, the singlet-triplet change, $S_1 \rightarrow T_1$ (often called **intersystem crossing**), may occur for a very considerable proportion of the excited singlet molecules.

The triplet state, like the singlet state, can return to the ground state by nonradiative processes (p. 680) but in many cases, a radiative transition ($T_1 \rightarrow S_0$) occurs, even though it has low probability. Such transitions result in emission of light of considerably longer wavelength than either that absorbed originally or that emitted by fluorescence. This type of radiative transition is called **phosphorescence.** Because phosphorescence is a process with a low probability, the T_1 state may persist from fractions of a second to many seconds. For benzene at −200°, absorption of light at 2540 A leads to fluorescence centered on 2900 A and phosphorescence at 3400 A with a half-life of 7 sec.

EXERCISE 28-2   What visible color would you expect the substance to have whose spectrum is shown in Figure 28-1?

EXERCISE 28-3   Suppose absorption of light by a diatomic molecule A-B in the lowest vibrational level of the ground state always resulted in dissociation into A and B atoms. Would this necessarily mean that the molecule could not exist in an excited electronic state in which the atoms were bonded together? Explain.

EXERCISE 28-4   The fluorescence of many substances can be "quenched" (diminished or even prevented) by a variety of means. Explain how concentration, temperature, viscosity, and presence of dissolved oxygen and impurities might affect the degree of fluorescence observed for solutions of a fluorescent material. Would you expect similar effects on phosphorescence? Explain.

EXERCISE 28-5   Explain qualitatively how temperature could have an effect on the appearance of the absorption spectrum of a system such as shown in Figure 28-2, knowing that most molecules are usually in their lowest vibrational state at room temperature.

28-2 LIGHT ABSORPTION AND STRUCTURE

We have already considered some aspects of the general relation of electronic spectra to structure. For example, in Chapter 9 it was shown how the changes in wavelength of absorption of conjugated systems could be accounted for in terms of differences in the degree of resonance stabilization between ground and excited states. However, most of the compounds considered absorbed principally in the ultraviolet and not in the visible region of the spectrum, although it was mentioned that for relatively long conjugated systems of multiple bonds the absorption moves sufficiently toward longer wavelengths such that visible light is absorbed. Thus, 1,2-diphenylethene is colorless (λ_{max} 3190 A), whereas 1,10-diphenyl-1,3,5,7,9-decapentaene is orange (λ_{max} 4240 A).

colorless   orange

(λ_{max} 3190 A)   (λ_{max} 4240 A)

In general, the more extended a planar system of conjugated bonds is, the smaller is the energy difference between the ground and excited states. The importance of having the bonds coplanar should be obvious from consideration of preferred geometries of the resonance structures with formal bonds and/or charge separations. The contribution of such structures to stabilization of the ground state is expected to increase with an increase in length of the conjugated system; however, stabilization of the excited state is expected to increase even more rapidly, so that the over-all energy difference between ground and excited states is expected to decrease and hence the wavelength required for excitation will shift to longer wavelengths. This effect is shown schematically in Figure 28-4.

The effect of substituents on colors associated with conjugated systems is of particular interest in the study of dyes, because, with the exception of β-carotene, which is an orange-red conjugated polyene occurring in a variety of plants

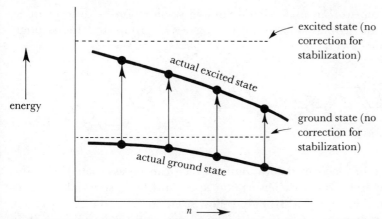

energy

Figure 28-4   Schematic relationship between stabilization of ground and excited states of systems
with n conjugated double bonds.

and which is commonly used as a food color, most dyes have relatively short
conjugated systems and would not be intensely colored in the absence of substituent groups.

β–carotene (all *trans* double bonds)
(λ_{max} 4500 A, ϵ 140,000)

A typical example is 2,4-dinitro-1-naphthol (Martius Yellow), a substance that
is useful for dyeing wool and silk.

Martius Yellow

Naphthalene rates as a conjugated system but is colorless, as is pure 1-naphthol.
2,4-Dinitronaphthalene is a pale yellow, so the red-orange color of crystalline
Martius Yellow is clearly due to a special combination of substituents with a conjugated system.

Substitution of a group on a conjugated system which is capable of either donating or accepting electrons usually has the effect of extending the conjugation. This is particularly true if an electron-attracting group is connected to one
end of the system and an electron-donating group at the other. Thus, with *p-*

nitrophenolate ion, we can expect considerable stabilization because of inter-action between the strongly electron-donating —$O^{\ominus}$ group and the strongly electron-accepting —NO_2 group.

The high degree of electron delocalization which can be associated with this system is clearly related to its absorption spectrum because, while p-nitro-phenolate ion in water gives a strongly yellow solution (λ_{max} 400 A, ϵ 15,000), p-nitrophenol produces a less intensely colored greenish-yellow solution (λ_{max} 3200 A, ϵ 9000). The important structural difference here is that the —OH group is not nearly so strong an electron-donating group as an —$O^{\ominus}$ group, and electron delocalization is therefore likely to be less important.

There are several connections in which changes of color resulting from inter-conversions of such substances as p-nitrophenol and p-nitrophenolate are impor-tant, including the practical one of the colors of acid-base indicators as a func-tion of pH. However, before discussing some of these, it will be well to make clear that, in visual comparisons of the colors of substances, it must be remem-bered that both wavelength and absorption coefficient are involved in judgments of color intensities. The change from p-nitrophenolate to p-nitrophenol pro-vides an excellent example of how both wavelength and absorption coefficient are affected by a structural change. It is possible for wavelength to shift with-out changing the degree of absorption and vice versa, so we must be careful in speaking of one substance as being more "highly colored" than another, as to which features of the spectra we are actually comparing.

The problems of correlating wavelength and absorption coefficient with struc-ture can be approached in a number of ways. In an earlier discussion (pp. 196-197), the excited electronic states were considered to have hybrid structures with important contributions from dipolar electron-pairing schemes. Thus for the first excited singlet state of butadiene, we may write the following contributing structures:

$$\overset{\oplus}{CH_2}-CH=CH-\overset{\ominus}{\underset{..}{C}H_2} \quad\leftrightarrow\quad \overset{\ominus}{\underset{..}{C}H_2}-CH=CH-\overset{\oplus}{CH_2} \quad\leftrightarrow\quad CH_2=CH-\overset{\ominus}{\underset{..}{C}H}-\overset{\oplus}{CH_2} \quad\leftrightarrow\quad etc.$$

[1]   [2]   [3]

Extension of this approach to benzene suggests the importance of resonance structures such as [4], [5], etc., for the excited singlet state of benzene.

It is not unreasonable to suppose that substitution of an electron-attracting group at one end of such a system and an electron-donating group at the other end should be particularly favorable for stabilizing the excited state relative to the ground state, wherein [4], [5], etc., are of negligible importance. At the same time, we should not expect that two electron-attracting (or two electron-donating) groups at opposite ends would be nearly as effective.

EXERCISE 28-6   The $\pi \to \pi^*$ absorption spectra of *trans,trans-*, *trans,cis-*, and *cis,cis-*1,4-diphenylbutadiene show maxima and ε values (in parentheses) at about 3300 A (5.5×10^4), 3100 A (3×10^4), and 3000 A (3×10^4), respectively. What is the difference in energy between the transitions of these isomers in kcal/mole? Why should the *trans,trans* isomer have a different λ_{max} than the other isomers? (It may be helpful to make scale drawings or models.)

EXERCISE 28-7   How would you expect the spectra of compounds [6] and [7] to compare with each other and with the spectra of *cis-* and *trans-*1,2-diphenylethylene (stilbene)? Explain.

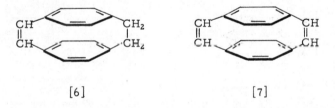

[6]   [7]

EXERCISE 28-8   Why must the resonance forms [1], [2], [3], etc., correspond to a singlet state? Formulate the hybrid structure of a triplet state of butadiene in terms of appropriate contributing resonance structures.

EXERCISE 28-9   a. *p*-Nitrodimethylaniline gives a yellow solution in water which fades to colorless when made acidic. Explain.
   b. *p*-Dimethylaminoazobenzene (p. 602) is bright yellow in aqueous solution (λ_{max} 4200 A) but turns intense red (λ_{max} 5300 A) if dilute acid is added. If the solution is then made very strongly acid, the red color changes to a different yellow (λ_{max} 4300 A) than the starting solution. Show how one proton could be added to *p*-dimethylaminoazobenzene to cause the absorption to shift to *longer* wavelengths and how addition of a second proton could shift the absorption back to shorter wavelengths.

EXERCISE 28-10   The well-known indicator and laxative, phenolphthalein, undergoes the following changes as a neutral solution is made successively basic:

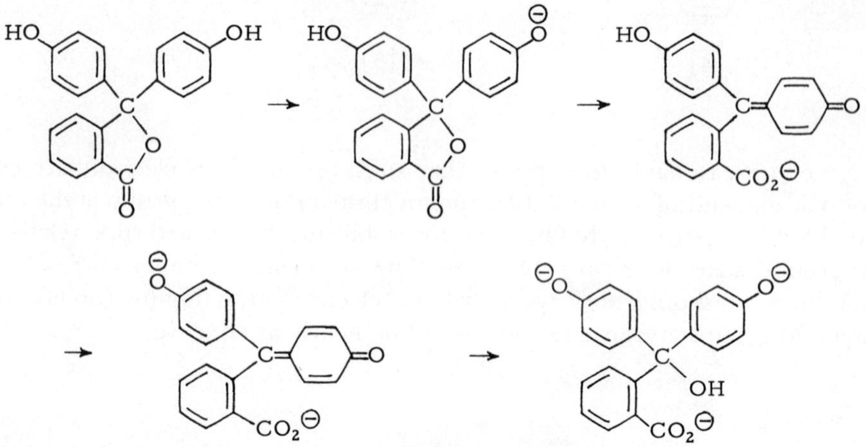

Some of these forms are colorless, some intensely colored.   Which would you expect to absorb at sufficiently long wavelengths to be visibly colored?   Give your reasoning.

The problem of predicting the absorption intensities is a difficult and complicated one.   An important factor is the ease of displacement of charge during the transition. On this account we expect substances such as p-nitrophenolate ions, which have roughly equivalent electron-donating and electron-attracting groups in each of their principal structures, to absorb particularly strongly.

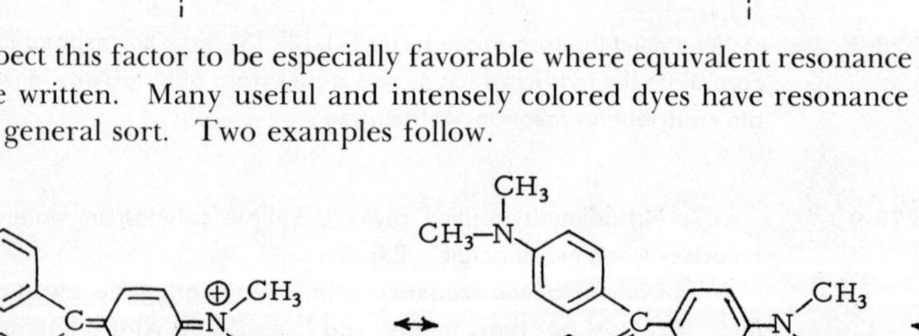

| electron attracting | electron donating | | electron donating | electron attracting |

We expect this factor to be especially favorable where equivalent resonance structures may be written.   Many useful and intensely colored dyes have resonance structures of this general sort.   Two examples follow.

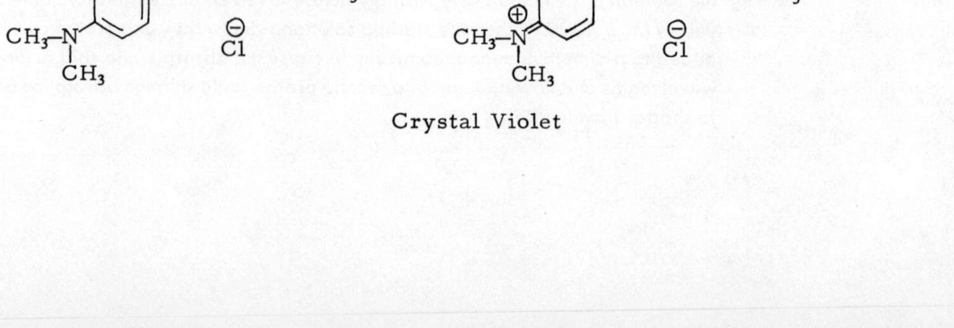

etc.

Crystal Violet

Pseudocyanine

(orange)

EXERCISE 28-11   Aqueous solutions of Crystal Violet turn from violet to blue to green to yellow on addition of successive amounts of acid. The color changes are reversed by adding alkali. What kind of chemical changes could be taking place to give these color changes?

DYES

28-3 METHODS FOR APPLYING DYES TO FABRICS

The subject of dyes can be approached in a variety of ways; for example, through consideration of the organic structures that correspond to particularly useful colors, or perhaps from the standpoint of the historical development of the dye industry. However, perhaps a more logical approach is possible through study of the methods of introducing color into fibers or fabrics because the factors involved in the dyeing process determine almost as much as anything what types of colored organic compounds have practical uses as dyes. The need for a variety of methods and a variety of dyes should be clear from the diversity of substances used as fibers in modern technology. At the nonpolar extreme of the spectrum are substances such as polypropylene, a long-chain hydrocarbon; in the middle is cotton, a polyglucoside with ether and hydroxyl linkages; at the polar end is wool, a polypeptide structure, cross-linked by cysteine and containing free acid and amino groups.

In virtually all dyeing processes it is necessary to have the dye do more than just color the surface of the fiber. Actually, the dye must penetrate all through the fiber. The problem then is to keep it in the fiber, particularly during washing and cleaning operations, which by their very nature are designed to remove foreign materials and, right or not, dyes seem to come under the category of foreign materials. The result is that a water-soluble color applied directly to medium- or nonpolar fibers normally is poorly wash-fast, and some stratagem has to be developed to keep it in the fiber. Some of the methods of producing wash-fast dyes follow.

A. Dyes with Polar Groups

Substitution of polar groups such as amino and sulfonic acid groups into colored molecules often improves wash-fastness by enabling the dye to combine with polar sites in the fiber. This is a particularly useful technique with wool and silk—both of which are polypeptides and contain many strongly polar groups. Martius Yellow (p. 683), which is strongly acidic, is a simple *direct* dye for wool and silk. For cotton, linen, and rayon, which are cellulose fibers, it is more difficult to achieve wash-fast colors by direct dyeing. Congo Red was the first reasonably satisfactory direct dye for cotton; it has polar amine and sulfonate groups which, in the fiber, can form hydrogen bonds to the cellulose ether and hydroxyl groups and to other dye molecules, thus reducing its tendency to be leached out in washing.

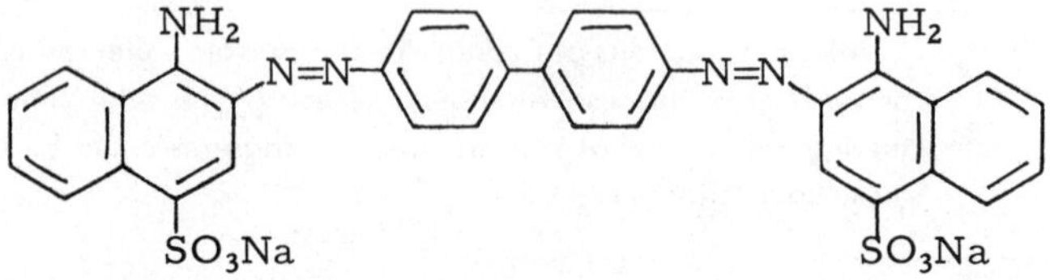

Congo Red

B. Disperse Dyes

The use of water-insoluble, fiber-soluble ("disperse") dyes is helpful for many of the medium- and less-polar fibers. Such dyes usually give true solutions in the fiber—the absorption of the dye not being dependent on combination with a limited number of polar sites. Disperse dyes are usually applied in the form of a dispersion of finely divided dye in a soap solution in the presence of some solubilizing agent such as phenol, cresol, or benzoic acid. The process suffers from the fact that usually the absorption of dye in the fiber is slow and is best carried out at elevated temperatures in pressure vessels.

1-Amino-4-hydroxyanthraquinone is a typical dye which can be used in dispersed form to color Dacron (polyethylene glycol terephthalate). Absorption of this dye is a solution process, as indicated by the fact that, even up to high dye concentrations in the fiber, the amount of dye in the fiber is directly proportional to the equilibrium concentration of dye in the solution.

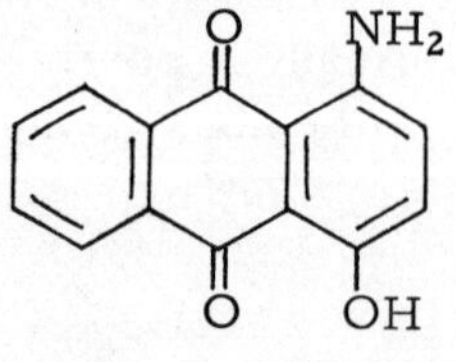

1-amino-4-hydroxyanthraquinone

(red-violet, pink dye)

C. Developed Dyes

In many cases, excellent and quite fast colors can be produced by forming the dye directly in the fiber by reactions such as azo coupling. The formation of Para Red provides a simple example, although it is a dye that is now of more historical than practical interest. Here, the fabric is soaked in an alkaline solution of β-naphthol; it is then dried, and the red azo dye is formed in the fiber by immersion of the cloth in a solution of p-nitrobenzenediazonium chloride.

Para Red

There are many variations on this kind of process, many of which are particularly useful in making printed fabrics.

D. Mordant Dyes

One of the oldest known methods of producing wash-fast colors is with the aid of metallic hydroxides to form a link between the fabric and the dye. The production of cloth dyed with "Turkey red," the coloring material of the root of the madder plant, using aluminum hydroxide as a binder or "mordant," has been carried out for many centuries. The principal organic ingredient of Turkey red has been shown to be 1,2-dihydroxyanthraquinone ("alizarin") and this substance is now prepared synthetically from anthraquinone.

1, 2-dihydroxyanthraquinone

(alizarin)

Mordant dyes are useful on cotton, wool, or silk, and are applied in a rather complicated sequence of operations whereby the cloth is treated with a solution of a metallic salt in the presence of mild alkali and a wetting agent for the purpose of forming a complex of the fiber with the metal cation. The dye is then introduced and an insoluble complex salt (often called a "lake") is formed in the fiber. With alizarin and aluminum hydroxide, it is probable that the binding to the dye involves salt formation at the 1-hydroxyl and coordination to aluminum at the adjacent carbonyl group.

Apparently, this chelated type of structure is important in contributing to the excellent light-fastness of most mordant dyes.

A variety of metals can be used as mordants, but aluminum, iron, and chromium are most commonly used. Mordant dyes normally have reasonably acidic phenolic groups and some kind of an adjacent electron-attracting group which fills the function of the carbonyl group in alizarin.

E. Vat Dyes

Another and very effective way of making fast colors, which is not different in principle from the developed dyes, is to introduce the dye in a soluble form (which may itself be colorless) and then generate the dye in an insoluble form within the fiber. Most commonly, the soluble form of the dye is a reduced form, the dye being produced by oxidation. The over-all process is known as "vat dyeing," the name arising from the vats used in the reduction step.

The famous dyes of the ancients, indigo and Tyrian purple (royal purple), can be applied in this way—reduced, soluble forms of these dyes occur naturally. In the case of indigo, this is the glycoside, indican (p. 669), which occurs in the indigo plant. Enzymic or acid hydrolysis of indican gives 3-hydroxy-indole ("indoxyl"), which exists in equilibrium with the corresponding keto form.

indoxyl

Air oxidation of indoxyl produces indigo—probably by a free-radical mechanism.

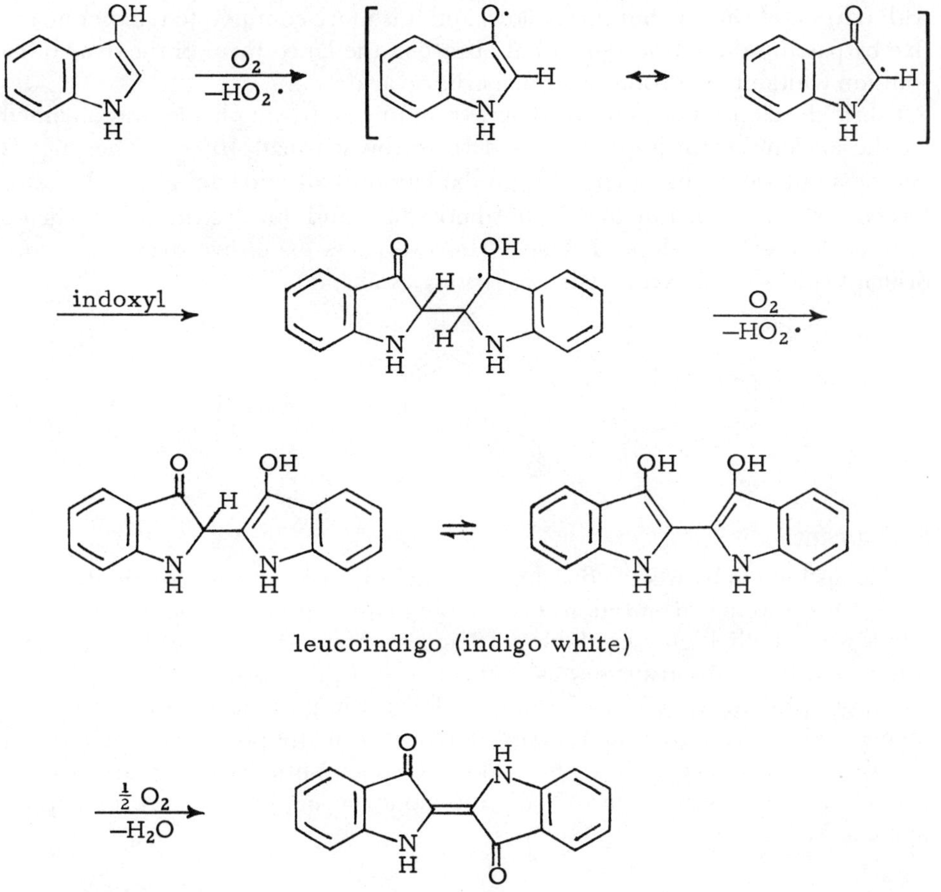

OH

$$\xrightarrow[-HO_2\cdot]{O_2}$$

indoxyl $\longrightarrow$

$$\xrightarrow[-HO_2\cdot]{O_2}$$

$\rightleftharpoons$

leucoindigo (indigo white)

$$\xrightarrow[-H_2O]{\frac{1}{2}O_2}$$

indigo

The last stage of this reaction, the oxidation of leucoindigo, will be seen to resemble conversion of hydroquinone to quinone. X-ray studies have shown that indigo has the *trans* configuration of the double bond. Indigo is very insoluble in water and most organic solvents. It absorbs strongly at 5900 A.

In the ordinary dyeing process, indigo is reduced to the colorless **leuco** form which, as an enol, is soluble in alkaline solution and is applied to fabric in this form. In the early days of vat dyeing, the reduction step was often achieved by fermentation, but sodium dithionite (sodium hydrosulfite, $Na_2S_2O_4$) is currently the favored reducing agent.

$$\overset{\oplus}{Na}\ \overset{\ominus}{O}\ \overset{O}{\underset{\|}{S}}\ \overset{O}{\underset{\|}{S}}\ \overset{\ominus}{O}\ \overset{\oplus}{Na}\ +\ 2\,\overset{\ominus}{O}H \longrightarrow 2\,NaHSO_3\ +\ 2\,e$$

That alkaline solutions are required for solubilization of the leuco form of most vat dyes restricts the use of such dyes to fabrics such as cotton and rayon which, unlike wool and silk, are reasonably stable under alkaline conditions.

Oxidation of the leuco form to the dye in the fiber can be achieved simply with oxygen of the air; but this is slow, and it is more common to regenerate the dye by passing the fabric, which has absorbed the leuco form of the dye, into a solution containing chromic acid or perboric acid.

Fabric dyed with the famous color Tyrian purple (royal purple) was obtained by the ancients from juice expressed from the sea-snail *Murex*. The juice is colorless but yields the purple dye on oxidation in air and sunlight. The color has been shown to be due to 6,6'-dibromoindigo, and this dye can now be made synthetically on any desired scale. However, less expensive dyes with more brilliant colors of the same type are readily available.

Tyrian purple

F. Pigments

The distinction between a dye and a pigment is that a dye is actually absorbed by the material to be colored, whereas a pigment is applied to the surface. Pigments are usually highly insoluble substances. Many inorganic substances that would be wholly unsatisfactory as dyes are useful pigments.

Copper phthalocyanine is an example of a very important class of organic pigments. They are tetraazatetrabenzo derivatives of the porphyrin compounds discussed in Chapter 27 (pp. 664-666). Copper phthalocyanine arises from condensation of four molecules of phthalonitrile in the presence of copper metal at 200°.

copper phthalocyanine

EXERCISE 28-12   Congo Red in neutral water solution has a λ_{max} in the visible spectrum at 4970 A. In acid solution it shows absorption maxima at 6470 and 5895 A. What colors are likely to be observed for neutral and acidic Congo Red solutions? How could addition of acid to a neutral Congo Red solution cause the absorption maximum to shift to *longer* wavelengths? What would you expect to happen to the color in very strong acid solution?

EXERCISE 28-13   Outline a possible synthesis of the red dye 1-amino-4-hydroxyanthraquinone from anthraquinone, knowing that sulfonation of anthraquinone with fuming sulfuric acid in the presence of mercuric sulfate gives anthraquinone-1-sulfonic acid.

EXERCISE 28-14   The color of alizarin-dyed fabrics depends on the mordant used. Aluminum gives red, iron violet, and chromium brownish-red.   Why should the color be dependent on the metal salt used?

EXERCISE 28-15   The formation of indigo by oxidation of indoxyl in alkaline solution might be formulated as involving formation of isatin and condensation of this substance with indoxyl in the aldol manner.

isatin

However, the reaction of isatin and indoxyl actually takes a different course and produces a colored isomer of indigo known as Indigo red, which does not form leucoindigo when reduced with sodium dithionite. What is the structure of Indigo red likely to be and why is it formed in preference to indigo in the condensation reaction?

EXERCISE 28-16   How might one make a phthalocyanine-type molecule which could be soluble enough in water to be a dye?   How might the phthalocyanine structure be modified to give a phthalocyanine vat dye?

28-4 OTHER COMMERCIAL USES OF LIGHT-ABSORBING COMPOUNDS

A. Photographic Sensitizers. Cyanines

A simple emulsion of silver bromide in gelatin is mainly sensitive to blue, violet, or ultraviolet light. As a result, a photograph made with such an emulsion represents blue and violet subjects as white and all other subject colors as gray or black. That organic dyes can act as photosensitizers for silver bromide emulsions was first discovered in 1873 and, as the result of many extensive studies, it is possible to make photographic emulsions which are sensitive over the whole region of the visible spectrum as well as into the infrared. Since the dyes themselves absorb light of the wavelengths to which they sensitize silver bromide, it appears that light-activated dye molecules can transfer their energy to silver bromide and thus produce activated silver bromide capable of being reduced by suitable developing agents (p. 620).

The most useful sensitizing dyes are called cyanines and have the following basic structural unit:

$$-\ddot{N}\!\!\left(\!\!-\overset{|}{C}=\overset{|}{C}\!\!\right)_{\!n}\!\!\overset{|}{C}=\overset{\oplus}{N}\!\!-$$

This type of system is expected to be strongly light-absorbing by virtue of having electron-attracting and electron-donating groups at the opposite ends of a conjugated system.   Two examples of useful cyanine photosensitizers follow.

Pinacyanol

(violet–blue)

Kryptocyanine

(purple–black)

Pinacyanol sensitizes silver bromide emulsions powerfully to red light; Kryptocyanine is effective for both red and infrared radiation.

B. Ultraviolet Screening Agents

The destructive action of ultraviolet radiation on dyes, plastics, fabrics, etc., is well known and there has been considerable research directed toward development of suitable protective agents which would act as preferential absorbers of ultraviolet light. Such substances are often called **ultraviolet screening agents,** and in practical applications they usually have to have properties consistent with a variety of other requirements.   For example, a sunburn preventive agent must be nontoxic, nonstaining, nonvolatile, reasonably soluble in and stable to water, and able to filter out the burning but not the tanning component of sunlight.   Glyceryl p-aminobenzoate is a screening agent which has a good balance of properties for this purpose.

Many ultraviolet screening applications require a substance which is not itself colored, is highly stable to light, and is an effective absorber.   It is particularly desirable to have a sharp drop in absorption coefficient at the edge of the visible coloration. These requirements are well met in many applications by o-hydroxyphenylketones, o-hydroxybenzophenones being particularly useful.   2-(2-Hydroxyphenyl)-benzotriazoles also possess excellent properties as screening agents.

2, 2'–dihydroxy–4, 4'–dimethoxy–
benzophenone

(Uvinol)

2–(2–hydroxy–4–methyl–
phenyl)–benzo[d]triazole

(Tinuvin P)

As with many other dyes, the presence of intramolecular hydrogen bonds greatly improves light fastness. Possibly, such substances have a high probability for radiationless transitions back to the ground state.

ORGANIC PHOTOCHEMISTRY

An extraordinarily wide variety of reactions of organic compounds are known to occur under the influence of visible and ultraviolet light. It is not our purpose here to review this kind of chemistry in detail—we shall mention a few types of important photochemical reactions and show how the courses of some of them can be explained on the basis of the principles that were discussed earlier with respect to light absorption, fluorescence, phosphorescence, etc.

28-5 PHOTODISSOCIATION REACTIONS

We have already mentioned (pp. 71-73) how the chlorine molecule undergoes dissociation with near-ultraviolet light to give chlorine atoms and thereby leads to free-radical chain chlorination of saturated hydrocarbons. Photochemical chlorination is an example of a photochemical reaction which can have a high *quantum yield*—that is, many molecules of chlorination product can be generated per quantum of light absorbed (p. 73). The quantum yield of a reaction is said to be unity when 1 mole of reactant is converted to product(s) per einstein of light absorbed. The symbol for quantum yield is usually Φ.

Acetone vapor undergoes a photodissociation reaction with 3130-A light with Φ somewhat less than unity. Although the reaction has been extensively studied, agreement is not unanimous on the details of how the photodissociation occurs. Despite this, the photochemical decomposition of acetone is of interest in illustrating some of the things which are taken into account in the study of photochemical processes.

Absorption of light by acetone results in the formation of an excited state which has sufficient energy to undergo cleavage of a C—C bond (the weakest bond in the molecule) and form a methyl free radical and an acetyl free radical.

$$CH_3-\overset{O}{\overset{\|}{C}}-CH_3 \quad \xrightarrow{h\nu} \quad \left[CH_3-\overset{O}{\overset{\|}{C}}-CH_3 \right]^* \quad \longrightarrow \quad CH_3-\overset{O}{\overset{\|}{C}} \cdot + CH_3 \cdot$$

At temperatures much above room temperature, the acetyl radical breaks down to give another methyl radical and carbon monoxide.

$$CH_3-\overset{O}{\overset{\|}{C}} \cdot \quad \longrightarrow \quad CH_3 \cdot + C{=}O$$

If this reaction goes to completion, the principal reaction products are ethane and carbon monoxide.

$$2\,CH_3 \cdot \quad \longrightarrow \quad CH_3-CH_3$$

If the acetyl radical does not decompose completely, then some biacetyl is also formed. This reaction is quite important at room temperature or below.

$$2\ CH_3\!-\!\overset{\overset{\textstyle O}{\|}}{C}\!\cdot\quad\longrightarrow\quad CH_3\!-\!\overset{\overset{\textstyle O}{\|}}{C}\!-\!\overset{\overset{\textstyle O}{\|}}{C}\!-\!CH_3$$

biacetyl

Lesser amounts of methane, hydrogen, ketene (see p. 348), etc., are also formed in the photochemical dissociation of acetone.

A variety of dissociation-type photochemical reactions have been found to take place with other carbonyl compounds. Two examples are

$$CH_3\!-\!\overset{\overset{\textstyle O}{\|}}{C}\!-\!CH_2CH_2CH_3\quad\xrightarrow[\text{vapor phase}]{h\nu}\quad CH_3\!-\!\overset{\overset{\textstyle O}{\|}}{C}\!-\!CH_3\ +\ CH_2\!=\!CH_2$$

$$\xrightarrow[\text{vapor phase}]{h\nu}\qquad \begin{matrix} CH_2\!-\!CH_2 \\ | \qquad | \\ CH_2\!-\!CH_2 \end{matrix}\ +\ CO$$

EXERCISE 28-17   The quantum yield in photochemical chlorination of hydrocarbons such as methane is quite sensitive to the experimental conditions. How would you expect it to vary with (a) the *intensity* of the incident light, (b) the wavelength of the incident light from 2500 to 4500 A, (c) the presence of oxygen, and (d) the presence of alkenes? Explain.

EXERCISE 28-18   The vapor-phase photochemical decomposition of acetone proceeds in the presence of iodine vapor but the amount of carbon monoxide formed becomes very small. Explain how this result argues against the one-step process, acetone $\xrightarrow{h\nu}$ $2\ CH_3\!\cdot + CO$. What do you expect the products to be in the presence of iodine?

28-6   PHOTOCHEMICAL REDUCTION.   BENZOPINACOL FORMATION

One of the classic photochemical reductions of organic chemistry is the formation of benzopinacol, as brought about by the action of light on a solution of benzophenone in isopropyl alcohol. The yield is quantitative.

The light functions to energize the benzophenone, and the activated ketone removes a hydrogen from isopropyl alcohol.

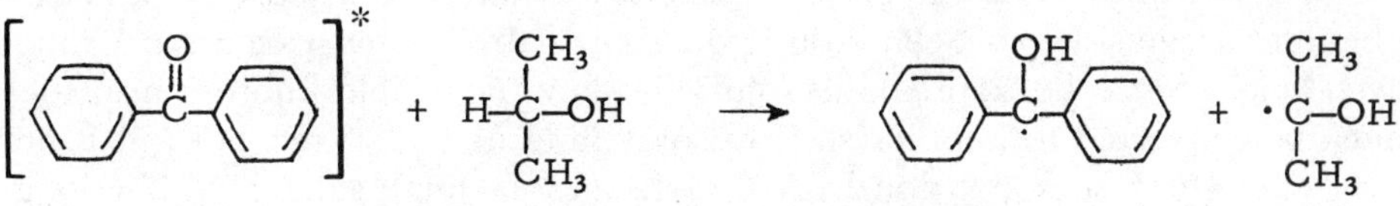

benzhydrol radical

[8]

Benzopinacol results from dimerization of benzhydrol radicals [8].

Since the quantum yields of acetone and benzopinacol are both nearly unity when the light intensity is not high, it is clear that *two* benzhydrol radicals [8] must be formed for each molecule of benzophenone that becomes activated. This is possible if the hydroxyisopropyl radicals formed by Eq. (28-1) react with benzophenone to give benzhydrol radicals.

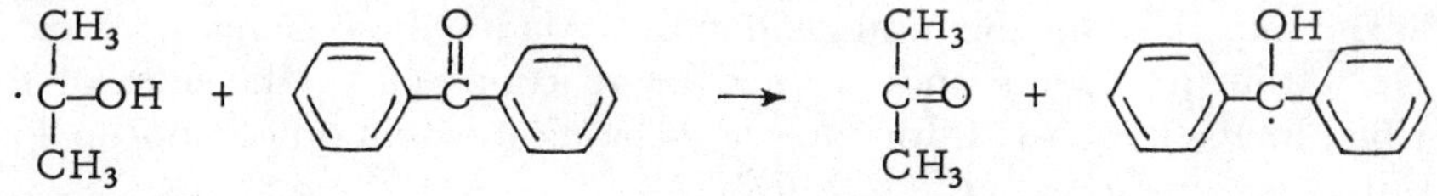

This reaction is expected to be energetically favorable because of the greater possibility for delocalization of the odd electron in the benzhydrol radical than in the hydroxyisopropyl radical.

Photochemical formation of benzopinacol can also be achieved from benzophenone and benzhydrol.

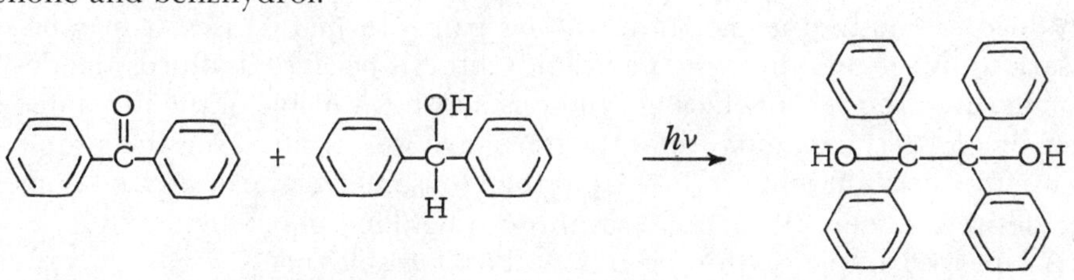

The mechanism is similar to that for isopropyl alcohol as the reducing agent except that now two benzhydrol radicals are formed.

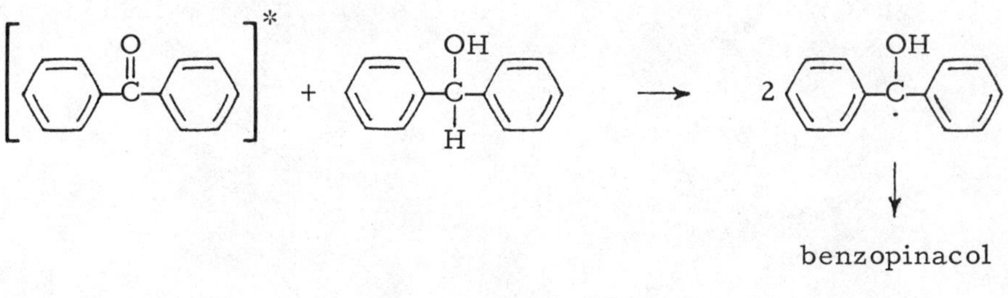

benzopinacol

This reduction is believed to involve the triplet state of benzophenone by the following argument. Benzopinacol formation is reasonably efficient even when the benzhydrol concentration is low; therefore, whatever excited state of benzophenone accepts a hydrogen atom from benzhydrol, it must be a fairly long-lived one. Since benzophenone solutions show no visible fluorescence, they must be converted to another state in something like 10^{-10} sec, but this is not long enough to seek out benzhydrol molecules in dilute solution. The long-lived state is then most reasonably a triplet state.

EXERCISE 28-19   Irradiation of benzophenone in isopropyl alcohol in the presence of oxygen gives no benzopinacol (the benzophenone is not consumed), acetone (with Φ equal to unity), and hydrogen peroxide (with Φ nearly unity). The reaction does not occur readily in the absence of benzophenone. Explain how benzophenone acts as a photosensitizer for the oxidation of isopropyl alcohol by oxygen.

28-7 PHOTOCHEMICAL OXIDATION

The lack of stability of many organic substances toward light in the presence of oxygen is well known. The light fading of dyes provides an important practical example of photochemical oxidation. Many photochemical oxidations involve sensitizing agents and proceed by reactions along the lines of those described in Exercise 28-19 for the photochemical oxidation of isopropyl alcohol with benzophenone as the sensitizer.

28-8 PHOTOCHEMICAL ISOMERIZATION OF *CIS*- AND *TRANS*-UNSATURATED COMPOUNDS

An important problem in many syntheses of unsaturated compounds is to produce the desired isomer of a *cis-trans* pair. In many cases, it may be necessary to utilize an otherwise inefficient synthesis because it affords the desired isomer, even though an efficient synthesis may be available of the unwanted isomer or of an isomer mixture. An alternative way of attacking this problem is to use the most efficient syntheses and then to isomerize the undesired isomer to the desired isomer. In many cases this can be done photochemically.

A typical example is afforded by *cis*- and *trans*-stilbene.

trans   *cis*

Here the *trans* form is easily available by a variety of reactions and is much more stable than the *cis* isomer because it is less sterically hindered. However, it is possible to produce a mixture containing mostly the *cis* isomer by irradiating a solution of the *trans* isomer in the presence of a suitable photosensitizer. This process in no way contravenes the laws of thermodynamics, because the input of radiant energy permits the equilibrium point to be shifted from what it would be normally.

In the practical use of the sensitized photochemical equilibration of *cis* and *trans* isomers, it is normally necessary to carry out pilot experiments to determine what sensitizers are useful and the equilibrium point which each gives. A specific example is provided by the equilibration of 1-bromo-2-phenyl-1-propene.

The *trans* isomer is formed to the extent of 95 per cent in the dehydrohalogenation of 1,2-dibromo-2-phenylpropane.

Photoisomerization of the elimination product with aceto-β-naphthone as sensitizer produces a mixture containing 85 per cent of the *cis* isomer.

28-9 PHOTOCHEMICAL CYCLOADDITIONS

We have discussed thermal 1,2- and 1,4-cycloadditions in some detail in Chapter 10 (pp. 206–210). Similar reactions occur photochemically with or without sensitizers and, in many cases, afford highly unusual products. Butadiene provides an excellent example of the differences between thermal and photochemical cycloadditions.

A wide variety of photochemical cycloaddition reactions are known, many of which are impossible to achieve thermally. Among many examples are the following:

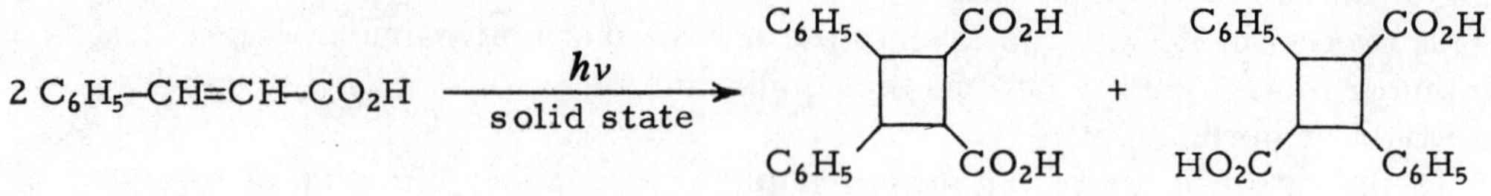

mixture of *cis* and *trans* isomers

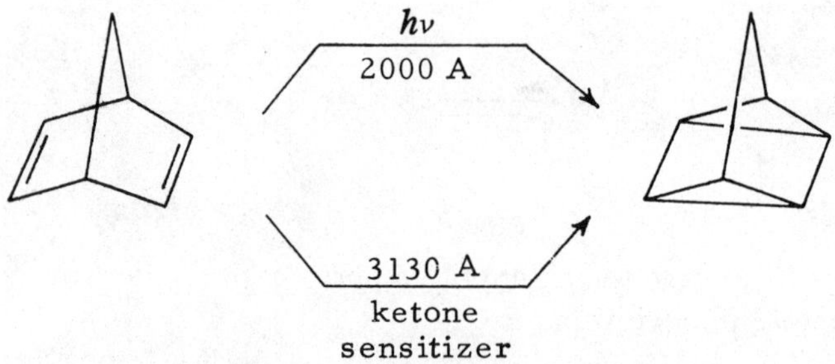

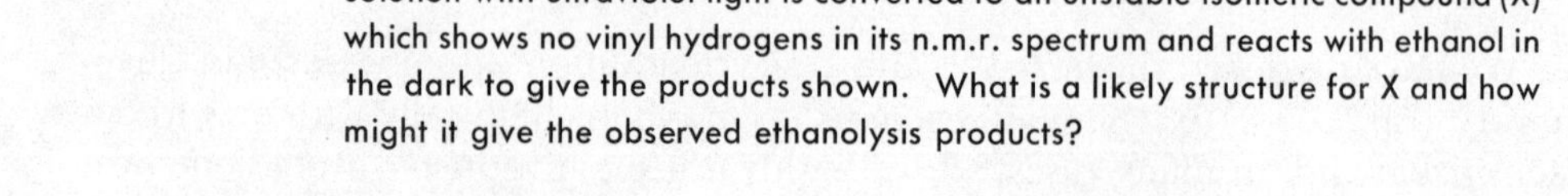

EXERCISE 28-20   3,5-Cholestadiene (see partial structure below) on irradiation in pentane solution with ultraviolet light is converted to an unstable isomeric compound (X) which shows no vinyl hydrogens in its n.m.r. spectrum and reacts with ethanol in the dark to give the products shown. What is a likely structure for X and how might it give the observed ethanolysis products?

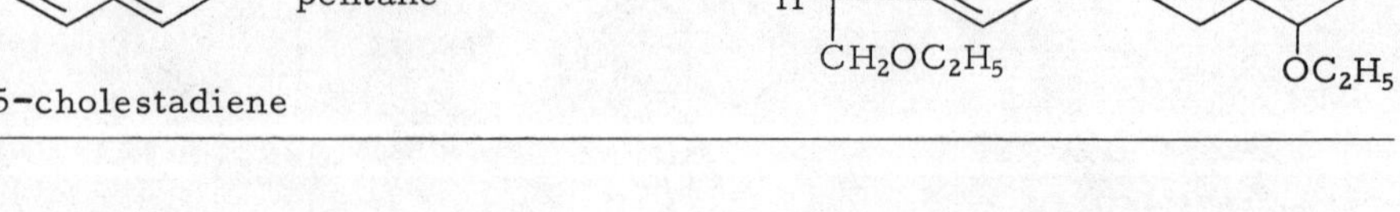

3, 5–cholestadiene

Polymers

*P*olymers are substances made up of recurring structural units, each of which can be regarded as derived from a specific compound called a monomer. The number of monomeric units is usually large and variable, a given polymer sample being characteristically a mixture of molecules with different molecular weights. The range of molecular weights encountered may either be small or very large.

The properties of a polymer, both physical and chemical, are in many ways as sensitive to changes in the structure of the monomer as are the properties of the monomer itself. This means that to a very considerable degree the properties of a polymer can be tailored to particular practical applications. Much of the emphasis in this chapter will be on how the properties of polymers can be related to their structures. This is appropriate because we have already given considerable attention in earlier chapters to methods of synthesis of monomers and polymers, as well as to the mechanisms of polymerization reactions.

Polymers

The thermal polymerization of cyclopentadiene by way of the Diels-Alder reaction provides a simple concrete example of how a monomer and a polymer are related.

monomer   dimer   trimer

tetramer   polymer

The first step in this polymerization is formation of the dimer, which involves cyclopentadiene's acting as both diene and dienophile. This step occurs readily on heating but slowly at room temperature. In subsequent steps, cyclopentadiene adds to the relatively strained double bonds of the first-formed polymer. These additions require higher temperatures (180 to 200°). If cyclopentadiene is heated to 200° until substantially no further reaction occurs, the product is a waxy solid having a *degree of polymerization n* ranging from two to greater than six.

Polycyclopentadiene molecules have double bonds for *end groups* and a complicated *backbone* of saturated fused rings. The polymerization is reversible and, on strong heating, the polymer reverts to cyclopentadiene.

EXERCISE 29-1   Write a reasonable mechanism for the thermal depolymerization of cyclopentadiene tetramer. How could one chemically alter the tetramer to make thermal breakdown more difficult? Explain.

EXERCISE 29-2   Suppose a bottle of cyclopentadiene were held at a temperature at which polymerization is rapid, but depolymerization is insignificant. Would the polymerization result in conversion of all of the cyclopentadiene into essentially one gigantic molecule? Why or why not? How would you carry on the polymerization so as to favor formation of polymer molecules with high molecular weights?

29-1 TYPES OF POLYMERS

Polymers can be classified in several different ways — according to their structures, the types of reactions by which they are prepared, their physical properties, or their technological uses. However, these classifications are not all mutually exclusive.

From the standpoint of general physical properties, we recognize three types of solid polymers: **elastomers** (rubbers or rubberlike elastic substances), **thermoplastic** polymers, and **thermosetting** polymers. These categories overlap considerably but are nonetheless helpful in defining general areas of use and types of structures. Elastomers (uncured) and thermoplastics typically have long polymer chains with few, if any, chemical bonds acting as **cross links** between the chains. This is shown schematically in Figure 29-1.

Such polymers, when heated, normally become soft and more or less fluid and can then be molded into useful shapes. The main difference between an elastomer and a thermoplastic polymer is in the degree of attractive forces between the polymer chains, as discussed on pp. 707 and 709. Thus, although elastomers, which are not cross-linked, are normally thermoplastic, not all thermoplastics are elastomers.

Cross links are extremely important in determining physical properties' because they increase the molecular weight and limit the motion of the chains with respect to one another. Only two cross links per polymer chain are required to connect together all the polymer molecules in a given sample to produce one gigantic molecule. As a result, introduction of only a few cross

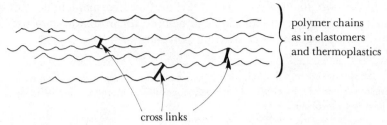

polymer chains
as in elastomers
and thermoplastics

cross links

Figure 29-1   Schematic representation of a polymer with few cross links.

links acts to greatly reduce solubility and tends to produce a **gel** polymer, which, although insoluble, will usually absorb (be swelled by) solvents in which the uncross-linked polymer is soluble. The tendency to absorb solvents decreases as the degree of cross linking is increased.

Thermosetting polymers are normally made from relatively low molecular weight, usually semifluid substances which, when heated in a mold, become highly cross linked, thereby forming hard, infusible, and insoluble products having a three-dimensional *space network* of bonds interconnecting the polymer chains (Figure 29-2).

Elastomers, thermoplastic and thermosetting polymers, are usually prepared by two different types of polymerization reactions—*addition* and *condensation* reactions. In addition polymerization, all of the atoms of the monomer molecules become part of the polymer; in condensation polymerization, some of the atoms of the monomer are split off in the reaction as water, alcohol, ammonia, or carbon dioxide, etc. Some polymers can be formed by either addition or condensation reactions. An example is polyethylene glycol, which, in principle, can form either by dehydration of ethylene glycol (condensation) or by polymerization of ethylene oxide (addition).

$$n \cdot HO-CH_2-CH_2-OH \quad \longrightarrow \quad HO(CH_2-CH_2-O)_n H \; + \; (n-1) \cdot H_2O$$

$$n \cdot CH_2-CH_2 \; + \; H_2O \quad \longrightarrow \quad HO(CH_2-CH_2-O)_n H$$
$$\underset{O}{\diagdown\diagup}$$

Other addition polymerizations were discussed earlier and include the formation of polycyclopentadiene, alkene polymers (pp. 152-156), polyalkadienes

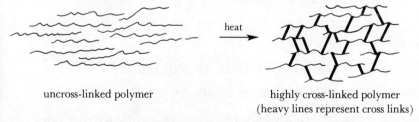

heat

uncross-linked polymer

highly cross-linked polymer
(heavy lines represent cross links)

Figure 29-2   Schematic representation of the conversion of an uncross-linked polymer to a highly cross-linked polymer.

(pp. 210-213), polyfluoroalkenes (pp. 251-252), and polyformaldehyde (pp. 324-325). Either addition or condensation can be used for preparation of useful elastomers, thermoplastic or thermosetting polymers.

EXERCISE 29-3   Show how each of the following polymer structures might be obtained from suitable monomers by either addition or condensation. More than one step may have to be involved.

a. $-CH_2-CH_2-CH_2-CH_2-CH_2-CH_2-CH_2-$

b. $-N-CH_2-CH_2-N-CH_2-CH_2-N-CH_2-CH_2-$
     $\quad\ |\qquad\qquad\quad |\qquad\qquad\quad |$
     $\quad CH_3\qquad\quad\ CH_3\qquad\quad\ CH_3$

c. $-CH-CH-CH-CH-CH-CH-$
     $\quad\ |\quad\ |\quad\ |\quad\ |\quad\ |\quad\ |$
     $\quad CH_3\ CH_3\ CH_3\ CH_3\ CH_3\ CH_3$

d. $\qquad\qquad\qquad\ O\qquad\qquad\qquad\qquad\ O\qquad\qquad\qquad\ O$
     $\qquad\qquad\qquad\ ||\qquad\qquad\qquad\qquad ||\qquad\qquad\qquad ||$
     $-O-CH_2-CH_2-C-O-CH_2-CH_2-C-O-CH_2-CH_2-C-$

e. $-CH_2-CH-CH_2-CH-CH_2-CH-$
     $\qquad\ |\qquad\qquad\ |\qquad\qquad\ |$
     $\qquad O-C-CH_3\ \ O-C-CH_3\ \ O-C-CH_3$
     $\qquad\qquad ||\qquad\qquad\ ||\qquad\qquad\ ||$
     $\qquad\qquad O\qquad\qquad\ O\qquad\qquad\ O$

f. $-CH_2-CH-CH_2-CH-CH_2-CH-$
     $\qquad\qquad |\qquad\qquad\ |\qquad\qquad\ |$
     $\qquad\quad OH\qquad\quad OH\qquad\quad OH$

g. $-CH_2-\langle\bigcirc\rangle-CH_2-CH_2-\langle\bigcirc\rangle-CH_2-CH_2-\langle\bigcirc\rangle-CH_2-$

h. $\qquad\qquad\qquad\qquad\ O\qquad\qquad\ O$
     $\qquad\qquad\qquad\qquad\ ||\qquad\qquad\ |$
     $-O-CH_2-CH-CH_2-O-C-O-CH_2-CH-CH_2-O-$
     $\qquad\qquad\ |$
     $\qquad\qquad\ O$
     $\qquad\qquad\ |$
     $\qquad\qquad\ C=O$
     $\qquad\qquad\ |$
     $\qquad\qquad\ O\qquad\qquad\qquad\qquad O$
     $\qquad\qquad\ |\qquad\qquad\qquad\qquad ||$
     $-O-CH_2-CH-CH_2-O-C-O-CH_2-CH-CH_2-O-$
     $\qquad\qquad\qquad\qquad\qquad\qquad\qquad\ |$
     $\qquad\qquad\qquad\qquad\qquad\qquad\qquad\ O$
     $\qquad\qquad\qquad\qquad\qquad\qquad\qquad\ |$

PHYSICAL PROPERTIES OF POLYMERS

29-2 FORCES BETWEEN POLYMER CHAINS

Polymers are produced on an industrial scale primarily, although not exclusively, for use as structural materials. Their physical properties are particularly important in determining their usefulness, be it as rubber tires, sidings for buildings, or solid rocket fuels.

Polymers that are not highly cross linked have properties that depend upon the degree and kind of forces that act between the chains. By way of example, consider a polymer such as polyethylene which, in a normal commercial sample, will be made up of molecules having 1000 to 2000 CH_2 groups in continuous chains. Since the material is a mixture of different molecules, it is not expected to crystallize in a conventional way.[1] Nonetheless, X-ray diffraction shows polyethylene to have very considerable crystalline character, there being regions as large as several hundred angstrom units in length, which have ordered, zigzag chains of CH_2 groups oriented with respect to one another like the chains in crystalline low-molecular-weight hydrocarbons. These crystalline regions are often called *crystallites*. Between the crystallites of polyethylene are amorphous, noncrystalline regions in which the polymer chains are more randomly ordered with respect to one another (Figure 29-3). These regions essentially constitute crystal defects.

The forces between the chains in the crystallites of polyethylene are the so-called **van der Waal's** or **dispersion** forces, which are the same forces acting between hydrocarbon molecules in the liquid and solid states, and, to a lesser extent, in the vapor state. These forces are relatively weak and arise through synchronization of the motions of the electrons in the separate atoms as they approach one another. The attractive force that results is rapidly overcome by repulsive forces when the atoms get very close to one another (see Fig. 3-6, which shows how the potential energy of pairs of neon atoms varies with the internuclear distance).

In other kinds of polymers, much stronger intermolecular forces can be produced by hydrogen bonding. This is especially important in the polyamides, such as the nylons, of which nylon (66) or polyhexamethyleneadipamide is most widely used.

possible hydrogen-bonded structure for
crystallites of nylon (66), polyhexamethyleneadipamide

---

[1] Quite good platelike crystals have been formed from dilute solutions of certain polymers, such as polyethylene. In the crystals, the polymer chains seem to run back and forth in folds between the large surfaces of the plates.

The effect of temperature on the physical properties of polymers is very important to their practical uses.   At low temperatures, polymers become hard and glass-like because the motion of the polymer chains in relation to each other is slow.   The approximate temperature below which glass-like behavior is apparent is called the **glass temperature** and is symbolized by T_g.   When a polymer containing crystallites is heated, the crystallites ultimately melt, and this temperature is usually called the **melting temperature** and is symbolized as T_m.   Usu-

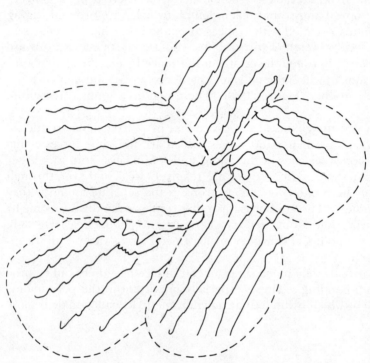

Figure 29-3   Schematic diagram of crystallites (enclosed by dotted lines) in a largely crystalline polymer.

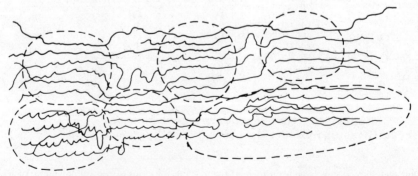

Figure 29-4   Schematic representation of an oriented crystalline polymer produced by drawing in the horizontal direction. The crystalline regions are enclosed with dotted lines.

ally, the molding temperature will be above T_m and the mechanical strength of the polymer will diminish rapidly as the temperature approaches T_m.

Obviously, another temperature of great importance in the practical use of polymers is the temperature near which thermal breakdown of the polymer chains occurs. Decomposition temperatures will obviously be sensitive to impurities, such as oxygen, and will be influenced strongly by the presence of inhibitors, antioxidants, etc. Nonetheless, there will be a temperature (usually rather high, 200 to 400°) at which uncatalyzed scission of the bonds in a chain will take place at an appreciable rate and, in general, one cannot expect to prevent this type of reaction from causing degradation of the polymer. Clearly, if this degradation temperature is comparable to T_m, as it is for polyacrylonitrile, difficulties are to be expected in simple thermal molding of the plastic. This difficulty is overcome in making polyacrylonitrile (Orlon) fibers by dissolving the polymer in N,N-dimethylformamide and forcing the solution through fine holes into a heated air space where the solvent evaporates.

Physical properties such as tensile strength, X-ray diffraction pattern, resistance to plastic flow, softening point, and elasticity of most polymers can be understood in a general way in terms of crystallites, amorphous regions, the degree of flexibility of the chains, and the strength of the forces acting between the chains (dispersion forces, hydrogen bonding, etc.). One way to approach the problem is to make a rough classification of properties of solid polymers according to the way the chains are disposed in relation to each other.

1. An **amorphous** polymer is one with no crystallites. If the forces between the chain are weak and if the motions of the chains are not in some way severely restricted, such a polymer would be expected to have low tensile strength and be subject to plastic flow in which the chains slip by one another.

2. An **unoriented crystalline** polymer is one which is considerably crystallized but has the crystallites essentially randomly oriented with respect to one another as in Figure 29-3. Such polymers, when heated, often show rather sharp T_m points, which correspond to the melting of the crystallites. Above T_m, these polymers are amorphous and undergo plastic flow, which permits them to be molded. Other things being the same, we expect T_m to be higher for the polymers with stiff chains (high barriers to internal rotation).

3. An **oriented crystalline** polymer is one in which the crystallites are oriented with respect to one another usually as the result of a **cold-drawing** process. Consider a polymer such as nylon, which has strong intermolecular forces and is in an unoriented state like the one represented by Figure 29-3. If the material is subjected to strong stress, say along the horizontal axis, at some temperature (most easily above T_g) where at least some plastic flow can occur, elongation will take place and the crystallites will be drawn together and oriented along the direction of the applied stress (Figure 29-4).

An oriented crystalline polymer usually has a much higher tensile strength than the unoriented polymer. Cold drawing is an important step in the production of synthetic fibers.

4. **Elastomers** are intermediate in character between amorphous and crystalline polymers. The key to elastic behavior is to have a polymer that has either

sufficiently weak forces between the chains or a sufficiently irregular structure to be very largely amorphous. The tendency for the chains to orient can often be considerably reduced by random introduction of methyl groups which, by steric hindrance, inhibit ordering of the chains. An elastomer needs to have some crystalline (or cross-linked) regions to prevent plastic flow and, in addition, should have rather flexible chains (which means T_g should be low). The structure of a polymer of this kind is shown schematically in Figure 29-5 — the important difference between this elastomer and the crystalline polymer of Figure 29-3 is the size of the amorphous regions. When tension is applied and the material elongates, the chains in the amorphous regions straighten out and become more nearly parallel. At the elastic limit, a semicrystalline state is reached, which is different from the one produced by cold drawing a crystalline polymer in that it is stable only while under tension. The forces between the chains are too weak in the absence of tension to maintain the crystalline state. Thus, when tension is released, contraction occurs and the original, nearly amorphous, polymer is produced.

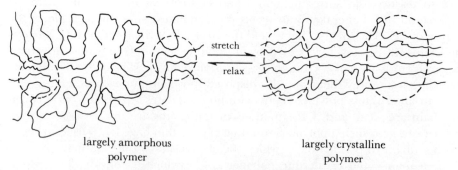

largely amorphous
polymer

largely crystalline
polymer

Figure 29-5   Schematic representation of an elastomer in relaxed and stretched configurations. The crystalline regions are enclosed by dotted lines.

A good elastomer should not undergo plastic flow in either the stretched or relaxed state, and when stretched should have a "memory" of its relaxed state. These conditions are best achieved with natural rubber (*cis*-polyisoprene, p. 212) by *curing* (*vulcanizing*) with sulfur. Natural rubber is tacky and undergoes plastic flow rather readily, but when heated with 1 to 8 per cent by weight of elemental sulfur in the presence of an *accelerator,* sulfur cross links are introduced between the chains. These cross links reduce plastic flow and provide a sort of reference framework for the stretched polymer to return to when it is allowed to relax. Too much sulfur completely destroys the elastic properties and gives hard rubber of the kind used in cases for storage batteries.

29-3 CORRELATION OF POLYMER PROPERTIES WITH STRUCTURE

With the aid of the concepts developed in the previous section, it is possible to correlate the properties of many of the technically important thermoplastic and elastic polymers with their chemical structures. We can understand why the simple linear polymers such as polyethylene, polyformaldehyde, and polytetrafluoroethylene are crystalline polymers with rather high melting points. Polyvinyl chloride, polyvinyl fluoride, and polystyrene as usually prepared are much less crystalline and have lower melting points; with these polymers, the stereochemical configuration is very important in determining the physical properties. Polystyrene, made by free-radical polymerization in solution, is **atactic,** which means that, if we orient the carbons in the polymer chain in the form of a regular zigzag, the phenyl groups will be randomly distributed on one side or the other when we look along the chain, as shown in Figure 29-6. Polymerization of styrene with Ziegler catalysts (p. 720) produces **isotactic** polystyrene, which is different from the atactic polymer in that all of the phenyl groups are located on one side of the chain or the other. The difference in properties between the atactic and isotactic materials is considerable. The atactic polymer can be molded at much lower temperatures and is much more soluble in most solvents than is the isotactic product. There are many other possible types of stereoregular polymers, one of which is called **syndiotactic** and has the side-chain groups oriented alternately on one side and then the other, as shown in Figure 29-6.

Polypropylene, made by polymerization of propylene with Ziegler catalysts, appears to be isotactic and highly crystalline with a melting point of 175°. It

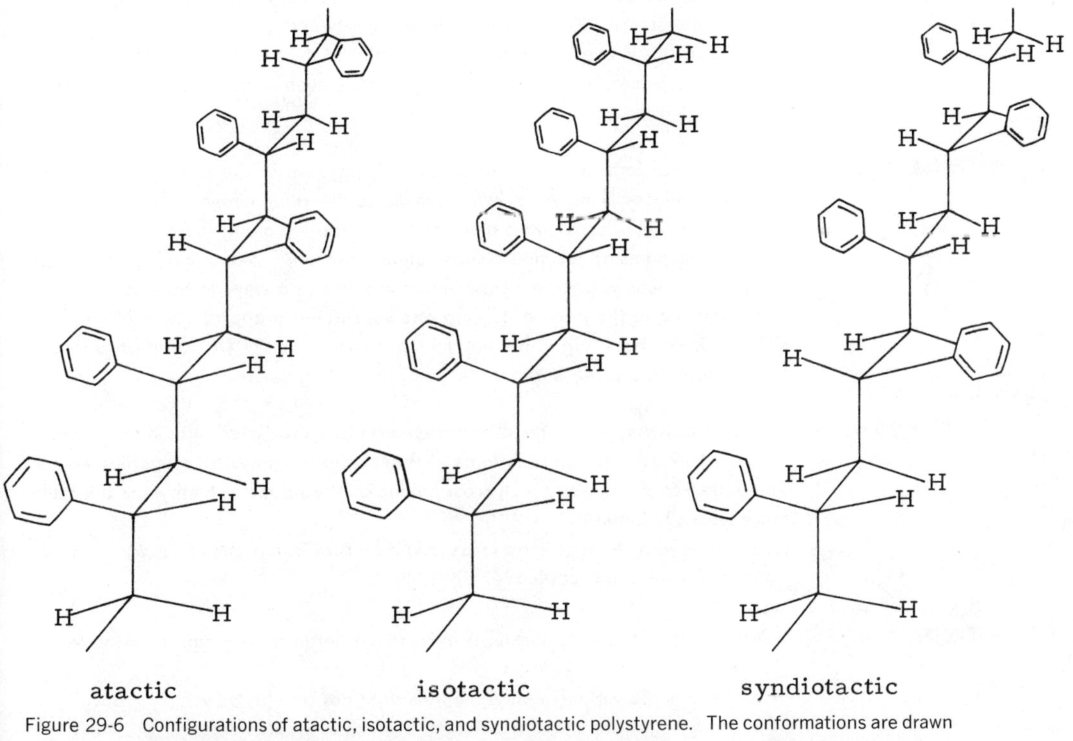

atactic   isotactic   syndiotactic

Figure 29-6 Configurations of atactic, isotactic, and syndiotactic polystyrene. The conformations are drawn to show the stereochemical relations of the substituent groups and are not meant to represent necessarily the stable conformations of the polymer chains.

can be drawn into fibers that resemble nylon fibers although, as might be expected, they do not match the 270° melting point of nylon and are much more difficult to dye.

Although both linear polyethylene and isotactic polypropylene are crystalline polymers, ethylene-propylene copolymers prepared with the aid of Ziegler catalysts are excellent elastomers. Apparently, a more or less random introduction of methyl groups along a polyethylene chain reduces the crystallinity sufficiently drastically to lead to a largely amorphous polymer.

Polyvinyl chloride, as usually prepared, is atactic and not very crystalline. It is relatively brittle and glassy. The properties of polyvinyl chloride can be improved by copolymerization, as with vinyl acetate, which produces a softer polymer ("Vinylite") with better molding properties. Polyvinyl chloride can also be *plasticized* by blending it with substances of low volatility such as tricresyl phosphate and di-*n*-butyl phthalate, which, when dissolved in the polymer, tend to break down its glass-like structure. Plasticized polyvinyl chloride is reasonably elastic and is widely used as electrical insulation, plastic sheeting, etc.

Table 29-1 contains information about a number of representative important polymers and their uses. Some similar data on diene elastomers has already been given (p. 213).

EXERCISE 29-4   High-pressure polyethylene (p. 155) differs from polyethylene, made with the aid of Ziegler catalysts (p. 720), in having a lower density and lower T_m. It has been suggested that this is due to branches in the chains of the high-pressure material. Explain how such branches might arise in the polymerization process and how they would affect the density and T_m.

EXERCISE 29-5   Free-radical induced chlorination of polyethylene in the presence of sulfur dioxide produces a polymer with many chlorine and a few sulfonyl chloride ($-SO_2Cl$) groups, substituted more or less randomly along the chains. Write suitable mechanisms for these substitution reactions. What kind of physical properties would you expect the chlorosulfonated polymer to have if substitution is carried to the point of having one substituent group to every 25 to 100 CH_2 groups? How might this polymer be cross linked? (A useful product of this general type is marketed under the name of Hypalon.)

EXERCISE 29-6   When polyethylene (and other polymers) are irradiated with X-rays, cross links are formed between the chains. What changes in physical properties would you expect to accompany such cross linking? Would the polyethylene become more elastic? Explain.

Suppose polyethylene were cross linked by irradiation above T_m, what would happen if it were then cooled?

EXERCISE 29-7   Answer the following questions in as much detail as you can, showing your reasoning:
   a. Why is atactic polymethyl methacrylate not an elastomer?
   b. How might one make a polyamide which is an elastomer?
   c. What kind of physical properties are to be expected for atactic polypropylene?

Table 29-1   Representative Synthetic Thermoplastic and Elastic Polymers and Their Uses[a]

Monomer(s)	Formula	Type of polymerization	Physical type	T_g, °C	T_m, °C	Trade names	Uses
ethylene	$CH_2{=}CH_2$	radical (high pressure)	semi-crystalline	$\ll 0$	110	poly-ethylene, Alathon	film, containers, piping, etc.
		Ziegler	crystalline		130		
vinyl chloride	$CH_2{=}CHCl$	radical	atactic, semi-crystalline	80	180	polyvinyl chloride, Geon	film, insulation, piping, etc.
vinyl fluoride	$CH_2{=}CHF$	radical	atactic, semi-crystalline	45		Tedlar	coatings[b]
vinyl chloride vinylidene chloride	$CH_2{=}CHCl$ $CH_2{=}CCl_2$	radical	crystalline	variable		Saran	tubing, fibers, film
chlorotrifluoroethylene	$CF_2{=}CFCl$	radical	atactic, semi-crystalline	$\ll 0$	210	Kel-F	gaskets, insulation[c]
tetrafluoroethylene	$CF_2{=}CF_2$	radical	crystalline	$<{-}100$	330	Teflon	gaskets, valves, insulation, filter felts, coatings[d]
propylene	$CH_2{=}CHCH_3$	Ziegler	isotactic, crystalline	-20	175		fibers, molded articles
hexafluoropropylene vinylidene fluoride	$CF_2{=}CFCF_3$ $CH_2{=}CF_2$	radical	amorphous	-23		Viton	rubber articles[c]

Continued on p. 714

Table 29-1 Representative Synthetic Thermoplastic and Elastic Polymers and Their Uses[a] (Continued)

Monomer(s)	Formula	Type of polymerization	Physical type	T_g, °C	T_m, °C	Trade names	Uses
isobutylene	$CH_2=C(CH_3)_2$	cationic	amorphous	−70		Vistanex, Oppanol	pressure-sensitive adhesives
isobutylene isoprene	$CH_2=C(CH_3)_2$ $CH_2=C(CH_3)CH=CH_2$	cationic	amorphous			butyl rubber	inner tubes
chloroprene	$CH_2=C(Cl)CH=CH_2$	radical	amorphous	−40		Neoprene	rubber articles[e]
isoprene	$CH_2=C(CH_3)CH=CH_2$	Ziegler, Li	amorphous (cis-1,4)	−70	28	natural rubber, Ameripol, Coral rubber	rubber articles
styrene	$CH_2=CHC_6H_5$	radical	atactic, semi-crystalline	85	<200	Styron, Lustron	molded articles, foam
styrene	$CH_2=CHC_6H_5$	Ziegler	isotactic,	100	230		
vinyl acetate	$CH_2=CHO_2CCH_3$	radical	amorphous	40		polyvinyl acetate	adhesives
vinyl alcohol	$(CH_2=CHOH)$[f]	hydrolysis of polyvinyl acetate	crystalline		dec.	polyvinyl alcohol	water-soluble adhesives, paper sizing
vinyl butyral		polyvinyl alcohol and butyraldehyde	amorphous			polyvinyl butyral	safety-glass laminate

714

				T_g	T_m		
formaldehyde	$CH_2{=}O$	anionic	crystalline		179	Delrin	molded articles
acrylonitrile	$CH_2{=}CHCN$	radical	crystalline	100[g]	>200	Orlon	fiber
methyl methacrylate	$CH_2{=}C(CH_3)CO_2CH_3$	radical	atactic amorphous	105		Lucite, Plexiglas	coatings, molded articles
		anionic	isotactic crystalline	115	200		
		anionic	syndiotactic, crystalline	45	160		
ethylene terephthalate	HO_2C⟨⟩$CO_2C_2H_4OH$	ester interchange between dimethyl tere- phthalate and ethylene glycol	crystalline	56	260	Dacron, Mylar, Cronar, Terylene	fiber, film
hexamethylenediamine adipic acid salt	$NH(CH_2)_6NH_2$ $CO(CH_2)_4CO_2H$	anionic condensation	crystalline	50	270	nylon, Zytel	fibers, molded articles

[a] Much useful information on these and related polymers is given by F. W. Billmeyer, Jr., "A Textbook of Polymer Chemistry," Interscience, New York, 1957; J. K. Stille, "Introduction to Polymer Chemistry," Wiley, New York, 1962; F. Bueche, "Physical Properties of Polymers," Interscience, New York, 1962, and W. R. Sorenson and T. W. Campbell, "Preparative Methods of Polymer Chemistry," Interscience, New York, 1961.

[b] Exceptional outdoor durability.

[c] Used where chemical resistance is important.

[d] Excellent self-lubricating and electrical properties.

[e] Used particularly where ozone resistance is important.

[f] These monomers are not the starting materials used to make the polymers, which are actually synthesized from polyvinyl alcohol.

[g] T_g is 60° when water is present.

d. What would you expect to happen if a piece of high-molecular-weight polyacrylic acid $\text{+CH}_2\text{—CH+}_n$ were placed in a solution of sodium hydroxide?
$$\underset{CO_2H}{|}$$

e. What kind of properties would you expect for high-molecular-weight poly-*p*-phenylene?

poly-*p*-phenylene

f. Are the properties, listed in Table 29-1, of polychloroprene as produced by radical polymerization of chloroprene (2-chlorobutadiene) such as to make it likely that *trans* 1,4-addition occurs exclusively?

EXERCISE 29-8   The material popularly known as "Silly Putty" is a polymer having an —O—Si(R)$_2$—O—Si(R)$_2$—O— backbone. It is elastic in that it bounces and snaps back when given a quick jerk but rapidly loses any shape it is given when allowed to stand. Which of the polymers listed in Table 29-1 is likely to be the best candidate to have anything like comparable properties? Explain. What changes would you expect to take place in the properties of Silly Putty as a function of time if it were irradiated with X rays (see Exercise 29-6)?

PREPARATION OF SYNTHETIC POLYMERS

A prevalent but erroneous notion has it that useful polymers, such as those given in Table 29-1, can be, and are, made by slap-dash procedures applied to impure starting materials. This is far from the truth and, actually, the monomers used in most large-scale polymerizations are among the purest known organic substances. Furthermore, to obtain uniform commercially useful products, extraordinary care must be used in controlling the polymerization reactions. The reasons are simple—namely, that formation of a high-molecular-weight polymer requires a reaction that proceeds in very high yields, and purification of the product by distillation, crystallization, etc., is difficult, if not impossible. Even a minute contribution of any side reaction that stops polymer chains from growing further will seriously affect the yield of high polymer.

In this section, we shall discuss some of the more useful procedures for the preparation of high polymers, starting with examples involving condensation reactions.

29-4 CONDENSATION POLYMERS

There are a very wide variety of condensation reactions that, in principle, can be used to form high polymers. However, as explained above, high polymers can only be obtained in high-yield reactions, and this limitation severely restricts the number of condensation reactions having any practical importance. A specific example of an impractical reaction is the formation of polytetramethylene glycol by reaction of tetramethylene bromide with the sodium salt of the glycol.

$$\overset{\oplus}{Na} \overset{\ominus}{O}\!\!-\!\!(CH_2)_4\!\!-\!\!\overset{\ominus}{O} \overset{\oplus}{Na} + Br(CH_2)_4Br \longrightarrow \overline{O\!\!-\!\!(CH_2)_4\!\!-\!\!O}_n + NaBr$$

It is unlikely that this reaction would give useful yields of any very high polymer because E2 elimination, involving the dibromide, would give a double-bond end group and prevent the chain from growing.

A. Polyesters

A variety of polyester-condensation polymers are made commercially. Ester interchange (p. 381) appears to be the most useful reaction for preparation of linear polymers.

$$CH_3O_2C\!\!-\!\!\langle\bigcirc\rangle\!\!-\!\!CO_2CH_3 + HOCH_2CH_2OH \xrightarrow[\sim 200°]{\text{metal oxide catalyst}}$$

dimethyl terephthalate   ethylene glycol

$$\overline{O\!\!-\!\!\overset{O}{\underset{\|}{C}}\!\!-\!\!\langle\bigcirc\rangle\!\!-\!\!\overset{O}{\underset{\|}{C}}\!\!-\!\!O\!\!-\!\!CH_2\!\!-\!\!CH_2}_n \qquad + CH_3OH$$

polyethyleneglycol terephthalate

(Dacron)

$$HO\!\!-\!\!\langle\bigcirc\rangle\!\!-\!\!\overset{CH_3}{\underset{CH_3}{C}}\!\!-\!\!\langle\bigcirc\rangle\!\!-\!\!OH + (C_6H_5O)_2CO \xrightarrow{300°} \overline{O\!\!-\!\!\langle\bigcirc\rangle\!\!-\!\!\overset{CH_3}{\underset{CH_3}{C}}\!\!-\!\!\langle\bigcirc\rangle\!\!-\!\!O\!\!-\!\!\overset{O}{\underset{\|}{C}}}_n + C_6H_5OH$$

bisphenol A   diphenyl   polybisphenol A carbonate
                       carbonate   (Lexan)

Thermosetting space-network polymers are often prepared through the reaction of polybasic acid anhydrides with polyhydric alcohols. A linear polymer is obtained with a bifunctional anhydride and a bifunctional alcohol, but if either reactant has three or more reactive sites, then formation of a three-dimensional polymer is possible. For example, 2 moles of glycerol can react with 3 moles of phthalic anhydride to give a highly cross-linked resin, which is usually called a **glyptal.**

glyptal resin

B. Nylons

A variety of polyamides can be made by heating diamines with dicarboxylic acids. The most generally useful of these is nylon (66), the designation (66) arising from the fact that it is made from the six-carbon diamine, hexamethylenediamine, and the six-carbon dicarboxylic acid, adipic acid.

$$HO_2C(CH_2)_4CO_2H + NH_2(CH_2)_6NH_2 \xrightarrow{280°} \left[\begin{matrix} O & O & H & H \\ \| & \| & & \\ C(CH_2)_4C-N(CH_2)_6N \end{matrix}\right]_n + H_2O$$

The polymer can be converted into fibers by extruding it above its melting point through spinnerettes, then cooling and drawing the resulting filaments. It is also used to make molded articles. Nylon (66) is exceptionally strong and abrasion resistant.

The starting materials for nylon (66) manufacture can be made in many ways. Apparently, the best route to adipic acid is by air oxidation of cyclohexane by way of cyclohexanone.

Hexamethylenediamine is prepared from the addition product of chlorine to butadiene (pp. 188-189) by the following steps:

$$CH_2=CHCH=CH_2 \xrightarrow{Cl_2} \underset{Cl}{CH_2}-CH=CH-\underset{Cl}{CH_2} + CH_2=CH-\underset{Cl}{CH}-\underset{Cl}{CH_2}$$

$$\xrightarrow[\text{-2NaCl}]{\text{2NaCN}} \quad NCCH_2CH=CHCH_2CN \quad \xrightarrow[\substack{\text{metal} \\ \text{catalyst}}]{H_2} \quad H_2N(CH_2)_6NH_2$$

C. Phenol-Formaldehyde (Bakelite) Resins

One of the oldest-known thermosetting synthetic polymers is made by condensation of phenol with formaldehyde using basic catalysts. The resins that are formed are known as **Bakelites.** The initial stage in the base-induced reaction of phenol and formaldehyde yields a hydroxybenzyl alcohol.

This part of the reaction closely resembles an aldol addition and can take place at either an *ortho* or the *para* position.

The next step in the condensation is formation of a dihydroxydiphenyl-methane derivative which for convenience is here taken to be the 4,4'-isomer.

This reaction is likely to be an addition to a base-induced dehydration product of the hydroxybenzyl alcohol.

Continuation of these reactions to all of the available *ortho* and *para* positions of the phenol leads to a cross-linked three-dimensional polymer.

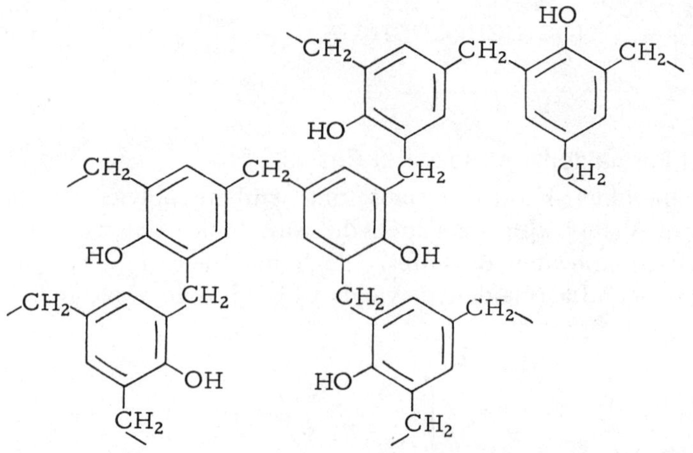

phenol–formaldehyde resin

EXERCISE 29-9   What kind of a polymer would you expect to be formed if p-cresol were used in place of phenol in the Bakelite process?

29-5 ADDITION POLYMERS

We have already discussed the synthesis and properties of a considerable number of addition polymers in this and earlier chapters. Our primary concern here will be with some aspects of the mechanism of addition polymerization that influence the character of the polymers formed.

A. Vinyl Polymerization

The most important type of addition polymerization is that of the simple vinyl monomers such as ethylene, propylene, styrene, etc. In general, we now recognize four basic kinds of mechanisms for polymerization of vinyl monomers — free-radical, cationic, anionic, and coördination. The elements of the first three of these have been outlined (pp. 152-156). The possibility, in fact the reality, of a fourth mechanism is essentially forced on us by the discovery of the Ziegler and other (mostly heterogenous) catalysts, which apparently do not involve "free" free-radical, cations or anions, and which can and usually do lead to highly stereoregular polymers. Although a great deal of work has been done on the mechanism of coördination polymerization, the details of how each unit of monomer is added to the growing chains is mostly conjecture. With titanium-aluminum catalysts, the growing chain probably has a C—Ti bond; further monomer units are then added to the growing chain by coördination with titanium, followed by an intramolecular rearrangement to give a new growing-chain end and a new vacant site on titanium where a new molecule of monomer can coördinate.

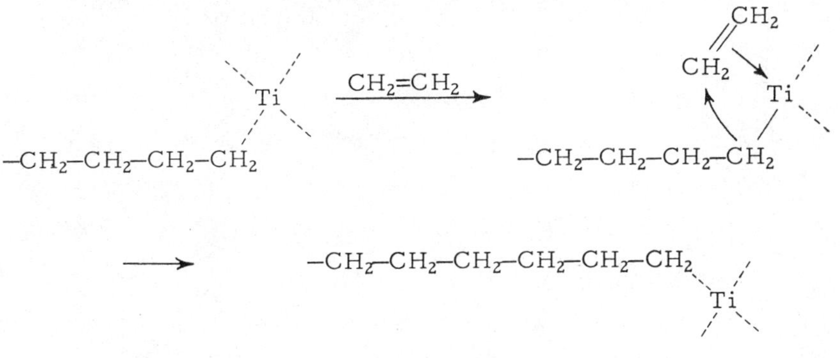

In the coördination of the monomer with the titanium, the metal is probably behaving as an electrophilic agent and the growing-chain end may well be transferred to the monomer as an anion. Since this mechanism gives no explicit role to the aluminum, it is surely a considerable oversimplification. Ziegler catalysts polymerize most monomers of the type $RCH{=}CH_2$, provided the R group is one that does not react with the organometallic compounds present in the catalyst.

B. Free-Radical Polymerization

In contrast to coördination polymerization, formation of vinyl polymers by free-radical chain mechanisms is reasonably well understood—at least for the kinds of procedures used on a laboratory scale. The first step in the reaction is the production of free radicals; this can be achieved in a number of different ways, the most common being the thermal decomposition of an *initiator,* usually a peroxide or an azo compound.

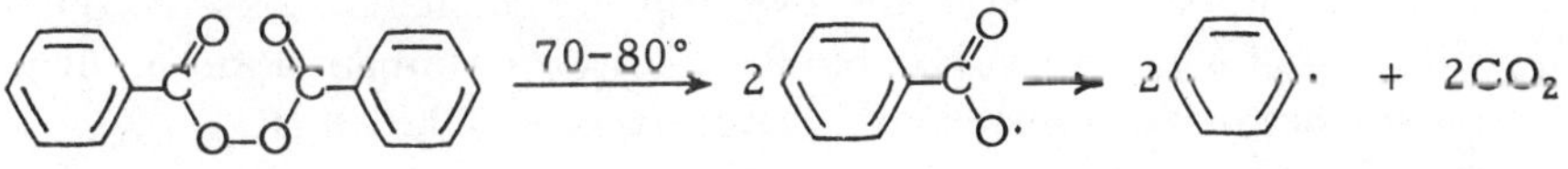

benzoyl peroxide

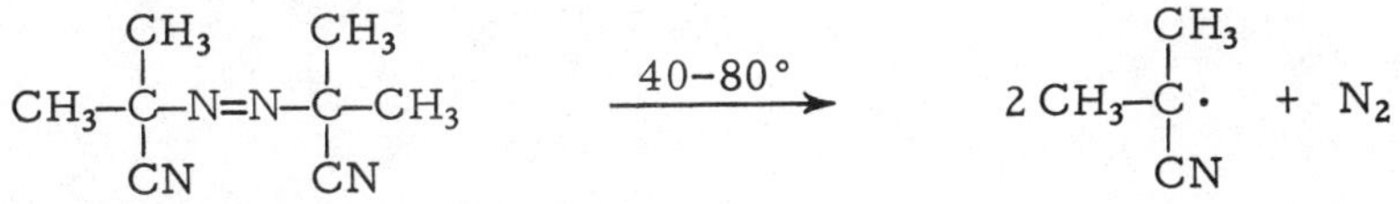

azobisisobutyronitrile

Many polymerizations are carried out on aqueous emulsions of monomers. For these, water-soluble inorganic peroxides, such as persulfuric acid, are often employed.

Addition of the initiator radicals to monomer produces a growing-chain radical which combines with successive molecules of monomer until, in some way, the chain is terminated. It will be seen that addition to an unsymmetrical monomer, such as styrene, can occur in two ways.

$$X_2 \quad \longrightarrow \quad 2\,X\cdot \qquad\qquad \text{initiation}$$

All evidence on the addition of free radicals to styrene indicates that the process by which $X\cdot$ adds to the CH_2 end of the double bond is greatly favored over addition at the CH end. This direction of addition is in accord with the considerable stabilization of the benzyl type of radicals relative to the alkyl type of radicals (see pp. 634-636). Polymerization will then result in the addition of styrene units to give phenyl groups only on alternate carbons ("head-to-tail" addition).

In general, we predict that the direction of addition of an unsymmetrical monomer will be such as to give always the most stable growing-chain radical.

The process of addition of monomer units to the growing chain can be interrupted in different ways. One is chain termination by combination or disproportionation of radicals. Explicitly, two growing-chain radicals can combine with formation of a carbon-carbon bond, or disproportionation can occur with a hydrogen atom being transferred from one chain to the other.

The disproportionation reaction is the free-radical equivalent of the E2 reaction.

Which mode of termination occurs can be determined by measuring the number of initiator fragments per polymer molecule. If there are two initiator fragments in each molecule, termination must have occurred by combination. One initiator fragment per molecule indicates disproportionation. Apparently styrene terminates by combination; but, with methyl methacrylate, both reactions take place, disproportionation being favored.

EXERCISE 29-10   Polymerization of methyl methacrylate with benzoyl peroxide labeled with ^{14}C in the aromatic ring gives a polymer from which only 57 per cent of the ^{14}C can be removed by vigorous alkaline hydrolysis. Correlation of the ^{14}C content of the original polymer with its molecular weight shows that, on the average, there are 1.27 initiator fragments per polymer molecule. Write mechanism(s) for this polymerization that are in accord with the experimental data, and calculate the ratios of the different initiation and termination reactions.

EXERCISE 29-11   The free-radical polymerization of styrene gives atactic polymer. Explain what this means in terms of the mode of addition of monomer units to the growing-chain radical.

EXERCISE 29-12   Polyvinyl alcohol prepared by hydrolysis of vinyl acetate (Table 29-1) does not consume measurable amounts of periodic acid or lead tetraacetate (pp. 309-310). However, the molecular weight of a typical sample of the polymer decreases from 25,000 to 5000. Explain what these results mean in terms of the structure of polyvinyl alcohol and of polyvinyl acetate.

EXERCISE 29-13   Ozonizations of natural rubber and gutta-percha, which are both polyisoprenes, give high yields of levulinic aldehyde ($CH_3COCH_2CH_2CHO$) and no acetonylacetone ($CH_3COCH_2CH_2COCH_3$). What are the structures of these polymers?

EXERCISE 29-14   Devise a synthesis of polyvinylamine, remembering that vinylamine itself is unstable.

C. Cationic Polymerization

Polymerization by the cationic mechanism is most important for isobutylene and α-methylstyrene, which do not polymerize well by other methods, and was discussed earlier in considerable detail (pp. 153-154).

D. Anionic Polymerization

In general, we expect that anionic polymerization will be more favorable when the monomer carries substituents that will tend to stabilize the anion formed

when a basic initiator, such as amide ion, adds to the double bond of the monomer.

$$H_2\overset{\ominus}{N}: \ + \ CH_2=\underset{H}{\overset{R}{C}} \qquad\longrightarrow\qquad H_2N-CH_2\overset{\ominus}{\underset{H}{\overset{R}{\ddot{C}}}}$$

Cyano and carbalkoxy groups are favorable in this respect and it is reported that
acrylonitrile and methyl methacrylate can be polymerized with sodium amide in
liquid ammonia. Styrene and isoprene undergo anionic polymerization under
the influence of organolithium and organosodium compounds, such as butyllith-
ium and phenylsodium.

E. Copolymers

When polymerization occurs in a mixture of monomers, there will be some
competition between the different kinds of monomers to add to the growing
chain and produce a *copolymer*. Such a polymer will be expected to have quite
different physical properties than a mixture of the separate *homopolymers*. Many
copolymers, such as GRS, ethylene-propylene, Viton rubbers, and vinyl chlo-
ride-vinyl acetate plastics are of considerable commercial importance.

NATURALLY OCCURRING POLYMERS

There are a number of naturally occurring polymeric substances that have a
high degree of technical importance. Some of these, such as natural rubber
(p. 212), cellulose, and starch (pp. 144-145), have regular structures and can be
regarded as being made up of single monomer units. Others such as wool, silk,
and deoxyribonucleic acid (pp. 505-508) are copolymers. Since we have considered the chemistry of most of these substances in some detail earlier, we shall
confine our attention here to silk, wool, and collagen, all of which have properties related to topics discussed earlier in this chapter.

29-6 SILK

Silk fibroin is a relatively simple polypeptide, the composition of which varies
according to the larva by which it is produced. The commercial product, obtained from the cocoons of mulberry silk moths, contains glycine, L-alanine, L-
serine, and L-tyrosine as its principal amino acids. Silk fibroin has an oriented-
crystalline structure. The polypeptide chains occur in sheets, each chain with an
extended configuration parallel to the fiber axis (not the α helix, p. 498),
and hydrogen-bonded to two others in which the directions of the peptide chain
are reversed (Figure 29-7).

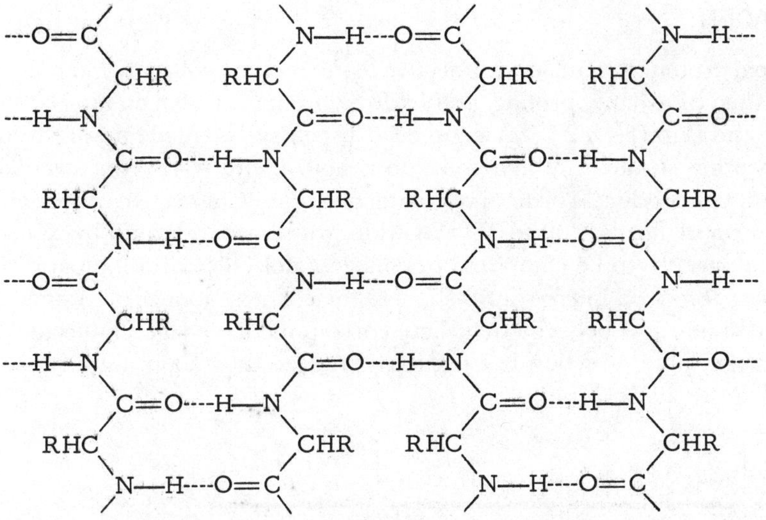

Figure 29-7   Hydrogen-bonded structure of silk fibroin. Note that the peptides run in different directions in alternate chains.

EXERCISE 29-15   How will the side chains on the L-amino acids of silk fibroin be oriented with respect to the fiber sheets?

29-7 WOOL

The structure of wool is more complicated than that of silk fibroin, because wool, like insulin (p. 498), contains a considerable quantity of cystine (p. 484), which provides disulfide cross links between the peptide chains. These disulfide linkages play an important part in determining the mechanical properties of wool fibers because, if the disulfide linkages are reduced, as with ammonium thioglycolate solution, the fibers become much more pliable.

$$RCH_2\text{–}S\text{–}S\text{–}CH_2R \ + \ 2\,HSCH_2CO_2^{\ominus}\ NH_4^{\oplus} \ \longrightarrow \ RCH_2SH \ + \ HSCH_2R$$

(wool disulfide cross link)

$$+ \ NH_4^{\oplus}\ {}^{\ominus}O_2CCH_2\text{–}S\text{–}S\text{–}CH_2CO_2^{\ominus}\ NH_4^{\oplus}$$

Advantage is taken of this in the curling of hair, thioglycolate reduction and curling being followed by restoration of the disulfide linkages through treatment with a mild oxidizing agent.

EXERCISE 29-16   Apparently the economically important chain reaction, wool + moths → holes + more moths, has, as a key step, scission of the disulfide linkages of cystine in the polypeptide chains by the digestive enzymes of the moth larva. Devise a method of mothproofing wool which would involve chemically altering the disulfide linkages (review Chapter 21).

29-8 COLLAGEN

The principal protein of skin and connective tissue is called collagen and is primarily constituted of glycine, proline, and hydroxyproline. Collagen molecules are very long and thin (14 × 2900 A), and each appears to be made up of three twisted polypeptide strands. When collagen is boiled with water, the strands come apart and the product is ordinary cooking gelatine. Connective tissue and skin are made up of fibrils, 200 to 1000 A wide, which are indicated by X-ray diffraction photographs to be composed of collagen molecules running parallel to the long axis. Electron micrographs show regular bands, about 700 A apart, across the fibrils; and it is believed that these correspond to collagen molecules, all heading in the same direction but regularly staggered by about a fourth of their length (Figure 29-8).

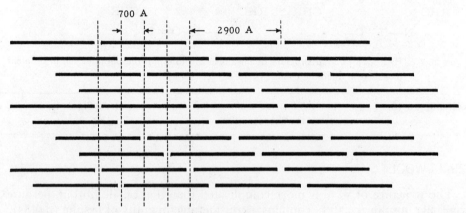

Figure 29-8   Schematic diagram of collagen molecules in a fibril so arranged as to give the 700 A spacing visible in electron micrographs.

The conversion of collagen fibrils to leather presumably involves formation of cross links between the collagen molecules. Various substances can be used for the purpose, but chromium salts act particularly rapidly.

The Chemistry of Natural Products

The area of organic chemistry that deals primarily with the structures and chemistry of the compounds which are synthesized by living organisms is extremely large and highly variegated. Many types of natural products, including the carbohydrates, amino acids, proteins and peptides, and alkaloids (discussed in earlier chapters), have been investigated in such detail that whole volumes or series of volumes have been, or could be, devoted to their occurrence, isolation, analysis, structure proof, chemical reactions, synthesis, biological function, and the biogenetic reactions by which they are produced—to mention the more important topics which are of interest with respect to natural products.

It is not our intention here to catalog the kinds of natural products that are of general or of special interest; actually, we shall proceed on the basis that it is better to discuss one class of natural product in depth than to cover many classes sketchily. Our grounds for this are that approaches to the chemistry of most classes of natural products are rather similar and it may be more important to see how such approaches are made than it is to have a general smattering of knowledge about the kinds of structures that occur naturally.

A serious deficiency of this procedure is that the chemistry of many classes of natural products is of general interest, quite apart from their biochemical importance. Thus, the chemistry of the bicyclic terpenes contributed much to the interesting and unusual chemistry of such ring compounds long before satisfactory syntheses were available by the Diels-Alder reaction (Chapter 10). Similarly, studies of the chemistry of the steroids has added as much or more to our knowledge of conformations in cyclohexane rings as studies of cyclohexane derivatives themselves. Many other equally cogent examples could be cited.

Our plan in this chapter is to first consider in some detail how the structures of natural products are established, both by classical procedures and by modern instrumental methods. We shall then consider in an illustrative way two rather closely related classes of natural products, terpenes and steroids. Finally, we discuss some of the aspects and uses of biogenetic schemes for the syntheses carried on by living systems. Throughout, we attempt to show how much of the material covered earlier in this book is pertinent to the study of natural products.

The Chemistry of Natural Products

CHAPTER 30

The general procedure for the determination of the structures of organic compounds, such as natural products, has been outlined in Chapter 1 (pp. 17-20). We shall now illustrate the procedure in more detail by the elucidation of the structure of the important perfume ingredient, civetone. The structure of this substance, which was established in 1926 by Ruzicka, is a good example of what might be called a *classical* structure determination.

30-1 CIVETONE

The active principle of civet, a substance collected from the scent gland of the African civet cat, is called **civetone.** This compound and one of similar nature called **muscone,** isolated from a scent gland of the Tibetan musk deer, are used in preparation of perfumes. Although civetone and muscone do not themselves have pleasant odors, they have the property of markedly enhancing and increasing the persistence of the flower essences.

The starting material for Ruzicka's work on the structure of civetone was commerical civet imported from Abyssinia packed in buffalo horns—an inhomogenous, yellow-brown, unctuous substance, containing 10 to 15 per cent water, intermixed with civet-cat hairs, and possessing a less-than-pleasant odor. Of several methods of isolation of the active principle, the most useful involved destruction of the glycerides present by hydrolysis (pp. 362-363) with alcoholic po-

729

tassium hydroxide, fractional distillation of the unsaponifiable neutral material under reduced pressure, and treatment of the distillate of b.p. 140 to 180° (3 mm) with semicarbazide hydrochloride in the presence of acetate ion (pp. 325-326). The crystalline product formed was the semicarbazone of civetone, and the yield indicated that the starting material contained 10 to 15 per cent of the active principle. Decomposition of the purified semicarbazone with boiling oxalic acid solution gave, after reduced pressure distillation, crystalline civetone of m.p. 31°. The pure substance showed no optical activity.

Civetone is a ketone (an aldehyde would hardly have survived the alkaline isolation procedure) which was shown by its elemental analysis and molecular weight to be $C_{17}H_{30}O$. Saturated open-chain ketones have the general formula $C_nH_{2n}O$ and civetone has four hydrogens less, which means that it must have a triple bond, or two double bonds, or one double bond and one ring, or two rings. Civetone reacts with permanganate, gives a dibromide, and absorbs 1 mole of hydrogen in the presence of palladium. The presence of one double bond and one ring is therefore indicated, and a partial structure can be written as follows:

$$O=C \left\{ C_{14}H_{30} \right\} \begin{array}{c} >C \\ \| \\ >C \end{array}$$

Oxidation of civetone with cold potassium permanganate solution gave a dibasic keto acid which was at first thought to be $C_{16}H_{28}O_5$ (loss of a carbon) but later was shown to be $C_{17}H_{30}O_5$. The formation of this acid confirms the presence of a ring and shows that each of the double-bonded carbons carries a hydrogen, because otherwise a dibasic acid with the same number of carbons could not be formed.

$$O=C \left\{ C_{14}H_{28} \right\} \begin{array}{c} \ce{^{\backslash}CH} \\ \| \\ \ce{_{/}CH} \end{array} \xrightarrow{[O]} O=C \left\{ C_{14}H_{28} \right\} \begin{array}{c} -CO_2H \\ -CO_2H \end{array}$$

A key step in the determination of the structure of civetone was to find out how many carbon atoms separate the carbonyl group and the double bond. This was done by oxidation of civetone under conditions such as to lead to cleavage both at the double bond and at the carbonyl group (p. 330). Different oxidation procedures gave somewhat different results but in all cases mixtures of dibasic acids were formed, the mildest conditions leading to formation of pimelic acid, $HO_2C(CH_2)_5CO_2H$; suberic acid, $HO_2C(CH_2)_6CO_2H$; and azelaic acid, $HO_2C(CH_2)_7CO_2H$. The formation of azelaic acid indicates that there is at least one continuous chain of seven CH_2 groups forming a bridge between the carbonyl group and double bond.

$$O=C \begin{array}{c} (CH_2)_7 \\ \diagup \qquad \diagup \\ \qquad \qquad CH \\ \diagdown \qquad --\|-- \\ \qquad \qquad CH \\ \{C_7H_{14}\} \end{array} \xrightarrow{[O]} \begin{array}{c} HO_2C \diagup^{(CH_2)_7}\diagdown CO_2H \\ \\ HO_2C\diagdown_{(C_6H_{12})}\diagup CO_2H \end{array}$$

Since all the dicarboxylic acids isolated from the oxidation had continuous chains, Ruzicka inferred that the other seven carbons were also linked up in a continuous chain and that civetone is actually 9-cycloheptadecenone.

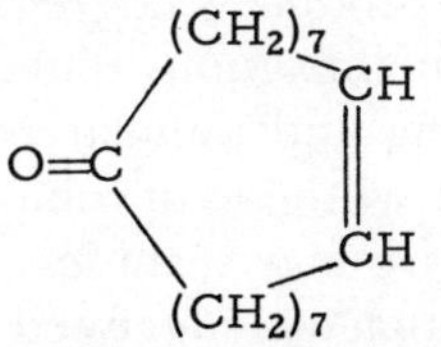

9-cycloheptadecenone

This was an exciting conclusion at a time when the largest known monocyclic compounds were cycloöctane derivatives, and, along with the demonstration of the existence of *cis*- and *trans*-decalin (1925), provided decisive evidence against the Baeyer theory of angle strain in large carbocyclic rings (pp. 92-93).

The postulated presence of a cycloheptadecene ring in civetone was supported by oxidation of dihydrocivetone by chromic acid to heptadecanedioic acid.

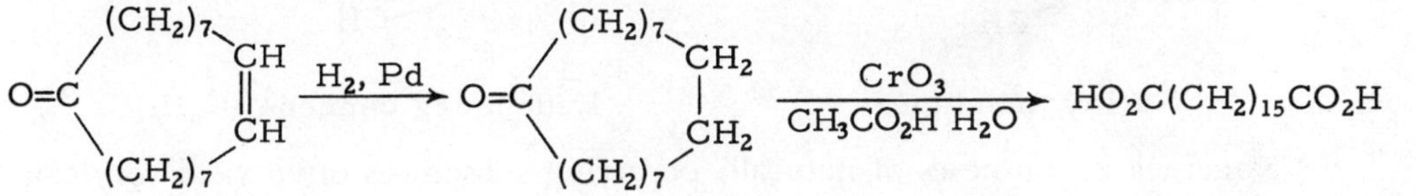

dihydrocivetone   heptadecanedioic
                                                          acid

Further evidence was obtained in confirmation of the structure of civetone, one particularly interesting series of transformations being as follows:

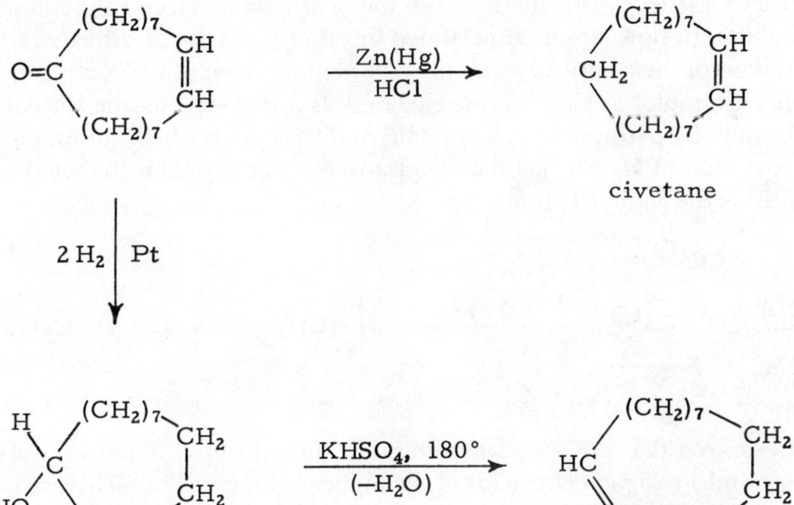

civetane

2 H$_2$ | Pt

dihydrocivetol   civetane

The interest in these reactions is the demonstration that the symmetry of the civetone ring is such that civetane (cycloheptadecene) produced by the Clemmenson reduction (p. 329) of civetone is identical with civetone obtained by reduction of civetone to dihydrocivetone and dehydration over an acidic catalyst (pp. 293-294).

In some quarters, the structure of a natural product is not regarded as really confirmed until a synthesis is achieved by an unambiguous route, and research aimed at such syntheses has been a fascinating and popular part of organic chemistry for many years. The achievement of syntheses of compounds already known to be stable because they occur in nature may seem less of a feat than preparation of tricyclobutane, or the structure that was suggested by Ladenburg in 1879 to best account for the properties of benzene, each of which is yet unknown and is expected to be rather unstable.

tricyclobutane   Ladenburg benzene (C_6H_6)

Nonetheless, syntheses of naturally occurring substances often yield very considerable benefits in the development of new synthetic reactions and furthermore may offer the possibility of preparing modified forms of the natural products which are of biochemical or medical interest.

In the case of civetone, a synthesis was not achieved until long after the structure was established, but the finding of the cycloheptadecane ring in civetone led Ruzicka to develop a method for the synthesis of large-ring compounds which, although now largely superseded by other procedures, afforded the first preparations of the complete series of cyclic ketones from C_9 to C_{21} and a number of higher examples as well. This reaction was a variation on the formation of cyclic ketones by pyrolysis of calcium salts of dibasic acids which, although useful for preparation of C_5 to C_7 ketones, leads to a 5 per cent yield with cyclooctanone and fails for the higher ketones.

Ruzicka showed that the corresponding thorium salts give 20 per cent of cyclooctanone and 1 to 5 per cent yields of the higher ketones. The yields are in the 1 per cent range from C_9 to C_{12}, where conformational difficulties are to be expected during and after ring formation (p. 94).

Musk-type odors are found to be associated with the C_{14} to C_{17} cycloalkanones, being particularly strong with cyclopentadecanone, which is available commercially under the name Exaltone. Interestingly, the odors of civetone and dihydrocivetone are the same. Further evidence for the presence of the seven-

teen-membered ring in civetone is supplied by the identity of synthetic cyclo-
heptadecanone with dihydrocivetone. The synthesis of civetone was reported
by Stoll and co-workers in 1948.

EXERCISE 30-1   Muscone, the active principal of Tibetan musk, is an optically active ketone of
formula $C_{16}H_{30}O$. On oxidation it gives a mixture of dicarboxylic acids. At least
two acids of formula $C_{16}H_{30}O_4$ are formed, along with some dodecanedi-
carboxylic acid and suberic acid.

Clemmenson reduction of muscone gives an optically inactive hydrocarbon
shown by synthesis to be methylcyclopentadecane. Muscone is not racemized
by strong acids or strong bases, although it does form a benzylidene
($=CHC_6H_5$) derivative with benzaldehyde and sodium methoxide.

What structure(s) for muscone are consistent with the above experimental evidence? Give your reasoning. What additional evidence would be helpful?

30-2 SPECTROSCOPIC METHODS IN THE DETERMINATION OF THE STRUCTURES OF NATURAL PRODUCTS

The use of the types of spectroscopic methods described in Chapter 2 has
greatly reduced the difficulty in determining the structures of the natural products of medium and low molecular weights. We have given many illustrations of
the kind of information which is obtained from ultraviolet, infrared, and n.m.r.
spectroscopy in earlier chapters. Application of these methods to the problem
of determining the structure of civetone would have been very helpful, but
probably not decisive, for the reason that civetone is mostly saturated hydrocarbon and distinction between some of the possible isomers would be difficult if not
impossible by spectroscopic methods.

EXERCISE 30-2   Explain how use of ultraviolet, infrared, or n.m.r. spectroscopy could be used to distinguish between the following possible structures for civetone.

a. 9-cycloheptadecenone and 2-cycloheptadecenone

b. cis-9-cycloheptadecenone and trans-9-cycloheptadecenone

c. 8-methyl-8-cyclohexadecenone and 9-cycloheptadecenone

d. 8-cycloheptadecenone and 9-cycloheptadecenone

Mass Spectroscopy

Considerable difficulty can be expected in structure determinations of cyclic
compounds which have several saturated rings with no functional groups to
permit degradation by selective oxidation. A typical example is afforded by
quebrachamine, an indole alkaloid (pp. 666-669) with a complex polycyclic
ring system.

quebrachamine

The ultraviolet spectrum of quebrachamine is typical of an indole and the n.m.r. spectrum shows that the indole system is substituted at the 2- and 3-positions. Oxidation fails to open the saturated ring system, and the only very useful degradative reaction found so far is distillation with zinc dust at 400°, which yields a complex mixture of nitrogen compounds, including several pyridine derivatives.

Fortunately, mass spectrometry is showing great promise in handling structural problems of just this variety and, rather than try to review the application of the other forms of spectroscopy to natural products, we shall concentrate here on mass spectrometry, which has hardly been mentioned since Chapter 2.[1]

One important use of mass spectrometry in the quebrachamine problem was in the identification of the components of the mixture of pyridine bases formed in the zinc-dust distillation. The mixture was separated by gas chromatography (pp. 15-17) and the fractions identified by their mass spectra (pp. 46-48).

The procedure for identification of compounds by mass spectrometry is first to determine m/e for the intense peak of highest mass number (see pp. 46-47). In most cases this peak corresponds to the positive ion (M^+) formed by removal of just one electron from the molecule (M) being bombarded, and the m/e value of M^+ is the molecular weight. Incorrect molecular weights are obtained if the positive ion M^+ becomes fragmented before it reaches the collector, or if two fragments combine to give a fragment heavier than M^+. The peak of M^+ is especially weak with alcohols and branched-chain hydrocarbons which readily undergo fragmentation by loss of water or side-chain groups. With such compounds the peak corresponding to M^+ may be 0.1 per cent or less of the total ion intensity.

The pressure of the sample in the ion source of a mass spectrometer is usually about 10^{-5} mm, and, under these conditions, buildup of fragments to give significant peaks with m/e greater than M^+ is rare. The only exception to this is the formation of ($M + 1$) peaks resulting from transfer of a hydrogen atom from M to M^+. The relative intensities of such ($M + 1$) peaks are usually sensitive to the sample pressure and may be identified in this way.

With the molecular weight available from the M^+ peak with reasonable certainty, the next step is to study the cracking pattern to determine whether the m/e values of the fragments give any clue to the structure. In the mixture of pyridine derivatives obtained by zinc-dust distillation of quebrachamine, the principal substance present showed M^+ at 107, and strong peaks at 106 and 92

[1] See K. Biemann, "Mass Spectrometry, Organic Chemical Applications," McGraw-Hill, New York, 1962.

(Figure 30-1). Loss of one m/e unit has to be loss of hydrogen, while loss of fifteen corresponds to NH or CH_3. Fragmentation of NH from a pyridine derivative seems to be a drastic change, but loss of CH_3 is reasonable, particularly if it would lead to a stabilized positive fragment. The m/e value of 107 corresponds to pyridine with one ethyl or two methyl groups. Using 3-ethylpyridine and 3,5-dimethylpyridine as specific examples, we could then have fragmentation reactions as follows:

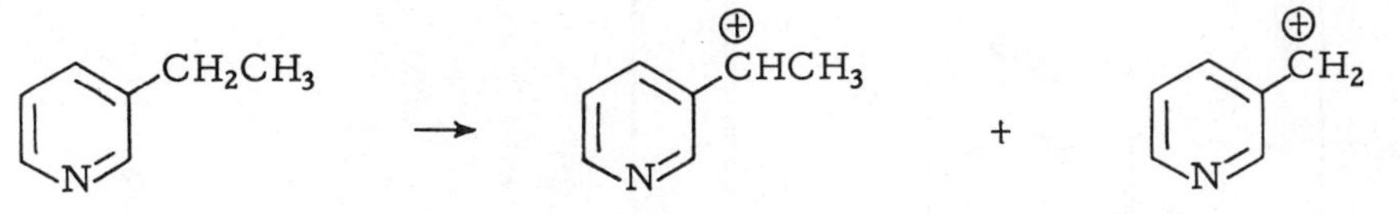

For both compounds, the fragment of mass 106 has a stabilized structure, but this is not true for mass 92—in one case, 92 represents a benzylic-type ion and, in the other, an unfavorable phenyl-type ion (pp. 571-572). Since the 92 peak is exceptionally strong, the substance is thereby indicated to be an ethylpyridine. Comparison of the mass spectra of the ethylpyridine isomers showed the product from quebrachamine to be actually 3-ethylpyridine.

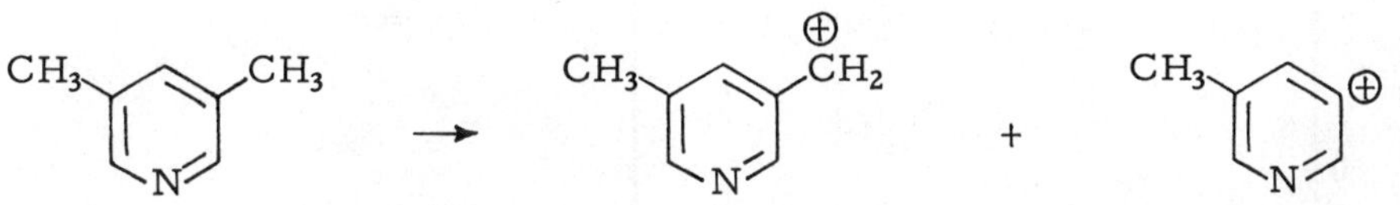

EXERCISE 30-3   How could one use deuterium labeling to show that the fragmentation of 3-ethylpyridine which occurs in the mass spectrometer results in loss of the CH_3 group and not an NH fragment? Be as specific as possible.

EXERCISE 30-4   The relative intensities of $(M-15)$ peaks for the 2- and 4-ethylpyridines are much less than for 3-ethylpyridine (see Figure 30-1). Suggest a reason for this. Can your explanation also account for the fact that intensity ratios $(M-15)/(M-1)$ for the different isomers fall in the ratio 3 > 4 > 2? Explain.

EXERCISE 30-5   Identify the fragments which produce the intensities which are off scale in the mass spectra of methyl ethyl ketone, propionaldehyde, and acetone in Figure 2-17 (p. 48).

Demonstration that the mixture of pyridines from zinc-dust distillation of quebrachamine contains 75 per cent of 3-ethylpyridine provided strong support for the presence of a 3-ethylpiperidine grouping in the alkaloid.

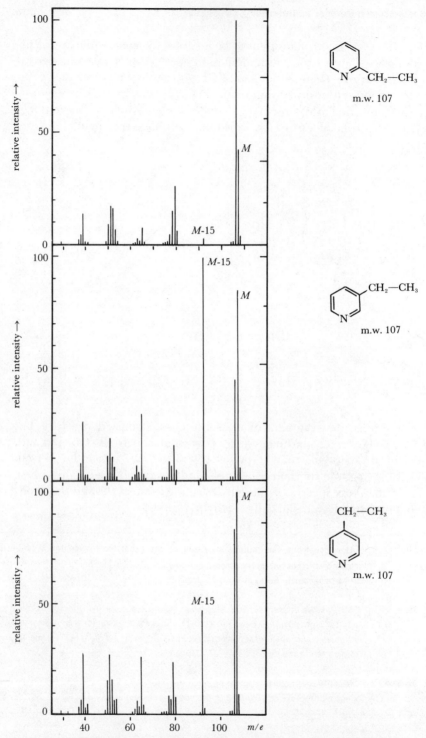

Figure 30-1   Mass spectra of 2-, 3-, and 4-ethylpyridines. The vertical scale is relative peak intensity.   The spectrum of the C_7H_9N base from the zinc-dust distillation of que-brachamine is the same as that of 3-ethylpyridine. (By permission from K. Biemann, "Mass Spectrometry, Organic Chemical Applications," McGraw-Hill, New York, 1962.)

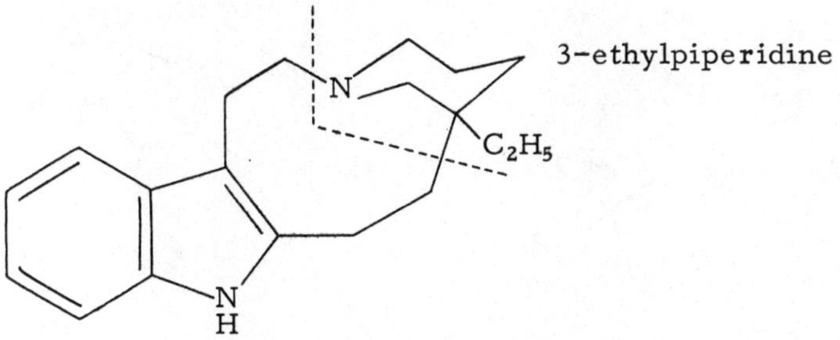

3-ethylpiperidine

Further evidence on the structure of quebrachamine was obtained by comparison of its mass spectrum with that of a transformation product [1] of a related alkaloid of known structure, aspidospermine.[1]

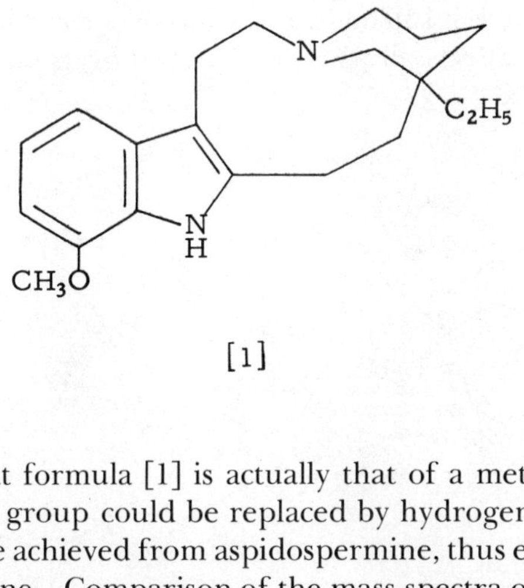

[1]

It will be seen that formula [1] is actually that of a methoxyquebrachamine and, if the methoxy group could be replaced by hydrogen, a synthesis of quebrachamine would be achieved from aspidospermine, thus establishing the structure of quebrachamine. Comparison of the mass spectra of [1] and quebrachamine is much easier and no less definitive. The spectra (Figure 30-2) at first glance look rather different, but careful examination shows that they are actually very similar from $m/e = 138$ downward. Furthermore, virtually all of the peaks that appear in quebrachamine from 143 up to that of M^+ (282) have counterparts in the spectrum of the methoxy compound just 30 units higher. This difference of 30 mass units is just the OCH_2 by which the molecular weight of the methoxyquebrachamine exceeds the molecular weight of quebrachamine itself.

Assuming the indole part of quebrachamine does not break up very easily, we would expect the *smallest* abundant fragments from that part of the molecule to have masses of 143 or 144.

---

[1] For the structure proof of aspidospermine, see H. Conroy, P. R. Brook, and Y. Amid, *Tetrahedron Letters,* **No. 11,** 4 (1959).

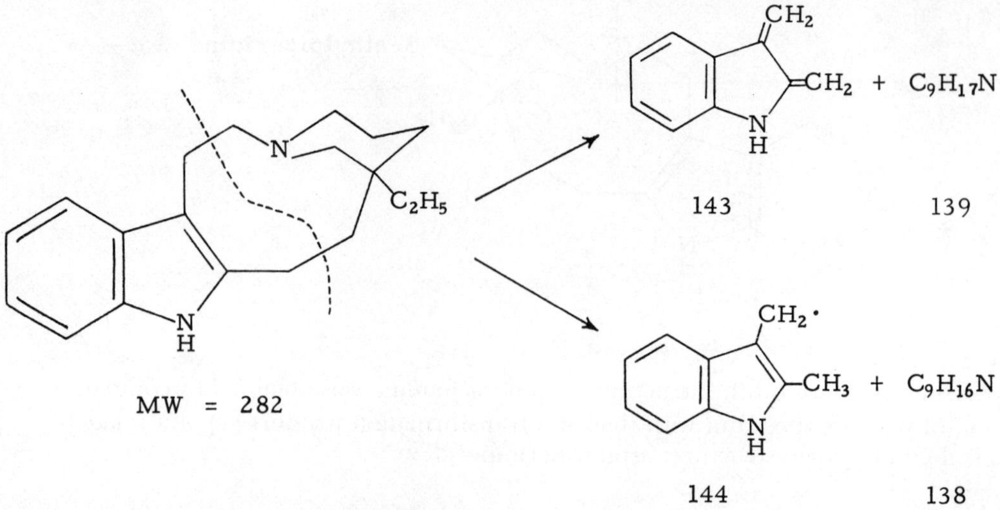
CH2
CH2 + C9H17N
N
H
143
139
N
C2H5
N
H
MW = 282
CH2·
CH3 + C9H16N
N
H
144
138

It is significant that the *largest* fragment from the saturated part of quebrachamine would then have *m/e* 138 or 139. From this we can see why substitution of the methoxyl group affects all peaks of 143 and over, but not those below this number.

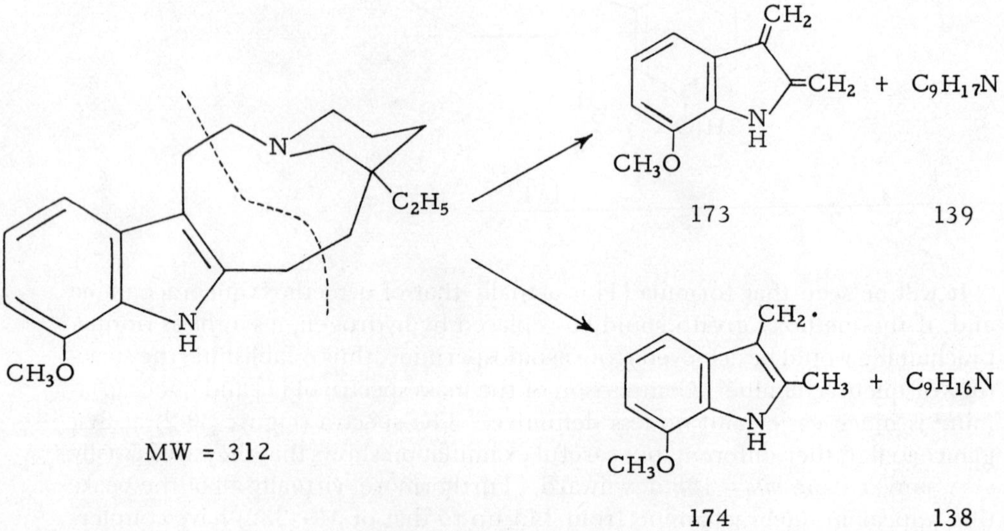
CH2
CH2 + C9H17N
N
H
CH3O
173
139
N
C2H5
N
H
CH3O
MW = 312
CH2·
CH3 + C9H16N
N
H
CH3O
174
138

EXERCISE 30-6 *a.* Identify the fragments in the mass spectrum of quebrachamine with *m/e* values of 267, 253, 157, and 125. Show your reasoning.

b. The very strong peak at 110 in the mass spectrum of quebrachamine has no counterpart at 172. How might a fragment of 110 mass units be reasonably formed by breakdown of the primary dissociation products?

It would be a serious error to imagine that in mass spectra nothing is observed but simple fragmentation of organic molecules on electron impact. Actually, even though

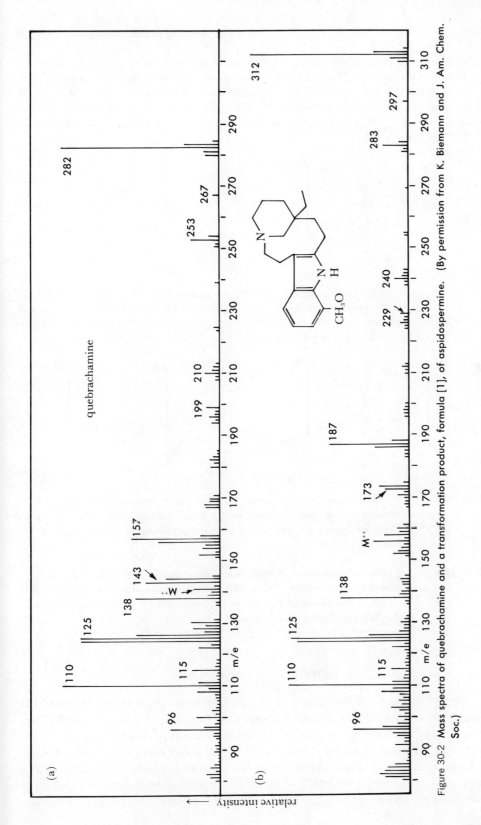

Figure 30-2 Mass spectra of quebrachamine and a transformation product, formula [1], of aspidospermine. (By permission from K. Biemann and J. Am. Chem. Soc.)

electron impact produces highly unstable molecular ions, there is a strong tendency for breakdown to occur by chemically reasonable processes (as with the ethylpyridines), and this may involve rearrangement of atoms from one part of the molecule to another. An excellent example of such a rearrangement is provided by the M^+ ion of ethyl n-butyrate, which breaks down to give ethylene and an M^+ ion of the enol form of ethyl acetate.

116   28   88

The postulated course of this fragmentation is supported by studies of the mass spectra of α-, β-, and γ-deuterated ethyl butyrate. The α,α-dideutero compound yields the enol ion, now with mass 90; the β,β-dideutero isomer gives the enol ion, with mass 88; while the γ,γ,γ-trideuterated ester produces enol, with mass 89.

89

EXERCISE 30-7   The mass spectrum of n-propylbenzene has a prominent peak at mass 92. When γ,γ,γ-trideutero-n-propylbenzene is run, the peak shifts to 93. Write a likely mechanism for breakdown of n-propylbenzene to give a fragment of mass 92.

EXERCISE 30-8   The mass spectra of alcohols usually show peaks of $(M - 18)$, which correspond to loss of water. What kind of mechanisms can explain the formation of $(M - 18)$ peaks, and no $(M - 19)$ peaks, from 1,1-dideuteroethanol and 1,1,1,3,3-pentadeutero-2-butanol?

ISOPRENOID COMPOUNDS

The odor of a freshly crushed mint leaf, like many plant odors, is due to the presence in the plant of volatile C_{10} and C_{15} compounds, which are called **terpenes.** Isolation of these substances from the various parts of plants, even from the wood in some cases, by steam distillation or ether extraction gives what are known as **essential oils.** These are widely used in perfumery, food flavorings and medicines, or as solvents. Among the typical essential oils are those obtained from cloves, roses, lavender, citronella, eucalyptus, peppermint, camphor, sandalwood, cedar, and turpentine. That such substances are of interest to us here is because, as was pointed out by Wallach in 1877, the components of the essential oils can be regarded as derived from isoprene.

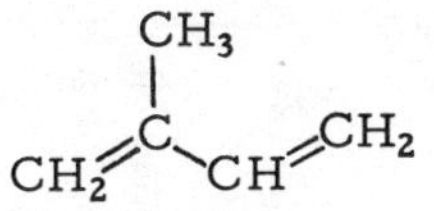

Not only are the carbon skeletons of these substances divisible into **isoprene units,** but the terpene hydrocarbons are exact multiples of C_5H_8. A typical example is afforded by myrcene ($C_{10}H_{16}$), which occurs in the oils of bay and verbena and is easily seen to have a carbon skeleton divisible into isoprene units.

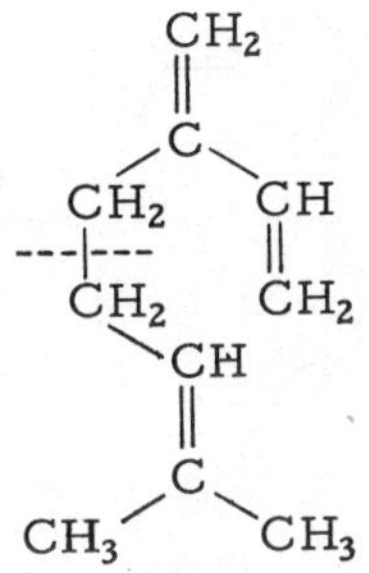

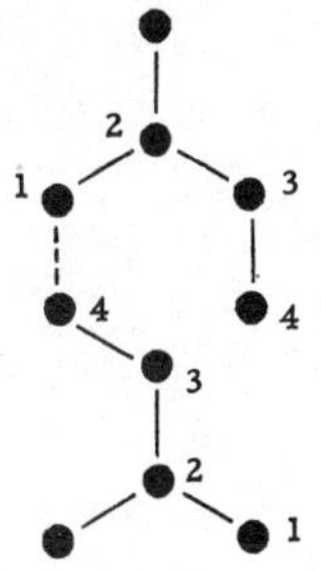

myrcene

The connection between the isoprene units in myrcene is between the 1- and 4-positions; this turns out to be more common than 1,1 or 4,4 linkages.

30-3 TERPENE HYDROCARBONS

A wide variety of cyclic terpene hydrocarbons are known and, as multiples of C_5H_8, these have fewer double bonds than the open-chain terpenes. Since it is time consuming to show all the carbon and hydrogen atoms of such substances, we shall represent the structures in a convenient short-hand notation wherein the carbon-carbon bonds are represented by lines, carbon atoms being understood at the junctions or the ends of lines. By this notation, myrcene can be represented by formulas like the following.

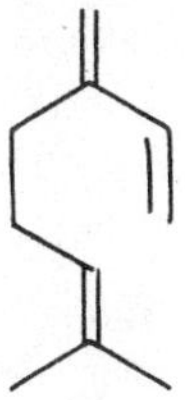

or

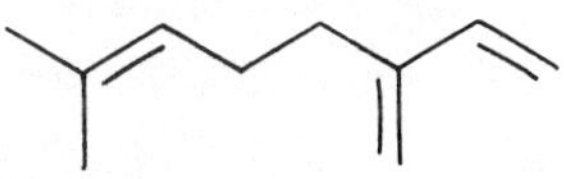

The semicyclic arrangement of the formulas is useful to show relationships with the open-chain (acyclic) and cyclic terpene hydrocarbons.

A number of terpene hydrocarbons are shown in Table 30-1. The designation "terpene" is actually by custom reserved for the C_{10} compounds, the C_{15}

Table 30-1   Some Isoprenoid Hydrocarbons

Type	Name	Structure	Origin
acyclic terpene $C_{10}H_{16}$	myrcene		bayberry wax; oils of bay, verbena
	ocimene		oil of *Ocimum basilicum*
acyclic sesquiterpene $C_{15}H_{24}$	α-farnesene		oil of citronella
acyclic triterpene $C_{30}H_{50}$	squalene[a]		shark-liver oil
acyclic tetraterpene $C_{40}H_{56}$[b]	lycopene[a]		plant pigment—tomatoes, pyracanthra, etc.

742

acyclic polyterpene $(C_5H_8)_n$		rubber (*cis*), gutta percha (*trans*)	*Hevea* latex (see pp. 272, 1092 and 1167)
monocyclic terpene $C_{10}H_{16}$		limonene	oils of lemon, orange, peppermint, etc.
		sylvestrene	Swedish or **R**ussian oil of turpentine[c]
monocyclic sesquiterpene $C_{15}H_{24}$		zingiberene	oil of ginger
monocyclic tetraterpene $C_{40}H_{56}$[b]		γ-carotene[a]	plant pigment

Continued on p. 744

Table 30-1 Some Isoprenoid Hydrocarbons (Continued)

Type	Name	Structure	Origin
bicyclic terpene $C_{10}H_{16}$	sabinene		oil of savin
	α-pinene		oil of turpentine (principal constituent)
	camphene		oils of ginger, citronella, etc.
bicyclic sesquiterpene $C_{15}H_{24}$	β-selinene		oil of celery
	caryophyllene		oil of cloves
$C_{15}H_{18}$[b]	vetivazulene		oil of vetiver (blue coloration, see pp. 563-564)

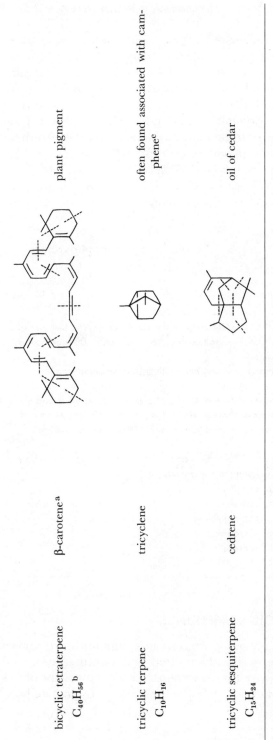

bicyclic tetraterpene
$C_{40}H_{56}$[b]

β-carotene[a]

plant pigment

tricyclic terpene
$C_{10}H_{16}$

tricyclene

often found associated with camphene[c]

tricyclic sesquiterpene
$C_{15}H_{24}$

cedrene

oil of cedar

[a] The structure shown is not necessarily correct with respect to *cis-trans* isomers but is drawn to show the relation of the isoprene units to one another.

[b] More unsaturated than calculated for a multiple of C_5H_8.

[c] Possibly not present in the plant itself but may be formed by isomerization of other substances in the essential oil.

compounds being known as **sesquiterpenes,** the C_{20} as **diterpenes,** C_{30} as **triterpenes,** etc. It should be apparent from Table 30-1 that the C_{10} and C_{15} compounds, which are the important components of essential oils, are in reality members of a much larger class of substances with carbon skeletons made up of isoprene units and occurring in both plants and animals. It is common to refer to all members of the group as **isoprenoid** compounds. The so-called *isoprene rule,* which correlates the structures of these substances, speaks for their synthesis in living systems from some common precursor with five carbon atoms. We can characterize the isoprenoid compounds as being *biogenetically* related. Isoprene itself does not occur naturally and appears to play no part in biosynthesis. The actual five-carbon intermediate appears to be isopentenyl pyrophosphate.

$$CH_3$$
$$\underset{CH_2}{\overset{|}{C}}{-}CH_2{-}CH_2{-}O{-}\underset{OH}{\overset{O}{\overset{||}{P}}}{-}O{-}\underset{OH}{\overset{O}{\overset{||}{P}}}{-}OH \qquad \text{isopentenyl pyrophosphate}$$

EXERCISE 30-9   *a.* Write out all of the possible carbon skeletons for acyclic terpene and sesquiterpene hydrocarbons that follow the isoprene rule. Do not consider double-bond position isomers.

b. Do the same for monocyclic terpenes with a six-membered ring.

EXERCISE 30-10   The terpene known as alloöcimene ($C_{10}H_{16}$) shows λ_{max} at 2880 A and gives among other products 1 mole of acetone and 1 mole of acetaldehyde on ozonization. What is a likely structure for alloöcimene? Show your reasoning.

EXERCISE 30-11   Write structures for each of the optical and *cis-trans* isomers that would be expected for the following isoprenoid compounds:

a. myrcene	*g.* camphene
b. α-farnesene	*h.* selinene
c. limonene	*i.* caryophyllene
d. zingiberene	*j.* tricyclene
e. sabinene	*k.* cedrene
f. α-pinene	

30-4 OXYGENATED ISOPRENOID COMPOUNDS

A great profusion of oxygen-containing isoprenoid compounds are known and, particularly in the polycyclic series, these often undergo interesting and unusual reactions which, however, are for the most part beyond the scope of this book. We shall confine our attention to a few representative oxygenated terpenes.

A. Oxygen Derivatives of Acyclic Terpenes

Of particular importance in the acyclic series are the alcohols, geraniol, nerol, and linaloöl, and the aldehydes, geranial (citral b), neral (citral a), and citronellal.

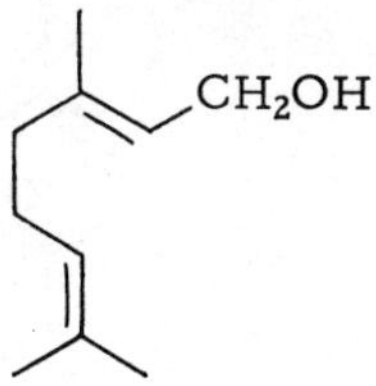

geraniol 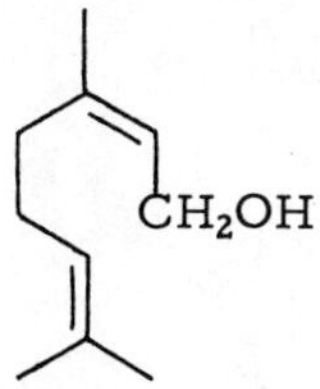   nerol 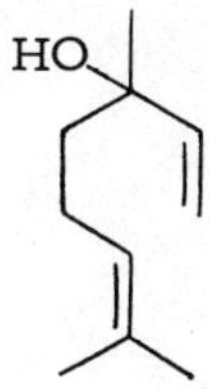   linaloöl

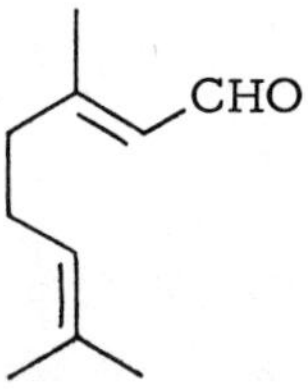

geranial   neral   citronellal
(citral *b*)   (citral *a*)

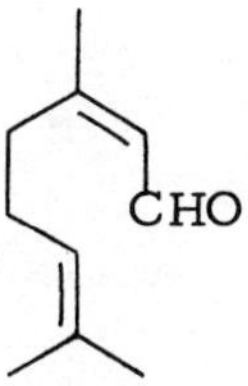

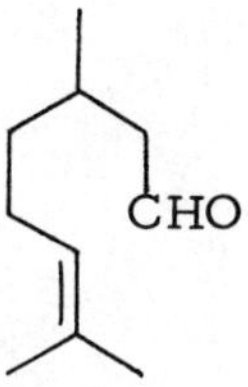

The alcohols occur in oil of rose and other flower essences. They have geranium or rose odors and are important perfume ingredients. The aldehydes have much stronger citrus-like odors and occur as major or minor constituents in many essential oils, such as oil of citronella, oil of lemon, etc.

EXERCISE 30-12   *a.* Nerol and geraniol cyclize under the influence of acid to yield α-terpineol. How could the relative ease of cyclization of these alcohols, coupled with other reactions, be used to establish the configurations at the double bond of geraniol, nerol, geranial, and neral? Write a mechanism for the cyclizations.

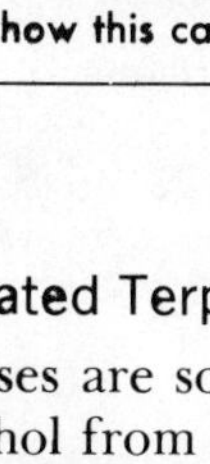

α-terpineol

b. Acidic cyclization of optically active linaloöl produces optically active α-terpineol. Explain how this can come about.

B. Monocyclic and Bicyclic Oxygenated Terpenes

Among the members of these classes are some familiar and interesting substances such as menthone and menthol from peppermint oil, 1,8-cineole from eucalyptus, and ascaridole, which is a naturally occurring peroxide from chenopodium oil.

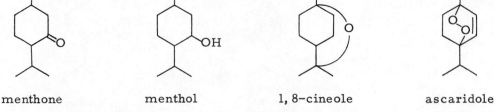

menthone   menthol   1, 8-cineole   ascaridole

Camphor is a particularly well-known bicyclic terpene ketone which has uses in medicine and as a plasticizer for nitrocellulose (p. 444).

$$CH_3 \quad CH_3$$
$$CH_3$$

camphor

For many years, the principal source of camphor was the Formosan camphor tree. It can be synthesized on a large scale from α-pinene (see Exercise 30-13). Some of the other types of naturally occurring bicyclic ketones follow:

thujone   verbenone   fenchone

EXERCISE 30-13   Camphor can be made on an industrial scale from α-pinene (turpentine) by the following reactions, some of which involve carbonium-ion rearrangements of a type particularly prevalent in the bicyclic terpenes and the scourge of the earlier workers in the field trying to determine terpene structures.

α-pinene $\xrightarrow[180°]{TiO_2 \cdot H_2O}$ camphene $\xrightarrow[H\oplus]{CH_3CO_2H}$ isobornyl acetate O_2CCH_3

$\xrightarrow{H_2O}$ isoborneol OH $\xrightarrow{[O]}$ camphor

Write mechanisms for the rearrangement reactions noting that hydrated titanium oxide is an acidic catalyst.

Two important *diterpene alcohols* are phytol, which occurs as an ester of the propionic acid side-chain of chlorophyll (p. 428), and vitamin A.

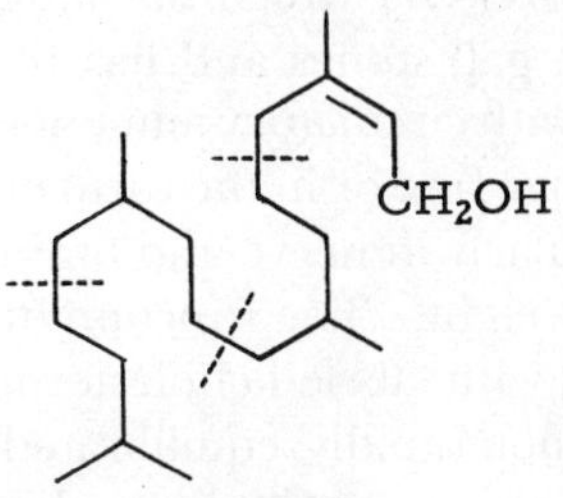

phytol 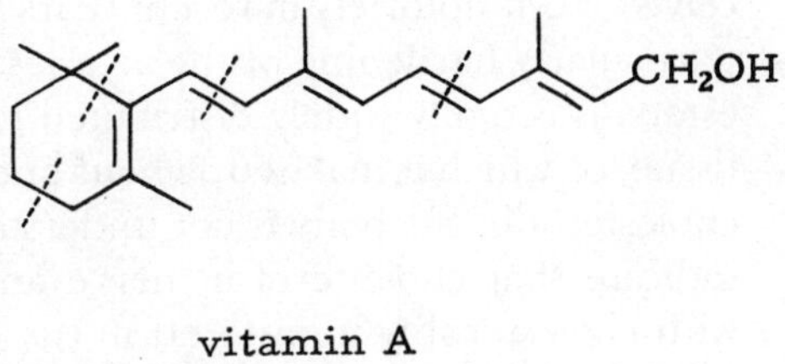   vitamin A

The phytyl group appears also as a side chain in vitamin K_1 (p. 622).

β-Carotene (p. 683) has vitamin A activity and is apparently oxidized in the body at the central double bond to give 1 mole of vitamin A.

The *diterpene acid*, abietic acid, is a major constituent of rosin, which is obtained as a nonvolatile residue in the manufacture of turpentine by steam distillation of pine oleoresin or shredded pine stumps. Abietic acid is the cheapest organic acid by the pound and is used extensively in varnishes and as its sodium salt in laundry soaps.

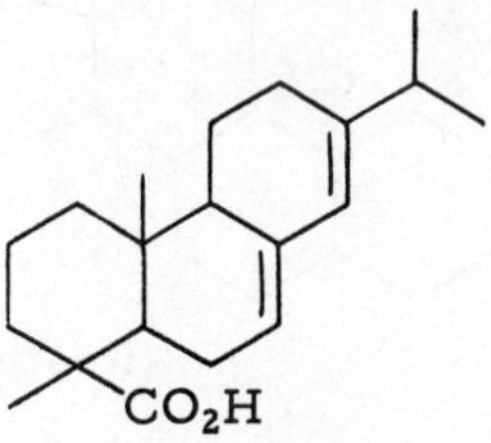

abietic acid

STEROIDS

In the discussion of the isoprenoid compounds it was our intention to show how the occurrence, structures, and properties of a large and important class of natural products can be correlated. To keep the discussion within reasonable bounds it was not possible to show how the various structures were established, or give any one compound particular attention. With steroids, we shall take the opposite approach of considering one member of the class, cholesterol, in some detail and then show only the structures of some other representative steroids. The term **steroid** is generally applied to compounds containing a hydrogenated cyclopentanophenanthrene carbon skeleton.

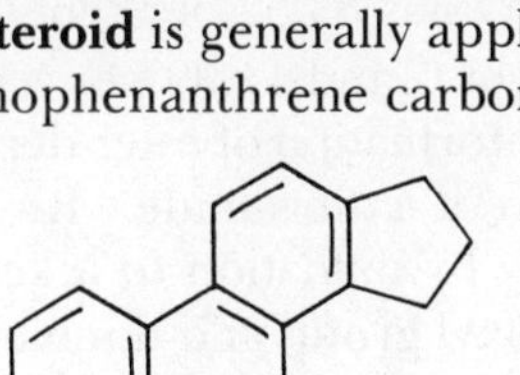

cyclopentanophenanthrene

Most of these compounds are alcohols, and sometimes the name **sterol** is used for the whole class. However, sterol is better reserved for the substances that are actually alcohols.

30-5 CHOLESTEROL

Cholesterol is an unsaturated alcohol of formula $C_{27}H_{45}OH$ which has long been known to be the principal constituent of human gall stones and has received fresh notoriety in recent years for its connection with circulatory ailments, particularly hardening of the arteries. Cholesterol, either free or in the form of esters, is actually widely distributed in the body, particularly in nerve and brain tissue, of which it makes up about one-sixth of the dry weight. The function of cholesterol in the body is not understood—experiments with labeled cholesterol indicate that cholesterol in nerve and brain tissue is not rapidly equilibrated with cholesterol administered in the diet. Two things are clear: Cholesterol is synthesized in the body and its metabolism is regulated by a highly specific set of enzymes. The high specificity of these enzymes may be judged from the fact that the very closely related plant sterols, such as sitosterol, are not metabolized by the higher animals, even though they have the same stereochemical configuration of all the groups in the ring and differ in structure only near the end of the side chain.

cholesterol   sitosterol

Although cholesterol was recognized as an individual chemical substance in 1812, all aspects of its structure and stereochemical configuration were not settled until about 1955. The structural problem was a very difficult one, because most of cholesterol is saturated and not easily degraded. Fortunately, cholesterol is readily available, so that it was possible to use rather elaborate degradative sequences which would have been quite out of the question with some of the more difficultly obtainable natural products.

The first step in the elucidation of the structure of cholesterol was the determination of the molecular formula, first incorrectly as $C_{26}H_{44}O$ in 1859 and then correctly as $C_{27}H_{46}O$ in 1888. The precision required to distinguish between these two formulas is quite high, since $C_{26}H_{44}O$ has 83.82 per cent C and 11.90 per cent H, whereas $C_{27}H_{46}O$ has 83.87 per cent C and 11.99 per cent H. Cholesterol was shown in 1859 to be an alcohol by formation of ester derivatives and in 1868 to possess a double bond by formation of a dibromide. By 1903 the alcohol function was indicated to be secondary by oxidation to a ketone rather than an aldehyde. The presence of the hydroxyl group and double bond when combined with the molecular formula showed the presence of four carbocyclic rings. Further progress was only possible by oxidative degradation.

Most of cholesterol is wholly saturated and oxidative reactions are not expected to proceed very well. However, chromic acid has the property of attacking tertiary hydrogens, probably by removal of H:$^{\ominus}$ and formation of a carbonium ion. Under the conditions, E1 elimination is expected, and this is likely to give the most highly substituted alkene which would then be cleaved by chromic acid. With the side chain of cholesterol, two points of cleavage are expected to be favored.

cholesterol
(partial structure)

Both processes occur, although the yields are poor. Formation of methyl isohexyl ketone by cleavage of the side chain was important in that it gave the first identifiable fragment of known structure. Actually, the second point of cleavage was much more significant, because it permitted correlation of cholesterol with another series of compounds, known as the *bile acids*, which offered better opportunities for oxidative degradation. The principal bile acids are *cholic acid* and *desoxycholic acid*.

cholic acid   desoxycholic acid

These substances occur in bile as sodium salts of N-acyl derivatives of glycine (RCONHCH$_2$CO$_2^{\ominus}$Na$^{\oplus}$) and taurine, β-aminoethanesulfonic acid (RCONHCH$_2$-CH$_2$SO$_3^{\ominus}$Na$^{\oplus}$). The function of the salts in bile is to aid in the solubilization and assimilation of fats and hydrocarbons, such as carotene. The bile acids are obtained by alkaline hydrolysis of the peptide bonds.

It will be seen that each of the six-membered rings in cholic acid carries a hydroxyl group, and this is most important, because it provides an entry into the rings by various kinds of oxidative processes. Furthermore, the side chain is seen to be the same length as in one of the chromic acid-oxidation products of cholesterol. The general similarity of the structures of the bile acids and cholesterol, including the stereochemical relations of the rings, strongly suggests that one is the precursor of the other in the body. Tracer experiments have shown that cholic acid can, in fact, be manufactured from dietary cholesterol.

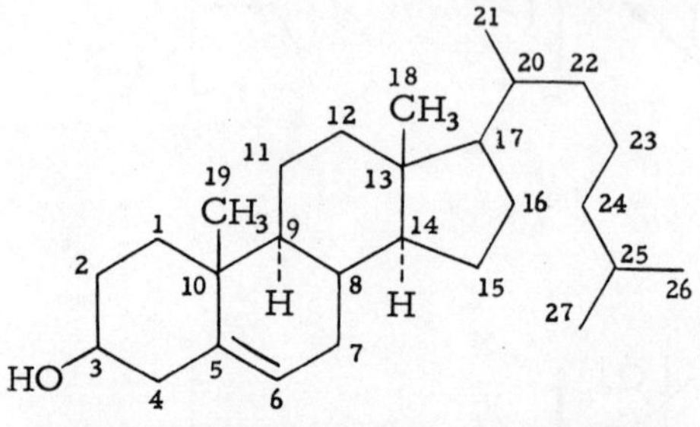

stereochemical configuration and
numbering system of cholesterol

Proof that cholesterol and the bile acids have the same general ring system was achieved by reduction of cholesterol to two different hydrocarbons, *cholestane* and *coprostane*, which differ only in the stereochemistry of the junction between rings A and B.

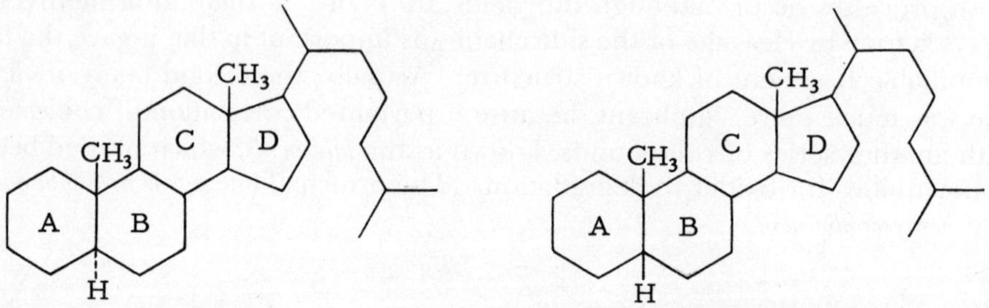

cholestane

coprostane

Oxidation of coprostane, but not cholestane, gave an acid which turned out to be identical with *cholanic acid* obtained by dehydration of cholic acid at 300° followed by hydrogenation.

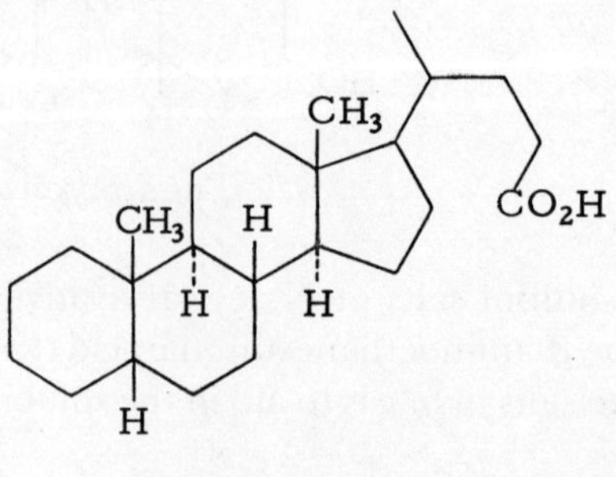

cholanic acid

EXERCISE 30-14   How many optical isomers are possible for cholic acid?

EXERCISE 30-15   Assuming cholesterol has the stereochemical configuration shown by [2], draw a similar configurational structure for cholic acid (including the hydroxyl groups).

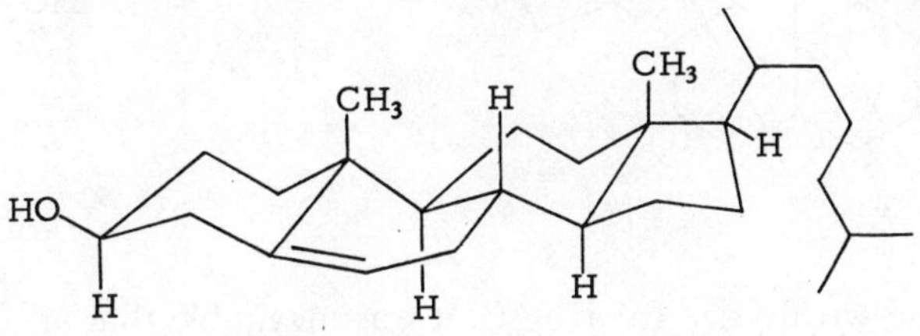

[2]

Determination of the sizes of the rings in cholesterol and the bile acids was achieved in part by use of the so-called **Blanc rule,** which states that a six-carbon dicarboxylic acid on heating will give a ketone, whereas a five-carbon dicarboxylic acid will give an anhydride (pp. 393-394). Reduction of cholesterol to cholestanol followed by oxidation yielded a dibasic acid, which on heating formed a ketone. This indicated the ring on which the hydroxyl was located to be a six-membered ring.

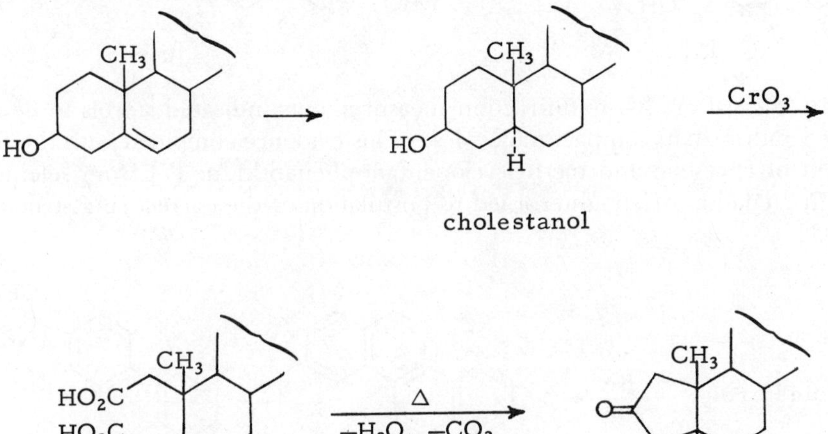

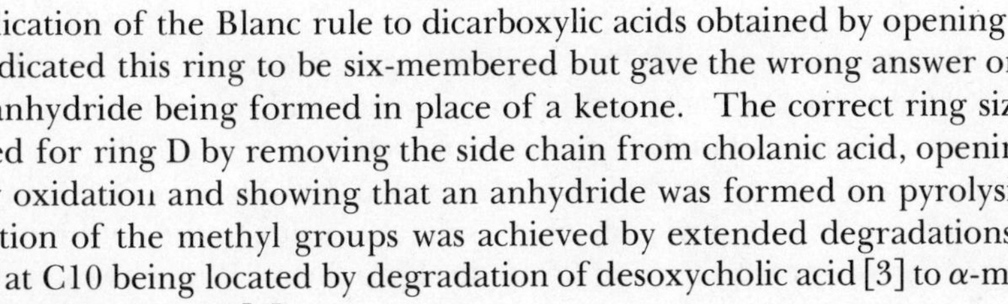

cholestanol

Application of the Blanc rule to dicarboxylic acids obtained by opening the B ring indicated this ring to be six-membered but gave the wrong answer on ring C, an anhydride being formed in place of a ketone. The correct ring size was obtained for ring D by removing the side chain from cholanic acid, opening the ring by oxidation and showing that an anhydride was formed on pyrolysis.

Location of the methyl groups was achieved by extended degradations—the methyl at C10 being located by degradation of desoxycholic acid [3] to α-methyl-α-carboxyglutaric acid [4].

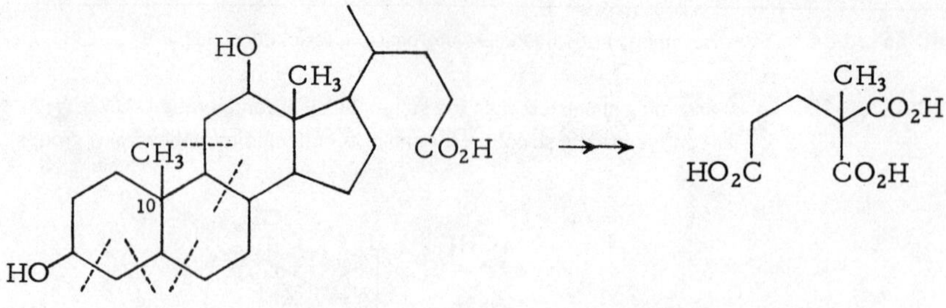

HO

CH₃

CH₃

10

HO

CO₂H

[3]

CH₃

CO₂H

HO₂C   CO₂H

[4]

With the wrong size for ring C, it was inevitable that at some stage incorrect structures would be proposed for cholesterol and the bile acids. Tentative structures [5] and [6] proposed in 1928 for desoxycholic acid and cholesterol, respectively, show a resemblance to the structures now known to be correct, but have a five-membered ring fused to ring A.

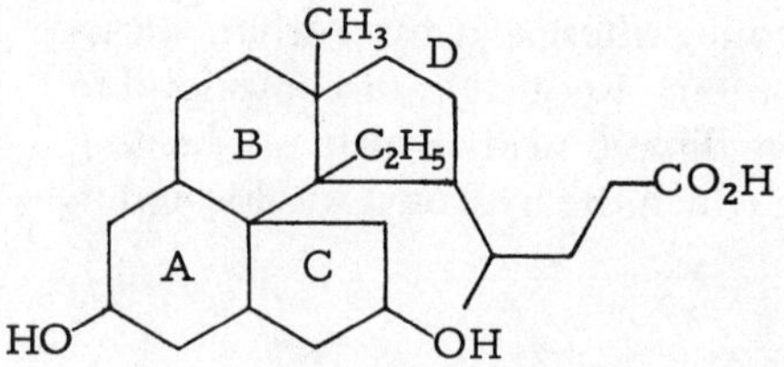

CH₃

D

B   C₂H₅

A   C

HO   OH

—CO₂H

[5]

CH₃

D

C   C₂H₅

A   B

HO

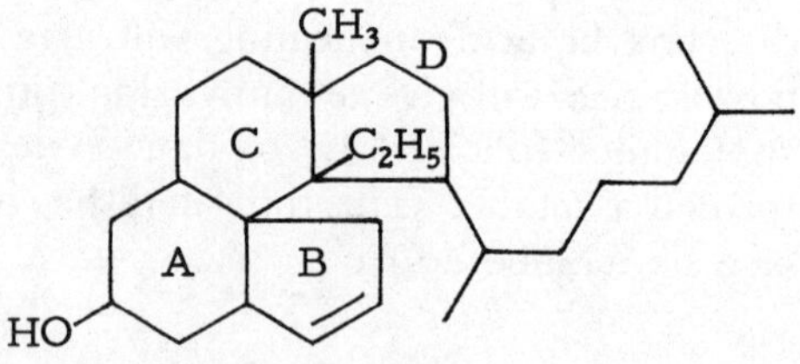

[6]

Shortly thereafter, X-ray diffraction measurements indicated sterols to be extended rather than compact molecules. This evidence combined with the formation of chrysene and methylcyclopentanophenanthrene [7] from selenium dehydrogenation of cholesterol led to postulation of the correct ring structure in 1932.

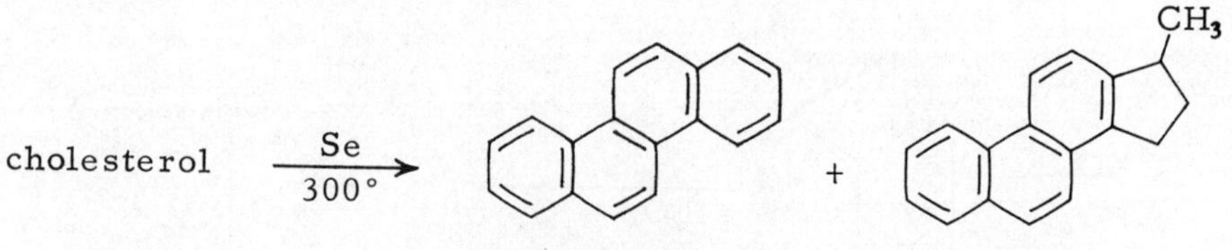

cholesterol $\xrightarrow[300°]{Se}$

chrysene

+

CH₃

[7]

The absolute configuration of the sterols and bile acids was established in 1955. Cholesterol has eight asymmetric centers and therefore there are 256 possible stereoisomers, but only cholesterol itself occurs naturally.

The proton n.m.r. spectrum of cholesterol at 100 Mcps is shown in Figure 30-3. Such spectra are obviously of considerable value in the determination of the structures of even quite complex natural products. With cholesterol, many of the protons at or near the functional groups stand out quite clearly.

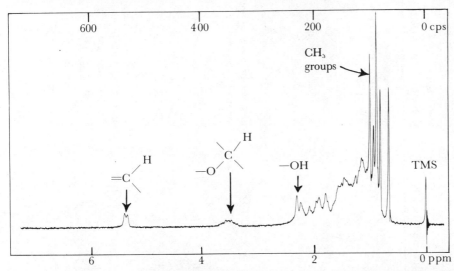

=C⟨H   −O−C⟨H   −OH   TMS   CH₃ groups

Figure 30-3   Proton n.m.r. spectrum of cholesterol at 100 Mcps as a 10 per cent solution in deutero-chloroform with reference to TMS at 0.00.   At 60 Mcps the chemical shifts are smaller and many of the features of the spectrum between 0.7 and 2.4 ppm are run together and less distinct. (Spectrum kindly furnished by Varian Associates.)

EXERCISE 30-16   When the sodium salt of 12-ketocholanic acid is heated to 330°, 1 mole of water and 1 mole of carbon dioxide are evolved and a hydrocarbon "dehydro-norcholene" is formed. Selenium dehydrogenation of this substance gives methylcholanthrene.

methylcholanthrene   12–ketocholanic acid

What is a likely structure for "dehydronorcholene" and how does the formation of methylcholanthrene help establish the location of the sterol side chain on ring D?

30-6   REPRESENTATIVE STEROIDS

The structures and physiological functions of a number of important steroids are shown in Table 30-2. Total syntheses have been achieved for the important sterols, sex hormones, and adrenal cortical hormones. The need for large quantities of cortisone and related substances for therapeutic use in treatment of arthritis and similar metabolic diseases has led to intensive research on synthetic approaches for methods of producing steroids with oxygen functions at C11, which is not a particularly common point of substitution in steroids.

Table 30-2 Representative Steroids

Structure and name[a]	Occurrence and physiological properties	Structure and name[a]	Occurrence and physiological properties
 ergosterol	sterol of yeast, gives vitamin D_2 when irradiated (see p. 758)	 vitamin D_2	antirachitic factor, formed by ultraviolet irradiation of ergosterol
 stigmasterol	plant sterol, soybean oil	 equilenen	female sex hormone of horse, regulates sexual cycle
 estrone	human estrogenic hormone, the corresponding C17 alcohol (OH *trans* to the C13 methyl) is even more active (estradiol)	 progesterone	human pregnancy hormone, secreted by the corpus luteum

756

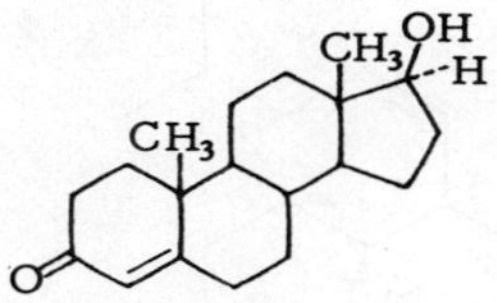

male sex hormone, regulates development of reproductive organs and secondary sex characteristics

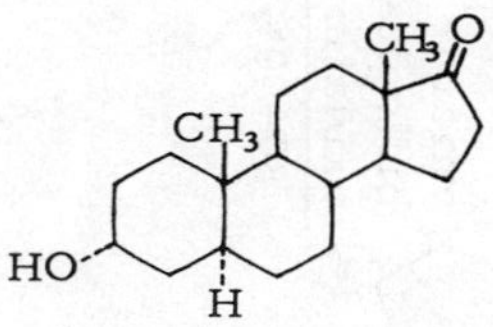

testosterone

androgenic hormone of less potency than testosterone

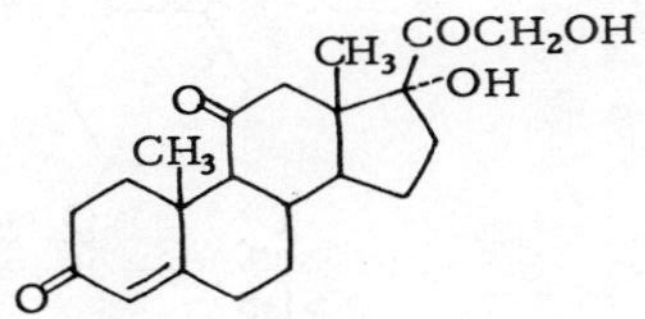

androsterone

hormone of adrenal cortex, used for treatment of arthritis; 6- and 9-fluoro derivatives have higher activity

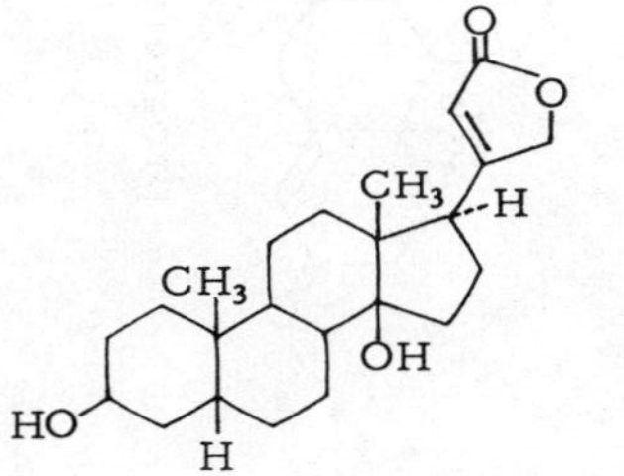

cortisone

as a complex glycoside at the 3-hydroxyl in digitalis plants, potent cardiac poison, used in small doses to regulate heart action

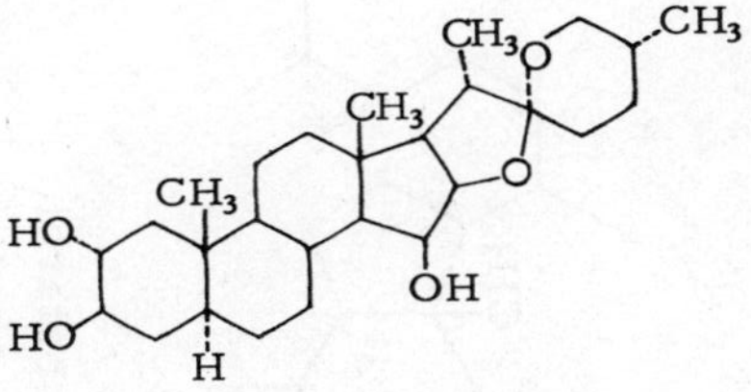

digitoxigenen

a saponin, occurs as a complex glycoside (glucose, galactose, and xylose) in digitalis plants[b]

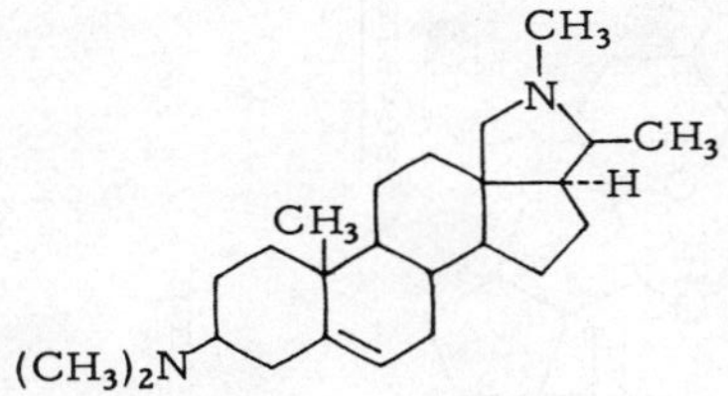

digitogenin

a representative alkaloid possessing a steroid nucleus

conessine

[a] The stereochemistry of the B/C and C/D ring junctions are as in cholesterol and the cholic acids; A/B stereochemistry is indicated where necessary.

[b] Digitogenin as the glycoside, digitonin, has the remarkable property of forming insoluble precipitates with the sterols having the 3-hydroxyl equatorial, but not those in which the hydroxyl is axial.

The most efficient way of doing this is by microbiological oxidation, and cortisone can be manufactured on a relatively large scale from the saponin diosgenin, which is isolated from tubers of a Mexicam yam of the genus *Dioscorea*. Diosgenin is converted to progesterone, then by a high-yield (80 to 90 per cent) oxidation with the mold, *Rhizopus nigricans*, to 11-hydroxyprogesterone and finally to cortisone.

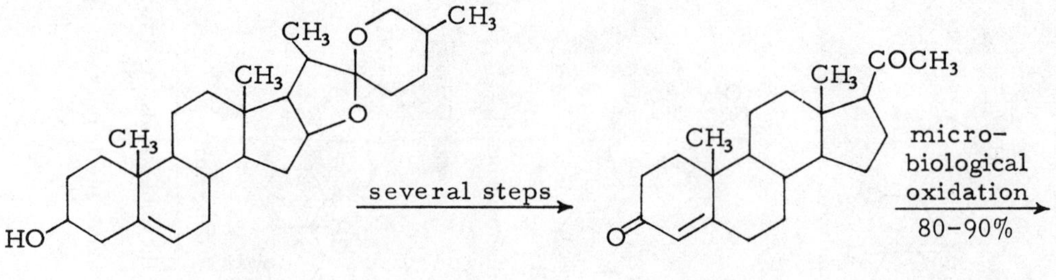

several steps →

diosgenin

micro-
biological
oxidation
80–90%

progesterone

several steps →

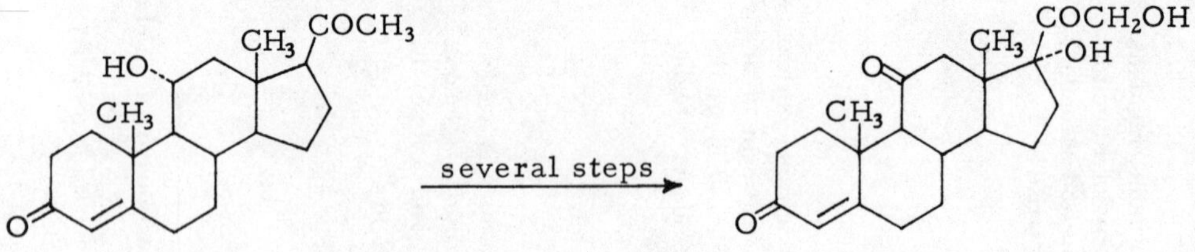

cortisone

Vitamin D is of special interest as a photochemical transformation product of ergosterol.

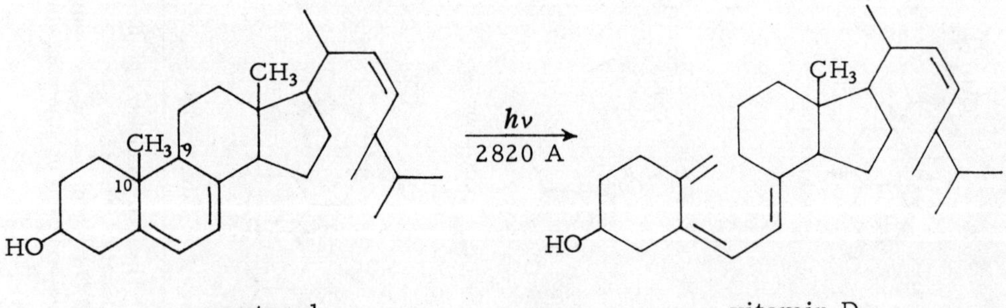

$\xrightarrow[2820\ \text{A}]{h\nu}$

ergosterol

vitamin D_2

(X-ray diffraction studies indicate the
transoid configuration of the 6, 7 bond
in the crystal)

BIOGENESIS OF THE TERPENES AND STEROIDS

Inspection of the structures for the typical pentacyclic triterpene, β-amyrin, and cholesterol shows such a striking resemblance between the carbon skeletons that it is not hard to imagine that the way in which these substances are synthesized, their **biogenesis,** may be closely related.

β-amyrin   cholesterol

This idea is heightened by the structure of lanosterol, a tetracyclic triterpene alcohol, which occurs along with cholesterol in wool fat and has properties so much like those of the sterols that it is better known as a sterol than a triterpene.

lanosterol

Concrete evidence that terpene and steroid biogenesis are actually related is provided by the finding that isotopically labeled lanosterol is converted to cholesterol by liver tissue. In fact, lanosterol is very likely to be a key intermediate in the formation of cholesterol from acetic acid, which, it turns out, is the raw material used for the biosynthesis of terpenes and steroids. A considerable part of the problem of biosynthesis of the steroids is therefore clearly tied up with the biosynthesis of the terpenes.

30-7 CHOLESTEROL BIOGENESIS

Isotopic labeling experiments indicate cholesterol to be derived from acetate by way of squalene and lanosterol. The evidence for this is that homogenized liver tissue is able to convert labeled squalene to labeled lanosterol and thence to labeled cholesterol. The conversion of squalene to lanosterol is particularly interesting because, although squalene is divisible into isoprene units, lanosterol is not—a methyl being required at C8 and not C13.

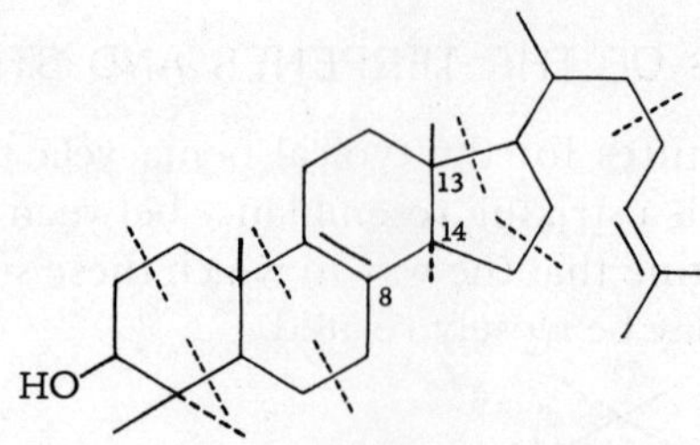

lanosterol

As a result, some kind of rearrangement must be required to get from squalene to lanosterol. The nature of this rearrangement becomes clearer if we write the squalene formula so as to take the shape of lanosterol.

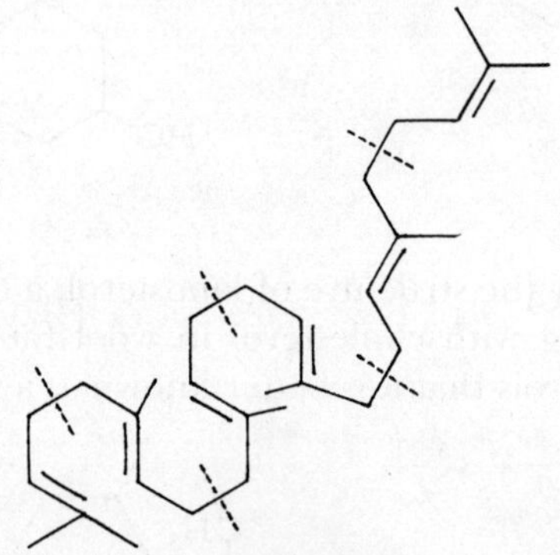

squalene

When written in this form, we see that squalene is beautifully constructed for cyclization to lanosterol. Each of the two carbons between which a ring bond is to be made is an unsaturated carbon, and we can imagine an essentially synchronous process for the formation of the rings if some oxidizing agent could furnish $HO^{\oplus}$ at C3.

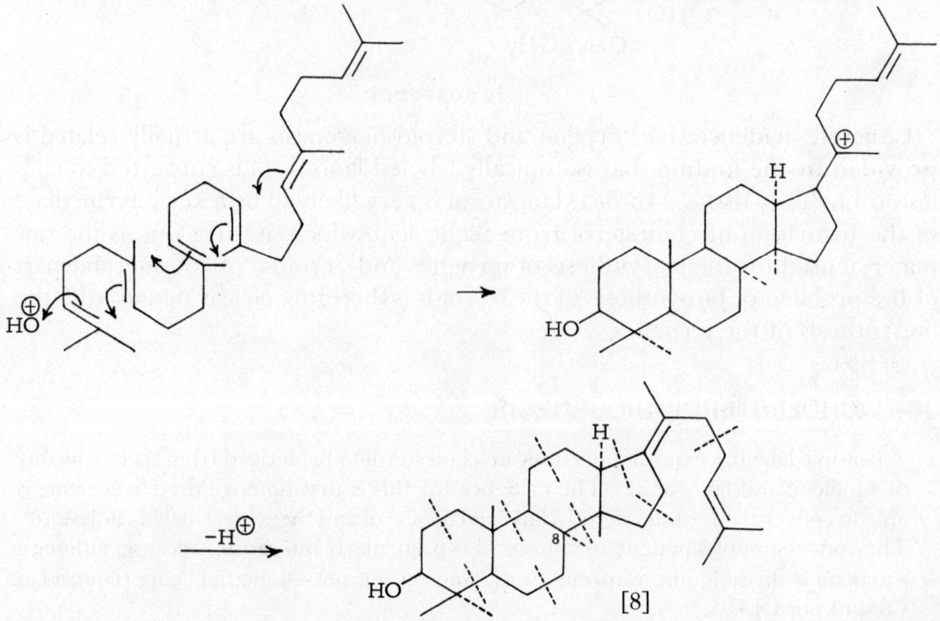

$-H^{\oplus}$ ⟶

[8]

The product [8] would be an isoprenoid isomer of lanosterol. Now if a sequence of carbonium-ion type rearrangements occurs we can see how [8] could be readily converted to lanosterol.

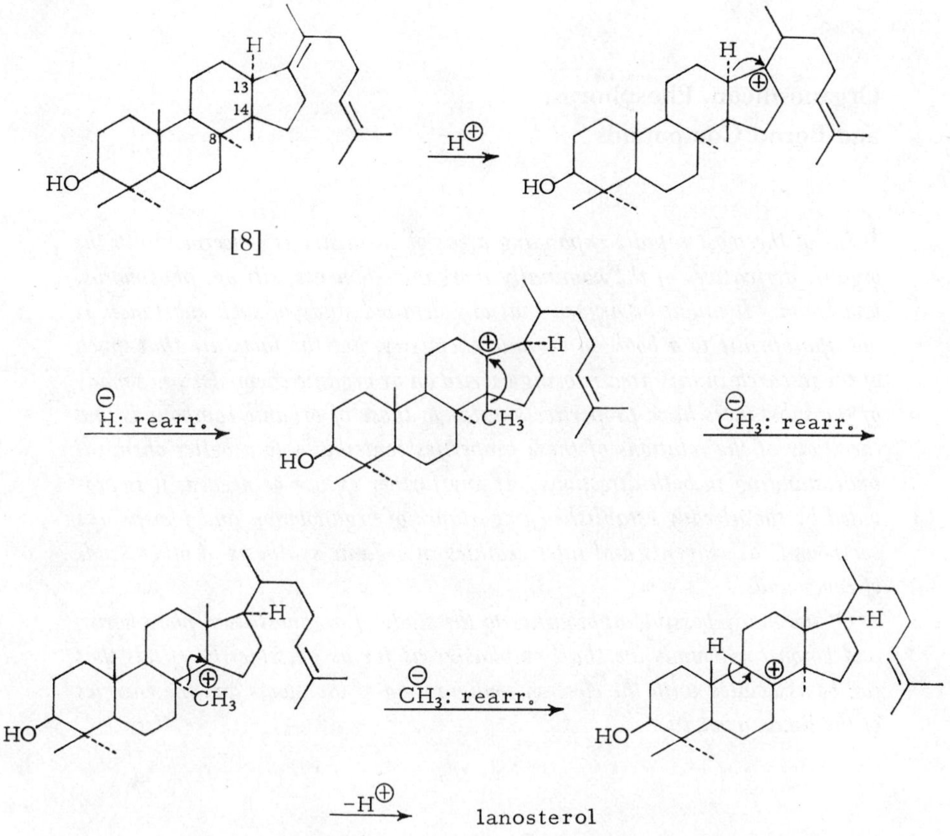

[8]

lanosterol

The evidence is strong that the biogenesis of lanosterol actually proceeds by a route of this type. With squalene made from either methyl- or carboxyl-labeled acetate, all the carbons of lanosterol and cholesterol are labeled as predicted. Furthermore, ingenious double-labeling experiments have shown that the methyl at C13 of lanosterol is the one that was originally located at C14, whereas the one at C14 is the one that came from C8.

The conversion of lanosterol to cholesterol involves removal of the three methyl groups at the 4,4- and 14-positions, shift of the double bond at the B/C junction to between C5 and C6, and reduction of the C24-C25 double bond. The methyl groups are indicated by tracer experiments to be eliminated by oxidation to carbon dioxide.

The **biogenesis of alkaloids** has also been extensively studied and, although for a time, it was thought that alkaloids arose primarily from amino acid precursors, strong evidence is now available that acetate is also involved. One experimental problem is the difficulty of feeding suitably labeled precursors to plants.

Organosilicon, Phosphorus, and Boron Compounds

*O*ne of the most rapidly expanding areas of chemistry is concerned with the organic derivatives of the nominally inorganic elements, silicon, phosphorus, and boron. It might be argued that any detailed study of such substances is not appropriate to a book on organic chemistry, but the facts are that much of the research in this area is being carried on by organic chemists, since many of the substances have properties similar to those of organic compounds and the study of the relations of these properties contributes to a better chemical understanding in both directions. If any further excuse be needed, it is provided by the already established importance of organoboron and phosphorus compounds as reagents and intermediates in organic synthesis of other kinds of compounds.

Of the many possible approaches to the study of organosilicon, phosphorus, and boron compounds we shall emphasize as far as possible the effects that can be associated with the electron configuration of the atoms and the energies of the bonds involved.

Organosilicon, Phosphorus, and Boron Compounds

ORGANOSILICON COMPOUNDS

Carbon and silicon are both members of Group IV of the periodic table and have similar configurations of outer electrons (see Figure 31-1). As a result, we expect a degree of resemblance in the chemistry of these elements even though they differ in the size of their atoms, their electronegativities, and the energies of their outer-shell electrons. In particular, the chemistry of silicon but not of carbon is expected to have the possibility of being influenced by the availability of empty $3d$ orbitals that are not greatly higher in energy than the silicon $3s$ and $3p$ orbitals (Figure 31-1). In the discussion to follow we shall try to show and rationalize the similarities and the differences that exist between carbon and silicon, as they are illustrated by comparison of the chemistry of organosilicon compounds with that of analogously constituted carbon compounds.

31-1 TYPES OF ORGANOSILICON COMPOUNDS

Several types of organosilicon compounds are listed in Table 31-1, together with the corresponding carbon compounds. It will be seen that silicon, like carbon, normally has a valency of four and forms reasonably stable bonds to other silicon atoms, to carbon, hydrogen, halogens, oxygen, and nitrogen. Some idea

Table 31-1   Principal Types of Organosilicon Compounds and Their Carbon Analogs

Organosilicon compound		Carbon compound	
silanes and organosilanes:		*alkanes:*	
$H_3Si—SiH_3$	disilane	$CH_3—CH_3$	ethane
$CH_3—SiH_3$	methylsilane	$CH_3—CH_3$	ethane
$(CH_3)_4Si$	tetramethylsilane	$(CH_3)_4C$	neopentane
organosilyl halides (halosilanes):		*alkyl halides (haloalkanes):*	
$(CH_3)_3SiCl$	trimethylsilyl chloride	$(CH_3)_3CCl$	*t*-butyl chloride
H_2SiCl_2	dichlorosilane	CH_2Cl_2	dichloromethane
CH_3SiCl_3	methylsilyl trichloride	CH_3CCl_3	1,1,1-trichloroethane
silanols:		*alcohols:*	
H_3SiOH	silanol	H_3COH	methanol (carbinol)
$(CH_3)_3SiOH$	trimethylsilanol	$(CH_3)_3COH$	trimethylcarbinol (*t*-butyl alcohol)
$(CH_3)_2Si(OH)_2$	dimethylsilanediol	$(CH_3)_2C(OH)_2$	acetone hydrate (unstable)
$CH_3Si(OH)_3$	methylsilanetriol	$CH_3C(OH)_3$	orthoacetic acid (unstable)
siloxanes and alkoxysilanes:		*ethers:*	
$(CH_3)_3SiOSi(CH_3)_3$	hexamethyldisiloxane	$(CH_3)_3COC(CH_3)_3$	di-*t*-butyl ether
$(CH_3)_3SiOCH_3$	trimethylmethoxy-silane	$(CH_3)_3COCH_3$	methyl *t*-butyl ether
$(CH_3)_2Si(OCH_3)_2$	dimethyldimethoxy-silane	$(CH_3)_2C(OCH_3)_2$	acetone dimethyl ketal
$CH_3Si(OCH_3)_3$	methyltrimethoxy-silane	$CH_3C(OCH_3)_3$	methyl orthoacetate
silyl esters:		*alkyl esters:*	
$(CH_3)_3Si—\overset{\overset{O}{\|\|}}{O}CCH_3$	trimethylsilyl acetate	$(CH_3)_3C—\overset{\overset{O}{\|\|}}{O}CCH_3$	*t*-butyl acetate
silazanes (silylamines):		*amines:*	
$(CH_3)_3SiNH_2$	trimethylsilazane (tri-methylsilylamine)	$(CH_3)_3CNH_2$	*t*-butylamine
$(H_3Si)_2NH$	disilazane (disilyl-amine)	$(CH_3)_2NH$	dimethylamine
$(H_3Si)_3N$	trisilylamine	$(CH_3)_3N$	trimethylamine

of the strength of these bonds relative to analogous bonds involving carbon may be obtained from the average bond energies shown in Table 31-2. Significantly, the Si—Si bond is *weaker* than the C—C bond by some 30 kcal/mole, whereas the Si—O bond is *stronger* than the C—O bond by some 22 kcal/mole. These bond energies account for several differences in the chemistry of the two elements. Thus, while carbon forms a great many compounds having linear and branched

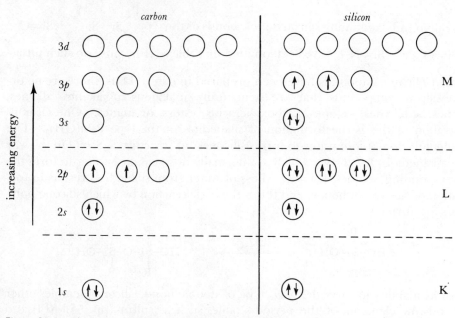

Figure 31-1   Electronic configurations of carbon and silicon.

chains of C—C bonds, silicon is less versatile; the silanes of formula Si_nH_{2n+2} analogous to the alkanes of formula C_nH_{2n+2} are relatively unstable and react avidly with oxygen.   On the other hand, the silicone polymers have chains of Si—O—Si bonds and have a high thermal stability as corresponds to the considerable strength of the Si—O bond.

Table 31-2   Average Bond Energies

Bond	Bond energy, kcal/mole	Bond	Bond energy, kcal/mole
Si—Si	53	C—C	82.6
Si—C	76	C—Si	76
Si—H	76	C—H	98.7
Si—O	108	C—O	85.5
Si—N		C—N	72.8
Si—F	135	C—F	116
Si—Cl	91	C—Cl	81
Si—Br	74	C—Br	68
Si—I	56	C—I	51

EXERCISE 31-1   Name the following compounds according to the nomenclature used in Table 31-1:

a. $(C_6H_5)_4Si$ d. $(CH_3)_3SiOSiH_3$

b. $(C_2H_5)_2SiBr_2$ e. $CH_3SiH_2NH_2$

c. $(C_6H_5)_2Si(OH)_2$ f. $C_6H_5CONHSi(CH_3)_3$

Compounds containing silicon double bonds of the type $\diagdown\!\!Si\!\!=\!\!Si\!\!\diagup$, $\diagdown\!\!Si\!\!=\!\!C\!\!\diagup$, $\diagdown\!\!Si\!\!=\!\!O$, or $\diagdown\!\!Si\!\!=\!\!N\!\!-$ have been omitted in Table 31-1 because no such unsaturated silicon compounds have been prepared to date. Thus, there are no organosilicon compounds that are structurally analogous to alkenes, alkynes, arenes, aldehydes, ketones, carboxylic acids, esters, or imines. One clear illustration of this is the formation of silanediols of the type $R_2Si(OH)_2$. The silanediols do not lose water to form "silicones" of structure $R_2Si\!\!=\!\!O$ in the way the alkanediols, $R_2C(OH)_2$, which are normally unstable, lose water to form the corresponding ketones, $R_2C\!\!=\!\!O$. Loss of water from silanediols results in formation of Si—O—Si bonds, and this is the basic reaction by which silicone polymers are formed.

$$\underset{\underset{R}{|}}{\overset{\overset{R}{|}}{2\ HO-Si-OH}} \quad \xrightarrow{\ -H_2O\ } \quad \underset{\underset{R}{|}\quad\underset{R}{|}}{\overset{\overset{R}{|}\quad\overset{R}{|}}{HO-Si-O-Si-OH}}$$

In its inability to form the p_π-p_π type of double bond, silicon resembles other second-row elements of the periodic table, such as sulfur (pp. 513-514) and phosphorus. The reasons for this are not clear, but may be due to relatively poor $3p_\pi$-$3p_\pi$ or $3p_\pi$-$2p_\pi$ overlap, possibly because of the larger sizes of the second-row atoms. Nonetheless, silicon, like sulfur (Chapter 21), does have a tendency to form a different type of double bond, involving d orbitals with elements like oxygen, nitrogen, and the halogens. This type of bonding is associated with d_π-p_π overlap and is sometimes called "backbonding."

31-2 BONDING INVOLVING d ORBITALS IN ORGANOSILICON COMPOUNDS

Silicon is normally tetracovalent in organosilicon compounds and, by analogy with carbon, we may reasonably suppose the bonds involved to be of the sp^3 type and the substituent groups to be tetrahedrally disposed in space. Evidence that this is so comes from the successful resolution of several silicon compounds having a center of asymmetry at the silicon atom; for example, both enantiomers of 1-naphthylphenylmethylsilane [1] have been obtained.

[1]

$[\alpha]_D = \pm\ 32°$

Also, X-ray and electron-diffraction studies of silicon tetraiodide, silicon tetra-chloride, and tetramethylsilane indicate tetrahedral structures. It would, how-ever, be incorrect to conclude that all silicon compounds are tetravalent and tetrahedral, because substances with hexacovalent silicon such as hexafluosilicate ion, $SiF_6{}^{2\ominus}$, are known, and this indicates that silicon can expand its valence shell to accommodate 10 electrons by utilizing the $3d$ orbitals. The silicon $3d$ orbitals are involved in a different way in compounds of the type $\diagdown\!\!\!\!\overset{\diagdown}{\underset{\diagup}{Si}}\!\!-\ddot{X}$,

where X is an atom or group having electrons in a p orbital so situated as to be able to overlap with an empty $3d$ orbital of silicon. The result is a Si—X bond with partial double-bond character of the d_π-p_π type, in which the silicon has an expanded valence shell. The bonding can be symbolized by the following reso-nance structures:

$$-\!\!\!\overset{\diagdown}{\underset{\diagup}{Si}}\!\!-\ddot{X} \quad\longleftrightarrow\quad -\!\!\!\overset{\diagdown}{\underset{\diagup}{Si}}\!\!\overset{\ominus}{=}\overset{\oplus}{X}$$

Examples of X include oxygen, nitrogen, halogens, as well as unsaturated groups like vinyl and phenyl groups.

EXERCISE 31-2　　　Write electron-pairing schemes for trimethylsilanol and vinylsilane involving silicon d orbitals.

EXERCISE 31-3　　　Explain why trisilylamine, $(SiH_3)_3N$, is a weaker base than trimethylamine and why trimethylsilanol, $(CH_3)_3SiOH$, is a stronger acid than t-butyl alcohol.

31-3 PREPARATION AND PROPERTIES OF ORGANOSILICON COMPOUNDS

A. Preparation of Organosilanes

The source of virtually all silicon compounds is silica, SiO_2. Secondary sources are elementary silicon and the silicon tetrahalides, SiF_4 and $SiCl_4$, which can be prepared on a commercial scale from silica by the following reactions:

$$SiO_2 + C \longrightarrow Si + CO_2$$

$$SiO_2 + 4\,HF \longrightarrow SiF_4 + 2\,H_2O$$

$$SiO_2 + 2\,Cl_2 + C \longrightarrow SiCl_4 + CO_2$$

Organosilicon compounds are prepared from elementary silicon or the silicon halides. A particularly valuable synthesis of organochlorosilanes involves heat-ing an alkyl chloride or even an aryl chloride with elementary silicon in the presence of a copper catalyst. A mixture of products usually results; nonethe-less, the reaction is employed commercially for the synthesis of organochloro-silanes, particularly the methylchlorosilanes.

$$CH_3Cl + Si \xrightarrow[300°]{Cu\,(10\%)} SiCl_4 + CH_3SiHCl_2 + CH_3SiCl_3 + (CH_3)_2SiCl_2$$
$$\qquad\qquad\qquad\qquad\quad 9\% \qquad 12\% \qquad 37\% \qquad 42\%$$

The reaction between a silicon halide and an organometallic reagent, either a Grignard reagent or an organolithium compound, provides a versatile laboratory synthesis of organosilicon compounds; three examples follow:

$$(C_6H_5)_3SiCl + C_6H_5CH_2MgCl \longrightarrow (C_6H_5)_3SiCH_2C_6H_5 + MgCl_2$$

$$SiCl_4 + 4C_6H_5Li \longrightarrow (C_6H_5)_4Si + 4LiCl$$

$$(CH_3)_2SiCl_2 + CH_3MgCl \longrightarrow (CH_3)_3SiCl + MgCl_2$$

These reactions are analogous to the nucleophilic coupling reactions of organic halides with Grignard reagents (see pp. 269-270).

$$\overset{\delta\ominus}{CH_2}=CH-CH_2\!:\ MgCl + \overset{\delta\oplus}{Cl}-CH_2-CH=CH_2 \longrightarrow CH_2=CHCH_2CH_2CH=CH_2 + MgCl_2$$

With a silicon halide, nucleophilic attack occurs at silicon.

$$\overset{\delta\ominus}{CH_2}=CH-CH_2\!:\ MgCl + \overset{\delta\oplus}{Cl}-SiH_3 \longrightarrow CH_2=CHCH_2SiH_3 + MgCl_2$$

Silicon halides are much more reactive than organic halides of comparable structure. This is not surprising, because silicon is more electropositive than carbon. An example of the reactivity difference follows wherein breaking of C—Cl and Si—Cl bonds is in direct competition, and only the chlorine attached to silicon is displaced.

$$\begin{array}{c} CH_3 \\ \diagdown \\ \diagup \quad Si \\ CH_3 \quad \diagdown Cl \end{array} \!\!\!\! \begin{array}{c} CH_2{-}Cl \\ \\ \end{array} + C_2H_5MgCl \longrightarrow \begin{array}{c} CH_3 \\ \diagdown \\ \diagup \quad Si \\ CH_3 \quad \diagdown C_2H_5 \end{array} \!\!\!\! \begin{array}{c} CH_2Cl \\ \\ \end{array} + MgCl_2$$

Silicon fluorides as well as chlorides, bromides, and iodides all react with organometallic reagents, particularly with organolithium reagents.

B. Properties of the Organosilanes

The physical properties of representative organosilanes may be seen from Table 31-3 to be roughly similar to those of analogously constituted carbon compounds. The chemical reactivity of organosilanes is generally much greater than that of alkanes. The Si—C bond is cleaved more readily than a C—C bond by both electrophilic and nucleophilic reagents, nucleophilic attack occurring at silicon and electrophilic attack at carbon.

Table 31-3   Physical Properties of Some Representative Silicon Compounds
and Their Carbon Analogs

Silicon compound	B.p., °C	M.p., °C	Carbon compound	B.p., °C	M.p., °C
SiH_4[a]	-112	-156.8	CH_4	-162	-184
SiH_3SiH_3[a]	-14.5	-133	CH_3CH_3	-88.3	-172
CH_3SiH_3	-57.5	-156.8	CH_3CH_3	-88.3	-172
$(CH_3)_4Si$	27		$(CH_3)_4C$	9.5	-20
$(CH_3)_3SiC_6H_5$	172		$(CH_3)_3CC_6H_5$	169	-58
$(C_6H_5)_4Si$	430	237	$(C_6H_5)_4C$	431	285
$SiCl_4$	57.6	-70	CCl_4	76.8	-22.8
$SiHCl_3$	33	-134	$CHCl_3$	61	-63.5
SiH_2Cl_2	8.3	-122	CH_2Cl_2	40	-96.7
CH_3SiCl_3	65.7		CH_3CCl_3	74	
$C_6H_5SiCl_3$	201		$C_6H_5CCl_3$	214	-5
$(CH_3)_3SiOH$	98.6		$(CH_3)_3COH$	82.8	25.5
$(CH_3)_2Si(OH)_2$		100			
$(CH_3SiH_2)_2O$	34.5	-138	$(CH_3CH_2)_2O$	35	-116
$(CH_3)_3SiOCH_3$	56		$(CH_3)_3COCH_3$	106	
$\overset{O}{\overset{\|}{CH_3COSi(CH_3)_3}}$	103	-32	$\overset{O}{\overset{\|}{CH_3COC(CH_3)_3}}$	97	
$(CH_3SiH_2)_3N$	109		$(CH_3CH_2)_3N$	89.5	-115

[a] Spontaneously flammable in air.

nucleophilic
attack at silicon

electrophilic
attack at carbon

Typical electrophilic reagents for these reactions are the halogens, Cl_2, Br_2, and I_2, and strong acids such as H_2SO_4 and $HClO_4$. Cleavage of Si—C bonds with both types of reagents occurs, although metal halide catalysts may be necessary for cleavage by halogens.

31-4 SILANOLS, SILOXANES, AND POLYSILOXANES

The silanols are generally prepared by hydrolysis of silicon halides and some-times by hydrolysis of hydrides and alkoxides.

$$R_3SiCl + H_2O \longrightarrow R_3SiOH + HCl$$

$$R_2SiCl_2 + 2H_2O \longrightarrow R_2Si(OH)_2 + 2HCl$$

$$R_3SiH + H_2O \xrightarrow{\overset{\ominus}{OH}} R_3SiOH + H_2$$

The reaction conditions have to be controlled to avoid condensation of the silanols to siloxanes, especially when working with silanediols.

$$R_2Si(OH)_2 + R_2Si(OH)_2 \xrightarrow{-H_2O} \begin{array}{cc} R & R \\ | & | \\ HO-Si-O-Si-OH \\ | & | \\ R & R \end{array}$$

This may necessitate working in neutral solution at high dilution.

The silanols are less volatile than the halides and siloxanes because of inter-molecular association through hydrogen-bonding, and the diols $R_2Si(OH)_2$ are more soluble in water than the silanols, R_3SiOH. Compared to alcohols, silanols are more acidic and form stronger hydrogen bonds. This can be ascribed to d_π-p_π bonding of the Si—O bond (p. 767).

$$R_3Si—O-H \longleftrightarrow R_3\overset{\ominus}{Si}=\overset{\oplus}{O}-H$$

In the presence of either acids or bases, most silanols are unstable and con-dense to form siloxanes.

Acid-catalyzed condensation:

$$R_3SiOH + H^{\oplus} \rightleftharpoons R_3Si\overset{\oplus}{OH_2}$$

$$R_3Si\overset{\frown}{O} + R_3Si-\overset{\oplus}{OH_2} \longrightarrow R_3SiOSiR_3 + H_2O \longrightarrow R_3SiOSiR_3 + \overset{\oplus}{H_3O}$$

Base-catalyzed condensation:

$$R_3SiOH + \overset{\ominus}{OH} \rightleftharpoons R_3Si\overset{\ominus}{O} + H_2O$$

$$R_3Si\overset{\ominus}{O} + R_3Si-OH \longrightarrow R_3SiOSiR_3 + \overset{\ominus}{OH}$$

The same type of condensation reaction, when carried out with the silanediols, leads to linear chains and cyclic structures with Si—O and Si—C bonds which are called polysiloxanes.

$$(CH_3)_2Si(OH)_2 \xrightarrow{\ H^{\oplus}\ or\ ^{\ominus}OH\ } \begin{array}{c} (CH_3)_2 \\ Si \\ O \diagdown \quad \diagup O \\ \ | \qquad\qquad | \\ (CH_3)_2Si \diagdown_{O}\diagup Si(CH_3)_2 \end{array}$$

$$+ \quad HO-\underset{\underset{CH_3}{|}}{\overset{\overset{CH_3}{|}}{Si}}-O \left(\underset{\underset{CH_3}{|}}{\overset{\overset{CH_3}{|}}{Si}}-O \right)_n \underset{\underset{CH_3}{|}}{\overset{\overset{CH_3}{|}}{Si}}-OH$$

The higher-molecular-weight products are the "silicone polymers."

The linear silicone polymers are liquids of varying viscosity depending on the chain length. They remain fluid to low temperatures and are very stable thermally, which makes them useful as hydraulic fluids and lubricants.

Cross linking results in hard and sometimes brittle resins, depending upon the ratio of methyl groups to silicon atoms in the polymer.

EXERCISE 31-4   Suggest possible reasons why silicone oils and rubbers have low glass temperatures (T_g). See pp. 708-710 for a discussion of T_g.

ORGANOPHOSPHORUS COMPOUNDS

31-5 TYPES OF PHOSPHORUS COMPOUNDS

Phosphorus is a second-row element in Group V of the periodic table and the configuration of its outer-shell electrons is similar to that of nitrogen, as shown in Figure 31-2. We might therefore expect some resemblances in the organic chemistry of the two elements. However, there are many striking differences, some of these being quite evident on comparing some of the main types of organic compounds formed by both elements, as is done in Table 31-4. There are no nitrogen compounds having more than four covalent bonds to the nitrogen atom; phosphorus compounds are known with three, four, and five covalent bonds to phosphorus. Furthermore, phosphorus does not appear to form stable unsaturated compounds having $p_\pi\text{-}p_\pi$ double bonds to oxygen, nitrogen, or carbon analogous to nitro, nitroso, azo, diazo, azido, nitrile, and imino compounds. Likewise, phosphorus does not give stable aromatic heterocyclic compounds analogous to pyridine. Thus, phosphorus resembles other second-row elements, such as sulfur and silicon, in its reluctance to form $p_\pi\text{-}p_\pi$ double bonds (see pp. 513 and 766).

The ability of phosphorus to form compounds with five covalent bonds, as in pentaphenylphosphorane ($C_6H_5)_5P$), means that phosphorus can accommodate 10 electrons in its outer shell by utilizing its empty $3d$ orbitals. Formation of

Table 31-4   Principal Types of Organophosphorus and
Organonitrogen Compounds

Organophosphorus compounds		Organonitrogen compounds	
		Tricovalent	
phosphines	*prim.* RPH_2	amines	*prim.* RNH_2
	sec. R_2PH		*sec.* R_2NH
	tert. R_3P		*tert.* R_3N
biphosphine	$H_2P{-}PH_2$	hydrazine	$H_2N{-}NH_2$
phosphorous acid (unstable with respect to phosphonic acid, $HP(O)(OH)_2$	$HO{-}\overset{\displaystyle OH}{\underset{\displaystyle OH}{P:}}$	hydrated form of nitrous acid, HONO (unstable)	$H{-}\overset{\displaystyle OH}{\underset{\displaystyle OH}{O{-}N:}}$
phosphorous acid derivatives	$:P(OR)_3$ $:PCl_3$	trichloramine	$:NCl_3$
phosphonous acid (unstable relative to phosphinic acid, $RHP(O)OH$)	$R{-}\overset{\displaystyle OH}{\underset{\displaystyle OH}{P:}}$	hydrated form of monomeric hyponitrous acid, HNO (unstable)	$H{-}\overset{\displaystyle OH}{\underset{\displaystyle OH}{N:}}$
phosphonous acid derivatives	$RP(OR)_2$ $RPCl_2$	dichloramine	$HNCl_2$
phosphinous acid [unstable relative to phosphine oxide, $R_2HP(O)$]	$R{-}\overset{\displaystyle OH}{\underset{\displaystyle R}{P:}}$	hydroxylamine	$H{-}\overset{\displaystyle OH}{\underset{\displaystyle H}{N:}}$
		chloramine	H_2NCl
phosphinous acid derivatives	$R_2P(OR)$ R_2PCl	O-alkylhydroxylamines N-chloramines	R_2NOR R_2NCl
		amide	$\overset{\displaystyle O}{\overset{\displaystyle \|}{RC}}{-}NH_2$
		nitroso	$RN{=}O$
		azo	$RN{=}NR$
		diazo	$RN{\equiv}\overset{\oplus}{N}$
		imino	$R_2C{=}NR$
		nitrile	$RC{\equiv}N$
		pyrrole	
		pyridine	

Continued on p. 773

Table 31-4   Principal Types of Organophosphorus and
             Organonitrogen Compounds (*Continued*)

Organophosphorus compounds		Organonitrogen compounds	
	Tetra- and pentacovalent		
phosphonium salts	$R_4P^{\oplus}\ X^{\ominus}$	ammonium salts	$R_4\overset{\oplus}{N}\ \overset{\ominus}{X}$
phosphine oxides	$R_3P{=}O$	N-oxides	$R_3\overset{\oplus}{N}{-}\overset{\ominus}{O}$
		nitro	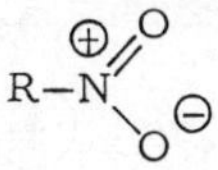 $R{-}\overset{\oplus}{N}\underset{O^{\ominus}}{\overset{O}{\diagup\!\!\!\backslash}}$

phosphoric acid[a]	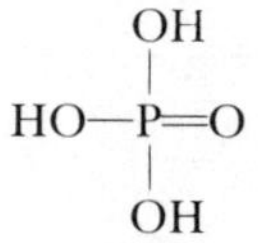 HO—P=O with OH above and OH below		
phosphonic acids	R—P=O with OH above and OH below		
phosphinic acids[b]	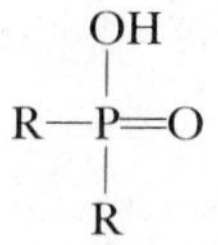 R—P=O with OH above and R below		
phosphoranes	R—P—R with R above and R, R below (pentacovalent)		
alkylidenephosphoranes	R—P=CR$_2$ with R above and R below		

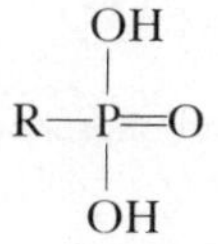

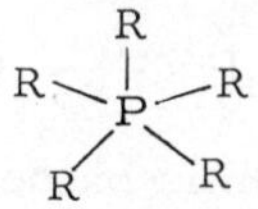

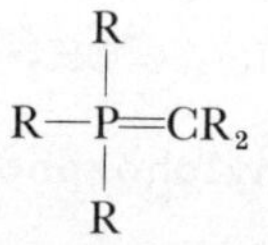

---

[a]Organic derivatives of phosphoric acid (such as esters, amides, etc.) are not strictly organophosphorus compounds, since they have no C-P bonds.

[b]Phosphinic acid itself $H_2P(O)OH$ is often called hypophosphorous acid.

---

analogous pentacovalent nitrogen compounds is precluded by the high energy of the nitrogen $3d$ orbitals relative to the $2s$ and $2p$ orbitals.

Some of the other types of organophosphorus compounds listed as pentacovalent in Table 31-4 involve p_π-d_π bonding and can be formulated as hybrids of electron-pairing schemes such that the phosphoryl group (P=O) of the oxy-

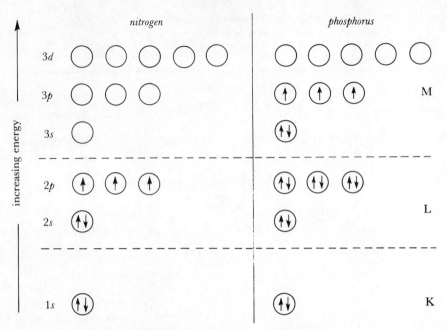

Figure 31-2   Electronic configurations of nitrogen and phosphorus.

acid derivatives and the P=C bond of the alkylidenephosphoranes have both dipolar and double-bond character.

$$(C_6H_5)_3\overset{\oplus}{P}-\overset{\ominus}{O}: \quad \longleftrightarrow \quad (C_6H_5)_3P{=}O \quad \sim \quad (C_6H_5)_3\overset{\delta\oplus}{P}{\cdots}\overset{\delta\ominus}{O}$$

triphenylphosphine oxide

$$(C_6H_5)_3\overset{\oplus}{P}-\overset{\ominus}{CH_2} \quad \longleftrightarrow \quad (C_6H_5)_3P{=}CH_2 \quad \sim \quad (C_6H_5)_3\overset{\delta\oplus}{P}{\cdots}\overset{\delta\ominus}{CH_2}$$

methylenetriphenylphosphorane

Whether the structure of the phosphoryl group is written as P=O or $\overset{\oplus}{P}-\overset{\ominus}{O}$ is immaterial provided we recognize its hybrid character. We have chosen here to use the representation P=O.

The physical properties of some representative organophosphorus compounds are listed in Table 31-5.

Table 31-5   Physical Properties of Some Organophosphorus Compounds

Compound	Formula	M.p., °C	B.p., °C	K_A, 25°, H_2O
methylphosphine	CH_3PH_2		14	
triethylphosphine oxide	$(C_2H_5)_3P{=}O$		128	
triphenylphosphine	$(C_6H_5)_3P\!:$	80		
triphenylphosphine oxide	$(C_6H_5)_3P{=}O$	156		
phenylphosphinic acid	$C_6H_5\overset{\displaystyle OH}{\underset{\displaystyle H}{P}}{=}O$	70		
phenylphosphonous dichloride	$C_6H_5PCl_2$		90–92[10 mm]	
diethyl phenylphosphonite	$C_6H_5P(OC_2H_5)_2$		100[5 mm]	
ethyl phenylphosphinate	$C_6H_5\overset{\displaystyle H}{\underset{\displaystyle OC_2H_5}{P}}{=}O$		120[4 mm]	
dimethylphosphinic acid	$CH_3{-}\overset{\displaystyle OH}{\underset{\displaystyle CH_3}{P}}{=}O$	88		3.2×10^{-4}
methylphosphonic acid	$CH_3{-}\overset{\displaystyle OH}{\underset{\displaystyle OH}{P}}{=}O$	105		1.7×10^{-3} [a] 8.2×10^{-8} [b]
ethylphosphonic acid	$C_2H_5{-}\overset{\displaystyle OH}{\underset{\displaystyle OH}{P}}{=}O$	59		7.2×10^{-3} [a] 9.2×10^{-9} [b]
methylphosphonic dichloride	$CH_3{-}\overset{\displaystyle Cl}{\underset{\displaystyle Cl}{P}}{=}O$		65[20 mm]	

[a] The first ionization constant, K_1.
[b] The second ionization constant, K_2.

31-6   NOMENCLATURE OF PHOSPHORUS COMPOUNDS

Unfortunately, the practice of naming organophosphorus compounds is largely unsystematic. However, a nomenclature system published in 1952 by both the American Chemical Society and the Chemical Society (London) has been widely adopted by English-speaking countries. It considers organophosphorus compounds to be derivatives of phosphorus hydrides, oxyacids, and oxides. The parent compounds in question, some of which are unstable and cannot be isolated, are:

phosphine $H_3P:$

phosphorane H_5P

$$\text{phosphonic acid}\quad H\!-\!\overset{\displaystyle OH}{\underset{\displaystyle OH}{P}}\!\!=\!\!O$$

$$\text{phosphonous acid}\quad H\!-\!\overset{\displaystyle OH}{\underset{\displaystyle OH}{P}}\!:$$

$$\text{phosphinic acid}\quad H\!-\!\overset{\displaystyle OH}{\underset{\displaystyle H}{P}}\!\!=\!\!O$$

$$\text{phosphinous acid}\quad H\!-\!\overset{\displaystyle OH}{\underset{\displaystyle H}{P}}\!:$$

$$\text{phosphine oxide}\quad H\!-\!\overset{\displaystyle H}{\underset{\displaystyle H}{P}}\!\!=\!\!O$$

Compounds with carbon-phosphorus bonds are named as substitution products resulting by replacement of hydrogen of a hydrogen-phosphorus bond with an alkyl or aryl group. Thus methylphosphonic acid has the structure $CH_3\!-\!\overset{\displaystyle O}{\overset{\|}{P}}(OH)_2$. Esters of the oxyacids are taken to be formed by replacing hydrogen of an O—H bond by an alkyl or aryl group; therefore, dimethyl methylphosphonate has the structure $CH_3\!-\!\overset{\displaystyle O}{\overset{\|}{P}}(OCH_3)_2$. Compounds having phosphorus-halogen bonds or phosphorus-nitrogen bonds are considered to be acid halides or amides formed by replacement of the acidic OH group of the phosphorus oxyacid by halogen, NH_2, NHR, or NR_2. Methylphosphonic dichloride and methylphosphonic diamide therefore have the respective structures $CH_3\overset{\displaystyle O}{\overset{\|}{P}}Cl_2$ and $CH_3\overset{\displaystyle O}{\overset{\|}{P}}(NH_2)_2$. Further examples follow:

phenylphosphonous dichloride $C_6H_5\!-\!\overset{..}{P}\!\!\overset{Cl}{\underset{Cl}{\diagdown}}$

methyl dimethylphosphinite $\overset{CH_3}{\underset{CH_3}{>}}\overset{..}{P}\!-\!OCH_3$

dimethylphosphinous chloride $\overset{CH_3}{\underset{CH_3}{>}}\overset{..}{P}\!-\!Cl$

N,N'-dimethyl phenylphosphonic diamide $C_6H_5\!-\!\overset{\displaystyle NHCH_3}{\underset{\displaystyle NHCH_3}{P}}\!\!=\!\!O$

diethylphosphinic chloride

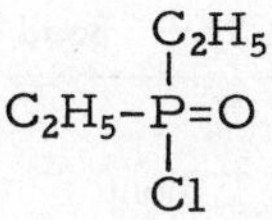

$$C_2H_5-\underset{\underset{Cl}{|}}{\overset{\overset{C_2H_5}{|}}{P}}=O$$

dimethyl phosphonate[1]

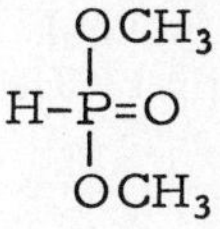

$$H-\underset{\underset{OCH_3}{|}}{\overset{\overset{OCH_3}{|}}{P}}=O$$

methylethylphosphine

$$CH_3-\underset{\underset{H}{|}}{\overset{\overset{C_2H_5}{|}}{P}}:$$

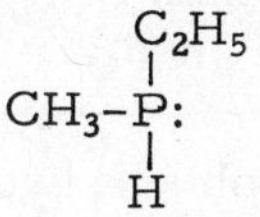

ethylidenetriphenylphosphorane

$(C_6H_5)_3P=CH-CH_3$

methylethylphosphine oxide

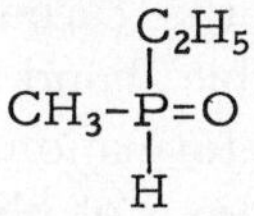

$$CH_3-\underset{\underset{H}{|}}{\overset{\overset{C_2H_5}{|}}{P}}=O$$

methylethylphosphonium bromide

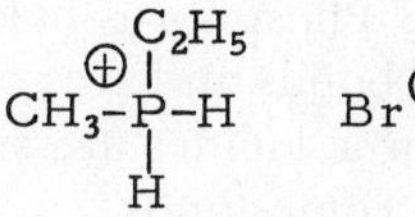

$$CH_3-\overset{\oplus}{\underset{\underset{H}{|}}{\overset{\overset{C_2H_5}{|}}{P}}}-H \qquad Br^{\ominus}$$

EXERCISE 31-5   Name the following compounds:

a. $CH_3PHCH_2CH_3$

b. 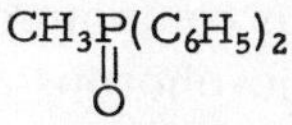 $CH_3\underset{\underset{O}{\|}}{P}(C_6H_5)_2$

c. $\underset{\underset{H}{|}}{\overset{\overset{CH_2-CH_2}{\diagdown \diagup}}{P}}$

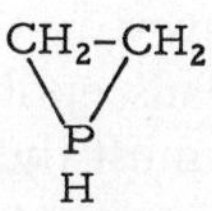

d. $P(OC_2H_5)_3$

e. $O=P(OC_2H_5)_3$

f. 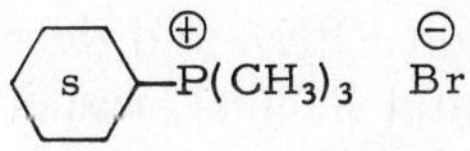 (thiophene ring)$-\overset{\oplus}{P}(CH_3)_3 \quad Br^{\ominus}$

g. $(C_6H_5)_2P-N(C_2H_5)_2$

h. CH_3PHCl

i. 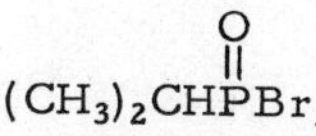 $(CH_3)_2CHPBr_2$ (with O double bond above P)

j. 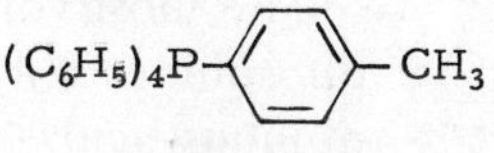 $(C_6H_5)_4P-\!\!\langle benzene \rangle\!\!-CH_3$

k. 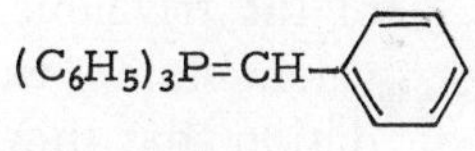 $(C_6H_5)_3P=CH-\!\!\langle benzene \rangle$

l. 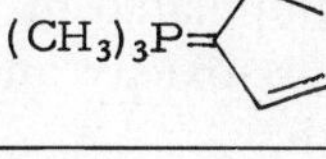 $(CH_3)_3P=\!\!\langle cyclopentadiene \rangle$

31-7 GENERAL CONSIDERATIONS OF REACTIVITY OF ORGANOPHOSPHORUS COMPOUNDS

A. Bond Energies

A tabulation of bond energies for various types of bonds to phosphorus is given in Table 31-6, and may be compared with the corresponding bond energies for nitrogen. The important points to note from the data in Table 31-6 are:

[1] Sometimes named as dimethyl phosphite or dimethyl hydrogen phosphite.

Table 31-6   Bond Energies in Phosphorus and Nitrogen Compounds

Bond	Bond energy, kcal/mole	Bond	Bond energy, kcal/mole
P—H (in PH_3)	77	N—H (in NH_3)	93.4
P—C [in $P(CH_3)_3$]	63	N—C	72.8
P—O	~95	N—O	~50
P=O	~140	N=O (in RONO)	145
P—Cl (in PCl_3)	78	N—Cl (in NCl_3)	46
P—P (in P_4)	48	N—N (in H_2NNH_2)	30

1. Phosphorus-hydrogen bonds are substantially weaker than nitrogen-hydrogen bonds.

2. The phosphorus-oxygen single bond is a fairly strong bond – stronger in fact than the carbon-oxygen single bond – while the P=O or phosphoryl p_π-d_π "double" bond is about 45 kcal stronger than the P—O single bond. The energy of formation of the phosphoryl group provides the driving force for many reactions of phosphorus compounds.

3. Phosphorus-halogen bonds are appreciably stronger than nitrogen-halogen bonds and are comparable in strength to carbon-halogen bonds. The phosphorus halides are similar to alkyl halides in being reasonably stable but reactive compounds.

4. Phosphorus-carbon bonds are comparable in strength to carbon-carbon bonds, and reactions involving their cleavage are not common.

B. Trivalent Phosphorus Compounds

The most common types of trivalent organophosphorus compounds are the phosphines R_3P, R_2PH, and RPH_2, and derivatives of phosphorous and phosphinous acids, $RP(OH)_2$ and R_2POH, respectively. An outstanding property of the trivalent compounds is the ease with which they convert to the pentavalent state. In fact, the lower phosphorus hydrides are so susceptible to oxidation that they are spontaneously flammable in air. They must therefore be manipulated in the absence of oxygen, and this inconvenience combined with their toxicity and unpleasant odors makes them difficult compounds to work with.

$$RPH_2 \xrightarrow{\ [O]\ } RP(OH)_2 \quad (O)$$

$$R_2PH \xrightarrow{\ [O]\ } R_2P(OH) \quad (O)$$

$$R_3P \xrightarrow{\ [O]\ } R_3P{=}O$$

In general, a hydroxyl group bonded to trivalent phosphorus ($\overset{..}{P}$—OH) is unstable, the stable structure being H—P=O. For this reason, diesters of phosphorous acid are unstable, and exist as diesters of phosphonic acid.

$$\begin{matrix} C_2H_5O \\ \ddot{~}\!P-OH \\ C_2H_5O \end{matrix} \quad \rightleftharpoons \quad \begin{matrix} OC_2H_5 \\ H-P=O \\ OC_2H_5 \end{matrix}$$

       diethyl phosphite   diethyl phosphonate

31-8 ORGANOPHOSPHORUS COMPOUNDS AS NUCLEOPHILIC REAGENTS

The most evident property of trivalent organophosphorus compounds is their ability to utilize the unshared electron pair on phosphorus to form bonds to other atoms. In this respect, the phosphines resemble amines and are weakly basic compounds forming phosphonium salts with proton acids and adducts with Lewis acids; they also act as nucleophilic reagents, forming phosphonium salts by attack at carbon of an alkyl halide.

$$(CH_3)_3P: + HCl \longrightarrow (CH_3)_3\overset{\oplus}{P}H\ \overset{\ominus}{Cl}$$

                      trimethylphosphonium chloride

$$(CH_3)_3P: + BCl_3 \longrightarrow (CH_3)_3\overset{\oplus}{P}:\overset{\ominus}{B}Cl_3$$

                      trimethylphosphine trichloroborane

$$(CH_3)_3P: + CH_3Cl \longrightarrow (CH_3)_4\overset{\oplus}{P}\ \overset{\ominus}{Cl}$$

                      tetramethylphosphonium chloride

The phosphines are actually more nucleophilic than the corresponding amines, probably because phosphorus is a larger, more electropositive atom than nitrogen, and its outer-shell electrons are consequently less firmly held and more polarizable.

Other nucleophilic reactions that lead to the formation of P—C bonds occur with phosphorus compounds possessing P—H bonds. Since the P—H bond is weaker and more acidic than an N—H bond, it can usually be broken by a base to give a powerfully nucleophilic phosphorus anion that can attack carbon of either an alkyl halide of good S_N2 reactivity or an alkene bearing electronegative substituents. The parent phosphorus compound can be a phosphine, R_2PH or RPH_2; a dialkyl phosphonate, $(RO)_2P(O)H$; or a secondary phosphine oxide, $R_2HP(O)$.

$$(CH_3)_2\overset{\oplus}{P}\overset{\ominus}{H} + NaNH_2 \longrightarrow (CH_3)_2\overset{\ominus}{P}:\overset{\oplus}{Na} + NH_3$$

     dimethylphosphine   sodium dimethylphosphide

$$(CH_3)_2\overset{\ominus}{P}: \ + \ CH_3CH_2Br \ \longrightarrow \ (CH_3)_2PCH_2CH_3 \ + \ Br^{\ominus}$$

dimethylethylphosphine

31-9 ORGANOPHOSPHORUS COMPOUNDS AS ELECTROPHILIC REAGENTS. NUCLEOPHILIC REACTIONS AT PHOSPHORUS

Substances in which the phosphorus atom is bonded to electronegative groups such as halogens and alkoxy groups are susceptible to attack by nucleophilic reagents, since the phosphorus atom is thereby made relatively deficient in electrons and hence has electrophilic character. Thus phosphorus-chlorine bonds can be hydrolyzed to P—OH bonds; they may be reduced with metallic hydrides to P—H bonds, and converted to P—C bonds with organometallic reagents.

$$H_2O \ + \ \overset{\delta\oplus}{R_2P}\!\!-\!\!\overset{\delta\ominus}{Cl} \ \longrightarrow \ R_2POH \ + \ HCl$$

$$\updownarrow$$

$$\underset{R_2PH}{\overset{O}{\underset{\|}{}}}$$

$$\overset{\ominus}{H:} \ + \ \overset{\delta\oplus}{R_2P}\!\!-\!\!\overset{\delta\ominus}{Cl} \ \xrightarrow{\text{LiAlH}_4} \ R_2PH \ + \ Cl^{\ominus}$$

$$\overset{\delta\ominus}{R':}\overset{\delta\oplus}{MgX} \ + \ \overset{\delta\oplus}{R_2P}\!\!-\!\!\overset{\delta\ominus}{Cl} \ \longrightarrow \ R_2PR' \ + \ MgXCl$$

Reactions of a phosphorus halide with an organometallic reagent provides a useful method for preparation of organophosphorus compounds, as the following examples show.

$$PCl_3 \ + \ 3\,CH_3MgBr \ \longrightarrow \ (CH_3)_3P \ + \ 3\,MgBrCl$$

phosphorus   trimethylphosphine
trichloride

$$POCl_3 \ + \ 3\,C_2H_5MgCl \ \longrightarrow \ (C_2H_5)_3P{=}O \ + \ 3\,MgCl_2$$

phosphorus oxychloride   triethylphosphine oxide
(phosphoryl trichloride)

31-10 FREE-RADICAL REACTIONS

The usual P—H bond is some 20 kcal weaker than the usual C—H bond. Consequently, a hydrogen can be removed from a P—H compound relatively easily by free radicals, giving phosphorus radicals which, however, are energetic enough to add to carbon-carbon double bonds. These reactions permit addition of P—H compounds to alkenes by a free-radical chain mechanism; the direction of addition being opposite to that expected by Markownikoff's rule, as in the chain addition of hydrogen bromide (pp. 146-148). The reaction sequence is well illustrated by the addition of phosphine to 1-butene.

Initiation:

$$PH_3 \xrightarrow[(-H \cdot)]{h\nu} \cdot PH_2$$

Propagation:

$$\left\{ \begin{array}{l} \cdot PH_2 + CH_3CH_2CH=CH_2 \rightarrow CH_3CH_2\overset{\cdot}{C}HCH_2PH_2 \\ CH_3CH_2\overset{\cdot}{C}HCH_2PH_2 + PH_3 \rightarrow CH_3CH_2CH_2CH_2PH_2 + \cdot PH_2 \end{array} \right.$$

$$n\text{-butylphosphine}$$

Reaction does not usually stop at the monoalkylphosphine stage but proceeds further, to give varying amounts of dialkyl- and trialkylphosphines.

$$PH_3 + CH_3CH_2CH=CH_2 \xrightarrow{h\nu} CH_3CH_2CH_2CH_2PH_2 + (CH_3CH_2CH_2CH_2)_2PH$$
$$\qquad\qquad\qquad\qquad\qquad\qquad\quad 38\% \qquad\qquad\qquad\quad 10\%$$

$$+ (CH_3CH_2CH_2CH_2)_3P$$
$$2\%$$

31-11 STEREOCHEMISTRY OF ORGANOPHOSPHORUS COMPOUNDS

The successful resolution of asymmetric quaternary phosphonium salts of the type $R_1R_2R_3R_4P^{\oplus}X^{\ominus}$ [2], with the R groups all different, shows that these compounds resemble tetracovalent carbon compounds and quaternary ammonium salts in their stereochemistry.

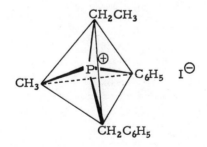

methylethylphenylbenzylphosphonium iodide

$$[\alpha]_D^{25} = \pm 24°$$

[2]

Likewise, tertiary phosphine oxides, $R_1R_2R_3P\!\!=\!\!O$ [3], have nonplanar configurations, since they can normally be separated into enantiomeric forms.

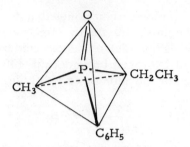

methylethylphenylphosphine oxide

$$[\alpha]_D^{25} = \pm 22.8°$$

[3]

More surprising is the fact that tertiary phosphines of the type $R_1R_2R_3P$: can be obtained optically active. For example, the optically active phosphonium salt [4] gives, by electrolytic reduction, optically active methylpropylphenyl-phosphine [5].

$$\left[\begin{array}{c} C_6H_5 \\ | \\ CH_3-P-C_3H_7 \\ | \\ CH_2C_6H_5 \end{array}\right]^{\oplus} \quad Br^{\ominus} \quad \xrightarrow[(-C_6H_5CH_3)]{[H]} \quad \begin{array}{c} C_6H_5 \\ | \\ CH_3-P-C_3H_7 \\ \cdot\cdot \end{array}$$

[4]   [5]

The optical stability of this phosphine contrasts very strikingly with the behavior of the corresponding amines which have not yet been resolved, apparently because they undergo inversion too rapidly (p. 456). The phosphines do not invert their configuration nearly as easily — in fact, the optically active phosphine [5] must be heated in boiling toluene for 3 hours for complete racemization to occur. The configurational stability of the phosphines resembles that of the sulfonium salts (p. 521).

$$\begin{array}{c} C_6H_5 \\ \diagdown \\ C_3H_7 ----- P: \\ \diagup \\ CH_3 \end{array} \quad \underset{\longleftarrow}{\overset{\text{slow}}{\longrightarrow}} \quad \begin{array}{c} C_6H_5 \\ \diagup \\ : P -----C_3H_7 \\ \diagdown \\ CH_3 \end{array}$$

31-12 REACTIONS OF QUATERNARY PHOSPHONIUM COMPOUNDS

There are interesting differences in behavior of quaternary ammonium and quaternary phosphonium salts toward basic reagents. Whereas tetraalkyl-ammonium salts with hydroxide or alkoxide ions generally form alkenes and trialkylamines by E2-type elimination (p. 460), corresponding reactions of tetra-alkyl- or arylphosphonium salts lead to phosphine oxides and hydrocarbons.

$$(CH_3)_3\overset{\oplus}{N}CH_2CH_3 \; + \; \overset{\ominus}{O}H \; \longrightarrow \; (CH_3)_3N \; + \; CH_2{=}CH_2 \; + \; H_2O$$

$$(C_6H_5)_3\overset{\oplus}{P}CH_2CH_3 \; + \; \overset{\ominus}{O}H \; \longrightarrow \; (C_6H_5)_2\overset{\overset{O}{\|}}{P}CH_2CH_3 \; + \; C_6H_6$$

EXERCISE 31-6 The rate of decomposition of quaternary phosphonium salts by bases has been established as dependent on the product $[R_4P^{\oplus}][OH^{\ominus}]^2$. Which step of the over-all reaction is likely to be the rate-determining step?

There is an alternative course of reaction of quaternary phosphonium salts with basic reagents. It involves attack of a base, usually phenyllithium, at a hydrogen *alpha* to phosphorus. The product [6] is called an alkylidenephosphorane.

$$\underset{\overset{\ominus}{X}}{R_3\overset{\oplus}{P}{-}CH_2R'} \; + \; C_6H_5Li \; \longrightarrow \; R_3\overset{\oplus}{P}{-}\overset{\ominus}{\underset{..}{C}}HR' \; + \; C_6H_6 \; + \; \overset{\oplus}{Li} \; \overset{\ominus}{X}$$

$$[6]$$

Although compounds of this type are frequently written as dipolar structures, they are better considered as hybrids of the contributing structures [6a] and [6b] involving p_π-d_π bonding.

$$\underset{[6a]}{R_3\overset{\oplus}{P}{-}\overset{\ominus}{\underset{..}{C}}HR} \quad \longleftrightarrow \quad \underset{[6b]}{R_3P{=}CHR}$$

Alkylidenephosphoranes are reactive, often highly colored substances, that rapidly react with oxygen, water, acids, alcohols, and carbonyl compounds—in fact with most oxygen-containing compounds. Several of these reactions are illustrated here for methylenetriphenylphosphorane and again the driving force is formation of the phosphoryl group, often at the expense of a phosphorus-carbon bond.

$$(C_6H_5)_3\overset{\oplus}{P}CH_3 \; \overset{\ominus}{Br} \quad \xrightarrow[{-HBr}]{C_6H_5Li} \quad (C_6H_5)_3P{=}CH_2$$

methyltriphenylphosphonium
bromide

methylenetriphenyl-
phosphorane

$$(C_6H_5)_3P{=}CH_2 \; + \; H_2O \; \longrightarrow \; (C_6H_5)_2\overset{\underset{\displaystyle CH_3}{|}}{P}{=}O \; + \; C_6H_6$$

methyldiphenylphosphine
oxide

$$(C_6H_5)_3P{=}CH_2 \; + \; \langle\!\!\!\bigcirc\!\!\!={=}O \; \longrightarrow \; (C_6H_5)_3P{=}O \; + \; \langle\!\!\!\bigcirc\!\!\!={=}CH_2$$

triphenylphosphine   methylene-
      oxide   cyclohexane

The preparation of alkenes from the reactions of alkylidenetriphenylphos-phoranes with aldehydes and ketones is known as the **Wittig reaction.**

ORGANOBORON COMPOUNDS

31-13 TYPES OF BONDING IN BORON COMPOUNDS

As can be seen in Figure 31-3, boron has three L-shell electrons available for bonding. Boron utilizes these three electrons to form predominantly covalent sp^2 bonds in compounds of the type BX_3; typical examples being boron trifluoride BF_3, trimethylborane $B(CH_3)_3$, and boric acid $B(OH)_3$. In such compounds the boron normally has only six electrons in three of the four available bonding orbitals and therefore is said to be "electron-deficient." There is a considerable tendency for boron to acquire an additional electron pair to fill the fourth orbital and so attain an octet of electrons. The boron halides and the organoboranes (BR_3) are Lewis acids and may accept an electron pair from a base to form tetracovalent boron compounds in which the boron atom has a share of eight electrons.

trimethylborane   ammonia trimethylborane
  (planar)   (tetrahedral)

A change in configuration at boron occurs in these reactions because tetracovalent boron is tetrahedral (sp^3 hybrid orbitals), whereas tricovalent boron is planar (sp^2 hybrid orbitals).

Although it is conceivable that boron might form double-bonded compounds such as $RB{=}BR$, $RB{=}O$, $RB{=}CR_2$, and $RB{=}NR$, so far such substances have not been isolated. However, there is evidence of double-bond character for $B{-}X$ bonds in compounds of the type BX_3, where the X atom possesses a pair of unshared electrons. Here, the unshared pair can participate in bond formation resulting from $p_\pi{-}p_\pi$ overlap between a p orbital on X and the vacant p orbital on boron. This bonding can be described by the following electron-pairing schemes:

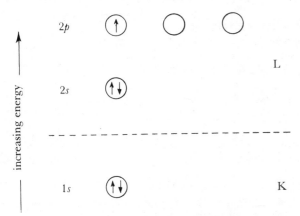

Figure 31-3   Electronic configuration of boron.

The fact that the trimethoxyboranes $B(OR)_3$ and triaminoboranes $B(NR_2)_3$ have little or no tendency to complex with amines is taken as evidence supporting p_π-p_π bonding, since this would reduce electron deficiency at boron and discourage coördination.

$$RO\underset{RO}{\overset{RO}{\diagdown}}B-\ddot{O}R \quad \longleftrightarrow \quad RO\underset{RO}{\overset{RO}{\diagdown}}\overset{\ominus}{B}=\overset{\oplus}{O}R$$

The best evidence in support of p_π-p_π bonding is afforded by a particularly interesting class of compounds known as **borazines.** These compounds are six-membered heterocycles with alternating boron and nitrogen atoms. They are formally analogous to benzene in that there are six electrons—one pair at each nitrogen—which could be delocalized over six orbitals—one from each boron and nitrogen in the ring.

[7a]   [7b]   [7c]

The similarity between benzene and borazine is obvious from the Kekulé-type structures [7b] and [7c]. The degree to which these structures can be regarded to contribute to the actual structure of the borazine molecule has been and remains a topic of interest and controversy. However, the weight of evidence, which is mainly physical, favors at least some aromatic character in borazine and certain of its derivatives. The borazine molecule has a planar ring with 120° bond angles and six equivalent B—N bonds of length 1.44 A, which is shorter than the expected value of 1.54 A for a B—N single bond and longer than the calculated value of 1.36 A for a B=N double bond.

EXERCISE 31-7   Which compound in each of the following pairs would you expect to be more
                       stable? Give your reasons.
                       a. B,B,B-trimethylborazine or N,N,N-trimethylborazine
                       b. borazine or B,B,B-trichloroborazine
                       c. B-methoxyborazine or B-(trifluoromethyl)-borazine
                       d. ammonia complex of $(CH_3)_2B$—$N(CH_3)_2$ or the ammonia complex of
                           $(CH_3)_2B$—$P(CH_3)_2$

EXERCISE 31-8   Would you expect boron-phosphorus analogs of borazines to have aromatic
                       character?

EXERCISE 31-9   Which would you expect to form a more stable addition compound with
                       ammonia, trivinylborane or triethylborane? What all-carbon system has an elec-
                       tronic structure analogous to dimethylvinylborane?

31-14 MULTICENTER BONDING AND BORON HYDRIDES

The simple hydride of boron, BH_3, is not stable, and the simplest known
hydride is diborane, B_2H_6. Higher hydrides exist, the best known of which are
tetraborane, B_4H_{10}; pentaborane, B_5H_9; dihydropentaborane, B_5H_{11}; hexa-
borane, B_6H_{10}; and decaborane, $B_{10}H_{14}$. These compounds are especially
interesting with regard to their structures and bonding. They are referred to
as "electron-deficient" because there are insufficient electrons with which to
form all normal electron-pair bonds; this will become clear from the following
description of the structure of diborane.

The configuration and molecular dimensions of diborane resemble ethylene
in that the central B—B bond and four B—H bonds form a planar framework.
However, the remaining two hydrogens are centered above and below this
framework and form bridges across the B—B bond, as shown in Figure 31-4.
The presence of two kinds of hydrogens in diborane is also consistent with its
infrared and nuclear magnetic resonance spectra.

If we try to write a conventional electron-pair structure for diborane, we see
at once that there are not enough valence electron pairs for six normal B—H
bonds and one B—B bond. Seven normal covalent bonds require fourteen

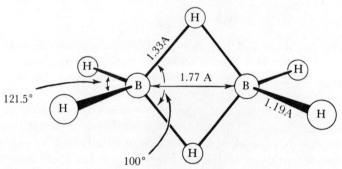

Figure 31-4 Configuration of diborane.

bonding electrons, but diborane has only twelve bonding electrons. The way the atoms of diborane are held together would therefore appear to be different from any we have thus far encountered, except perhaps in some carbonium ions (pp. 142-143). Nonetheless, it is possible to describe the bonds in diborane in terms of electron pairs if we adopt the concept of having *three* (or more) atomic centers bonded by an electron pair in contrast to the usual bonding of *two* atomic centers by an electron pair. We can formulate diborane as having two **three-center bonds,** each involving an electron pair, the two boron atoms, and a bridge hydrogen.

The three-center bonds can be represented in different ways—one possible way being with dotted lines, as in [8].

[8]

The structures of many of the higher boron hydrides, such as B_4H_9, B_5H_9, B_5H_{11}, B_6H_{10}, and $B_{10}H_{14}$, have been determined by electron and/or X-ray diffraction. These substances resemble diborane in having an over-all deficiency of electrons for the total number of electron-pair bonds formed unless formulated with multicenter bonds.

The structure of pentaborane is shown in Figure 31-5. This molecule has twenty-four valence electrons; of these, ten can be regarded as utilized in forming five *two-center* B—H bonds (solid lines) and eight in forming four *three-center* BHB bonds (dashed lines). The remaining six electrons can be taken to contribute to *multicenter* binding of the boron framework (dashed lines).

A number of alkylated diboranes are known, and their structures are similar to diborane.

sym–tetramethyldiborane

However, when a boron atom carries three alkyl groups, three-center bonding does not occur, and the compound is most stable in the monomeric form. Apparently, alkyl groups are unable to form very strong three-center bonds with boron.

EXERCISE 31-10   *a.* Show how monomethyl-, dimethyl-, trimethyl-, and tetramethyldiborane could be formed on mixing trimethylborane with diborane.

b. Formulate a mechanism whereby compounds of the type $RBCl_2$ and R_2BCl are formed on heating BCl_3 with BR_3.

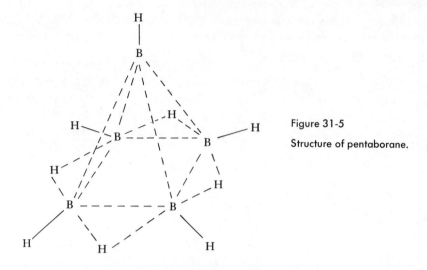

Figure 31-5

Structure of pentaborane.

31-15 NOMENCLATURE AND PHYSICAL PROPERTIES OF ORGANOBORON COMPOUNDS

The literature on organoboron compounds is inconsistent as to nomenclature, and many compounds are often called by two or more names. For example, the simple substance of formula $B(CH_3)_3$ is called variously trimethylborane, trimethylborine, or trimethylboron. Insofar as possible, we will name organoboron compounds as derivatives of borane, BH_3. Thus, substitution of all the B—H hydrogens by methyl groups gives $B(CH_3)_3$, trimethylborane. Several more examples follow:

$$B(C_6H_5)_3 \qquad\qquad B_2H_6 \qquad\qquad C_6H_5BCl_2$$

triphenylborane   diborane   phenyldichloroborane

$$(CH_3)_2BCl \qquad\qquad (CH_3)_3\overset{\oplus}{N}-\overset{\ominus}{B}H_3 \qquad\qquad (CH_3)_2N-BH_2$$

dimethylchloroborane   trimethylamine borane   dimethylaminoborane

Many boron-oxygen compounds are frequently described as derivatives of the boron oxyacids, boric acid, $B(OH)_3$; boronic acid, $HB(OH)_2$; and borinic acid, $H_2B(OH)$; the latter two parent acids being unknown. Thus trimethoxyborane can also be called trimethyl borate. We shall not use these names, but they are indicated below in parentheses. Further examples follow:

$$C_6H_5B(OH)_2 \qquad\qquad (C_6H_5)_2B-OH \qquad\qquad CH_3B(OCH_3)_2$$

phenyldihydroxyborane   diphenylhydroxyborane   methyldimethoxyborane

(phenylboronic acid)   (diphenylborinic acid)   (dimethyl methylboronate)

$(CH_3)_2B-OCH_3$ $Cl-B(OC_2H_5)_2$ $Cl_2B-OC_2H_5$

dimethylmethoxyborane   chlorodiethoxyborane   dichloroethoxyborane

(methyl dimethylborinate) (diethyl chloroboronate)   (ethyl dichloroborinate)

Heterocyclic boron compounds are known, and the best known and most interesting of these are the *boroxines* and the *borazines*. Both are six-membered ring compounds, the boroxines having alternate boron and oxygen atoms and the borazines having alternate boron and nitrogen atoms.

boroxine   triphenylboroxine   borazine   B, B, B–trimethylborazine

---

EXERCISE 31-11   Write names for the following compounds.

a. $CH_2=CH-CH_2-B(CH_3)_2$

b. $(C_2H_5)_2BHBH_3$

c.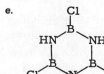

d. $(CH_3)_2N-B(CH_3)_2$

e. 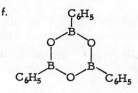   f.

EXERCISE 31-12   Write structures for the following:

a. di-*n*-butyl-(*p*-dimethylaminophenyl)-borane

b. di-*p*-tolylchloroborane

c. dichloromethoxyborane

d. borazepine

e. tri-(dimethylphosphino)-borane

31-16   PREPARATION AND CHEMICAL PROPERTIES OF ORGANOBORON COMPOUNDS

A. Formation of B—C Bonds

The most generally useful method of preparing compounds with boron-carbon bonds is based on the fact that trivalent boron is electrophilic and is easily attacked by carbanions.

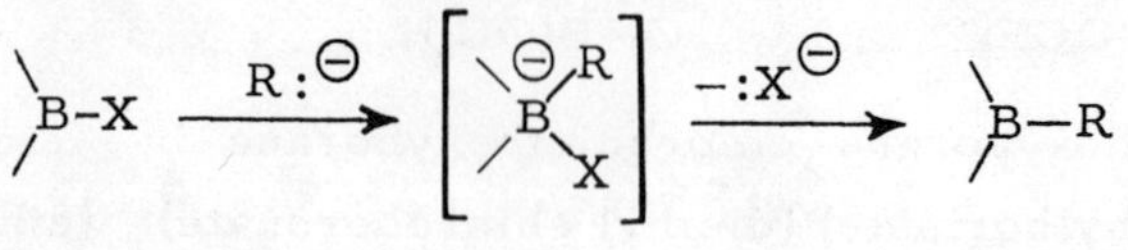

$$\begin{matrix} \diagdown \\ \diagup \end{matrix}\!\!B\!-\!X \quad \xrightarrow{\;R:^{\ominus}\;} \quad \left[\begin{matrix} \diagdown \\[-2pt] \diagup \end{matrix}\!\!\overset{\ominus}{B}\!\!\diagup^{R}_{\diagdown X} \right] \quad \xrightarrow{\;-:X^{\ominus}\;} \quad \begin{matrix} \diagdown \\ \diagup \end{matrix}\!\!B\!-\!R$$

The boron compounds generally used in synthetic reactions are the halo- or alkoxyboranes. The carbanion reagents are typically organometallic compounds of magnesium, lithium, zinc, mercury, or tin.

$$BX_3 \;+\; 3RMgX \;\longrightarrow\; BR_3 \;+\; 3MgXCl$$

$$X = \text{halogen or OR}$$

Whether one, two, or three X groups are displaced depends on the amount of organometallic reagent used, on the nature of X and R, and on the reaction temperature. By a suitable choice of reagents and conditions, mono-, di-, or trisubstitution can be achieved; this type of reaction therefore provides a route to a variety of substituted boranes and also to tetraorganoboride salts, $M^{\oplus}[BR_4]^{\ominus}$.

$$B(OR')_3 \;+\; RMgCl \;\longrightarrow\; RB(OR')_2 \;+\; Mg(OR')Cl$$

$$B(OR')_3 \;+\; 2RMgCl \;\longrightarrow\; R_2B(OR') \;+\; 2Mg(OR')Cl$$

$$B(OR')_3 \;+\; 3RMgCl \;\longrightarrow\; R_3B \;+\; 3Mg(OR')Cl$$

$$R_3B \;+\; RMgCl \;\longrightarrow\; \overset{\oplus}{Mg}Cl\,[BR_4]^{\ominus}$$

Special techniques are usually necessary for isolation and handling of the products because of the sensitivity of boron compounds to oxidation and hydrolysis. In fact, compounds of the type RBX_2, where X is halogen, are not often isolated but are converted to the corresponding hydroxy- or alkoxyboranes.

$$RBX_2 \quad \begin{cases} \xrightarrow{\;H_2O\;} & RB(OH)_2 \;+\; 2HX \\[6pt] \xrightarrow{\;ROH\;} & RB(OR)_2 \;+\; 2HX \end{cases}$$

EXERCISE 31-13   Write structures for the principal products of the following reactions:

a. $(CH_2\!\!=\!\!CH)_4Sn \;+\; BCl_3 \;\longrightarrow$

b. 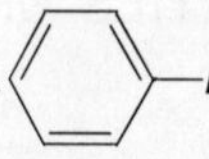 ⬡—$MgCl \;+\; BF_3 \;\longrightarrow$

c. $Br(CH_2)_4Br \;\xrightarrow[\text{ether}]{\;Li\;}\; \xrightarrow{\;C_6H_5BF_2\;}$

d. $(n\text{-}C_4H_9O)_3B \;+\; n\text{-}C_4H_9MgBr \;\longrightarrow$

e. $B(OC_2H_5)_3 \;+\; Al(C_2H_5)_3 \;\longrightarrow$

A second useful method of preparing trialkylboranes is through addition of boron hydrides to multiple bonds. In general, these reactions of boron hydrides conform to a pattern of cleavage of B—H bonds in the direction $\overset{\oplus}{B}:\overset{\ominus}{H}$, with boron acting as an electrophile.

$$\text{\}\text{C}{=}\text{C}\text{/} \ + \ \text{\}\text{B}{-}\text{H}\text{/} \ \rightleftharpoons \ {-}\overset{|}{\underset{\underset{\text{B}}{|}}{\text{C}}}{-}\overset{|}{\underset{\underset{\text{H}}{|}}{\text{C}}}{-}$$

Addition of a B—H linkage across the double bond of an alkene is known as **hydroboration** and has been discussed earlier (pp. 148-149 and 170-171).

$$CH_3CH{=}CH_2 \ + \ BH_3 \ \rightarrow \ CH_3CH_2CH_2BH_2 \ \xrightarrow{CH_3CH{=}CH_2} \ (CH_3CH_2CH_2)_2BH$$

$$\xrightarrow{CH_3CH{=}CH_2} \ (CH_3CH_2CH_2)_3B$$

B. Cleavage of B—C Bonds

While the boron hydrides are reactive compounds, especially toward oxygen, water, alcohols, halogens, and halogen acids, the trialkyl- and triarylboranes are much less reactive. For although the more volatile compounds are spontaneously inflammable in air, they are resistant to hydrolysis and alcoholysis, and react relatively slowly with halogens and halogen acids. A striking example of the relative reactivities of B—H and B—C bonds is seen in the hydrolysis of methyldiborane; the B—H bonds are all converted to B—OH bonds, whereas the B—C bond remains unattached.

$$\begin{array}{c}\text{H} \qquad \text{H} \qquad CH_3 \\ \text{B}{:}{:}{:}{:}\text{B} \\ \text{H} \qquad \text{H} \qquad \text{H}\end{array} \ + \ 5\,H_2O \ \longrightarrow \ B(OH)_3 \ + \ CH_3B(OH)_2 \ + \ 5\,H_2$$

trihydroxyborane   dihydroxymethylborane

(boric acid)   (methylboronic acid)

Cleavage of B—C bonds of organoboranes is possible with halogen acids but a much more rapid reaction occurs with carboxylic acids, and has proved to be a useful reaction for the formation of alkanes from alkenes by hydroboration (p. 149).

$$BR_3 \ + \ HCl \ \longrightarrow \ R_2BCl \ + \ RH$$

$$3\,RCH{=}CH_2 \ + \ BH_3 \ \longrightarrow \ (RCH_2CH_2)_3B \ \xrightarrow{C_2H_5CO_2H} \ RCH_2CH_3 \ + \ B(OCOC_2H_5)_3$$

EXERCISE 31-14   Formulate a reasonable mechanism for the reduction of acetaldehyde by triethylborane to give ethoxydiethylborane.

$$CH_3CHO + B(C_2H_5)_3 \longrightarrow CH_3CH_2OB(C_2H_5)_2 + CH_2{=}CH_2$$

Oxidative-cleavage of B—C bonds is readily accomplished, and mention has already been made of the flammability of organoboranes. Controlled air oxidation gives successively monoalkoxy- and dialkoxyboranes.

$$BR_3 \xrightarrow[H_2O]{O_2} R_2BOR \xrightarrow[(dry)]{O_2} RB(OR)_2$$
$$\xrightarrow[(dry)]{O_2}$$

EXERCISE 31-15   Suggest a possible reason why the oxidation of a trialkylborane stops at the monoalkoxyborane stage in the presence of moist air.

Oxidation of organoboranes with hydrogen peroxide is of value for the preparation of alcohols from alkenes by hydroboration (p. 149).

$$3RCH{=}CH_2 + BH_3 \longrightarrow (RCH_2CH_2)_3B \xrightarrow[\ominus OH]{H_2O_2}$$

$$3RCH_2CH_2OH + B(OH)_3$$

The reaction is catalyzed by base and has been formulated as a nucleophilic attack of $^\ominus OOH$ at boron followed by a rearrangement of an organic group from boron to oxygen.

$$H_2O_2 + \overset{\ominus}{O}H \rightleftharpoons H_2O + \overset{\ominus}{O}OH$$

$$R_3B + \overset{\ominus}{O}OH \rightleftharpoons \left[\begin{array}{c} R \\ | \\ R{-}B{-}OOH \\ | \\ R \end{array} \right]^{\ominus} \longrightarrow \left[\begin{array}{c} R \\ | \\ R{-}B{-}\overset{..}{\underset{..}{O}}: \\ | \\ R \end{array} \right] + \overset{\ominus}{O}H \rightarrow \begin{array}{c} R \\ \diagdown \\ B{-}OR \\ \diagup \\ R \end{array}$$

The alkoxyborane so produced can be similarly oxidized to a dialkoxyborane and thence to the trialkoxyborane.

$$R_2BOR \xrightarrow[\underset{OH}{\ominus}]{H_2O_2} RB(OR)_2 \xrightarrow[\underset{OH}{\ominus}]{H_2O_2} B(OR)_3$$

C. Addition Compounds. Amine Boranes

The tendency of trivalent boron to accept an electron pair from a donor atom such as nitrogen, oxygen, hydrogen, or carbon and attain an octet of valence electrons is illustrated by the following reactions of trimethylborane.

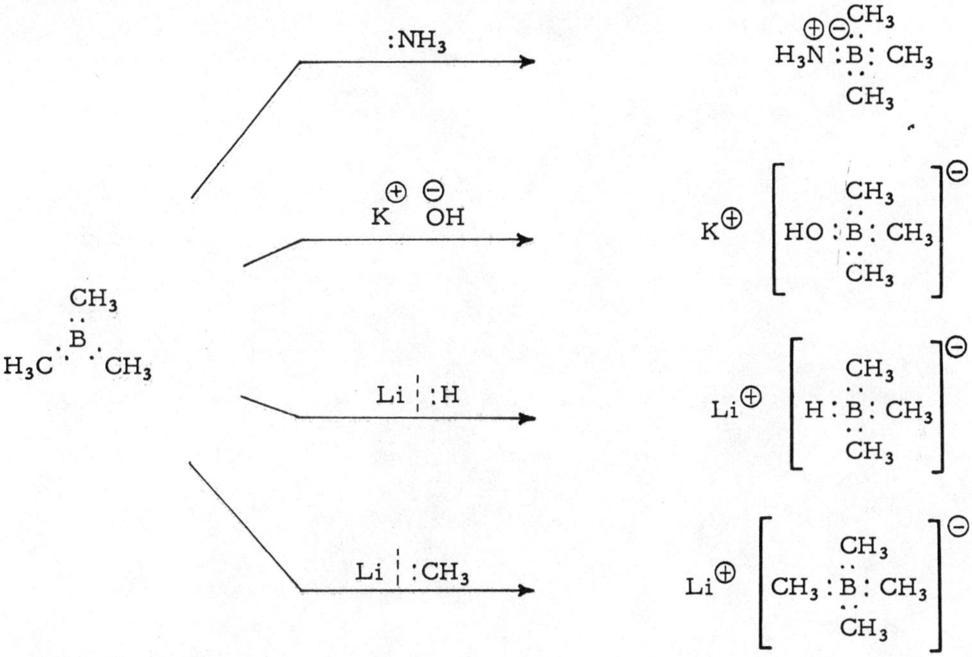

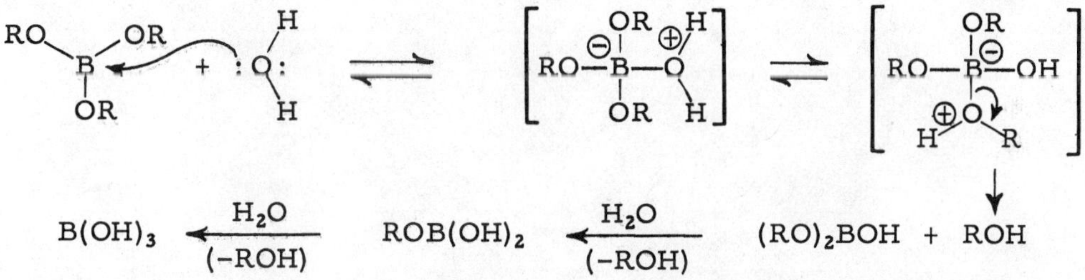

$$\overset{\oplus}{H_3N} : \overset{\ominus}{\underset{\cdot\cdot}{B}} \overset{CH_3}{\underset{CH_3}{:}} CH_3 \qquad :NH_3$$

$$K^{\oplus}\left[HO : \overset{CH_3}{\underset{CH_3}{B}} : CH_3 \right]^{\ominus} \qquad \overset{\oplus}{K}\ \ \overset{\ominus}{OH}$$

$$H_3C \overset{\overset{\cdot\cdot}{B}\cdot\cdot}{\underset{}{\cdot\cdot}} CH_3 \qquad \overset{CH_3}{}$$

$$Li^{\oplus}\left[H : \overset{CH_3}{\underset{CH_3}{B}} : CH_3 \right]^{\ominus} \qquad Li\ \vdots\ :H$$

$$Li^{\oplus}\left[CH_3 : \overset{CH_3}{\underset{CH_3}{B}} : CH_3 \right]^{\ominus} \qquad Li\ \vdots\ :CH_3$$

$$RO \overset{OR}{\underset{OR}{B}} + :\overset{H}{\underset{H}{O}}: \ \rightleftharpoons\ \left[RO - \overset{\overset{OR}{|}}{\underset{\underset{OR}{|}}{B}} - \overset{\overset{H}{\diagup}}{\underset{H}{O}} \right] \ \rightleftharpoons\ \left[RO - \overset{\overset{OR}{|}}{\underset{\underset{O}{\oplus}}{\underset{H\ \ R}{B}}} \overset{\ominus}{O}H \right]$$

$$B(OH)_3 \xleftarrow[\ (-ROH)\ ]{H_2O} ROB(OH)_2 \xleftarrow[\ (-ROH)\ ]{H_2O} (RO)_2BOH + ROH$$

Many of the reactions of trivalent boron compounds appear to involve tetra-covalent intermediates of this type. An example is provided by trialkoxybo-ranes which hydrolyze with considerable ease. This is probably the result of prior coördination with a molecule of water, which facilitates cleavage of a B—O bond.

General Index

Page numbers printed in *italic* refer to physical properties; **boldface** refers to syntheses or formation reactions.

Page numbers printed in *italic* refer to physical properties; **boldface** refers to syntheses or formation reactions.

Page numbers printed in *italic* refer to physical properties; **boldface** refers to syntheses or formation reactions.

Page numbers printed in *italic* refer to physical properties; **boldface** refers to syntheses or formation reactions.

Page numbers printed in *italic* refer to physical properties; **boldface** refers to syntheses or formation reactions.

Page numbers printed in *italic* refer to physical properties; **boldface** refers to syntheses or formation reactions.

conformation of, 92
heat of combustion of, 93
strain in, 93
Cyclopropanecarbonitrile, reduction of, 311
Cyclopropanecarboxaldehyde, **311**
Cyclopropanecarboxylic acid, **339**
Cyclopropenyl cation and anion, 190
Cyclopropyl chloride, reactivity of, 247
Cyclopropyl cyanide, 311
Cyclopropylacetonitrile, alkylation of, 472
Cyclopropylcarbinyl chloride, 247
Cyclopropylisobutyronitrile, **472**
Cyclopropyne, 156
Cysteine, *484*
cystine from, 482
Cystine, *484*
in chymotrypsin, 502
cysteine from, 482
in insulin, 499
in wool, 725
Cytosine, in DNA and RNA, 506–507
Cytosine deoxyribonucleotide, 507
Cytosine deoxyriboside, 507

Dacron, 715, **717**
dyeing of, 688
uses of, 715
DDT, 639
Deadly nightshade, 670
Decaborane, 786
Decahydronaphthalene (*see* Decalin)
Decalin, 99
conformations of, 99
stereochemistry of, 99
Decane, *59*
isomers of, 52
n-Decyl alcohol, *281*
1-Decyne, *166*
heat of combustion of, 166
Degenerate orbitals, 106
Dehydrobenzene (*see* Benzyne)
Dehydrogenation
of arenes, with selenium, 754
Dehydrohalogenation (*see* Elimination reactions)
Dehydronorcholene, 755
Delphinidin chloride, 674
Delrin, 325, *715*, 715
uses of, 715
Denaturation, of enzymes, 501
of proteins, 493, 497
2-Deoxy-D-ribose, 429, 506
N-glycosides of, 440–441
Deoxyribonucleic acid (DNA)
base composition of, 508
base sequences in, 509–510
dissociation of, 505
enzymic hydrolysis of, 508
and genetic control, 505, 509–510
modification of, 509–510

molecular weights of, 505
replication of, 509–510
structures of, 505–508
synthesis of, 510
Deoxyribonucleoproteins, 504
Deoxyribonucleosides, 441
Desoxycholic acids (*see also* Bile acids), 751
degradation of, 753–754
old formula for, 754
Desulfonation, of arenesulfonic acids, 551
Detergents, alkanesulfonates as, 524
Deuteration of arenes (*see also* Electrophilic aromatic substitution), 551
Deuterium, and n.m.r. spectra, 39–40
Developed dyes, 689
Dextrorotatory, definition of, 400
Diacetone alcohol, **341–342**
dehydration of, 344
n.m.r. spectrum of, 39
Dialdehydes, 351
Dialkyl sulfates, 219, **293**
nucleophilic reactions of, 226
and sulfuric acid, 219
Dialkylaluminum hydrides, and alkenes, 271
Diamines, polymers from, 718–719
1,3-Diaminobenzene (*see* m-Phenylenediamine)
p-Diaminobenzene (*see* p-Phenylenediamine)
2,4-Diaminophenol, as developer, 620
Diastase, 444
Diastereomers, and asymmetric induction, 419–420
definition of, 407
physical properties of, 407
separation of, 417–418
Diatomic molecules, electronic excitation of, 679–680
1,2-Diazine (*see* Pyridazine)
1,3-Diazine (*see* Pyrimidine)
Diazirines, 477–478
Diazo compounds, preparation and properties of, 477–478
Diazo coupling, dyes from, 689
of furan, 655
mechanism of, 601–602
of pyrrole, 654
substituent effects on, 602
Diazoalkanes (*see* Diazomethane)
1,3-Diazole (*see* Imidazole)
Diazomethane, *477*, **477**
carbenes from, 249
explosive properties of, 477
as methylating agent, 477
with enols, 477
with ketones, 694
with unsaturated carbonyl compounds, 477
structure of, 477–478
toxicity of, 477
Diazonium salts (*see also* Aryldiazonium salts), nucleophilic reactions of, 226
Dibenzoyl (*see* Benzil)
Diborane, 148
alkyl derivatives of, 787
with propylene, 791

Page numbers printed in *italic* refer to physical properties; **boldface** refers to syntheses or formation reactions.

Eclipsed hydrogens, 86–88
Egg white, denaturation of, 497
Eicosane, *59*
  number of isomers, 52
Einstein, definition of, 26
Elastomers (*see* Polymers, elastomers)
Electrical effects, on light absorption, 682–687
Electrolytic reduction, of aryldiazonium salts, 601
  of phosphonium salts, 782
Electron delocalization, 178
Electron diffraction, 25
Electron microscopy, 499
Electron pairing, 178
Electron pairs, 105, 107
Electron paramagnetic resonance spectroscopy (*see*
      E.p.r. spectroscopy)
Electron repulsion (*see* Interelectronic repulsion)
Electron-deficient compounds, 143
Electronic configurations, of atoms, 106–107
Electronic excitation, 32–33, 678–681
Electronic spectra, 25, 32–34
  absorption coefficient and structure of, 684
  absorption process of, 679–681
  of aldehydes, 313, 365
  of alkanes, 60
  of alkenes, 126
  of alkynes, 165
  of arenes, 536–539
  of arylamines, 595–597
  benzene chromophore, 537–538
  benzenoid band, 538–539
  of carboxylic acids, 365
  of charge-transfer complexes, 593
  of conjugated polyenes, 196–197
  of cycloalkanes, 83
  of ketones, 313, 365
  of nitro compounds, 474
  of phenols, 606–607, 609
  of polyenes, 682–683
  resonance and, 196–198, 682–687
  substituent effects on, 683–687
  of α,β-unsaturated carbonyl compounds, 346
  and vibrational and rotational energy levels on, 33
Electronic spectrum, of acetaldehyde, 365
  of acetic acid, 365
  of acetone, 34, 365
  of *p*-aminophenol, 606
  of aniline, 538, 595, 596
  of anthracene, 539
  of benzaldehyde, 537
  of benzene, 537–539
  of benzidine, 596
  of biphenyl, 537
  of butyraldehyde, 365
  of butyric acid, 365
  of β-carotene, 683
  of catechol, 606
  of Congo Red, 692
  of *p*-cresol, 606
  of N,N-dimethylaniline, 596
  of diphenylamine, 596
  of hydroquinone, 606

  of *p*-hydroxybenzaldehyde, 607
  of indigo, 691
  of iodobenzene, 538
  of N-methylaniline, 596
  of naphthacene, 539
  of naphthalene, 539
  of 2-naphthol, 607
  of 1-naphthylamine, 597
  of 2-naphthylamine, 597
  of *m*-nitroaniline, 595, 596
  of *p*-nitroaniline, 595, 596
  of nitrobenzene, 474
  of *p*-nitrophenol, 606, 684, 686
  of *p*-nitrophenolate ion, 684, 686
  of pentacene, 539
  of phenol, 538, 606
  of phenoxide ion, 538
  of *p*-phenylenediamine, 596
  of picric acid, 606
  of quebrachamine, 734 ·
  of resorcinol, 606
  of salicylaldehyde, 606
  of stilbene, 537, 682
  of styrene, 537, 538
  of toluene, 538
  of *p*-toluidine, 596
  of triphenylamine, 597
Electronic transitions, 537–538, 680
Electron-pair bonds, 177–178
Electron-pairing schemes, of benzene, 182–183
Electrophilic aromatic substitution (*see also* Hetero-
      cyclic compounds, electrophilic substitution of,
      Nitration, Halogenation, *etc.*), of arylamines,
      598
  effect of substituents on, 552–557
  features of, 540–543
  orientation in, 552–557
    with alkyl substituents, 553–555
    of benzene derivatives, 552–554
    with disubstituted benzenes, 557
    electrical effects on, 554–557
    isomer identities, 552
    isomer ratios, 552, 562
    Körner's method, 552
    of polynuclear arenes, 560–563
    resonance effect on, 554–557
    theory of, 551–557
  partial rate factors in, 552–553
  of phenols, 612–613
  of polyhydric phenols, 617
  of polynuclear arenes, 558–563
  reactivity effects in, 551–557
  reagents for, 542–543
  of tropolones, 623
Electrophilic displacement, first-order
      racemization in, 273
    retention of configuration in, 273
    stereochemistry of, 272–273
Electrophilic displacement reactions, 272–273
  first-order vs. second-order, 272–273
  second-order, stereochemistry of, 273
Electrophilic reagents, 136

Page numbers printed in *italic* refer to physical properties; **boldface** refers to syntheses or formation reactions.

Page numbers printed in *italic* refer to physical properties; **boldface** refers to syntheses or formation reactions.

Gentiobiose, in amygdalin, 637–638
Geometrical isomerism, 129–131
  of substituted cycloalkanes, 96
Geranial, 747
Ginger, oil of, 743
    camphene from, 744
Glass temperatures of polymers, definition of, 708
Glucaric acid, from glucose, 434
Gluconic acid, from glucose, 434
D-Glucose, **433**
  acetals from, 434
  aldehyde form of, 434, 438, 439
  with amines, 434, 439
  anomers of, 435
  carbonyl derivatives of, 434
  in cellulose, 443
  configuration of, 432
    absolute, 415
  conformations of, 436–437
  derivatives of, 440
  determination of structure of, 432–433
  in glycogen, 445
  hydroxyl reactions of, 434
  with methanol, 434
  mutarotation of, 438
  occurrence and structure of, 429, 430
  oxidation of, 434
  with phenylhydrazine, 439
  from photosynthesis, 427
  reducing properties of, 434
  reduction of, 434
  ring structure of, 428, 430, 435–438
  in starch, 444–445
  in sucrose, 431, 441–443
Glucose phenylosazone, 439
Glucose 2,3,4,6-tetraacetate, 437
Glucosylamines, 439
Glutamic acid, *484*
  as acidic amino acid, 481
Glutamine, *484*
Glutaric acid, *392*
  pyrolysis of, 394
Glutaric anhydride, **394**
Glyceraldehyde, **324**
  absolute configuration, determination of, 413–417
  as configurational standard, 414
  projection formulas for, 414
Glyceraldehyde diethyl acetal, **324**
  hydrolysis of, 324
Glyceric acid, in photosynthesis, 427
Glycerides, 363
  in civet, 729
  soap from, 363
Glycerol, 244, *298*, 299
  as constituent of fats, 299, 363
Glycerol esters, 363
Glycerol trinitrate, 299
Glyceryl p-aminobenzoate, as screening agent, 694
Glycin, as photographic developer, 620
Glycine, **482,** *483*
  acid-base properties of, 486–487
  and bile acids, 752

  in collagen, 726
    with benzyl chloroformate, 496
  in silk, 724
  titration curve of, 486
Glycogen, 431
Glycogens, 445
Glycolic acid, **351**
1,2-Glycols, from alkenes, 309
  oxidative cleavage of, 309–310
  properties of, 298–299
  rearrangements of, 311
Glycosides, definition of, 431, 440
  plant pigments as, 673–674
  of steroids, 757
N-Glycosides, 440
O-Glycosides (*see also* Disaccharides), 440
Glyoxal, 351
  Cannizzaro reaction of, 351
Glyptal, 718
Gomberg, M., 635
Gramines, structure of, 667
Grape flavoring, 639
Greek letters, for substituent positions, 221–222
Grignard reagents (*see* Organomagnesium compounds)
Grignard, V., 263
GRS rubber, 213
Guanidine, base strength of, 458
Guanine, in nucleoproteins, 506
Gum arabic, 431
Gutta percha, 212
  as polyterpene, 743

Hair, curling of, 725
Halides, types of, 9
Halide ions, nucleophilic reactivities of, 236
Haller-Bauer alkylation, 345–346
Haloacetylenes, reactivity of, 246
N-Haloamines, **464**
  hydrolysis of, 464
α-Halocarboxylic acids (*see* Carboxylic acids, α-halo)
Haloform reaction, 339
Halogenation, of alkanes, 75–77
  of carbonyl compounds, 335–339
    mechanism of, 336–339
  of pyridine, 656
  of pyrrole, 654
  of thiophene, 655
Halogenation of arenes (*see also* Electrophilic aromatic
    substitution), of anthracene, 562–563
  catalysts for, 546–547
  mechanisms of, 547
  of naphthalene, 560
  of phenanthrene, 562
Halogens, charge-transfer complexes of, 547
  with thiols, 520
Harmala alkaloids, 668
Heart poisons, 757
Heat of activation, 74

Page numbers printed in *italic* refer to physical properties; **boldface** refers to syntheses or formation reactions.

Page numbers printed in *italic* refer to physical properties; **boldface** refers to syntheses or formation reactions.

Isobutyl bromide, equilibrium with *t*-butyl bromide, 145
Isobutylene, 240, 294
  addition of hydrogen bromide to, 144–146
  cationic polymerization of, 153–154
  conversion to isobutyraldehyde, 312
  copolymers of, 213, 714, 723
  hydration of, 138
  polymers of, 714
Isobutylene glycol, conversion to isobutyraldehyde, 312
Isobutyraldehyde, **312**, *315*
  equilibria in acetal formation, 324
Isobutyric acid, *364*
  ionization constant of, 364
Isoelectric point, of amino acids, 483–485
  definition of, 487
  of proteins, 500
Isoeugenol, **638**
  vanillin from, 638
Isohexane, *60*
Isohydrazone, 478
Isolated double bonds, 123
Isoleucine, *483*
d,l-Isomers (*see* Enantiomers)
Isomers, definition of, 14
Isonitriles (*see* Isocyanides)
Isoöctane, 154
Δ³-Isopentenyl pyrophosphate, as biological isoprene unit, 743
Isoprene, anionic polymerization of, 724
  copolymers of, 714
  heat of combustion and stabilization energy of, 194
  synthetic rubber from, 210–213
  as unit in terpenes, 741
Isoprene unit, 741
Isoprenoid compounds, 740–749
  biogenetic relationships of, 746
  oxygenated derivatives of, 746–749
Isopropyl acid chromate, **297**
Isopropyl alcohol, chromic acid oxidation of, 297
  commercial synthesis of, 286
  equilibria in acetal formation, 320–323
  in photochemical reduction, 696–697
p-Isopropylbenzaldehyde from isopropylbenzene, **631**
Isopropylbenzene, *534*, **548**
  formylation of, 631
  phenol from, 608
Isopropyl bromide, 147
Isopropyl magnesium halides, with diisopropyl ketone, 270
Isopropyl methyl ether, 287
4-Isopropyltropolone, 622
Isoquinoline, 644
  electrophilic substitution of, 658
  natural products related to, 669–670
Isotactic polymers, definition of, 711
Isovaleric acid, with thionyl chloride, 371
Isovaleryl chloride, **371**
Isoxazole, structure of, 647
Isoxazolines, from 1,3-cycloadditions, 663
IUPAC rules, for acyl halides, 279

for alcohols, 219–220
for aldehydes, 278
for alkanes, 55–57
for alkenes, 121–123
for alkynes, 164
for carboxylic acids, 221
for heterocyclic compounds, 644–647
for ketones, 279
for sulfur compounds, 516–517

Jet engine fuels, 63
Jute, 444

Kekulé, A., 179
Kel-F, 252, *713*, **713**
Keratin, 501
Kerosine, 63
Ketene, *349*, **349**
  as acetylating agent, 349
  with carboxylic acids, 349
  with 1,3-cyclopentadiene, 210
  dimerization of, 350
  with water, 349
Ketene dimers, 350
Ketenes, 348–350, **348–349**
Ketimines, **269**
α-Keto acids, amino acids from, 482
Ketoaldehydes, 352
Keto-enol tautomers, 352–353, 384–386
Ketohexoses (*see* D-Fructose)
Ketoketenes (*see* Ketenes)
Ketones, **309–312**, *312–313*, 549–550
  from acetoacetic esters, 389
  alcohols from, 327–329
  from alcohols, 296–297
  aldol additions of, 340–343
  from alkenes, 312
  alkylation of, 344–346
  from alkynes, 170
  from carboxylic acids, 393
  gem-chloro compounds from, 327
  in Claisen condensation, 388
  cyanohydrins from, 317–320
  from dicarboxylic acids, 393
  from 1,2-diols, 309–312
  electronic spectra of, 313, 365
  enolate anions of (*see* Enolate anions)
  enolization of, 337–338
  general properties of, 312–313
  from 1,2-glycols, 309–312
  from Grignard additions, 266, 269
  α-halo, **335–339**
    in nucleophilic displacements, 339
  hydration of, 298
  infrared spectra of, 313
  large-ring, **732**

Page numbers printed in *italic* refer to physical properties; **boldface** refers to syntheses or formation reactions.

Page numbers printed in *italic* refer to physical properties; **boldface** refers to syntheses or formation reactions.

Page numbers printed in *italic* refer to physical properties; **boldface** refers to syntheses or formation reactions.

Page numbers printed in *italic* refer to physical properties; **boldface** refers to syntheses or formation reactions.

Page numbers printed in *italic* refer to physical properties; **boldface** refers to syntheses or formation reactions.

Page numbers printed in *italic* refer to physical properties; **boldface** refers to syntheses or formation reactions.

Page numbers printed in *italic* refer to physical properties; **boldface** refers to syntheses or formation reactions.

Page numbers printed in *italic* refer to physical properties; **boldface** refers to syntheses or formation reactions.

Page numbers printed in *italic* refer to physical properties; **boldface** refers to syntheses or formation reactions.